Practical

KNOWLEDGE

For All

Volume

ONE

COURSES IN THIS VOLUME

A Complete List of Lessons in the Course appears on each of the pages above indicated.

COLOUR PLATES IN THIS VOLUME

For Ready Reference to any item in text or illustrations, consult GENERAL INDEX, end of Vol. 6.

MASTERPIECE OF RENAISSANCE ART

In such paintings as Giovanni Bellini's masterly portrait of Loredano, Doge of Venice in 1501, we have not only a superb example of a great painter's art, but a direct illustration of one of the most brilliant and fascinating chapters in the human story.

National Gallery, London

The Universal Self-Educator

PRACTICAL KNOWLEDGE
FOR ALL

Edited by
SIR JOHN HAMMERTON

FIFTY EDUCATIONAL COURSES

*in Literature · Language · History · The Arts · Natural and
Applied Sciences · Geography · Economics and other Subjects
arranged in Progressive Lessons for Home Study*

Entirely New & Complete Edition
in Six Handy Volumes

With over 3,250 Illustrations
and 52 Plates in Full Colour

VOLUME ONE

LONDON
THE WAVERLEY BOOK CO. LTD.

MADE AND PRINTED IN GREAT BRITAIN BY PURNELL AND SONS, LTD.
PAULTON (SOMERSET) AND LONDON

The Editor's Remarks

ALTHOUGH *it bears a title already familiar to the British public, this set of six books is offered as essentially a New and Original Compendium of Self-instruction in the main branches of Practical Knowledge. Hence, the Editor feels that an explanation is due to his reader. Fully told, the bibliography of 'Practical Knowledge For All' would read like a real romance of British publishing, but the barest facts are all that need be recorded in this place.*

WHEN we witness no more than a fraction of the colossal material destruction involved by Total War, our first inclination is to reckon how many years it may take to repair the ravages of a few minutes' bombing. But do we as readily consider the less palpable, yet even greater, loss that has been suffered in the things of the mind ? I doubt if we do. Those five years or more when all the young men and women in the British Empire and Commonwealth of Nations should have been enriching their minds with knowledge, general and specific, equipping themselves for that peaceful battle of life in which they must engage long after total war has ceased, have been expended upon tasks of vital urgency, yet transient and disturbing . . . 'the years which the locust hath eaten.'

At no time have the younger and the middle generations of our people stood in such need of mental refreshment. Never have they so willingly turned to instructive reading as a means of repairing, in such measure as their individual needs demand, their intellectual loss in those precious years of national service and self-sacrifice.

No publishing house is in better case than that which had issued edition after edition of PRACTICAL KNOWLEDGE FOR ALL before the War and during the War. For the pre-war diffusion of that work had attained to a figure unapproached by any set of books ever produced in any country. But for the paper restrictions, which have pressed with undue severity upon its publishers, it would ere now have stood at no fewer than 500,000 sets, or a total of 3,000,000 volumes. The demand seemed to increase in inverse ratio to the possibilities of supply.

The publishers were entirely in accord with the Editor when, about midway in the War, he proposed that the continued public call for this famous sextet of books would justify so bold and costly an enterprise as the re-making of the set entirely anew, greatly augmented as to literary and pictorial contents and planned on improved lines. The outcome of that resolution is now in the reader's hands, and might well be left to speak for itself, were it not that he should be conversant with some of the steps by which this unique compilation has attained to its present and finalised form.

Re-arrangement of the Work. This presents the greatest novelty, and is so different from the method pursued in all preceding editions, or in any kindred publication of the past, that it is our chief claim to uniqueness. Instead of the Lessons in each Course being dispersed through the whole six volumes, each Course is completed within one continuous sequence of pages : the set of six volumes therefore housing, as it were, fifty different and distinct treatises : a library of fifty books within six handy volumes ! The advantage of this calls for no further emphasis.

The old arrangement thus discarded was a legacy of the original serial publication, whereas this edition has been designed from the first page to the last for publication in book form only.

Number of Courses. In earlier editions of Practical Knowledge For All the Courses numbered twenty-nine. This has been increased to fifty, in order to cover the much wider field of instruction decided upon, and also to present many alternative studies. No reader can reasonably complain that the choice of Courses is less than representative or more than desirable. And here I would point out that the contents of these six volumes have not been determined by the educational needs of any one reader ; they are intended to provide the means of ' a liberal education ' to all members of the family circle.

Languages. There were five Language Courses in our previous editions ; here we provide a total of nine. More important than the increased number is the different treatment. With the exceptions of Greek, Latin, and English, all the

languages are now presented on the ' Basic ' principle originated by Mr. C. K. Ogden, which Mr. Winston Churchill has so strongly approved for the teaching of English to natives of foreign countries. Not only that, but Mr. Ogden and his colleague, Mr. Charles Duff, editor of the Orthological Institute, Cambridge, are themselves responsible for these Courses appearing here. The single fact that the possessor of this edition has at his elbow the means of acquiring a good working knowledge of French, German, Italian, Spanish, Portuguese, or Russian on the basic principle, in addition to Greek, Latin, and English on standard lines, is enough to give special distinction to these six volumes.

New Courses. While all the original twenty-nine Courses of Study are here repeated in company with twenty-one new ones, there is not one of the original Courses which has not undergone heavy revision and in many cases, notably Architecture, Aeronautics, and Mathematics, entire re-writing at the hands of the best available experts.

Our Illustrations. The whole work has been completely re-illustrated in conformity with the most modern methods of pictorial instruction, and this at a cost which only the assured demand for the new set of Practical Knowledge For All could justify. It now contains more than double the number of illustrations that appeared in any of the earlier editions : some 3,250 in half-tone and line reproductions, and fifty-two fine art plates in full colours, including folding maps and charts ; a wealth of educational pictures which no other set of six handy volumes has ever assembled. A notable achievement, it might be claimed, for any publication devised and produced in the midst of a Total War.

Our Title. So markedly does the present edition differ from its fore-runners, it might well have been presented to the public under a new name; but its title is now so well-known that it seemed inadvisable to change it. I would point out, furthermore, that I have resisted suggestions from those friendly critics who deem the word 'Practical' to be here misapplied. They argue that it suggests something too material, too technical, too mechanistic.

As it happens, I have but recently found that the celebrated Sir Edwin Arnold of the Daily Telegraph wrote: 'No knowledge is wasted in journalism; sooner or later everything you know or have seen, every experience of life, every bit of *practical knowledge* is valuable.' And this surely applies to the reader, whether he or she aims at being a journalist, a B.B.C. announcer, or an accountant, a secretary, an institutional manager, or a motor salesman, or, indeed, to any person desirous of increasing his general knowledge. I have also found in a recent re-reading of some chapters in 'Modern Painters,' that Ruskin talks about 'the laborious study of *practical art*.' So that when I wrote in my introduction to an earlier issue: ' we use the adjective "practical" not because we offer only information of a technical nature, but because we offer a range of studies in general knowledge, presented in a " practical " manner for the self-instruction of the reader,' I did not know that I had two such eminent authorities to support me.

Our Contributors. I have had the valued assistance of a devoted editorial staff, and a galaxy of expert contributors in the preparation of this work, far exceeding in number the fifty Courses of Study. But their cooperation has been so closely interlaced, in many instances three or four contributors and departmental editors being engaged upon one Course, that it would be difficult, if not invidious, to specify their individual contributions. To all of them I express grateful thanks for their collaboration. I can, however, assure my readers that I have gone to the best-known authorities wherever highly specialized knowledge has been required in preparing the Courses, and many of these collaborators bear names famous in their respective spheres.

' Practical Knowledge For All ' is offered to the public not upon the warranty of such names as might be mentioned, but upon its already established reputation.

Public acceptance is the ultimate verdict that stands, and there must be some merits in the conception and presentation of PRACTICAL KNOWLEDGE FOR ALL which have made it in its earlier and less complete editions one of the world's best sellers.

FULL LIST OF COURSES

*H*ERE, *arranged in alphabetical order according to the volumes in which they appear, although not printed in this order in their respective volumes, the whole series of Courses may be seen at a glance. This list is not repeated in subsequent volumes, but on page ii of the preliminary pages in each volume a list of the contents in that particular volume, with the corresponding page numbers, and a list of its colour plates, are provided. For General Index to all text and illustrations see end of Volume Six.*

ART

*T*HIS *Course traces the progress and developments of art from early times to the 20th Century, beginning with ancient Egypt. Both painting and sculpture throughout historic times are considered. For the remarkable art of prehistoric man reference should be made to the Course on* ARCHAEOLOGY *also in this volume. An associated Course of practical importance is that on* DRAWING AND DESIGN *in Volume IV, which not only describes the methods of self-tuition in drawing in line and wash, and perspective, but also covers design, modelling and sculpture, lettering, and caricature.*

The history and principles of ARCHITECTURE *are presented in another Course in Volume III.*

22 LESSONS

New Art and Old Masters

THERE is no satisfactory definition of the nature of Art. Philosophers, writers on aesthetics, and art historians have tried times without number to confine its functions within narrow limits, or to express precisely the essence of Art. Others, like Tolstoi, have devoted volumes to the question : ' What is Art ? ' without finding any satisfactory answer. Croce possibly summarized the true function of Art when he asserted that it was ' vision or intuition.'

At one time it was held that Art was exclusively concerned with beauty. But inasmuch as nobody could provide a comprehensive definition of beauty, and the human idea of what constitutes beauty has undergone revolutionary changes in recent times, no such simple label could hold the field. Indeed, latter-day criticism has shown itself so eager to divorce Art from the idea of beauty that—in some quarters, at any rate—Art would seem to be associated chiefly with the cult of ugliness.

But if it is uncertain what the function of Art should be, it is tolerably clear what it has been and can be. Briefly, it has introduced pleasure into the lives of nearly everybody—so much so that complete enjoyment of life would seem to be impossible without Art. It has opened the eyes of Man to the loveliness of the world, and suggested to him the depth and sanctity of the finest human emotions. Regarded as a language for expressing the emotions, it has taught some of the most precious lessons learned by humanity.

The Functions of Art. Formerly its educational and moral value was more direct and definite. When the knowledge of letters was practically confined to monks and a very small minority of students, the painted picture and the carved relief had to serve as educational instruments, and great religious doctrines, as well as history, were taught to the people by the direct appeal through the eye to the brain. Even today it has, and always must have, a refining influence on human progress. It is no exaggeration to say that Art is almost as great a human need as speech. Art might be called the emotional statement of life as speech is the intellectual statement.

Whatever may be his religion or his philosophy, the most interesting thing to man is the life of man. There are two ways in which we may know about life. We know it by living it ourselves, and we know *of* it through the experience of others. Now, we can only know what the rest of the world, outside ourselves, know and feel through the power of communication with our fellow-creatures ; and just as the thinker conveys the thoughts he has conceived through the spoken or written word, so does the artist convey his emotions through Art. As, in music, certain sounds produce melancholy and others pleasure, so in painting we use gay colouring to give a sensation of gaiety, and sombre colours to give solemnity ; and so in the plastic arts we play upon the human emotions through the appropriate form or pose. We express emotion, and the measure of what we express is the measure of our individual artistry.

Importance of Old Masters. A clear conception of the universal significance of Art is essential to prevent the would-be artist from being side-tracked by the ideals of some particular school or clique into a blind alley of fruitless endeavour. Not less essential is a study of the Art of the past. There are ultra-modernists who would vigorously combat the idea that any practical good can come from the study of the ' old masters.' The artist's job, they say, is to create, not to copy or resurrect ; he will be unhampered if he starts with only the visible world, reinforced by latter-day artistic science, as his model and mentor. For such a view there is just a grain of substantiation in the fact that certain practitioners of Art have gone back into the past and stayed there. But they were not artists in the truest sense, though they may have been competent craftsmen.

A sojourn among the masters of old cannot but be highly useful, if only because their example will teach us that the advance in Art has been anything but along a straight, continuous line. The truth is that Art, like other branches of human progress, is as much re-creative as creative, and no masterpieces worthy of the name can be discarded safely as dead or obsolete.

In many ways the old masters are nearer to us today than they were to our great-grandfathers, by whom they were treated with considerably more reverence. We have discovered that Velazquez had more than a little in common with the Impressionist School, although that school can hardly be said to have come into existence until the later years of the 19th century ; and the same claim could be made, perhaps with even stronger reason, for the later Spanish genius Goya. It is extremely doubtful whether in the 17th century anybody talked about the application of the geometrical principle to artistic composition; yet Rubens' ' Descent from the Cross ' at Antwerp is now seen to be built up on perfectly orthodox geometrical lines, and it would be possible to discover the same instinctive science in some of the compositions of Tintoretto. Even Jacob Epstein found inspiration in the far less sophisticated art of ancient Assyria before he turned to the simplicity of African motives.

The marked tendency towards the abstract in modern Art, especially in painting and design, is dealt with in a later Lesson, but no student can safely embark upon the study of this fascinating phase without establishing a standard of comparison for himself beforehand—by studying the best Art of the past and present in its more concrete forms. For that reason, if for no other, the old masters must not be neglected. But when setting out on his voyage of exploration the student should remember that it is the sum of his accumulated experience that will count for gain, rather than any particular inspiration he may derive from this or that painter or school No

school of painters is wholly right ; none is wholly wrong. No isolated piece of sculpture will give him the secret of a modern masterpiece, but a sense of the vast possibilities to his hand will surely come from the thoughtful contemplation of many, which will teach him to think and dream in terms of his medium. And in looking at life through the eyes of acknowledged masters, he will eventually learn to look at it through his own eyes and to interpret it according to his vision.

THE DESCENT FROM THE CROSS. One of the best-known works of Peter Paul Rubens (1577–1640), whose painting marks the highest development of Flemish art. It will be noticed on analysis that its composition is based upon a sort of geometrical scaffolding, a method of building up a design found in the works of many old masters.

Arts in Ancient Egypt

THE study of art history can but begin with the art of ancient Egypt, since the valley of the Nile gave birth to the oldest civilization in the world. Research has proved that the civilization of the early historic period of Egypt was preceded by one still older, which takes us back at least another 4,000 years ; and that even in this dim and distant age Egyptians had arrived at a high degree of artistry in the carving of hard stone and ivory. In the beginning, undoubtedly, their art instinct, like that of other primitive races, expressed itself in personal decoration ; from the earliest pictorial representations of human figures on pottery and on the walls of tombs it would appear that the men and women painted their bodies with red and yellow colour respectively, and tattooed them with figures of animals and other symbolic marks. There is evidence also that when they turned from the decoration of themselves to wall-painting, their art was more or less naturalistic—as opposed to the hierarchic symbolism found in the dynastic period.

It was not until Egypt's dynastic rulers began to hold sway that Egyptian art first assumed its peculiar individuality. To understand the direction it took one has to remember that the dynastic kings of Egypt were also high priests and almost gods. As temporal rulers, they had to impress their subjects with their power ; hence the ideals of size and massiveness that inspired the building of their temples to the dead or living. Thus, although mammoth architecture is commonly supposed to be essentially a modern conception, the Great Pyramid of Cheops still dwarfs the largest modern buildings in Cairo. With the idea of size went that of stability and permanence. If the purely human instinct to perpetuate a name and memory was partly responsible for this characteristic, the old Egyptian ' cult of the dead ' was still more so. Life, in ancient Egypt, was a conscious preparation for death. The pyramids are the world's last word in permanence, and they are but temple tombs ; and one may say that although the ruling Egyptian may sometimes have built his house for a lifetime only, he built his tomb for eternity and even called it his ' house of everlasting.'

There remains the third element—mystery. Every powerful priesthood in history has for its own purposes appealed not to the reason but to the superstitions of its humble but indispensable votaries ; but the Egyptians went beyond all others in impressing their people with the superhuman power of priest-kings and divinities. The mystic element in Nature has never found more fitting expression in art, and even today ancient Egyptian motifs and ideas are employed whenever there are mysteries to be suggested.

The artistic genius of the dynastic Egyptian was architectural and sculptural, not pictorial ; and with the knowledge of the three main characteristics of that architecture just enumerated—massiveness, permanence, and mystery—the student should be prepared to examine some of the most wonderful monuments for himself. He will notice that with the passing of the centuries the main characteristics become intensified. There is a vast difference between the earliest pyramid, the Step Pyramid built by King Zeser of the Third Dynasty (2900 B.C.) with its comparatively modest base of 394 by 351 feet, and the Great Pyramid of Cheops, of the next dynasty, which is more than half a mile round, and its companion pyramids of Gizeh. He will

THE SPHINX AT GIZEH, one of the greatest achievements of Egyptian art. It is a portrait-statue of King Khafra (or Cheops) of the 4th dynasty, and the long-buried temple between the massive outstretched paws can be clearly seen.
' *The Times* ' *copyright*

EGYPTIAN STATUARY. *Wooden effigy of a fifth dynasty official (' Sheik El Beled '), and gold-plated wooden statuette of Tutankhamen as Horus.*

Cairo Museum and Harry Burton, Metropolitan Museum, New York

accompanied by greater technical perfection. Square, unadorned stone pillars, such as were used in the causeway leading to the second pyramid at Gizeh, gradually took the shape of articulated columns.

One can trace the progress in the rock tombs of Beni-Hassan. First the pillar has eight facets, then sixteen, each facet being hollowed out into a groove to accentuate the edges. Architrave is crowned by cornice, and a square slab introduced between pillar and architrave. A circular slab connects the pillar with the ground. Next comes simple grooving of the shaft, so that it seems, as it were, to consist of four stalks, tied together at the top to form the base of the capital ; and the boldly carved four leaves of the latter represent a closed flower —the lotus of Greek and Roman architecture. At Karnak, where both walls and columns are covered with paintings and hieroglyphics, the lotus form is simplified in some shafts and capitals, but in others the flower is opened in a way that vividly suggests the volutes of the Ionic capital.

Famous early Egyptian sculptures include the ' Scribe,' now in the Louvre in Paris, and the ' Sheik El Beled,' to be seen in the Cairo Museum. Firmly and masterfully modelled, with a marvellous breadth and dignity of treatment, they bear the impress of personal portraiture, of having been done from life. Yet in a human sense there is little or no life in them. Although

see also that a certain lightness of style that characterizes the Step Pyramid is not present in the huge unbroken sides of the works over which the colossal sphinx—by some considered the greatest achievement of Egyptian art—stands guardian.

With regard to the temples, the most wonderful of all is that of Karnak, near Luxor. Strictly speaking, this is not a temple, but a city of temples, tombs, avenues of sphinxes, and sacred lakes, with its encircling wall complete. This House of Amen-ra was already a vast and splendid building when the kings of the Nineteenth Dynasty cast their eyes upon it, and decided to erect in front of the existing building the famous Hypostyle Hall, 338 feet long and 170 broad, with the roof 80 feet in height, supported by no fewer than 134 columns.

Increase in the size of tomb or temple was

TEMPLE OF AMEN-RA AT KARNAK. *It was started by Pharaohs of the Twelfth Dynasty (c. 2000 B.C.) and finished by the Ptolemies (c. 200 B.C.). The columns and walls were sculptured with inscriptions and reliefs, and a long processional way, flanked by sphinxes, led from here to the temple at Luxor*

Royal Air Force Official

the muscles of the body are at times indicated, they lack all accent and expression, all suggestion of potential movement. Always the expressionless face looks straight ahead.

The laws governing Egyptian art were extremely rigid. Figures became increasingly conventionalized and ' static ' postures were invariably adopted as opposed to those evoking breadth of movement.

A later and more vivid aspect of Egyptian art was revealed by the excavation at Karnak of the tomb of Tutankhamen. Egyptian art is considered by experts to have reached its highwater mark in the Old Kingdom between 2800 and 2500 B.C. This relic of the New Empire (1580 B.C. onwards) was found to contain many objects in metal and wood of a lighter craftsmanship. The story of the tomb must be read elsewhere, but one may mention among its contents thirty statuettes of wood, plated with gold, of which one, representing Tutankhamen himself as Horus the Avenger, has a grace and animation that mark a definite break with the old tradition of impassiveness. Among the other finds were examples of polychromatic art that make the typical reliefs—with their curious convention by which face, legs, and feet are drawn in profile, and the shoulders and torso full face— seem dead and rigid. The craftsmen of Tutankhamen's age contributed a most refreshing touch to the tradition before darkness finally descended upon the great Egyptian civilization.

LESSON THREE

Oriental Art (1): Assyria, Persia, India

COMPARED with the knowledge we have of the art of the ancient Egyptians, our reconstruction of the art of the early Asiatic empires, of Babylonia (now known, with its next-door neighbour Chaldea, as Iraq) and Assyria, is comparatively fragmentary. Their monumental works were not as durable as those of the Nile valley, owing to the destructibility of the building material, which consisted mainly of sun-dried bricks clad with coloured and glazed tiles, and alabaster slabs decorated with relief carvings.

A few shapeless sandhills are all that is left of the mighty city of Babylon, but we know from ancient records the colossal extent of the strong walls by which the city was encircled. We know that the pyramidal Temple of Baal was built in eight terraces on a base of about 800 ft., and that the famous ' Hanging Gardens ' of Semiramis were laid out in similar fashion on pyramidal terraces. Some Chaldean bas-reliefs and statues of extraordinarily skilled workmanship unearthed about 1900 at Tello, the site of a royal palace, date from about 3000–2000 B.C.

There was a striking difference between the Chaldean and the Egyptian art ideal. In Egyptian sculpture we have found a striving for monumental repose, and a simplification of form which often resulted in smooth surfaces without even a suggestion of bones and muscles. The diorite statues from Tello, notably that now known as ' The Architect of Tello,' are marked by that sharp characterization and pronounced realism that are the most striking feature of Chaldean and Assyrian plastic art.

But the Tello discoveries do not represent the whole artistic achievement of Chaldea. Much more recently the Pennsylvania Joint Expedition to the site of Ur, the city of Abraham, found proof that as far back as 3500 B.C. Sumerian workers in the valley of the Euphrates were turning out veritable masterpieces of design and technique in gold and silver, copper, stone, and shell. Thorough excavation revealed the traces not only of temple and palace, but of domestic architecture showing familiarity with the main principles of modern construction, and dated about 2100 B.C. From evidence here, at any rate, it is clear that much of the material was imported for the making of artistic treasures, though the houses were built of the native burnt brick.

Assyria. Assyrian reliefs are far less naïve in the treatment of the human form than those of Egypt, the attitudes being perfectly natural. As regards animals, too, they reached a perfection of realistic statement that has never been surpassed in the history of art. In the world-famed ' Dying Lion ' at the British Museum the suggestion of form and muscular development is the more astounding because the relief is very little raised above the surface of the background. The artistic importance of this work is greater than that of those curious inventions of the Assyrian genius, the winged bull or lion with a bearded man's head and five legs, or even the winged angel, though the latter has been handed down somewhat modified to play an important part in Christian art.

In architecture the Assyrians invented the vault and the cupola. Their palace buildings rose terrace-like in several storeys, each storey being crowned by a little gallery with short columns, which provided the interior with light and air. The use of columns played a very subordinate part. Where they occur, they are generally of moderate height, and carry a curious form of capital, consisting of two pairs of volutes placed one on the top of the other. Sometimes these short columns rest on the backs of walking lions, a device frequently resorted to by the Italian sculptors of the thirteenth and fourteenth centuries.

Of the enormous extent of some of these palace buildings, the excavations at Khorsabad may give some idea. The brick terrace on which the palace was raised has been calculated to have occupied about 40,000,000 cubic feet. About 210 apartments, many of which were decorated with wall-paintings, were arranged around thirty courts. The temple pyramid by the side of the palace had seven steps, four of which—each 20 feet high—are still extant. Each of the seven storeys was resplendent in a different colour, symbolic of one of the seven planets. The porches had round arches of wedge-shaped enamelled bricks.

Persia. The art of ancient Persia was of a distinctly eclectic type, and never reached any degree of independence. The love of dazzling display evidenced by the

powerful dynasty that ruled over Persia after the fall of the Assyrian empire in the middle of the sixth century B.C. was grafted on to the artistic traditions of Assyria, of the Ionian Greeks in Asia Minor, and, to a lesser extent, even of Egypt. The only form developed by the Persians themselves is the thoroughly characteristic and generally rather over-decorated capital, consisting sometimes of a pair of bulls or unicorns back to back ; or, again, of two flower-cups—one upright, the other and lower one turned downwards—upon which rest some pairs of volutes, rather like those of the Assyrian capitals, but placed upright instead of horizontally. The relief sculpture has something of the hierarchic dignity of Egyptian, and something of the realism of Assyrian art.

It is in the remains of the royal palaces at Susa and Persepolis that we can best study Persian art of the early periods (see colour plate facing page 8). After its conquest by Alexander in the 4th century B.C. the history of Persia becomes fragmentary, and from the standpoint of its art the next great period arose under the Sassanid

MOVEMENT IN STONE. *Assyrian sculptors were unsurpassed in the ancient world as regards the naturalistic representation of the human form and of animals. Their extraordinary powers are well seen in these bas-reliefs showing chariots crossing a pontoon and (above) a fine study of a lion mortally wounded. With humped shoulders the animal grips the ground with all four feet in a last effort to prevent himself from rolling over on to the sand.*

BULL CAPITAL, one of the very few original contributions made by Persia to ancient art.
Louvre; photo, Maurice

dynasty, 226–651 A.D. The most famous examples of Sassanian art are to be found chiselled under the rock tombs of the Achaemenians at Persepolis. These bas-reliefs, seven in number, begin with two equestrian figures in a somewhat archaic style. In a garden (Tak-i-Bustan, the ' Garden of the Grotto ') near Kermanshah, there are bas-reliefs representing a stag hunt and also a boar hunt. These varied reliefs are the supreme expression of Sassanian art.

In this period fine goldsmith's work—cameos, intaglios, and coins—was also produced. The best extant specimen of Sassanian metal work is the ' Cup of Chosroes.' The frame is composed of a network of hammered gold, in which are inserted medallions of crystal and of green or red glass. In the centre is a large medallion of rock crystal, cut in relief to represent Chosroes II (Parviz). According to ancient tradition this cup, which for many centuries was known as the Cup of Solomon, was presented to Charlemagne by Haroun-al-Raschid. There is also a famous sardonyx cameo which represents Shapur charging Valerian and making him prisoner by seizing his left arm.

India. The earliest remains of Indian art belong to the 3rd century B.C. The Emperor Asoka (273–232) was a convert to Buddhism, and his peaceful and prosperous reign resulted in a high artistic development. He issued a series of edicts which were incised upon the highly polished surfaces of rocks and monolithic pillars. Among

the fragmentary remains of the pillars known to us is one, found in the ruins of Sarnath, of which some 17 feet of the original 50 remain. It was surmounted by a lion-capital, 7 feet high, which is the finest piece of ancient Indian sculpture surviving from a golden age that lasted until the Mahomedan conquest of 1001.

The magnificent series of Buddhist wall decorations, painted and sculptured, in the cave temples at Ellora, Ajanta and Karli, which date from the 2nd century B.C. to the 8th century A.D., constitute one of the greatest achievements of Asiatic art.

The theory that Indian art was of Greek origin is no longer tenable. It is not concerned with the real or the temporal, but with the spiritual and eternal, not with physical beauty as such, but with the soul. It is idealistic and symbolic.

The Mahomedan prohibitions in the Koran against images and pictures not only repressed the pursuit of art, but also fanatically encouraged the mutilation of existing works, and a great many fine examples of Indian painting were destroyed in the 11th century A.D.

AKBAR HUNTING, a fine specimen of Mogul art by a painter at the court of the great emperor.
British Museum

ART OF PERSIA. These archers of King Darius (reigned B.C. 521–486), on enamelled bricks from the Palace of Susa, present an example of the cosmopolitan art of the Persian kings, derived largely from Mesopotamia.

The Louvre

EARLY CHINESE PAINTING

The earliest known Chinese painting is a silken roll of about A.D. 370, illustrating 'The Admonitions of the Preceptress to the Court Ladies.' In the portion above the Lady Feng shows her bravery in the face of a bear. Below is an exquisite landscape copied in the Sung period from a work of Wang Wei (699–759) of the T'ang period.

Indian painters wrought chiefly in fresco, a method still practised, since it is peculiarly adapted to interior decoration in dry, tropical climates, and, with care, is more durable than oil painting. While we have few examples of early Indian painting, a number of small Nepalese paintings, recovered from Tun-huang on the western borders of China, reveal the consummate artistry of their creators.

The sculptors were averse from portraiture, partly because individualism was repugnant to the spirit of their faith. Their aim was to produce an impersonal type of face. In the sculpture of animals there is nothing to surpass the gigantic war horse at the Black Pagoda at Kanarak, in Orissa.

Indian art raised its head again after the Mongols had overthrown Arab rule (at the beginning of the 16th century), and under the Mogul emperors the famous school of miniaturists reached its apogee.

At the Mogul court at Delhi Akbar (1542–1605), the grandson of Babur (founder of the dynasty), greatly encouraged the arts, and under his patronage painting received a fresh stimulus. Many of his artists were Hindu ; others came from Persia, and during the first phase of his rule Persian miniatures were imitated. Basawan is the most famous of Akbar's artists ; his style is distinctive and far removed from Persian models.

By the 17th century the Persian element had been completely absorbed, but Indian painting received a setback during the reign of Aurungzebe towards the end of the century, since that emperor was a strict Muslim. During the 18th century Hindu themes became popular, and by the time that British rule was firmly established European influence was making itself felt in the works of many artists.

The present century has seen a revival of Indian art based on traditional methods. Lyrical in mood, allied to folk-song and dance, these works express the idealistic nature of the Indian viewpoint. This modern school has received great encouragement from such artists as Abanindro Nath Tagore, Nanda Lal Bose, and Surendra Nath Ganguly.

Oriental Art (2): China and Japan

THE Chinese claim that their civilization is at least 5,000 years old. It seems certain that the beginnings of this culture had its roots north of the Yangtse Valley in the third millennium before Christ. In China the past is a living tradition and Chinese culture is a synthesis of ancient and modern.

A miraculous sense of rhythm and form is displayed in the early pottery and bronzes, in the Buddhist sculptures and in great examples of the T'ang and Sung periods. As regards painting, this was considered by the Chinese to be a branch of calligraphy. The importance of technique lay in the quality of the brush stroke expressed on paper or silk. Painting, therefore, was related to writing, and writing to painting, and this view is still strongly held at the present day. Naturalistic representations, studies of nature or of human beings, are alien to the Chinese mind. One thought, one mood, is conveyed in a picture or a piece of sculpture, and this convention has imposed a strict discipline, a single-mindedness, not easily appreciated by the uninitiated Westerner.

The Chinese are extremely conscious of their great traditional inheritance, for their culture has survived successive barbaric invasions. China has, nevertheless, absorbed many alien influences.

Bronzes. In spite of the diversity of styles over a period of three thousand years, Chinese art is homogeneous. The talents of the Shang dynasty (c. 1500–1100 B.C.) are shown in the casting of bronze, an art which was brought to perfection. These early bronzes express rhythm, balance, space, sensitive treatment of bird, animal and flower motifs. The Shang craftsmen realized, as few artists realized before or since, the limitations of their medium. In the Chou period (c. 1100–481 B.C.) a greater perfection of technique appears in the bronzes (*see* Archaeology, Lesson 28).

Han Period Sculptures. The paintings of the Han era (c. 206–221 A.D.) have long since disappeared, though references to them occur in the literature of the time, and copies in stone engraving have been discovered in tombs dating from the third century after Christ. Movement is emphasized, and forms are expressed in thin lines. Han sculpture is mainly represented by small objects of bronze, jade or clay. Later on, the process of dry lacquer was invented, which combined hardness with lightness and durability. That plastic art, however, had outgrown the stage of infancy long before it was transformed by Buddhist influence, as is attested by the fine bas-reliefs found in the tombs of the Later Han. In these reliefs the delineation of the figures is simple and masterly.

The earliest known specimen of Chinese painting dates from about 370, and is in the form of a silken roll containing exquisitely drawn figure subjects by Ku K'ai-chih for a tract called ' The Admonition of the Preceptress to the Court Ladies ' (*see* Plate facing p. 9). Of the painting of the 5th and 6th centuries no authentic specimen survives.

T'ang Art. The T'ang age (618–907 A.D.) was the begetter of China's grandest and most vigorous art, but no original painting of the most distinguished artist of that period—Wu Tao-tze—has survived. He was the creator of stupendous designs and initiator of an expressive, calligraphic use of outline. Examples of his work, however, are to be seen in medieval copies.

GEM OF SUNG ART. *Charming study of a bird on a bough by an anonymous Chinese painter. The Sung school reached perfection in depicting scenes from Nature.*
Eumorfopoulos Collection

T'ANG STATUETTES. *Left, priest-like figure in painted glazed pottery, from the tomb of T'ing-hsün (d. 728). Right, a court lady in unglazed ware, a little work of art showing great technical skill.*
Eumorfopoulos Collection

T'ang painters excelled in portraying action and movement, which is not characteristic of later Chinese art. A new school of landscape was founded by Wang Wei (699–759) and specimens of his work were copied by a later master, the great Chao Meng-fu (late Sung).

Tombs dating from the T'ang dynasty have furnished many beautiful examples of both glazed and unglazed pottery, including vigorously modelled animal and human figures, and painted vases with incised ornamentation of flowers.

The 11th century saw the birth of a special academy of painting at the Chinese court and the development of the suave, accomplished style of landscape-painting of which Ma Yuan is the typical exponent. At the court of Hui Tsung (himself a painter of importance) there arose a reaction against stereotyped and traditional modes of representation, which synchronized with an intellectual movement against Confucianism. The emperor and his artists discarded ancient models and devoted themselves to the study of birds, flowers, and animals, which they drew vividly from life.

Sung School. This impressionistic style was exemplified by the Sung School (960–1279 A.D.). Ink was used rather than colour. A fashion for ugliness, distortion and abnormality in the religious representations of saints and Buddhas characterized certain aspects of Sung art. At the same time, the painting of birds and flowers reached an astonishing perfection. It was the great age of landscape painting, and the mysteries of Nature were expressed in visible form ; indeed, the greatness of Chinese art is to be found not in its reverence for Nature alone, but in the unity of Man with Nature. These painters of the 10th–12th centuries showed that art was no mere imitation, but reality experienced at first-hand. A certain sect of Buddhism, the Dyana or Zen sect of Contemplation, strongly influenced Sung painting.

In 1264 the Sung dynasty fell before the invading Mongols, but Chinese civilization absorbed the conquerors. The resultant period (1280–1368) ended with the establishment of the Ming dynasty.

Ming Period. The great period of the Ming era extends from 1368 to 1644. There is a noticeable change of style : more intense colouring, and an increasing trend towards the external aspect of objects. In time this influence led to artificiality and over-stylization, and it was examples of the Later Ming period that propagated many false notions regarding Chinese art current in the West during the 18th century. Yet there are many admirable examples of Ming art, and decorative motifs reached a high degree of colour and harmony.

Later Chinese Art. China's isolation from the outside world and foreign contacts from the 16th to the middle of the 19th century had an inhibiting effect on many works of art. With the establishment of the Manchus (Ch'ing dynasty, 1644–1912) tradition fettered imagination, and artistic styles tended to be reduced to a formula. Nevertheless, Chinese art was still vigorous during the 18th century. Calligraphic rhythm was increasingly discarded, and this led to a traditional academism. At the present day there is no great school of painting in China. Traditional art forms

have been, in certain cases, allied to Western ideas. Chinese painters maintain that innate fidelity to experience so vividly expressed by the majority of their countrymen.

Japanese Beginnings. With the adoption of Chinese civilization and the introduction of Buddhism into Japan in the 6th and 7th centuries painting became the major art of that country. Few works of this period have survived, yet it is evident that Japanese artists of the 7th century derived their ideas from the Chinese T'ang period and even made copies of their masterpieces.

Three hundred years passed before a native painter of outstanding ability and original genius appeared in Kanaoka, the founder of the Kose School. He might well be termed the precursor of Japanese pictorial art. Religion restricted artistic genius, yet it was a priest who finally broke the long spell of mediocrity. This was Meicho, or Cho Densu of Kyoto (1351–1427), a painter of originality and vigour. His work is impressionistic and is distinguished by light and silvery tones. Cho Densu rescued Japanese art from insularity, but at the same time there was danger that the cult of Chinese models might become pedantic. Landscapes in the Chinese style were painted by Japanese artists who had never been to China.

Kano School. The inevitable reaction produced the Kano school, of which Masanobu was the founder. Many of the painters belonging to this school were Buddhist priests, and they sought to restore

CHINESE CERAMIC ART. *Left, wine jar with three-colour glaze and relief ornament of the Chinese 'Rip Van Winkle' watching the fairy draught-players (15th cent.). Right, above, stand for artist's colours, Chia Ching period ; below, porcelain wine vessel, incised (' Chang Te,' 1506-21).*
Eumorfopoulos Collection and British Museum

colour, for which the earlier Japanese artists had been renowned.

The second phase of the Kano school is known as the Momoyama Period. Magnificent screens painted on a gold ground were among the fine productions of this time. The fourth phase (Tokugawa) is remarkable for its light colouring and simpler style. Greens and blues predominate.

16th–18th Centuries. The Popular School of Japan in the 16th century concerned itself with everyday affairs and caricature. Hishigawa Moronobu (c. 1646–c.1716) carried on this tradition and introduced sketches of contemporary manners and customs. These provide valuable examples of Japanese life at that period, and also led to the establishment of a school of wood-engravers. Hanabusa Itcho (1651–1724) freely introduced wit and humour into his drawings of open-air life. Ogata

Korin (1657–1716) was one of the most personal of Japanese painters. The revolutionary assault upon the classical tradition, however, was initiated by Maruyamo Okio (1733–95), who established a school in Kyoto expressly to practise naturalistic art, and whose achievements were supported by Mori Sosen (1747–1821).

The eighteenth century saw the flowering of the art of the colour-print—that aspect of Japanese design with which Europeans are most familiar. The greatest genius of this school was Hokusai (1760–1849). He found endless subjects in Man and Nature, and his views of Fuji are world-famous. He had a unique gift for composition, and his drawings are highly imaginative. With him may be grouped Hiroshige (1797–1858), whose colour-blocks have also acquired a well-merited and universal reputation.

LESSON FIVE

The Minoans and Mycenae

THE civilization of Crete and Mycenae is of great antiquity and remarkable interest. Crete, indeed, was the first European land to attain any high achievement in art between 2200 and 1600 B.C. The chief cities of this pre-Hellenic culture were Troy in Asia Minor, Mycenae and Tiryns in Greece, Cnossus and Phaestus in Crete itself.

The name Minoan has been given to phases of Bronze Age civilization in Crete. Minoan art is divided into Early (c. 3600–2100 B.C.), Middle (c. 2100–1600 B.C.), and Late (c. 1600–1200 B.C.) periods. The golden age of Crete—in the Late Minoan —lasted about a century (1500–1400 B.C.), towards the end of which the Mediterranean island was invaded by the more robust Mycenaeans and the palace of Cnossus burnt. The remains of this intricately built palace (*see* Archaeology, Lesson 17), with the ancient Labyrinth, exhibit architectural and decorative talent of an unusual order.

MINOAN BULL. *The bull entered largely into Cretan life and art. This fine head came from Cnossus.*

Photo. G. Maraghianni

Some excellently preserved wall paintings (fresco) show processions, bull-ring scenes (*see* Social History, Lesson 4), warriors and their women seated in their courts or looking out from balconies, landscapes and seascapes, and other scenes of national life. The human figures are narrow-waisted and long-limbed. From the fresco paintings which decorated the public rooms and main corridors of the palaces, from the delicate work of the gem engravers and, above all, from statuettes and plaques in glazed earthenware, one is aware of a complex civilization and a sophisticated art.

Furniture and household goods, costume and weapons show little change throughout the three periods, but during the Late Minoan age the polychrome vase-painting, characteristic of Middle Minoan pottery, gave place to black silhouette-drawing on a light ground. Vases were usually wheel-made, of dignified but not very varied shapes. The floral designs ceased to be naturalistic and became formal combinations of a few popular forms — lily, iris and rosette. Spiral ornament, so easily reproduced and adapted, became customary. Magnificent work, of a more realistic kind, was still done in fresco painting, ivory carving, stone work and gem cutting, and there was presumably fine metal work copied in commoner materials, though the originals have perished. A number of smaller objects executed by the artist-craftsmen of the time prove that great skill and efficiency had been attained at this remote period in goldsmith's work, enamelling, cameo-cutting and pottery. A table of gold-plated ivory set with crystal plaques, backed with silver and blue enamel, was one of the most beautiful of the Cnossus discoveries.

During the course of the Late Minoan age the southern regions of the Greek mainland developed a similar culture. There were native communities in Aegina and on the Corinthian Isthmus, settlements in Attica and Euboea. The Aegean islands took the lead in the decoration of pottery by painted instead of incised ornament. Whence they learned this art is not certain ; possibly it was from the Greek mainland, where it had been practised for a long time in Thessaly.

Mycenae. Guarding the pass through the hills to Corinth and the north, Mycenae was the fortress of Agamemnon in the days of the Trojan War. By reason of its geographical position the city could hardly have avoided the fame and prosperity which befell it as soon as the Greek mainland began to share the dawning civilization of Crete and the Aegean Islands some 3,000 years B.C. Schliemann's excavations on the site of Mycenae, which were started in 1876, revealed an astonishing array of gold rings and necklaces, embossed and intricately decorated gold fittings and platings for furniture and clothing, of which the perish-

MINOAN FRESCO. ' The Prince,' fragment from a brilliant wall decoration in the royal palace at Cnossus, where frescoes, paintings and carvings give evidence of a high standard of art.

Courtesy of Hellenic Society

able parts are dust or splinters. Schliemann's discoveries brought to light not only an elaborate craftsmanship and a wealth of complicated design but a whole style of art, with traditions and ideals of its own, not merely pre-Hellenic, but, at the time of these excavations, unrelated to any comparable discoveries.

Early shaft graves, or repositories for grave contents, reveal as nothing else has done the great wealth of the Mycenaean civilization. Much of the funerary equipment is of gold: drinking cups, personal ornaments, embossed plaques for the decoration of robes or hangings or wooden chests now perished. These were found in great numbers and in a wide variety of design, with spiral patterns commonly, but as a rule with figures of animals and plants and occasional human scenes, such as that of the famous lion hunt inlaid in a dagger blade with alloys of several colours.

Silver is curiously rare, bronze abundant and worked in bold designs, which serve to explain some peculiarities of the pottery belonging to this period and also to identify as Minoan work some of the vessels brought from Mycenae in tribute to the Egyptian Thothmes III (16th century B.C.). Mycenaean ornamentation corresponds partly to that of the ancient Egyptians and partly to that of the Bronze Age in Northern Europe.

The Mycenaean civilization came to an abrupt end about 1000 B.C., when the Dorian invasion from the north drove the Mycenaeans (or Achaeans) to the Aegean Islands and to Asia Minor, where their influence made itself felt among the Lydians and Phrygians. Greece itself relapsed into a state of semi-barbarism. Not until the 7th century B.C. did the current of culture return and flow from east to west, and Greece experience a period of artistic development and great achievement such as has never been equalled in the history of the world.

LESSON SIX

Arts of Ancient Greece

THE ancient Greek conceived his gods and goddesses in human form, and made his statues of them accordingly. Just as in his temple building (*see* Volume III, Architecture, Lesson 2) he confined himself to what was essential and permanent, so in fashioning the human figure of his deity he strove to achieve by means of balance and proportion the utmost perfection of which this form was capable, and to keep out the accidental and personal elements. His human gods or heroes are generalized ; they are persons, yet they are impersonal. Again, his art arose naturally from his daily life. A natural instinct for beauty was constantly fed by the sight of the graceful movement of beautifully developed bodies, draped or nude, engaged in dance or physical exercise. The last was almost as much a part of his religion as was his physically perfect god.

The earliest Greek works of plastic art— Greek as differing from Minoan and Mycenaean—point clearly to Egyptian and Assyrian influences, though already in these archaic works there is an undeniable striving after truth, a searching for form, even beneath the draperies. The Greeks imbued their statuary with a general feeling of flight. For the first time in the history of art man had learned to soar away from his surroundings. With the dawn of the 6th century B.C. the emancipation from the archaic is well on its way. French

excavations at Delphi have resulted in the unearthing of a wonderful bronze statue of a charioteer, life-size, in which the strongly realistic treatment of the feet contrasts with the conventionalized drapery. Skilled reconstruction has thrown a little fresh light on some of the work of this period. Professor Furtwängler's restoration (at Munich) of the pediment of a temple at Aegina, representing nude athletes fighting across the bodies of their stricken comrades, revealed an unsuspected freedom from stiffness and lack of variety in the composition.

But the great period of Greek sculpture begins with the Argive school about 480 B.C., with Polycleitus, Myron, and Pheidias. The famous ' Doryphorus ' of Polycleitus was one of the earliest statues in which the weight of the body, instead of resting on both feet, is thrown on to one foot, while the other leg is ' free standing ' with the heel raised from the ground ; a wonderfully easy pose results. According to the Greek writers Polycleitus interested himself specially in the study of human proportions and produced the work just alluded to as a model of the human form at rest.

Myron was one of the first to discard the rigid uprightness of chest and head, and to show the full flexibility of the body in action. His statues of athletes, among them the well-known ' Discus Thrower,'

FINEST FLOWER OF ATHENIAN YOUTH. The frieze round the top of the cella wall of the Parthenon, inside the colonnade and high up under its roof, is generally regarded as the finest pictorial representation in low relief in the world. In the portion shown here we see the well-born youths of Athens riding on their spirited steeds in the procession in honour of Athena, the city's patron goddess.
British Museum

are notable instances of his art. This school reached its culminating point in Pheidias, who was undoubtedly the leading spirit in the sculptural decoration of the Acropolis, and was responsible for the colossal statue of Athena, forty feet high, by which this group of buildings was once dominated. It is considered likely that the sculptures of the Parthenon, if not actually Pheidias' work, were made under his direction.

The fifth century, especially that part of it which is known as the age of Pericles, witnessed the highest point reached by Greek art, but for at least another hundred years it remained at the summit of excelence. In the fourth century, however, the sculptor's ideal became modified; instead of aiming merely at the interpretation of a robust physical life and spiritual serenity, he sought the expression of human emotion and passion. The three great masters of this period are Scopas, Praxiteles, and Lysippus. To Scopas has been assigned a head from the temple at Tegea (in the Athens National Museum), and world-masterpieces such as the Niobe group and the Nike of Samothrace are ascribed at least to his influence.

The most famous of the ascriptions to Praxiteles are the Venus of Cnidus, at the Vatican in Rome, and the Hermes with the infant Dionysus at the Olympia museum —works that show less passion and more dreamy tenderness than is seen in the art of

HUMAN GRACE AND BEAUTY IMMORTALIZED IN STONE. Upper left, the Doryphorus of Polycleitus ; right, the Discobolus (discus thrower) of Myron. Below, left, Hermes carrying the infant Dionysus, ascribed to Praxiteles ; and right, the Nike (Victory) statue found in Samothrace, representing the goddess poised with outstretched wings on the prow of a warship.

The Vatican; Glyptothek, Munich; Olympia Museum; The Louvre

Scopas. There is much human charm in the figure of the Hermes, but this hardly extends to the child, whose man-like expression is curiously suggestive of those representations of the child Christ in early Christian art. Lysippus, who is said to have executed a vast number of statues, including many of Alexander the Great, delighted in the rendering of physical vigour, as in the Apoxyomenus of the Vatican.

Historians of artistic development draw a sharp line of division between the art that followed the death of Alexander the Great and that of the preceding period. The change in political conditions caused by the formation of independent states under various princes is held to have been responsible for a certain debasement of the artistic ideal. The works of the Hellenistic schools of Rhodes and Pergamum—notable among which are the Laocoon group (Vatican), the Farnese Bull (Naples), the Apollo Belvedere and the Dying Gaul—are considered to mark a decline. The first and last of those named have been accused of ' playing to the gallery.' But there are works of genius and real beauty belonging to the same age.

In order to arrive at a just estimate of Greek plastic and glyptic art, the student should have regard not merely to the works ascribed to the major sculptors, but to the far more homely aspect of life represented by the workers in terra-cotta. In the fourth and third centuries Greek sculptors produced thousands of terra-cotta figures of a purely *genre* type, richly illustrative of Greek daily life and charmingly free from the classic conventions. In this phase of the art they would seem to have had much in common with the Etruscan realists, and to have expressed to no slight extent their own sense of humour. A very attractive form of this lighter Greek sculpture is seen in the Tanagra figurines, thousands of which have been found in graves. Again, in the

arts of cutting cameos and striking coins the Greeks achieved perfection.

There is no extant Greek painting on which to form a judgement, apart from the Greek vases and the Pompeian wall-paintings executed by Greek artists during the late Hellenistic period. But there is no lack of literary records, and many names of Greek painters have come down to us. We know that they used the fresco technique for wall paintings, and tempera for panels, and—in the best period—the encaustic method, painting with dry wax-sticks and burning the colours into the carefully prepared surface. Later came the mosaic work which was to become vulgarized in the decoration of Roman houses.

The decorative paintings of Polygnotus and Micon were, it is safe to assume, coloured outline drawings, without modelling, shadow or perspective. According to the records, Agatharchus, at the end of the fifth century, was one of the first artists to study the problem of perspective. Then came Apollodorus, a pioneer in light and shade ; and those reputed masters of realism, Zeuxis, Parrhasius, and Apelles.

Although we have no means of comparing a single example of Greek painting with medieval or modern work in that medium, we have at any rate the evidence of the red and black figure pottery to guide us in our estimate of the painters' progress in general. This ware, produced in great quantities from the 6th to the 4th centuries and distributed through the Mediterranean countries, represents in many cases the loveliest combination of ceramic design and pictorial embellishment ever devised.

GREEK VASE PAINTING. Left, two Attic vases of the 6th cent. B.C., with lustrous black figures on clay of a rich orange-red colour ; the first, an amphora, depicts the end of the third labour of Heracles ; the second, a hydria, decorated in panel style, shows three maidens with their water pitchers, between Dionysus and Hermes. Next is a late 6th century amphora with red figures on black. Finally, we have a 5th cent. B.C. funerary oil vase (lekythos), the painting being in colours on a white ground.

Outline of Roman Art

THE statement by Horace that ' conquered Greece led her conqueror captive ' in the arts has frequently been taken to mean that the Romans were mere plagiarists from the older civilization. This is true only in so far as they were content for a time to sit, metaphorically, at the feet of their artistic masters and learn. The Romans were soldiers and practical men of affairs ; the Greeks were philosophers, poets, artists, with the wisdom in such matters that centuries of peaceful endeavour can give. They were scientists whose pre-eminence lay in the science of beauty.

At the beginning Roman art was avowedly Hellenistic and derivative. Later came certain developments to fit the needs of its patrons. The Roman's pride in his own home was at variance with that of the Greek. It is in the decoration of the Roman villa that the social history of the Empire is reflected.

Etruscan Origins. Researches have brought into prominence a truth which the 19th-century enthusiasm for Greek art tended to obscure, namely that there is such a thing as Roman art, pursuing its own lines independently of Greek influences with which it never completely coalesced. The origin of this art we must seek in the neighbouring region of Etruria. The latter State, although in the first place owing its culture largely to Greek sources, yet embarked on an artistic course peculiarly its own from the beginning of the 6th century B.C. onwards. Roman art from the time of the Kings down to the middle of the republican period was in reality Etruscan.

The Etruscans handed on their gift for realistic portraiture to their Roman successors. Two salient features of Etruscan civilization were belief in a future life, and a reverence for ancestors, and both were displayed in their funerary urns and sarcophagi, surmounted by a bust or full-size model of the deceased. Many Roman tombs were Etruscan in style, especially the effigies on cinerary urns.

Roman Portraiture. Sculpture became largely a vehicle for personal portraiture. The Greeks had made statues of their gods, of mythological heroes, and of athletes ; whereas statuary in Rome was towards a perpetuation of the forms and features of living personalities. Where the Roman gods were depicted in sculpture considerable scope was allowed. The Romans thus found full expression for their realistic tendencies, and it was maintained down to the days of the later Empire. Many busts in our museums represent unknown individuals and show ' with matter of fact, even pitiless realism the Roman gentleman as he was.'

The radical difference between Greek and Roman portraiture is worth noting. The realism of Roman portraits is well exemplified at the beginning of the imperial age by portraits of Julius Caesar and Augustus (about 60 and 20 B.C.). In the succeeding period, from Augustus to

ETRUSCAN PORTRAITURE. From the 6th century B.C. onwards the wealthier Etruscans were buried in elaborate sarcophagi, mostly of terracotta, like this one, decorated with scenes of mythology or civic life and surmounted by figures of the occupant or occupants, here a man and his wife.
British Museum

Vespasian, it is not in the imperial personages that we find the best specimens of the art, but in the portraits of unknown persons. In Roman sculpture the anonymity of the artist forbids identification of his work, and there are no schools of sculptors as in Greek art, in which the creation of a type often enables us to recognize the artist.

Under the Flavian emperors portraiture reaches its highest point, and extraordinary skill is shown in the combination of the Hellenic and Roman elements. Good examples are of the two portraits of Titus, in the British Museum and the Vatican. The great impetus given to art under the Flavian emperors, which is exemplified in the portraits of the time (A.D. 80 onwards),

was due to the increased skill of the native Roman artist, who broke free from the conventions of the Augustan age and produced a new national art full of vigour and realism. During the century from Vespasian to Marcus Aurelius Roman art was at its best.

Mural Painting. Owing to the preservative action of the volcanic ashes, many of the mural paintings in the villas at Pompeii and Herculaneum (buried A.D. 79) were discovered in a remarkably fresh condition. It should be emphasized that the easel picture was unknown to the Romans, but their mural pictures were frequently as illusionist as any easel picture.

One of the chief illusions aimed at and achieved was that of extra space to a room.

ROMAN PORTRAIT SCULPTURE. *Top left, Agrippina the Younger (c. A.D. 15–59), wife of Claudius and mother of Nero ; lower left, Caracalla, emperor A.D. 211–217 ; right, Augustus, first Roman emperor, who reigned from 27 B.C. to A.D. 14.*

Ny Carlsberg Museum, Copenhagen; Berlin Museum; Vatican

SILVER GOBLETS used by a wealthy Roman. Found at Boscoreale, they are decorated with skeletons preaching the doctrine 'be merry, for to-morrow we die.'

Bibliothèque Nationale, Paris; photo, Giraudon

Openings imitated in the panels of a wall were made to frame landscapes representing the open country outside. By the clever disposition of painted columns and scenic effects, a completely enclosed room could be made to resemble a cloistered court. One of the frescoes of the villa of Livia at Pompeii occupies an entire wall with the representation of a garden that achieves both realism and considerable decorative charm as well.

The colours, unusually brilliant, were flat. A panel or a figure was thrown into relief by black or by that Pompeian red which is still the keynote of many modern schemes of decoration. Landscape, allegory and myth naturally demanded light and tender colours. Modern authorities have called attention to the curiously free handling of some of these frescoes, finding in it a foretaste of that species of impressionism which is associated with the school of Fragonard. Certainly the Pompeian painters outstripped the Greek and other conventions in mural painting in their efforts to satisfy their essentially practical and realistically-minded patrons.

Mosaic. It is a curious fact that the destruction of Pompeii seems to have synchronized with the almost complete disappearance of the art of painting in the Roman world. Its place was taken by a new method of decoration, that of mosaic, which, despite its obvious limitations, yet proved an effective form of graphic art. Originally practised in the East, it was introduced first into Italy about the middle of the 2nd century B.C., and was used for floors and for wall decoration. Subsequently it spread to the provinces, often with a very skilful and happy pictorial result, and some of its finest

WALL DECORATION in the House of the Vettii at Pompeii. In this every device of 'illusionism' is used to suggest an extent and number of rooms that had no existence in actual fact.

Photo, Brogi

achievements during the Empire are to be found in the pavements of houses in France, Germany and Britain.

Minor Arts. The Roman potter inherited technical skill from his Etruscan prototype, profited considerably from Greek designers, and achieved a striking success in the well-known Arretine ware, in which the decoration is stamped in relief by moulds. The pottery itself was made of red clay. In the Portland vase in the British Museum we have a triumphant exposition of Roman genius in glass work, which, indeed, following the invention of the blow-pipe, was frequently made to take the place of pottery in everyday use. From glass was developed the so-called mosaic glass used by the Romans for producing ware unequalled in richness of colour. Gold and silver plate, bronze articles for household use or ornament have been found at Pompeii and the former port of Ostia.

LESSON EIGHT

Byzantine Art and its Influence on the West

WHILE Christian art may be said to have started in the obscurity of the catacombs, there is not very much in what remains of the frescoes and carvings of these underground refuges that denotes a definite artistic impulse distinct from what had preceded it in pagan Rome. The Christians of the catacombs took over many of the motifs and subjects that the pagan artists had used, and gave them, so

BYZANTINE 'MOSAIC. Adopted from oriental sources, mosaic work played a great part in Byzantine decoration. This picture of Christ is a large example of portable mosaic made of stone tesserae.
National Museum, Florence

far as their craftsmanship allowed, a new symbolic meaning. Floral patterns such as the vine were equally applicable to the New Testament and to the worship of Bacchus, and many a pagan myth lent itself to the illustration of a Christian precept. There was, however, one important difference. The early Christians were strongly averse to rendering the divine story in terms of the human form, and employed unpretentious symbols, such as the fish, the alpha and omega, the cross, the palm branch and the lamb, wherever they could. When the human form is represented it is an abstraction, a symbol, not a naturalistic interpretation.

Yet this art of the catacombs was extraordinarily widespread. Although the known number of catacombs beneath Rome itself has been added to by the discoveries of the Pontifical Commission of Sacred Archaeology, and many highly interesting finds have been recorded, the Roman catacombs were but a fragment of the whole. There are catacombs at Naples, where the Christians used old quarries ; at the once magnificent city of Syracuse in Sicily ; at Ziza, near Palermo, in the same island ; and in north Africa, at Alexandria and other places where the Roman colonists had penetrated. It is important to remember the existence of these outlying catacombs, if only as evidence of the far-flung growth of the Christian sect, whose members, though separated by vast distances, were yet united in a common ideal, the ideal that was later to find its complete expression in Byzantine art.

In A.D. 330 the emperor Constantine, having formally adopted Christianity as the state religion, moved his capital from Rome to Byzantium (Constantinople). With

Rome relegated to the position of a provincial city, her importance as an artistic centre rapidly dwindled and her craftsmen forsook her for the new capital. At the same time Christian artists and worshippers in Greece, in Egypt, and in Syria, who had all along developed their faith and the art connected with it on eastern rather than on Roman lines, gravitated to the new centre. Byzantium became a mighty rallying ground for world-Christian art.

In the shaping of Byzantine art this eastern influence proved a good deal more potent than the western. To the eastern artists Christianity presented itself in terms of colour rather than of form, and it was colour that assumed the predominance in the eastern capital and later spread its influence through the west. The naturalistic ideal of Rome dis-

BEAUTIFUL BYZANTINE TAPESTRY. The silkworm was introduced into the Empire in the 6th Century and superb textiles were produced at Constantinople and elsewhere. This early specimen, representing Samson wrestling with the lion, was probably made at Alexandria
Victoria and Albert Museum

appeared ; sculpture in the round almost entirely perished, except in the art of the ivory workers, who developed the very highest skill, as is seen in the 5th-century panel of St. Michael illustrated in Archaeology Lesson 27 (page 470). Decoration became flat once more, relying on colour to give it a sensuous appeal.

Mosaic work is a typically Byzantine form of art, conveying, often with resplendent light and colour, images which, though conventionalized, have a most impressive nobility of design. In Roman times, coloured glass and gold had been used, but by the time of Constantine these materials were replaced by fragments of inlaid marble and other hard stones, enriched with brilliant enamels and glasswork and gold. On a stucco foundation the innumerable tiny pieces were fitted together with amazing skill and polished smooth. Originally applied to pavements, in imitation of carpet, mosaic art produced rich geometric designs ; later it was used for mural

decorations, confined at first to the interior of churches but by the 12th century appearing on the façades also.

Architecture alone continued to develop along Roman lines. Descriptions of the early Christian basilica, in which the Byzantine builders introduced their new principle of dome construction, will be found in our Course on Architecture, Lesson 5 (Vol. III). The Byzantine style of church building lent itself admirably to the use of colour. Craftsmen in stone, wood, ivory, metal, enamel and glass produced superb carvings and mouldings, plaques, candelabra and altar furniture, including chalices of outstanding beauty. At the same time, the textile workers of the East were kept busy designing and executing the richest of ecclesiastical raiment. Nor must we forget the illuminators of manuscripts whose exquisite work has never been surpassed. Excepting architecture, the major arts languished, but all the radiance of the East was brought into the service of Byzantine decoration.

LESSON NINE

Precursors of the Renaissance in Italian Art

THE great movement in art and letters known as the Renaissance had its origin in Italy at the end of the 14th century ; early in the 15th it was becoming international in scope. Then it was that under the rule of the Medici family in Florence humanism became a cult. Scientists and men of letters, architects, painters, and sculptors devoted themselves to the study of classic literature and antique art. The writings of Greek and Roman philosophers were popularized, fragments of ancient sculpture unearthed, ruins of classic buildings investigated, and the lessons learnt from them applied to the creation of new monumental buildings. In a short time what remained of the Gothic taste was swept away. The gradual flowering of the Renaissance was the outcome of five hundred years of darkness, of a period that had lost the flexibility and aesthetic discrimination of the best Greek and Roman epochs.

Humanism stood for much more than the mere study of the antique. It was identified also with the liberation of thought and ideas. Even as early as the 13th century the Gothic architects and sculptors of the North were reaching out towards a more individual conception of art than had previously been permitted by the Church. In the North the new ideas of the 15th century coincided with the Reformation. In Italy there was no Reformation in the Church, but in Florence arose the new religion of science ; it arose with such force

that it spread over Europe. The numerous city states into which Italy was divided were presided over by merchant princes who challenged the lay authority of the Pope while themselves remaining within the body of the Church. Under their patronage and that of the wealthy citizens who supported them, art became to a great extent secularized, and artists were encouraged to work under less restricted conditions. The building and decoration of the palace and civic building became at least as important as that of the church and the cathedral.

The theory that Renaissance art merely repeated antique classical art has long since been exploded. Even in architecture it was very far from being a mere reproduction of rediscovered Greek and Roman forms. The great designers put so much genius into scientific interpretation of realism that, though the Renaissance style is based on the revival of the Classic Orders, these are applied in an entirely new manner, designed as a means of scientific expression and to meet constructive exigencies arising from new types of building.

Cimabue and Pisano. Historically the Renaissance flourished in the 15th century. More than a hundred years earlier than this Cimabue (1240–1302) is no longer controlled by the Byzantine models ; his work shows a form of impressionism. He executed several important frescoes in both the churches of St. Francis at Assisi. His last work is said to have been the mosaic of Christ in Glory in the apse of the cathedral at Pisa. His work in this medium was without equal at the period.

Niccola Pisano (c. 1206–78), the creator of the sculptures (1260) on a famous pulpit at Pisa and of those on the great pulpit in Siena cathedral, revived the noble grandeur of classic form ; he was also a skilled engineer and great architect. Giovanni Pisano, his son, executed the pulpit of St. Andrea at Pistoia, which gives an early glimpse of that naturalism and emotional expressiveness which were to become so marked a feature of later Renaissance painting. These artists represent already the twin currents of Renaissance thought — humanism

MOSAIC IN PISA CATHEDRAL, representing 'Christ in Glory.' It is believed to have been Cimabue's last work (1301).

and the urge to realism—
at their source.

Giotto. The first to paint
objects in a manner that
enables the spectator to
realize their likeness to
actuality without mental
effort was Giotto (1266–
1337). He preserved traditional ideals, but created
reality. His form is not
merely plastic, but shows
the constructive lines of
composition. There is a
vital suggestion of drama,
a striving for more than
mere beauty of line and
colour. There is more
form in his work but less
vision, less grandeur than
in that of his predecessors.
A great series of frescoes
at Assisi and a famous
altarpiece in St. Peter's
at Rome bear witness to

**PULPIT OF SIENA CATHEDRAL, one of
the best known works of Niccola Pisano,
dating from 1268.**

his naturalistic genius and sincerity. He
had several followers in painting, but
their work—mostly uninspired—did little
towards the development of the master's
ideals. It was a sculptor, Andrea Pisano,
who did more than any contemporary
painter to further the movement away
from the old conventions that Giotto
had set on foot. Andrea and his pupils
infused vigorous life into the art of relief
sculpture, and there are few things finer in
that art than this master's bronze gate to
the Florence baptistery.

Side by side with the school of Florence
another school arose at Siena, of which
Duccio di Buoninsegna was perhaps the
greatest member. But in the early paintings
of the Sienese school there is only a slight
advance from the immobility of the Byzantine models ; the style never quite freed
itself from the hierarchic tradition. It had
not the vitality of the Florentine school, and
was soon left behind the latter in the race
for pre-eminence. Outside Tuscany, the
influence of Giotto's art was shown in
the work of painters of Rimini, while the
Venetians remained more faithful to the
Byzantine tradition.

One characteristic of these precursors
remains to be mentioned—their many-
sidedness. Giotto was not only painter
but also architect and sculptor. The great
campanile by the Duomo at Florence is
striking testimony to his achievement in
both the latter arts. Orcagna Andrea

Pisano's most celebrat-
ed pupil, was equally
famed as Florentine pain-
ter, sculptor, goldsmith,
and architect. Even in
these early days to know
one art was to be con-
versant with many, if not
actually distinguished in
more than one ; and as
the Renaissance matured,
this habit of versatility
became more marked, un-
til the culmination was
reached in those two giants
of artistic endeavour,
Michelangelo and Leo-
nardo da Vinci. The rest-
less intellect of Leonardo,
indeed, could not be kept
within the confines of art,
but ventured courageously
and effectively into military engineering and the
then unknown science of
aeronautics. In the Renaissance the barriers
between the various arts were largely broken
down in a common effort for the enrichment of life.

**VIRGIN WITH ANGELS, a fresco by Giotto in
the Chapel of the Arena at Padua. He was the
earliest and supreme Italian master in the suggestion of relief or rounded form in painting.**
Photo, Alinari

LESSON TEN

Masters of the Italian Renaissance

IN the early days of the Italian Renaissance the Florentine school of painting took the lead, Siena occupying the second place. The subsequent history of the movement in the arts reveals the rise and development of several other local schools, each of them being identified with the name of at least one great master ; in fact, there was hardly a town of any importance that did not have its school of artists. Thus the schools of Rome and Venice developed when the influence of Florence began to wane ; Milan, Bologna and Genoa, Parma, Naples and Modena, Ferrara, Pisa and Lucca—all had their periods of artistic activity and fame. Most art historians do not adopt a severely local classification, but range the painters under more general headings, such as Tuscan or Umbrian or Lombard, finding in those within the category some common bond in style or technique. Many of the great artists travelled and were influenced by other schools or imparted their own knowledge to them.

It is not always easy to distinguish between these schools, especially those of central Italy, where the influence of Florence was dominant. But, so far as pictorial art is concerned, a difference was to develop in the early part of the 16th century between the Florentine school and that of Venice. Whereas the Florentines thought mainly in terms of form and line, the Venetians were, first and foremost, colourists. Venice was always less concerned with the revival of the ancient learning than with the colourful amenities of her own life—the pomp and ceremony of government, the pageants of her canals, the domestic luxuries—anything that gave pleasure and relaxation from the daily cares of this sternly mercantile republic. These wealthy traders demanded an art that should be neither academic nor didactic, an art that should not reflect classic knowledge or otherwise exact an effort of the intellect, but that should reproduce the splendour of their surroundings and appeal directly to the senses through harmony of colour. Venice had never lost touch with those aesthetic motifs that had come from Byzantium ; and Byzantine art was an art of colour.

Of the painters working in the 15th century, Fra Angelico, Giovanni Angelico da Fiesole (1387–1455), a Dominican monk, who is associated with the Florentine school, stands on the threshold of the Renaissance, yet nevertheless apart. His was the triumph of the Gothic style. His frescoes in the museum of San Marco in Florence, and those in the chapel of Nicholas V in the Vatican, at Cortona and elsewhere, are considered examples of purest religious art. In the National Gallery, London, is one of his easel pictures : a ' Glory ' of Christ with 265 saints. The deeply sincere yet joyous nature of his art has often been stressed.

Fra Filippo Lippi (c. 1409–1469) expressed emotions of a different character. A Carmelite, he studied under Masaccio (1401–c. 1428), a master who improved perspective in art and the relation of figures and objects to the background. Fra Filippo found beauty in Italian peasants, painting religious subjects from the human

BOTTICELLI'S ' LA PRIMAVERA' (Spring). Sandro Botticelli (c. 1444–1510) was famed among the Italian painters for his marked success in conveying the suggestion of open air and for the beauty of his linear compositions.

rather than from the idealistic viewpoint. His art reveals emancipation from the exaggerated religious fervours of some of his contemporaries. Lippi's frescoes in the choir of Prato cathedral, depicting events in the lives of SS. John the Baptist and Stephen, are remarkable for their grouping and colour. His son, Filippino Lippi (1457–1504), is generally considered to be Raphael's truest precursor. His work displays meekness and piety, whereas the elder Lippi's is robust and turbulent.

Sandro Botticelli (c. 1444–1510), Filippo Lippi's most brilliant pupil, was frankly Greek in spirit. With unequalled beauty of decorative line and rhythm, Botticelli stood apart from the scientific aims introduced into the art of the Renaissance by such masters as Donatello, Masaccio and Pollaiuolo. Though Botticelli could express blithe and lovely pagan feeling—for example, in his famous ' Primavera ' in the Florence Academy—he also possessed the capacity for deep and sincere feeling. From 1482 to 1492 his style, from the brilliant and exquisitely fanciful, becomes more austere. Examples of this period are his religious pictures of the Annunciation and the lovely circulars of the Madonna ; also the magnificent pagan decorative painting of ' The Birth of Venus.' His frescoes in the Sistine Chapel of the Vatican are representative of his greatest work.

Piero della Francesca (c. 1416–1492) gave to his paintings a crystalline purity of light and colour. He was a master of perspectival composition and regularity of form. A pupil of his, Luca Signorelli (c. 1441–1523), painted a number of frescoes, and of his easel pictures there are several examples in the National Gallery, London. He shows himself in these, and in his frescoes in the Cathedral at Orvieto, as excelling in the painting of the human body in terms of muscular activity. Pietro Perugino (1446–1523) is perhaps chiefly noted as the master and forerunner of Raphael, but his paintings, though charming in colour and graceful in form, possess an almost cloying sweetness.

Raphael. Modern critical opinion has somewhat modified the former acceptance of Raphael Santi (1483–1520)—born at Urbino and commonly known as Raphael —as the greatest artistic figure of the

A RAPHAEL ' HOLY FAMILY.' The Madonnas of Raphael (1483–1520) are generally considerd to be the greatest works of their kind in the world.
Prado, Madrid

Renaissance. His earlier work closely resembles Perugino's—which was natural, as he helped him in painting pictures, after the custom of the time for apprentices in the studio of a master. Later, having acquired all the graceful sense of form that Florence could teach him, he was influenced by both Michelangelo and Leonardo da Vinci. In common with them, Raphael passed easily from religious to pagan themes. He was, however, on his own account a technically perfect painter. It has been said of him that he was the symbol of the Italian spirit of sublime grace. Of the new classical humanist school, he reproduced antique character in fine designs expressive of lovely movement and action.

Correggio (1494–1534), unrivalled as a master of chiaroscuro, possessed excellent command of technique and of his medium, whether oils or fresco. There are oil paintings by him in the National Gallery, London, but his greatest work was the fresco of the Assumption of the Virgin in the dome of Parma Cathedral.

Leonardo da Vinci. The two greatest artists of the Renaissance are Leonardo

ITALIAN RENAISSANCE PORTRAITURE. Left, *Vincenzo Morosini, by Jacopo Robusti (' Tintoretto ') ; he wears a senator's ermine-trimmed crimson robe.* Right, *Mona Lisa, wife of Francesco del Giocondo (hence the name of La Gioconda), by Leonardo da Vinci.*

Vatican, Rome; Louvre, Paris

da Vinci (1452–1519) and Michelangelo Buonarroti (1475–1564). The former is best known to the world by reproductions of his pictures ' The Last Supper ' on the wall of the church of St. Maria delle Grazie at Milan, and the ' Mona Lisa ' at the Louvre, the only existing example of Leonardo's work in portraiture. A pupil of Verrocchio, Leonardo advanced towards a new synthesis of the scientific aims of the precursors of the Renaissance. Now linear perspective was not enough—aerial perspective is added. The figures in the composition are subordinated in detail to the whole and conform to effects of light. An outstanding example of the magnificent arrangement of his lighting effects is seen in the Louvre version of ' The Virgin of the Rocks.' Leonardo is the great structural painter, investigating everything and putting his knowledge clearly into his drawing of forms.

Michelangelo. Painter, sculptor, engineer and architect, Michelangelo astounds in all four branches with the grandeur and vastness of his artistic conception. It would seem almost incredible that the man who executed the fresco of the ' Last Judgement ' on the vault of the Sistine Chapel, with its titanic tortured figures, its overwhelming sense of violence, should also have carved the classically beautiful and infinitely solemn figures of the Medicean tombs (in San Lorenzo, Florence), and yet found energy and time to carry out the duties of architect-in-chief of St. Peter's and design a dome for that mighty cathedral.

MICHELANGELO'S ' LAST JUDGEMENT.' *This fresco on the vault of the Sistine Chapel was painted by the ' mighty seer of the Renaissance ' when he was more than sixty years of age. Displayed on Christmas Day, 1541, it is perhaps the most famous single picture in the world, and was the master's final achievement in painting.*

Sistine Chapel. Rome

Michelangelo carries to its limits the modelling of the human form. His output of sculpture alone is enormous. He could strike the classical note impressively, as in the Medicean figures, or more lightly, as in his 'David' (Florence Academy). He could also express the most tender and sincere religious feeling, as seen in the Pietà in St. Peter's, Rome. In none of his work does he consciously aim at beauty, but at grandeur and sublimity.

Venetian School. The Venetian school may be said to have been founded with Giovanni Bellini (c. 1430–1516) and Gentile Bellini (c. 1426–1507) in the 15th century, in so far as both these artists were in search of that rich colour that was to become characteristic of the later

MANTEGNA'S 'TRIUMPH OF CAESAR.' *This Renaissance painter owed much to Roman art, as may be seen from this reproduction of one of his most famous pictures—a sculpturesque rendering of a common scene from Roman history.*

school (*see* Frontispiece). But maturity was not reached till the turn of the century, the age of Giorgione (1477–1510) and Titian (c. 1480–1576), and, in its latter half, of Tintoretto and Paolo Veronese. Giorgione is the real creator of the Venetian school ; he liberated Venetian art from servitude to Florentine form and established a new relationship between colour and light and shade. Titian, his greatest pupil, took the art of Giorgione as a starting point, but in later life developed and created new tonal harmonies splendid in their strength.

As a portraitist Titian ranks with Velazquez and Rembrandt. The great men of Venice, their characters, their pomp and trappings, live again vividly in the pictures of this aristocratic artist and citizen. The religious side of the most sumptuous colourist of any age is revealed in his gorgeous yet solemn 'Assumption' in the Venice Academy. Tintoretto (1518–1594) and Veronese (1528–1588) upheld and developed the traditions of Venetian painting when the Renaissance throughout the rest of Italy had lost its fire.

With Tiepolo (1696–1770) the Venetian school may be said to have reached its

MICHELANGELO'S 'PIETÀ.' *A marble group in St. Peter's, Rome, representing the Madonna tending the body of the dead Christ.*

close. Tiepolo was a prolific painter, and the amount of work accomplished by him in fresco, on vast ceilings and wall spaces of Venetian villas and palaces, was enormous. His compositions are grandiose, and his colour and draughtsmanship display an astonishing power.

During the 15th century Venetian art was strongly influenced by the neighbouring school of Padua, represented by Schiavone (c. 1435–1474) and Mantegna (1431–1506) ; and these were essentially classical painters, exponents of the new humanism. Mantegna added his enthusiasm for archaeological construction and the asceticism of the engraver's line. He stands above his contemporaries as a classical artist with a Roman rather than a Greek interpretation.

Sculpture. Two great sculptors of the early Renaissance period are Ghiberti (1378–1455) and Donatello (1386–1466). Ghiberti's greatest work is the two bronze gates of the Baptistery at Florence. The grandeur and yet graceful composition displayed in this work are unexcelled.

Donatello also worked in metals, being first apprenticed to a goldsmith. He was the greatest of the early Tuscan sculptors, and his work created an epoch in the art of sculpture, of which he has been called the founder in its modern aspect. He

CELLINI'S MASTERPIECE. *'Perseus with the Head of Medusa' was executed in bronze for Cosimo de' Medici in 1553.*

Loggia de' Lanzi, Florence; photo, Alinari

had complete mastery in the art of relief. Although influenced and inspired by the antique he caught the personal character of the subject, and his work thrills with life. His bronze equestrian statue at Padua, the ' Gattamelata,' challenges the more famous Colleoni monument in Venice, the work of Verrocchio, for impressiveness and dignity.

Luca della Robbia (c. 1400–1482), a Florentine sculptor in bronze and marble, and the founder of a complete dynasty of workers in majolica or glazed and enamelled terracotta, broke fresh ground in his masterly and sympathetic interpretations of the homelier human emotions ; the mother's love, the happiness of children. Amongst his works are medallions in polychrome and enamelled reliefs. He is also specially famed for the two panels of children carved in marble for the singing gallery of Florence Cathedral.

An important figure in the later Renaissance is Benvenuto Cellini (1500–1571), the greatest goldsmith of all time, who sculptured also in bronze. His ' Perseus and Medusa,' executed for Cosimo de' Medici, is a superb plastic creation in bronze ; but he displayed the same passion for perfection in designing and making so small a piece as a gold salt-cellar for the king of France.

LESSON 11

European Art in the Age of the Renaissance

WE may now glance at the effect of the Italian Renaissance upon the art of other countries. The upward surge of the aesthetic and intellectual revival in Italy spread gradually throughout Europe. This new-found freedom of expression caught the imagination of men's minds in other countries, and owing to the increased facilities of communication the Renaissance spread its roots to France, Germany and Flanders, Spain and England.

In a cursory survey of this revival it is difficult to separate architecture from the fine arts, for much of the sculpture and painting of the period was designed for the embellishment of churches and other buildings of the Renaissance.

France. In France the influence was felt much earlier than elsewhere. This was due to the almost continuous political connexion between the two countries during the 15th century. Social manners in France became Italianized ; French scientists and men of letters visited the lecture rooms of Tuscany and Lombardy ; Italian artists, notably Andrea del Sarto and Leonardo da Vinci, received warm welcome from the French Court. Early in the 16th century French architects began to plan along the lines of the classic Renaissance builders. Yet, as is shown by Chambord and other examples of château architecture at this date, the vitality of the French style was such that it never became completely dominated by the Italian example. Then, as now, it was the striking achievement of French artistic genius to borrow and re-create. When the real Renaissance in French architecture matured in the 17th century, it had achieved a synthesis of northern feeling with classical abstraction.

In church building the Gothic ideals realized in the cathedrals died very hard. Lemercier's church of the Sorbonne, built in the days of the Grand Monarch, is one of the few examples that show a purely classic spirit. The châteaux of the previous century mostly represent either the imposition of classic details upon a Gothic plan or Gothic details retained in a classic plan. In painting, Italian ideas did not really manifest themselves until Nicolas Poussin (1594–1665) translated them into the French language of art. Poussin (*see* Lesson 13) lived and worked in Rome as well as in Paris ; he was profoundly influenced by antique sculpture, and his mastery in the use of geometrical shapes and solid composition (the comprehension of form which makes things appear solid) has had a lasting influence on French art. He has been called the ' father of the Post-Impressionists.'

Germany and Flanders. In Germany and Flanders the influence of the Renaissance had generally an individual rather than an artistic significance. The northerners were not greatly interested in the revival of learning in so far as it related to Greek and Roman philosophy ; but their scholars and churchmen were interested in the Greek and Hebrew texts of the Bible as a department of ' learning,' and there was much intercourse with Italy for the purpose of elucidating these texts and so preparing the way for the spreading of the Reformers' gospel. Thus, by the irony of events, humanism, which in Italy connoted the pagan classics, became an active instrument of the Christian Reformation ; although Protestantism, developing into Puritanism, was the negation of the Renaissance spirit. The Italian influence hardly affected either German or Flemish art during the 16th century. There is, indeed, nothing more striking, in view of the intellectual intercourse with Italy, than the consistently national character of the austerely great art of Albrecht Dürer (1471–1528) and of the Holbeins, or of the contemporary Flemish painters. Later both Germans and Flemings took something from Renaissance architecture, but the former never appreciated its simplicity, and overloaded their ' classic ' buildings with exuberant Teutonic ornament. In the Low Countries Renaissance architecture was more discreetly adapted, and in the 17th century painting began to reveal, in the art of Rubens and Van Dyck, a nobility of conception and grandeur of scale associated with Renaissance ideals ; but by this time the Renaissance in Italy was dead.

Spain. Any direct impression the rise of humanism might have made on Spain was checked by the Counter-Reformation. The Church held life and art alike in a firm grip. Yet the writings of Cervantes and Calderon, the mystical paintings of El Greco and the realistic paintings of Velazquez, the exploration of the oceans by Columbus, the conquest of Mexico and Peru—all indicate a time of intense mental and physical activity arising at the same period of history as the Renaissance. In the domain of architecture, there were already several points of contact between the Moorish and classic styles ; but Italy's influence made no appreciable difference. The Escurial, indeed, built in the 17th century, is a classical building, but of a type that suggests an origin in passing fashion rather than in feeling.

England. Of English art it may be said that it was at first but lightly touched by the Renaissance. In painting, England was virtually attached to the Netherlands till the 18th century. The Tudor style of architecture has been described as an attempt to translate the Renaissance style into the English vernacular. ⌐ Yet the numerous and stately country mansions it produced have an individuality at least as attractive and appropriate as the characteristic French château. Later, Inigo Jones —working when Van Dyck and Rubens were painting in England—gave us in ' Palladian ' an austere but dignified Greek classical architecture. Sir Christopher Wren (1632–1723), builder of St. Paul's and other beautiful London churches, evolved an independent style that was peculiarly suited to English aesthetic needs. In painting and sculpture there was no native soil prior to the 18th century in which Renaissance ideas could take root and flourish.

LESSON 12

Old Masters of Northern Europe

L ITTLE is known of the personalities and
lives of the early artists in Germany.
In the fourteenth and fifteenth
centuries there were fairly vigorous schools
of art at Prague, Cologne, Augsburg and
some of the cities on the Rhine, but the
' masters ' preferred to remain anonymous. The asceticism of the medieval
spirit was translated in Germanic art into
terms of the stark horror of realism. This
is especially noticeable in the treatment of
religious subjects, such as martyrdoms or
the Crucifixion. At best, these painters
desired to be truthful at all costs, their work
possessing a tortured passion of sincerity ;
at worst, they twisted the truth into un-
endurable ugliness. The work of Mathias
Grünewald shows both aspects.

Albrecht Dürer. Towards the end of the
15th century Albrecht Dürer (1471–1528),
with his freedom from Italian influence and
the Renaissance cult of classical beauty
before all, represents everything that was
greatest in German national art, which was
intellectual rather than aesthetic. He
brought to his work immense dignity and
supreme technical ability ; it combines
characteristics of his nation in its homeliness and mysticism and of himself in its
expression of his search after scientific and
moral truth. In such works as the Nativity
triptych in the Dresden Gallery and his

' Adam and Eve ' at Madrid, these qualities
and his talent for forcible composition are
magnificently asserted. Had he never painted
a picture, he would, however, still be among
the world's greatest artists ; his splendidly
designed woodcuts and copper-plates for
engravings exhibit the highest degree of
finish with boldness of line, imagination,
and grasp of the technical requirements of
his materials. His drawings, of which there
are many examples in the British Museum,
show his supreme skill as a draughtsman.
During his later years the thought of this
profound artist was influenced by Luther—
himself fundamentally a German patriot.
With zeal for the doctrines of the Reformation Dürer inscribed admonitory texts from
the Epistles—taken from Luther's translation—on his pair of vigorously painted
panels of the Evangelists, given to the
council of Nuremberg, his native town, and
later transferred to Munich.

Contemporary with Dürer, a lesser, but
also celebrated, German master, Lucas
Cranach (1472 – 1553), painted sacred,
classical and contemporary scenes in oils
on panel. He also executed designs for
various wood and copper engravings, but,
unlike Dürer, his drawing is somewhat
defective ; his chief interest is as a colourist.

Holbein. The next great master produced by Germany was Hans Holbein the
Younger (c. 1497–
1543). He was born
at Augsburg and
there instructed by
his father, the elder
Hans, himself at the
time an honoured
painter, though later
to be eclipsed by his
famous son. For a
while the younger
Holbein worked at
Basle, Zürich and
Lucerne, and im-
portant paintings
and drawings by him
are in the Museum
at Basle. Here he
was seriously em-
ployed in making
designs for wood-
engravers, of which
art, like Dürer, he

DÜRER'S NATIVITY TRIPTYCH. *Albrecht Dürer (1471–1528) was one of the
greatest artists of Germany and the world. The triptych (painting on three panels
hinged together) in the Dresden Gallery, showing the Madonna and Child in the
centre, flanked by St. Anthony and St. Sebastian, is among his most famous works.
It belongs to his earlier Nuremberg period, and is painted in tempera on linen.*

MASTERPIECES OF PORTRAITURE. Left : ' The Ambassadors,' painted by Holbein the Younger in 1533, portrays Jean de Dinteville, Lord of Polisy, and George de Selve, Bishop of Lavaur. Right : Jean Arnolfini, a merchant of Lucca, with his wife and terrier, painted by Jan Van Eyck (c. 1385-1440) in 1434.
National Gallery

was a supreme master. About 1527 he visited England, and subsequently became court painter to Henry VIII. During this period he executed remarkably fine portraits in oil of contemporary personages and also a number of portrait drawings preserved in the Royal Collection at Windsor. His paintings, 'The Ambassadors' and the exquisite masterpiece, 'Queen Christina of Denmark,' are in the National Gallery. Darmstadt possesses the curiously interesting ' Meier Madonna,' so called from its being actually a portrait group of Jacob Meier's family. Holbein's most famous woodcuts of the ' Dance of Death ' are distributed between London, Paris and Munich. He learned something of his pictorial composition from the Italians—notably Mantegna and Leonardo da Vinci—but his art is characteristically German in its intellectual veracity and attention to the minutest details. His keen observation of human character, together with his unerring technical ability, places him amongst the world's greatest portrait painters.

The Van Eycks. The great commercial activity of Flanders in the 14th and 15th centuries provided a powerful stimulant to the development of art. Although oil painting had been previously practised, Hubert and Jan Van Eyck (the former born

about 1366, some twenty years before the latter) perfected the use of this medium, so that the brilliance and finish of their work are unique today. The brothers painted in partnership at Ghent for some years ; then Jan was employed at Bruges in the service of Philip the Good of Burgundy. Hubert's great work, ' The Adoration of the Lamb,' an altar-piece with folding doors for the cathedral of St. Bavon, in Ghent, was completed after his death by his brother Jan. The National Gallery, London, possesses in the portrait-painting of Jean Arnolfini and his wife a masterpiece by Jan Van Eyck in which the homely characters and setting reveal the perfection of his technique. The Van Eycks painted their sacred subjects also, literally and faithfully, from the models they met in their daily lives, the landscapes and architecture they looked upon, the familiar objects in their homes.

Rogier van der Weyden (1400-64) was rather less literal, a little more emotional, in his transcripts from the life. His reputation extended into Germany and France, and he was the moving spirit in the foundation of a school of Flemish realists who, in common with the early German masters, painted zealously the horrors of tortured bodies and the realism of beggars' wretchedness, the effects and ravages of disease. Pieter Brueghel (1525-69) depicted such

PIETER BRUEGHEL painted village scenes, religious subjects and landscapes, with figure interest like his 'Robbing the Birds' Nest' above, executed with a strong sense of composition and colour.

Kunsthistorisches Museum, Vienna

scenes with forceful composition and good colour. His work has of later years attracted interest and appreciation. He could also paint merry-makings and village scenes with remarkable veracity. Quentin Matsys (c. 1466–1530) linked the Flemish and Dutch schools. He ranks highly as a colourist, and his pictures are exquisitely finished.

Rubens. The most famous painter of the Flemish school, Peter Paul Rubens (1577–1640), came under Italian influence, especially that of the Venetian school, early in his career. He may be said to have taken from Italy all that was necessary for the full development of his own robust Flemish art. He was a brilliant colourist. The superabundant vitality of his style expressed itself occasionally in the opulence of his nude figures and in excess of movement, which takes the eye of the spectator out of the picture. He does not equal the gracefulness and dignity of his pupil Van Dyck in aristocratic portraiture, but his range was considerably wider. Though not primarily a religious painter, Rubens rises in some of his religious compositions, notably the Antwerp ' Descent from the Cross ' (*see* p. 3) to magnificence.

Gerard van Honthorst (1590–1656), born at Utrecht, acquired in his youth the style of Caravaggio (1569–1609), an Italian painter notable for his brilliant use of colour. His work attracted the notice of Charles I, and in 1628 he painted a series of allegorical pictures for Whitehall Palace. Towards the end of his life he devoted himself entirely to portraiture.

Court painter to Charles I, Van Dyck (1599–1641) has left us a collection of

TWO FAMOUS OLD MASTERS. Left, Sir Anthony Van Dyck's painting of William II of Orange and Mary Stuart on the occasion of their marriage in 1641. Right, ' The Lute Player ' of Frans Hals of Haarlem; the model was Adrian Brouwer, a favourite pupil, depicted in the act of serenading the lady of his choice.

Rijks Museum, Amsterdam

portraits of the English and Continental royalty and aristocracy of the day. He, like Rubens, learnt his art in Italy, studying the masterpieces of Titian and Veronese, and if as a colourist he was less courageous than Rubens, he was more subtle. In addition to his fine portraiture, he painted religious subjects with distinction and great beauty of form ; he was also a master etcher and executed a series of line portraits of contemporaries, later published as engravings.

Dutch Painters. The Dutch School of the 17th century arose directly out of the Puritanism of the Reformation. North Flanders, or Holland, generally accepted the strictest Protestant doctrines. In the unpretentious new churches there was no room or desire for religious pictures, but the Dutch burghers had grown well-to-do, and demanded small paintings for the decoration of their private houses, not of the sacred or pagan classical subjects of the Renaissance, but landscapes of the country they lived in, and

scenes of the daily life of burgher and peasant at work or recreation. The demand was met by painters of landscapes like Hobbema and Cuyp, by seascape painters like Van der Velde, and a host of ' little masters,' among whom stand out the names of Ruysdael, Vermeer of Delft, Jan Steen, Terburg and Gerard Dou ; the younger Teniers, though a Fleming, may be joined to their number. Technically these men are superb. Never have cabinet pictures been produced with a keener appreciation

of the handling of pigment.

R i s i n g among these excellent little masters, Hals assumes a great, and R e m b r a n d t Van R i j n a gigantic, stature. Frans Hals (c. 1 5 8 0 – 1 6 6 6) achieved his greatest triumphs in portraiture, especially in group portraiture, such as the fine series of Burgomasters at Haarlem. Remarkable in their spontaneity are his renderings of the expressions on the faces of his subjects, as seen in his famous works, ' The Laughing Cavalier' and ' The Lute

LANDSCAPES OF THE DUTCH SCHOOL. *Above, the Avenue, Middelharnis, painted by Meindert Hobbema (1638–1709), a fine example of the work of one who excelled in the representation of the placid beauties of the Dutch countryside. Hobbema's paintings were little appreciated by the art patrons of his day and he died in obscure poverty. Below is the ' View of Delft,' by Jan Van der Meer (1632–75), more often called Vermeer of Delft.*

National Gallery; Hague Museum

C

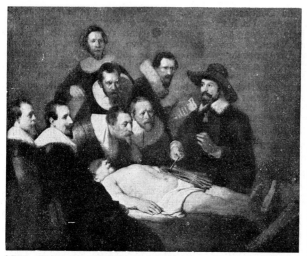

' THE ANATOMY LESSON,' by Rembrandt. The demonstrator is Nicholaes Tulp, and those watching the dissection are members of the Amsterdam Guild of Surgeons. In this picture, painted in 1632, Rembrandt's handling of light is masterly.

Mauritshuis, The Hague

Player.' He founded the Dutch School of figure painting.

Rembrandt. Rembrandt (c. 1607–1669), the first great master of chiaroscuro since Correggio—though neither always so consistent nor so true in this respect as the Italian painter—combined a rich gift of individual characterization with the power of dramatic effect. He was able as a rule to use light and shade in an arbitrary manner to suit his purpose because he understood nature, but occasionally, he overstressed his contrasts and thus limited his range of colour. That he could paint in starkly realistic fashion his fine ' Anatomy Lesson ' at The Hague bears witness. The dramatic intensity of ' The Night Watch,' and those profoundly human portrait studies of his mother and of himself in old age, reveal his art at its highest. Among his supreme masterpieces are the self-portrait, in the National Gallery, 'Hendrikje Stoffels,' in the Louvre, the ' Supper at Emmaus,' ' The Mill,' and ' An Old Woman Cutting Her Nails.' He was a great etcher as well as a painter ; indeed, it has been asserted not without exaggeration that the arts of etching and dry point began and ended with Rembrandt. His life work possesses immense variety, imaginative power and sympathetic insight. Both Hals and Rembrandt have been called impressionists because in their work there is a sense of focus, objects in the centre being more clearly seen than those on the outside of the field of vision.

LESSON 13

Early Painters of France and Spain

THE earliest French artist of international interest is Jean Pucelle. In the first half of the 14th century, at his famous atelier in Paris, illuminators, miniaturists and other painters, both native and foreign, worked under his direction. This School of Paris influenced the art of northern Europe, and English painters studied there ; it inspired the three great pieces of medieval painting—the Parement of Narbonne, the portrait of Richard II in Westminster Abbey, and the Wilton Diptych in the National Gallery. The next painter of note whose name emerges from among anonymous primitive masters is Jean Fouquet (c. 1420–c. 1480). He studied in Rome and worked at Tours, was at the court of Charles VII of France and painted a remarkably subtle portrait of the king ; also at about the same period a lovely diptych, the right wing of which is in the Museum at Antwerp and the left at the Museum, Berlin. The latter represents St. Stephen and also has a fine portrait of Étienne Chevalier, minister of finance to Charles, while the right wing shows the Virgin and Child surrounded with blue seraphim and scarlet cherubim. Fouquet

THE WILTON DIPTYCH, *of which the right-hand panel is reproduced here, was painted by an unknown French artist between 1381 and 1394.*

National Gallery

also excelled as a miniaturist and book illuminator.

Jean and François Clouet, often called Janet, painted portraits on panel, in oil. (In some cases the medium is not determined.) Jean Clouet came to France from the Netherlands about 1516 and worked in Paris till 1540. He painted a splendid portrait of his patron, François I. François Clouet, in Paris 1522–1572, painted many notable persons, including Charles IX. Both are known as miniaturists.

The Neo-Classicists. In 1530 Primaticcio, a second-rate Italian painter, was summoned to Fontainebleau by François I, and his sojourn there led to the foundation of the 'School of Fontainebleau,' which was mainly a collection of Italian mannerists who produced no great artist from their ranks. These were followed early in the 17th century by the Neo-Classicists, headed by the great painter, Nicolas Poussin (1594–1665), who may be regarded as the founder of a dynasty of painters in the grand, otherwise classical, manner. In the latter half of the 19th century Poussin's work was discredited, but again today the same degree of admiration expressed for it by Sir Joshua Reynolds and Gainsborough is accorded by most critics. Poussin used geometrical and thoroughly architectural shapes in his pictorial compositions. He has been called ' the father of the Post-Impressionists,' because, like them, he bestowed his attention not on tone, but on that comprehension of form which makes things appear solid. His self-portrait, at the age of 56, reveals strength and intellectual nobility. The finest collection of his works is at the Louvre, but he is represented at the National Gallery and at Dulwich. Gaspard Poussin, his nephew, was a landscape painter of some note.

Associated in period with Nicolas Poussin, but widely different in style, is Claude Gelée, usually known as Claude of Lorraine (1600–1682). Concerned — as were the

POUSSIN'S 'BACCHUS AND ARIADNE.' *Poussin, who was appointed King's Painter by Richelieu in 1640, was an ardent exponent of the classical ideals of the Renaissance and often went to the pagan mythologies for a theme.*

Impressionists after him—with light as it affected colour, his achievement may be described briefly as the discovery of sunlight as a governing factor in landscape ; it was this aspect of his art that provoked Turner to victorious emulation and Constable to unbounded admiration. Though Claude never painted a landscape without paying homage to the classic ideal by including classic architecture, the varying effects of sunlight were the real subjects of his pictures, and his trees and clouds and winding rivers ceased to be mere forms conventionally coloured. Both Poussin and Claude influenced decisively the rise of modern landscape painting in England.

Brothers Le Nain. Working about the same time were the three brothers, Antoine (1588 – 1648), Louis (1593 – 1648), and Mathieu Le Nain (1607 – 1677), renowned for their paintings of French peasant life. These pictures were remarkable in a period

WATTEAU'S 'FETE CHAMPETRE'. *Antoine Watteau (1684–1721) led the artistic revolt against the ponderous classicism of the days of Louis XIV. Light yet strong, there is nothing weak about his work and he never lost sight of good draughtsmanship and composition. One of his most representative paintings is shown above.*
National Gallery of Scotland, Edinburgh

when art was mainly devoted to classical subjects and landscapes, or to portraits of great persons, and throw much light on the humbler domestic life during the first half of the reign of Louis XIV. A contemporary Court painter was Le Brun, who directed the decoration of the palace of Versailles. as well as the organization of the Gobelins Tapestry factory. He possessed great influence at the time, but his work had little artistic value.

French painting became frigid and statuesque at the end of the 17th century. Rigaud (1659–1743) and Mignare (c. 1608–1666) were the high priests of academic artificiality. Rigaud's portraits of the famous people of his time, which are exhibited in the chief European art galleries, have mainly an historical value.

Watteau and his Pupils. With the turn of the century a new epoch in French painting arrived, and the artist who set the fashion for this epoch, Antoine Watteau (1684–1721), though born at Valenciennes, was of Flemish origin. Penniless, he arrived in Paris and at the age of eighteen found employment in various studiofactories. After much hard work he painted his diploma picture in 1717, when he attained full membership of the French Academy of Art, founded by Louis XIV in 1648. This picture, ' The Embarkation for Cythera,' is now in the Louvre. Subsequently he painted portraits, decorative panels, Court and camp scenes. His 'fêtes champêtres' and 'fêtes galantes ' mark a reaction against the stiffly set styles of Rigaud and Mignard. Gaiety, airy and sparkling effects characterize his elegant groups arranged under trees, thus breaking the tradition of stuffy interiors and cold classical vistas of corridors. He made them alive with an atmosphere of charm and humanity. His arcadian scenes—French courtiers and their ladies masquerading as harlequins and shepherdesses in appropriate gardens—held up a faithful mirror to the artificial life of 18th-century

society. But his sub-
jects throughout re-
mained free from
the coarse sugges-
tiveness introduced
by some of his fol-
lowers. Grace and
poetry are manifest
in all his work—
etchings as well as
paintings. - His deli-
cate, brilliant colour
is inimitable in the
latter, and so, in
both branches of his
art, is his fluent
drawing. Following
in the Watteauesque
tradition, J. B. J.
Pater (1695–1736)
excelled in ' fêtes
galantes.' Watteau's
pupil, Lancret (1660–
1743), was a charm-
ing painter, with-
out the genius of
his master; Nattier
(1685–1766) was a
successful portrait-

EL GRECO'S 'AGONY IN THE GARDEN.' El Greco counts today as the most modern of all Spanish painters. His geometry of design and brilliant colour—notably in this picture—make a strong appeal to present-day artists.
National Gallery

ist of the Rococo period; Boucher (1703–
1770) and Fragonard (1732–1806) were
much influenced by Watteau. The former was a fine etcher and decorator, and
his portraits of Madame de Pompadour
are well known. Fragonard, who studied
in Rome and outlived the Revolution, was
also a Court painter and an etcher. He
decorated the apartments of Madame du
Barry with exquisite skill. He was apprenticed to a great artist, Jean Baptiste
Simeon Chardin (1699–1779), an exquisite
portraitist, and one of the most important
French painters of the 18th century. He
was famed for his still life, flower and genre
paintings. An artist whose pictures possess
delicacy of colour and charm is Jean
Baptiste Greuze (1725–1805), but his work
is spoilt by pretty sentimentality and somewhat weak draughtsmanship.

French sculptors followed dutifully in
the footsteps of a classic fashion that had
ost all vitality, until a climax was reached
n the domination of Europe by Canova
and Thorwaldsen, whose uninspired perfection held sway till the 19th century was
well advanced. A few French names have
survived, but not gloriously.

Spanish Art. The ' historical ' period
dates from the School of Seville towards the
end of the 16th century. The first name to

stand out is Zurbaran. Francisco Zurbaran
(1598–1662) most truly represents the som-
breness of the national character at this
time ; he was pre-eminently the painter of
the monks and of the dramatic side of the
Catholic Reaction. His is emotional art,
indeed, with the emotion pitched in one
key ; yet he has a fine sense of form and
handles his limited palette skilfully.

El Greco and Velazquez. Earlier than
Zurbaran was working the celebrated mystic
painter, Theotocopuli, known as El Greco
(1545–1614), who, though born in Crete,
became a Spanish master, painting in
startling contrast to the school represented
by Zurbaran and the greatest of all Spanish
artists, Velazquez (1599–1660). El Greco
was influenced by the religious mysticism of
Ignatius Loyola, the founder of the Jesuit
Order. This mysticism is noticeable in all
his pictures. In comparing the technique of
El Greco with that of Velazquez it is
important to note that the latter is always
grasping at essential things in the world as
he saw it, while the former is always concerned with the world of the spirit. The
technique of Velazquez is stronger and more
perfect, but he lacks the imagination and
creative originality which distinguish the
work of El Greco in such a masterpiece as
' Christ's Agony in the Garden.' On the

Art 13

PORTRAIT BY GOYA of Doña Isabel Cobos de Porcel. *In addition to his portraiture of notable persons, he depicted with unflinching realism scenes from the contemporary life of the streets and of war.*

National Gallery

human character may be studied in a long series of portraits of the Bourbons and the men who stood behind them, now scattered throughout the European galleries. One marvels the more at his achievement since the Court to which he was painter held etiquette hardly second to religion, and every one of its members wore a mask of cold dignity to conceal his inner self from the world. But Velazquez penetrated the masks. Perhaps the greatest and most human of his portrait groups is ' Las Meniñas ' (the Maids of Honour). The National Gallery has examples of his work—portraits, historical scenes and the Rokeby Venus.

Ribera (1588–1656), though associated for the greater part of his life with Naples, must be classed as belonging to the Spanish School. His large historical pictures were influenced by Caravaggio.

Goya. Compared with El Greco and Velazquez, Murillo (1617–1680) is merely a journeyman painter, though he enjoyed an enormous popularity. His subjects are marred by over-sweetness and strained sentiment. Spanish painting remained quiescent and undistinguished till the later part of the 18th century, when Goya (1746–1828) ' arrived.' A talented artist of immense versatility, Goya was a rebel by nature, and much of his art is keen satire directed against the effete and corrupt Church and State. The vitriolic pungency of his work is expressed in his famous etchings. His portraits are characterized by uncompromising realism.

other hand, El Greco could not render contours and textures so delicately or so truthfully, yet his grey tones are an extraordinary anticipation of modern art. ' The Burial of the Count of Orgaz ' in the church of Santo Tomé, Toledo, is considered to be one of his greatest works.

In his first years of painting Velazquez followed Zurbaran in colouring. The Spanish school loved warm colours—reds, yellows, orange —and painted their shadows in browns. The effect was heavy and lacking in variety. Velazquez developed his magnificent sense of colour after his visit to Italy. Like Rembrandt, he has been called an Impressionist. His insight into

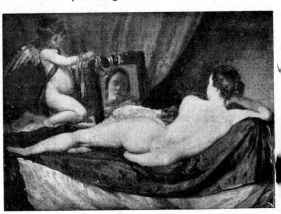

THE 'ROKEBY VENUS.' *This Venus and Cupid by Velazquez was painted for Philip IV of Spain and is an excellent example of the great master's realism and modernity. Velazquez was one of the first painters to suggest detail without actually painting it.*

National Gallery

A Note on English Painting to the 16th Century

THE earliest English painting is in the form of illuminated manuscripts. Illumination was introduced into this country from Scotland, whither it had arrived from Ireland. Early painting, therefore, had a strong Celtic influence. The Book of Kells, dating from the 7th century, is a copy of the Gospels remarkable for its brilliant colour, though it contains Byzantine elements not found in other work of Celtic origin. Book ornamentation achieved a high level of artistry in the monastic settlements of Northern Britain, notably at Lindisfarne on Holy Island off the coast of Northumbria. The Lindisfarne Gospels, dating from the 8th century, were executed in honour of St. Cuthbert and provide a striking proof of early Northumbrian Christian art.

Illumination. Craftsmen from Byzantium assembled at Charlemagne's Court at the beginning of the 9th century, and the resultant art developed into the Carolingian style which has been described as Franco-Saxon. From this root there spread widely differing branches across Western Europe. In Britain during the 10th century illumination was practised increasingly. Scandinavian motifs were introduced into native art about this time, and a further development of the linear style took place. Anglo-Saxon painting surpassed the Carolingian in delicacy and beauty of line. The earliest Winchester manuscript, now in the British Museum, was given by King Edgar in 966 to the New Minster on its reconstitution.

Under the Normans a large number of churches modelled on the style of the Abbaye aux Dames and the Abbaye aux Hommes, which William I had built at Caen, introduced the Romanesque style to this country. Scope was thus given for wall painting and interior decoration. A fine style of decoration was encouraged by the Cluniac monks, both in architecture and illumination. The cult of the Virgin attained

greater importance during the Romanesque period, and a further source of development took the form of bestiaries—books of allegorical stories wherein the characters were animals. The colours were red, green or blue, and the bestiaries were partly in verse and partly in prose.

Matthew Paris (c. 1200–1259), who entered the Benedictine monastery of St. Albans, gives a vivid description in his Chronicles of the early Gothic age. He illustrated his historical works with pen and ink drawings. In his ' Chronica Minora ' he drew his own portrait. This is the earliest self-portrait of an English artist. Decoration became ornate during the Middle Gothic period and emancipation from strictly ecclesiastical motifs became more marked. The three Gothic periods—Early, Middle and Late—stand for simplicity, romanticism and realism.

Portraiture. The invention of printing dealt a death-blow to illumination, and, at the same time, the Renaissance encouraged a contempt for forms of English art. With the Reformation early ecclesiastical art was largely destroyed. English painting was discouraged, and during late Tudor and Stuart times art was imported. Portraiture took the place of ecclesiastical themes. Many of these portraits, painted on wood, were conceived as flat, rather stereotyped studies in which dress and ornament were of paramount interest.

Foreign portraitists who influenced English painters of the Tudor period were the Dutch Sir Anthony More (Antonis Mor) (1519–1578), the German Hans Holbein (*see* Lesson 12), and the Italian Federigo Zucchero (1543–1609), who painted portraits of Queen Elizabeth and Mary Queen of Scots. English painters such as John Bettes (c. 1530–1573) and Hans Eworth (d. 1574) were strongly influenced by the lavish colour and masterly technique of Holbein.

Nicholas Hilliard (1537–1619) was a superb miniaturist. His miniature of his father, Richard Hilliard, and

HEAD OF A KING, an example of 13th century English painting. It was copied from a fresco in the cloisters of St. George's Chapel, Windsor, by Prof. E. W. Tristram

Victoria & Albert Museum

his 'Queen Elizabeth' are outstanding examples of his art. The Hilliard tradition was continued by Isaac Oliver (d. 1617) and his son Peter (1594–1647). Other important English painters of a slightly later date include John Hoskins (d. 1664) and his nephew, Samuel Cooper. Hoskins' miniature of Charles I at Windsor Castle has been described as the most revealing portrait in existence of that monarch.

English Painters of the 17th and 18th Centuries

THREE great foreign artists dominated portraiture in England during the Stuart period—Sir Anthony Van Dyck (1599–1641), Flemish Court painter to Charles I, Sir Peter Lely (1618–1680), Dutch Court painter to Charles II, and the German, Sir Godfrey Kneller (1646–1723). All three had much influence on the magnificent epoch of British painting which immediately succeeded them and continued throughout the reigns of the four Georges. Lely is famous for the series of ' Beauties ' at Hampton Court, though his masterpieces are his splendidly individualized ' Admirals ' at Greenwich Hospital. Kneller's popularity as a portraitist was so prodigious that his large output of work is of necessity unequal. Two fine examples, which combine delicacy of modelling with firmness and reveal his skill as a colourist, are the portraits of Sir Christopher Wren and ' The Duke of Monmouth after execution,' both in the National Portrait Gallery.

Genre Pictures. Kneller was governor of the first art school in London, situated near Lincoln's Inn Fields. He had, therefore, ample opportunity to influence the technique and style of the rising generation of painters, although amongst them a distinctively English art was forming, while a demand was being created among the well-to-do public for a different type of picture. Large portraits and vast paintings of classical subjects were suitable for palatial buildings and the stately mansions of the great ; but now the prosperous professional classes and city merchants required smaller pictures to adorn the panelled walls of their Georgian houses, which were being erected by terrace and square in city and town, while sporting squires wished for paintings of hunting scenes and of their horses and dogs. The immediate demand, therefore, was for something more after the Dutch type of *genre* pictures. William Hogarth (1697–1764), the first definitely English painter of genius in the 18th century, arose to supply this demand with his extraordinary output of narrative pictures, stage scenes, ' moralities ' and small ' conversation pieces.' The last-named type of portrait groups, in which all the members of the family introduced were united in some occupation or interest, were exceedingly popular throughout the century. The painters John Zoffany (1733–1810) and George Stubbs (1725–1806) are particularly noted for their fine work in this style of portraiture (*see* colour plate facing p. 41). The latter artist also excelled as an animal painter.

Sir James Thornhill (1675–1734), who succeeded Sir Christopher Wren as M.P. for Melcombe Regis, is mainly remembered for his decorative painting. This includes the Painted Hall at Greenwich Hospital, the interior of the dome of St. Paul's Cathedral, and the great hall at Blenheim Palace. Thornhill is the only English exponent of large-scale baroque decoration. He was Hogarth's father-in-law, and founded the academy of painting which Hogarth subsequently reorganized in St. Martin's Lane.

Hogarth. Hogarth was born in Smithfield, the son of a schoolmaster, and was an engraver before he began to paint in oils at the age of thirty. His industry was almost as amazing as his gift of memory and the fluent swiftness of his art. He professed much contempt for foreigners, though he derived great benefit from the study of Dutch pictures ; his method of composition by means of light and shade was influenced by Rembrandt. He may also be compared with Hals in the talent which they both possessed of being able to catch to perfection momentary facial expressions. The ' Shrimp Girl ' in the National Gallery, London, is the finest example of Hogarth's work of this kind. Excellent also in their lifelike characterization, though without unity of composition, are the six heads of his ' Servants ' in the National Gallery.

Hogarth lived and worked through a troubled period. It was an age of violent

GAINSBOROUGH. 'The Blue Boy,' a masterpiece now in America, is the portrait of the son of an ironmonger of Soho painted by Gainsborough about 1770 in defiance of Reynolds' dictum that a cool colour such as blue could not be used as the main colour of a painting.

GROUP PAINTINGS. Both George Stubbs (1725–1806) and George Romney (1734–1802) excelled in group portraiture. Above, a squire and his reapers painted and aquatinted by Stubbs in 1791 ; below, the Beaumont Family by Romney, who is ranked only after Reynolds and Gainsborough. His male portraits are excellent.

contrast between the upper and the lower classes of society, of wild experiments in government and finance, of State lotteries, of the South Sea Bubble, of the most flagrant abuses of power, privilege, and common human decencies. He hated hypocrisy and showed up some of these abuses in such pungent fashion that they were uprooted. The fame of his pictorial series of moralities—'Marriage à la Mode,' 'The Rake's Progress,' 'The Harlot's Progress,' etc.—is not, however, based only on their moral or narrative interest. The six pictures of the first-mentioned series belong to his most brilliant period, as also does that masterpiece—portraying the contemporary misery and destitution of the poor in France—'Calais Gate,' painted in 1749, in which he records his arrest while sketching the town.

Charles Johnson, official lecturer at the National Gallery, London, in 'English Painting' (Bell, 1932), says of Hogarth :

His wide sympathy inspired in him a curiosity to investigate every aspect of human life, so that he proved that anything can be interesting and even picturesque. His excitement in noting movement and life naturally led to a swift enjoyable method of painting figures ; just as his perception of the beauty of lighting led to a transparent painting of its gradations. The same wide sympathy led him to moralize. Whether this was also good for his art has been doubted. Certainly it often caused him to overstress his meaning or overcrowd his canvas, and sometimes to become obscure or even to forget the requirements of a picture altogether. It has been said that he was at his best as a cool, detached observer. But sympathy makes complete detachment impossible ; and without such sympathy with the inner workings of men's minds he could never have recorded their outward actions with such vivacity.

Reynolds and Gainsborough. By the time that Hogarth had arrived at the height of his powers two younger painters were coming to the fore. Sir Joshua Reynolds (1723–1792) and Thomas Gainsborough (1727–1788) were rivals throughout their careers, and their relative merits have been vigorously contested. Though the former artist exercised a more lasting influence on portraiture, Gainsborough was the more versatile painter—he would have been famous for his landscapes alone—and possessed the deeper insight. Some of his most exquisite masterpieces are now in America, notably the lovely painting of Eliza Linley (afterwards Mrs. Richard Brinsley Sheridan) and her brother ; a most delightful portrait of a little girl, 'Miss Juliet Mott,' and the famous 'Blue Boy.' (*see* colour plate facing page 40). In London, his 'Miss Singleton' (Nat. Gal.) and 'Mrs. Robinson' (Wallace Col.) are beautiful examples of his genius for painting women.

Gainsborough never laboured his art ; poetry was implicit in what he saw. He derived an additional dexterity from the study of the work of the Flemish masters, Van Dyck and Rubens ; Hogarth also influenced his portraiture, while in

HOGARTH'S 'CALAIS GATE.' *William Hogarth (1697–1764) painted the tragedy and folly of real life, and thereby drew upon himself the displeasure of the critics of his day. He lacked the 'grand manner' of his contemporaries and his work was therefore misunderstood. 'Calais Gate'—based on an incident that occurred during his visit to France in 1748—is one of his best-known compositions and is a biting commentary on greed and avarice.*
National Gallery

landscape he deeply appreciated and studied the technique of the French artists Nicolas Poussin and Claude of Lorraine. Gainsborough was great enough to learn from others and yet evolve his own individual style. Much of his work is painted thinly with rare beauty of execution and luminous colour, for, unlike Wilson or Turner, he never made his subject poetical. Ruskin said he was the greatest colourist since Rubens.

Sir Joshua Reynolds was founder and first president of the Royal Academy in London (1768). Steeped in the tradition of the great Italians—and also receiving the mantle of Sir Godfrey Kneller as his successor in portraiture in the grand manner and following him in the use of a rich impasto—he painted both portraits and historical pieces. But whereas he lives through his portraiture, he was comparatively mediocre in the historical compositions, which he himself believed to be the more important part of his work, painted according to the doctrines which he preached in his famous 'Discourses.' To some extent his portraiture is also intellectual in character. In his earlier work he was always making experiments and so striving after perfection that his painting lost the freshness which characterizes that of his great rival Gainsborough ; but, in many of Reynolds' portraits the psychological insight is penetrating and sympathetic, showing his wide understanding of humanity. He is usually at his best in his portraits of men, but the exquisite ' Nelly O'Brien,' painted in 1763 and now in the Wallace Collection, London, is one of his finest masterpieces. In this portrait he has combined spontaneity with the complete finish which he loved.

Romney, Raeburn and Lawrence. George Romney (1734–1802) followed Reynolds in the grand manner of portraiture and classical grouping (*see* colour plate facing p. 41), and also was one of those encouraged by his teaching to study historical composition, but he had great individual qualities. His work is less even in quality than that of either Gainsborough or Reynolds, but he possessed a strong sense of beauty ; most of his many portraits of Lady Hamilton reveal her loveliness enhanced by exquisite decorative arrangement.

The Scottish artist Sir Henry Raeburn (1756–1823) ranks with Gainsborough and Reynolds. His portraits of lairds and old ladies are superb. Of all British portraitists of his day he had the finest sense of character ; his technique was forceful and brilliant. Many of his finest portraits were painted in the first decade of the 19th century. In England John Hoppner (c. 1758–1810), though not comparable with Raeburn in acute or sympathetic penetration of character, was carrying on the tradition of great painting. John Opie (1761–1807), of Cornish origin, is at his best as a realistic recorder of country scenes ; his more ambitious historical compositions suffer from theatricality, while his later more sophisticated portraits lack the sincerity of his earlier work.

With Sir Thomas Lawrence (1769 – 1830) the great Reynolds tradition in portraiture came to an end. Though possessed of extraordinary facility as a capable draughtsman and executant with his brush, this most successful portrait painter in the time of George IV lacks sincerity in his work.

TWO BRITISH PORTRAITS. *Left, Miss Nelly O'Brien, a famous beauty of her time, painted by Sir Joshua Reynolds in 1763. Right, Sir Henry Raeburn's portrait of Sir John Sinclair Laird. Raeburn set up as a portrait painter in Edinburgh and quickly became famous and fashionable, excelling in male subjects.*
Wallace Collection; National Portrait Gallery

Blake. Working in London during this highly creative period, but, on account of his imaginative genius, somewhat removed from it, was the great mystic, who was both painter and poet, William Blake (1757–1827). He was influenced by Sir Joshua Reynolds' ideas insomuch as he produced historical compositions (this term included literary or classical subjects not taken from everyday life), the greatness of which Reynolds had always held to be infinitely superior to portraiture. Among other illuminating remarks on Blake, Charles Johnson ('English Painting,' 1932) says :

The power to express movement is one of Blake's greatest gifts. Most of the distortions of which his enemies complain—the lengthened limbs or twisted bodies—are introduced for no other purpose. Had Blake avoided them and accurately copied the pose of a moving figure at an instant of time, the effect upon the eye, as in an instantaneous photograph, would have been that of a sudden cessation. For vision is continuous and not instantaneous, and those like Blake, who can make a figure run or swim or fly, always produce their effect by combining what happens at different instants of time.

Experiments in tempera and in illumination led to a medium which Blake used for

WILLIAM BLAKE'S ' PITY,' an example of his genius for illustration. He found in this design a complete vision of the double image in Shakespeare's lines (Macbeth, Act I, sc. 7), ' And pity, like a naked new-born babe, striding the blast ; or heaven's cherubin hors'd upon the sightless couriers of the air . . . '.
In the possession of Mr. W. Graham Robertson

some of his most impressive designs — his colour-printed drawings. He also painted transparent water-colours, some examples of which are at South Kensington, and a fine collection of his work is at Millbank. His last undertaking was that of engraving a series of designs for Dante's ' Divina Commedia,' but his finest engravings are perhaps the twenty-one illustrations for the Book of Job (at the British Museum).

LESSON 16

British Landscape from Wilson to Constable

DURING the reigns of the four Georges the art of landscape painting was not neglected in England. The names pre-eminent in this branch, besides Gainsborough—whose beautiful landscape painting is referred to in the preceding Lesson—are Wilson, Girtin, Morland, Bonington, Crome, Turner and Constable. The Welsh artist, Richard Wilson (1714–1782), studied in London and Rome, and produced a series of excellent landscapes in the grand manner both of subject and treatment. These were unappreciated during his lifetime. Unity characterizes his work and the effect of his wonderful power of rendering light and space. Thomas Girtin (1775–1802), a Londoner, left behind him, in spite of his short life, works of enduring beauty ; his paintings are of cathedrals and abbeys, and far exceed works by his contemporaries. George Morland (1763–1804) painted obvious rustic scenes and had a robust sense of character and colour. Richard Parkes Bonington (1801–1828) has been called the Keats of English painting. Like the poet, he loved beauty, like him, he influenced successors in his art by exquisite work, and he died young of consumption. Many of his watercolours, noted for bright colouring and delicate drawing, were acquired for the Wallace Collection, London.

Towards the end of the 18th century a school of landscape painters flourished at Norwich, the leading spirit of which was

John Crome (1768–1821). Known as 'Old Crome,' he was nearly forty when he produced his first masterpiece, ' Moonrise on the Marshes of the Yare,' now in the National Gallery. Crome's eye for colour was subtle and his sense of design exquisitely delicate.

Turner. One of the greatest — by some authorities considered the greatest— of English painters and of landscape painters in the world, William Turner (1775–1851) was the son of a barber and born in London. He

' WINDSOR.' Painted in 1808, this picture of the great castle in its pastoral setting is a product of Turner's ' Wordsworthian mood,' when he was intent on depicting the beauties of the English landscape. He first exhibited at the Royal Academy in 1790 and in the course of his long life executed hundreds of paintings and nearly 20,000 drawings. *Tate Gallery, Millbank*

was apprenticed at the age of thirteen to Thomas Malton, an excellent draughtsman of architecture. This training brought out Turner's wonderful power for the explanation of structure in his later work, which enabled him to combine in his pictures— more completely than any other artist had been able to do—the solidity of all natural forms introduced with his understanding of the atmospheric qualities of light and air. Turner learnt much from the best of the older English landscape painters—Wilson, Gainsborough, Crome and Girtin; indeed, his debt to the exquisite work of Girtin was considerable. He greatly admired both Poussin and Claude, paying them all the compliment of some imitation. To the National Gallery, London—to be hung next to two fine examples of Claude's work— Turner bequeathed his ' Sun rising through Vapour ' and ' Dido building Carthage ' as an acknowledgement and a challenge.

' MOONRISE ON THE MARSHES OF THE YARE.' John Crome (1768–1821) was born in Norwich, and many of his most famous paintings, including the one shown here, are of scenes in the Norfolk countryside. He was the leading spirit of the Norwich Society of landscape painters, and to their exhibitions he contributed nearly 300 works. *National Gallery*

While ready to learn about gradations of light and classical composition from the French master, Turner's genius joined almost mathematical precision of drawing with atmospheric softness, and as a draughtsman of trees he is unsurpassed.

In water-colour Turner achieved the strongest possible contrast between lights and darks. In his earlier landscapes in this medium the colours are subdued and their luminous quality depends on gradations of light and shade. He did

'ON THE WYE.' Richard Wilson (1714–82) studied portrait-painting, but soon turned to landscape. He won fame with his '*Niobe*' in 1760 and was one of the original Academicians in 1768. *'On the Wye'* is in the National Gallery.

period, and 'Windsor' is a beautiful example at the Millbank Gallery. After the Wordsworthian mood had passed came the idea of rivalling Claude in classical composition, and it was not till Turner was forty-four that he first visited Italy, and the series of lovely water-colours of Venice resulted, together with some important oil paintings, such as the exquisite 'Bay of Baiae.'

The year 1829 marks the beginning of the final phase of Turner's career,

not use oil-colour until after he was twenty-one, and the work belonging to his first period of oil-painting was too dark in tone as a whole. He was at his best when painting sea pieces, ships and the men in them.

Charles Johnson, in 'English Painting' (1932), considers that the spirit of Turner's earlier work—pictures of ruined castles, stormy seas and frowning mountains—is akin to that of Byron, while, after his continental tour in 1802, his eyes being opened to the beauty of a type of English scenery hitherto neglected, his mood became Wordsworthian: 'though Turner had probably not read Wordsworth's poetry, but rather was inspired, like the poet, by a spirit belonging to the age.' 'The Sun rising through Vapour' and 'Frosty Morning,' both at the National Gallery, belong to this Wordsworthian

as he then adopted his individual technique as a colourist. An example of this perfected sense of rich colour is 'Ulysses deriding Polyphemus' (National Gallery). Mr. Johnson places 'The Fighting Téméraire' (National Gallery) highest of Turner's achievements ; painted when he was sixty-three, it contains 'all the glory of his later colour without any vagueness. It has all

'LOCK ON THE STOUR.' Painted in 1817 by John Constable (1776–1837), this Suffolk landscape demonstrates his remarkable gift for the expression of atmosphere and movement of the wind in sky and trees. Constable was a native of East Bergholt, in Suffolk, and he was never so much at home as in his pictures of his East Anglian flats.   *Victoria and Albert Museum. S. Kensington*

his splendour of invention, with all his depth of feeling.'

The output of Turner's work is vast ; throughout his lifetime from the age of twelve he painted continuously. He pointed a new way in his later work ; with its concentration on the problem of light and its relation to colour, it formed the starting point of French Impressionism.

Constable. Contemporarily with Turner was working that other celebrated landscape painter, John Constable (1776–1837), the son of a Suffolk miller. After early apprenticeship in his father's business Constable became an artist at twenty-three. Technical ability was slow in arrival and his best work was done after the age of forty ; his great ambition was to be a ' natural painter.' Though far less ambitious and greatly inferior to Turner in draughtsmanship, Constable had an exquisite sense of local colour, and after much labour produced a style of his own which won wide appreciation and recognition in France, and he practically became the leader of a new school of realistic landscape painting.

Constable was supremely able to depict lovely colour in meadow and forest, the movement of foliage in the breeze, of the sea in sunlight, and of clouds in the sky. The beauties of nature took on a new significance in his hands. The 18th century convention of painting brown trees received its coup de grâce at the hands of Constable.

Green trees appeared in his canvases, and caused a sensation when they were first exhibited. After Constable had taught painters to use their eyes when they studied nature, no one thought further of brown trees. Canvases became lighter, landscapes scintillated. Constable's natural medium was oils, and he handled his paint superbly. Examples of his work at his happiest period are ' Flatford Mill ' (National Gallery) and the beautiful ' Cottage in a Cornfield ' and ' Lock on the Stour ' at the Victoria and Albert Museum, both painted in 1817. In his later work he made lavish use of his palette knife to dab on impasto high lights, which sometimes led him into clumsiness of technique. In contrasting Constable with Turner Charles Johnson says :

They have both been called Impressionists, and were both in many ways pioneers of the movements of that name. For they were both students of light. But while Constable loved to record a fleeting instant of time when light was passing, Turner's peculiar gift lay in representing the gradual increase or decrease of light upon an abiding spacious area. Turner was ultimately always concerned with form. Even when most vague in his drawing he aimed at making the horizon appear immeasurably far away. Turner's accuracy of perception of tone, combined with the system of colour he used in his later works, makes him the forerunner of the scientific Impressionists. Constable's indifference in his sketches to fact and absorption in the momentary effect make him the forerunner of the emotional Impressionists.

LESSON 17

Influence of the Pre-Raphaelites

TOWARDS the middle of the 19th-century portraiture was almost at zero, and subject pictures by the popular artists, Landseer, Leslie and Frith, were sentimental, theatrical or trivial. The necessary art revival came with the pre-Raphaelite Brotherhood, but just before that movement George Frederick Watts (1817–1904) and Alfred Stevens (1817–1875) had begun their careers. Both of these artists remained outside the pre-Raphaelite movement, and both were influenced by Greek sculpture and Italian painting—Watts by the great Venetian colourists and Stevens by the masters of the Renaissance period. Watts, having gained a premium for a cartoon for the decoration of the palace of Westminster, studied in Italy, and

from the time of his return to England, in 1847, became one of the most noted artists of his day. His famous series of portraits of the intellectual leaders—John Stuart Mill, Carlyle, Cardinal Newman, Tennyson, Matthew Arnold, Gladstone and others—with the gift of which he enriched the National Portrait Gallery, London, prove him to be a great painter. His allegories constitute the supreme instance of didactic art, and are neglected by present-day schools. He possessed—though he used them unequally —both the gift for grand design and the mastery of technique. ' Time, Death and Judgement ' (Millbank) and ' Love and Death ' (Millbank) are among his finest symbolic pictures, most of which are powerfully imaginative in conception, showing forth the strangely mingled agnosticism and faith which composed Watts' religion. He painted many good landscapes, but achieved only transient success as a sculptor.

Alfred Stevens, on the contrary, was a sculptor of genius. He was also an excellent painter and a faultless draughtsman. While studying in Italy, he worked under the Danish sculptor Thorwaldsen, and on his return designed, amongst other decorations for public buildings, the four mosaics of the Prophets for the dome of St. Paul's. He was unable himself to complete his greatest work—the monument of Wellington in St. Paul's—owing to lack of means and the magnificence of his conception; it was finished from his model thirty-seven years after his death. In addition to his many lovely cartoons—notable among them being those for Dorchester House—he painted some excellent portraits, a fine example of which is ' Mrs. Collmann ' (Millbank). Frederick, Lord Leighton, Sir Edward Poynter and many other painters in the classical style, whose work was profusely exhibited during the nineteenth century, never attained the level of Stevens' art. His classicalism was inherent, and no imitation of ancient Greek sculptors or Italian masters of the Renaissance.

Holman Hunt and his Followers. The originators of the pre-Raphaelite movement, William Holman Hunt (1827–1910), Dante Gabriel Rossetti, the painter-poet (1828–1882), and Sir John Everett Millais (1829–1896), determined at the outset of their careers to substitute romance and poetry for the trivial subject pictures painted by most of the popular artists of the day. They desired to shake themselves free of traditions which had mainly degenerated into superficial presentments of academic art. They set out to revive the humble and conscientious attitude towards Nature which had characterized the work of the Italian Primitive painters. In 1849, a year after the pre-Raphaelite Brotherhood was established, its three members exhibited their first representative P.R.B. pictures : ' Rienzi,' by Hunt, ' Isabella and Lorenzo,' by Millais (the subject selected from Keats'

Mrs. Collmann, a portrait by Alfred Stevens. It has been described as the most beautiful by any English painter in Victorian times.
Tate Gallery, Millbank

poem ' Isabella and the Pot of Basil '), and ' Girlhood of the Virgin,' by Rossetti.

Though these first pictures received some favourable criticism, abuse was soon directed against the P.R.B. The very name for which these initials stood was obnoxious to academic critics, who considered Raphael the greatest of all painters and the Primitives of comparatively little interest. So bitter was the attack on Rossetti's beautifully designed picture, ' The Annunciation,' exhibited in 1850, that he never publicly showed his work again during his lifetime ; while the pictures exhibited by Hunt and Millais, at the same Academy Exhibition, fared little better. In strenuous opposition to the new movement was Charles Dickens, who wrote a scathing article in his magazine ' Household Words.' Swiftly defensive appeared Ruskin's letters in ' The Times,' demanding fair play for the youthful painters and pointing out the value of the revival of the medieval spirit.

Holman Hunt was the only one of the pre-Raphaelites—into whose circle also came Ford Madox Brown, William Morris and Sir Edward Burne-Jones—to paint unswervingly throughout his career within the laws laid down by the youthful aspirants. Hunt was a man of powerful individuality and strong religious convictions, which influenced his work. His faults were a certain rigidity in the posing of his figures, a superabundance of detail and crudity in the colours he used—the results of painting everything as he knew it to be rather than as he actually saw it. These faults were overcome in some of his work, notably in ' The Hireling Shepherd ' (Manchester City Art Gallery) and in ' Claudio and Isabella ' (Millbank). Many of his pictures reveal great beauty of design—for example, the ' Triumph of the Innocents ' (Millbank) and ' The Scapegoat ' (Port Sunlight)—but require to be studied in detail for true appreciation of his genius.

Millais' most successful pictures in the P.R.B. manner are his ' Ophelia ' (Nat. Gallery), ' The Blind Girl ' (Birmingham Art Gal.), and his realistic ' Christ in the House of His Parents ' (Millbank). A peculiarity of this artist's work—though not originated by him, as he adapted it from the Flemish masters—was his method of painting with transparent pigment over a white groundwork ; this accounts for the brilliant richness of the resultant colour. He cannot be regarded as an inspired painter ; possessed of far greater facility than

anticipated their ideas. His defect—a not uncommon result of pre-Raphaelitism— was an over-conscientious desire for improvement of his painting, which led him into a bad habit of re-touching ; his great qualities were his understanding of fine linear design and his sense of colour. Notable pictures are ' Work ' (Manchester City Art Gal.) ' Last of England ' (Birmingham), and his masterpiece, ' Christ Washing Peter's Feet ' (National Gallery).

Sir Edward Burne-Jones (1833–1898) and William Morris (1834–1896), though both influenced by Rossetti, worked with entirely different aims. The latter actually had a very small pictorial output, but is famous for his influence on the art of his day, and even more so for his championship of the social aims of the people; for that insistence on the necessity of beautifying things in common use which revolutionized many

Hunt, Millais' work was more popular, but is unquestionably of less importance. In the 'sixties he was largely concerned with book illustrations, with which he achieved real success. His later paintings were marred by dullness, due to his lack of imagination and sentimental choice of subjects. His commercial attitude made him a popular painter, but separated him from the earnest aims and ideals of the pre-Raphaelites.

Ford Madox Brown (1821–1893) was in sympathy with them and to some extent

PICTURES BY THE PRE-RAPHAELITE LEADERS. Above, left, is ' The Annunciation ' painted by Dante Gabriel Rossetti (1828–1882), with its formal and beautiful design. Right : ' Claudio and Isabella,' by Holman Hunt (1827–1910), a harmony of dramatic appeal and decorative pattern. Below is the ' Ophelia ' of Sir John Everett Millais (1829–1896), jewel-like in its brilliance of colour.

Top left and bottom, National Gallery; top right, Tate Gallery, London

homes throughout the land, by leading to the foundation of the firm of Morris & Co. This celebrated firm undertook the beautifying of everything from wall papers and furniture to table ware and tapestry. Unfortunately, influenced by Ruskin, Morris refused to recognize the possibility of beauty in machine-made goods, and thus, instead of being a forward movement, much of his work was retrograde, while designs for the machine-made goods of his day were divorced from aesthetic authority.

The earliest work of Burne-Jones was in water colour. In these pictures and in his subsequent oil paintings was a special appeal to the literary public on account of their ' poetical and conventional art.' Influenced by the lovely linear designs of Botticelli, Burne-Jones possessed great imagination and a highly decorative sense of pattern. He devoted much time to designs for stained glass windows, to be carried out by William Morris, and prepared many illustrations for the Kelmscott Press, notably for the Morris edition of Chaucer.

In spite of the subsequent confusion of its motives, pre-Raphaelitism undoubtedly acted as a spur to British art, even after Ruskin's championship of it had ceased to reverberate. It urged sincerity in art-thought and honesty of craftsmanship, and although the ' precious ' technique associated with it died out, much of the courageous independence shown by British artists towards the end of the century was due to the new spirit it inculcated. English sculpture also, which up to the middle of the century knew only that solitary genius Alfred Stevens—though hardly equalling the French achievement—asserted itself as never before. The work of Sir Alfred Gilbert (1854–1934), sculptor of ' Eros ' in Piccadilly Circus, represents the dignified taste of the period ; that of Alfred Drury shows decorative skill. He is specially noted for his groups of sculpture at Leeds.

LESSON 18

Rise of the Romantics and Impressionists

To assume that the French mind is inherently classical in art is a hasty generalization. Tradition is certainly upheld and culture widely appreciated, but a review of the great pictorial productions proves that the French genius is capable of the most amazing departures from academic standards and of the highest original conceptions. After the turmoil of the French Revolution there was certainly a harking back to the antique, but this developed from mere imitation into a creative movement, a feeling for order out of chaos, of which Jacques Louis David (1748–1825) was the leader.

State artist under the Republic, Master of the Ceremonies for the Republican festivals, David was appointed Court painter when Napoleon arose and the Empire style in art and decoration appeared. Greco-Roman forms were the fashion. Laurel wreaths, acanthus leaves, columns, eagles, the toga, classical draperies and sandals were affected in sculpture and as details in settings and costumes both in contemporary portraits and in historical paintings. This movement lasted until 1830, and the Empire style was reflected in England by the classical decoration and architecture of the Regency period.

Well-known pictures by David are his early painting of ' Marat Assassinated,' his portrait of Madame Récamier, and, among his historical paintings, ' The Rape of the Sabines.' His work is distinguished by a sculpturesque quality of clear-cut accuracy of form and is occasionally marred by resultant hardness of texture and by some monotony of colour. His most famous pupil was Jean Auguste Dominique Ingres (1780–1867), who also shows fine restraint of style and superb draughtsmanship, carrying on the nationalized classical tradition in all his work. The National Gallery, London, has an excellent example of Ingres' portraiture, ' M. de Norvins,' and also two small historical paintings. ' La Grande Odalisque ' in the Louvre is, perhaps, his most celebrated picture.

Completely opposed to Ingres was Eugène Delacroix (1798–1863), the leader of the Romantic movement, who has been called the Byron of French art. He was considered a revolutionary, but his mastery of colour was officially recognized and he was employed to decorate a ceiling in the Louvre and the interior of the Chamber of Deputies. A famous picture is his ' Liberty Leading the People,' now in the Louvre. In his landscapes he was influenced by the art of John

Constable. A number of lithographs for the book trade evinced the imagination and vitality of his talent. Until recently his art was quite out of fashion, while that of Ingres, duly admired as being based on simplicity of form and unblurred line, continued to be greatly admired ; its directing structural influence pointed to the development of Cubism.

With Delacroix, however, began that revolt against official art which set a fashion of being proud when work

BEAUTY OF SPRING AT BARBIZON. *Jean-François Millet (1814–75), whose realistic art was poetic and not objective, was the son of a peasant and famous for his pictures of French peasant life. He worked chiefly at Barbizon, where 'Le Printemps' (above) was painted.*   The Louvre

was refused by the Academy and of painting to please oneself. Théodore Rousseau (1812–67), another Independent, known as 'Le Grand Refusé,' was at first entirely outside the pale of recognized art. He, after settling in Barbizon, became the founder of that school of landscape painters also made famous by the work of his associates, Diaz,

Daubigny, Millet and Corot. We have seen in Lesson 16 that the painting of John Constable profoundly influenced the Romantic landscapists of the Barbizon school. It can also be claimed that he and Turner showed the way to the French Impressionists ; but if French art owed a debt to England in the first half of the 18th century, France repaid it in the second half, and since has set the pace for the world.

Barbizon School. The classical painters had been in bondage to the past in choice and treatment of subject. The Romantics of the Barbizon school and elsewhere established the artist's right to take subjects from every phase of life and paint them according to personal vision, a right afterwards consolidated by both Impressionists and Post-Impressionists. Of the Independents in Barbizon, J. F. Millet (1814–75) stands out by reason of the simple directness of his vision. The son of a peasant,

ATMOSPHERIC ART OF COROT. *Prominent among the members of the Barbizon school was Jean Baptiste Camille Corot (1796–1875), whose work is characterized by perfection of technique. 'A Flood,' reproduced above, is a typical example of his later landscape manner.*   Tate Gallery

who had spent his boyhood in his father's fields, he had one motive in all his works: 'Man goeth forth to his labour until the evening.' Visualizing rustic France with complete understanding and sympathetic power, he is recognized as one of its greatest painters. Well-known pictures by him are 'The Gleaners,' 'The Angelus,' 'The Man with the Hoe,' and that composition in lovely light, 'Le Printemps,' a landscape at Barbizon of a field traversed by a path between fruit trees, the fresh green of which stands out against the dark sky arched by a brilliant rainbow.

The work of Jean-Baptiste Corot (1796–1875), one of the finest landscapists who ever lived, differed from that of the other Barbizon painters in that it united Classicism with Romanticism. Perfection of technique characterizes his composition and painting; he combined breadth with exquisite delicacy. He is well represented in British galleries. His reputation suffered somewhat owing to the vast number of spurious works attributed to him, which were produced by copyists to meet the great demand for his pictures. Among his masterpieces are 'Tivoli from the gardens of the Villa d'Este,' 'Danse des Nymphes,' and many of his numerous paintings of misty rivers and lakes, serene moonlight and trees.

An interesting independent painter with a strong dramatic sense was Honoré Daumier (1808–79), who began as a caricaturist and poster artist. Later he excelled as a sculptor, modelling his 'masques' of politicians from memory. As a painter, though one of the pioneers of realism, he was able to visualize in imagination his Don Quixote series. The Parisian scenes which he illustrated in his pictures were mostly of the seamy side of life. If Delacroix may be called the Byron, Daumier was the Charles Dickens of French art. Another realist, Gustave Courbet (1819–77), portrait painter and landscapist, whose work is imbued with a frank realism, was one of the artists from whom Edouard Manet (1832–83) learned, though he owed more to Titian, Hals, Rembrandt and Velazquez.

French Impressionists. With Manet we arrive at the French Impressionists. The word came into use in the eighteen-seventies, when an equally famous leader of the group, Claude Monet (1840–1926), named one of his pictures 'Sunrise—an Impression.' The other great French painters connected with this movement, the most important in the art of the time, were Edgar Degas (1834–1917), Alfred Sisley (1840–99), Pierre Auguste Renoir (1841–1919), Camille Pissarro (1850–1903), and Manet's pupil, Berthe Morisot (1840–95).

Within a few years of the pre-Raphaelite agitation in England Manet painted his 'Olympia,' a work in which the seemingly deliberate ugliness of the subject was a direct challenge to all previous ideas of beauty in art. It may be regarded as Manet's declaration of independence with which to startle Paris and shock the critics, and the picture certainly made a great sensation. Many of his other paintings are, however, delightfully amusing in their sympathetic portrayal of character, as, for example, 'Chez le Père Lathuile,' or his earlier picture, 'Le Bon Bock.' His work has penetrative quality; he revealed by his fine perception of colour and form. In his earlier pictures his designs are more compact and structures are more definitely explained, but in his later work colour in its relation to light is his supreme interest. 'La Servante de Bocks' (Millbank), a scene in a Paris cabaret, is a good example of his later style.

PAINTING BY A PIONEER OF REALISM. Honoré Daumier (1808–79), a French master of the 19th century, was little appreciated in his lifetime. Like the Spanish artist Goya, Daumier excelled in scathing satires and in portraying scenes from the common life of the people. Intensely dramatic, he also possessed imagination, as his picture, reproduced above, of 'Don Quixote and Sancho Panza' reveals, with its tilting knight and eerie shadows.
National Gallery, Millbank

In all his work his aim was to state ordinary things and people with pictorial truth.

Light studied scientifically was the keynote of Impressionism. Claude Monet, after studying Turner's work in England, began to paint with broken strokes of the brush, laid down in touches of pure primary colour. The effect produced is both brilliant and luminous, as may be seen in his ' Vetheuil : Sunshine and Snow,' at Millbank. There is no structural solidity in some of Monet's pictures ; he deliberately sacrifices it to atmospheric effects. In Pointillism, of which the inventive Georges Seurat (1859–91) was the most famous exponent, this absolute painting of daylight was carried

EXAMPLES OF IMPRESSIONISM. *Edouard Manet (1832–1883) and Pierre-Auguste Renoir (1841–1919) were two of the leaders of the French Impressionist movement. Above, Manet's ' La Servante de Bocks '; right, Renoir's ' Les Parapluies.'*
Tate Gallery, Millbank

farther by painting in spots (*points*) of primary colour. It was in Turner's later work that the scientific juxtaposition of the three primary colours, red, blue and yellow, throughout a picture was first introduced, though Gainsborough, Watteau and Rubens had made occasional and partial use of the method in landscape to obtain sunny effects.

Edgar Degas was another Impressionist of genius who, with Manet and Monet, has influenced English art. In addition to his fine rendering of light and atmosphere, he possessed a mastery of anatomical construction, and a superb vitality of movement characterizing his pictures of the circus, the ballet and the racecourse. Alfred Sisley's landscapes, drawn directly with the brush, possess a spontaneous charm. Renoir's sensitive and brilliant painting is seen to perfection in his many portraits and genre pictures : one of his best-known paintings is ' La Loge,' in which a woman, in a black and white evening dress, is seated in a box at the theatre with a man in evening dress. Both figures are superbly realized. Renoir painted with long strokes of the brush, using a preponderance of red and green, which gave great brilliancy to his work. Two fine works are ' Les Parapluies ' and ' La Première Sortie,' both in the Tate Gallery. Toulouse-Lautrec was strongly influenced by demi-mondaine types. His ' Absinthe Drinkers ' is especially outstanding.

The art of the poster dates from the Impressionists. In France the finest poster designers were Toulouse-Lautrec and Chéret, while in England Dudley Hardy and the Beggarstaff Brothers (James Pryde and William Nicholson) were famous pioneers. Puvis de Chavannes (1824–98), though a

' refusé ' from the Salon, is not an Impressionist. His mural paintings were an inspiration to later generations, and he greatly influenced decorative art in England.

Whistler. The Impressionist movement spread through Europe. In England one of the greatest exponents was James A. McNeill Whistler (1834–1903), an American by birth who had studied in Paris. With his contemporary, Edouard Manet, he desired to break away from the academic in art. His ' White Girl ' (Nat. Gal.) roused as great excitement and protest in the ' Salon des Refusés ' (inaugurated by Napoleon III) of 1863 as Manet's ' Déjeuner sur l'herbe.' Whistler's arrival in England was a landmark in the history of our art. His interest in Japanese art and its influence on his work —an influence exercised on most of the French Impressionists, including Manet and Degas—helped to turn attention away from the classical tradition and to present an entirely novel aspect of painting, in which freedom of design—with an understanding that empty spaces could add value to its beauty—and new effects of perspective played an important part. Whistler also helped to form the close alliance with French art so marked in England at the end of the 19th and turn of the 20th century.

Among Whistler's most famous paintings are the portrait of his mother, painted in 1872 and subsequently bought for the Louvre, the portrait of Thomas Carlyle (Glasgow), the ' Princesse du Pays de la Porcelaine,' the lovely design of ' Old Battersea Bridge ' (Millbank), known also as ' Nocturne—Blue and Gold.' His etchings and lithographs are unique in their delicate craftsmanship. His perfection of taste in composition and art of selection have seldom been equalled by English painters, although his ' Nocturnes ' were adversely criticized by Ruskin in ' Fors Clavigera.'

The great revival in English landscape painting during the last fifty years owes much to the French Impressionists. Only a few names can be mentioned here. Wilson Steer (1860–1942), Henry Tonks (1862–1937), Lucien Pissarro (1863–1944), Sir Charles Holmes (1868–1936), and Sir George Clausen (b. 1852) are all Impressionists—using the word in its highest sense—whose greatest gifts are for painting atmosphere and lovely effects of sunlight. Steer was also a sympathetic portraitist ; and Holmes was one of the first painters to discover beauty and pictorial pattern in factory chimneys.

Sargent and Sickert. In portraiture the Impressionists in England include J. S. Sargent (1856–1925)—who, like Whistler, was of American parentage and studied in Paris—and Whistler's pupil, Walter Richard Sickert (1860–1942). Sargent was a prolific and often fine painter, though unequal as a colourist ; like his master, Carolus Duran, he was inspired by Velazquez ; his style is characterized by loose brushwork and greatly influenced contemporary artists.

Sickert, in addition to his portraits, was a great painter of landscape and genre —indoor and outdoor scenes of cosmopolitan life. His highest gift was the power of expressing not only physical but emotional atmosphere. He often painted a cool tint—such as a mauve shadow—over a warm colour—such as an orange ground— representing sunlight. A typical work is the ' Café des Tribunaux, Dieppe,' at Millbank. Sickert's method, like that of the Old Masters, was to prepare a series of the most careful drawings so that the subject was learnt by heart and then to paint from them in a systematic scale of tones in a given colour scheme.

A WHISTLER NOCTURNE. In his series of night pieces on the Thames—one of the loveliest of which, ' Old Battersea Bridge,' is reproduced above— Japanese influence is seen.
Tate Gallery, Millbank

The Reaction of Post-Impressionism

BECAUSE human nature is suspicious of the unfamiliar, new forms of art seem ugly, sometimes even comical, on their first appearance ; gradually, if the idea has been truthfully stated—and the truth may be abstract or concrete—beauty is revealed to the beholder, as understanding increases and prejudice lessens. The perfection of naturalistic and luminous painting had been reached by the masters of the Romantic and Impressionist movements ; nothing more along their lines seemed possible. Manet and Degas had combined realism of atmosphere with superb draughtsmanship ; Seurat had taken Monet's brilliant colour schemes scientifically farther with Pointillism and, in addition, achieved, in such pictures as ' The Woman Powdering Herself ' (Courtauld Collection) and ' The Bathing Party ' (Millbank), a monumental solidity which was a step towards one of the demands of the rising school of painters—the demand for architectural form, lacking in the work of the Impressionists.

Roger Fry named these new painters at the end of the 19th century Post-Impressionists. They declared that their predecessors had sacrificed structure for atmospheric effect—theories of light had become too complex. Though the Impressionists had shown people aspects of Nature which they would otherwise have missed, naturalism was condemned : art is not Nature, they said ; ' it is a pattern or rhythm of design that we impose on Nature.' Mere unselective copying was despised : it was challenged by the camera. They argued that a photographic study could be more realistic than any painting.

Cézanne. All reactions in art are exaggerated ; if they were not they could not gain sufficient impetus to attract attention or become a movement. Movements arise out of exasperation against narrow mental conceptions and attempts at standardization in art. The desire to avoid the faults of the previously accepted school restores balance by a swing-over. But this one-sidedness, however useful as a corrective, does not help progress ; only strongly creative leadership is able to do that. Paul Cézanne (1839–1906), striving towards perfection with unceasing experiments, hit upon the method which revolutionized modern painting.

Though Paul Gauguin (1848–1903) and Vincent Van Gogh (1853–1890) were also originally in this revolutionary movement — which only reached the London public at the Grafton Galleries' Post-Impressionist exhibition in 1910, when the chief painters represented were dead — they were independents. It was Cézanne who inspired numerous followers; it was Cézanne whose very failures were stepping stones for other artists. In his many uncompleted efforts they could see what he had been striving for technically ; what they could not

EXAMPLE OF POINTILLISM. *Georges Pierre Seurat (1859–1891) studied art in Paris and invented a method of painting scintillating light by means of dots. His drawing and composition are monumental and ' solid,' as may be seen in this reproduction of ' La Baignade.'*
National Gallery (Tate), Millbank

emulate was his possession of spontaneous emotion — he was always going beyond impressions in his search for some poetic, spiritual quality. Turning to painting rather late in life, though a genius, he was never able to acquire facility or a good figure memory; also he disliked working from models. He set himself a difficult ideal: to combine the best efforts of impressionism with the structural qualities of Nicolas Poussin — light and colour with architectural drawing and form. Cézanne has been declared a bad draughtsman. His aim was not to outline, but to suggest modelling. Everything in his estimation could be resolved into geometrical forms — all shapes simplified into cylinders, cones and spheres: his very brush strokes were mostly angular. He was thus the man behind Cubism, which, however, did not develop as an art movement till 1908. He made still-life pictures like patterns, just for the pleasure a pattern can give. He considered that a beautiful invention was better than the meticulous copying of grouped objects.

Though Cézanne was often unable to carry out his pictorial conceptions, his successes with ' The Card Players ' (Louvre), ' The Young Philosopher,' and his masterpiece ' La Montagne Sainte Victoire ' (Courtauld Collection), with its solidity of mountain form, have a fine massive simplicity and sometimes a colour value as sensitive as Turner's own. An example of his subtle colour modulation in landscape is given in the colour plate facing page 64.

Beginning with Cézanne, the Neo-impressionists—with only a few exceptions —demanded the ' illusion of solidity.' In common with the English pre-Raphaelites their aims were structural, not merely visual like those of the Impressionists. The pre-Raphaelites, however, with all the mass of structural detail which they introduced

DECORATIVE PAINTING OF PRIMITIVE PEOPLE. *Hatred of civilization drove Paul Gauguin from Paris to Tahiti, where he painted many studies of native life, such as his ' Te Rerioa ' reproduced above. His work is characterized by magnificent colour and design.*
Courtauld Collection

into their pictures, could never attain the same ' roundness ' seen in the work of Cézanne with his simplification of forms. In Turner's painting the structural and visual aims were nearly reconciled . Roger Fry maintained that each reform in the history of painting has been an attempt to balance these two aims.

Gauguin. Paul Gauguin's links with Cézanne were repudiation of naturalism and a certain defiance of perspective. Partly Peruvian on his mother's side, he developed on individual, exotic lines as a supremely decorative artist. Violent in colour and design, his art has chiefly influenced designers for decorative industries. His aims are apart from the modern in serious painting. and for this reason he is not so important as Cézanne. The consistent illusion of solidity does not appear to trouble him. Using a heavy outline frequently to unify his design, Gauguin makes his figures either quite flat or in relief —sometimes in the same picture. While negligent of scientific lighting effects, he produced deeply psychological atmosphere in many of his works painted in Tahiti, where he went in 1891, specializing thenceforth in poetic and faithful renderings of the rich colour and spirit of the South Sea Islands. Notable among his pictures are ' Contes Barbares,' a barbaric idyll of two women and a man amongst lovely and strange flower forms ; ' The Spirit Watchers,' ' Nevermore ' and ' Te Rerioa,' studies of native women charged with mysterious or tragic feeling ; also his portrait of Van Gogh.

Van Gogh. This artist (1853–90), a Dutchman, began to paint in Paris in 1886. His work was chiefly influenced at the outset by Pissarro, Renoir, Cézanne and Seurat. In common with Renoir he used much green and red, with resultant masses of splendid colour in his vigorous designs. His painting is somewhat hard, applied with heavy strokes, sacrificing, after the fashion of the Post-Impressionists, delicate qualities of texture to structure and form. He concerned himself, as did Cézanne, chiefly with pattern. This did not impair his power of characterization in his portraits, while it gave a strange clear-cut beauty to his flower pieces and landscapes (*see* colour plate facing page 64). During his lifetime he sold few canvases—the most he received for a picture amounted to a few francs. Today his masterpieces are exhibited in the chief galleries of the world, where they are a source of inspiration.

Matisse. The most distinguished associate of the three Post-Impressionists already named was Henri Matisse, born in 1869, who carried the search for abstract pattern still farther—so far, indeed, that some of his subjects are deprived of resemblance to Nature. He painted landscape, figure, interiors and flower pieces. Beginning under the influence of Cézanne, later Matisse led the Fauves, at one time termed ' the incoherents.'

Fauvism was taken up in other European countries and found particular acceptance

' VASE OF FLOWERS ' by Henri Matisse shows how, as leader of the Fauves, he pursued flat linear design instead of compositions of ' solid ' form.
Syndicat de la Propriété Artistique

in Germany. The group headed by Matisse returned to direct simplicity of expression. He, like a Primitive, worked freely with colour and line ; like the early Italians, he submitted to the ' discipline of rhythm,' but not to the discipline of Nature. Copyists of Matisse failed because he could make no rules for their guidance. He paints each picture with the treatment he feels that it requires, inventing new qualities in the sensitive relations of colour and in line. Breaking away from Cubism, he painted flat, ignoring alike shadow, modelling and perspective.

LESSON 20

Developments in Modern Painting

A FTER the Post-Impressionists and the Fauves arose, in 1908, the Cubists, with Pablo Picasso (b. 1881) as their leader. Cubism, as the name implies, is mathematical in form ; in its purest style it deals solely with abstract patterns, and its aim has been defined by Roger Fry as an ' abstract language of form—a visual music.' Carrying Cézanne's geometrical simplification farther, the Cubists declared that the abstract primitive form is the cube ; circles are merely edge-worn cubes ; flat

instead of curved surfaces are, therefore, emphasized in their compositions. Six cubes can form a primitive human figure —four for the limbs and two for the head and trunk. Cubes lend themselves readily to making fine geometrical patterns. Anyone who looks at what is known today as ' modern ' design in rugs, tapestry, wallpaper, dress fabrics or pottery is really seeing patterns which owe their origin to the art experiments of the Cubists and Fauves ; receiving their form from the first

—cubes being split up into facets at will—and line and colour from the second group, with a few subsequent developments and profuse adaptation.

The excellent side of the Cubist training is the ability it gives to resolve things to their simplest forms and to grasp their essential shapes ; to hate alike sentimentality and vague treatments ; to regard a weak, blurred outline as a crime and to prefer even a distortion. Cubist pictures are hard and definite, their atmosphere and texture sacrificed to their technique, but the method of splitting the object up into facets of flat planes means that its structure has been understood and the result can never be pretty-pretty or dull. The Cubist—or any structural painter—values light as a means of explaining form ; faces of planes are differentiated to the eye by the tones resultant from the angle at which the surfaces are to the light ; painting these tones lighter or darker gives the object its ' solid ' shape.

Picasso. Pablo Picasso, though born at Malaga, is counted among leading French painters ; he settled in Paris in 1903, and came into the reactionary group of the Post-Impressionists. His earliest paintings are both poetic and realistic, notable achievements. Like Watteau, Daumier, and Degas before him, he often chose his subjects from the picturesque behind-the-scenes of the entertainment world—pierrots, the harlequinade, circus characters, the ballet. After a brief incursion into ' l'Art Nègre ' Picasso, drawing inspiration from El Greco and Cézanne, formulated Cubism. In this movement Juan Gris, a Spaniard born at Madrid (1888–1927), was soon associated. His portrait of Picasso, painted in 1912, is a clear example of early Cubist technique, with its effect of a first stage in a wood-carving. About some of Picasso's work at this time is an extraordinary feeling of disintegration, expressive of the analytical thought and general disruptive tendencies of the decade preceding the First Great War. He sometimes put his portraits together in fragments from different points of view (after the manner of ancient Egyptian reliefs) ; they may show the eye full face in a profile, the shoulders square to the spectator and the legs again viewed sideways. Such experiments on his part were not imitative but were directed

towards the clearing away of his old concepts and creating afresh. To Picasso the subject had ceased to be important in order that it might be suggested (in the abstract) instead of rendered.

Picasso about 1915, with the French painter Georges Braque (b. 1881), began studies in abstract pattern, not to imitate but to create form ; perspective and realism quite vanished from his pictures. Both painters used objects such as violins, jars, pipes and tools, merely for their intrinsically decorative shapes, to form compositions ; from these things they created not ordinary still-life pictures, but new patterns. It was during this period of his experiments that Picasso so greatly influenced modern design ; Cubism has practically changed the forms of nearly everything made within the last thirty years. Of late his painting, still in the experimental stage perhaps, has become even more difficult to understand, but he is accepted as a master of organized form and constructive design, and both architecture and sculpture have been influenced by him, as well as industrial design.

Later developments in France include ' Beyond Cubism,' or Purism ; Dadaism, which appeared in 1920, machinery forming the basis of its designs ; the Surrealists ; and the New Independents, reacting against Cubism. Le Corbusier, the famous French architect and leader of Purism, defines style as ' unity of principle animating all the

PAINTINGS BY FOUNDERS OF CUBISM. Picasso's ' Pierrot ' (left) is after his early manner, poignantly expressive. Later he became leader of the Cubist group, another member of which was Juan Gris who, in 1912, painted the portrait of Picasso (right) in unequivocal Cubist style.
Left, photo by permission of Alex. Reid and Lefèvre, Ltd. ; right, courtesy of ' Art Work '

work of an epoch, the result of a state of mind which has its own special character.' Our own epoch is determining day by day its own style. Out of all these movements mingled, we have the modern style.

Futurism and Vorticism. Of Futurism, which started in Italy in 1910, under the leadership of the Italian writer Marinetti, and of Vorticism, there is only space for briefest mention here. These movements originated in the years before the First Great War in a wave of dynamic violence in art, with its increasing interest in machinery and its wild desire for emancipation from the past. In Futurism arbitrary symbols — ' force lines and rhythms ' together with quasi-geometric patterns — are substituted for realistic representation ; a work of art is a purely subjective expression in an absolute, personal ' language.' Attempts to paint the passage of time—

THE SMILING WOMAN. The portraiture of Augustus John, R.A. (b. 1878), is penetrative and individual. The painting reproduced above is representative of his distinctive and powerful style.

National Gallery, Millbank

by drawing, for instance, ten arms to represent a single arm in motion—are a phase of Futurism which is a synthesis of the movements of living creatures or of objects in activity. Vorticism, a variation of Cubism and Futurism, found its appropriate subjects in the mechanism of modern weapons, and in vast armies of robot-like creatures at drill or on the march. Wyndham Lewis is the chief exponent of Vorticism in England, with his compositions of planes and wedges, the cast-iron countenances of his inhuman figures, the symbolism of mass production and general mechanism of the machine-ruled modern world.

The term Futurism was misapplied by many people in England to include all modern art. As a vital force, however, this ' tubular ' method of painting barely survived the outbreak of war in 1914. During the subsequent period (1918-1939) feverish experimentalism set in, and the twenties saw a formidable array of 'isms. In the immediate post-war years these battled for supremacy among the advanced groups of painters. By the early thirties, up till the London exhibition of Surrealism

in 1936, the general tendency in this country was towards a modified form of Expressionism.

Surrealism, the chief exponent of which was Dali, greatly influenced un-academic European painting, though the full effects were hardly discernible in England until the middle and late thirties. Many of the surrealistic paintings were prophetic, inasmuch as they foretold world disaster and the threat to the civilization of Western Europe. Among the younger English painters whose work was surrealistic were Graham Sutherland, John Armstrong, Edward Bawden, Leslie Hurry, John Tunnard and Edward Burra.

Artists whose reputations were established shortly before and immediately after the last War—Duncan Grant, Vanessa Bell, Harold Gilman, Spencer Gore (the last two belonging to the Camden Town Group founded by Sickert)—displayed a feeling for internationalism. The period between the two Wars intensified this international tendency. It was an age the extreme eclecticism of which produced the subtle distortions of a Marie Laurencin and the abstractions of an Edward Wadsworth. French painters of the 1920's were strongly influenced by Cézanne, Gauguin and the mystical Odilon Redon (1840-1916). At the end of the twenties a reaction had set in and there was a turning back to 15th-century Italian styles. Bonnard, Roussel and Vuillard are important painters in the Expressionist tradition. Modigliani (1884-1920) stands in a class apart. His compositions are curiously foreboding, and were in advance of their time. Contemporary painters in France and England were greatly influenced by Picasso, the Spanish idiom being adopted by the younger French artists.

The Nash Brothers. The art of the woodcut returned to favour during postwar years. Leading figures in its revival were the brothers Paul and John Nash, born respectively in 1889 and 1893. The work of both these artists is of extraordinary interest. Examples of their war pictures show the strong influence of Cubism, in their striking patterns and three-dimensional solid compositions. Even in later work their methods are powerfully structural, the very antithesis in landscape of those of the Impressionists. John Nash, however, shows a tendency to revert to naturalism ; without losing his fine sense of pattern he is dropping certain mannerisms and increasing his breadth of handling masses and sense of atmosphere. Paul Nash has a wide range —from such pictures as his terrifying war landscape, ' Menin Road,' to his fine sea-scapes, sympathetic water colours, dramatic woodcuts and posters.

Augustus John. Though born in 1878, Augustus John is essentially a modern painter while independent of prevailing ' isms.' His painting is vigorous ; his skill in composition, especially in his large group pictures, is magnificent, as may be seen from the study of his decorative cartoon ' Galway ' at Millbank. His portraits are dramatic and spontaneous—the latter quality ranks John in the opinion of some critics among the Impressionists—remarkable alike for fine draughtsmanship and rich colour. Notable examples are his ' Madame Suggia,' ' The Smiling Woman ' and ' The Yellow Jacket,' at Millbank ; in Manchester are ' Meirikli ' (Platt Hall), the portrait of a dark-haired woman of interesting personality, comparable in its fine design and painting with a Venetian master's work, and the ' Boy ' (City Art Gallery), with its simplified yet accurate treatment and fine brushwork.

War Painters. During the First World War the painting of such men as the Nash brothers, C. R. W. Nevinson, Stanley Spencer and Henry Lamb in their tragic war pictures combined vivid reality with the hard definite style, which is, in great part, their individual development of Cubism. Their war pictures should be studied in the Imperial War Museum, together with others by artists for bare mention of whom there is no space here.

As Charles Johnson, in ' English Paint-ing,' has well pointed out, Henry Lamb's great war pictures, ' Irish Troops among the Judean Hills ' (Imp. W. M.) and ' The Advanced Dressing-Station on the Struma ' (Manchester City Art Gallery), exhibit pre-Raphaelite minuteness of detail. In his later work this painter has shown deeply sympathetic insight into character in portraiture.

Stanley Spencer is a very accomplished, original and deeply sincere painter. Apart from his war pictures, which include a series of mural paintings on the walls of an oratory at Highclere, his most successful works—or, at least, his most popularly appreciated—are his landscapes. His mys-tical paintings, ' Christ bearing the Cross ' and his large ' Resurrection ' (both at Millbank), show extraordinary distortions of bodily types and inhumanity of faces. It appears impossible for the painter to combine his mystical ecstasy with the convincing realism which marks such beautiful pattern-compositions as ' Fighting Swans ' and ' Swan Upping at Cookham.'

The Second World War saw the gradual isolation of English painting from the main stream of European movements. This trend was stressed by John Piper (b. 1903) in his studies of war-scarred buildings (such as Coventry Cathedral)—English architectural style blended with dramatic intensity.

The Official War Artists Exhibition at the National Gallery attracted thousands of people whose interest in art was ready to be stimulated by the widest set of standards and values. The tendency during the years preceding the War was to bridge the gap between life as led by ordinary people and the higher realms of imaginative art. Expressionism was therefore encouraged, and the doctrine of art for art's sake (fostered by the aesthetic movement of the

TWENTIETH CENTURY MYSTICAL PAINTING.
Stanley Spencer, A.R.A., a deeply sincere modern British artist, has a certain affinity with the pre-Raphaelites. In his picture ' Christ bearing the Cross ' a fantastic element is introduced ; the curtains of the windows, from which people gaze, blow out with the effect of wings.
National Gallery, Millbank

80's and 90's of the previous century) suffered a decline, and a broader conception of the aims of painters and sculptors was realized.

The broad result of all these intellectual — mathematical and philosophical — art movements has been to promote in English painting structural composition, sincerity, and an echo of that affection for painstaking detail which marked the work of the great pre-Raphaelite Holman Hunt.

There is no direct road to the appreciation and understanding of art. The student is recommended to visit all notable picture galleries and loan collections within reach, and also to attend lectures on painting, when opportunity arises.

Sculpture since the Renaissance

AFTER the apogee to which the genius of Donatello and, later, of Michelangelo had raised the art of sculpture (*see* Lesson 10), it languished throughout Europe for the best part of two centuries, only galvanized from torpidity by flamboyant design and the ' movement ' which characterizes decorative art of the rococo period. This decadence may be broadly described as the aftermath of the revival of interest in everything Greek by scholars and pedants—purveyors of the dead letter of the Renaissance as opposed to its living spirit of scientific inquiry and adventure. It was largely due to the profiteering by the antique dealers—who arose in the Renaissance era and flourished thereafter on the sales of spurious and restored Greco-Roman statues, to propaganda of dealers and collectors, and to the popular taste created thereby for everything pseudo-classical, which came to be recognized as the standard of beauty irrespective of the sculptural merit of the particular piece. It was thus much easier to make a living as a restorer, as a copyist of the antique, or as a conventional sculptor of the ideal, than as an original artist.

In his provocative and interesting book ' The Meaning of Modern Sculpture ' (Faber & Faber), R. H. Wilenski analyses the unwholesome ingredients of what he calls ' prejudice-pie.' Of these the two most injurious to any mental digestion of creative modern ideas on sculpture are : (a) ' the Greek prejudice,' which imposes a belief that, first and last, absolute perfection in sculpture was reached by the Greeks, thus leaving every sculptor since at a dead end, and ignoring the previous glories of ancient Egyptian, Assyrian and Persian carvings ; (b) the ' Renaissance prejudice,' which assumes that the sculptors of this age imitated the Greeks to perfection, capturing the ancient Hellenic spirit

The third and least important ingredient of the pie is the ' Romantic prejudice.' This prejudice consists of extending the finality-form of good sculpture to admit as worthy companions of the Greek the works of Rodin and other works like them. ' The average person's concept of sculpture is thus a finality-form operating as a prejudice against modern sculpture, which is placed outside the prejudice-pie both in point of time and point of value.'

Carving v. Modelling. Mr. Wilenski observes that Donatello, the most typical of 15th-century figures, far from copying the antique, forestalled the Romantics of the 19th century ; that his work has been of cardinal service to Epstein as a modeller for bronze ; that Donatello's art was not Greek, was not even specifically Italian, but international and intensely Gothic in character. ' It is not till we get to Michelangelo's work in the 16th century that we encounter sculpture that is no longer Gothic, and Michelangelo's attitude . . . . was more like that of the original sculptors of our day.' The last statement refers to the Italian master's preference for *carving* as opposed to *modelling in clay*, a preference shared by many modern sculptors.

Michelangelo himself carved his own statues directly into marble, generally without the aid of a preliminary model, except a small sketch in wax or clay. He regarded carving as essentially sculpture and modelling as an art similar to painting. Obviously, plastic clay is the most suitable medium for the subtleties of naturalistic sculpture or portraiture embodying the Romantic doctrines ' that art is nature seen or imagined through the artist's temperament, and that sculptural beauty is emotionally expressive character ' (Wilenski, *ibid.*). Direct carving demands greater accuracy, labour and clarity of concept. Michelangelo considered that ' the finest artist has no concept which the marble alone does not contain within itself.' This idea that essential sculpture is ' collaboration between the sculptor and the block of resistant substance beneath his hand ' is also in the creed of the modern artist who appreciates his material.

Precursors of Michelangelo, the medieval architectural sculptors, were also concerned with helping stones to symbolize life ; they were not concerned, as are modellers of the Romantic school, with ' converting living figures into dead material.'

The worship of the ' antique ' was just as annoying to the independent and scientific minds of the Renaissance creative sculptors as ' prejudice-pie ' is to those of our own day.   Donatello's and Michelangelo's work was regarded by contemporary collectors as utterly inferior to the ideal, restored statues finished with more or less appeal of sensual beauty, according to the customer's requirement.   The output of Greco-Roman sculpture was vast ; practically every Roman house, every public building and place in the Empire, east and west, was decorated with statuary, either looted by the Romans from Greece in the 2nd century B.C. or produced by their own sculptors.   Almost equally vast was the scale of statue-breaking by the Goths and Vandals in their raids over Latin-Hellenic territory and, in the 8th century, of the iconoclasts who destroyed countless statues for religious reasons, while others, surviving the icono- 'clast fury, were refashioned from the original Greek into Christian images.

Concoctions of Antique Statues.   By the 10th century a whole antique statue would be a rare find indeed—the bulk were either melted down if of bronze, or, if of stone, were in fragments buried in the ground. With the revival of Greek culture during the Renaissance gangs of diggers were set to unearth these fragments, and tremendous work in restoration and concoction by the lesser sculptors and assistant craftsmen started forthwith.   The dealers in antiques thenceforth supplied the Vatican, the courts of Europe, noble collectors and museums with ideal restored or faked antiques.

World-renowned pieces as we see them today—the ' Venus of Milo ' and the ' Victory of Samothrace,' to mention only two in the Louvre—are concoctions of fragments put together by restorers.   The torso alone of the ' Victory' consists of 118 pieces stuck together after arrival in Paris in 1863, the fragments having been sold to a Frenchman in the island of Samothrace. How can all these fragmentary compositions—even if the result is sometimes beautiful — be considered authentic antique sculpture ? Mr. Wilenski, with reference to the ' Victory,' says, ' If this concoction had been concocted a hundred years earlier, it is, I submit, only reasonable to suppose that we should know it in quite other and

EFFETE PAGANISM AND DIGNIFIED REALISM.   The decadence that followed Michelangelo is shown in the work (left) of Giovanni Lorenzo Bernini (1598–1680). In direct contrast is the statue of Washington by Jean-Antoine Houdon (1741– 1828), a copy of which stands outside the National Gallery, London.
Left, Galleria Borghese, Rome; photo, Anderson

more Greco-Roman shape.' In Lesson 6 a more conserva- tive view is expressed of Hel- lenistic art. Today the sculptor is apt to react too violently against it owing to the abuse of the Greek tradition.

Bernini. The Middle Ages were free from the Greek prejudice, and much fine and vigorous sculpture was directly carved in stone on Gothic. cathedrals, etc. After the Renaissance the work of that elegant craftsman Lorenzo Bernini (1598-1680) affords a striking example of the de- plorable decadence which set in. Successful in his day as sculptor, painter and architect (in architecture his most notable achievement is the colonnade of St. Peter's, Rome), on contemporary sculpture he exercised a bale- ful influence, with his pseudo-

VOLTAIRE by the great French sculptor, Houdon. Executed in bronze, it is considered to be one of his finest portrait busts.

The Louvre; photo, Giraudon

classicalism, his extravagance of design and his emotional theatricality. Some of his work, after the type of ' Apollo pursuing Daphne,' possesses a pretty grace which, when dwindled to the proportions of chimney-piece ornaments, could serve as an inspiration for the designers of mytholo- gical figure groups in the china factories. His portrait busts of royal and noble personages show his delight in the long hair or huge wigs and in the intricate patterns of the lace collars in vogue at the time.

The sculptors of the Re- naissance were so scientifically curious that in their endeavour to arrive at naturalistic por- traits they used death-masks and casts from life as studies : Bernini could turn out an admired bust in his most expensive style from two pain- tings—without seeing the original and without imaginative vision—all blemishes omitted.

Houdon. Jean Antoine Houdon (1741– 1828), the French sculptor, working in the latter half of the 18th and early 19th centur- ies, forestalled Rodin in his Romantic interest in emotional character, realistic detail and expression. He certainly put in the blemishes. His portrait bust of Gluck, the composer, shows on the animated face traces of small-pox. Away from the conventional allegorical figure is Houdon's ' Negress,' designed during the French revolution for a foundation to commemorate the abolition of slavery, proclaimed by the National Convention, February 4, 1794. Ideal groups were sculptured by him, but it is as a portrait-sculptor that he is famous ; busts and statues include J. J. Rousseau, Voltaire, Mirabeau, Lafayette, Franklin, Washington (he visited America to execute this statue) and Napoleon.

Contemporary with Houdon were the Italian sculptor Antonio Canova (1757–1822), who produced a vast amount of highly finished work on academic pseudo-classical lines, and John Flaxman (1755–1826) in England. Flaxman, also, was academic in style, and his chief claim to admiration lies in his designs for engravings to illustrate Dante's ' Divine Comedy,' and in his decorative line ' Illustrations to Homer,' rather than in his sculptures.

FINE ALLEGORICAL GROUP. ' Truth and False- hood,' one of the groups designed for the Wellington monument in St. Paul's Cathedral, by Alfred Stevens (1817–75).

Victoria and Albert Museum

Alfred Stevens. A follower of Canova's artificial tradition of smooth grace, and equally hidebound in ' Greek ' convention as understood in his day, was Bertel Thorwaldsen (1770–1844), a Danish sculptor who worked in Rome for forty years and executed many allegorical and ' pagan ' statues. A portrait bust of Byron by him is at Cambridge, but the principal collection of his works is at Copenhagen. His pupil assistant, Alfred Stevens (1817–1875), possessed, in common with other great artists—Poussin, David, Ingres and Turner, for instance—the faculty of abstracting knowledge for his own purposes from his profound study of the work of Michelangelo and other masters. Stevens returned to England in 1842, the most thoroughly educated artist of the 19th century. His was the inherently classical temperament—using the word classical in its meaning of austerely grand and dignified, and not Greco-Roman (*see* Lesson 17). A representative collection of his work is at Millbank, and plaster models for the Wellington monument, St. Paul's, and of the fireplace for Dorchester House (Dorchester Hotel now stands on the site of this famous mansion) are at the Victoria and Albert Museum.

Rodin. Seeking and experiment are the keynotes of original artists : sculptors have had their part in the movements briefly described in the previous Lessons in this Course. The greatest sculptor of the Romantic movement in the 19th century was Auguste Rodin (1840–1917), who began his artistic training in the studio of Antoine Barye (1795–1875), a French sculptor noted for his bronze animal groups and statues, such as his famous lions at the Louvre. Like the Impressionist painter Manet, Rodin's first recognition by the art critics was effected by shock. In 1864 he exhibited the statue of a ' man with a broken nose.' By 1877 he had ' arrived.' His ' Age of Bronze,' in

the Salon, was acquired by the State, and placed in the Luxembourg Gardens. Between 1882 and 1885 he sent to the Salon busts of Victor Hugo and of the sculptors Dalou and Carrier-Belleuse.

A bronze replica of his ' Burghers of Calais '—which outraged all the conventions of his day—was set up in the Victoria Tower Gardens, London, while his magnificent gift of representative sculptures to the British nation during the First Great War is at the Victoria and Albert Museum. His famous ' Thinker,' his ' Eve,' which excited quite as much protest and initial disgust as any statue of Epstein's, and his greatest work, ' The Gate of Hell,' illustrating Dante's ' Inferno,' containing 186 figures—which took up almost all his lifetime from 1880, and was

FAMOUS ROMANTIC MASTERPIECES. When ' The Age of Bronze ' *(right) was exhibited in plaster by Rodin in the Paris Salon of 1877, some critics asserted that it had been moulded from life, not modelled. Vasari, critic and biographer contemporary with Michelangelo, implies that the same charge—with equal injustice—was brought against Donatello (1386–1466), the pioneer of romantic sculpture, with regard to his glorious bronze ' David ' (left).*

Left, *Museo Nazionale, Florence; photo, Anderson. Right, Victoria and Albert Museum* left unfinished—all these show his dramatic expression and power of conveying emotion by gesture and pose. His habit of leaving a figure emerging from an unfinished block is intentional and characteristic of his Romantic tendency, not only to force contrasts but also to focus the spectator's attention on the particular point of interest which the sculp-tor wishes to stress by completing that portion and leaving all else in the rough.

Rodin never carved ; clay modelling was the only possible medium for his work. The varied surfaces when cast in bronze aid the impressions he desires to create. Marble versions of his statues were produced by independent marble workers.

LESSON 22

Universal Forms in Sculpture

To label the art of our period the end of the Romantic-Impressionist movement and return to Classicism (using the last word in its austere meaning) is partial truth. Form is certainly set above feeling, structure before impression ; there is appeal to the intelligence rather than to sentiment, reliance on mathematical axiom and fundamental shapes rather than on association of ideas ; but it is here that we branch away from the Classic revivals of the past. The French artist-architect Le Corbusier has said : ' Art is no longer anecdotal, it is a source of meditation ; after the day's work it is good to meditate.' Painters and sculptors have been experimenting and concentrating on patterns and shapes of abstract beauty, or of universal character, rather than on literal representation, individual or story interest ; where their work possesses such interest it is subordinated to the formal design. Everywhere art is simplified, drastically liberated by being stripped of excess and shams. There has been a return to the elemental in the endeavour to state the problem afresh.

Experiments continue ; an immense clearing and productive work has been accomplished which has had the effect of changing all ideas in industrial art since Picasso formulated Cubism (*see* Lesson 20). Not that it is possible, or even remotely desirable, to fetter art to industry ; but by such means a synthesis has been arrived at which will be known to history as the style of our period—still, perhaps, in its early stages after thirty years of experiments. There is harmony between the new architecture, sculpture and painting ; between these great arts and all their decorative dependants — pottery, metal, glass, furniture, mural and textile design.

Modern original sculptors, like the painters seeking productive inspiration, have endeavoured to return to the starting point and re-educate themselves. They began with the idea of essential sculpture as an activity consisting in the fashioning of form ; a work which has sculptural meaning, i.e. the meaning of its form, need have no anecdotal or sentimental meaning.

Ruskin, in ' The Seven Lamps of Architecture,' tells us :

I have said that all art is abstract in its beginnings ; that is to say, it expresses only a small number of the qualities of the thing represented. Curved and complex lines are represented by straight and simple ones ; interior markings of form are few and much is symbolical and conventional.

In some cases sculptors have advanced towards greater completion of their work ; in others they have continued of their own free will along the line of what Ruskin terms ' noble abstraction,' that is, to gather out of objects ' those arrangements of form which shall be pleasing to the eye in their intended places,' or they have experimented with the essential characters of symbolical life.

Ruskin, over sixty years ago, defined sculpture as 'the reduction of any shapeless mass of solid matter into an intended shape,' and he displayed a crystal sphere as the essential type of sculptured form in the round (i.e. not relief carving) ; thus—as R. H. Wilenski points out—foreshadowing the modern sculptors' initial creed and their initial concept of form :

They thought of themselves as architects of sculptures in the round ; and their first concern was to discover the simplest type of three-dimensional meaning. That type they found in the sphere, the cube and the cylinder ; and they sought to fashion statues which would be apprehended in the way that the sphere, the cube and the cylinder are apprehended . . . And in the early stages they rigorously restricted their studies to this field.

Geometrical Harmony in Art. Greek philosophy has been placed above Greek

POST-IMPRESSIONISTS. Above, Van Gogh's 'Landscape with Cypress Trees' exemplifies his concern with pattern and clear-cut beauty of colour (*see* p. 56). The Cézanne landscape below shows the artist's subtle power of colour modulation.

Van Gogh, National Gallery of British Art

PAUL NASH. The entirely modernist work of Paul Nash (b. 1889) is the antithesis of the Impressionists both in the striking patterns which he employs and in his powerfully structural methods. This painting 'Battle of Britain' clearly displays these characteristics. Nash has a very wide range including war landscapes, seascapes, water colours, dramatic woodcuts and posters (*see* p. 58).

To face p. 65

ART, Lesson 19

art. According to Plato's 'Philebus,' Socrates affirms that geometric forms are not only relatively beautiful, 'but they are eternally and absolutely beautiful,' while that which is commonly termed art is mere guess-work plus skilful craftsmanship. The sculptors Brancusi and Gaudier-Brzeska (1891–1915) made pioneer experiments in geometrization early in this century. The former, in accordance with the Socratic idea of beauty, has made sculptures which only have meaning as universal or decorative shapes ; the latter resolved figures into geometrical forms and also formalized natural structures. Gaudier-Brzeska was killed in the First Great War ; three small pieces of his sculpture are at the Victoria and Albert Museum : 'The Fallen Workman,' a bronze cast from an early study ; a marble torso of a girl, and a statuette in plaster, 'The Dancer.'

With regard to formalization of natural structures, the modern sculptor shares with the sculptors of the Renaissance the scientific spirit of inquiry. Just as the latter were deeply interested in anatomy and death masks for the purpose of realism, so the former are interested in results of photo-micrography. Back to Nature they may go, but from a new and scientific view-point —not the guess-work which Socrates condemned—which has revealed the almost unbelievable perfection of detail in the geometrical construction of organisms. Fossilized skeletons of minute sea-plants— diatoms, for instance—when magnified hundreds of times, show octagonal, hexagonal and pentagonal varieties in absolute symmetry. The spiral curve, which is the plan on which the ammonite shell was developed millions of years ago, has been used throughout the history of art and again appears in modern geometric sculptured compositions.

In his two volumes of series of remarkable photographs, entitled 'Art Forms in Nature,' Professor Karl Blossfeldt shows that an almost inexhaustible variety of lovely geometrical designs exists in plant organisms. When magnified, all idea of their haphazard growth is dispelled. In his fore-

word to the second series Professor Blossfeldt says :

Every sound expansion in the nature of art needs stimulation. New strength and stimulus for its healthy development can only be derived from Nature. . . . The plant may be described as an architectural structure, shaped and designed ornamentally and objectively. Compelled in its fight for existence to build in a purposeful manner, it . . . combines practicability and expediency in the highest form of art. Not only then in the world of art, but equally in the realm of science, Nature is our best teacher.

By such studies sculptors have arrived at what Mr. Wilenski (p. 60) calls ' the concept of the universal analogy of form, the concept of all human, animal and vegetable forms as different manifestations of common principles of architecture, of which the geometric forms in their infinity of relations are all symbols ' ; thus we see that modern sculpture is an effort towards truth to Life, and not merely truth to Nature in the old individualistic sense. The next generation of sculptors will probably achieve balance by proceeding along more individualistic lines, but they will have learnt much from these experiments, just as the modern painters learnt much from Cézanne (*see* Lesson 19).

Although Greek statues are viewed by them without sentimental bias, various modern sculptors have taken a backward

GEOMETRICAL FORMS IN NATURE. The young fruit of the common rue with calyx (right) and the opened seed capsule of the nettle (left), selected from a series of enlarged photographs from Nature, dispel the idea of a wild, ragged and haphazard plant life. They reveal, in common with minute animal organisms, definite shapes of intentional order and logical development, from which the artist derives basic forms to be reassembled in his work.

Photographs from Prof. Karl Blossfeldt's 'Art Forms in Nature,' by courtesy of Messrs. A. Zwemmer

D

glance at Greek art without becoming enslaved in past academic tradition. Aristide Maillol (b. 1861), who, with Jacob Epstein, may be termed a transitional master between Rodin and the modern sculptors, went in 1909 to Olympia, there to study the Greek temple fragments, and afterwards to Athens and to Naples. A pupil of Rodin, Maillol reacted against the emotive quality of the great Romantic, but did not become a convert to the antique ; his work is modern in his creation of generic and not particular forms. The most famous of his sculptures are the monument to Cézanne and the War Memorial at Elne ; various important works are in collections in Germany, where he has had a great vogue, and he has been a constant exhibitor in Paris at the Salon des Indépendants. His French followers are many, and in England Frank Dobson has developed Maillol's work along somewhat academic lines. One of his most famous works, the bronze figure of 'Truth' (1930), was acquired for the nation.

Zadkine and Archipenko, who are not French but who exhibited in Paris before

STONE CARVED SYMBOL OF NIGHT. *Jacob Epstein in executing the sculptures of Day and Night (the latter shown above) for the Underground Building, Westminster, carved them directly in stone. They are thus interesting contributions to modern architectural sculpture.*
Courtesy of London Passenger Transport Board

the Second World War, are other modern sculptors whose work shows traces of Greek affinity as differentiated from Asiatic. They find formal meaning in some of the archaic Greek statues in the round, though the essential cubic or cylindrical shapes of these were borrowed from the Egyptian academic tradition, which was already centuries old when the Greek sculptors used its formula. Picasso, abandoning painting for the time being, has made many interesting experiments in sculpture. He too seems to have looked with his eager and critical gaze at the Greek fragments, as well as at all other plastic forms of the past— to have constructed astounding models for himself from wood and from wire in order to wrench from these new patterns and forms.

R. H. Wilenski tells us that the creative modern sculptors have studied Chinese-Buddhist sculptures, to find that their concepts of plastic form are based on ' spheroid, ovoid and cylindrical forms,' and their flowing rhythm is accentuated by lines of drapery which are drawn in these shapes. He suggests that if we make our minds a blank, except for the cubic form of Egyptian sculpture, the

ARCHITECTURAL SCULPTURE IN BRICK. *This relief is one of a series carved by Eric Kennington in brick on the brick façade of the Shakespeare Memorial Theatre at Stratford-upon-Avon. The figures are over life-size and were executed in position without preliminary clay models.*
Courtesy of 'The Architectural Review'

linear rhythm of the Chinese-Buddhist carvings, and (with several other pietàs) Michelangelo's pietà in St. Peter's, Rome, then we are in a position to study Epstein's ' Night ' carved on the Underground Building over St. James's Park Station, Westminster. **Epstein.** Violent controversy has raged round the sculpture of Jacob Epstein (b. 1880) since 1907, when he first gained notoriety by his figures for the new buildings of the British Medical Association in the Strand, London. When these buildings were reconstructed for the Rhodesian Government, the figures were either broken up or left in a sadly depleted state. That his work is the expression of genius of a very high productive order is now generally conceded. His clay-modelled busts cast in bronze have found many admirers, because they are merely his own development of the Romantic style of Rodin and, farther back, of Donatello ; therefore they have shocked less than his direct carvings in stone, such as ' Rima,' ' Day ' and ' Night,' ' Genesis,' ' Ecce Homo,' ' Consummatum Est,' ' Adam ' and ' Jacob and the Angel ' (the last-named exhibited in London in 1942), and many others which he has exhibited in London and elsewhere.

Apart from his portrait busts, which are Romantic, Epstein has used a negroid or (as in ' Night ') a Mongolian facial type in his work, thus giving it an individualistic touch lacking in the more modern work of English sculptors such as Henry Moore, whose carvings in stone, wood and alabaster, ' Girl,' ' Mountains ' (a study of a recumbent woman), ' Harp Head ' and other sculptures, are symbols of life.

Moore, one of the most important sculptors in England today, follows the natural shape of the stone or wood, and in his ' drawings for sculpture ' he has vividly shown his method of working primitive forms. Other sculptors whose work displays abstraction from organic

' MOTHER AND CHILD,' by Barbara Hepworth, makes no attempt at portraiture, but seeks to symbolize in sculpture a permanent and universal idea of motherhood.

Courtesy of Messrs. A. Zwemmer

form include Barbara Hepworth, whose ' Musician ' and ' Mother and Child ' are essays in unified movement ; and Maurice Lambert, whose Sumerian studies have influenced his direct carving, but who can also produce a poetical abstraction of a yacht.

Carvings on buildings form a characteristic part of modern sculpture when they are integral to the building, and not merely modelled figures placed in certain positions as ornaments. Epstein's architectural sculpture is carved mainly in the position it is to hold and entirely by his own hand. An interesting experiment was made by the English sculptor, Eric Kennington, at Stratford-on-Avon on the Shakespeare Memorial Theatre with his series of large figure reliefs in brick on brick.

Whatever may be the particular reaction to modern sculpture, it is never dull ; future productions should be yet fuller of interest, with their new developments and efforts to embody the doctrine already expressed in the work of the Chinese artist-philosophers of the T'ang age (A.D. 700) :

' We react with satisfaction to works of art which make us realize that all forms in Nature are manifestations of the unity and harmony of Life.'

BOOK LIST

'The Meaning of Art,' Herbert Read (Faber) ; 'The Artist and his Public,' Eric Newton (Allen & Unwin) ; 'An Outline History of Painting,' S. C. Kaines Smith (Medici) ; 'Egyptian Art,' J. Capart (Allen & Unwin) ; 'Introduction to Persian Art,' A. U. Pope (Davies) ; 'The Hindu View of Art,' Mulk Raj Anand (Allen & Unwin) ; 'Painting in the Far East,' L. Binyon (Arnold) ; 'Art of Ancient Crete,' H. T. Bossert (Zwemmer) ; 'Greek Art,' H. B. Walters (Methuen) ; 'An Introduction to Italian Painting,' C. Holmes (Cassell) ; 'Flemish Art,' R. Fry (Chatto) ; 'Introduction to Dutch Art,' R. H. Wilenski (Faber) ; 'English Painting,' C. Johnson (Bell) ; 'An Account of French Painting,' C. Bell (Chatto) ; 'Modern Movement in Art,' R. H. Wilenski (Faber) ; 'A History of Sculpture,' Post and Chase (Harper) ; 'Meaning of Modern Sculpture,' R. H. Wilenski (Faber).

GEOFFREY CHAUCER, who lived in the 14th century, is the first great English poet and possesses a rare humour and tenderness. Here we see him at the period of his famous 'Canterbury Tales.'

From MS. in British Museum

THE EARL OF SURREY (HENRY HOWARD) did much to introduce the sonnet-form in early Tudor times. His most noteworthy achievement was the invention of blank verse.

After the portrait by Titian (photo, Mansell)

EDMUND SPENSER is known as 'the poets' poet' because of the ethereal beauty of his work. His magnificent 'Faerie Queene' is an allegorical romance of epic proportions.

. From a portrait owned by the Earl of Kinnoull

SIR PHILIP SIDNEY died at the early age of thirty-two, but he had already written many charming lyrics and sonnets, besides the prose romance 'Arcadia.'

By an unknown artist

ENGLISH LITERATURE

56 LESSONS

See also English Language, Philology, Foreign Literatures.

D*

LESSON ONE

Literature and Its Place in Life

EVERYONE realizes that it is necessary to take food in order to live. The proposition is as certainly, if not as quickly, demonstrable as the fact that fire burns, or that rain makes us wet. But there are other facts, quite as important to know and to understand, that cannot so easily be demonstrated. Of these is the fact that some knowledge of literature is essential to the living of a well-balanced life.

Many instances may be adduced that seem to prove the opposite, so far as either side of the question is capable of proof. The Vanderbilts, the Rothschilds, rose to great heights though they had no literary attainments ; the founder of the first family, it is said, could neither read nor write. Alas, with all his gains he remained poor ; and poor, indeed, are all who, waxing rich in worldly gear, still lack that imperishable furnishing of the mind which can be acquired only in communion with the great intellects that have made the world's literature.

Not poor merely, but intellectually dead. For, as surely as the body dies for lack of food, or grows unhealthy by improper feeding, so does the mind of man languish and die if mental nourishment be withheld. We have all met persons of gross body who have been blessed with material wealth, but whose minds were vacant places where no beautiful things were, yet where these might have been had the impulse come, the effort been made, at the proper time, towards literary culture.

Nevertheless, it must not be thought that the reading of books is the be-all and end-all of mental culture. Far otherwise. The simile of feeding may still be pursued. For just as there is over-development of the physical man—differently, but equally, by over-eating or excessive athleticism— it is no uncommon thing for a man to become attached to mere book-learning to the exclusion of many other essential elements of that culture which produces a well-balanced, four-square life.

The purpose of these Lessons, then, is not to praise book-learning with indiscriminate rhetoric, nor to exalt it unduly. There are nobler things than to be rich in the lore of the world ; but, let a man be never so well endowed in all the attributes of good character, he will still be the better man by some measure of acquaintance with the treasures of literature ; in fact, it is hard to know how he may acquire the more worthy traits of character without the ministry of literature, direct or indirect. A man who has no knowledge of books has the blinds close drawn on some of the windows of his soul.

Only within comparatively modern times has a class arisen that makes literature the sum of its life : the professional literary class. In ancient times the authors were men of action—travellers, architects, statesmen. They did not begin and end in a world of books ; they fought battles, they adventured in strange lands, they governed provinces, they made laws, they reared buildings ; and what they wrote was in large part derived from their contact with the life of the world in which they participated, not as authors on the quest for 'copy,' but as men.

The same is true, in a measure, of the monks, so long the conservators of letters ; they were primarily concerned with the business of living and the contemplation of a future life. The literary man of our day is in constant danger of looking at life from the ' literary ' point of view as distinct from that of human experience, and his real success is to be measured mainly by his evidence of deliberate detachment from the conditions which have made it possible for so many members of the community to become professional critics of life rather than men waging the common battle of existence.

Purpose of Reading. Clearly, for the literary class, as such, these Lessons have nothing to offer. Their utility is for those in whose lives literature has an ennobling part to play, but still only a part—that is, for the majority of the people. Bacon's dictum remains unsurpassed :

Read not to contradict or confute, nor to believe and take for granted, nor to find talk and discourse, but to weigh and consider.

'To weigh and consider'—that is the true purpose of all useful reading. We have not to read for the mere storing of our minds with multitudinous facts, nor yet with sensuous fancies, which seem to be the chief results of the tremendous consumption of modern printed matter. In truth, there is no reason to complain in these days that the British public reads too little; it reads quite enough, but without discrimination. In order to 'weigh and consider,' it is obvious that there must be discretion. At what age comes discretion? This is a point of great importance.

Biography teems with stories of prodigies who had 'read everything' at fifteen. Many of us have met in the flesh one of these wonders grown old, and have formed no exalted estimate of his literary judgement. By grace of genius a boy or girl of nineteen may be a poet, but the average healthy youth unvexed by genius is not usually at that age, and rarely earlier, capable of really intelligent reading. He may, truly, have read much and derived genuine and rational pleasure from his reading, but it will be in later life that the critical faculty will assert itself and judicial appreciation of that early reading be disengaged from the vague sensations of remembered pleasure and repulsion left by the books read before the development of the faculty of criticism. No dogmatic assertion can be made as to the incidence of that faculty; but it is seldom present before the age of twenty; whence it may be inferred that all the reading that matters in one's life is not done from sixteen to twenty-one or thereabouts.

The young people of sixteen who are ' for ever reading something or other ' are more than likely to become the least intelligent of readers, the least truly cultured. Not seldom do they in later life acquire a positive distaste for books; and in any case the greater part of their juvenile reading will count for little or nothing, since it was undertaken at a time when their understanding was unequal to the occasion.

Children should be permitted at most to acquire the habit of reading, and to that end the commonest of boys' or girls' papers serves its purpose. But by fifteen or sixteen years of age, when the greater number of British boys and girls are following some sort of employment, they are in train for guidance, and one may reasonably presume to direct their attention to such standard works as will at once give pleasure, while steadily fostering the taste for what is good and enduring in our literature—though it were foolish to expect from readers so young any well-founded judgement on the qualities of the books they read.

One cannot picture those of tender years 'weighing and considering' what they read. They have read as they have played skipping-rope or hand-ball—for pleasure and rightly so. But, just as in our later teens we put these games behind us, so we should then begin to read for a different purpose— the true purpose—the culture of the mind; with crude results at first, inevitably, yet thrilling with the now awakening knowledge that books are not merely inventions for passing the time, but the most precious of all the agencies for carrying us into a full manhood.

The purpose of art, we are told, is to please. But not all that pleases is art. Henry Drummond, as a boy, was in love with the red-painted inside of a toy trumpet, and wondered why God had not made the whole world red. Many a child has had the same delight and wonder. Deadwood Dick and Sweeney Todd have pleased innumerable thousands of healthy boys, but neither is a work of literary art.

The true pleasure of art is that arising from the joy of consciously appreciating the work of the artist, and realizing that it has wrought enlargement in our mind to the better understanding of our world and of the people around us. That is the kind of pleasure which should come when the reader has begun to understand that he is reading seriously; not until then has literature begun to take its place in his life.

The Reader's Contribution. But the reader must bring something to this reading of books if he would take something away. He must bring certain qualities of imagination, common sense, sympathy, in addition to the elements of school-learning, in order that what he reads he may 'weigh and consider,' and that when he has done this he may feel he has taken another step along the unending path of knowledge and self-culture. He will have his ordinary affairs to attend to; his daily tasks in office or workshop, his studies in whatever subject his taste or circumstances may dictate, his recreations, his love-making; since reading for literary culture must not displace any of these essentials of manhood and womanhood.

No one would advocate the breeding of a race of mere bookworms any more than one composed only of virile specimens of bone and brawn with brain devoid of grey matter. Yet even the humblest fitter in an engineering shop is capable of enlarging and beautifying his life by a judicious knowledge of literature. Years ago there lived an engineer's labourer whose taste in books was as cultured and accurate as that of many who live by criticism, whose knowledge of our standard authors was extensive and sound, who could write with great literary charm (he contributed to the 'Cornhill' and other magazines), and remained withal a sturdy British working-man.

He was an exception to the general rule ; but what is possible to one is open to many, and though one could not with equanimity contemplate the spectacle of numerous engineers' labourers bombarding the magazines with unsolicited contributions, one would rejoice to know that in the humblest walks of life as in the highest—and the need is equal in both—the pleasures of literature were rationally present.

It is to assist in realizing this ideal that the Lessons which follow are designed.

LESSON TWO

How to Get the Best Out of Books

No one is entitled to respect for his opinion on any book who has not read many books systematically. Most ordinary readers are totally unqualified to say whether a book is good or bad, for they have never developed the faculty of knowing how to judge. To aver that they like it or dislike it is another matter. They know what they like or dislike. Man Friday disliked salted food, but that did not prove salt a bad thing. The Papuan liked to make a meal of his grandmother, but the Briton has never esteemed this a toothsome dish. Many avid patrons of the circulating libraries are Papuans and Fridays, devouring with approval things that offend all regulated tastes, or spitting out the real salt of literature.

In all matters of taste and opinion we must allow for the personal equation. Even when we are receiving the opinion of a famous man eminently entitled to an opinion, we ought to examine it before acceptance, if only to cultivate in ourselves the critical faculty. Consider, for example, this injunction of Emerson's : 'Never read any book that is not a year old. Never read any but famed books. Never read any but what you like.' Regarded from the point of view of the average man, this advice is useless. 'Never read a book that is not a year old.' That is the soundest part, but a truly good book may appear this day ; why wait a year before you bring your mind into touch with this new expression of a living mind ? A year, if you like, before asserting that the new book is literature, and will endure ; that is another matter.

Nor is the vogue of a new book a wholly bad thing. To read what all others are reading has at least the merit of vivifying one's interest, though sober criticism may not come till later,—a year later, if you will,—years later. But deliberately to refrain from opening a book until it is a year old ; no. Even the ephemeral in literature is not to be utterly despised ; Hazlitt's oft-quoted advice as to reading an old book whenever a new one comes out is not to be taken as undervaluing all new literature, but as wise counsel not to allow the new books to crowd out the old and tried favourites.

'Never read any but famed books.' Dubious advice, since so much depends on what is meant by 'famed.' 'Don Quixote' is famed ; 'Gargantua,' 'Paradise Lost,' 'Pendennis'; so, too, 'Rebecca' and 'The Citadel'—and these are more than a year old. There is much that is worth reading in books that are not, and never will be, famed—even in poor and mediocre books.

As to ' never read any but what you like,' that, too, is unwise counsel. Johnson said that 'a man ought to read just as inclination leads him, for what he reads as a task will do him little good'—which is a very different line of thought from Emerson's, however similar it may at first appear. As a matter of common experience, it is not the things we like that most stimulate our thoughts, but the things we dislike.

The sheer pleasure of agreeing with another's thoughts tends for the time to lull our own thinking faculty, whereas the man or the writer whose avowals disturb our equanimity, ruffle our temper, strike us rudely, will energize our own thoughts ; rasp them, maybe, to smoothness and greater usefulness. It is conflict, not acquiescence, that produces activity, mental and physical ; and the authors we dislike may have as much for us as, if not more than, those we like. But—and here is the subtle difference between Emerson and Johnson—our inclination may lead us to bear company with an author we dislike, for the tonic effect of his opposing intellect. When we realize this, we may conclude that we are reading to some profit.

What we have to bear in mind about the method of reading is that there are many ways of getting the best out of a book, and that all are right. If the individual feels his own particular way to be right, it is right for him, though it might be the worst possible way for anyone else. The essential is, that he have a way—that he do not read aimlessly ; that if he presume to utter an opinion on a book, he shall have deliberately come by that opinion as the result of reason and study, that it be no capricious expression of an irresponsible mind.

A Reader's Qualifications. The reader must not come empty-handed to the author. He should at least know the rudiments of grammar and composition. It is necessary that he bring some other quality, if it be only a conscious ignorance of the subject of study. But more usually he takes up a book already knowing something of the matter with which it deals, of the author's reputation, characteristics, previous works. Unless he is an aimless person he has also a reason for taking up a book,—must have. That reason may be wise or mistaken ; enough that it is a reason, that the reader is not merely bent on passing an idle hour.

There are, of course, numerous reasons for reading a book. Local interest will count for something ; he is on safe ground who familiarizes himself with all the notable writers identified with his town or district. And it is well to have some one branch of literature, or even one author, that attracts us more than others, though never allowing this study to weaken our interest in general reading. The innate promptings of our nature must be permitted to influence us in following these by-paths of study ; they will never take us astray if we are consciously in search of good.

Gibbon had a system of self-examination before reading any book, whereby he took stock of his own knowledge of the subject, glancing over the work to secure a rough idea of its scope before beginning seriously to study it. Thus he would know with precision how much the author had taught him when he had finished the reading of the book. John Morley tried this method and commends it. It is, at least, one that depends upon no personal idiosyncrasy and is open to all of us.

We must never 'skip' a preface. It is unfair to the author, foolish to ourselves, to omit hearing what he has to say in his preface. A possible exception to this rule is offered by Scott's novels, which are over-burdened with prefaces and appendices. Most of these can be read with enjoyment, but they are hardly essential to the pleasure of the fiction ; and if they were, then the fiction had surely failed of its purpose. But ordinarily a preface is as much a part of a book as a door is part of a house.

Having read carefully the preface or introduction—sometimes we find both, and rarely, if it be a good book, without a reason—we begin the actual reading.

Points to Examine. We have now to decide upon the qualities to observe in the work before us. These cannot be detailed in the present Lesson, but some working examples must be given, and these shall be taken from History and Fiction.

In reading a historical work we have to consider :
(1) The author's point of view. The more picturesque and readable a historian is, the more need is there to keep a sharp look-out for bias. We are pretty likely to find evidence of this, and whenever we suspect it we must refer to some other historians on the same point in order to correct our impressions.
(2) The author's knowledge of men and motives, great movements, will call for examination—nothing being taken for granted unless it be an obvious statement of uncoloured fact.
(3) His style will demand especial attention, as in a historian it is of equal importance with accuracy, and, indeed, his manner will largely determine his accuracy —one who is excessively fond of picturesque description and epigrammatic comment (Macaulay, for instance) being always open to the suspicion of letting his manner unduly colour his matter.

In a work of fiction we look for :
(1) A story. This is the first essential, and we have to ask ourselves whether it appeals to us as being an ingenious invention and credible.
(2) Next we consider the sequence of the story. Is it unfolded naturally, inevitably ? Are the events contrived as in actual life they might be ? Or are they forced to fit the ends of the author ? All these questions may be answered in the negative, although the first consideration be fully admitted.
(3) Are the characters such as might exist in life, and do they act for just those reasons which would influence living people ? Here, while (1) and (2) might be granted, (3) might be only partially allowed.
(4) The vital question of style, which includes humour, sympathy, method, per-

sonality, must be always, in some degree, present with the reader.

It happens often that the reading of one book leads to the reading of others by mention of them being made in the work just laid down. Thus, in Boswell's voluminous ' Life of Johnson ' a host of other books are named, the reading of which will be rendered (at the beginning, at least) the more piquant from knowing what Johnson thought of them. To note carefully the books which are mentioned as having been favourites with a man whose life we admire, and to determine on a first-hand acquaintance with these, were an excellent feature of any system which the reader may eventually evolve for himself.

When one has mastered the art of reading, he may be left to apply it to the best of his understanding. This may be said, however : that no reading of a book is complete until the reader has carefully reviewed the whole work in his mind, turned back to passages which may have puzzled him in the earlier

parts and revised his first impressions in the light of his finished reading—as the end of a book, and especially of a work of fiction, may modify the opinions formed in the earlier stages of its study.

A good plan, if the book we have just read happens to be the first of that author's with which we have made acquaintance, is to take up some other of his writings, and not to allow the fact of its having displeased or disappointed us to restrain us from bearing him company a second or a third time. Indeed, it should be rather an incentive to our doing so, lest we allow ourselves, on the strength of one book, to form an erroneous opinion of any writer.

It is doubtful if we should ever set ourselves the task of reading in succession all the works of any one author, especially if he be as voluminous as Scott or Dickens. If the sequence be broken by turning to other writers, we shall be the better able to compare their styles, and so to appreciate all with greater justness.

LESSON THREE

Poetry: Highest Form of Human Expression

POETRY is the first, as it is the highest, expression of the human mind. Of all forms of human expression it is the most natural and direct, and the heart of a people always responds to it in moments of exaltation. Even those who confess they are unable to read poetry cannot escape its influence ; since there is in the nature of mankind the stuff of poetry, which must at times manifest itself in all our lives.

But what we really mean by poetry is not merely the ingenious arrangement of words and phrases in lines beginning with capital letters and ending with words of similar sound ; it is one of the elemental things of nature, like electricity, and perhaps, in its deeper significance, no better understood.

The Aeolian harp may be taken as an illustration. This stringed instrument of the ancients, placed where the wind could play upon it, gave forth sweet sounds. Man made the instrument, but Nature produced the music ; neither acted alone —it was a relation of interdependence.

So with poetry ; it is not merely Homer or Dante, not Shakespeare or Milton, who plays upon our feelings and our senses when we read his poems. He offers the magical, emotion-fraught words, and we

the listening hearts ; but it is the soul of all remembered emotions and aspirations in each one of us—the very rhythm of life— that attunes these words to the needs and possibilities of each individual nature, and thus applies poetry.

It was by first discovering the power to utter words potent to awaken responsive emotions in their fellows—having fitted first of all their own emotions, of which the words were an essential part—that men began that intercommunion of souls which, in the course of ages, creating for itself certain conventions of form, shaped itself finally into poetry.

Function of the Bards. In the earliest recorded history of our own land the bard had his place in the social scheme, articulating what his fellows felt but dimly and were quite unable to body forth ; and both as historian and as prophet interpreting his age to itself and to posterity.

These old Gaelic singers were often warriors as well ; but many of them were more akin in their social status to the modern professional men of letters than any poets or historians in the intervening ages. The need of singers to arouse enthusiasm for battle, to celebrate victories, to mourn over defeats and commemorate fallen heroes, was as great in those rude days of Fionn, Oisin, and Merlin as the need of the political pamphleteer and leader-writer of modern times ; but the bard was more dignified, more in tune with Nature.

Thus, in our own land, as some twelve centuries earlier in Greece, when Homer celebrated the Trojan war in the first great poem of imperishable genius, the beginning of poetry as a literary expression was associated with the hero and heroic deeds. In the ancient poetical books of the Bible it was associated with the divine aspirations of the soul, and the real beginning of English poetry was also religious, much of the poetic energy of our race, first expressed by Caedmon in the seventh century, being informed by a deep devotional spirit, which remains characteristic of English poetry.

Fundamentals of Poetry. We must not be tempted at this stage into the history of poetry ; this will be the subject of succeeding Lessons. What will be of immediate practical use to us is a working knowledge of its constituents and varieties. This may be thought a wrong phrase to employ, smacking as it does of the laboratory ; but while it is tolerably certain that the greatest poets were almost unconscious of art, their exalted thoughts taking on an exalted and inevitable rhythm in perfect harmony with the canons of art, because above art and of a piece with that elemental voice of nature expressed in the well-known line from the Book of Job, 'When the morning stars sang together'—because of this, it is possible to make a scientific analysis of poetry, no less than of any other energy of nature.

It would be difficult to select a more controversial subject than the ' scientific ' criticism of poetry. This much, however, may be declared : that, as everything in life may be submitted to scientific analysis, there is no conclusive reason why poetry should not also be subjected to such analysis. At any rate, none of the varying criteria whereby men have attempted to define and judge the poet's art has quite met the case, and the criticism of poetry is today about as difficult to define as poetry itself. For criticism has changed as persistently as art in standards of taste, and to apply the standards of one age to the judgement of the art produced in another is shown by certain historical examples to be futile. It is the glory of Aristotle's system of criticism that so much of it may still be applied to modern art. But criticism gener-

ally works out thus : after we have examined and accepted so many principles, the great new artist—a Walt Whitman, for instance—arrives and upsets our theories.

One thing that does seem to be within the range of even timorous assertion is that rhythm and verse-form are the essential characteristics of poetry. Yet many eminent critics, Carlyle among them, have contended that prose can possess all the necessary qualities of poetry. It is commonly agreed, however, that both poetry and prose have their rhythm, while metre is the added quality of poetry, and this metre is not mere ornament, but of the very fabric of the thought itself ; in other words, the emotions or thought-material of the poet whom we loosely call inspired have an inherent, rhythmic, metrical quality, which is not the mere literary decoration of the artist, but the very voice of Nature herself. Rhyme, on the other hand, is purely ornamental, and not an essential of poetry, though so scholarly a critic as Dr. Johnson had a great distaste for blank verse, and Bernard Shaw once asserted that a cat might be taught to write it. And, in truth, much of the free verse produced in late years on both sides of the Atlantic would seem to be well within the feline capacity.

Among the many writers on prosody who have sought to explain to the ordinary reader the significance of the difference between prose and poetry so that its largeness would be unmistakable, none would appear to have hit upon a better plan than that of an American professor, Mark H. Liddell, in his 'Introduction to the Scientific Study of English Poetry.' While there is much in that work that does not compel assent, it does supply at least a good working test of the fundamentals of poetry, and this it behoves us to examine before proceeding to note its metrical varieties. Professor Liddell takes this passage from 'Macbeth,' wherewith to test the qualities that render poetry distinct from prose :

Duncan is in his grave ;
After life's fitful fever he sleeps well ;
Treason has done his worst : nor steel, nor poison,
Malice domestic, foreign levy, nothing,
Can touch him further.

This we will presume to be poetry. The professor re-casts the passage in what may be called literary or rhythmic prose :

Duncan lies in his grave. Life, that racks my soul with succeeding ague-fits of fear, for him is over and he sleeps in peace beyond the reach of treason. The assassin's steel or poisoned cup, secretly fomented strife at home, treacherously assisted hostility from abroad—none of these can harm him now.

He next reduces it to a bald statement of fact, as follows :

The life of Duncan is extinct, and he is no longer affected by the personal vicissitudes and dangers of government, such as assassination, treason, rebellion, and foreign invasion, which produce this anxiety in my mind.

Liddell then proceeds to examine these three forms of the same thought. The last (which, for this experiment, may be regarded as the first form of the thought) is, he considers, so plain and dispassionate a statement of the fact that it would hardly awaken any strong emotions in the breast of anyone save Macbeth himself. It is not poetry. But the second is framed in words charged with emotional qualities, which must necessarily affect the feelings of all readers, though not invariably touching them to the same issues.

This added quality in the second stage we are to denote as human interest, and this Liddell rightly considers the determining element of literature : 'that common and general interest, which its thought possesses for all men who think, regardless of those peculiar attitudes toward life that arise from peculiar pursuits and occupations'—a doctor, for instance, not looking on death in the same way as a non-medical man or woman, nor an undertaker finding in the word ' grave ' the same emotions as one to whom the surroundings of the tomb are less familiar. Still, the second stage is not recognizable as a poetic form.

But in the third stage (or, properly, the first Shakespearian form) the thought material is, both in substance and in form, in warp and woof, as it were, poetical. The change is due chiefly to the regular rhythm and the metrical movement of the verse, which punctuate the thought ; marking off its different impulses, its units, and projecting vividly into the mind of the reader what was in the mind of Macbeth—not, let us note, merely what was in the mind of Shakespeare, for this is an instance of what Watts-Dunton calls absolute vision, the vision of dramatic poetry. The thought and expression here seem to us one and indivisible, which may prove even more than Liddell set out to prove : that in the two forms into which he altered the passage he must have taken away more than expression, so that his bald statement of the fact was really not a statement of the fact at all, the real full fact existing only in the thought and form of Shakespeare's verses.

There is one great dividing line in poetry itself which is nowhere so clearly defined as by Theodore Watts-Dunton in his famous article on Poetry in the 'Encyclopædia Britannica' (Ninth Ed.). He there says :

Of poetic imagination there are two distinct kinds : (1) the kind of poetic imagination seen at its highest in Aeschylus, Sophocles, Shakespeare, and Homer ; and (2) the kind of poetic imagination seen at its highest in Pindar, Dante, and Milton, or else in Sappho, Heine, and Shelley. The former, being in its highest dramatic exercise unconditioned by the personal or lyrical influence of the poet, might perhaps be called absolute dramatic vision ; the latter, being more or less conditioned by the personal or lyrical impulse of the poet, might be called relative dramatic vision !

Let us bear this in mind, as it will greatly help us to appreciate poetical values.

LESSON FOUR

The Structure of English Poetry

To enjoy to the full the reading of poetry, one must be able to appreciate the technical skill underlying the poet's inspired expression ; this in turn requires some knowledge of the mechanical structure of verse forms.

Hazlitt, in one of his Essays, writes :

Poetry is the language of the imagination and the passions. It relates to whatever gives immediate pleasure or pain to the human mind. It comes home to the bosoms and businesses of men ; for nothing but what comes home to them in the most general and intelligible shape can be a subject for poetry. Poetry is the universal language which the heart holds with nature and itself. . . . Wherever there is a sense of beauty, or power, or harmony, as in the motion of a wave of the sea, in the growth of a flower, there is poetry in its birth. . . . It is not a branch of authorship ; it is ' the stuff of which our life is made.' The rest is mere oblivion, a dead letter ; for all that is worth remembering in life is the poetry of it. . . .

A modern critic, Robert Lynd, in his delightful essay, ' On Poetry and the Modern Man,' says :

In poetry we are continually being re-born into new fairy lands. . . . Poetry begins as a random voyage among the blue seas of fancy, though it may end with the return of a laden treasure-ship of the imagination into the harbours of home.

When, therefore, the student has grasped the immense extent of the subject matter of poetry, he should become acquainted with its architecture. An intelligent, well-read person, who has studied prosody (i.e. the grammar of verse), can write verse, but that great indefinable gift which we call inspiration is necessary before the verse writer can be promoted to the rank of poet. It is indeed this quality of inspiration which is never absent from great poetry.

How, then, is it possible to distinguish poetry from prose, seeing that the subject-matter of the former is so all-embracing ? A simple example may help. Imagine you have a gardening friend who meets you one day and says : ' Red carnations are coming out in my garden now.' He makes a prosaic, though perhaps interesting, statement. But if he says :

Red carnations in my garden now are out . . .

the fact is the same, put in a different form. The essential difference is the introduction of what is known as rhythm.

Human beings, even from earliest childhood, have an instinctive sense of this. Writers of verse, therefore, should know how to obtain certain rhythms, and also how to use, at times, another device, called rhyme. Rhythm, rhyme, and certain verse forms will be here described. The subject, however, is a large one, and lack of space will not allow it to be dealt with exhaustively. It should also be borne in mind that there is no reason why writers should not invent new poetic forms, just as musicians compose new and pleasing tunes. There is, indeed, a close affinity between poets and painters, and poets and musicians. The painter uses his pigments to produce his effects ; the musician has all the instruments of the orchestra at his service, though their fellow artist, the poet, has only words to use. With these he must appeal to both mind and ear.

Thus he should be a master of his material, and, as Coleridge states, should learn to use ' the best words in the best order.'

A final warning is necessary before verse forms are defined and set forth. We have no native words to describe our devices, and are driven to employ terms used in classical verse, in which they mean something different. In Latin, metre (=measure) is controlled by the quantity of the vowel. Thus a vowel, in Latin, is always long if it comes immediately before two consonants, not necessarily in the same word. English metre is in no way affected by the length of a vowel, but simply by the stressing, or not, of syllables.

Rhythm. Rhythm is produced by a well-balanced recurrence of pauses and stresses. Oratory and good prose have a rhythm of their own, different from that possessed by verse, and easily distinguished from it, for it does not exhibit anything like the regularity found in poetry.

The curfew tolls the knell of parting day. . .

is an example of a well-marked poetic rhythm. It is produced by a stressed syllable following regularly an unstressed one. It is actually the rhythm which appears to be most suited to the genius of the English language, and more will be said about it later.

Rhyme. This word should really be spelt rime, since it is derived from the Old French *rime* ; its present form is due to a false analogy with rhythm. Rhyme is produced by a repetition of the same sound at the ends of two or more lines which must follow on at once, or be near enough to enable the resemblance to strike the ear. In English rhyme it is necessary that the consonants preceding the rhyming vowels be different. Rhymes consisting of one syllable, such as ' main ' and ' brain,' ' hill ' and ' still,' are called masculine. Double rhymes such as ' ocean ' and ' motion,' or ' follow ' and ' swallow,' are called feminine.

It will be noted that rhyme does not depend on spelling, but only on pronunciation. Indeed, words with similar spelling often do not rhyme at all, thus 'love' and 'move,' 'farm' and 'warm' : these are called ' eye ' (or printers') rhymes. Anyone who has read a number of hymns will realize the absurdities that have been committed by their writers in search for words to rhyme with 'God,' 'blood,' and 'love.'

English, unlike French, is very limited in the number of its rhymes. Sometimes more than two syllables are employed in order to obtain a rhyme : this is often done for a humorous effect. Thus Sir W. S. Gilbert, a master of light verse, uses such rhymes as 'diurnally,' 'externally,' 'infernally' ; 'in fear of him,' ' in rear of him ' ; and 'frolicking,' 'rollicking.'

Assonance is a term applied to an incomplete rhyme, where the vowels are identical, but not the consonants which immediately follow : thus 'sane' and 'fate' ; 'feet' and 'deep' ; and 'roaming' and 'floating.'

Alliteration. The term alliteration is used when two or more words in one line begin with the same consonant or vowel. Thus :

> For apt Alliteration's artful aid . .
>
> Five miles meandering with a mazy motion..

Some misguided anonymous writer exercised his ingenuity in writing an entire piece of verse, each line being completely alliterative, and the whole alphabet being employed :

> An Austrian army awfully arrayed,
> Boldly by battery besieged Belgrade . . .

and so on. Alliteration was an essential part of all Old English metres, and of many in Middle English. It had a fresh blossoming as late as Langland, whose ' Piers Plowman ' begins thus :

> In a somer seson, when soft was the sunne,
> I shope me in shrouds as I a shepe were.

Metre. In poetry a specific combination of stressed and unstressed syllables is called a *metric foot*. The four feet most commonly used in English verse are shown in the table.

Syllables	Name of Foot with its Adjective	Examples
Non-stress + stress	Iamb(us), iambic	ap/pear, at/tack
Stress + non-stress	Trochee, trochaic	ho/ly, stu/pid
Stress + two non-stresses	Dactyl, dactylic	mess/enger, mus/ical
Two non-stresses + stress	Anapaest, anapaestic	colon/nade, re-ap/pear

Besides these quite frequently used feet, a *spondee* is occasionally to be found. This consists of two equally stressed syllables ; examples : hunchback, Rolls Royce, clothes-prop. An *amphibrach* is also sometimes employed. This has a

stressed syllable in the middle, between two which are unstressed ; thus, revengeful, amazing. It is not an easy form of verse to write, but Shakespeare used it very successfully in :

> Most friendship / is feigning,
> Most loving / mere folly ;
> Then heigh-ho / the holly,
> This life is / most jolly.

According to the number of *stresses* in a line, the verse is said to be monometer (1), dimeter (2), trimeter (3), tetrameter (4), pentameter (5), hexameter (6), heptameter (7), or octometer (8). To make matters clear, the lines quoted here are scanned. Scansion is the division of poetic lines into feet, the stresses being marked. It will be noted that some stresses are heavier than others and that variations occur ; it is seldom that we find an unfailingly regular metre.

The poetic line which suits English best is the five-stress one, the *iambic pentameter*. When this does not rhyme it is called blank verse. When lines rhyme in pairs we have heroic couplets. The following lines from ' King Henry V ' are an example of the regular iambic pentameter :

> By Jove, / I am / not cov/etous / for gold,
> Nor care / I who / doth feed / upon / my cost ;
> It yearns / me not / that men / my gar/ments wear ;
> Such out/ward things / dwell not / in my / desires.

The way Pope handled the heroic couplet —a metre he much liked—is shown below :

> Know then / thyself, / presume / not God / to scan ;
> The pro/per stud/y of / Mankind / is Man. /
> Plac'd on / this is/thmus of / a mid/dle state, /
> A be/ing dark/ly wise / and rude/ly great. /

Many of our great works have been composed in blank verse. Shakespeare used it for his plays ; Milton showed himself its master in ' Paradise Lost ' and ' Paradise Regained ' ; Wordsworth chose it for ' The Prelude ' and ' The Excursion ' ; while Tennyson, in ' The Idylls of the King,' Thomas Hardy in ' The Dynasts,' and later poets, down to T. S. Eliot and Roy Campbell, wrought, in their different ways, the music of a mighty line.

One of the pitfalls against which the poet must take precautions is monotony. This is particularly the case in poems of any length where a metre, strictly adhered to, might have a soporific effect on the reader.

So various devices are employed. The poet sometimes starts his line with a trochee instead of an iamb; he adds an extra unstressed syllable at the end of the line, or he omits one syllable at its beginning. He avoids having too many end-stopped lines—that is, making each line a complete sentence in which the sense coincides with the metre—by carrying his sentences on from one line to the next. Examples are to be found in the quotations given.

Variation in the position of the *caesura* is a potent device against monotony. The caesura is the pause which occurs when the line is read aloud, and its position is clearly dictated by the sense. The opening lines of Milton's ' Paradise Lost ' show this:

Of man's first disobedience ‖ and the fruit
Of that forbidden tree, ‖ whose mortal taste
Brought death into the world and all our woe
With loss of Eden, ‖ till one greater Man
Restore us ‖ and regain the blissful seat,
Sing, Heavenly Muse, ‖ that on the secret
top . . .

Monometers and *dimeters* are uncommon, though both have been written by that master of dainty verse, Robert Herrick. But *trimeters* and *tetrameters* are not at all uncommon. They are frequently found in hymns. The well known :

O God, / our help / in ag/es past, /
Our hope / for years / to come, /
Our shel/ter from / the storm/y blast, /
And our / eter/nal home. /

is written in alternate tetrameters and trimeters. The formula *a* for the first, *b* for the second, and so on, is the convention for briefly describing the rhyme of a verse. The scheme here is therefore *ab ab* ; the second rhyme is an ' eye ' one, for, though spelt similarly, ' come ' and ' home ' are imperfect rhymes.

The octosyllabic couplet, a form of the tetrameter, in which each line rhymes with the next, came to us from the French, and has been a favourite form for long narrative poems from the Middle English period to John Masefield.

The pentameter has already been described and its outstanding importance underlined. The *hexameter, heptameter,* and *octometer* are long lines which are not very suitable for the music of English verse, but have nevertheless been employed by skilled poets. A form of iambic hexameter, called the alexandrine, constitutes the final line of the Spenserian stanza (*see* below and Lesson 9) ; it was ridiculed by Pope, thus :

That like / a wound/ed snake / drags its / slow length / along /

Macaulay used the heptameter in his stirring poem, ' The Armada ' :

Attend / all ye / who list to hear / our no/ble Eng/land's praise /

and Tennyson attempted the longest line of all, the octometer, in ' Locksley Hall ' :

Comrades, / leave me / here a / little, / while as / yet 'tis / early / morn.

This is a trochaic measure with a syllable lacking in the final foot.

Longfellow produced in 'Hiawatha' unrhymed *trochaic tetrameters :*

Then the / little / Hia/watha
Learned of / every / bird the / language . . .

'Evangeline' is in unrhymed *hexameters :*

This is the / forest pri/meval, the / murmuring / pines and the / hemlock . . .

In Tennyson's 'Charge of the Light Brigade' there are unrhymed *dactylic dimeters :*

Cannon to / right of them,
Cannon to / left of them,
Cannon in / front of them . . .

Byron used *anapaestic tetrameters* in :

The Assyr/ian came down / like a wolf /
on the fold, /
And his co/horts were gleam/ing in pur/ple
and gold ; /
And the sheen / of their spears / was like
stars / on the sea, /
When the blue / wave rolls night/ly on
deep / Galilee. /

J. E. Flecker produced an outstanding piece of verbal music in 'The War Song of the Saracens' :

And the spear / was a Des/ert physic/ian
who cured / not a few / of ambition,
And drave / not a few / to perdi/tion, with
med/icine bitt/er and strong :
And the shield / was a grief / to the fool /
and as bright / as a des/olate pool,
And as straight / as the rock / of Stamboul /
when their cav/alry thun/dered / along.
For the cow/ard was drowned / with the
brave / when our bat/tle sheered up /
like a wave,
And the dead / to the des/ert we gave, /
and the glo/ry to God / in our song.

Flecker obtains a remarkable effect not only on account of his mastery of the anapaest, but because of his unusual arrangement of rhyme. He uses the *internal rhyme* (known as the *Leonine*, or bisecting rhyme), as well as rhyme at the end of the line. Thus 'physician' and 'ambition' in the first line rhyme with 'perdition' in the middle of the second line ; 'fool' in the third line rhymes with 'pool,' which in turn rhymes with 'Stamboul' in the fourth, and so on. In addition to this, the words at the end of the second, fourth, and sixth lines also rhyme. The result of all this elaboration is a poem which moves with a splendid swing.

Other metres than those described here are used from time to time, and the student is strongly advised to try to analyse the metre of the poem he reads. He will find it a valuable and interesting exercise. He must bear in mind that the whole basis of English prosody is stress, and not quantity, and the English poet is not slavishly bound to use exactly the same number of syllables in every line of a piece of verse he has chosen to write in a given measure. An attempt was made in Elizabethan times to write verse on the classical model based on the quantity and length of the vowel. It was a complete failure.

Vers Libre. Another experiment in verse writing is taking place today. It is the production of Free Verse, or Vers Libre. It is by its nature very indefinite, and therefore is difficult to define. It may, however, be described as a form of verse writing in which there is no fixed regular system of rhyme or rhythm. Words and phrases have to be so chosen as to give an effect less continuous than that which is found in prose. Walt Whitman, the American poet, first used this kind of verse writing in his 'Leaves of Grass,' published in 1855, so the experiment is nearly a hundred years old. It has made some progress of late, and there are parallel movements in Music and Art.

Classification of Poetry. According to the poem's function, it may be classified.

The Epic takes a theme of high purpose and immense scope, and ranges over a great variety of episodes, embellished with all the devices of the poet's art. In a number of 'books' or parts, it narrates the deeds of its heroic figures and describes the scenes and persons they encounter, preserving always the balance and unity of the composition. In Greek we have the 'Iliad' and 'Odyssey' (each consisting of 24 books); in Latin, the Aeneid (12 books) ; in English, Milton's 'Paradise Lost' (12 books) and 'Paradise Regained' (4 books).

Lyrics are poems of emotional content, so called because the earliest specimens were intended to be sung to the lyre.

The Ode is a species of lyric, with a noble theme lending itself to profundity of thought ; it has a varied and irregular metre, usually rhymed, and a certain magnificence of style. Dryden's 'Ode on St. Cecilia's Day,' Gray's 'Ode on a Distant Prospect of Eton College,' Wordsworth's 'Ode on Intimations of Immortality,' Shelley's 'Ode to the West Wind' and 'Ode to a Skylark,' and the six Odes of Keats are famous examples.

Dramatic poetry explains itself ; all poetic plays come under this heading.

Pastoral poetry describes rural life ; it usually consists of conversations between shepherds, relating to their loves and their flocks ; Spenser's 'Shepherd's Calendar' typifies this almost extinct form.

The Elegy is a lament in verse. Gray's 'Elegy in a Country Churchyard,' Shelley's beautiful 'Adonaïs' (written on the death of Keats), and Tennyson's long 'In Memoriam' may be given as instances.

Ballads are short tales, often legendary, told in a light and rapid metre and suitable for recitation.

Types of Stanza. There are several poetic stanzas, composed of certain fixed lines, which are readily recognizable. The *ballad stanza* is strictly composed of four lines alternately of four and three iambic feet :

> O come ye here to fight, young lord,
> Or come ye here to play ?
> Or come ye here to drink good wine
> Upon the weddin'-day ?

The *elegiac stanza* is an iambic pentameter quatrain, rhyming *abab* :

Full many a gem of purest ray serene
The dark unfathom'd caves of ocean bear :
Full many a flower is born to blush unseen,
And waste its sweetness on the desert air.

The same metre with a rhyme scheme *aaba*, in which the first, second and fourth lines rhyme and the third does not, is known as the 'Omar Khayyam' stanza, because it was used in Edward FitzGerald's beautiful paraphrase of the Persian poet's 'Rubaiyat':

For some we loved, the loveliest and the best *a*
That from his Vintage rolling Time hath prest,*a*
Have drunk their cup a Round or two before, *b*
And one by one crept silently to rest. *a*

The *Spenserian stanza* (*see* Lesson 9) was so named after its inventor, who used it for 'The Faerie Queene.' It consists of eight iambic pentameter lines followed by an alexandrine. The rhyme scheme is *abab bcbcc.* This stanza has been used by Thomson in 'The Castle of Indolence,' Burns in 'The Cottar's Saturday Night,' Byron in 'Childe Harold's Pilgrimage' and Shelley in 'Adonaïs.' A verse from 'Adonaïs' will illustrate this form :

He has outsoared the shadow of our night, *a*
Envy and calumny and hate and pain, *b*
And that unrest which men miscall delight, *a*
Can touch him not and torture not again. *b*
From the contagion of the world's slow stain *b*
He is secure ; and now can never mourn *c*
A heart grown cold, a head grown grey, in
vain— *b*
Nor, when the spirit's self has ceased to burn, *c*
With sparkless ashes load an unlamented urn. *c*

Before Spenser's time the 7-line stanza was common. Chaucer uses it in his 'Troilus and Creseyde' and other poems, for instance—

O soth is seid, that heléd for to be
As of a fevere or other gret siknesse,
Men mosté drink, as men may alday see,
Ful bittré drinke ; and for to han gladnésse
Men drinken ofte peyne and gret distresse ;
I mene it here, as for this aventure,   [cure.
That through a peyne hath founden all his

The *Octave Stanza,* or Ottava Rima, consists of eight iambic pentameters. The rhyme is *ab ab ab cc.* This form was borrowed from Italy. It was used by Byron in 'Don Juan,' 'Beppo,' and 'The Vision of Judgement.' Both Shelley and Keats used it very successfully. The example is taken from Byron's ' Beppo ':

They lock them up, and veil, and guard them
daily, *a*
They scarcely can behold their male relations, *b*
So that their moments do not pass so gaily *a*
As is supposed the case with northern nations;*b*
Confinement, too, must make them look quite
palely ; *a*
And as the Turks abhor long conversations, *b*
Their days are either passed in doing nothing, *c*
Or bathing, nursing, making love, and
clothing. *c*

The 'In Memoriam ' stanza, although not invented by Tennyson, was used in his poem. It consists of four lines, each with four iambic feet, rhyming *ab ba :*

And so the Word had breath, and wrought *a*
With human hands the creed of creeds *b*
In loveliness of perfect deeds, *b*
More strong than all poetic thought. *a*

The *Sonnet* is a complete poem of fourteen lines with special rules as to the number and place of the rhymes. Each line is an iambic pentameter. There are two main sonnet forms, each with some variations. They are the Italian (or Petrarchan) type, actually dating from 1220, and the English variety. Sonnets were written in Italy by Petrarch, Dante, and Tasso, by Camoens in Portugal, by Ronsard and du Bellay in France.

The first English sonnets may be found in 'Tottel's Miscellany,' published in 1557 ; they were paraphrases from Plutarch, made by Sir Thomas Wyatt and the Earl of Surrey. Sir Philip Sidney's 'Astrophel and Stella' (1591) gave the sonnet its vogue, and it has been computed by Sir Sidney Lee that more than two thousand were published between 1591 and 1597, including cycles by Constable, Daniel, Lodge, Drayton, Chapman and Campion. Spenser used his own variant and so did Shakespeare ; both had many followers. Later came Drummond of Hawthornden, and Donne composed two sequences of religious sonnets. Milton wrote some noble sonnets, but after his time the sonnet-form was neglected. Wordsworth revived it, and Keats, Mrs. Browning, D. G. Rossetti and Christina Rossetti all composed beautiful examples.

Each sonnet is divided into an octave, the first eight lines, and a sestet, the last six. In the strict Italian form there is a marked break between the octave and sestet ; in the modified form, which Milton and other poets followed, there is no such break. The rhyme scheme in the orthodox form is: *abba, abba, cde, cde.* In the modified form the rhymes are the same in the octave, and the variations, which are many, occur in the sestet ; thus the scheme is *abba abba, cd cd cd,* or *cd cd ee,* and many other varieties. An excellent example of a beautiful sonnet, with rhyme variations in the sestet, is Christina Rossetti's ' Remember ':

Remember me when I am gone away, *a*
Gone far away into the silent land ; *b*
When you can no more hold me by the hand, *b*
Nor I half turn to go, yet turning stay. *a*
Remember me when no more day by day *a*
You tell me of our future that you plann'd : *b*
Only remember me ; you understand *b*
It will be late to counsel then or pray. *a*
Yet if you should forget me for a while *c*
And afterwards remember, do not grieve : *d*
For if the darkness and corruption leave *d*
A vestige of the thoughts that once I had, *e*
Better by far you should forget and smile *c*
Than that you should remember and be sad. *e*

Shakespeare's form of sonnet really consists of three quatrains and a rhyming couplet, thus : *abab cdcd efef gg.* Spenser's sonnet has a more closely knit rhyme scheme, as follows : *abab bcbc cdcd ee.* There is no division into octave and sestet.

A good example of one of Shakespeare's sonnets is :

Shall I compare thee to a summer's day ? *a*
Thou art more lovely and more temperate : *b*
Rough winds do shake the darling buds of
   May, *a*
And Summer's lease hath all too short a
   date: *b*
Sometime too hot the eye of heaven shines, *c*
And often is his gold complexion dimm'd ; *d*
And every fair from fair sometime declines, *c*
By chance or nature's changing course un-
   trimm'd : *d*
But thy eternal Summer shall not fade *e*
Nor lose possession of that fair thou owest ; *f*
Nor shall Death brag thou wanderest in his
   shade, *e*
When in eternal lines to time thou growest : *f*
So long as men can breathe, or eyes can see, *g*
So long lives this, and this gives life to thee. *g*

It will be noted that in the Italian forms the maximum number of rhymes is five, and may be only four. Shakespeare uses seven rhymes, and Spenser five. Rupert Brooke in his well-known group of sonnets, which are quite irregular in structure, uses seven rhymes.

'Poetic' Diction. Finally it must be remembered that poetry possesses no particular form of language, peculiar to itself. In the eighteenth century poetry became linked up with a peculiar form of diction. Birds were 'the feathered quire,' men were 'swains,' heaven was 'the azure vault,' the moon became 'the refulgent lamp of night,' and so on. The publication of 'The Lyrical Ballads' in 1798, together with Wordsworth's outspoken and oft-repeated opinion that the language of everyday life was the proper raw material for the poet, helped to give a mortal blow to artificiality of diction. The poet of to-day enjoys considerable latitude ; he need not simplify, any more than he need elaborate. He may use inversions, and in general, his vocabulary and syntax are not limited to that which would be found in prose. There is infinite scope for variety.

English is a noble, flexible and expressive language, and in it poets of genius have produced poetry unsurpassed in any European literature.

LESSON FIVE

Old English Verse

IT is hardly possible to overestimate the value and importance of English literature. It has the distinction of being the greatest literature in the world. This claim is due not only to the fact that it started earlier than any other European literature, but also because in the merit of its various forms, and in quantity, it excels all others, and from its early beginnings it has shown an astonishing vitality.

A great part of Early English literature was written in metre, and this will form the subject of the present lesson, the prose being dealt with in a later section (*see* page 148). First, however, a word must be said about the language which these primitive writers used.

The earliest form of English—from the beginning to about one hundred years after the Norman Conquest—is sometimes called Anglo-Saxon, but more generally Old English. By its vocabulary and system of inflexions it is seen to be of West Germanic stock, but it also contains a considerable element of Latin loan words. In appearance it looks like a foreign tongue, and many are the changes and simplifications it

has undergone in its passage through the years. Hence, except to the specialist student, all the earliest works are a closed book save in translation.

In order that the student may have some idea of the difficulty of Old English, one of the best known pieces in our language, the Lord's Prayer, is given below in the Anglo-Saxon translation of 995.

Fŏder ure ŏu ŏe eart on heofonum, si ŏin nama gehalgod ; to-becume ŏin rice ; gewurŏe ŏin willa on eorþan swa swa on heofonum ; urne dŏghwamlican hlaf syle us to-dŏg : and forgyf us ure gyltas, swa swa we forgyfaþ urum gylentendum ; and ne gelod us on costnunge ac alys us of yfele. Soplice.

(þ (thorn) and ŏ (eth) were runes which survived in the Old English alphabet ; they were interchangeable, and equivalent to 'th.')

The oldest English poetry is to be found in the pagan 'Charms,' which have been only partially Christianized. There are other pagan remnants, somewhat later in origin ; these are obviously the work of experienced writers. 'Beowulf,' the greatest and longest of all early European poems— its length is 3,183 lines—exists in one manuscript in the British Museum. Three other ancient volumes, the Exeter Book, the Vercelli Book, and the Junian manuscript, contain nearly all the rest of Old English poetry.

Early Metric Usage. The chief characteristics of Old English poetry are :

(1) Long lines divided into half lines by a well-marked pause in the middle.

(2) The two halves of the line are linked together by alliteration either of vowels or of consonants.

(3) In each half line there are two accented syllables, which may be marked either by the alliteration, or by the natural emphasis of the sense, and a varying number of unaccented syllables.

(4) The versification relies on alliteration and accent ; rhyme is practically unknown before the Norman Conquest.

The verses were made for oral delivery, and were probably chanted by a minstrel. As Mr. George Sampson says:

Possibly the nearest approach we have to Anglo-Saxon verse is the 'pointing' of the Psalms in the Church Service, i.e. the fitting of verses with no fixed number of syllables to form a chant with a fixed number of accents.

Of the smaller poems which have survived, the first is 'Widsith,' or 'the man who has travelled widely.' In a difficult poem of 143 lines, the bard speaks of his wanderings and the kings of whom he has heard, how at the court of Eormanric he sang the praises of the lady Ealdhild, and how he and his mate Scilling were held in honour wherever they went. 'Widsith' may date from the fifth century, with later interpolations.

'Deor's Complaint' is a poem of 42 verses. It is possibly contemporary with 'Beowulf.' It is the story of Deor, a minstrel, who has been supplanted by his rival, Heorrenda. He consoles himself, however, by thinking about the troubles of others, and each verse ends with the refrain :

þæs ofereode : þisses swa mæg.
(That was lived through : so this can be.)

'The Wanderer' is an elegy of 115 lines telling of the wandering of a man who has lost his protecting lord and travels upon the waters to find a resting-place. In this moving poem the poet dreams of his former happiness, and reflects on the trials and changes of this life. The last verse has been translated thus :

All is full of trouble, all this realm of Earth !
Doom of Wyrds* is changing all the world below the skies ;
Here our fee is fleeting, here the friend is fleeting,
Fleeting here is man, fleeting is the kinsman !
All the Earth's foundation is become an idle thing.
(*Wyrd [weird] means Fate or Destiny)

'The Seafarer' is 100 lines in length. It may be a monologue, but is considered by some scholars to be a dialogue between an old seaman who knows both the hardships and the attractions of a sailor's life, and a young man who will not be deterred, whatever the consequences, from a life of adventure on the sea.

'The Ruined Burg,' a short poem of 35 lines, describes the devastation by the Saxons of a Roman town, probably Bath. It shows, with real feeling, the contrast between the prosperity of the past and the desolation of the present.

'The Wife's Complaint ' and 'The Husband's Message ' are two fragments obscure at times because of the imperfection of the manuscript in the Exeter Book. In the former the wife complains of her banishment from her lord through false tongues. 'The Husband's Message' is a call to a woman from her husband who has been compelled to leave his home through a blood feud. He has prospered in a foreign land, and asks his wife to sail and join him.

From this early period there are also two fragments, 'Waldhere,' in which a warrior flees with his love from the Huns, and 'The Battle of Finnsburg,' from an old saga.

One feature which these poems all have in common is parallelism ; the thought expressed in the first half of a line is repeated in paraphrase in the second half. Another feature is their paganism, though Christian sentiments have sometimes been added.

'Beowulf' is by far the most important of all the Old English poems, not only on account of its length, but because it is the earliest and best of the northern hero-poems. The story tells how Beowulf, hearing that the man-monster Grendel haunts Hrothgar's hall and devours his thanes, sets sail to deliver him. He wrestles with the creature and tears out his arm, and Grendel escapes only to die through loss of blood. Next day, Grendel's mother takes vengeance, and Beowulf has to seek her out and slay her with his magic sword. He returns to Hrothgar in triumph and is laden with gifts. Years later, as an old man, he has his last fight with a dragon which guards a hoard of treasure ; he slays the dragon, but is himself wounded to death, and the poem ends with an account of his burial pyre.

The customs of the times are revealed, the attitude towards women, and the hard and joyless lives which our forefathers endured. We learn much that is interesting of the communal life of the warriors, as spent in the hall of their lord. The long northern nights brought fear and uncertainty. Against men and beasts men could fight bravely, but against the workings of Wyrd they felt helpless.

The manuscript that we possess of the poem is in the West Saxon dialect, and belongs to some period between the tenth and twelfth centuries. Where ' Beowulf ' is not legend it deals with historical events which occurred about A.D. 520. In substance it is heathen, but it contains several passages distinctly Christian in sentiment. It shows signs of having had more than one revision.

Early Christian Poetry. The remaining poems with which the student is concerned are Christian in character. Thus inexorable Wyrd gives place to an all-loving Father, and the darkness of the terror-haunted yields to light and hope. Christ and the saints now inspire the poets' work.

The first English poet whom we know by name is Caedmon (fl. 670). The great Bede (673–735), in his ' Ecclesiastical History of England ' (written in Latin), tells this beautiful story of him.

Caedmon used to tend the cattle in the monastery at Whitby. One night he fell asleep in the stable and there came to him the vision of One who said : 'Caedmon, sing me something.' He answered : 'I cannot sing, and for this cause left I the feast.' 'Yet,' said the divine visitant, 'you must sing to me.' ' What shall I sing ?' asked Caedmon. 'Sing,' the other replied, 'the beginning of created things.'
At once Caedmon began a hymn in praise of the Creator, and when he awoke he remembered it. He became a monk, and continued in the Abbey till joyfully he died at peace. He sang each day the Scripture history and about the Judgement Day.

It is probable that we have very little now that can with any degree of certainty be attributed to Caedmon, though there are poetic versions of Genesis, Exodus, and Daniel, together with a poem called ' Christ

and Satan,' which, if not by the master himself, were certainly written by members of his school. The Hymn quoted by Bede in his 'Ecclesiastical History' is his only authentic composition.

The one other poet of outstanding importance is Cynewulf, a Northumbrian, who flourished in the latter part of the eighth century. To him are attributed poems on New Testament subjects and legends of the martyrs. Of these, the finest is his 'Crist,' which in three splendidly conceived episodes presents the Nativity, the Ascension and the Day of Judgement.

Deep creation thunders, and before the Lord
　　shall go
Hugest of upheaving fires o'er the far-spread
　　earth !
Hurtles the hot flame, and the heavens burst
　　asunder,
All the firm-set flashing planets fall out of
　　their places.
Then the sun that erst o'er the elder world
With such brightness shone for the sons of men
Black-dark now becomes, changed to bloody
　　hue.
And the moon alike, that to men of old
Nightly gave her light, nither tumbles down ;
And the stars also shower down from Heaven,
Headlong through the roaring rift, lashed by
　　all the winds.

Remarkable, too, is Cynewulf's 'Elene,' which describes the discovery of the true cross by the Empress Helena, mother of Constantine. His other poems were 'The Fates of the Apostles' and the fragmentary 'Descent into Hell.' He wrote part, at least, of 'Guthlac,' which relates the life and death of the Mercian saint. There is reason to suppose that he was also author of the beautiful 'Dream of the Rood' and of 'Andreas.' The dull 'Juliana' is his early work ; with this exception, all his poems are characterized by their imaginative force. Of the 95 'Riddles' extant, many are attributed to Cynewulf.

Old English verse, after its first flowering, showed a complete collapse which it is difficult to explain. Apart from the poem on the Battle of Brunanburh (937), found in the Anglo-Saxon Chronicle, there are only two poems of any importance. The first is ' Judith,' a lively fragment of 350 lines giving part of the Apocryphal story. The second is ' The Battle of Maldon,' a vigorous poem of which the end is lost. It describes the fight between the English, under ealdorman Byrhtnoth, and the raiding Northmen under Anlaf, in 991. With these fragments Old English poetry ends.

LESSON SIX

Middle English Metrical Romances

Of all European literatures, English was clearly the most important up to the end of the tenth century. Then, for the next two hundred years, it suffered an almost complete eclipse. From the time of the Norman Conquest until about the end of the thirteenth century, French literature was predominant in nearly every branch. In the fourteenth century, owing mainly to its three giants—Dante (1265–1321), one of the greatest poets the world has ever known, Petrarch (1304–1374), and Boccaccio (c. 1313–1375)—Italian literature obtained the leadership, until, in the last quarter of the century, Chaucer regained the supremacy for England.

It is not difficult to understand the decline of English letters in the eleventh and twelfth centuries. In 1066 there took place the conquest of England by the Normans (= North men), who, although sprung from a stock similar to the English, brought with them a new language and new ideas which were to form a close link with Continental culture. Moreover, there was to be a struggle between Norman-French and English for mastery. English, deep-rooted in the soil and of sturdy growth, was to survive with a much increased vocabulary. Thus before 1150 there emerged a form of our language, known for convenience by the name of Middle English, which embodied a large number of new words from Norman and Continental French. With it came a new form of literature which exhibited an amalgamation of English and Continental features. In metrical composition the French definitely won a victory, for rhyme was introduced and widely used. In dealing with the poetry of this period it is important to recall that writings could only be circulated in manuscript. Many of them, moreover, were still intended for chanting by minstrels.

Medieval Romances. The influence of imported subject matter was henceforth strongly marked. Romance became the great subject for the poet, and this was divided into three ' matters ': (1) 'The matter of France' dealt with stories about Charlemagne and the Twelve Peers, with such outstanding heroes as Roland, Oliver, Ferumbras, Ogier the Dane, Huon of Bordeaux, and the Four Sons of Aymon. (2) 'The matter of Britain' was the Arthurian legend. (3) 'The matter of Rome the Great' embraced the whole of classical antiquity, including stories of Troy and Thebes, and several about Alexander, who by poets' magic was transformed into a feudal monarch. There are other stories which do not fall within these classifications.

The stories dealing with Charlemagne (742–814) and his knights are filled with adventure. They not infrequently describe gallant fights on the battlefield between Christian knight and Saracen warrior. A good example is ' Sir Otuel,' whose hero, a Saracen who insults Charlemagne, is challenged by Roland and finally converted to Christianity.

Arthurian Legends. The importance of the Arthurian legend is so great that a very brief explanation of its origins and influence must be given. The romantic figure of King Arthur has possibly some historical basis, and there is reason to believe that he was a chieftain or general in the fifth or sixth century. Mention is found in annals of the battle of Mount Badon in 518, ' in which Arthur carried the cross of Lord Jesus Christ on his shoulders.' It is also stated that he fell at the battle of Camlan in 539.

King Arthur first appears as a hero of romance in Geoffrey of Monmouth's famous 'History of the Kings of Britain.' This Latin work is not very reliable as history ; the author sometimes allowed too much rein to his vivid imagination. He owns his indebtedness to a very ancient work in the British tongue, brought from Brittany.

According to Geoffrey, Arthur is the son of Uther Pendragon and Igraine, wife of Gorlois of Cornwall, whom Uther wins by means of Merlin's magic. He becomes King of Britain at the age of fifteen, and fights against Picts, Scots and Saxons. With ' Caliburn ' (Excalibur), his sword, he conquers Scotland, Iceland, Ireland and the Orkneys. He marries Guinevere, a noble Roman lady, and conquers many lands on the mainland of Europe. His court is at Caerleon on Usk. When summoned to pay tribute to the Emperor Lucius of Rome, he refuses and declares war. Guinevere and his kingdom are left in charge of his nephew, Modred. Arthur slays the giant of St. Michael's Mount when he is on his way to Rome. As Arthur's envoy, Sir Gawaine defies the Emperor, and bears himself well in the combat which follows. Arthur is about to enter Rome when he is warned that Modred has seized Guinevere and the kingdom. He returns with Gawaine, who is killed when he attempts to land. Modred and his recreant knights retreat into Cornwall, and in the final battle on the river Camel he is slain with all of them. Arthur, mortally wounded, is taken to the isle of Avalon for the healing of his wounds. Guinevere becomes a nun.

This is the Arthurian story in the barest outline. It has been expanded and modified in many details by subsequent writers. The Norman poet Wace mentions the Round Table as a means of settling precedence among Arthur's knights. The wounded king is expected to return from Avalon and resume his reign. Wace's work was used by Layamon in his poetic chronicle 'Brut,' which introduces a supernatural element into the story ; elves are present at Arthur's birth, and his sword and spear are of magical origin.

The story was developed by French writers, and Arthur became the centre of many legends. He is the chief figure only in the tales of his earlier years and of his death. His court, however, is the gathering-place for adventurous knights, when the king himself is but a figure-head. It is worthy of note that the gallant Gawaine is concerned in more deeds than any other knight. Some of Arthur's adventures are used by Malory, in his 'Morte d'Arthur,' which Tennyson borrowed as the basis of his 'Idylls of the King.' But the exploits of Arthur and his knights of the Round Table, the quest of the Holy Grail, the loves of Lancelot and Guinevere, and of Tristram and Iseult, have inspired many writers in different lands.

Other Medieval Poems. Thus in Middle English there is to be found a very considerable body of literature, which cannot here be examined in detail. It will only be possible to deal with some of the more important metrical romances. It must be borne in mind also that a new kind of love poetry was being introduced through France, by the influence of the wandering minstrels, the troubadours. Moreover, the attitude of men to life, and especially towards women, was becoming profoundly influenced by the chivalry of the Middle Ages.

Probably one of the most important poems of this period is the 'Brut' of Layamon. It is written in a blend of the old alliterative verse with some rhyming octosyllabic forms according to the French pattern, and shows metre in its transitional form. It traces the ' history' of England from the arrival of a legendary Brutus to Cadwalader (A.D. 689) and includes the first versions in English of the stories of Lear and Cymbeline.

'The Owl and the Nightingale,' a poem of about 1,800 lines in the Dorset dialect, is of importance. It is written as a political debate, with legal formality, between the nightingale, who represents the world, and the grave owl, who represents the cloister. The poet shows considerable skill in the way he handles his octosyllabic couplets, and the result is a delightful poem. 'Havelok the Dane,' another poem of importance, tells how a Danish prince and an English princess come into their own again after being defrauded by wicked guardians. 'King Horn' is another good story of lovers thwarted but eventually reunited. A little later came the racy romance of 'Richard Coeur de Lion,' in 7,000 lines. The popular 'Guy of Warwick' is tedious and relates in long-winded fashion how Sir Guy saved England from Colbrand the Dane. 'Sir Bevis of Hamtoun,' a poem of about 4,000 lines, is of special interest ; it contains nearly all the exciting ingredients which made a poem popular with our forefathers. The fighting against a dragon, which had now become a usual feature of medieval romance, is described with great effect.

'Sir Tristrem' tells the love story of the knight and Iseult ; 'Sir Launfal' deals with the love of a fairy for a mortal ; 'Sir Orfeo' is the tale of Orpheus and Eurydice related as a Celtic fairy story ; 'Ywaine and Gawain' describes the fight between the two knights until recognition brings the combat to an end ; in 'The Wedding of Sir Gawain' the knight saves the life of Arthur by marrying a loathsome hag who turns into a lovely maiden. 'Amis and Amiloun' is one of the most moving of these stories. 'The Romance of William of Palerme' (Palermo), a free translation from the French, is an exciting narrative marked by real characterization.

All these are examples of subject-matter chosen from a considerable number of metrical romances. They have certain features in common. They are nearly all anonymous : they have their being in a world of the imagination far divorced from every-day life, and they not infrequently strike the note of a Christendom constantly at war with the powers of darkness.

The most important group of these romances consists of four poems : 'Pearl,' 'Patience,' 'Cleanness,' and 'Sir Gawayne and the Grene Knight.' It is within the bounds of possibility that they are all the work of the same author. The poet combines variations of the old alliterative measure with rhyme. 'Pearl' is probably an allegory on a dead child. The precious pearl has been lost in the ground, and the 'joyless jeweller,' in his sorrow, searches for it. He sees the maiden in dazzling white raiment covered with pearls, and she shows him a vision of the celestial city. But he wakes and finds himself on the hillside—alone. 'Patience' tells the Biblical story of Jonah, and contains a spirited description of a storm at sea. 'Cleanness,' or 'Purity,' is a rather long poem which illustrates, by means of stories from Scripture, the vices opposed to cleanness.

But the greatest of these poems is without doubt 'Sir Gawayne and the Grene Knight.' Written in a rather difficult Lancashire dialect, it consists of 2,530 lines in alliterative and rhyming verse, broken from time to time by a short refrain. The poem deals with one of King Arthur's knights and is a graceful comedy of temptation. It combines vitality with mystery, and excels in descriptions of the delights of hall-feast and hunt, and of a lonely ride taken by Sir Gawayne through the silence of the forest and the deep snow.

Tales from the Orient. The Crusades (1096–1270), with their many contacts, were important in breaking down barriers between West and East. The European knights learnt, for the first time, how to enjoy hot baths, and to take elementary precautions to prevent their bodies from being constantly verminous, and they brought back a number of Eastern tales.

One of the best of these is 'Flores and Blancheflour,' which relates the romance of a Christian princess, carried off by the Saracens, and brought up with a Christian prince, Flores. Other interesting tales from the East are 'The Seven Sages of Rome,' a poem of some length in which the main story is set in a framework of fourteen short tales ; and 'Ypotis,' about Epictetus the Stoic, who flourished in the first century A.D., and held that virtue is mainly endurance and abstinence.

The tale of 'Barlaam and Josaphat' is a real literary curiosity. It is a Christianized version of the legend of Buddha and was widely circulated as a Christian work until its Buddhist origin was discovered much later. It has a further interest for us because it contains a casket story which, with certain modifications, was used by Shakespeare in 'The Merchant of Venice.'

Early Lyrics. The eleven short poems of Laurence Minot, written during 1333–52, are of interest mainly because they are the only verses of the period which are not anonymous. They celebrate in fervidly patriotic strain England's successes in battle under Edward III.

The lyric was just beginning to appear. From an unknown poet came the charming

> Sumer is i-cumen in
> Lhude sing cuccu. . . . . .

The original manuscript of this poem, set to music, is in the British Museum. It has the added interest of being the first known English musical manuscript.

Religious Poems. A certain number of devotional works in verse must be mentioned. The 'Poema Morale,' or 'Moral Ode,' consists of a series of reflections on the shortness of human life, the failure of wisdom to coincide with increase in years, the coming of judgement, and the joys of heaven. Metrically it is particularly notable, being written in rhyming couplets of fourteen syllables. The 'Cursor Mundi,' a long poem of some 24,000 lines, written mainly in eight-syllabled couplets, has many episodes falling within seven 'ages' which cover Biblical history and include the mythical finding of the Cross ; the last section deals with Judgement Day. The poem was evidently very popular, since many manuscripts of it still exist. Well worth study, too, is the dramatic 'Harrowing of Hell,' which renders in lively verse the legend of Christ's visit to Hell to redeem the worthy who had died before His coming to earth.

The 'Ormulum,' another long poem of which there now survive 20,000 lines, written alternately in eight and seven syllables, is concerned with the Gospel for each day, with expositions thereon. It is the work of a monk named Orm or Ormin, who introduced a form of phonetic spelling, and by doubling the consonant after each short vowel has preserved for us a valuable record of the pronunciation of his day. In 1303 Robert Mannyng, a canon of the order of St. Gilbert of Sempringham, translated into eight-syllabled verse, under the title of 'Handlyng Synne,' the 'Manuel des Pechiez' of William of Waddington, but he added freely to the original and, by means of anecdote and satire, made it far from dull reading.

There is also a fine 'Story of Genesis and Exodus,' and a notable Northumbrian version of the Psalter.

Chaucer and the Rise of English Poetry

IF one were to begin the study of poetry with the works of Geoffrey Chaucer, it is doubtful whether one's progress would be immediate and sustained. For the study of Chaucer requires of the student some degree of cultured love for poetry, which is not so necessary to the immediate enjoyment of Shakespeare or Tennyson, since both of these great geniuses are comprehensible to us, using language not too far removed from our daily speech.

It is otherwise with Chaucer and the writers of the later medieval period. While the body of the language in which Chaucer wrote is the essential English with which we are all familiar, it is different in so many little ways that the reader never quite accepts it as his own tongue, but always finds in it a quaint and somewhat foreign flavour. For this very reason, however, there is the more need that we should familiarize ourselves with it. Only so shall we discover the charm of Chaucer.

Chaucer's Language. We have already noted that in Chaucer's day the rude and vigorous Anglo-Saxon speech of the common people had absorbed from the Norman-French of the aristocracy numerous words and idioms not yet assimilated, which, later on, were vastly to enhance the beauty and expressiveness of the language. Old French words, later modified in spelling and pronunciation, still continued to bear a resemblance to their originals ; thus 'chamber' is *chaumbre*, 'error' is *errour*, 'authority' is *auctoritee*.

Many verbs retain the old Germanic suffix '-en' for the infinitive, while the past participle has the 'y-' or 'i-' prefix, which had taken the place of the old 'ge-.'

Chaucer was no affected writer, but true to the speech of his day. As J. R. Lowell says pithily :

He found our language lumpish, stiff, unwilling, too apt to speak Saxonly in grouty monosyllables, but left it enriched with the longer measure of the Italian and Provençal poets. He reconciled, in the harmony of his verse, the English bluntness with the dignity and elegance of the less homely southern speech.

Pronunciation. Here we can indicate only a few of the principles which Chaucer recognized ; they are substantially the principles of French poetry.

Note that most words ending in '-e' have to be read as though this letter formed a separate syllable, except when the word immediately following begins with a vowel, or sometimes when it begins with an 'h.'

Professor Skeat instructs us to sound the final '-e' when it occurs at the end of a line. The medial 'e' is also sounded as a rule, and thus certain words ending in '-ed' or '-es' take a syllable more than they require in our modern speech.

A little care will enable the general student to enjoy to the full some of the grandest poetry in our language. Be assured that Chaucer, once taken up as a task, will be continued as a pleasure.

Metre. Chaucer enriched English poetry with two new measures—the 7-line stanza and the decasyllabic couplet. The 7-line stanza, a decasyllabic measure rhyming *ababbcc*, afterwards became known as 'rime royal' when James I of Scotland used it for his lovely Chaucerian 'Kingis Quhair' (King's Book). It came into general use for serious verse until, a hundred years later, Spenser's 9-line stanza displaced it. We may see in 'Troilus and Creseyde' how fluent and adaptable the measure could be. The following lines, addressed to the Virgin Mary, are from the Prologue to the Prioress's Tale :

Lady ! thy bountee, thy magnificence,
Thy vertu, and thy great humilitee,
There may no tonge expresse in no science ;
For som-tyme, lady, er man praye to thee,
Thou gooest biforn of thy benignitee,
And getest us the light, thrugh thy preyere,
To gyden us unto thy sone so dere.

The decasyllabic couplet, used in 'The Canterbury Tales,' consists of iambic pentameters rhymed, with an easy overflow from one line to the next.

And I seyde, his opinioun was good.
What solde he studie and make himselven wood [1]
Upon a book in cloistre alway to poure,
Or swinken [2] with his hendes and laboure
As Austin [3] bit [4] ? How shal the world be served ?
Let Austin have his swink to him reserved.

---

[1] mad.   [2] toil.
[3] St. Augustine.   [4] bid.

Life and Work. We should know a little about the poet's life, because of its influence on his work. . . .

Chaucer was born about 1340, the son of a London vintner who was in the service of the King. The boy Geoffrey entered the household of the Duke of Clarence, brother to the King. He bore arms against the French, was pensioned by Edward III, and married Philippa, a lady of the court, whose sister was the third wife of John of Gaunt, another royal duke. Chaucer became one of the King's esquires, and was sent abroad on several missions. Thus he made contact with the leading personalities of his day, and from this full and varied experience he gained the shrewdness and worldly wisdom which characterize his work. He held many lucrative posts, and in 1386 sat in Parliament, but this same year a decline in his fortunes set in. He died in 1400, and was the first poet to find a resting-place in Westminster Abbey.

Chaucer must have had little time for writing poetry until his retirement from office in 1386. The early poems, such as 'The Dethe of Blaunche the Duchesse' (wife of John of Gaunt) and the much finer ' Dethe of Pité,' have tenderness and charm but no sustained power. His first great work was 'Troilus and Creseyde,' written about 1380–3 ; 'The Parlement of Foules' is a charming allegory, celebrating the betrothal of the new king, Richard II, to Anne of Bohemia ; then came 'The Hous of Fame,' written under the influence of Dante, though in lighter mood, and left unfinished, like the admirable 'Legende of Good Women.' 'The Canterbury Tales' were begun in 1386 and left incomplete.

During his lifetime these poems were circulated in manuscript copies. They were first printed by Caxton, who issued an edition of 'The Canterbury Tales' about 1477 ; the earliest complete edition of his works was that by Godfray in 1532. Of modern texts, Skeat's is accepted as the best.

Chaucer's Characteristics. We shall find no poet more human than Geoffrey Chaucer, hardly one with whom the reader would be more willing to have personal acquaintance. His intense humanity comes out so inevitably in everything he wrote ; his sympathy with his fellows, his delight in Nature's ways, his jovial humour, his reverence, his occasional ribaldry and his sorrow for his follies—all these qualities serve to make his a most lovable personality. Lowell refers to him as 'a truly epic poet, without knowing it,' and indeed we find in his poems occasional evidence of 'absolute dramatic inspiration,' which, were it continuous instead of occasional, would carry him into the highest rank of the world's great poets.

Sources. Creative though he was, Chaucer's genius was awakened by the influence of Continental literature, with which, as a scholar and traveller, he early made acquaintance. The French and Italian poets and storytellers were familiar to him in the original, and he drew largely upon them for his material. His heaviest debt is to Boccaccio, his great Italian contemporary, whom, as well as Petrarch, he is popularly supposed, on somewhat slender evidence, to have met during a diplomatic mission to Italy. It is also probable that Dante's 'Divina Commedia' affected him to a considerable extent. His verse-form was derived from the *trouvères* of France, who, for more than two hundred years before him, had been composing those epic poems which the *jongleurs* recited in castle halls.

Yet, with all his borrowings, and even when he seemed only to have translated, Chaucer so wonderfully transmuted by his genius the material wherewith he worked that it was re-created, as is the case with all great artists. Boccaccio himself, from whose 'Decameron' Chaucer drew so much for his 'Canterbury Tales,' and whose 'Filostrato' he so closely follows in 'Troilus and Creseyde,' took his stories from the popular medieval fiction of his time, and gave them classical form. But the artist mind of Chaucer is well illustrated in 'The Canterbury Tales,' where every personage tells a tale that is suited to the teller's character, taste, or condition of life. No such dramatic fitness is observed in the 'Decameron.'

The Canterbury Tales. This is the work with which Chaucer's name is always associated. Its plan is familiar. A company of twenty-nine pilgrims, journeying to the shrine of Thomas Becket at Canterbury, forgather in Southwark at the Tabard Inn, where the poet meets them and proposes to make one of the company. The landlord of the Tabard also offers to join the party and to act as guide. It is he who suggests that, in order to beguile the tedium of the journey, each pilgrim should undertake to tell two stories, both going and returning, and that the teller of the story which is voted the best will, on the return to the Tabard, be entertained to supper at the common cost. Chaucer did not complete the task of relating every one of the stories to be told by the pilgrims. Twenty-four tales—several of them unfinished — exist, with linking material, forming only a fragment of his design ; but a glorious fragment, which for nearly two hundred years remained the unequalled gem of English literature.

In the Prologue, which is the very acme of Chaucer's achievement, the characters of the different persons are so vividly drawn that they live again for us in the very atmosphere of the Middle Ages.

The tales themselves vary in merit. The Knight's Tale of Palamon and Arcite is usually regarded as the finest, with the Clerk's Tale of Patient Griselda and the Man of Law's Tale of Constance running it close, together with the robustly humorous Nun's Priest's Tale of the Fox and Hen; the Prioress's Tale of little St. Hugh is a moving piece of work, and in yet another vein we have the grim Pardoner's Tale.

The poet apologizes for including certain stories more racy than polite :

And therefore every gentil wight I preye,
For goddes love, deemeth nat that I seye
Of evel entente, but that I moot nedes
Hir tales alle, be they bettre or werse,
Or elles falsen som of my matere.
And therfore, who-so list it nat y-here,
Turne over the leef, and chese another tale.

This seems true enough from the artistic point of view, and from that of historical truth it is equally cogent, for it has to be borne in mind that the poet reflected in his mirror the manners of a rude age despite the fact that it was the time 'when knighthood was in flower.' We see no reason, therefore, to suppose he wrote thus 'with his tongue in his cheek,' as some critics have suggested.

Troilus and Creseyde. Though Chaucer is best remembered for his 'Canterbury Tales,' his 'Troilus and Creseyde,' based on the 'Filostrato' of Boccaccio, ranks at least equally high as a poetic masterpiece, and has the advantage of being a composite whole. It is, indeed, one of the loveliest works of poetry in the English language.

For the young reader, we recommend that a start should be made with those exquisite little poems comprising 'The Legende of Good Women,' in which the poet relates the tragic love-stories of Cleopatra, Thisbe, Dido, Ariadne, and other faithful women who had suffered through the selfishness of the men they loved.

The reader who has borne Chaucer company through two or three of these poems will require no counsel to cultivate acquaintance with the writings of this merry, wise and gentle poet, who was a scholar, a lover of books and ancient lore, but not the less a lusty Englishman, rejoicing in the out-of-door world.

LESSON EIGHT

British Poets from Chaucer to Spenser

So commanding is the figure of Geoffrey Chaucer in English medieval literature that more than two hundred years have to pass before another stands beside him on the same plane. Spenser acknowledged Chaucer as his master, but they have really little in common.

John Gower. A friend of Chaucer's, John Gower may be described as a man of great talent, ripe scholarship and character, though lacking the divine fire of genius.

He wrote three large works, in French, Latin, and English respectively. The first is no longer in existence ; the second gives an account of the rising under Wat Tyler, and thus has some value in the eyes of the historian. His English work has been reprinted under the editorship of Professor Henry Morley. It is entitled 'Confessio Amantis' (A Lover's Confession), and its interest is mainly for the philologist. Gower died in 1408 ; the effigy on his tomb in St. Saviour's Cathedral, Southwark, shows him with his head pillowed on his three ponderous works.

William Langland. Open-air vigour and downright satire are the two dominant characteristics of 'The Vision of Piers Plowman,' generally accepted as the work of William Langland (c. 1330–1400), a clerk, or minor priest, born at Cleobury Mortimer in Shropshire. The years 1362 to 1398 have been established as the date of its composition, and the dark and light colouring of life in the 14th century—the increasing corruption of the Church on the one hand and the general spread of popular intelligence on the other—are clearly reflected in it. The poem, which comprises some 7,300 alliterative lines on the Old English model, was written for the people, and won considerable popularity.

This long work makes difficult reading, but is of considerable importance for the light it throws upon the period. Next to Chaucer's 'Canterbury Tales', it is by far the most important work in Middle English. 'Piers Plowman' has been described as 'a vision of Christ seen through the clouds of humanity.' It is divided into nine dreams. In the allegory many personifications are introduced, the most important of which are Meed (worldly success), Falsehood, Repentance, Reason, Truth, Hope, Conscience. Piers Plowman, first introduced as the type of the poor and simple, becomes gradually transformed into the Christ. Later in the 'Vision' appear Do-well, Do-bet, Do-best. In this poem, and its additions—for in its original form it appeared in 1362, and in its final form in 1398 or 1399—the writer says a good deal about the abuses of his time, and discusses their remedy.

It should be noted that Professor Manly advances, with many arguments, the theory that the 'Vision' is not the work of one, but of several writers, and that William Langland is therefore an assumed, and not a personal, name.

John Skelton. Skelton (c. 1460–1529) cuts no mean figure in 15th-century literature, despite the adverse criticism to which he has always been subjected. 'Beastly Skelton' is how Pope dismisses him, and Puttenham in his 'Arte of English Poesie' —which, published in 1589, was one of the critical works that accompanied the Elizabethan literary revival—says of him : 'Being indeed but a rude rayling rimer, and all his doings ridiculous ; he used short distances and short measures, pleasing only the popular eare.' The best reply is made by the poet himself :

> For though my ryme be ragged,
> Tattered and jagged,
> Rudely rayne beaten,
> Rusty and moth eaten,
> If ye take it well therwith
> It hath in it some pyth.

Skelton was the English Rabelais, with a good deal of the Frenchman's learning, his unrestrained delight in word-play, something of his satire, much of his coarseness and his joviality. He was also capable of tender humour, as we see in 'Philyp Sparwe,' a girl's lament for her tame sparrow, killed by a cat.

Among the lesser English poets of the 15th century we need merely mention Thomas Hoccleve and John Lydgate, followers of Chaucer, and Stephen Hawes, whose long allegory, 'The Pastime of Pleasure,' is his best-known work. It contains a magnificent epitaph :

> O mortall folk ! you may beholde and se
> Howe I lye here, sometime a myghty knyght,
> The end of joye and all prosperitee
> In deth at last, thorough his course and myght :
> After the day there cometh the derke night :
> For though the day be never so longe
> At last the belles ringeth to evensonge.

In considering English literature, we find that Scottish writers have played an important part. The lamp of culture burned low in England during the 15th century, but it was kept well alight in the sterner regions of the north.

John Barbour. The first great Scottish poet, John Barbour, presented, in 'The Bruce,' a 13,500-line national epic in octosyllabic verse, full of movement and observation, and accepted by authorities as historically accurate. The original is perhaps a little more difficult to read than Chaucer, whom Barbour resembles in his love of Nature. Most collections of Scottish poetry include passages, notably the one beginning :

> A ! fredome is a nobill thing !

The following lines occur in the description of the launching of Bruce's galleys, with his little army of three hundred men, from the island of Arran, to cross the Firth of Clyde to Turnberry :

> This was in Ver[1], quhen wynter tyde,
> With his blastis hidwyus[2] to byde
> Was our drywyn,[3] and birdys smale,
> As turturis[4] and the nychtyngale,
> Begouth rycht sairely to syng,
> And for to mak in thair singyng
> Swete notis, and sownys ser,
> And melodys pleasand to her.

> [1]Spring.   [2]Bitter blasts.
> [3]Overpast.   [4]Turtle-dove.

Barbour, who was born in 1316, and died in 1395, was archdeacon of Aberdeen for about forty years, and made several journeys through England and France, chiefly, it has been thought, to collect material for his books. It is unfortunate that his 'History of the Scottish Kings' is lost ; it was, no doubt, a racy annal.

James I. King James I of Scotland (1394–1437) during his long imprisonment in England wrote many poems—notably 'The Kingis Quhair' (Book) and 'A Ballad of Good Counsel'—which are models of good English, graceful in style, and at times approach Chaucer in music and imagination. The student should read, in this connexion, Washington Irving's 'A Royal Poet,' in 'The Sketch Book.'

Robert Henryson. Of this poet we know little except that he was a schoolmaster at Dunfermline and is among those named in Dunbar's 'Lament for the Makers,' printed in 1508. Henryson's 'Fables' were popular ; his modest genius is well shown in the 'Taill of the Uplandis Mous and the Burges Mous' (the Country Mouse and the Town Mouse).

William Dunbar. Like Skelton, Dunbar was a priest, but on the whole he shows a better-balanced character ; and although he can rival his contemporary in coarseness when he cares—which is much too often— he displays public spirit in his satires, grace and wit in his allegories, and is at times capable of real pathos. Born about 1460-65, most of his life was spent at the Scottish court and his most famous poem, 'The Thrissill and the Rois' (The Thistle and the Rose), was an allegory on the marriage of James IV with Margaret, eldest daughter of Henry VII. It is supposed that he accompanied the ambassadors who went to England to arrange the marriage. Dunbar probably died about 1520.

Gavin Douglas. The third son of Archibald, earl of Angus, Gavin Douglas (c. 1474–1522) was important politically as well as in literature. It was about 1500 when he produced his earliest and longest original work now extant, 'The Palice of Honour,' and in 1513 he rendered the 'Aeneid' into Lowland Scots, this, though it was not printed for nearly forty years, being the first translation of a Latin classic published in Britain. Douglas became bishop of Dunkeld in 1515, and in 1520, on the fall of his nephew, the sixth earl of Angus, fled to England and died suddenly in London of the plague. He was buried in the church of the Savoy.

Wyatt and Surrey. Sir Thomas Wyatt and his friend Henry Earl of Surrey were the English originators of amatory verse.

Sir Thomas Wyatt (1503–42) wrote many graceful sonnets and lyrical poems characterized by a grave courtliness rather than the light touch of the true love-poet. It was he who introduced the sonnet into England from Italy. The Earl of Surrey (1517–47) was the first English poet to write in blank verse ; he used this metre for his translation of the second and fourth books of Virgil's 'Aeneid.'

With Wyatt and with Surrey, whom the French critic H. A. Taine, in his 'History of English Literature,' describes as an English Petrarch, our language had at length acquired greater literary possibilities than it had before possessed. 'Those who have ideas now possess an instrument capable of expressing them,' says Taine.

Indeed, Wyatt's lyrics are a fitting prelude to the glorious music of the Elizabethan age. Most often quoted are his lines beginning :

> Forget not yet the tried intent
> Of such a truth as I have meant ;
> My great travail so gladly spent,
> Forget not yet !

and the stanza :

> And wilt thou leave me thus,
> That hath lov'd thee so long
> In wealth and, woe among ?
> And is thy heart so strong
> As for to leave me thus ?
> Say nay ! say nay !

Surrey lacked this lightness of touch, but his name will always be remembered with gratitude as the inventor of blank verse. Though his lines sometimes limp, they opened up a new epoch. We give these lines as an example :

> Who can express the slaughter of that night,
> Or tell the number of the corpses slain,
> Or can in teares bewail them worthily ?
> The auncient famous citie fallen down,
> That many yeares did hold such seignorie.

Ballads. Medieval poetry reaches its finest flowering not in any of these poets (except Chaucer himself), but in simple balladry. Some of these ballads, like 'The Battle of Otterbourn,' tell a vividly dramatic story of contemporary events ; others build up a series of legends round a central figure such as 'Robin Hood' ; others again are pure romance, like 'Young Beichan' or 'Clerk Saunders.' As an example of the lilting charm of these verse narratives, we may take the opening lines of 'Robin Hood and the Monk ' :

> In somer, when the shawes be sheyne
> And leves be large and long,
> Hit is full mery in feyre foreste
> To here the foulys song ;

> To se the dere drawe to the dale,
> And leve the hilles hee,
> And shadow hem in the leves grene
> Under the grenewood tre.

The Scottish ballads are particularly notable for their liveliness, genuine poetic qualities and sense of the supernatural.

The ballad metre is a quatrain, made up of alternating octosyllabics and hexasyllabics.

The Poetry of Sidney and Spenser

WHEN we turn our attention to the poetry of the Elizabethan age, it is as though we were looking with unskilled eyes upon a starry heaven, so bewildering and so brilliant are the names that glitter in the literary firmament of that wonderful age, with Shakespeare as the 'bright, particular star.' With the awakening of the English nation to a new and grander perception of patriotism, the dusky clouds of medievalism had been suddenly dispersed by the bright sun of a new day.

There was nothing miraculous in the outburst of poetry which heralded and accompanied the Elizabethan age. If from the time of Chaucer the genius and imagination of the country had languished, scholarship, at least, had ripened ; and the medieval age did not pass away without leaving a legacy to the age that followed.

The English language had assumed, in the poetry of Wyatt and Surrey, a perfection of form which it had not hitherto possessed. It was now to be used by writers imbued with loftier idealism than that of the age of chivalry and old romance. But during the transition period we should naturally expect to find the older notions of life still actuating writers who chronologically are to be reckoned Elizabethans. This is true in some measure of Spenser and Sidney, both of whom were born some four years before the accession of Elizabeth.

Sir Philip Sidney. Thoroughly attractive as a human being and capable of very high achievement as a poet and prose-writer, Sidney, despite the shortness of his life, won for himself a high place in the regard of his contemporaries and has been held in affection ever since.

He was born in 1554 at Penshurst, in Kent, and in early youth was sent to Court, under the auspices of his uncle, the famous Earl of Leicester. He attracted the Queen's favour, but this did not last long. Sent to the Netherlands with the small contingent which was grudgingly allotted to assist the Dutch in their resistance to Spanish aggression, he was fatally wounded at the Battle of Zutphen in 1586 and died with a characteristically noble gesture, directing that the water brought to him should be given to a wounded soldier— ' Thy need is greater than mine.' He was

indeed the *beau ideal* of the age—' a verray parfit gentil knight.'

His progress as a poet is shown in the sonnet-sequence ' Astrophel and Stella.' The early part is weak and artificial, until at length

' Fool ! ' said my Muse to me, ' look in thy heart and write ! '

He soon gains in emotional strength, and two of these sonnets reach the heights. We quote here :

With how sad steps, O Moon, thou climb'st the skies !
How silently and with how wan a face !
What ! may it be that even in heavenly place,
That busy archer his sharp arrows tries ?
Sure, if that long-with-love-acquainted eyes
Can judge of love, thou feel'st a lover's case ;
I read it in thy looks ; thy languish'd grace,
To me, that feel the like, thy state descries.
Then, even of fellowship, O Moon, tell me,
Is constant love deem'd there but want of wit ?
Are beauties there as proud as here they be ?
Do they above love to be lov'd, and yet
Those lovers scorn whom that love doth possess ?
Do they call virtue there ungratefulness ?

Equally famous is the sonnet beginning ' Come sleep, O sleep, the certain knot of peace,' and among the lyrics scattered throughout the prose romance ' Arcadia ' is the charming sonnet ' My true love hath my heart and I have his.' Another memorable lyric is the splendidly song-like

Ring out your bells, let mourning shows be spread,
For Love is dead :
    All Love is dead, infected
    With plague of deep disdain ;
    Worth, as nought worth, rejected,
And Faith fair scorn doth gain.
    From so ungrateful fancy,
    From such a female frenzy,
    From them that use men thus,
    Good Lord, deliver us.

Sidney was one of the most modest of men, and it is to his sister, the Countess of Pembroke, that we owe the preservation of most of his work. In so short a life he achieved more than most writers. His dignified 'Defence of Poesy ' showed him to be a penetrating and learned critic. The ' Arcadia ' is discussed later.

Edmund Spenser. A poetical star of much greater magnitude, Spenser was born in London about 1552, the son of a working clothmaker who managed to give him his education at Merchant Taylors' School and Cambridge. He won the friendship of Sir Philip Sidney, and it was through Sidney's influence that he received an appointment in Ireland. For ten years he occupied Kilcolman Castle in County Cork. Here he was visited by Sir Walter Raleigh, who became his friend and to whom he read the manuscript of ' The Faerie Queene.' Instantly recognizing the quality of this stupendous poem, Raleigh took the poet under his protection and presented him to the Queen. In 1598 he was made Sheriff of Cork. The same year saw Tyrone's rebellion in Ireland ; Kilcolman Castle was sacked and burned, and it is believed that Spenser's young son, a baby, perished in the flames. The poet was sent to London with a dispatch to Queen Elizabeth. In 1599 he died in a Westminster tavern, ' for lacke of bread,' says Ben Jonson.

' The Faerie Queene.' Spenser's fame rests chiefly on his ' Faerie Queene,' which, though only half finished, is a masterpiece dwarfing all his other work, lovely as that often was.

The Faery Queen, Gloriana, is holding her annual feast, of twelve days' duration. On each day a complaint of injustice is brought to her, and one of her knights rides forth to redress the wrong. His adventures are described at length, each in a separate book running to many cantos. The poem is an allegory, each knight representing some noble quality which is brought into conflict with a personification of evil. Thus St. George, the Knight of the Red Cross, is Holiness, setting forth to slay the Dragon, which is Wickedness. Sir Guyon, hero of Book II, is Temperance ; the lady Britomart, in knightly armour, is Chastity. Sometimes, too, there is a subsidiary allegory ; Gloriana is Glory and she is also Queen Elizabeth.

Into this magnificent poem Spenser wove his thoughts and his dreams. It is his vision of life, harmonious, colourful, lit with 'the light that never was on sea or land.' Prolix it may be, and lacking in constructive skill, but those who have yielded to the spell of its incomparably gorgeous pageantry will read on with unflagging zest, caring not at all if there be no blueprints whereby one can examine the proportions of this faery structure.

The allegorical purpose of the poem is never obscured. Spenser's women are the embodiment of beauty and virtue ; in his Una, Britomart, Amoret, Florimel, Serera, Pastorella, and Belphoebe, he has given us unforgettable portraits. In landscape effects, too, he excelled, and in the magical modulations of sense and sound-rhythms. He is indeed 'the poet's poet.'

Of the twelve books intended, Spenser wrote six, together with the splendid Canto of Mutability. He used the stanza since associated with his name—eight iambic pentameters with the addition of an alexandrine, rhyming *a b a b b c b c c :*

A gentle knight was pricking on the plain,
  Yclad in mighty arms and silver shield,
Wherein old dints of deep wounds did remain,
  The cruel marks of many a bloody field ;
  Yet arms till that time did he never wield ;
His angry steed did chide his foaming bit,
  As much disdaining to the curb to yield ;
Full jolly knight he seem'd, and fair did sit,
As one for knightly jousts and fierce encounters
  fit.

Spenser was already famous before the publication of ' The Faerie Queene.' His first work, ' The Shepherd's Calendar,' is pastoral poetry, often with an undercurrent of allegory. Later poems include ' Muiopotmos, or the Fate of the Butterfly,' a delicate fairy tale ; ' The Ruins of Time,' an exquisite series of elegies ; 'The Tears of the Muses,' an inferior poem ; a paraphrase of Virgil's 'Gnat' ; the satirical 'Mother Hubbard's Tale,' which deals with the corruption of the court, and the struggle between the Reformed Church and the Papacy ; the elegy 'Daphnaïda' ; 'Colin Clout's Come Home Again,' a tribute to Raleigh ; the glorious 'Epithalamion' for his own wedding, which overshadows the 'Prothalamion' ; the 'Amoretti,' a sonnet-sequence in thanksgiving for the happiness of his married life ; and the 'Four Hymns' in honour of Love, Beauty, Heavenly Love and Heavenly Beauty.

There can be no manner of doubt as to the eminent place of Spenser among the English poets. He is a master of the romantic epic, his invention is inexhaustible, the rhythm of his verse the very perfection of poetic form, his imagination so rich and sensuous that Campbell aptly called him ' the Rubens of English poetry.'

In his own day Spenser was immensely popular and had many followers. Somewhat surprisingly, he was also much admired by Dryden, Cowley and Pope. In the early days of the Romantic revival, Thomson, Shenstone and others brought him into fashion. His influence may be traced in Wordsworth, in Shelley and Keats, in Byron, and later in Tennyson, Browning, Morris and other poets.

Lyric Poets of the 16th and 17th Centuries

IT was one of the glories of the age that nearly every man of note was the possessor of literary talent.

Raleigh. Though only incidentally a poet, Sir Walter Raleigh (1552–1618), whose prose is mentioned elsewhere, wrote verse which is graceful and free from the more pronounced affectations of the period. A well-known example is his 'Pilgrimage':

> Give me my scallop-shell of quiet,
> My staff of faith to walk upon,
> My scrip of joy, immortal diet,
>   My bottle of salvation ;
> My gown of glory, hope's true gage,
> And thus I'll take my pilgrimage.

Drayton. A Warwickshire man and a friend of Shakespeare, who entertained him and Ben Jonson at Stratford a few weeks before his death, Michael Drayton (1563–1631) was a lyric and descriptive poet of very unusual qualities. His chief work, 'The Polyolbion,' is a topographical account of England, displaying wonderful learning and containing many glowing descriptions, but utterly mistaken in its medium, which should have been prose. His 'Barons' Wars,' another long poem, abounds in passages of great spirit, and 'Nymphidia' is a delightful fairy poem. Best known of all his work is the lively 'Ballad of Agincourt' and the magnificent sonnet :

> Since there's no help, come let us kiss and part.
> Nay, I have done ; you get no more of me ;
> And I am glad, yea, glad with all my heart
> That thus so cleanly I myself can free.
> Shake hands for ever, cancel all our vows,
> And when we meet at any time again
> Be it not seen in either of our brows
> That we one jot of former love retain.
> Now at the last gasp of Love's latest breath
> When, his pulse failing, Passion speechless lies,
> When Faith is kneeling by his bed of death
> And Innocence is closing up his eyes,
> Now, at the last, when all have given him over,
> From Death to Life thou might'st him yet recover.

Drummond. An accomplished minor poet and scholar was William Drummond (1585–1649), of Hawthornden, near Edinburgh, the friend of Drayton and Ben Jonson. Besides miscellaneous verse, he wrote some fine sonnets.

Daniel. Jonson dismisses Samuel Daniel (1562–1619) as 'a good, honest man, but no poet.' His chief work was a lengthy 'History of the Civil Wars between York and Lancaster,' but he also wrote some beautiful sonnets, which were greatly admired by Drummond.

Donne. John Donne (1573–1631) was the greatest preacher of his day and the leading exponent of the 'metaphysical' school of poetry. His 'Life' ranks high among Izaak Walton's masterpieces. Donne's poems were first collected in 1633. With him passed the scholasticism of the Middle Ages. His religious poems, apart from their 'metaphysical' style, express rare qualities of purity and intensity and his 'essential joy in this life and the next.' 'The Progress of the Soule' is his most serious effort, but is unfinished. Besides the 'Divine Poems,' Donne's highest achievements were his 'Songs and Sonnets.' We give here the first stanza of 'The Anniversary,' an example from that volume.

> All kings, and all their favourites,
> All glory of honours, beauties, wits,
> The sun itself, which makes time, as they pass,
> Is elder by a year now than it was
> When thou and I first one another saw,
> All other things to their destruction draw,
>   Only our love hath no decay :
> This no tomorrow hath, nor yesterday ;
> Running, it never runs from us away,
> But truly keeps his first, last, everlasting day.

George Saintsbury summed up the poet's quality as proceeding from his 'fiery imagination shining in dark places, the magical illumination of obscure and shadowy thoughts with the lightning of fancy.'

Wither. The most prolific writer of the time was George Wither (1588–1667). Dryden wrote of him :

> He fagotted his notions as they fell,
> And if they rhym'd and rattled, all was well.

But, though his work is of unequal merit, he will always be remembered for his captivating lyric, 'The Manly Heart.' Here is the first verse :

> Shall I, wasting in despair,
>   Die because a woman's fair ?
> Or make pale my cheeks with care
>   'Cause another's rosy are ?
>
> Be she fairer than the day,
>   Or the flowery meads in May—
>   If she thinks not well of me,
>   What care I how fair she be ?

Campion and Quarles. A delightful poet is Thomas Campion (c. 1575–1620). Born in London and educated at Cambridge, he was at one time a member of Gray's Inn and afterwards practised as a physician. He was held in high esteem as an authority on music by his contemporaries, and the words and music of his English airs are full of charm. Representative of his talent is the song beginning :

If she forsake me I must die ;
　Shall I tell her so ?
Alas, then straight she will reply
　' No, no, no, no, no.'
If I disclose my desperate state,
She will but make sport thereat,
　And more unrelenting grow.

Francis Quarles (1592–1644), who was a voluminous author, enjoyed an immense popularity in his own day and afterwards, as a writer of religious poems. While he was one of Dr. Donne's school of metaphysical, or allegorical, poets and something of a Puritan, he possessed a lively fancy and felicity of expression that do something to mitigate the effect of his strained conceits, and his 'Divine Emblems' are still worthy of attention.

Herrick. In Robert Herrick (1591–1674)—it is curious to note, by the way, that the lyric poets were longer-lived than most of the dramatists of this period—the first great age of English lyric poetry reaches its culmination and finds its crowning star. Described by Swinburne as 'the greatest song-writer—as surely as Shakespeare is the greatest dramatist—ever born of English race,' Herrick was a creative and inventive singer who surpassed all his rivals in quantity of good work, and his 'Hesperides' is a collection of lyrics unrivalled in their quality of spontaneous instinct and melodious inspiration, and charged with a charm so incomparable and so inimitable that even English poetry can boast of nothing quite like it or worthy to be named after it. Of the man himself and his life, very little is known. Born in London, the youngest child of a goldsmith who died the year after his son's birth, he became the ward of his uncle, Sir William Herrick, goldsmith and moneylender to James I. He was educated at Cambridge, and later became a disciple of Ben Jonson, and found patrons and friends at Court. At what date he took Holy Orders is not known, but in 1629 the King presented him to the vicarage of Dean Prior, near Ashburton, in Devonshire. Ejected by the Puritans in 1647, he returned to London and gave his attention to the publication of his poems ' Hesperides ' and ' Noble Numbers.' One of the most characteristic poems from ' Hesperides ' is quoted here :

To Daisies, Not to Shut so Soon.

Shut not so soon ; the dull-eyed night
　Has not as yet begun
To make a seizure on the light,
　Or to seal up the sun.

No marigolds yet closèd are ;
　No shadows great appear ;
Nor doth the early shepherd's star
　Shine like a spangle here.

Stay but until my Julia close
　Her life-begetting eye ;
And let the whole world then dispose
　Itself to live or die.

After the Restoration he was restored to Dean Prior, where, according to the parish register, he was buried, October 15, 1674.

That Herrick's conception of religion and views as to the rule that should govern a country parson's life were not identical with those of 'holy George Herbert' is obvious enough from the robust vigour of all his verse and from the not infrequent coarseness and the even offensive blemishes that sometimes deform the loveliness of his genius. But the man was no hypocrite, and it is impossible to believe that the 'Noble Numbers' are in the least insincere. It has been said that he was the last of those poets who entirely relished earthly life while wholeheartedly believing in another and a better. On the whole it is a pleasant picture that emerges from his poems—a country clergyman on excellent terms of easy familiarity with his poor parishioners, enjoying a care-free bachelor existence, with a spaniel and, according to tradition, a tame pig for his constant companions, and one faithful old maidservant to keep house for him. And for his own intellectual occupation this marvellous gift of song. A happy man, this ; certainly not one to make any parade of piety in his daily bearing, but one nevertheless with very definite principles of private conduct. Of poets he says :

Wanton we are, and though our words be such
Our lives do differ from our lines by much.

And the discerning reader will not fail to see the special significance of Herrick's choice of a similar distich for the final poem in the original edition of ' Hesperides ':

To his book's end this last line he'd have
　placed :
Jocund his muse was but his life was chaste.

George Herbert. George Herbert (1593–1633) was yet another poet whose work was influenced to its disadvantage by his admiration for his friend John Donne. But marred though it is by the often irritating conceits that distinguish the school, his chief work, 'The Temple,' is packed with thought and precept and has poetical merit of a very rare, lofty, and original order that makes it rank with the best religious verse in the language. The manuscript, now in the Bodleian, was given by Herbert on his deathbed to his friend Nicholas Ferrar, who effected its publication at Cambridge in the same year (1633), when it ran through two editions. By 1670, when Izaak Walton published his 'Life' of Herbert, 20,000 copies had been circulated. The issue has been very large ever since, and the reputation of the poem is still on the increase. Of the 'Sacred Poems and Private Ejaculations,' planned in reference to church architecture, numbering over 160, of which 'The Temple' is composed, the one that is perhaps the best known is this beautiful piece on Virtue :

Sweet Day, so cool, so calm, so bright,
The bridal of the earth and sky,
The dew shall weep thy fall tonight ;
For thou must die.

Sweet Rose, whose hue angry and brave,
Bids the rash gazer wipe his eye,
Thy root is ever in its grave,
And thou must die.

Sweet Spring, full of sweet days and roses,
A box where sweets compacted lie,
My Music shows ye have your closes,
And all must die.

Only a sweet and virtuous soul,
Like season'd timber, never gives ;
But though the whole world turn to coal,
Then chiefly lives.

Remarkable alike as poet and prose-writer was Thomas Traherne (1636?–1674), a mystic, whose work remained undiscovered until the beginning of this century (*see* Lesson 31). Besides using the pliant verse-forms of his contemporaries, he wrote in a form of *vers libre* similar to that of Walt Whitman.

Minor Lyric Poets. In the space available it is impossible to do more than note the names of Phineas and Giles Fletcher, William Browne, Sir John Davies, and Thomas Carew, 'that delectable versifier,' among the many minor lyric poets born in the sixteenth century. The number of them is indeed surprising, and there is hardly one of them but was capable of writing distinguished verse.

Lyrics of the Dramatists. It has been deemed convenient for the purpose of these Lessons not to follow the usual plan of dividing the Elizabethan age into two periods, but to review at once the poets who are epic, as Spenser, narrative, as Drayton, or lyric, as Sidney, and to reserve the dramatic writers for separate consideration. Naturally, some of the dramatists wrote lyrical verse : John Lyly, for example, whose exquisite 'Cupid and Campaspe' is sheer perfection ; Robert Greene, admirably represented in this genre of poetry by his 'Farewell to Folly' and 'Sephestia's Song to Her Child' ; Ben Jonson, whose 'Drink to Me Only with Thine Eyes' (quoted below), one of the most engaging songs in our language, appeared in a collection of fifteen lyrics, entitled 'The Forest,' in 1616 ; and many another, including Shakespeare himself ; but in this Course they must be regarded and dealt with as essentially dramatic poets. The arrangement adopted, if somewhat arbitrary, serves at least to give some idea of the poets of the lesser order immediately preceding, contemporary with, and following Shakespeare and the Elizabethan dramatists.

To Celia
Drink to me only with thine eyes,
    And I will pledge with mine ;
Or leave a kiss but in the cup
    And I'll not look for wine.
The thirst that from the soul doth rise
    Doth ask a drink divine ;
But might I of Jove's nectar sup,
    I would not change for thine.

I sent thee late a rosy wreath,
    Not so much honouring thee
As giving it a hope that there
    It could not withered be ;
But thou thereon didst only breathe
    And sent'st it back to me ;
Since when it grows, and smells, I swear,
    Not of itself, but thee.

Translators. Sir John Harington (1561–1612) translated the 'Orlando Furioso' of Ariosto, the Italian poet. Edward Fairfax (c. 1580–1635) made an admirable version of Torquato Tasso's 'Jerusalem Delivered.'

The ordinary reader may be content to study all the poets mentioned in this Lesson in volumes of specimens, since a fair conception of their respective merits and of their united influence upon the literature of our country can be obtained by reading some of their larger poems and a selection of their minor pieces.

LESSON 11

The Early Dramatic Writers

THE drama, so long and bitterly condemned by the Puritans, is not only one of the world's oldest and noblest arts, but one that had its origin in religious worship. The art which produced in Shakespeare the greatest genius of all time was in ancient Greece an evolution of pagan ceremonial. In its modern form it might be described as a graft on the priestly propaganda of the medieval miracle plays and mystery plays.

Study of the Greek drama, important though it is, does not fall within the scope of this work. (For this the translations by Gilbert Murray are an admirable basis.) Here only such incidental references to it are made as may be necessary in discussing English drama. But let us be clear on this point : the art of the dramatist, both in the ancient and the modern world, has attracted the mightiest intellects ever devoted to creative literature, and in proportion to the whole body of the drama, the works of genius it contains outnumber those in any other division of literature.

It is necessary to state this in the most emphatic manner, because a measure of prejudice against everything associated with the theatre still endures—the legacy, on one side, of Puritanism, and the outcome, on the other, of the sterility of our stage throughout most of the Victorian era. Of late years, and despite the setback which it received during the First Great War, the English drama, in a literary sense, has been showing signs of renewed strength. Still, it is mainly to the printed page, and not to the theatre, that we must turn to study the drama. It may be said that this is as it should be, since the dramatist, not less than any other poet, is for the study. But the fact remains that what is called 'a drama for the closet' is no drama at all ; the play which cannot be acted is for that reason no play, and equally the play which is only tolerable when acted is not literature.

Our drama might almost be said to have begun and ended in one great burst of glory ; for if all that has been written since the last of the Elizabethans, with few exceptions, were to be wiped away, our dramatic literature would not be greatly impoverished. The evolution of the English drama is sometimes ascribed to the old Mysteries invented by the medieval clergy for the purpose of teaching the ignorant mob some smattering of Biblical knowledge. These crude representations of sacred history gave place gradually to the morality play, wherein the teachers of the people endeavoured to visualize before their dim intelligences the Christian virtues. From this it was but a step to the stage representation of the common life, and that step had been taken before the reign of Elizabeth, Heywood's 'Interludes' forming a link between the morality play and the drama proper.

George Gascoigne (c. 1525–77) was one of the earliest dramatists, and a poet of no mean place among the Elizabethans, his spirited satire, 'The Steel Glass,' being the longest and one of the most virile compositions in blank verse before Milton. But it is evident in his dramatic work that he was influenced not so much by the disappearing morality play as by the ancient classical drama ; his 'Jocasta' is an adaptation from Euripides, while his 'The Supposes,' from which Shakespeare borrowed for his 'Taming of the Shrew,' was translated from Ariosto's 'I Suppositi' and is the first prose comedy in English.

Indeed, it is hardly correct to speak of any link between the modern drama and the morality play, as in all countries the rise of the drama was the outcome of a revival of learning which led the writers to look back across the ages and to find their models in the ancient classical drama. The machinery of the stage, however, was ready to their hand as it existed for the purpose of the moralities. The first English comedy in rhyming verse, 'Ralph Roister Doister,' written by Nicholas Udall (1506–56), master of Eton, for a holiday performance by the Eton boys, was modelled on the comedies of Plautus and Terence, while Sackville and Norton's 'Gorboduc,' our first English tragedy, produced in 1561, was modelled on the tragedies of Seneca and is in blank verse.

As an example of 'transition' farce 'Gammer Gurton's Needle' must be mentioned. The farce was at one time thought to be older than 'Ralph Roister Doister,' owing to a mistake as to its date of publication. One attributed to Bishop Still it is the work of a certain William Stevenson, a Fellow of Christ's College, Cambridge, where it was played in 1566; it was printed in 1575. It is rougher in character, more vigorous in action, than 'Roister Doister'—'a piece of low humour,' says Sir Walter Scott, 'the whole jest turning upon the loss and the recovery of the needle with which Gammer Gurton was to repair the breeches of her man Hodge ; but in point of manners it is a great curiosity.' It contains the first drinking song of any merit to be found in our language—which may be, as some think, the work of Skelton. A verse of this rollicking rhyme may be quoted :

I cannot eat but little meat,
  My stomach is not good :
But sure I think that I can drink,
  With him that wears a hood.
Though I go bare, take ye no care,
  I nothing am a-cold ;
I stuff my skin so full within
  Of jolly good ale and old.
Back and side go bare, go bare,
  Both foot and hand go cold ;
But belly, God send thee good ale enough,
  Whether it be new or old.

Comedy shaped itself into true dramatic form earlier than tragedy, and the art owed well-nigh as much to such writers as Greene and Peele as tragedy did to Marlowe. Most of the early dramatists were poet-scholars, men who had been educated at Oxford and Cambridge, and who, to their knowledge of classical models, added a racy intimacy with the life of the day, which enabled them, while observing the ancient ideas of drama construction, to appeal to the common people with subjects of living interest. In fact, these men of rare wit and scholarship were only too familiar with the life of their times, and their biographies, so far as we can ascertain them, are for the most part melancholy records of lives untimely sacrificed to debauchery.

It is noteworthy that Shakespeare, the great king of them all, was almost the only one who had no university training, and, in the then accepted definition of scholar, could rank with few of his contemporaries. He, too, was among the group who showed a better-balanced character, and observed a standard of conduct which today would have made him a person of almost 'suburban' manners.

No detailed chronicle of the early drama can be attempted here ; the poets only, rather than their art, can be dealt with, and even so only a few of the more notable of the dramatists. Among these some mention must be made of John Lyly (1553-

1606), as his name is, for other reasons than his talent, conspicuous in the early Elizabethan period. He is not a dramatist of any great ability, his comedies in prose and verse being unworthy of attention today, except from the close student of the Elizabethan drama. As stated in a previous Lesson, he had a lyrical rather than a dramatic gift, some of his songs in his plays being wholly delightful.

George Peele (c. 1558-? 98) made more valuable contributions to comedy, though his plays are stronger in poetic fancy and form than they are in dramatic construction. His comedies, such as 'The Arraignment of Paris' and 'The Old Wives' Tale,' are as pretty and engaging as his tragedies, such as 'The Battle of Alcazar,' are bombastic and preposterous.

Robert Greene (c. 1558-92) was a poet of very similar gifts to his boon companion Peele. A follower of Lyly as a novelist, the best of his genius is to be seen in the beautiful lyrics which are introduced in his prose romances and his plays. Shakespeare went to Greene's novel 'Pandosto' for the outline of 'The Winter's Tale.' Perhaps the most noteworthy of his dramatic pieces is 'Friar Bacon and Friar Bungay.' One characteristic of Greene's dramas deserves notice, and that is his capacity for drawing lovable women, who foreshadow Shakespeare's peerless heroines.

While both Peele and Greene have no great interest for the general reader, the student desiring to familiarize himself with this period of our drama must not neglect either of these writers.

Although not strictly in place, we cannot refrain from quoting some lines from Greene's 'Farewell to Folly' as illustrative of his lyrical poetry.

Sweete are the thoughts that savour of content,
  The quiet mind is richer than a crowne ;
Sweete are the nights in carelesse slumber spent,
  The poor estate scorns Fortune's angrie
    frowne :
Such sweete content, such mindes, such sleepe,
  such bliss,
Beggars enjoy when princes oft doe miss.

Another of the 'University Wits' was Thomas Kyd (1558-94), a scrivener's son, whose violent play in the Senecan manner, 'The Spanish Tragedy,' was for over 200 years the most widely performed Elizabethan drama outside Shakespeare's works and set the style for Kyd's contemporaries. He is also the supposed author of the lost play of 'Hamlet' on which Shakespeare is said to have based his great tragedy.

Marlowe: Herald of English Drama

THE real herald of the English drama, the first great name in its annals, was Christopher Marlowe, than whom there is no more melancholy figure in all our literary history. Son of John Marlowe, a shoemaker of Canterbury, he was christened, the register informs us, in the parish church of St. George the Martyr in that city on the 26th day of February, 1564, exactly two months before, on the 26th of April, William, son of John Shakespeare, was baptized in the church of Stratford-upon-Avon. Had their deaths synchronized as nearly as their births, had Marlowe not fallen a victim to a vicious and irregular life at the early age of twenty-nine, he might, his splendid powers ripened and exercised with the restraint of maturer judgement, have stood no more than a step behind Shakespeare himself.

As a native of Canterbury, Marlowe enjoyed the opportunity of acquiring his early education at the famous King's School there, whence he proceeded to Benet, now Corpus Christi, College, Cambridge, perhaps at the expense of some wealthy patron. He graduated as B.A. in 1583 and as M.A. in 1587, employing part of the intervening time in London in literary and dramatic work ; it is established that both parts of his remarkable drama 'Tamburlaine the Great' had been publicly performed in London at least as early as 1587.

Disfigured though it is by much bombast and fustian—faults, be it noted, that had not a little to do with its immediate immense popularity—'Tamburlaine the Great' is alive with real drama, and its style is instinct with poetic feeling. In the evolution of English blank verse this play, moreover, marks a cardinal point. Unrhymed iambic pentameter verse had been used both for epic and dramatic purposes before Marlowe's time ; but, composed strictly on the classical model, with a pause at the end of each line, it had acquired a monotony which deprived it of all freedom of movement.

Not yet had Marlowe perfected his own use of the measure, indulging too freely in sonorousness and rotundity of declamation, but already his 'mighty line' is an accomplished fact destined to have a permanent influence on the whole subsequent development of this verse form.

Records of the production of Marlowe's works are somewhat confused, but it is probable that his 'Tragical History of Doctor Faustus' was composed soon after 'Tamburlaine.' 'Faustus,' his greatest and best-known work, is founded on the legend of the German magician who, for twenty-four years of unrestrained life, sold himself to the devil both body and soul. It is also the theme of Goethe's greatest poem. 'There is,' says Hallam, 'an awful melancholy about Marlowe's Mephistopheles, perhaps more impressive than the malignant mirth of that fiend in the renowned work of Goethe. But the fair form of Margaret is wanting ; and Marlowe has hardly earned the credit of having breathed a few casual inspirations into a greater mind than his own.' Goethe himself, however, was enthusiastic in his praise of Marlowe's version of the legend.

Of 'The Jew of Malta,' which was probably the third in chronological order of Marlowe's plays, not much need be said here, unless it be to draw the attention of the student to the astonishing inequality of the workmanship. The first two acts, in Hallam's judgement, are 'more vigorously conceived, both as to character and to circumstance, than any other Elizabethan play, except those of Shakespeare,' presenting in the Jew Barabas a character that, developed on the same scale, would have matched Shylock. Never before had a play opened with a scene charged with such concentrated drama as this of Barabas in his counting-house, contemptuously disparaging as 'trash' the heaps of gold before him, and voicing his insatiable avarice in language that stirs the dullest imagination :

Give me the merchants of the Indian mines
That trade in metal of the purest mould ;
The wealthy Moor that in the Eastern rocks
Without control can pick his riches up,
And in his house heap pearls like pebble-stones,
Receive them free and sell them by the weight ;
Bags of fiery opals, sapphires, amethysts,
Jacinths, hard topaz, grass-green emeralds,
And seld-seen costly stones of so great price
As one of them, indifferently rated
And of a carat of this quantity,
May serve, in peril of calamity,
To ransom great Kings from captivity.

Dignity and beauty characterize the first two acts of this play, revealing Marlowe's genius in maturity, and then the whole

MICHAEL DRAYTON wrote much verse of fine quality. His most ambitious effort was the ' Polyolbion,' a patriotic topographical survey of England.

National Portrait Gallery

JOHN DONNE, who became Dean of St. Paul's, wrote fine love poetry and sacred poetry in metaphysical vein and was also noted for his sonorous prose.

Portrait by or after G. Oliver

GEORGE HERBERT, Rector of Bemerton, wrote much religious verse, of which ' The Temple' is best known. He was influenced by Donne.

From an engraving by R. White in the British Museum

ROBERT HERRICK, whose lyrics are of outstanding quality, was vicar of Dean Prior near Totnes, and wrote religious verse as well as charming secular poems.

Frontispiece to the ' Hesperides' (1648)

GEORGE GASCOIGNE, one of the earliest English dramatists, is here seen presenting a copy of his works to Queen Elizabeth. Besides plays, he wrote much verse.

From a MS. of 1575

101

Mr. WILLIAM

SHAKESPEARES

COMEDIES,
HISTORIES, &
TRAGEDIES.

Published according to the True Originall Copies.

LONDON

Printed by Isaac Iaggard, and Ed. Blount. 1623.

IVDICIO PYLIVM, GENIO SOCRATEM, ARTE MARONEM
TERRA TEGIT, POPVLVS MÆRET, OLYMPVS HABET

STAY PASSENGER WHY GOEST THOV BY SO FAST,
READ IF THOV CANST, WHOM ENVIOVS DEATH HATH PLAST,
WITH IN THIS MONVMENT SHAKSPEARE: WITH WHOME,
QVICK NATVRE DIDE: WHOSE NAME, DOTH DECK Y TOMBE,
FAR MORE, THEN COST: SIEH ALL, Y HE HATH WRITT,
LEAVES LIVING ART, BVT PAGE, TO SERVE HIS WITT.
OBIT ANO DOI 1616.
ÆTATIS 53 DIE 23

WILLIAM SHAKESPEARE, the greatest figure in English literature, seems to have had no portrait painted during his lifetime. The engraving by Martin Droeshout (shown above) appears in the frontispiece of the First Folio or first collected edition of his plays (1623), and was highly commended by Ben Jonson. The bust (on right) erected over his grave in the chancel of Holy Trinity Church, Stratford-on-Avon, was the work of Gerard Janssen, a Southwark monumental mason of Dutch ancestry, in 1616. It is supposed to have been modelled from a death mask, and was touched with colour and gilt. Shakespeare was only fifty-two when he died.

Droeshout engraving from First Folio in British Museum

SHAKESPEARE'S THEATRE. This view of Southwark in the year of Shakespeare's death is taken from a panoramic picture of London engraved by Visscher in 1616. On the right is the Globe theatre, where Shakespeare acted and in which he held shares. Built of wood in 1599 and holding 1,200 people, it was burnt in 1613 but rebuilt the following year, and finally pulled down in 1644. This district bordering the river was then known as Bankside, and the picture shows the Bear Garden where men indulged in the sport of bear and bull baiting.

BEN JONSON, *distinguished alike as dramatist, poet and prose-writer, was one of the greatest figures of his age. His plays are satiric, the best known being 'Every Man in His Humour.'*

After Gerard Honthorst, National Portrait Gallery

PHILIP MASSINGER *wrote many interesting plays; fifteen of them survive. He sometimes collaborated with Fletcher (below). His masterpiece is 'A New Way to Pay Old Debts.'*

From an engraving by H. Robinson after T. Cross

FRANCIS BEAUMONT *collaborated with John Fletcher in many plays, including 'Philaster,' 'The Maid's Tragedy,' and 'The Knight of the Burning Pestle,' which in their day were more popular than Shakespeare's plays.*

Engraving by P. Audinet in British Museum

JOHN FLETCHER *wrote the greater part of the Beaumont and Fletcher plays and also collaborated with other dramatists, including Shakespeare, besides writing much independent work, notably 'The Faithful Shepherdess.'*

From a print in the collection of the Earl of Clarendon

LESSONS 15 AND 16

WILLIAM WYCHERLEY, next to Congreve, was the most important dramatist of the Restoration period, his chief plays being ' The Country Wife ' and ' The Plain Dealer.' Though his dialogue was distinctly licentious, he was brilliantly witty.

From an engraving after the painting by Lely

WILLIAM CONGREVE, wittiest of Restoration dramatists, reached the summit of his fame with ' Love for Love ' and ' The Way of the World,' outstanding example of . ' ' d,. ' . a superb gift for repartee.

Portrait by Kneller, National Portrait Gallery

OLIVER GOLDSMITH, a versatile genius, is best remembered for the delightful play, ' She Stoops to Conquer,' and for ' The Vicar of Wakefield,' a landmark in the history of the novel ; he also wrote attractive verse.

Portrait by Reynolds, National Portrait Gallery

RICHARD BRINSLEY SHERIDAN wrote those brilliant specimens of the comedy of manners, ' The School for Scandal ' and ' The Rivals,' besides the entertaining ' Critic.' This happy-go-lucky Irishman was a political orator of bravery and integrity.

After Sir Joshua Reynolds

LATE VICTORIAN DRAMATISTS. Oscar Wilde (left), unhappy founder of the cult of aestheticism, wrote several witty plays, which still retain their popularity. His other work includes the memorable but unpleasant novel, ' The Picture of Dorian Gray,' and some moving poetry, of which the best was written during his imprisonment. His volume of fairy stories (' The Happy Prince ') is wholly delightful. Henry Arthur Jones (centre) was the popular writer of many social comedies, now outmoded ; ' The Silver King ' was his first hit. Sir Arthur Wing Pinero, in ' The Second Mrs. Tanqueray ' struck a new note of seriousness which he followed with many other successful plays, notably ' Trelawny of the Wells ' and ' The Gay Lord Quex.'

SIR JAMES MATTHEW BARRIE, creator of ' Peter Pan,' turned from novel-writing to drama, in which he was immensely successful. His plays have a sentimental appeal and a tender humour which make them perennial favourites.

GEORGE BERNARD SHAW, brilliant and unconventional as dramatist and as critic, delighted audiences by his witty and outspoken satire. An earnest Socialist, he tilted at many windmills, stirred up much controversy.

E

John Drinkwater   St. John Ervine   Somerset Maugham

Frederick Lonsdale   James Bridie   Noel Coward

Lady Gregory   J. M. Synge   Sean O'Casey

DRAMATISTS OF RECENT YEARS. To each of these dramatists a considerable measure of popularity has deservedly been given. Drinkwater's 'Abraham Lincoln' is a classic of the stage, and St. John Ervine, Somerset Maugham, Frederick Lonsdale and Noel Coward have been immensely successful with many fine plays dealing with the contemporary scene in various phases. James Bridie has shown striking originality of theme and treatment. Lady Gregory and the incomparable Synge were, with W. B. Yeats, the main pillars of the Irish Revival, which is now most vividly exemplified in the brilliant work of Sean O'Casey.

Photos, Noel Coward by Dorothy Wilding, J. M. Synge by courtesy of his publishers, Allen & Unwin Ltd., and Sean O'Casey by G.P.A.

JOHN MILTON, the greatest literary figure of his period, became blind at the age of 44, but nevertheless produced his majestic epic, 'Paradise Lost,' followed by 'Paradise Regained' and ' Samson Agonistes.' He was one of the most learned of poets.

Engraving by W. Faithorne, Nat. Portrait Gallery

JOHN DRYDEN was poet laureate in Restoration days. His verse is mainly satire (notably ' Absalom and Achitophel ') of a witty and good-humoured kind. He was a distinguished dramatist and also wrote excellent prose, notably the ' Essay of Dramatic Poesy.'

Painting by Kneller, National Portrait Gallery

ALEXANDER POPE was the leading poet of the early 18th century. He wrote brilliant satire. ' The Rape of the Lock,' ' The Dunciad ' and ' The Essay on Man ' are his most famous works, together with his translation of Homer.

William Hoare, National Portrait Gallery

THOMAS GRAY wrote little, but so graceful and musical was his work that he is among the famous poets. Besides the immortal ' Elegy Written in a Country Church Yard,' he composed some splendid Pindaric odes ; he was a delightful letter writer.

J. G. Eccardt, National Portrait Gallery

107

WILLIAM COWPER was a sincerely religious poet, with a true love of nature, witty yet tender. His work has a simple eloquence, his most sustained effort being ' The Task.' As a letter-writer, he is charming ; and he translated Homer.

Engraving by Stocks after Romney

ROBERT BURNS, Scotland's most idolized poet, made himself immortal by his lyrics and by the matchless ' Tam O'Shanter.' He was utterly sincere and human, and unsparingly attacked hypocrisy. There is a rich variety in his work.

Portrait by Nasmyth, National Gallery of Scotland

WILLIAM BLAKE, one of the great mystics, wrote ineffably beautiful poetry and was equally remarkable as an artist. **WILLIAM WORDSWORTH** revolutionized English poetry by his philosophy, summed up as ' return to Nature.' His output was very large, and included some of the finest lyrics and sonnets in our literature.

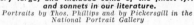
Portraits by Thos. Phillips and by Pickersgill in the National Portrait Gallery

thing suffers lamentable deterioration ; the characters become caricatures, the drama buffoonery. Bullen suggests that the play may have been called for at very short notice, and that the last three acts were only roughly sketched out by Marlowe and filled in by some other person, who took it upon himself to supply the grotesque farcical addition which gave the play its popularity with the vulgar while spoiling it for the fastidious. Whether or not this be the true explanation, it draws attention to one quality in which Marlowe's genius was entirely deficient—the radiant humour which was one of Shakespeare's most enchanting gifts.

'Edward the Second,' written, according to Warton, in the year 1590, is the most elaborate of Marlowe's works and is generally agreed to be the best historical play in our language before Shakespeare. Charles Lamb is not unduly enthusiastic when he says :

> The reluctant pangs of abdicating royalty in Edward furnished hints which Shakespeare scarcely improved in his 'Richard II,' and the death scene of Marlowe's king moves pity and terror beyond any scene, ancient or modern, with which I am acquainted.

Two other dramatic works by Marlowe remain to be mentioned, 'The Massacre at Paris' and 'The Tragedy of Dido, Queen of Carthage' (written with T. Nash), but neither of these productions is worthy of the poet's undoubted genius. Perhaps the opinion of Thomas Warton, the erudite historian of English poetry, gives the best critical summary of Marlowe's work :

> His tragedies manifest traces of a just dramatic conception ; but they abound with tedious and uninteresting scenes, or with such extravagances as proceed from a want of judgement, and those barbarous ideas of the times over which it was the peculiar gift of Shakespeare's genius alone to triumph and to predominate.

Nor must his beautiful fragment 'Hero and Leander' be neglected, a poem which, in Swinburne's words, 'stands out alone amid all the wild and poetic wealth of its teeming and turbulent age as might a small shrine of Parian sculpture amid the rank splendour of a tropic jungle.' Only the first two sestiads are Marlowe's, and these were first published in 1598—a second edition, with the continuation by his friend Chapman, appearing the same year. The poem leaped into immediate popularity, and is a masterpiece of rhymed heroics.

Suggested parallels are occasionally treacherous and misleading. Nevertheless it is difficult to find in all our literature a more interesting study than to read Marlowe's 'Hero and Leander.' 'Edward the Second,' and 'The Jew of Malta ' side by side with Shakespeare's 'Venus and Adonis,' 'Richard the Second,' and 'The Merchant of Venice.'

LESSON 13

Shakespeare: Greatest Poet of All Time

IF we were to shear away every name in English dramatic poetry but that of Shakespeare, we could still claim for it such pre-eminence, especially in tragedy— the highest form of drama—that not even the glorious art of Greece could be said to transcend it. Indeed, tragedy, which sprang from the worship of the god Dionysus or Bacchus—the altar and the chorus of the pagan temple having their counterparts in the Greek theatre—and rose into supreme poetic form in the tragedies of Aeschylus, Sophocles, and Euripides, may be said to have culminated in the works of William Shakespeare (1564-1616), whose 'Hamlet,' 'Othello,' 'Macbeth,' and 'King Lear' are the four greatest tragedies in the world. But it is Shakespeare's unmatched glory that he excelled in both tragedy and comedy.

As Coleridge points out very aptly, Plato in his 'Symposium' had, two thousand years before, framed 'a justification of our Shakespeare' when he argued that 'it was the business of one and the same genius to excel in tragic and comic poetry, or that the tragic poet ought, at the same time, to contain within himself the powers of comedy.' This in Plato was prophetic, as it laid down a canon utterly opposed by all the ancient critics, and quite unsupported by any example from the Greek dramatists, to whom tragedy and comedy were incompatible elements, having but one quality in common—ideality. To quote Coleridge further :

> Both were alike ideal ; that is, the comedy of Aristophanes rose to as great a distance above the ludicrous of real life as the tragedy

E*

of Sophocles above its tragic events and passions ; and it is in this one point of absolute ideality that the comedy of Shakespeare and the old comedy of Athens coincide. In this also alone did the Greek tragedy and comedy unite ; in everything else they were exactly opposed to each other. Tragedy is poetry in its deepest earnest ; comedy is poetry in unlimited jest.

Thus we see at a glance why Shakespeare's was the one intellect which, while comprehending all human passions and emotions, could equally express all.

No one will expect to find here anything so audacious as an effort to condense within a page or two a study of Shakespeare. Betterton, the first great tragedian, at the end of his career, when performing Hamlet for the last time, said that he had seldom in fifty years, and with all his continuous study, discharged that rôle without finding in the character some new beauty. If this be true of only one of the multitude of characters created by Shakespeare, one might devote a lifetime of study to his works and leave them unexhausted at the end. Nay, many men of great and original talent have done so, and many more will do the same. Shakespeare is not only to be regarded as a great author and a department of study, but as a life and a literature.

Vast Literature and Scant Biography. So limitless is the literature which has grown around the name of Shakespeare in all the languages of European culture that only a man of the ripest scholarship and linguistic attainments can hope ever to obtain more than a partial knowledge of this mighty genius. But that should in no way deter anyone from entering upon the study and enjoyment of a series of works which, if one read no others, would furnish the mind with the very essence of intellectual joy. It is not the least of Shakespeare's distinctions that he commands the devotion and lifelong service of the best scholars, while he entertains the most ordinary reader and the common playgoer.

Although it is often said that some half-dozen facts are all that we possess of the poet's life, the untiring industry of biographers and critics, especially during the last century, has supplemented the few historical facts with so much inferential knowledge that there is no difficulty in realizing for ourselves an adequate conception of the man, and in understanding the poet, to the best of our individual capacities.

Almost alone among the Elizabethan dramatists Shakespeare was not a university scholar ; but it is fair to suppose that he received his education at the free school of Stratford, being under fourteen years of age when his father, who had hitherto been prosperous and prominent in the public life of the town, fell upon evil times, and had to withdraw his son in order to put him to a trade. It has been thought that the boy was apprenticed to a butcher, though some critics, on the strength of the legal knowledge displayed in his works, have supposed that he may have been for a time an attorney's clerk.

He was not eighteen when he married Anne Hathaway, a yeoman's daughter, eight years older than himself ; and three or four years later, now the father of three children and a social failure in his own town, he came to London, where in 1592 we find him an actor and a rising playwright. It is in this year that Greene, in his 'Groatsworth of Wit,' gibes at him as a 'rude groome,' who 'supposes he is as well able to bumbast out a blanke verse as the best of you '—the sneer of a practised dramatist at a younger and more promising member of his craft.

Shakespeare attained to no great distinction as an actor, but his connexion with the stage brought him in the way of literary work such as altering old plays, retouching the writings of other dramatists when the manager employing him desired to revive their plays. Playwrights were then in the habit of selling to the theatrical managers for a few pounds the entire copyright of their plays, and as actors thought it prejudicial to their interests that the plays should be published, only a few plays of the period were printed, chiefly in unauthorized versions, during their authors' lifetime.

Chronology of the Plays. The chronology of Shakespeare's early plays has undergone many changes at the hands of different critics, but there is no great difficulty in deciding upon the approximate order of the thirty-seven plays attributed to him, or in distinguishing those of which he was only part author. As Sir Sidney Lee observes :

The subject-matter and metre both afford rough clues to the period to which each play may be referred. In his early plays the spirit of comedy or tragedy appears in its simplicity ; as his powers gradually matured, he depicted life in its most complex involutions, and portrayed with masterly insight the subtle gradations of human sentiment and the mysterious workings of human passion. Comedy and tragedy are gradually blended, and his work finally developed a pathos, such as could only come of ripe experience. Similarly, the metre undergoes emancipation from the hampering restraints of fixed rule, and becomes flexible enough to respond to every phase of human feeling.

For this reason the works of Shakespeare are best read in something like chronological order. It is well, therefore, not to begin with the plays, but with the two long narrative poems, 'Venus and Adonis' and 'The Rape of Lucrece,' as the former, published in 1593, was almost certainly the first effort of Shakespeare's muse, and the latter, appearing in the succeeding year, did much to establish the fame of the young play-actor, whose name was becoming familiar to patrons of the theatre as an adapter of plays. These were the works which first won him renown among his contemporaries, and, apart from their great poetic beauty, they are interesting to us for that reason. They are elaborately classical both in matter and in manner, typical of what we know as the Pagan Renaissance. Both poems are dedicated to Shakespeare's youthful patron and friend, Henry Wriothesley, 3rd Earl of Southampton, who is also depicted in the 'Sonnets.' 'Venus and Adonis' is erotic almost to the point of licence, but the exuberant fancy of the poem, the sensuous beauty of its imagery and its rhythmic sweetness give it distinction. Its success was so great that in the nine subsequent years it went into seven editions.

'The Rape of Lucrece,' which deals with the tragic story of the lawless passion of Tarquin's son for the chaste and devoted wife of Collatinus, was that 'graver labour' which the poet promised in his dedication of the first work. It gives evidence of such maturity in its reflective passages, and so great an increase of art in its whole conception and construction, that there is good reason for supposing 'Venus and Adonis' to have been an effort of the poet's youth, considerably antedating even the first of his attempts at play revising. At all events, these two poems, if read before the plays, will help to the better understanding of the unfolding of Shakespeare's genius.

LESSON 14

A Brief Outline of Shakespeare Study

IN the preceding Lesson we saw that subject matter and metre enable us approximately to determine the chronology of the plays of which Shakespeare was the author, in whole or in part. Below, we set forth the names of the plays as they have been arranged by Sir Sidney Lee, marking with an asterisk those of which Shakespeare was only part author.

1. Early Dramatic Work

Love's Labour's Lost	1591
Two Gentlemen of Verona	1591
The Comedy of Errors	1592
Romeo and Juliet	1592
*Henry VI (Part I)	1592
*Henry VI (Part II)	1592
*Henry VI (Part III)	1592
Richard III	1593
Richard II	1593
*Titus Andronicus	1593
Merchant of Venice	1594
King John	1594

2. The Development of Dramatic Power

A Midsummer Night's Dream	1594–5
All's Well that Ends Well	1595
Taming of the Shrew	1595
Henry IV (Part I)	1597
Henry IV (Part II)	1597
The Merry Wives of Windsor	1597
Henry V	1598

3. Maturity of Genius

Much Ado About Nothing	1599
As You Like It	1599
Twelfth Night	1600
Julius Caesar	1601
Hamlet	1602
Troilus and Cressida	1603

4. The Highest Themes of Tragedy

Othello	1604
Measure for Measure	1604
Macbeth	1606
King Lear	1607
*Timon of Athens	1608
*Pericles	1608
Antony and Cleopatra	1608
Coriolanus	1609

5. The Latest Plays

Cymbeline	1610
A Winter's Tale	1611
The Tempest	1611
*Henry VIII	—

It is not suggested that the student of Shakespeare is to procure himself a good edition of the plays and poems and read them through precisely in the order given above. But it is well, so far as it may be practicable, to read Shakespeare with more regard to the chronological order of the plays than to their grouping as comedies, histories, and tragedies—the arrangement adopted in so many popular editions.

Many influences will control the reading of the plays, especially theatrical representation, for no student of Shakespeare should miss any opportunity of seeing his plays performed by good companies, and there are few towns of any considerable size where such opportunities do not occur occasionally. He is a poet for both the stage and the study.

It will sometimes happen that the reader may have an opportunity of seeing a Shakespearian play which he has not read, and which, if he were following the above order of reading, he would not be likely to read for some time. The opportunity must not be lost, more especially if it be to witness one of the plays less frequently staged, such as 'Cymbeline' or 'Coriolanus.' The play should be read before seeing the theatrical representation of it, and again immediately afterwards. Following this course, one will be struck by the revelation of the subtler passages which results from witnessing a play, already familiar by reading, in its natural atmosphere of the stage. It was said of a great tragedian that to see him act was like reading Shakespeare by flashes of lightning. The phrase was not quite happy, as it is not well to read anything by lightning flashes. But what the critic meant was true : that the actor often interprets passages of the poet, which thus become illumined as by a flash of bright light, to the student, who may have missed their significance when reading the play for himself.

In very few of the popular editions of Shakespeare's plays is any hint given as to the sources whence the poet derived his subjects — sometimes, indeed, his very thoughts and words. But no adequate understanding of Shakespeare can be arrived at without these data, and the reader is counselled to study Shakespeare in some of those editions which give each play in a separate volume, with an introduction and notes by a competent scholar, sometimes giving the full text of the original stories from which the poet has drawn the foundations of his work.

Aid from the Commentators. It is in this way that a true critical estimate of the dramatist may be formed ; but at the same time we are not to place ourselves unreservedly in the hands of the critics and commentators. It is always better, no matter how we may blunder in the first instance, to come by our own opinions in our reading through the exercise of our own intelligence. What we have found out for ourselves is of far more value to us and the development of our mind than what we have received from any teacher.

In Shakespearian study, we must accept a vast amount from the expositors of his text, but in doing so, we can at the same time cultivate our own critical faculty ; and to this end we cannot do better than read a play for the first time in an edition which is not annotated. In this way we are forced to form some independent judgement, and it is relatively of very little importance whether that judgement be right or wrong ; the conscious effort has been made, and only thus can critical aptitude ever be attained.

After we have received our personal impressions of the poet's appeal to our understanding, and formed our own opinions of his work we can, with far more profit to ourselves, place ourselves in the hands of a scholarly editor, whose notes, elucidations, and parallel quotations will enable us to shape in our own mind an adequate conception of the poet's work, from which we may eliminate the mistaken notions formed in our first unguided reading, whilst still retaining the tested results of independent judgement. Indeed, this method of reading is not limited in its application to the study of Shakespeare, though it is better adapted to the study of the dramatists and the poets generally than to the writers of prose.

Shakespeare can best be understood by following the sequence of his works. His Sonnets (an example was given in page 82) should be read with the plays of his second period, as most of them were written in the year 1594, though the collection was not published until 1609. Extraordinary interest has centred in these, the only other important work of Shakespeare's pen, and a whole library of books has been devoted to the discussion of the 'mystery of the sonnets' ; but it is neither possible nor necessary to deal with the subject here.

The tale of Shakespeare's works from 1592 until his final retirement to Stratford, in 1611, supplies most that we know of his life. He had become part owner of the Globe Theatre, the leading London playhouse, in 1599. His income, which in his later years must have been about £600 per annum in the money of the time—equal to at least seven or eight thousand pounds today—was derived chiefly from his share in this theatre. Two years earlier he had purchased New Place, in Stratford-on-Avon, where he died, April 23, 1616.

Master Dramatists of the Elizabethan Age

THE greatness of Shakespeare could not be better illustrated than by contrast with Ben Jonson (c. 1573–1637). In almost any age Jonson would have been accounted a writer of the most extraordinary parts. His scholarship was profound—indeed, Shakespeare's learning is, by comparison, almost superficial—but in all his serious efforts to produce a supreme dramatic work he gives evidence of scholarship only, and not of that divine, ineffable quality which makes the poetry of Shakespeare as harmonious a part of the world's intellectual life as seed-time or harvest is of its physical life.

Ben Jonson. It is hard to determine how Jonson came by his vast learning, for we have evidence of only a few weeks spent at St. John's College, Cambridge, in his sixteenth year, after leaving Westminster School. In his youth he worked for a time, to his never-forgotten disgust, at his stepfather's trade of bricklaying, and he was a soldier in the Low Countries when only eighteen years of age. It has been asserted that at nineteen he returned to Cambridge and completed his studies, but this theory rests rather on the desire to explain his wonderful knowledge of the Latin poets than on evidence. He was as injudicious as his great contemporary in contracting an early marriage. Perhaps poverty, as much as inclination, led him to become an actor. His acting seems to have been undistinguished. Steeped in the works of the pagan poets, his native genius was undoubtedly more lyrical than dramatic in inspiration, though he gives evidence of a certain saturnine temper which, inclining to tragedy, but modified by the former impulse, expresses itself in satire. It was with a comedy, however, that he first essayed to win success on the stage, and 'Every Man in His Humour,' produced in 1596, and performed two years later by the company of which Shakespeare was a member, secured a popularity which led to his following it with the play, 'Every Man Out of His Humour.'

Both are admirable comedies, and, like his two tragedies, 'Sejanus' and 'Catiline,' follow classical models ; but the author is so obviously subjected to the strict rules of classical composition that his work lacks spontaneity and natural grace in the comedies and tenderness in the tragedies.

This is the fault of all his plays ; they are overlaid with the weight of his learning ; made coldly accurate by the careful observance of his models ; and neither in tragedy nor in comedy does he sound the depths of human emotions. Though the character is always perfectly observed and represented, Jonson fails to reveal the hidden springs, as Shakespeare, less by art than by intuition, does. For these reasons Jonson's dramatic works earned small popularity in his time, and have ever since been dead to all but students of literature. 'Every Man in His Humour' has occasionally been revived on the stage, but never with lasting success.

Three of his most outstanding plays were : 'Volpone, or the Fox,' 'Epicoene, or the Silent Woman,' and 'The Alchemist.' 'Bartholomew Fair,' a violently satirical play, is a bitter attack on Puritanism.

Court Masques. Such prosperity as Jonson enjoyed came from the composition of masques, which were a favourite amusement of the Court and the aristocracy. The masque is a form of stage entertainment midway between a pageant and a play. During the reign of Elizabeth it rose into extreme popularity, and most of the dramatists, with the notable exception of Shakespeare, set themselves to supply their lordly patrons with such entertainments. They were written in both prose and verse, the dialogue being interspersed with songs, and afforded opportunities for the display of gorgeous costumes and scenic decoration quite foreign to the stage of the time, where no attempt was made at scenic effect or accuracy of make-up. Women also took part in these private theatricals, whereas on the stage all the feminine parts were played by boys or young men. The finest example of this class of poetic composition is Milton's 'Comus,' written for the Earl of Bridgewater, and acted at his residence, Ludlow Castle, in Shropshire, on Michaelmas night, 1634. In 'Comus' the masque, as an acted entertainment, may be said to have culminated, for it died out under the Commonwealth and has never been revived.

Some of the best specimens of Jonson's verse are to be found in his masques, including the lovely 'Hymn to Diana,' from 'Cynthia's Revels.'

Jonson, in his personal character, had some traits which suggest likeness with his great namesake of the eighteenth century, and 'rare Ben' anticipated Samuel's satirical treatment of the Scots. He came near to having his ears clipped for making fun of King James's countrymen in 'Eastward Ho,' a drama in which he collaborated—a rare thing for him, for he was vain of his personal achievement—with Chapman and Marston. He died on August 6, 1637, having experienced loss of friends and favour in his later years. His gravestone, in Westminster Abbey, is inscribed, 'O Rare Ben Jonson.'

Beaumont and Fletcher. Collaboration was a favourite method of work among the Elizabethan, as it is in our own time with the French, dramatic writers. The most noteworthy example of the practice was furnished by Beaumont and Fletcher, who were so intimately associated in their lives that they had house and clothes in common. Both were of gentle birth, scholars, and men of genius. Their plays—chiefly comedies— were even more popular than Shakespeare's, being, if anything, more in harmony with the temper of the period. Francis Beaumont (1584-1616) probably became acquainted with his friend John Fletcher (1579-1625) at the meetings at the celebrated Mermaid Tavern, frequented by Shakespeare, Jonson, and the wits of the time, as celebrated by Beaumont in his verses to Jonson :

What things have we seen
Done at the Mermaid ! heard words that have been
So nimble, and so full of subtle flame,
As if that every one from whence they came
Had meant to put his whole wit in a jest,
And had resolved to live a fool the rest
Of his dull life.

Together Beaumont and Fletcher wrote 'The Knight of the Burning Pestle,' 'The Maid's Tragedy,' 'Philaster,' and many other plays. Fletcher had usually the greater share in the composition of the plays which bear their joint names, and alone he wrote at least twenty, including the lovely 'Faithful Shepherdess.' Shakespeare is supposed to have collaborated with him in ' The Two Noble Kinsmen,' while Fletcher also had a hand with Shakespeare in the writing of 'Henry VIII.'.

It is hard to differentiate between Beaumont and Fletcher, though it seems easy enough by comparing their individual and their joint productions ; but perhaps it is not wrong to say that the one had a more strongly marked lyrical gift, while the other was essentially dramatic in his inspiration. Both men were immensely popular with their contemporaries, and theirs will ever remain among the great names of Elizabethan drama.

As an interesting summary of the most important characteristics of the two famous collaborators, the following passage from Thomas Campbell's 'Specimens of the British Poets' cannot be improved upon :

There are such extremes of grossness and magnificence in their dramas, so much sweetness and beauty, interspersed with views of nature either falsely romantic or vulgar beyond reality ; there is so much to animate and amuse us, and yet so much that we would willingly overlook, that I cannot help comparing the contrasted impressions which they make to those which we receive from visiting some great and ancient city, picturesquely but irregularly built, glittering with spires and surrounded with gardens, but exhibiting in many quarters the lanes and haunts of wickedness. They have scenes of wealth and high life, which remind us of courts and palaces frequented by elegant females and high-spirited gallants, whilst their old martial characters, with Caractacus in the midst of them, may inspire us with the same sort of regard which we pay to the rough-hewn magnificence of an ancient fortress.

LESSON 16

Some Minor Contemporaries of Shakespeare

MANY names must now be dismissed briefly, though most of them are almost as worthy of some detailed notice as Beaumont or Fletcher.

Tragic Dramatists. Philip Massinger (1583-1640), who was laid in the same grave as Fletcher, at St. Saviour's, Southwark, was so associated with him and other dramatists in play-writing that it is difficult to appreciate his individual work. But he is no less gifted in comedy than Beaumont and Fletcher, and in tragedy he displays real power. His only play that has held the stage is 'A New Way to Pay Old Debts,' a brilliant and mordant comedy.

John Ford (1586-c. 1640) was a dramatist of real tragic power, to whom only the darker emotions of the heart seemed to appeal.

His plays are sombre and unredeemed by the finer feelings of fancy and imagination. His 'Perkin Warbeck' is a good historical drama, and ''Tis Pity She's a Whore' is a remarkable tragedy. He collaborated in several plays, notably 'The Witch of Edmonton,' with Thomas Dekker (c. 1570–1641), a prolific and able writer of both tragedy and comedy. 'The Shoemaker's Holiday' and 'Old Fortunatus' are Dekker's best-known comedies.

Dekker, in turn, was associated with John Webster (c. 1580–1625), of whose life hardly anything is known. Webster was a dramatist of extraordinary power in tragedy, and over his works gloom, profound and chilling, seems ever to brood. 'The Duchess of Malfi' must rank with the finest of the period ; but it is easy to understand he had scant favour with contemporary audiences.

Elizabethan Comedies. Thomas Middleton (1570–1627) wrote many charming comedies, while William Rowley (c. 1585–c. 1642), an actor-playwright of no remarkable qualities, collaborated at various times with the five last-mentioned dramatists, and also with Thomas Heywood (c. 1570–1641), who claims to have had a large share in the writing of 220 plays up to the year 1633. 'A Woman Killed with Kindness' has real pathos and simplicity to distinguish it, and is possibly the best of Heywood's plays.

John Marston (c. 1575–1634) was a poet of most unequal achievement, associated with Jonson and George Chapman (1559–1634) in the production of 'Eastward Ho.' Chapman was greater in comedy than in tragedy : 'All Fools' is an excellent play of the former class, while his tragedies are usually marred by bombast and fustian. His great achievement was the translation of Homer's Iliad and the Odyssey into rhymed verse of fourteen and ten syllables respectively. These translations, despite numerous faults, are in many ways unsurpassed by Pope's more familiar versions of the same works.

With James Shirley (1596–1666) we reach the last of this school of dramatists, for, though he was but a boy when the reign of the Virgin Queen ended, his early associates were the later Elizabethans, and all the influences on him were Elizabethan ; he had come to manhood at the time of Shakespeare's death. Charles Lamb says of him :

James Shirley claims a place among the worthies of this period, not so much for any transcendent talent in himself, as that he was the last of a great race, all of whom spoke nearly the same language, and had a set of moral feelings and notions in common. A new language and quite a new turn of tragic and comic interest came in with the Restoration.

This, rather than Campbell's somewhat perfervid panegyric of the dramatist, is a proper view of Shirley, for while the tragic and pathetic passages of his plays, which are chiefly tragi-comedies, are often distinguished by great tenderness and true feeling, he fails on the whole to rise to the level of his models, Beaumont and Fletcher and Ben Jonson. Of his thirty-odd plays 'The Lady of Pleasure,' designed on the lines of Massinger's 'City Madam,' and his tragedy, 'The Traitor,' have been justly commended. As a writer of masques ('The Triumph of Beauty,' 'The Triumph of Peace') he is second only to his 'acknowledged master' Ben Jonson.

The Elizabethan Spirit. We have now reached the end of an important stage of our study, for on our knowledge of, and sympathy with, the poets from Chaucer to Shirley will depend much of our understanding of English literature. The Elizabethans, especially, are the beacon lights of the English spirit, if the metaphor will pass. To know them well is to have the whole character of England illumined for our better appreciation. They represent more directly than any body of writers in England, before or since, the spirit of their time and country. This may be thought an overstatement, when we remember how the spirit of the eighteenth century is reflected in writers of the period. But that was not the real genius of England ; it was a passing phase ; whereas the spirit of the Elizabethan age is the very pulsing of England's heart.

In a sense, the Elizabethans are more in touch with us of this later day than are the writers of the eighteenth century. We shall even find that the literature of the Victorian age, rich to abundance though it is in great writers and in great works, is not so thoroughly in tune with the English spirit as is that of the Elizabethan age. For the creators of the latter were poets to a man, and the poet is ever the truth-teller. He is not so apt to temporize with passing moods and whims as the prose-writer is ; he utters himself with greater freedom, fearless because 'It is in me, and shall out.'

It was the glory of the Elizabethan age to be the epoch in which there lived, surely by no mere chance but inevitably, a splendid company of poets whose poetry enshrines for all time the English spirit—patriotism, heroism, idealism, the love of liberty, beauty, nature, domesticity.

That the Elizabethan poets were as capable of expressing grossness as of voicing the noblest aspirations is no argument against them. Every country and every age of any country has its own standards. That of the Elizabethan was different from that of our day; just as that of fifty years hence will again be different.

The Elizabethan poets—since, for all their superiority to the multitude, they were still men of their time—necessarily reflect in their writings the looseness of their age in the treatment of morals. And it is Shakespeare, again, who towers above his glorious company of contemporaries in his comparative freedom from all besmirching elements. By that token he is really less the mirror of his age—but more the mirror of the English spirit—than, for example, Beaumont and Fletcher. He is the most modern writer in our language. It would seem that in one fruitful moment the genius of England gave birth to a poet who interpreted his country to itself and to the world once and for all time; his thought and language are the everlasting mind and utterance of his race at the highest.

His contemporaries are small when ranged beside him, yet mighty in their individual and collective strength.

We may take leave of the Elizabethans by quoting the summary with which Taine begins his study of the theatre in his ' History of English Literature ':

Forty poets, among them two of superior rank, as well as one, the greatest of all artists who have represented the soul in words ; many hundreds of pieces, and nearly fifty masterpieces ; the drama extended over all the provinces of history, imagination, and fancy—expanded so as to embrace comedy, tragedy, pastoral and fanciful literature—to represent all the degrees of human condition, and all the caprices of human invention—to express all the perceptible details of actual truth, and all the philosophical grandeur of general reflection ; the stage disencumbered of all precept and freed from all imitation, given up and appropriated in the minutest particulars to the reigning taste and public intelligence ; all this was a vast and manifold work, capable by its flexibility, its greatness and its form, of receiving and preserving the exact imprint of the age and the nation.

Such is the Elizabethan drama, the most important of all periods of English literature, not to the student only, but to the general reader who desires a knowledge of our great literary heritage.

LESSON 17

Dramatists from Dryden to Sheridan

THE reader who would make closer acquaintance with the writers for the Restoration stage cannot do better than begin by reading Macaulay's brilliant disquisition on ' The Comic Dramatists of the Restoration ' in his Essays, written originally as a review of Leigh Hunt's edition of the Works of Wycherley, Congreve, Vanbrugh and Farquhar. Nothing more is attempted here than the sketchiest review of the more noteworthy figures of that period.

The first name to engage our attention is that of Sir William Davenant (1606–68), whose work reflects the spirit of reaction against Puritanism. His ' Siege of Rhodes ' is the germ of English opera, and he introduced many accessories to the theatre, among them the orchestra.

John Dryden (1631–1700) wrote at Davenant's suggestion his absurd adaptation of ' The Tempest,' and a capital blank verse tragedy, ' All for Love,' on the lines of ' Antony and Cleopatra.' Dryden adapted the heroic couplet to the English drama. His characters are, in the main, abstractions ; he uses noble language to convey ideas full of extravagance. But his tragedies of ' Don Sebastian ' and ' Cleomenes,' together with the comedies of ' Marriage à la Mode ' and ' The Spanish Friar,' contain much that is eminently readable. Considering the volume and variety of his literary output in other directions, it is remarkable that his position as a dramatist stands as high as it does. The student should not miss his ' Essay on Dramatic Poesy.'

Wycherley and Congreve. Only the reader who cares to familiarize himself with the indifferent for the sake of the picture of contemporary manners to which it may give completeness need spend time with the plays of Etherege, D'Urfey, Shadwell, and Aphra Behn, all of whom reflect the least agreeable features of the time. When we turn to William Wycherley (c. 1640–1716), however, we are in company with genius, and if he can compete with any of them in indecency, he at least offers compensations. Wycherley was one of the two great lights of Restoration comedy. Like Dryden, but with greater success, he sought and found inspiration in France and Spain. He may be described as one of the originators of our comedy of manners. He was a faithful mirror of his own time. His chief comedies are ' The Plain Dealer ' and ' The Country Wife.' The one is founded on Molière's ' Le Misanthrope,' and is praised by Hazlitt as ' a most severe and poignant moral satire ' ; the other loses our respect and much of such admiration as its workmanship claims when compared with its sources, Molière's ' L'Ecole des Maris ' and ' L'Ecole des Femmes.'

It was in the works of William Congreve (1670–1729) that the comedy of manners attained its apogee. ' The Old Bachelor,' ' The Double Dealer,' ' Love for Love ' (which has been described as the finest prose comedy in the English language), ' The Mourning Bride,' and ' The Way of the World ' were all written before their author was thirty years old. Then came sinecures and literary sterility. His later career shows him to have sacrificed his genius for the worship of rank. His social success was remarkable, and he amassed a large fortune. Congreve was, and remains, a master of repartee and polished insolence. As Macaulay writes in his essay on ' The Comic Dramatists ' :

In every point Congreve maintained his superiority to Wycherley. Wycherley had wit ; but the wit of Congreve far outshines that of every comic writer, except Sheridan, who has arisen within the last two centuries. Congreve had not in a large measure the poetical faculty ; but, compared with Wycherley, he might be called a great poet. Wycherley had some knowledge of books, but Congreve was a man of real learning. Congreve's offences against decorum, though highly culpable, were not so gross as those of Wycherley, nor did Congreve, like Wycherley, exhibit to the world the deplorable spectacle of a licentious dotage.

Vanbrugh, Farquhar and Otway. What Sir John Vanbrugh (1664–1726) lacked in grace he had in coarse wit and facile inventiveness. The epitaph,

> Lie heavy on him, earth ! for he
> Laid many heavy loads on thee

alludes to his achievements as the architect of Blenheim and Castle Howard, not to his authorship of ' The Relapse,' ' The Pro-

voked Wife,' and ' The Confederacy.' With Vanbrugh may be compared George Farquhar (1678–1707), who, in some directions as a dramatist, improved on his predecessors in cogency of construction, and whose incidental verse indicates a power that—possibly for reasons connected with a hand-to-mouth existence—was never fully cultivated. He wrote best what he wrote last—' The Recruiting Officer ' and ' The Beaux' Stratagem.' He marks the transition from Restoration licence towards the cleaner, if more conventional, stage methods characterizing the reign of Queen Anne and the early Hanoverians.

In Thomas Otway (1652–85), it has been well observed, ' there is no relief, no pause from the war and clamour of passion.' He lived tragically, wrote tragedy, and died young. Gloomy as are his plays and devoid of lyrical beauty, they reach the heart by sheer force and knowledge of human nature. ' More tears,' said Scott, ' have been shed probably for the sorrows of Belvidera (in ' Venice Preserved ') and Monimia (in ' The Orphan ') than for those of Juliet and Desdemona.' Otway is a strayed tragedian, belonging by genius, if not by time, to the Elizabethans.

Late 17th and 18th Century Playwrights. The only other of the Restoration dramatists who need be mentioned here is Nahum Tate (1652–1715), whose version of ' King Lear,' in which Cordelia survives and marries Edgar, actually held the stage until the middle of last century. It was then the time of Shakespeare's partial eclipse, for although we constantly hear of Shakespeare's dramas being performed, the versions presented would have disconcerted the original begetter of the plays and he would have found the children of his brain as strangely ' translated ' as his own immortal Nick Bottom when he awoke in the wood.

The many-gifted Colley Cibber (1671–1757) was probably a better actor than playwright, yet it was Cibber's version of ' Richard III ' that was performed down to the beginning of the present century, and perhaps may still linger in provincial repertories. These late seventeenth-century playwrights must at least have had a sound conception of their craft.

Thomas Southerne's (1660–1746) drama, founded on Aphra Behn's 'Oroonoko,' was another instance of the vitality noted ; but the astonishing career of 'The Beggar's Opera' eclipses everything in the history of the English stage. That this prose farce, written by the poet John Gay (1685–1732) at the suggestion of Swift, as a burlesque of the Italian opera, then newly fashionable in England, should not only have won instant success with its witty dialogue and dainty lyrics—there were 69 of these arranged to popular airs of the day—but that after its revival on June 5, 1920, it should have drawn all London for three and a half years to a suburban theatre, suggests that it is informed with some rare and individual charm.

It is doubtful whether today an English audience would tolerate the arid accuracy of Addison's 'Cato,' a blank verse tragedy on the classical model, which, first produced at Drury Lane on April 14, 1713, made a hit, eight editions of the book being sold in the first year. But it is worth reading, if only to discover how deficient the rich and elegant scholarship of the eighteenth century could be in the elusive quality of genius which illumines not only Shakespeare's own plays but those of most of his contemporaries.

Goldsmith and Sheridan. In its dramatic taste the age of Queen Anne favoured the tragic, as a change from Restoration comedy. Sir Richard Steele (1672–1729), though full of faults as a dramatist, gave a start to the prose comedy of manners, which grew in favour in the days of the Georges until it culminated in two masterpieces which are unexcelled and enduringly fresh after a century and a half : 'She Stoops to Conquer,' by Oliver Goldsmith (1728–74), and

'The School for Scandal,' by Richard Brinsley Sheridan (1751–1816). Neither of these famous plays is a perfect work of art ; both are open to criticism in many ways ; but both have that 'blithe wine or bright elixir' which makes immortal, while many a work of perfect art lies dead for lack of it. They have justly been described as the greenest spots in the dramatic history of the period to which they belong, and as exhibiting wit without licentiousness, humour with extravagance, and natural delineation of character.

A man of superlative gifts, dramatist, distinguished member of Parliament, and magnificent orator in the House, Richard Brinsley Sheridan has been surpassed in genuine humour by Shakespeare alone. The quality is particularly expressed in 'The Rivals,' produced at Covent Garden theatre in 1775. With its excellently constructed plot, it is a better play than 'The School for Scandal,' which appeared at Drury Lane two years later. The latter comedy, though his greatest work in respect of masterly characterization, sheer brilliance of dialogue and fine acting scenes, lacks cohesion and all the dramatic unities. 'The Critic' is an even more loosely constructed play, which, however, always delights its reader or audience with its sparkling and unforced wit.

To the graceful humour of Goldsmith, Sheridan added the wit without the grossness of Congreve, and he set the model of witty dialogue for the English stage.

LESSON 18

Great Names in 19th Century Drama

WHEN the nineteenth century opened Shakespeare was coming into his own again. Goldsmith and Sheridan were widely popular, and there was no lack of minor playwrights striving to create masterpieces. The taste of the day was for the tragic and the heroic, with the darkly romantic ; the scene was being set for the entry of Byron. James Sheridan Knowles (1784–1862), a cousinly relative of Sheridan, came nearest to achieving greatness, working on the Shakespearian model, and many of his plays take a virile hold on the imagination of an intelligent audience. He wrote more than a score—'The Hunchback,' produced at Covent Garden in 1832 with the author in a leading part, being perhaps the most finished, although 'Virginius' has a greater dramatic intensity.

Two more of the early nineteenth-century dramatists who should be named here are Joanna Baillie (1762-1851), whose 'Plays on the Passions' contain some fine poetry if they are deficient in drama, and Elizabeth Inchbald (1753–1821), an actress and playwright, who is remembered today by her novel 'A Simple Story.'

The dramatic form was highly popular in the first half of the nineteenth century, and the literary drama, as distinct from the acting drama, had notable recruitment in Byron and Shelley, whose works are dealt with in a later Lesson (*see* pages 133, 134). 'Ion,' a Greek tragedy, by Sir Thomas Noon Talfourd (1795–1854), and 'Philip van Artevelde,' by Sir Henry Taylor (1800–86), are both works for the reader rather than the playgoer.

One of the most popular of the dramatists of the nineteenth century was Edward Bulwer, Lord Lytton (1803–73), whose plays, 'The Lady of Lyons,' 'Money,' and 'Richelieu,' despite their artificialities of sentiment, firmly held the stage. Such plays as 'Caste' and 'Ours,' by Thomas William Robertson (1829–71), when well revived, can still interest and exert a hold upon the public. This is true also of 'Masks and Faces' and 'It is Never too Late to Mend,' by Charles Reade (1814–84) ; 'Still Waters Run Deep,' by Tom Taylor (1817–80) ; ' Black-Eyed Susan,' by Douglas Jerrold (1803–57) ; 'London Assurance ' and 'The Colleen Bawn,' by Dion Boucicault (1822–90) ; and 'The Two Roses,' by James Albery (1838–89).

Comedy lightened into burlesque and extravaganza, on the one hand, the work of Planché, the brothers Brough, Henry James Byron and others ; and, on the other, into comic opera, of which those written by Sir William Schwenck Gilbert (1836–1911) are incomparably the best. The association of Sir Arthur Sullivan (1842–1900) with Gilbert in that memorable series of comic operas was one of the happiest things that distinguished the English stage of the nineteenth century. In the history of the theatre there has been no more precious contribution to human enjoyment.

19th Century Literary Drama. While the higher comedy was degenerating, the purely literary drama was again receiving some noteworthy additions in 'Strafford,' 'A Blot on the 'Scutcheon,' and other plays by Robert Browning (1812–89) ; but Lord Tennyson (1809–92) did more than add to the 'drama of the closet' in such poetical plays as 'Queen Mary,' 'Harold,' and 'Becket,' for those were staged with a fair measure of success.

William Gorman Wills (1828–91) was a better dramatist than Tennyson, and there was also a literary quality about such plays as 'Charles I,' 'Jane Shore,' and 'A Royal Divorce,' which might have made them tolerable in the study. Algernon Charles Swinburne (1837–1909) in his lyric dramas and poetic tragedies could have had no drooping eye on their ultimate staging, as they are all void of acting qualities, and the proper place of 'Rosamond,' 'The Queen Mother,' 'Bothwell,' 'Mary Stuart,' and the rest of them is among his collected poetry ; even there some of them may be found rather heavy going, despite their abundant metrical charm. A like judgement might have been passed upon the

poetic plays of Robert Bridges (1844–1930) had not their author affirmed that he meant them for the stage. As plays, then, they are of the still-born variety, and if we have had no opportunity to see them performed we can still read them in that quietude of our studies for which they were not intended !

There need be no hesitation in affirming that the closing quarter of the nineteenth century saw the English drama at a low ebb ; but, as happens so often in human mutations, it also saw signs of a revival which, still a little uncertainly perhaps, is endowing the British stage with a new and rich interest for all persons of literary taste. 'The theatre is the gold mine,' said Robert Louis Stevenson (1850–94), and with W. E. Henley (1849–1903) tried his luck in it, 'Admiral Guinea,' 'Beau Austin,' 'Deacon Brodie' and 'Macaire ' being the product of their joint venture ; and in the 'wonderful nineties' many literary men were hankering after the rich prizes of the theatre. There was a charming piece by Anthony Hope, 'The Adventure of Lady Ursula,' that seemed to presage a new master of comedy, although he is better known in connexion with the theatre as the originator of Ruritanian drama. After the adaptation of his novel, 'The Prisoner of Zenda,' by Edward Rose, there was a continuous output of romantic dramas set in imaginary Balkan kingdoms. Jerome K. Jerome (1859–1927) had several good comedies, characterized by sentimentality rather than sentiment, to his credit, but he did not produce 'The Passing of the Third Floor Back' until 1907, when the literary revival of the stage had already begun. Other names that may be recalled here are Sir F. C. Burnand, Sidney Grundy, George R. Sims, Henry Pettit, Robert Buchanan and Haddon Chambers—none of them, except Buchanan's, appealing in a literary way. Burnand was an author of some attainments, but his stage work was chiefly adapted from the French.

Oscar Wilde. There was, it is true, one real 'man of letters' who brought his brilliant gifts of ironic criticism and character drawing by means of witty dialogue to the enrichment of the *fin-de-siècle* theatre in 'Lady Windermere's Fan' and four other plays in which the literary and the dramatic are delightfully blended : and if Oscar Wilde (1856–1900)—who will rank in literary history with the tragic and helpless ones, like Villon and Marlowe, like Verlaine and Francis Thompson—did no more than show that an audience could be held by charm which was not only, nor largely, dramatic, yet that was a great thing, and his service towards the literary revival of the British stage is unforgettable.

The promise alluded to above was best seen in the work of a younger dramatist, Sir James Matthew Barrie (1860-1937), whose plays are considered in the next Lesson. Stephen Phillips (1864-1915), in 'Paolo and Francesca,' written in 1899 and produced at His Majesty's Theatre in 1902, was heralded as a new poet with the right sort of stage experience, who would bring many distinguished things to the theatre ; but his promise was unfulfilled.

Pinero and Henry Arthur Jones. Among all the dramatists of the period under review the two most distinguished figures were Sir Arthur Wing Pinero (1855-1934) and Henry Arthur Jones (1851-1929), both supreme craftsmen, but neither what is implied by the word 'literary.' Both of them took to printing and publishing their plays, perhaps with an idea that type gave a certain 'literary' illusion to things that were printed and bound up like books ; but, in fact, these two most able dramatists were essentially and exclusively 'men of the theatre.' Their plays when read distil no literary essence ; they depend largely for effect on stage direction, their dialogue requires the emphasis of the actor's voice. In short, they demand too much from the reader to revitalize them.

Yet Henry Arthur Jones must be declared a great playwright, who retained his com- mand of his medium to the end. His first great success was the melodrama, 'The Silver King,' produced in 1882, but he found his true vein with a social comedy, 'Saints and Sinners,' 1884, which was followed by a long series of successful plays—'The Dancing Girl,' 'The Case of Rebellious Susan,' 'Mrs. Dane's Defence,' and others—and 'The Lie,' produced in 1923, showed that his craftsmanship was unimpaired at the age of seventy-two.

Sir Arthur Pinero was an actor from 1874 until 1881, when he took to writing for the stage. After some preliminary success, notably with 'The Squire,' 1881, and 'The Magistrate,' 1885, he produced a series of brilliant comedies at the Court Theatre, 1885-93, a charming comedy of sentiment, 'Sweet Lavender,' 1888, and a dramatic play, 'The Profligate,' 1889 ; and then, in 1893, by virtue of 'The Second Mrs. Tan- queray,' he secured his place as the fore- most British dramatist of his period and one of the great creators of stage characters. Later plays include 'Trelawny of the Wells,' which, first produced in 1898, still exercises undiminished fascination when- ever it is revived, 'The Gay Lord Quex,' 'His House in Order,' 'Mid-Channel,' and 'Iris,' the whole long succession containing a most illuminating picture and criticism of contemporary manners. Pinero dis- played great versatility ; though he was a master of the technique of English comedy, he created, with his serious dramas, the vogue for the problem play in England.

LESSON 19

Barrie and Shaw

OF all the literary men whom the glittering prizes of the theatre have attracted, none has gathered more abundantly, or, let us add, more deservedly, than Sir James Barrie. When at the age of twenty-five, he settled down in London to the career of letters, early in 1885, we were on the eve of a revolution in public taste which has profoundly affected literary forms. The Nonconformist con- science was still so potent that the word 'novel' smelled a little suspiciously, and the thing so designated could be read on a Sunday only under fear of divine dis- pleasure. As for the theatre, no one fit to partake of 'the ordinances of the Church' would set foot in it, and certain low resorts known as music halls were out of bounds to all decent folk.

But few things in modern literary history are more noteworthy than the way in which J. M. Barrie, after contriving to win to his standard the whole army of religiously- minded readers with his humorous and sentimental sketches of life in the most restricted of Scottish religious communities, made himself master of the very difficult art of the theatre, and marched confidently to the conquest of an entirely antipathetic public. Nay, even the godless 'music halls' changed into respectable 'variety theatres,' so that on their vast stage this new Wizard of the North was enabled to display his mastery of the short dramatic sketch to immense audiences of fellow citizens representing all shades of opinion.

Barrie scored his first stage success in 1892 with 'Walker, London,' a charming light comedy, fresh and amusing, with a foretaste of the Barriesque in the whimsical notion of the newly-married barber going on his honeymoon, for reasons of economy, without his bride.

Once he was fairly under way with the stage he had but small conceit of his story-telling gifts, and no book came from him that mattered after 'The Little White Bird' in 1902, and that is chiefly of interest as containing the germ of his celebrated stage masterpiece, ' Peter Pan ' (1904). Who shall chide him for abandoning book-writing in order to give to the stage what it so greatly needed in that long series of comedies which includes 'The Professor's Love Story,' 1894 ; 'The Little Minister,' 1897; 'Quality Street' and 'The Admirable Crichton,' 1902; 'Alice Sit-by-the-Fire,' 1905; 'What Every Woman Knows,' 1908 ; 'A Kiss for Cinderella,' 1916; 'Dear Brutus,' 1917; 'Mary Rose,' 1920; and, finally, 'The Boy David,' 1936 ?

The success of all his plays is of the same essence as the success of his books—a quality of humour that is entirely free from artifice and is peculiar to J. M. Barrie. There is no recipe for it, and for this reason it is as difficult to define it as it would be to get a will-o'-the-wisp to pose for a portrait. But it conforms to the everlasting definition of all true humour in disclosing a deep and abiding sympathy with all lowly forms of life. It is also a form of amused self-criticism, as though the author were chuckling to himself not only about things around him and the fancies of his brain, but about his ego, whom, by virtue of his humorous outlook, he can regard with an affectionate detachment.

George Bernard Shaw (b. 1856) is perhaps the most elusive genius of our age and the most difficult to classify. From his earliest days he seems to have been resolved to be original and never to say a thing simply and quietly that might be said complexly and showily ; he was always out to stir up strife, and he got reactions from lethargic minds by shocking them into awakenment. But to suggest that he is nothing more than one who attracts attention by being unusual would be absurd. He has always been an independent thinker, who has wrestled with the problems of life in the loneliness of his own heart and sought solutions earnestly.

Shaw's idealism was none the less effec-tive for being purely rational. His concep-tion of a nobler world, free from shams and hypocrisy, was the logical outcome of those fundamental beliefs in the Life Force which he preached with all the fervour, if not with the mystery, of a religion. In 'Man and Superman' and, later, in 'Back to Methuselah,' a cycle of five plays, he gave vivid expression to his Nietzschean con-ception of progress based upon a theory of evolution inherited from Samuel Butler.

Shaw's God, the Life Force, expresses itself in matter, using the individual living thing as a tool. Neither omnipotent nor omniscient, it has to struggle against difficulties and limitations from which misery and pain in the world result. Evolu-tion represents the experiments of the Life Force to perfect an instrument for its purposes, and Shaw was for ever warning mankind that unless it, too, was prepared to aid the Life Force, it would be discarded as the prehistoric monsters had been. He looked forward to the time when the Ancients of 'Back to Methuselah' should people the world, and when life would be almost released from necessity of contact with matter. His seriousness when he is serious is as undeniable as his wit is irre-sistible when he is minded to indulge in his intellectual horseplay.

Of all dramatists, Shaw is the least obviously dramatic. He starts by having some point of view to expound ; some of his plays are propaganda pamphlets turned into dialogue for persons to repeat seated or standing in different positions on a stage. Sometimes the 'curtains' are merely arbi-trary stops : as though the super-talker (who is usually Shaw himself), seated 'off' and prompting each speaker in turn, had suddenly decided that the audience should have a breathing space to go out into the foyer and think over the brilliant stuff the persons on the stage have been saying.

In Shaw the literary drama, which has been gathering strength and purpose since the late nineties, may be seen at its brightest, and 'Saint Joan' certainly shows that this undramatic playwright, an he will, can be as dramatic as any. His 'Caesar and Cleopatra' is one of the wittiest comedies ever written for the English theatre. Such a wealth of intellectual pleasure is stored for us in the numerous volumes of his plays, with their fascinating prefaces, that it is hard to say whether preface or play gives the greater satisfaction. The first volume to be issued (1898) was 'Plays : Pleasant and Unpleasant,' containing 'Widowers'

Houses,' 'The Philanderer,' 'Mrs. Warren's Profession,' 'Arms and the Man,' 'Candida,' 'The Man of Destiny,' and 'You Never Can Tell.' Most popular of his later plays have been 'Major Barbara,' 'The Doctor's Dilemma' and 'Pygmalion.'

It is significant that during the present century a large public has appeared avid to read as well as to see plays. As was previously said, Pinero and Jones took to printing their plays, and their example was followed by a considerable number of dramatists in the beginning of this century.

More recently, however, what was once an individual experiment has become a general practice, and whereas it was formerly possible only to get printed editions of established classics in dramatic literature, it is now possible to procure copies of almost every play that has a run of even a few weeks. Every publisher's catalogue contains editions of the dramatic works of some author, well known or obscure, and students of this branch of literature can now keep themselves acquainted with the very latest developments of the literary drama.

LESSON 20

Some 20th Century Playwrights

IN 1906, John Galsworthy (1867–1933), who had been writing novels since 1898, achieved his first real success with 'The Man of Property.' The same year saw him turn to the theatre.

His first play was 'The Silver Box,' and he steadily cultivated the stage in the intervals of novel-writing, so that a long series of successful dramatic works such as 'Justice,' 'The Pigeon,' 'The Skin Game,' 'Strife,' and 'Loyalties,' proceeded from his pen. In all that he wrote for the theatre the same earnestness of purpose that distinguishes his fiction is present, and though there is the relief of humorously observed characterization there is never any effort to be amusing. Galsworthy stands for seriousness in all things, but the dramatic instinct which was strong in him never fails to awaken the interest of his audience in the social perplexities he sets out to elucidate. It is a high degree of art that enables an author to be serious without ever being dull. Galsworthy's plays rank among the best of the twentieth-century theatre.

William Somerset Maugham (b. 1874), who also started as a novelist, became one of our most admired playwrights, rivalling Barrie and Shaw in popularity. His 'Jack Straw,' 'Penelope,' 'Caroline,' 'The Circle,' are comedies that follow familiar lines but present contemporary character with unfailing freshness of treatment and humorous observation. Some of his later plays, such as 'Our Betters,' 'Rain,' 'For Services Rendered,' show satire and irony as his most marked characteristics.

John Drinkwater (1882–1937) has been disparaged by some people on the ground that his 'Abraham Lincoln' is not a play but merely biography presented in dramatic form. The dramatist has gone to biography for his material, but Shakespeare went to history for much of his, and as a quarry there is no distinction between history and biography. In any case, it is an achievement to take certain commonly known facts of a man's life and so to present these in stage dialogue that they hold the attention and enlarge the sympathies of widely contrasting audiences. The lives of Peg Woffington, Garrick, and Kean had served as subjects for comedies years ago, yet Drinkwater really opened a new vein in his series of fine plays based upon biographical data : 'Oliver Cromwell,' 'Mary Stuart,' and 'Robert E. Lee.'

What may be called a biographical play was seen at its best in 'The Barretts of Wimpole Street,' by Rudolf Besier, produced in 1930 at the Queen's Theatre. It dealt with the life of Robert and Elizabeth Barrett Browning in a manner that was at once dramatic and literary, and its theatre success was a tribute to the readiness of the playgoing public to accept good literature in dramatic form.

Frederick Lonsdale (b. 1881), on the other hand, owes all his theatrical successes to qualities which have little to do with literature. He has a perfect sense of the effective plot, seen to advantage in such plays as 'The Last of Mrs. Cheyney,' 'Aren't We All ?' 'On Approval,' and 'Canaries Sometimes Sing,' and a very distinguished gift of bright and effective dialogue.

Arnold Bennett (1867–1931) was, on the whole, something of a failure in his dramatic efforts, except when he was in association with a skilled man of the theatre like Edward Knoblock. 'Milestones,' which was an original dramatic idea, and 'The

'Great Adventure,' in which he adapted one of his novels, were the only two of his plays that had more than passing success.

Recent years have seen individual and isolated successes, such as 'Hassan,' the blank verse tragedy of the glamorous East of 'The Arabian Nights,' by the poet James Elroy Flecker (1884–1915), which was posthumously produced at His Majesty's Theatre in 1922, and 'Musical Chairs,' at the Criterion in 1932, by Ronald Mackenzie, who died in the same year, aged twenty-nine. Another outstanding success was 'Journey's End' (produced at the Savoy Theatre in 1929), the work of Robert Cedric Sherriff, a young dramatist—he was born in 1896—of very marked ability, whose later plays, however, were less successful. Clemence Dane, better known as a novelist, won recognition as a moving dramatist with 'A Bill of Divorcement' and her play in verse 'Will Shakespeare.'

Sustained popularity, first as novelist and then as playwright, has rewarded the work of Ian Hay (Major Beith, b. 1876), which includes 'Tilly of Bloomsbury,' 'A Safety Match,' 'The Sport of Kings,' and 'The Middle Watch.'

St. John Ervine has written many successful plays, including 'The Ship' (based on the tragedy of the 'Titanic') and the comedies 'Anthony and Anna,' 'The First Mrs. Fraser,' and 'Robert's Wife.' J. B. Priestley 'experimented with time' in his 'Time and the Conways,' and 'I Have Been Here Before.' Amongst his other plays are 'Dangerous Corner,' 'Laburnum Grove,' 'Eden End,' 'Cornelius,' 'Johnson Over Jordan,' and 'They Came to a City.'

Theatre of the Thirties. James Bridie (Dr. O. H. Mavor) won fame in 1931 with 'The Anatomist' and 'Tobias and the Angel.' 'Jonah and the Whale' and 'A Sleeping Clergyman' followed in 1932 and 1933 ; 'Storm in a Teacup,' a richly characterized comedy, in 1936, and 'Holy Isle,' which was produced at the Arts Theatre, London, in 1942. Emlyn Williams, who came to the fore in the nineteen-thirties, has several successful plays to his credit, including 'Night Must Fall,' 'The Corn is Green,' and 'The Morning Star.'

Dodie Smith (who formerly wrote under the name of C. L. Anthony) attracted large audiences to a number of comedies of modern life. Among them were 'Autumn Crocus,' 'Service,' 'Call It a Day,' 'Bonnet Over the Windmill,' and 'Dear Octopus.'

In Noel Coward (b. 1899) the modern theatre discovered a dramatist of the most versatile gifts. His numerous revues may be dismissed as successes of showmanship, but his pageant 'Cavalcade' (1931) has dramatic value, and he has shown himself, in such plays as 'The Vortex' (1924), 'Hay Fever' (1925), 'The Queen Was in the Parlour' (1926), 'Private Lives' (1930), 'Conversation Piece' (1934), and 'Blithe Spirit' (1940), a master of light comedy, satire and the dramatic form, composing his own music.

Abbey Theatre Dramatists. An event of importance in the history of the drama was the foundation of the Irish Literary Theatre in Dublin in 1898. In 1903 this organization developed into the Irish National Theatre Society, which produced in London two plays by W. B. Yeats, entitled 'The Hour Glass,' and 'Kathleen-ni-Houlihan,' and Lady Gregory's 'Twenty-Five.' So successful was this venture that in 1904 Miss Horniman opened the Abbey Theatre in Dublin for the free use of the Irish National Theatre Society. The plays of J. M. Synge (pron. Sing ; 1871–1909) were its chief mainstay, notably his 'Riders to the Sea,' 'The Shadow of the Glen,' and 'The Playboy of the Western World,' which are now securely established as classics. Other playwrights represented in the theatre were Edward Martyn, 'A. E.' (George Russell), George Moore, Padraic Colum, Norreys Connell, St. John Ervine, Lennox Robinson, Denis Johnston, and George Bernard Shaw. None of the later Irish dramatists has shown so complete a dramatic gift as that of Sean O'Casey (b. 1890), whose 'Juno and the Paycock' and 'The Plough and the Stars' —to mention only two plays which have enjoyed great popularity—are worthy to rank with the finest efforts of the modern British stage.

Provincial Drama. Reference should also be made here to the rise of a new provincial drama. Representative works in this category are the strong Lancashire play, 'Hindle Wakes,' by Stanley Houghton (1881–1913); Harold Brighouse's Lancashire comedy, 'Hobson's Choice'; 'Rutherford & Son,' a Yorkshire play, by Githa Sowerby; and many Devonshire plays by Eden Phillpotts (b. 1862), of which 'The Farmer's Wife,' in particular, enjoyed an immense success.

There is a mounting improvement in the state of drama from the late Victorian period to our own day. The sharp differentiation between the purely literary 'drama of the closet' and the theatrical drama, characterized for the most part by a certain artificiality, that existed throughout the greater part of the nineteenth century, has almost disappeared, and the list of effectively dramatic playwrights whose work is of real literary quality is a steadily growing one. It is no part of the plan of these Lessons to enlarge upon the dramatists of today, but it can be declared that the pleasure to be derived from study of our dramatic writers, from the Elizabethan onwards, shows no signs of failing under present conditions.

LESSON 21

Poetry in the Age of Milton

OUR necessarily rapid survey of English dramatic literature having been completed, we now resume the tale of English poetry, going back in point of time to the period in which the lessons urged by the critical school of Ben Jonson bore fruit, and beginning with John Milton (1608–74), the greatest name among the poets of the age that witnessed the rise of the Commonwealth and the downfall of the Stuart kings.

John Milton, 'God-gifted organ voice of England,' was the son of a scrivener who had been disinherited by his father for changing his faith to that of the Reformers. Though he wrote verses at the age of ten, and paraphrases of the Psalms (including the well-known 'Let us with a gladsome mind') as a schoolboy, we find him in the sonnet 'On Arriving at the Age of Twenty-Three' lamenting his 'late spring.' His early poems were chiefly inspired by the pastoral surroundings of Horton, in Buckinghamshire, where, after leaving Cambridge, Milton spent five years under the parental roof. 'L'Allegro' and 'Il Penseroso' are mirthful and pensive poems respectively, as their titles imply. Each has supplied the world with many oft-quoted phrases and lines. Among many familiar lines in the former is the couplet :

Quips and cranks and wanton wiles,
Nods and becks and wreathèd smiles.

In the latter is the phrase 'the cricket on the hearth' and the well-known reference to

. . . Storied windows, richly dight,
Casting a dim religious light.

'Comus' is a masque, beneath the exquisite allegory of which may be discerned the poet's political bent, and the whole is rich with promise of his later work. 'Lycidas' is an elegiac poem composed in memory of a college friend. A short extract is given in the next column. Some passages in the poem breathe such a contempt for the corrupt holders of ecclesiastical benefices as to make one wonder why it was not made the subject of a Star Chamber inquiry.

Alas ! what boots it with incessant care
To tend the homely, slighted shepherd's trade
And strictly meditate the thankless Muse ?
Were it not better done, as others use,
To sport with Amaryllis in the shade,
Or with the tangles of Neaera's hair ?
Fame is the spur that the clear spirit doth raise
(That last infirmity of noble mind)
To scorn delights, and live laborious days ;
But the fair guerdon when we hope to find,
And think to burst out into sudden blaze,
Comes the blind Fury with the abhorred shears
And slits the thin-spun life . . .

Having pondered these poems, the student should read the beautiful lines, 'At a Solemn Musick.' The works mentioned were composed between the years 1631 and 1637, when, to quote the words of Sir Edmund Gosse, Milton

contributed to English literature about two thousand of the most exquisite, the most perfect, the most consummately executed verses which are to be discovered in the language.

'Paradise Lost' is the best known of all Milton's writings. Though owing something, doubtless, to Spenser's 'Faerie Queene,' it is not only the first English epic ; it is unapproached. There are various forms of this particular class of poetry ; its foreign masters are Homer, Virgil, Tasso, Ariosto, and Dante. Milton's original conception was of a drama on the Arthurian legends. Perhaps the Civil War which intervened between the conception and the performance of the work supplied sufficient motive for a theme of a more sublime and solemn character than even that associated with the Round Table. But, as Milton's great editor, Professor Masson, reminds us, Milton inherited, as it were, a subject with which the imagination of Christendom had long been fascinated.

'Paradise Lost' is more than the outpourings of a richly stored mind saturated in the classics and the Bible. It is an epic that has no parallel in our own or in any other language. As Professor Masson says:

It is an epic of the whole human species—an epic of our entire planet, or, indeed, of the entire astronomical universe. The title of the poem, though perhaps the best that could have been chosen, hardly indicates beforehand the full nature or extent of the theme ; nor are the opening lines, by themselves, sufficiently descriptive of what is to follow. It is the vast comprehensiveness of the story, both in space and time, that makes it unique among epics, and entitled Milton to speak of it as involving

'Things unattempted yet in prose or rhyme.'

It is, in short, a poetical representation, on the authority of hints from the Book of Genesis, of the historical connexion between human time and aboriginal or eternal infinity, or between our created world and the immeasurable and inconceivable universe of pre-human existence.

Milton's ' Ode on the Morning of Christ's Nativity,' written in his Cambridge days, conveyed the theory that the pagan gods were fallen angels. ' Samson Agonistes ' was his last work. It is a drama founded on the Book of Judges, but, as the author expressly states, not designed for the stage. It is the work of one whose cause had been nobly fought for, and hardly lost. The thoughts uttered by Samson came from the heart of the poet. The work is severe in style, and derives its highest interest from the parallels it offers between the lives of Samson and Milton himself.

It is impossible to over-estimate the importance of the study of Milton's work to all who aspire to the proper and most effective use of their native language. To Milton may be ascribed Spenser's eulogy of Chaucer as 'a well of English undefiled.'

Milton's Contemporaries. The minor poets who were Milton's contemporaries will be considered very briefly. Thomas Randolph (1605-35) was one of the young writers who were honoured with the title of his 'sons' by Ben Jonson. The author of several plays, mostly in verse, as well as of a quantity of other poetry, he has a good deal of fancy and his verse flows melodiously, but in general his poetry has a bookish and borrowed air, and need not detain any but the advanced student. Edmund Waller (1606-87) was the most celebrated among the minor poets of the period between the Restoration and the Revolution. Of weak character, he was incapable of feeling or expressing any very generous emotion, and his poetry seldom or never strikes a powerful note ; yet he revived the heroic couplet in English poetry, and his verse abounds in ingenious thoughts, dressed to great advantage and exhibited with great transparency of style. Waller is remembered today only as the author of ' Go, Lovely Rose ' and 'Lines on a Girdle'—lyrics which, as his editor, Thorn Drury, says, 'might almost be chosen from English literature to serve as examples of the charms of simplicity and directness.'

Sir John Suckling (1609-42) was the author of a small collection of poems and of four plays. Fluent and graceful, he has a sprightliness and buoyancy all his own. He is saved from oblivion by a song beginning 'Why so pale and wan, fond lover ?' and his ballad of 'The Wedding,' the very perfection of gaiety in verse, containing the pretty simile :

Her feet beneath her petticoat
Like little mice crept in and out
As if they feared the light.

Sir Richard Lovelace (1618-58) wrote two small volumes of pleasant songs and other short pieces, mostly amatory. Among them are the poems 'To Lucasta, on Going to the Wars ' and ' To Althea, from Prison,' the last stanza of which begins with the lines :

Stone walls do not a prison make,
Nor iron bars a cage.

Sir John Denham (1615-69) is the author of a contemplative poem, 'Cooper's Hill,' which supplies, under the influence of Waller, an early model of the rhythmical couplet.

Richard Crashaw (1613-49), author of 'The Flaming Heart,' was a mystical poet of the highest order who influenced Coleridge, Shelley, and Swinburne. In his own day he was eclipsed by his friend Abraham Cowley (1618-67), than whom few poets have been more praised in their lifetime. Cowley belonged to what Johnson called the 'metaphysical' school of Donne, of which mention has been made in earlier Lessons, and indeed was in the main a mere modernization and dilution of Donne, somewhat less forced and fantastical, much less daring, but unfortunately also much less poetical. Considerable grace and dignity, however, occasionally distinguish his Pindaric Odes, and there is playfulness of style and fancy in his translations from and imitations of Anacreon. Today, however, Cowley is chiefly read for his prose.

Samuel Butler (1612-80), in his inimitable satiric poem 'Hudibras,' which was written in ridicule of the Puritans, displays much learning as well as wit, and not infrequently a surprising beauty both of thought and expression, while his epigrammatic sayings are most happily phrased. Andrew Marvell (1621–78) was a friend of Milton, played the part of laureate during the Protector's life, and wrote a 'Horatian Ode upon Cromwell's Return from Ireland,' which Trench specially commends to English students of Horace. Marvell's lines on the 'Emigrants in the Bermudas' are even better known than the Horatian ode. Henry Vaughan (1622–95) was a follower of George Herbert. As a whole his poetry is unequal in its quality, but he wrote some lovely elegies, and 'The Retreat' may be regarded as a forerunner of Wordsworth's 'Intimations of Immortality.'

LESSON 22

Dryden and Pope

SECOND in importance only to that of Milton in the period under review is the name of **John Dryden** (1631–1700). He excelled as a dramatist and as a writer of prose, but here we are concerned only with his poems. One of the first of his characteristics that strike us is his alertness to the significance of events in the world outside of his library. Witness his ' Annus Mirabilis ' (the wonderful year of 1666), wherein he celebrates the English victories over the Dutch at sea and the benefits of the Great Fire of London.

In ' Absalom and Achitophel ' Dryden directed the whole weight of his powerful intellect to the undoing of the Earl of Shaftesbury's scheme for inducing Charles II to nominate his illegitimate son, the Duke of Monmouth, as his successor to the throne against the lawful claim of the king's brother, James, who was a Romanist. At this time, it should be remembered, Dryden, though soon to adopt the Roman faith, was strongly Protestant, as may be proved by reference to ' Religio Laici,' the work that followed ' Absalom and Achitophel.' Taking as his model the story of Absalom's revolt against David, Dryden named the various parties to the Monmouth plot after the characters in the Second Book of Samuel. The portrait of Shaftesbury, beginning :

In friendship false, implacable in hate,
Resolved to ruin or to rule the State.

is the most telling example of passionately concentrated poetic portraiture in our literature.

Three other works by Dryden exhibit his splendid lyrical ability—the ' Ode to the Memory of Mrs. Anne Killigrew,' described by Johnson as the noblest in our language ; the ' Song for St. Cecilia's Day,' and ' Alexander's Feast.' Dryden's translations from Homer, Virgil, Ovid, Juvenal and Boccaccio are subjects for advanced study. One of his chief claims to attention is that directness and vigour of his language which almost any half-dozen lines in his verse would illustrate. James Russell Lowell says :

Amid the rickety sentiment looming big through misty phrase which marks so much of modern literature, to read Dryden is as bracing as a north-west wind. He blows the mind clear. In ripeness of mind and bluff heartiness of expression he takes rank with the best. His phrase is always a short cut to his sense. He had beyond most the gift of the right word ; and if he does not, like one or two of the Greek masters of song, stir our sympathies by that indefinable aroma, so magical in arousing the subtle associations of the soul, he has this in common with the few great writers that the winged seeds of his thought embed themselves in the memory and germinate there.

Of the poets who came between Dryden and Pope in order of their birth, four only can be selected for mention here. Matthew Prior (1664-1721) wrote a clever parody of Dryden's ' The Hind and the Panther,' called ' The Country and the City Mouse. ' His muse, as Hazlitt says, was a wanton flirt. His poems and lyrics are marked by an easy air of abandonment, but have at least the merit of originality as well as wit. Thomas Parnell (1679–1718), author of ' The Hermit ' and ' The Fairy Tale,' aided Pope in his translation of the ' Iliad ' and wrote an ' Elegy to an Old Beauty,' of which one line is often quoted :

We call it only pretty Fanny's way.

The ' Night Thoughts ' of Edward Young (1683–1765) have all the gloom but little of the grandeur of ' otherworldliness.' John Gay, the author of 'The Beggar's Opera' (*see* pages 117–8), was the author of several delightful songs.

Pope. Bracketed equal with Dryden by his contemporaries, and his successor in the complete mastery of the use of the heroic couplet, Alexander Pope (1688-1744) is the next great figure to detain us. The son of a London linen merchant, a Roman Catholic, he was excluded from public school and university by reason of his father's religion ; as a result he was in a great measure self-taught and self-cultivated. Pope tells us that

> As yet a child, nor yet a fool to fame,
> I lisp'd in numbers, for the numbers came.

Many critics maintain that they came too easily. These are they who hold that Pope's polish is as much a proof of an unpoetic soul as Whitman's ruggedness.

Indeed, there is more divergence of critical opinion concerning Pope than any other great poet. That may be due to his being a satirist, and to the merciless manner in which he ridiculed his contemporaries in 'The Dunciad,' the 'Epistles,' and his miscellaneous verse, which stirred up those animosities that cloud judgement and replace criticism with passion. Those whom he wounded and all who sympathized with them failed to appreciate his true greatness. That is always the danger for the satirist. When Voltaire built a church at Ferney and dedicated it to God, in all honesty and reverence, as a protest against the innumerable churches dedicated to Peter and Andrew and John and less familiar saints, he was widely contemned as a mocker. Who lives by ridicule shall perish by ridicule ; but Pope contrived to do the one and avoid the other, because he had vastly more in him than his un-matched powers of satire. This is shown even in one of his most famous satiric poems, the brilliant, mock-heroic 'Rape of the Lock,' of which Dr. Johnson said, 'It is the most airy, the most ingenious, and the most delightful of all Pope's compositions.'

Properly to appreciate Pope, we must know much more of his life and personality than can possibly be illustrated here. Yet the assertion can be made that he is one of the heroic figures in English poetry, and that he is one of our greatest poets, su-premely competent in the technique of his art, with a brilliant and comprehending mind, and a heart that could respond to Nature and to humanity, despite all the pother one has heard about his artificiality and his heartlessness.

It has been the fashion—perhaps it is not so now—to sneer at the smooth regu-larity and the rocking-horse rhymes of Pope's verse. He made the heroic couplet a great and enduring vehicle of expression, which not even the genius of Dryden had

achieved for it, and rhythmic regularity is of the essence of the heroic couplet. It is easy to make it appear trivial by reading in a sing-song manner ; even the noblest passages of 'Paradise Lost' can be turned into toneless prose if read aloud as one would read a newspaper paragraph. There must be in reading, as in witnessing a play, a contribution of make-believe from the reader, who should deliberately tune his ear to the movement of the verse and then submit to the poet's emphasis, pause and rhythm, if he would have the full pleasure of the verse he is reading.

Pope is a 'polished' poet. Sir Edmund Gosse traces this polish to the example of Boileau, the great French satirist, and that may be so ; but the whole age of Pope was intent on polishing, and making perfect to the point of artificiality. Nor is that altogether a fault. The conscious effort towards perfection is always in itself a good thing, and cannot mislead if the person making the effort has something worth saying. This Pope had in abundance.

The best and final test of a poet's con-tribution to the thought of the world is the extent to which his lines pass into the common speech. From such a test Pope emerges more successfully than any other English poet save Shakespeare alone.

> Hope springs eternal in the human breast ;
> Man never is, but always to be blest.

> Know then thyself, presume not God to scan ;
> The proper study of mankind is man.

> Vice is a monster of so frightful mien,
> As, to be hated, needs but to be seen ;
> Yet seen too oft, familiar with her face,
> We first endure, then pity, then embrace.

> A wit's a feather, and a chief a rod ;
> An honest man's the noblest work of God.

> Thou wert my guide, philosopher and friend.

These lines from 'An Essay on Man,' and hundreds more that might be cited, are familiar as household words to many thousands of readers who have never read one complete poem of Pope's.

Lesser 18th-Century Poets. In the poetry of James Thomson (1700–48) is heard an echo of that of Spenser. This echo is characteristic of much of the poetry of the eighteenth century. Thomson may be said to afford relief from the didacticism of Pope by singing of Nature sincerely, if in a somewhat affected style. His chief poems are 'The Seasons' and 'The Castle of Indolence,' which prepare the way for the beautiful odes of William Collins (1721–59) and the scholarly writings of Thomas Gray (1716–71), whose 'Elegy Written in a Country Churchyard' (Stoke Poges) did for 'the rude forefathers of the hamlet' what Pope accomplished for the fashionable folk of the town. Gray wrote little, but what he wrote was written supremely well. He was a man of leisure and refinement, the son—like Milton—of a scrivener. He drew inspiration from Milton and Dryden, and is one of the harbingers of Wordsworth.

Mention may here be made of Robert Blair (1699–1746), who wrote a sombre poem called 'The Grave,' which was still popular in the melancholy Victorian days ; William Shenstone (1714–63), whose 'Schoolmistress' is a tender tribute to a Leasowes teacher, Sarah Lloyd ; Mark Akenside (1721–70), whose 'Pleasures of the Imagination' is a poem too dull and too didactic in character to appeal to the modern reader ; and Oliver Goldsmith, poet of 'The Deserted Village' and 'The Traveller,' whom we have already met among the dramatists (page 118).

LESSON 23

The Poetry of Cowper, Burns and Crabbe

IN the words of William Cowper (1731–1800), 'it is a great thing to be indeed a poet, and does not happen to more than one man in a century.' It happened to him. Although his poetry has passed through periods of neglect in the century and more that has gone since his death, it has never been quite under eclipse. It was the religious nature of his work that earned its first great vogue. At the close of the eighteenth century and in the early years of the nineteenth, the whole middle-class community of England was 'brought up on Cowper.' Yet it was a piece of joyous ballad poetry, 'John Gilpin,' that first won the popular favour and will longest retain it. He was fifty-four when he published 'The Task,' which made him famous.

Begun in the winter of 1783, it was written at the suggestion of a friend, Lady Austen, and its success was complete, for here Cowper showed himself in his natural spirit. ' The Task ' has been said to be a poem about Cowper himself, and, although it contains hardly a hint of the tragedy of his life, in it his ailings, his walks, his friends, his abhorrence of slavery, and his religious views are delightfully portrayed. A modern appreciation of Cowper is to be found in Lord David Cecil's ' The Stricken Deer.'

Among Cowper's contemporaries were James Macpherson (1736–96), the self-styled translator of Ossian ; Charles Churchill (1731–64), author of the satirical ' Prophecy of Famine ' ; Michael Bruce (1746–67), who probably wrote that exquisite lyric, ' Ode to the Cuckoo,' which has also been claimed for John Logan (1748–88) ; and

Thomas Chatterton (1752–70), who produced the Rowley Forgeries at the age of sixteen, and the exquisite ' Balade of Charitie ' at eighteen.

> The marvellous boy,
> The sleepless soul that perished in his pride !

Chatterton came to London full of hope and confidence in his precocious powers. He died of starvation and poison in a wretched garret, and was buried in the paupers' pit of Shoe Lane Workhouse.

Burns. When Cowper talks about only one poet arising in a century, he is somewhat wide of the mark. His own century produced Pope, Crabbe, and Burns in addition to himself. To Robert Burns (1759–96), fame came early, and a sorry business he made of it.

> He left his land her sweetest song
> And earth her saddest story.

But the universal renown and affection which have grown for the works and character of Burns since his death are unprecedented in the history of literature. There are good reasons for this. The lyric gift of Burns more nearly touched perfection than that of any English poet before or since. The epithet ' English ' is used with a full sense of responsibility, because Burns is something more than an Ayrshire bard, and there are objections to the word ' British ' as applied to matters of taste. There is a further reason for emphasizing his English quality, despite what Cowper, who was admired by Burns, called his ' uncouth dialect,' and it is this.

Burns is a writer of the purest, smooth-flowing English. In all his serious poetry there is hardly one Scottish word. He reserves the Scottish tongue for his lighter moods, his satirical vein, and it is to be observed, in such a poem as ' The Cottar's Saturday Night,' that as the thought changes in character or deepens in seriousness the language changes also.

Wi' kindly welcome, Jenny brings him ben ;
  A strappin' youth ; he takes the mother's eye ;
Blythe Jenny sees the visit's no ill ta'en ;
  The father cracks of horses, ploughs, and kye.
The youngster's artless heart o'erflows wi' joy,
  But blate and laithfu', scarce can weel behave ;
  The mother, wi' a woman's wiles, can spy
What makes the youth sae bashfu' an' sae grave ;
Weel-pleased to think her bairn's respected like the lave.

O happy love ! where love like this is found ;
  O heart-felt raptures ; bliss beyond compare !
I've pacèd much this weary mortal round,
  And sage experience bids me this declare—
  ' If Heaven a draught of heavenly pleasure spare,
One cordial in this melancholy vale,
  'Tis when a youthful, loving, modest pair
In other's arms breathe out the tender tale,
Beneath the milk-white thorn that scents the evening gale.'

Burns himself tells us, in the famous dedication to the noblemen and gentlemen of the Caledonian Hunt, that the poetic genius of his country bade him sing the loves, the joys, the rural scenes and rural pleasures of his wild, native soil in his native tongue, and he tuned his ' artless ' notes as she inspired. There has been a tendency to accept him a little too much at his own valuation in that matter of art and artlessness. Actually he is one of the most finished of English poets and his prose is obviously that of one who is an artist in words. Let it be declared here that he was a conscious artist and no untutored genius of the plough.

It has to be remembered that Burns was no infant phenomenon of the muse. The bulk of the poetry on which his fame is based was written round about the age of 25—by no means an early age for a poet of genius—when his inspiration was at its freshest and his education had been carried far beyond the average of his class, both in reading and in writing. He was already an artist when he made his bid for fame. That is an aspect of the poet which students should consider. Burns was a ploughman,

but in the Scotland of his day, and perhaps in the Scotland of today, the ploughman may be a man of culture as well as agriculture. Burns was no counterpart of the English Hodge, plus inspiration. He was a well-educated, bookish young Scotsman of poor but decent parentage, a description that would be true of fifty per cent of his countrymen.

Robert Burns is the peculiar glory of Scotland. There never was a poet at once so local and so universal in his appeal. He brought the quality of pity into poetry and stirred it in the hearts of men at a time when the blighting shadows of Calvinism-cum-Knoxism still lay upon Scotland and made its religion bleak and forbidding. For every lowly thing, for all downtrodden unhappy folk, Burns was full of pity. And that pity has immortal expression in many of his poems, while there is also a wistfulness about much that he wrote that goes straight to our hearts and brings the poet there also.

Crabbe. Although in his birth George Crabbe (1754–1832) pre-dates Burns, his principal achievement falls within the nineteenth century, and Burns had died four years before that opened. ' Nature's sternest painter and her best,' says Byron : a description that is not free from poetic enlargement, though the first half of the line might safely be accepted. For Crabbe's chief work was to restore a sense of the realities ; to smash up the pretty-pretty, meretricious, porcelain stuff that had come to pass as pastoral poetry. This he did lustily, and in fine vigorous verse that pleased the ear while it sustained interest in the pity or the horror of his story. Humour is not Crabbe's strong point, and yet we grow to like the poet by reason of his evident sympathy with the unfortunate subjects of his verse. He is a satirist moved by a passionate attachment to the truth and a warm heart for human suffering, so that while others were seeing nothing but idyllic scenes in a rural England that never was—Goldsmith among them—and it was the fashion to pretend that the country life was arcadian in its unalloyed delights, Crabbe in his poem ' The Village ' could remind us of the sordid realities of ' the parish house ' in this fashion :

Theirs is yon House that holds the parish poor,
Whose walls of mud scarce bear the broken door ;
There where the putrid vapours, flagging, play,
And the dull wheel hums doleful through the day,
There children dwell who know no parents' care :

Parents who know no children's love dwell
  there ;
Heart-broken matrons on their joyless bed,
Forsaken wives, and mothers never wed,
Dejected widows with unheeded tears,
And crippled age with more than childhood
  fears ;
The lame, the blind, and, far the happiest they !
The moping idiot and the madman gay.

Influenced by Goldsmith, Gray and Pope, Crabbe may be considered the chief founder of the rural school and the forerunner of Wordsworth. We read Crabbe for what he says more than for his style, which, notwithstanding its vigour, is unequal and frequently faulty. His knowledge of humanity is extensive ; and he showed a charming lyric gift when he sought relief from the heroic couplet. ' The Parish Register,' published in 1807, is, perhaps, most worthy of study.

LESSON 24

From Blake to Wordsworth

THE poetry of the nineteenth century struck its roots in the soil of the eighteenth and its branches stretch into the twentieth. In its style, a notable characteristic is a certain reaction against artificiality and mere rhetoric. In its spirit is distinguishable the influence of the Germany of Goethe and Schiller, of the France of Rousseau and Victor Hugo, and of the ' problem' writers of Norway and Denmark. The movements towards political freedom in France, Italy and Greece, and the evolution of English democracy, all affected it. Thus, to its understanding must be brought some knowledge of the historic happenings amid which it arose and flourished.

It is possible to take the works of two or more of the greatest poets of the period, and to derive pleasure from the isolated perusal of them. But while there is much to be said for the study of the poetry of any writer for its own sake, the more we know of the main facts in the life and times of a great writer, the better we shall understand and appreciate what he has written.

Blake. The great name of William Blake (1757–1827) falls here because, though born two years before Robert Burns (p. 128), he forms a link between the Elizabethans and Wordsworth. He towers above lesser men of his own day by reason of his imaginative genius, and the authentic accounts of his life prove him, in the light of modern understanding, to have been of better balanced temperament than has sometimes been allowed. He was irritable, even violent in his bitterness against accepted forms of injustice, but enlivening his passionate sincerity was a great gift of humour. His love of children speaks to us in his exquisite ' Songs of Innocence' ; his feelings of horror at the cruelty of life in his 'Songs of Experience.'

He was a mystic, with a contrast of simplicity and subtlety in his work ; he felt keenly and expressed keenly social wrongs and ecclesiastical tyranny. Like Crabbe, he had to fight poverty and owed his knowledge to his own self-improving efforts.

In his youth Blake was fascinated by notions of an early mythological Britain. He was also imbued with the ideas of the mystic Swedenborg. These influences are traceable in the 'Prophetic Books,' in which he evolved a complete symbolism, and in which lovely passages abound amidst their strange and often obscure mysticism. We have space only to quote one of these, from 'The Four Zoas' :

What is the price of Experience ? Do men buy
  it for a song,
Or Wisdom for a dance in the street ? No ! it
  is bought with the price
Of all that a man hath—his house, his wife, his
  children.
Wisdom is sold in the desolate market where
  none come to buy,
And in the wither'd field where the farmer
  ploughs for bread in vain.

Born in London, where he lived for sixty-seven of his seventy years, in his day Blake met with little encouragement, though he had his own circle of friends and a devoted wife. Poet, engraver and painter, his illustrations to his poems are superb (*see* Art, Vol. I, Lesson 15, page 43). Of him, his friend, disciple and patron, John Linnell, wrote : 'He feared nothing so much as being rich, lest he should lose his spiritual riches.'

Among the lesser poets, Samuel Rogers (1763–1855) wrote a long poem in heroic metre on 'The Pleasures of Memory,' and caught, in his blank verse poem 'Italy,' some of the beauties of that southern land. Robert Bloomfield (1766–1823), first a rural 'hand' and then a shoemaker, wrote in a

London garret 'The Farmer's Boy,' which gives a sympathetic view of the life indicated by its title. He derived his style from Thomson's 'Seasons.' Another poet of humble life, though on a much higher level, is James Hogg (1770–1835), the 'Ettrick Shepherd,' who stands next to Burns in the order of Scotland's peasant-poets. He described himself to Scott, to whom he sent contributions for the latter's 'Border Minstrelsy,' as 'King of the Mountain and Fairy School of Poetry,' and this piece of self-description is accepted by the critics. 'When the Kye Come Hame' and 'Kilmeny' are among Hogg's most popular compositions.

Wordsworth. One of the greatest poets of the nineteenth century now claims attention in William Wordsworth (1770–1850). In his early days he was greatly influenced by the ideals of French republicanism and the teaching of William Godwin, the author of 'Political Justice,' a work basing morals on necessity. Godwin also had a marked influence on Coleridge. When France, having first debased her humanistic ideals, forsook them for dreams of world conquest under Napoleon, the effect on Wordsworth would have been disastrous but for the devotion of his sister Dorothy and the fact that a legacy of £900 left to the brother and a sum of £100 bequeathed to the sister enabled them to settle down quietly, first at Racedown, in Dorset—where Wordsworth's one tragedy, 'The Borderers,' was written—then at Alfoxden, by the Quantock hills—which district inspired his and Coleridge's contributions to the volume of 'Lyrical Ballads'—and, finally, at Grasmere. This was the home of the Wordsworths from 1799 till the poet's death. 'The Prelude ; or, the Growth of a Poet's Mind,' an autobiographical poem in blank verse, reflects the influence of ideas acquired during his visits to Germany, Italy, Switzerland and France. That poem and 'The Excursion' are parts of a scheme never completed.

Wordsworth has to be considered in three aspects—critic, teacher and poet. His critical opinions may be studied in the preface and appendix to the 'Lyrical Ballads,' the preface to 'The Excursion,' and in numerous letters. In the preface to the 'Lyrical Ballads' he writes :

It may be safely affirmed that there neither is, nor can be, any essential difference between the language of prose and metrical composition. We are fond of tracing the resemblance between poetry and painting, and accordingly we call them sisters ; but where shall we find bonds of connection sufficiently strict to typify the affinity between metrical and prose composition ? They both speak by and to the same organs ; the bodies in which both of them are clothed may be said to be of the same substance, their affections are kindred and almost identical, not necessarily differing even in degree.

The best proof of the error inherent in this view of poetry is to be found in Wordsworth's own work. Elsewhere, in his intense scorn for the artificial and the meretricious, which were so characteristic of much of the poetry of the eighteenth century, Wordsworth went to the verge of the trivial. But though he raised a storm of criticism, which delayed due recognition of his genius and is not yet exhausted, it is well to remember with Coleridge, one of the greatest of literary critics—especially where Wordsworth is concerned—that, but for the prefaces and appendices, much of what has been said against Wordsworth's poems would be reduced to absurdity. The few pages that gave such an opportunity to the pungent parodists of 'Rejected Addresses,' to Byron, to Leigh Hunt, to Jeffrey, and to others to pour scorn on Wordsworth, would, but for the fear that they represented an intention to overthrow the accepted canons of art, have been ' passed over in silence as so much blank paper, or leaves of a bookseller's catalogue,' and 'only regarded as so many light and inferior coins in a rouleau of gold.' Popularity and honours at length rewarded the poet. In 1839 Oxford gave him a Doctorate, he was given a civil list pension of £300 in 1842 and in 1843 he succeeded Southey as Poet Laureate.

As a teacher Wordsworth took his vocation seriously. 'The poet,' he averred, 'is a teacher. I wish to be considered as a teacher or as nothing.' What did he teach ? George Brimley, in one of the most brilliant of his essays, written in 1851 and still applicable, contends, with reason, that the value of Wordsworth's teaching—

lay mainly in the power that was given him of unfolding the glory and the beauty of the natural world and of bringing consciously before the minds of men the high moral function that belonged in the human economy to the imagination, and of thereby redeeming the faculties of sense from the comparatively low and servile office of ministering merely to the animal pleasures. . . . He has shown the possibility of combining a state of vivid enjoyment, even of intense passion, with the activity of thought and the repose of contemplation. He has, moreover, done more than any poet of his age to break down and obliterate the conventional barriers that, in our disordered social state, divide rich and poor into two hostile nations ; and he has done this, not by bitter and passionate declamation on the injustices and vices of the rich, and on the wrongs and virtues of the poor, but by fixing his imagination on the elemental feelings, which are the same in all classes, and drawing out the beauty that lies in all that is truly natural in human life.

Was Wordsworth a poet ? Indubitably ; as Dante was a poet. None but a great poet could have written such lines as those 'Composed a few miles above Tintern Abbey,' in 1798 ; or his ' Lines suggested by a picture ot Peele Castle in a Storm.' But Wordsworth's claim to rank among the immortals might be based on his sonnets alone. From whatever standpoint it may be looked at, the sonnet 'Composed upon Westminster Bridge, September 3rd, 1802,' quoted here, is one of the very finest in the language.

Earth has not anything to show more fair ;
Dull would he be of soul who could pass by
A sight so touching in its majesty ;
This city now doth like a garment wear
The beauty of the morning ; silent, bare,
Ships, towers, domes, theatres and temples lie
Open unto the fields, and to the sky ;
All bright and glittering in the smokeless air.
Never did sun more beautifully steep
In his first splendour valley, rock or hill ;
Ne'er saw I, never felt, a calm so deep !
The river glideth at his own sweet will ;
Dear God ! the very houses seem asleep :
And all that mighty heart is lying still.

There is nothing in the Elizabethan sonnet-writers to surpass it in perfection of form.

LESSON 25

Byron, Shelley, Keats and Other Early 19th Century Poets

CHIEF of Wordsworth's contemporaries was Samuel Taylor Coleridge (1772–1834). Coleridge was a talker, a preacher, a philosopher, and a mystic. His best work belongs to his early years, when he was inspired by his love of Nature and by the revolutionary idealism of France. His ballad epic of 'Christabel,' though a fragment, exercised in MS. form, some twenty years before it was published, a wonderful influence on Scott and other English poets.

For an explanation of the dreamland beauty of 'Christabel,' 'Kubla Khan' and the 'Rime of the Ancient Mariner,' some critics consider that recourse must be had to the German philosophers, particularly to Goethe, Herder, Schelling, and others of their school, to whom Coleridge was much indebted. The first stanza of 'Kubla Khan' displays his gift for poetic narrative.

In Xanadu did Kubla Khan
  A stately pleasure-dome decree :
Where Alph, the sacred river, ran
Through caverns measureless to man
  Down to a sunless sea.
So twice five miles of fertile ground
With walls and towers were girdled round :
And here were gardens bright with sinuous rills,
Where blossomed many an incense-bearing tree,
And here were forests ancient as the hills,
Enfolding sunny spots of greenery.

Sir Walter Scott (1771–1832) sought and restored to letters the romance of the past. 'The Lay of the Last Minstrel,' 'Marmion,' and 'The Lady of the Lake,' his best poems, are for the million what 'Christabel' and 'The Ancient Mariner' are for the comparatively few. For pure joy in Nature and love of humanity Scott was not excelled by either Wordsworth or Coleridge, but his verse is too mechanical to be classed with the greatest English poetry.

Robert Southey (1774–1843), as a poet, is little honoured today, though Professor Saintsbury boldly champions his cause. His choice of subjects and his ponderous treatment are reasons for neglect. Of his longer works, 'Roderick, the Last of the Goths,' is the best. The others are 'Thalaba, the Destroyer,' a rhymed epic of Arabia ; 'Madoc,' a semi-historical poem, descriptive of the adventures of a Welsh prince ; and 'The Curse of Kehama,' a poem in irregular rhymes, the theme of which is drawn from Hindu mythology. Southey is better known for his ballads 'The Battle of Blenheim,' 'The Well of St. Keyne,' and 'The Inchcape Rock.'

The place of Walter Savage Landor (1775–1864) is with the prose writers of the nineteenth century (*see* page 174), for he wrote poetry for amusement and prose as an occupation. But it was with a poem, 'Gebir,' that his genius first flashed into enduring flame. He also wrote some beautiful lyrics, notably the exquisite elegy that enshrines the name of his much loved Rose Aylmer, whose early death in India he never ceased to mourn. Of his 'Epigrams' the oft-quoted 'On His Seventy-fifth Birthday' is highly characteristic.

> I strove with none : for none was worth my strife.
> Nature I loved, and next to Nature, Art ;
> I warmed both hands before the fire of life.
> It sinks, and I am ready to depart.

Thomas Campbell (1777–1844) is, like Southey, best remembered by his lyrical poems—'Hohenlinden,' 'Ye Mariners of England,' 'The Soldier's Dream,' 'Lord Ullin's Daughter,' and the 'Song of the Evening Star' are among them. 'Pleasures of Hope' is an echo of Thomson and Gray.

Thomas Moore (1779–1852), the Bard of Erin, had in abundance the double gift of vocal and poetic melody. An Irishman by birth, he achieved the more enduring part of his reputation by his 'Irish Melodies,' lyrics of haunting beauty written to be sung to native airs instinct with an equally tender spirit of music. His social success was also due in part to his witty gift of political satire, characteristically exemplified in ' The Twopenny Post Bag' and 'The Fudge Family in Paris.'

While still at the zenith of his fame, he forsook lyrical for narrative poetry and in 1817 published 'Lalla Rookh,' a poem which, despite certain obvious faults, of which the chief is an excess of sensuousness, has many passages of rare beauty and some of splendour.

Moore rendered a real service to English verse by introducing a great variety into the use of the lyric metres. Poetry was still fettered by a too rigid insistence upon the iambic and trochaic metres and, possibly for the satisfaction of his own musical instinct, he made a free use of dactylic and anapaestic measures, managing them with astonishing dexterity and contributing greatly to the emancipation of all lyric poets who have followed him. It is Moore's great distinction, his fellow countryman Stephen Gwynn has remarked, that he brought into English verse something of the variety and multiplicity of musical rhythms.

Byron. Since the reaction following the excessive hero-worship to which he was at first subjected, George Gordon, Lord Byron (1788–1824), has enjoyed a greater popularity on the Continent than in England. He is a figure of romance. His poetry is part of his personality. He lived and moved in an atmosphere for ever electrical with presage of storm, joyous intervals of sunniest beauty alternating with others of sombre melancholy. In this he was intensely human ; he was exceptional only in being able to give to all his moods a romantic glamour, which made even his melancholy a thing of tenderness and human pity.

Of all our great poets, he is the most subjective : he found all his emotional material within himself. In everything that he wrote it is himself that clamours for expression : the personages of his poems are but varying aspects of the poet. His poetry may be regarded as really an extraordinarily brilliant and fascinating autobiography.

Thus it is especially true of Byron that without some knowledge of the successive stages of his short but crowded life, his belongings, his surroundings, his friendships and his fortunes, a great deal of his poetry lacks significance. His output was large. It comprises two epics, or quasi-epics, 'Childe Harold' and 'Don Juan'—which constitute his best work—twelve narrative poems, eight dramas, seven or eight satires and a multitude of occasional poems, lyrics, epigrams and jeux d'esprit. That his verse had many technical faults is true ; as Sir Edmund Gosse points out, 'he lacked the power to finish : he offended by a hundred careless impertinences : but his whole being was an altar on which the flame of personal genius flared like a conflagration.' A stanza from a lyric poem in 'Hebrew Melodies' shows him in his best vein.

> She walks in beauty, like the night
> Of cloudless climes and starry skies ;
> And all that's best of dark and bright
> Meet in her aspect and her eyes ;
> Thus mellowed to that tender light
> Which heaven to gaudy day denies.

Byron, indeed, had the true poetic glamour ; he could not be shackled by any laws of rhythm or rhyme. He was, however, shackled and mentally warped by his one personal defect—his lameness, which helped to make him cynical and jaundiced in his outlook on life.

His contemporary Trelawny, in 'Recollections of Shelley and Byron,' writes :

Byron's spirit was always on the fret and fume to be doing something new and strange ; he exhausted himself in speculating, plotting and planning ; but when it came to the point of execution, the inertness of his body and his halting gait held him fast, so that few men even among the poets did more in imagination and less in reality than he did.

The French author André Maurois has written valuable biographical studies of both Byron and Shelley ('Ariel, ou la vie de

Shelley') which have been translated into English and shed much light on the romantic picturesqueness of the former, and on the sensitive personality of the latter poet.

Shelley. Percy Bysshe Shelley (1792–1822) was, as Byron was, a herald of revolt ; but he was also, what Byron could hardly be said to be, an idealist. Byron was at times sincere ; Shelley always so. If Shelley erred against the social and religious conventions of his day, it was not out of contempt or in any spirit of reckless libertinism, but because he had constructed for himself a philosophy and adhered to it. Among his principal works are 'Queen Mab,' 'Alastor,' 'The Revolt of Islam,' 'Prometheus Unbound,' that dark and poignant drama 'The Cenci,' 'Julian and Maddalo,' 'The Witch of Atlas,' 'Epipsychidion,' 'Adonaïs,' and 'Hellas.' In 'Queen Mab' were expressed the mingled idealism and atheism of the Revolution. 'Prometheus Unbound' is well described as 'the finest example we have of the working out in poetry of the idea of a regenerated universe.' 'Adonaïs,' one of his loveliest poems and most finished pieces of art, was a lament for the death of John Keats. One verse is quoted in Lesson 4, page 81. A few lines from 'Epipsychidion' will indicate the quality of that poem.

There was a Being whom my spirit oft
Met on its visioned wanderings, far aloft,
In the clear golden prime of my youth's dawn,
Upon the fairy isles of sunny lawn,
Amid the enchanted mountains, and the caves
Of divine sleep, and on the air-like waves
Of wonder-level dream, whose tremulous floor
Paved her light steps ; on an imagined shore,
Under the grey beak of some promontory
She met me, robed in such exceeding glory,
That I beheld her not.

Shelley's was a divided personality ; he lived in the world, but all his thoughts soared into the empyrean. As a poet of the imagination, he was immeasurably superior to Byron. Of his lyrics, the 'Ode to the West Wind' is as imperishable as anything in English poetry.

In his introduction to 'The Life of Shelley,' as comprised in the three principal contemporary 'Lives' of the poet, by Hogg, Trelawny and Peacock (Dent, 1933), Mr. Humbert Wolfe, with his close knowledge of Shelley's life and work, writes :

Whatever brainstorms might from time to time have disturbed him, Shelley could and did reason more closely than almost any poet of them all. He held resolutely to the path of his ideal, and in all the relations of life if he was sometimes surprising as a man, it was because his Maker had painted him, in Browning's phrase, with only so much body as showed soul.

Keats. To turn from Byron and Shelley to John Keats (1795–1821) is like passing from a storm in which body and soul have been engaged to some sweet resting-place. Keats leaves the problems of passion— whether physical or purely intellectual— alone, and tunes his lyre to hymns of beauty and the praise of Nature. He is one of the first of modern literary poets, drawing his inspiration largely from ancient Greece and Elizabethan England, though the influence of his friendship for Leigh Hunt is distinguishable in his early poems. When the critics attacked 'Endymion,' the attack was meant to reach, through it, the detested politics of Leigh Hunt. Not only Browning and Tennyson, but Dante Gabriel Rossetti, William Morris, and Swinburne owe much to Keats.

'Hyperion' is a beautiful fragment ; the odes 'On a Grecian Urn' and 'To a Nightingale,' the sonnet, 'On first Looking into Chapman's Homer,' and the poems, 'The Eve of St. Agnes' and 'La Belle Dame Sans Merci,' stand by themselves in the foremost ranks of their kind. One stanza from the 'Ode to a Nightingale,' is quoted, including some of the lines best known in the whole world of poetry :

Thou wast not born for death, immortal Bird !
No hungry generations tread thee down ;
The voice I hear this passing night was heard
In ancient days by emperor and clown ;
Perhaps the self-same song that found a path
Through the sad heart of Ruth, when, sick
for home,
She stood in tears amid the alien corn ;
The same that oft-times hath
Charmed magic casements, opening on the
foam
Of perilous seas, in faery lands forlorn.

They are the work, be it always remembered, of one whose father worked in a livery stable, and who began life as a surgeon's apprentice and was dead at the age of twenty-six.

Lesser Poets. Other poets calling for brief mention are : Ebenezer Elliott (1781–1849), whose 'Corn Law Rhymes' have served to distract attention from his transcripts from Nature ; Leigh Hunt (1784–1859), whose reputation, largely due to his prose writings, would not be inconsiderable were it based only on 'The Story of Rimini' and his other and shorter poems, of which 'Abou Ben Adhem' and 'Jenny Kissed Me' are most familiar ; Thomas Love Peacock (1785-1866), who wrote a number of delightful lyrics which are to be found in his novels ; Bryan Waller Procter ('Barry Cornwall') (1787–1874), who, while he is better known for his appreciations of poetry than as a poet himself, wrote at least one good song, 'The Sea ' ; Sir Aubrey De Vere (1788–1846), who wrote several fine sonnets and two dramas of much poetic strength, 'Julian the Apostate' and 'Mary Tudor' ; Thomas Hood (1799–1845), whose 'I remember, I remember,' 'The Dream of Eugene Aram,' 'The Song of the Shirt,' and 'The Bridge of Sighs' are as truly poetry of the heart as his inimitable humour was original ; Lord Macaulay (1800–59), whose spirited 'Lays of Ancient Rome' used to be the popular ideal of the heroic ; William Barnes (1800–86), the pastoral poet of Dorsetshire ; Winthrop Mackworth Praed (1802–39), a writer of bright, witty 'society verse' ; and Robert Stephen Hawker (1803–75), the inspired poet-priest of Morwenstow.

Attention must be drawn to the poems of the gifted Brontë sisters, published in 1846 under the pen names of Currer, Ellis, and Acton Bell. Emily Brontë was the greatest genius of the family. Her poems show a sense of vision which those of the other sisters lack ; they have been slow in gaining the appreciation they deserve—though both Matthew Arnold and Swinburne fully recognized her genius—but as a poetess her place is now surely fixed.

Elizabeth Barrett Browning (1806–61), the publication of whose first volume of 'Poems' in 1844 was an event of importance in the history of Victorian literature, was gifted with fervour, imagination and sympathy. Among these poems was the often quoted 'Cry of the Children.' Her most notable work was her 'Sonnets from the Portuguese,' inspired by Robert Browning's courtship, and this was followed by 'Casa Guidi Windows,' the metrical romance 'Aurora Leigh,' and the posthumous 'Last Poems.' Her work is sometimes marred by slipshod rhythm and the diffuseness which was a fault more of the fashion of her period than innate.

LESSON 26

Greatest Poets of the Victorian Age: Tennyson and Browning

IN the crowded galaxy of Victorian poets, Alfred, Lord Tennyson (1809–92), is the ' bright particular star.' One of the most scholarly and exact of poets since Milton and Gray, he was, with the possible exceptions of Burns and Byron, the most popular since Shakespeare. Not even Wordsworth took his vocation more seriously. From a period of idealism he passed to one of something very like pessimism. Always hating the petty conventions of the present, he became in his later years too much of a social critic for his poetry to benefit. From first to last, however, he was a master of word-music, capable of rendering his impressions with almost miraculous fidelity.

Although, after half a century of extreme popularity among his contemporaries, Tennyson has suffered from the inevitable reaction, his value to the student is twofold. On the one hand, he teaches by example the qualities and possibilities of the English language ; on the other hand, his poems may not inaptly be described as 'the voice of the century' in all its modulations between the extremes of buoyant hope and despair. 'Locksley Hall,' and its sequel, 'Locksley Hall Sixty Years After,' sum up the difference between liberal aspiration and democratic achievement. In 'Maud,' his favourite work, he entered an eloquent protest against material views of life.

If it be granted that Tennyson's poetry did not profit by his sensitiveness to the social problems of the time, or by the way in which he criticized the trend of policies and the fickleness of public opinion, it can hardly be gainsaid that he was a great teacher. The best of Tennyson is not to be gathered by the pastime of hunting out plagiarisms from his poems. As the stirring events of Elizabeth's reign inspired Shakespeare, so was Tennyson inspired by the Battle of Waterloo and 'the fairy tales of science' to the vision of a time when

The war-drum throbb'd no longer, and the
   battle-flags were furl'd
In the Parliament of man, the Federation of the
   world.

But he saw the peril, first of an excessive insular patriotism, and then of mere 'talk.'

From a technical standpoint 'Maud' is regarded by competent critics as one of the best and most finished of Tennyson's poems ; it is the one, moreover, of which the poet himself was specially fond. It contains the exquisite lyric 'Come into the garden, Maud.'

Ahead of his time, Tennyson advocated the higher education of women in 'The Princess' (1847), which, like 'Maud' (1855), contains many exquisite lyrics. His greatest achievements were, perhaps, 'In Memoriam' (1850), enshrining his grief and musings over the death of his friend Arthur Hallam, and 'Idylls of the King' (1859-72), a noble epic in twelve episodes, centring round the Arthurian romance.

Perhaps the best of Tennyson's work was his earliest. That which penetrates the heart of the many is comprised in the lyrics, such as the song from 'Maud' referred to, together with 'Break, Break, Break,' 'Sweet and Low,' 'The Splendour Falls,' 'Tears, Idle Tears,' and his swan song, 'Crossing the Bar.' But the 'Idylls of the King' are also widely loved. 'The Lady of Shalott,' 'Mariana in the South,' 'The Miller's Daughter,' 'Oenone,' 'The Palace of Art,' 'The May Queen,' 'The Lotus Eaters,' 'A Dream of Fair Women,' 'The Morte d'Arthur,' 'Love and Duty,' and 'Locksley Hall ' have been rightly placed among the poems which have profoundly affected English literature. Tennyson showed exceptional skill in writing poetry at short notice for special occasions. A fine example is his 'Ode on the Death of the Duke of Wellington.' He was the obvious choice for the Poet Laureateship on Wordsworth's death in 1850, the year of publication of 'In Memoriam.'

Robert Browning. With Robert Browning (1812–89), 'form' was but a secondary consideration. Its requirements, in fact, constituted for him almost an obstacle to the flow of thought. He is as difficult and obscure as, for the most part, Tennyson is clear and easy to the common understanding. With Browning, far more than with Tennyson, it is necessary to consider the life and the poetry as interdependent and inter-explanatory. It has been well said that 'much of the apparent obscurity of Browning is due to his habit of climbing up a precipice of thought, and then kicking away the ladder by which he climbed.'

There is no gloom in Browning. He is all virility. His dramas and his poems are the appurtenances of an intellectual gymnasium. With Browning, 'Life is—to wake, not sleep,' 'Rise and not rest,' he cries ; but 'press—

> From earth's level, where blindly creep
> Things, perfected, more or less,
> To the heaven's height, far and steep,
> Where, amid what strifes and storms
> May wait the adventurous guest,
> Power is love.

Few poets have given rise to such a body of criticism and interpretation as Browning. But it is not always what is best worth knowing that is clearest of comprehension, and although many people would rather spend an evening with Tennyson for the certain solace of his word-music, the same time spent in mental sparring with Browning might be more stimulating in effect. Professor Dowden, who remains Browning's most competent critic, says :

Browning as a poet had his origins in the romantic school of English poetry ; but he came at a time when the romance of external action and adventure had exhausted itself, and when it became necessary to carry romance into the inner world, where the adventures are those of the soul. On the ethical and religious side he sprang from English Puritanism. Each of these influences was modified by his own genius and by the circumstances of its development. His keen observation of facts and passionate inquisition of human character drew him in the direction of what is termed realism. . . . His Puritanism received important modifications from his wide-ranging artistic instincts and sympathies, and again from the liberality of a wide-ranging intellect. . . . He regarded our life on earth as a state of probation and of preparation. . . . In his methods Browning would acknowledge no master ; he would please himself and compel his readers to accept his method, even if strange or singular. . . . His optimism was part of the vigorous sanity of his moral nature. . . . The emotions which he chiefly cared to interpret were those connected with religion, with art, and with the relations of the sexes.

It is especially important to remember that Browning's thought where it is most significant is often more or less enigmatical if taken by itself ; 'its energetic gestures, unless we see what they are directed against, seem aimless beating in the air.' That portion of his work, therefore, which is primarily polemical bids fair to fail in interesting posterity. His masterpiece is the living human epic of 'The Ring and the Book.' He wrote many long poems, of which ' Sordello ' and ' Fifine at the Fair,' though difficult, are among the most remarkable, together with 'Christmas Eve and Easter Day,' 'Paracelsus,' 'Bishop Blougram's Apology' and 'Andrea del Sarto.' 'How They Brought the Good

News from Ghent,' 'Saul,' 'The Lost Leader,' 'Home Thoughts from Abroad,' 'The Grammarian's Funeral,' 'Rabbi Ben Ezra,' 'The Last Ride Together,' 'Love Among the Ruins,' and 'The Pied Piper of Hamelin' are among his widely popular poems, as are the charming songs from 'Pippa Passes.' A more vitally dramatic poet than Browning never existed ; though his remarkable series of poetic dramas—

'Strafford,' 'A Blot on the Scutcheon,' 'Colombe's Birthday,' and others—lack the lucidity essential to the theatre, being too nimble in action and too clever for the audience to follow. He began to write dramatic lyrics about 1841, and some of them are included in the series, 'Men and Women,' published in 1855. They embody his most original, poignant, tragic, grotesque and lively genius of expression.

LESSON 27

The Pre-Raphaelites and Some Late Victorian Poets

SWINBURNE, D. G. Rossetti, Christina Rossetti, William Morris and Coventry Patmore were the leading poets of that romantic revival in art and literature, the Pre-Raphaelite Brotherhood. Both Tennyson and Matthew Arnold, though apart from the movement, showed in much of their poetry what may be defined as the ideal of Pre-Raphaelitism, a blend of serene clarity and refined luxury. The decadence of this ideal was an effete romanticism expressed by many of the poets of the 'nineties ; its revival can be traced in the work of such diverse modern poets as Edith Sitwell and Walter de la Mare.

Of **Algernon Charles Swinburne** (1837–1909), Tennyson said : ' He is a reed, through which all things blow into music.' A younger contemporary of Browning's, Swinburne was, indeed, a poet of a different mould. Browning was a thinker striving to utter his thoughts in poetic form, and never a stringer-together of mellifluous words for the sake of their metrical charm. Form was paramount with Swinburne, and the content of the verse seemed secondary. His verse is as near to actual music as that of any poet who ever lived. The following stanza forms part of a chorus from ' Atalanta in Calydon.'

> Before the beginning of years
>   There came to the making of man
> Time, with a gift of tears ;
>   Grief, with a glass that ran ;
> Pleasure, with pain for leaven ;
>   Summer, with flowers that fell ;
> Remembrance fallen from heaven,
>   And madness risen from hell ;
> Strength without hands to smite ;
>   Love that endures for a breath ;
> Night, the shadow of light,
>   And life, the shadow of death.

No English poet more definitely felt himself a poet than Swinburne did. From his earliest years he consecrated himself to the tuneful muses. Even when his verse is disfigured by excess of passionate phrase, it produces a sense of exaltation.

Our finest lyrist after Tennyson and an artist even more comprehensive in the mastery of varied metres, it would be wrong to leave the impression that Swinburne's concern was so fixed upon the form of his poetry that he was careless of its content, or, again, that he was obsessed by the sensuous side of life. His poetry abounds in passages where high thought and true emotions are expressed in lines of intense and enduring beauty, ample evidence that his soul was in tune with life's inmost and profound harmonies. His ' Tristram of Lyonesse ' should be compared with Tennyson's. He wrote a magnificent trilogy on Mary Stuart, and his ' Atalanta ' and ' Erechtheus ' are superb poetic dramas.

Matthew Arnold. Next in importance to Swinburne must be reckoned Matthew Arnold (1822–88), whose poems, austere in form, classic in spirit, breathe the indefinable sadness of culture threatened by anarchy. Swinburne uttered no criticism that rings more true than his dictum that Matthew Arnold's ' best essays ought to live longer than most ; his poems cannot but live as long as any of their time.' Matthew Arnold would have won lasting distinction among the few had he written only ' The Strayed Reveller ' (that perfect anticipation of modern free verse), ' Empedocles on Etna,' ' The Scholar Gipsy,' ' Sohrab and Rustum,' and his fine Arthurian poem ' Tristram and Iseult,' with its exquisite Pre-Raphaelite glamour and naturalism. Four verses from his poem ' Self-Dependence ' embody both his ideal of restraint and his power of word-painting.

' Ah, once more,' I cried, ' ye stars, ye waters,
  On my heart your mighty charm renew ;
Still, still let me be, as I gaze upon you,
  Feel my soul becoming vast like you.'

From the intense, clear, star-sown vault of heaven,
  Over the lit sea's unquiet way,
In the rustling night-air came the answer :
  ' Wouldst thou *be* as these are ? *Live* as
· they.

' Unaffrighted by the silence round them,
  Undistracted by the sights they see,
These demand not that the things without them
  Yield them love, amusement, sympathy.

' And with joy the stars perform their shining,
  And the sea its long moon-silver'd roll ;
For self-poised they live, nor pine with noting
  All the fever of some differing soul.'

The poems of Frederick Tennyson (1807–98) and Charles Tennyson Turner (1808–79) may be studied with those of their illustrious brother. With him they were joint authors of the famous ' Poems of Two Brothers.' Frederick's poem ' The Isles of Greece ' is well worth reading. Charles is best represented by his sonnets.

Rossetti and William Morris. Dante Gabriel Rossetti (1828–82) was the fountain-head of Pre-Raphaelitism. As A. C. Benson observes :

He has stimulated the sense of beauty, the desire to extract the very essence of delight from emotion, form and colour ; he has inculcated devotion to art.

A painter of outstanding merit, he was an excellent translator from Italian, French and German. His two talents interacted, for many of his poems were written as commentaries on his pictures. His sister Christina (1830–94) was, in all she wrote and in her attitude to life, an essential poet. A devotional writer of the finest quality, her lyric gift was rare and distinguished, and her poetry will engage the student's interest as conveying the Pre-Raphaelite ideal in its purest form. An example of her sonnets is given in page 81.

Mr. R. L. Megroz, in ' Modern English Poetry,' says that Coventry Patmore (1823–96) ' in his " Unknown Eros " odes opened a way in a new direction, for he was the least Romantic of the poets who contributed (as he does in the Odes) to Pre-Raphaelite poetry, and the most original after Rossetti.' Of that other great leader

in the P.R.B., William Morris (1834–96), Mr. Megroz (ibid) observes :

Morris always lacked the artistic mastery of the literary medium which might have made his poetic fame secure, but his genius as a poet of the day-dreaming imagination, like Masefield's indeed, is not to be denied, and will for a long time yet hold youthful readers in thrall.

We have now reached a stage in our survey when not even the pretence of naming the lesser poets of the period can be made. Their name becomes legion, and they must pass in scores unheralded. The explanation of the phenomenon is that there was now a steady raising of the mean of poetry ; and as the average rises and the number of competent artists swells, it would seem that poetic genius becomes diffused ; the sporadic outbursts which produced the giants are fewer or by contrast less astonishing.

Each reader will in his own way discover for himself favourite specimens of the work of other men whose reputation as poets was high among their contemporaries. Arthur Hugh Clough (1819–61), as shown by 'The Bothie of Tober-na-Vuolich,' was not altogether given over to the philosophic doubt usually associated with his name. In the Irish songs of William Allingham (1824–89) is to be traced something of Christina Rossetti and of the glamour of archaic things wherein lay the origin of the 'Celtic revival.'

Later Victorian Poets. The poetic output of Robert Louis Stevenson (1850–94), limited in quantity, is notable in quality. W. E. Henley (1849–1903) possessed an innate fineness which rings through his verse. George MacDonald (1824–1905) wrote many short lyrics ; his 'Diary of an Old Soul' was declared by Ruskin to be one of the three great religious poems of the century. Francis Turner Palgrave (1824–97) was greater as a critic than as a poet ; his 'Golden Treasury of Songs and Lyrics' bears witness to his powers of discrimination, though he owed much to the advice of Tennyson. Gerald Massey (1828–1907) wrote some tenderly emotional lyrical poetry, notably the exquisite 'Ballad of Babe Christabel.' T. E. Brown (1830–97), the Manx poet and a distinguished scholar, produced moving lyrics embodying his love of nature. Sir Edwin Arnold (1832–1904), in 'The Light of Asia,' interpreted Buddhism for Western readers.

Sir Lewis Morris (1833–1907), the author of 'The Epic of Hades,' an attempt to read the Greek myths in the light of Christian sentiment, 'The Ode of Life,' a review of life's stages, and 'A Vision of Saints,' was in his day the most popular poet next to Tennyson. James Thomson, (1834–82), who wrote under the initials 'B.V.' depicted the dark side of London in 'The City of Dreadful Night,' and ranks among the unfortunates of genius. The same might almost be said of Francis Thompson (1859–1907), that powerful visionary, the author of 'The Hound of Heaven,' whose intuition reached the 'smouldering core of mystery'; and of John Davidson (1857–1909), who, like his predecessor, James Thomson, fiercely revolted against the narrow prejudices and oppressions of contemporary life. Notable among his poems are the 'Fleet Street Eclogues' and his 'Ballads and Songs.'

There is the daintiest of art in everything of Austin Dobson (1840–1921). Yet other figures of the 'nineties were Wilfrid S. Blunt (1840–1922), a genuine poet, noted for his sonnet sequences and his versions of the 'Seven Golden Odes of Pagan Arabia'; Alice Meynell (1850–1922), the foremost woman poet of her time, whose work was marred by preciosity, but distinguished by charm; and Katherine Tynan (1861–1931), who made her first serious appeal as a poet with 'Ballads and Lyrics.'

Special mention must be made of George Meredith (1828–1909), whose poetry was influenced by the P.R.B. movement, and concerning whom critical opinion is still divided. In the modern mind there is little doubt that he is destined to live as a poet when his long novels will be little read. We find his natural voice in his poetry and

a forthright vigour of expression that is not characteristic of his prose. In 'Love in the Valley,' taken from his 'Poems and Lyrics of the Joy of Earth,' we have a characteristic example in which he also strikes clearly the romantic note. Here is the first stanza :

Under yonder beech-tree single on the green-
    sward,
Couched with her arms behind her golden head,
Knees and tresses folded to slip and ripple
    idly,
Lies my young love sleeping in the shade.
Had I the heart to slide an arm beneath her,
Press her parting lips as her waist I gather slow,
Waking in amazement she could not but
    embrace me :
Then would she hold me and never let me go ?

Sir William Watson (1858–1935) was certainly one of our chief poets of later times. He started and continued as a Wordsworthian, and has some of the defects as well as many of the merits of his master. His mastery of the sonnet form is complete, and he wrote odes of grave beauty and serene simplicity.

It is a commonplace of journalism to talk about the decadence of the eighteen-nineties, and that much of the poetry of that period reveals a moral and spiritual disorder, due to enervating external influences in operation at the time, is undoubtedly true. It can be seen in the work of Ernest Dowson, Richard Le Gallienne, Richard Middleton, Lionel Johnson, Arthur Symons, Oscar Wilde, Lord Alfred Douglas and others who, nevertheless, produced poetry of high merit when not marred by artificiality and egotism. The last-named, especially, is a poet of distinction, and a writer of some exceptionally beautiful sonnets.

LESSON 28

Outline of Modern Poetry

ENGLAND has had more good poets from 1900 to the present day than during any period of the same length since the early 17th century,' wrote W. B. Yeats in his introduction to 'The Oxford Book of Modern Verse,' first issued in 1936. In this Lesson it will be possible to give the reader merely a bare outline of the trend of modern poetry, and to instance only those poets whose work is most characteristic, in one aspect or another, of the age which called it forth.

The poetry of the present generation voices the spirit of revolt—revolt, at the beginning, against 'Victorianism,' a term connoting moral earnestness, eloquence, rhetoric, scientific description of natural phenomena, and all conventional 'poetic' diction. From this period survived several poets of maturity and distinction who continued to hold their place either because they appealed to a particular segment of the poetry-reading public, or because they embodied in their work something of the 'pure, gem-like flame' sought by the younger poets.

Among them is **Thomas Hardy** (1840–1928). Throughout his life Hardy had written verse, but it was not until his later years that he showed himself a tragic poet of genius who, in imaginative range and intellectual quality, is clearly one of the moderns. As in his novels, so in his poems, Hardy deals with the ironies and disappointments of life. He practises a great economy of words, his phrasing is direct and vigorous, and he not infrequently employs irony. His most ambitious piece of work, 'The Dynasts' (1904–1908), is an epic-drama giving a chronicle of the Napoleonic Wars. It deals with them as they touched every class of society, and Hardy shows considerable virtuosity in using vocabularies suitable to the very large range of characters introduced. His shorter lyric verse, which is of high quality, is to be found in the collections, 'Wessex Poems,' 'Poems of the Past and the Present,' ' Time's Laughing Stocks,' 'Satires of Circumstance,' and 'Moments of Vision.'

The poetry of **Gerard Manley Hopkins** (1844–1889) was not written with a view to publication. Most of his compositions were sent in letters to Robert Bridges, who printed a first collection in 1918. An enlarged edition appeared in 1930. All his poetic work fills about 100 pages, for he gave it up as a worldly vanity after becoming a Jesuit. Manley Hopkins is of importance largely because of his metrical experiments and his endeavour to concentrate into an economic use of words as full a poetic significance as they could carry ; he sometimes invented words. He had very considerable influence upon modern poets, from Eliot onwards. 'The Wreck of the Deutschland,' a great though obscure poem, should be noted.

Robert Bridges (1844–1930), a master of metre and a most scholarly poet, was made Laureate in 1913. Some of his best work is to be found in his sonnet sequence, ' Eros and Psyche,' and in ' The Growth of Love '; and nearly all his short lyrics are admirable. In his old age he published his most ambitious poem, 'The Testament of Beauty' (1929), an astonishing piece of work for one over eighty. Much varied criticism has been devoted to this long philosophical poem, and though Bridges may be remembered chiefly as an outstanding writer of lyrics, nevertheless 'The Testament of Beauty' will be recalled for its noble intention and its passages of magnificantly expressed wisdom.

As an example of his lyrical gifts we give here the first two stanzas of a short poem of which W. B. Yeats said : 'Every metaphor, every thought a commonplace, emptiness everywhere, the whole magnificent.'

> I heard a linnet courting
>> His lady in the spring ;
> His mates were idly sporting,
>> Nor stayed to hear him sing
>> His song of love.
> I fear my speech distorting
>> His tender love.
>
> The phrases of his pleading
>> Were full of young delight ;
> And she that gave him heeding
>> Interpreted aright
>> His gay, sweet notes,
> So sadly marred in the reading,
>> His tender notes.

A. E. Housman (1859–1936), Professor of Latin, first at London University and then at Cambridge, had all his work published in three slim volumes : ' A Shropshire Lad,' 'Last Poems,' and posthumously 'More Poems.' Housman was a master of the musical yet restrained lyric. He expressed a fatalism which had not been heard in English verse since FitzGerald's paraphrase of Omar Khayyam, and this may explain something of his popularity. Typical of his manner is this four-line epitaph :

> Here dead lie we because we did not choose
>> To live and shame the land from which
>> we sprung.
> Life, to be sure, is nothing much to lose ;
>> But young men think it is, and we were
>> young.

Rudyard Kipling (1865–1936) was a poet who knew exactly how to appeal to his public. At a time when the ideas of a somewhat superficial imperialism flourished, he sang of the deeds of the white men among their coloured brethren, and of soldiers under tropic skies. His 'Barrack Room Ballads,' 'The Seven Seas,' and 'The Five Nations' struck the same note, and the violence of the language used, while appealing to some, shocked the literary and aesthetic sense in others. Kipling had attempted to make the fighting man tell his own story in his own language. Other verses, some of quite a different character, are to be found in 'Songs from Books' and 'The Years Between.' But Kipling could not keep politics out of his verse, and this is probably responsible for the fact that

SAMUEL TAYLOR COLERIDGE belonged to the 'Lake School' of poets, founded by Wordsworth. He had an extraordinary gift of conveying the supernatural, as may be seen in 'The Ancient Mariner,' 'Kubla Khan' and 'Christabel,' while at the same time he was a shrewd critic.

Portrait by W. Allston

GEORGE GORDON, LORD BYRON, is one of the most striking figures in literature, unhappy because of the faults in his own character. He wrote moving lyrics, superb descriptive verse ('Childe Harold'), romantic melodrama (such as 'Manfred'), and brilliant satire ('Don Juan').

After Phillips, in the possession of Sir John Murray;
photo, Emery Walker

PERCY BYSSHE SHELLEY, supremely gifted lyric poet, was also capable of sustained magnificence, as in 'The Revolt of Islam' and 'Prometheus Unbound.' An impassioned idealist, his revolutionary sentiments were ahead of his times.

Portrait by Amelia Curran, National Portrait Gallery

JOHN KEATS, who died young, had a sensuous beauty of imagination and a felicity of phrase which made his work immortal. 'Endymion' and 'Hyperion' were his most ambitious work: the odes and sonnets are best known.

Portrait by W. Hilton, National Portrait Gallery

LESSON 25

POETESSES OF GENIUS. Elizabeth Barrett Browning (left), wife of the great poet, was herself famous for her tenderly passionate lyrics; her 'Sonnets from the Portuguese' and 'Aurora Leigh' show her splendid and courageous spirit. Emily Brontë wrote poetry of rare spiritual beauty; her 'Last Lines' ('No coward soul is mine') are deathless. She is, however, more generally known for her magnificent novel, 'Wuthering Heights.' The portrait is by her gifted but wastrel brother, Patrick Branwell Brontë.

Portrait of Mrs. Browning by W. Gordigiani; both in National Portrait Gallery

MASTER POETS OF THE VICTORIAN AGE. Alfred Lord Tennyson, poet laureate, had a remarkably large and varied output of poetic masterpieces, marked by nobility of thought and felicity of expression. Robert Browning, an intensely individual poet and thinker, was even more prolific; he was dramatic rather than lyric, with the gift of understanding character. The subtleties of his thought are reflected in his style. He spent much of his life abroad.

Browning's portrait by his son

A. C. Swinburne

Matthew Arnold

William Morris

Dante Gabriel Rossetti

Christina, sister of D. G. Rossetti, wrote exquisite lyrics with a mystical quality which sets them apart.

Drawing by D. G. Rossetti

Francis Thompson

W. E. Henley

Wilfrid Scawen Blunt

Robert Bridges

FAMOUS VICTORIAN POETS. *Matthew Arnold is classic in spirit ; Rossetti, Morris and Swinburne belong to the Pre-Raphaelite school ; Francis Thompson is one of the great mystics ; Henley was a vigorous poet and critic, and Wilfrid Scawen Blunt wrote accomplished verse, but neither is much read today. Bridges, poet laureate from 1913 to 1930, was a distinguished and scholarly writer, whose ' Testament of Beauty ' is a magnificent achievement.*

Portrait of Arnold by G. F. Watts (National Portrait Gallery); of D. G. Rossetti by himself; drawing of Thompson by permission of Burns, Oates & Washbourne; Photos, Elliott & Fry, F. Hollyer and Lafayette

'A. E.' (G. W. Russell)

W. B. Yeats

John Masefield

Alfred Noyes

Walter de la Mare

Lascelles Abercrombie

W. H. Auden

Edith Sitwell

T. S. Eliot

MODERN POETS. These cover a wide range. G. W. Russell (' A. E.') and Yeats led the Celtic Revival. Masefield, poet laureate, has written forceful poems, plays and novels ; Noyes was a prolific writer of wide appeal ; de la Mare, a profound psychologist with a gift for conveying the supernatural, wrote for children as well as for adults, short stories as well as poems ; Abercrombie was markedly intellectual. Auden, Eliot, and Edith Sitwell are among the most distinguished of the moderns.
Photos of Edith Sitwell and T. S. Eliot, Elliott & Fry

he has received less credit as a craftsman than is his due. At his best Kipling is a real poet ; always he is a skilled writer of vigorous verse. Sir Henry Newbolt (1862–1938), a contemporary of Kipling, was also a patriotic poet, but his note was more restrained. Two typical collections of his are 'Songs of the Sea' and 'Songs of the Fleet.'

Irish Poets. W. B. Yeats (1865–1939) is to be counted a modern, for, while already recognized at the end of the century as one of the greatest poets of the age, his remarkable powers of development, his eagerness to explore new worlds and new theories, made him the contemporary of three succeeding generations, on whose work he exercised great influence. The lyrical and emotional qualities of his shorter poems, and the mystical tendency always latent in him, entitle him to rank as the chief poet of the 'Celtic Twilight.' Yeats succeeded in creating a body of poetry and drama which reflected both the old Irish literature and the contemporary life of Ireland. His two best-known plays are 'Cathleen ni Houlihan' and 'The Land of Heart's Desire,' which are really poems in dialogue. His early poetry, e.g. that contained in the volume entitled 'Wind Among the Reeds,' tended to be over-elaborate ; his later work is distinguished by complete austerity of style.

We give here the last stanza of his poem 'Coole and Ballylee,' written in 1931 :

We were the last romantics—chose for theme
Traditional sanctity and loveliness ;
Whatever's written in what poets name
The book of the people ; whatever most can
  bless
The mind of man or elevate a rhyme ;
But all is changed, that high horse riderless,
Though mounted in that saddle Homer rode
Where the swan drifts upon a darkening flood.

G. W. Russell (1867–1935), better known as 'A.E.,' is another Irish poet whose genius is clothed with ancient legendary lore and symbolism. His collected poems reveal in almost everyday language rare beauties of vision and quiet rapture. J. M. Synge (1871–1909), Oliver St. John Gogarty (b. 1878), Padraic Colum (b. 1881) and F. R. Higgins (b. 1896) likewise draw upon the folk traditions of Ireland for the themes of their lyrics. Herbert Trench (1865–1923) went further afield, as did James Stephens (b. 1882), who published his collected poems in 1926 and subsequently.

Edward Plunkett, Lord Dunsany (b. 1878), is a distinguished poet who has also written

who has also written some of the greatest one-act plays in existence, but is perhaps best known for his highly original short stories. John Masefield (b. 1875), Poet Laureate, endeavoured in his 'Saltwater Ballads' and 'Ballads' to do for the sailor what Kipling had accomplished for the soldier. But by describing the slum and the drunkard with a lurid brutality, and being extraordinarily careless in both metre and rhyme, he easily became the victim of the parodist. He was, however, only carrying out his purpose declared in 'A Consecration' :

Others may sing of the wine and the wealth
  and the mirth . . .
Mine be the dirt and the dross, the dust and
  scum of the earth !

Masefield shows much narrative skill and has even been compared with Chaucer. The best of his earlier narrative poems are 'The Everlasting Mercy,' describing the conversion of a boxer ; 'Daffodil Fields,' the story of a murder placed in a spring setting ; 'The Widow in the Bye-street' which tells how the widow's son is seduced by a hussy ; and 'Dauber,' which relates the adventures of a would-be painter who ships as an ordinary seaman. Later he was to improve on these with 'Philip the King' ; 'Reynard the Fox,' the story of a great hunt, and 'Right Royal,' the story of a horse race. Among his plays in verse is 'Good Friday,' a tragedy giving the story of the crucifixion without bringing on the stage the figure of Christ.

Wilfrid Wilson Gibson (b. 1878) is of primary importance for his realistic poems of working life. He possesses far more restraint than Masefield, and obtains his effects by simplicity and restrained sincerity. In 'The Stonefolds' (blank verse), 'Daily Bread' (irregular unrhymed verse) and 'Fires' (rhymed dramatic monologues) he sings of the common sorrows and joys of everyday folk. 'Krindlesyke,' a play not written for dramatic production, is his most ambitious work. Edward Thomas (1878–1917) was another poet who drew upon everyday life in the countryside for the themes of his 'Poems' and 'Last Poems.' He was killed in action in 1917.

Hilaire Belloc (b. 1870), though of French birth, became greatly attached to the land of his adoption, and gloried in singing of the beauties of its countryside, and of its beer. He wrote some excellent comic verse in 'The Bad Child's Book of Beasts,' 'More Beasts for Worse Children,' and 'Cautionary Tales for Children,' while his

F

serious lyrics have memorable beauty. W. H. Davies (1871–1940), the tramp poet, was a natural lyrist of a very high order, and in such poems as 'Leisure,' 'A Great Time,' and 'The Kingfisher,' and many others, he has added to the store of imperishable English lyrics.

Walter de la Mare (b. 1873) is a poet of great individuality with the gift of being able to saturate his verse with a faery quality. He appears to move in a world of enchanted imagination. He also has the rare power of entering sympathetically into the working of the child mind, and his collection 'Peacock Pie' is deservedly popular with children. He is best studied in his collected works, where his pleasant variety can most be appreciated. Gordon Bottomley (b. 1874), whose most vigorous work is contained in his plays is nevertheless a poet of real power. His poem 'To Ironfounders and Others' sounds the note of revolt which is to be found in so much modern poetry. Bottomley's best work is collected in 'Poems of Thirty Years.'

G. K. Chesterton (1874–1936) as a poet had some points of resemblance to his friend Hilaire Belloc, and some of the journalistic gusto of Kipling, whose political views, however, were abhorrent to him. He used his verse as a medium for tilting against what he considered evils, and for airing in vigorous rhythm his prejudices and beliefs. In 'Lepanto' he reaches the heights.

Alfred Noyes (b. 1880) published his first volume of verse, 'The Loom of Years,' as long ago as 1902, and his careful and painstaking work has won for him higher praise in America than in his native land. He is a fine lyrist, and is one of the few recent poets to write an epic : 'Drake,' in blank verse. In 'The Torch Bearers' (1922–30), which relates, in blank verse interspersed with lyrics, the work of the great pioneers of thought and discovery, he produced his most ambitious work. The first two volumes are better than the final one, but all contain some splendid passages. His 'Tale of Old Japan' was set to music by Coleridge-Taylor.

Lascelles Abercrombie (1881–1938) was a very original poet who employed an unusual vocabulary. He wrote but few lyrics and specialized in the dramatic poem and poetic drama. The subjects he chooses are distressing, and at times full of horror, and the very strength of his presentation adds to their power. By the nature of his work, Abercrombie has secured a special place among modern English poets. The

most varied collection of his work is 'Emblems of Love.' Other important works are 'Interludes and Poems,' 'The Sale of St. Thomas,' and 'Twelve Idylls.'

John Drinkwater (1882–1937) was a writer of many charming lyrics. He will be remembered also as a playwright (*see* page 122) and as a writer of prose.

Humbert Wolfe (1885–1940), a Civil Servant by profession, produced work of sure poetic quality in his limited leisure. His ' Lampoons,' ' Kensington Gardens,' ' News of the Devil,' ' Cursory Rhymes,' and ' Requiem ' won for him an appreciative public, but it is probable that his magnificent verse translation of Rostand's ' Cyrano de Bergerac ' is his outstanding piece of work. Siegfried Sassoon (b. 1886) made a name as one of the poets of disillusion of the First Great War, but has since chiefly written much good prose in which similar opinions are expressed. Rupert Brooke (1887–1915), whose sonnet, ' If I should die,' is likely to endure as an immortal English poem, should be regarded as one of the poets of promise cut off by war.

It is not possible to deal at any length in this Outline with all the poets of importance, and in addition to those mentioned in some detail, the student should note the work of Charlotte Mew (1870–1928), James Elroy Flecker (1884–1915), D. H. Lawrence (1885–1930), Laurence Binyon (1869–1943), whose moving 'For the Fallen' was set to music by Elgar, Ralph Hodgson (b. 1871), Maurice Baring (b. 1874), Sir J. C. Squire (b. 1884), Edward Shanks (b. 1892), Robert Nichols (b. 1893), Wilfred Owen (1893–1918) and Edmund Blunden (b. 1896). Of the same generation, Edith Sitwell was one of the forerunners of the more modern poets, on whom she had considerable influence. Her ' Collected Poems ' were published in 1930.

T. S. Eliot, born in 1888 in the United States, became a naturalized British subject in 1927. He has been acclaimed as the leading spirit in the poetry of his time, and it is therefore important to examine his work and his outlook. It must be borne in mind that he started in a period of bitter disillusionment brought on by the First World War, and by the post-war failure of the politicians to build a land worthy for ' heroes to live in,' as the catchphrase of 1918 had it. His first great success was obtained with ' The Waste Land,' a poem of much obscurity to which the poet himself added explanatory notes which did not seem in any way to make it clearer. Eliot employs free verse as his medium and shows much technical skill in its use. In one of his most recent and satisfying poems, ' Little Gidding,' he explains his own ideal in the use of words. It is a form of writing

Where every word is at home,
Taking its place to support the others.
The word neither diffident nor ostentatious,
An easy commerce of the old and the new,
The common word exact without vulgarity,
The formal word precise but not pedantic,
The complete consort dancing together.

' Ash Wednesday ' appeared to competent critics as a distinct advance on ' The Waste Land,' and ' Murder in the Cathedral,' a Becket play written for Canterbury, was a fine piece of work with many noble passages, though at times marred by Eliot's frequent device of placing the sublime and the ridiculous side by side. The 'Collected Poems 1909-1935' gathered together most of his published poetry and included 'Sweeney Agonistes,' the choruses from 'The Rock,' 'Burnt Norton,' and also some poems in French. Later he published 'East Coker,' 'The Dry Salvages' and 'Little Gidding' which, with 'Burnt Norton,' were issued in 1944 as a single work, 'The Four Quartets.' 'Little Gidding' was a mystical poem written round the scene of the famous Nicholas Ferrar religious experiment.

Eliot has shown himself a master of rhythm, and employs a carefully wrought individual diction with an exquisite choice of words.

Let us see what Eliot himself says about ' modern ' poetry. In his interesting Preface to Anne Ridler's anthology, ' The Little Book of Modern Verse,' published in 1941, he writes :

Apart from these two great poets [Gerard Manley Hopkins and W. B. Yeats] we may take as within the term of modern poetry the work of those writers who had arrived at individual form and idiom during the four or five years immediately preceding the last war. Those who first found their speech during that war—whether we call them ' war poets ' or not—form a second age group ; and since 1918 at least two other poetic generations can be distinguished. One thing that must strike the reader of the last twenty years is the rapidity with which one literary generation has followed another ; and as each poet has continued to develop his own style, the impression may well be confusing. For this acceleration of change . . . the cause . . . is to be found, if at all, in the history of a changing and bewildered world . . . An explanation of what makes modern poetry would have to be an explanation of the whole modern world. . . .

As Michael Roberts says, prefacing his anthology ' New Signatures' (1932) :

It was inevitable that the growth of industrialism should give rise to ' difficult ' poetry. Because our civilization has hitherto depended directly on agriculture, and because our thoughts have hitherto made use of images taken from a rural life, our urban and industrial society leaves us uncomfortable and nostalgic. . . . The poet is . . . a person of unusual sensibility, he feels acutely emotional problems which other people feel vaguely, and it is his function not only to find the rhythms and images appropriate to the everyday experience of normal human beings, but also to find an imaginative solution of their problems, to make a new harmony out of strange and often apparently ugly material. . . .

Vers Libre. There is a considerable group of writers who have adopted the technique of free verse, as well as new modes of thought, often obscure and very difficult to follow. W. B. Yeats wrote :

Ten years after the war certain poets combined the modern vocabulary, the accurate record of the relevant facts, learnt from Eliot, with the sense of suffering of the war poets, that sense of suffering no longer passive, no longer an obsession of the nerves ; philosophy had made it part of all the mind. . . . They may seem obscure, confused, because of their concentrated passion, their interest in associations hitherto untravelled.

Janet Adam Smith, who in 1935 compiled ' Poems of Tomorrow' from 'The Listener,' touches on this matter of obscurity.

A supposed incomprehensibility is the charge most often brought against modern poetry. (But) too great an emphasis on factual meaning may make the reader blind to the other qualities of a poem ; it is possible to enjoy long before we comprehend.

Foremost among the poets who have arisen since 1930 is W. H. Auden (b. 1907), whose poetry has been well described as ' thought stripped to essentials,' approaching ' that integration, that acceptance of the dynamic nature of life which we are all seeking.' With Christopher Isherwood, he wrote the plays, 'The Dog Beneath the Skin,' ' The Ascent of F.6.' and ' On the Frontier,' all in noble verse with occasional prose.

We cannot do more than mention the names of Louis MacNeice, Stephen Spender, Cecil Day Lewis, the South African Roy Campbell (*see* p. 233), Charles Williams, W. J. Turner, Lady Dorothy Wellesley, Herbert Read, William Empson, Charles Madge, Dylan Thomas, Edward Thompson, John Lehmann and Laurence Whistler. All have made important contributions to modern poetry.

English Prose : Its First Eight Centuries

THE student confronted for the first time with even an elementary work on English prose may well ask himself why he should study it. What is the use, for example, of an anthology of English prose ? Is it compiled in order that the reader of it may be enabled to form some idea of the origin and development of the language at various periods of its history ? Yes ; and no. Philological considerations alone do not enter into such a work. There is as much fascination attached to the study of the growth of a language as there is to the pageant of history.

We apply our minds to classic prose, not only for the light it sheds upon the time in which it was written ; not merely because of its intrinsic value as a means of knowledge, but also because of its style. And for yet another reason—which some would place above all the rest—because behind the style is a living man. Herein, for the true student of literature, is the secret charm of our standard literature, and especially of our standard prose.

We learn, sooner or later, that the eloquence, the rhythm, the colour, the tone, the deft management of the period, are largely modelled by the great masters of English prose upon the works of men who wrote in Greece and Rome and the East some twenty centuries or more ago. But that is no cause for withholding our tribute of grateful admiration. What is allowed to the plastic artist, the painter, the sculptor, the architect, cannot be denied the artist in words. All highly developed art is rooted in classical tradition.

When we approach a work of living prose we may be certain that behind it is a great man, and something more—something of the character of the best of that man's contemporaries, of the spirit of the age in which he lived. Genius is the same in all ages, and writers in the rudest times, as well as those in more polished and enlightened eras, reached those limits beyond which the faculties of the human mind seem unable to penetrate. Thus, the elements of thought are only conditioned, not governed, by the outward circumstances of their expression.

Verse has been, certainly in English, far ahead of prose in the matter of settled law. Hence we can imitate the rhythm of Spenser without seeming old-fashioned. No cadence in modern verse is more pure, more perfect, than that of Shakespeare's sonnets and lyrics. But the prose of the masters and makers of it is even more personal ; it cannot be imitated.

All that can be attempted in the space available here is to indicate where the student must look for the leading examples of English prose, and to point out, as briefly as may be, the principal stages of our prose development.

Old English Prose. The chief characteristic of Anglo-Saxon prose reflects what is a chief characteristic of the English character—practicality. The language was direct and simple. Another point to be borne in mind is that, right up to and including the sixteenth century, our prose writers were, in the main, translators. Their works were, for the most part, educational, religious, and historical.

Influence of King Alfred. The coming of Alfred (849–901), who reigned over Wessex from 871 until his death, brought with it new life for English letters. At the time of his accession Alfred relates that no scholar could be found south of the Thames who could even read the Latin service books of the Church. The king gathered round him scholars from all parts and sent competent teachers to the monasteries. He himself began to translate Latin books into the West Saxon language, bringing in comment and original matter of his own. Among the books he translated and edited were : (1) ' The Handbook,' a collection of extracts on religious subjects. (2) The ' Cura Pastoralis ' of Gregory the Great, with a Preface by himself ; this has the distinction of being the first piece of English prose. (3) Bede's ' Ecclesiastical History of the English.' (4) Orosius's ' History of the World,' which he brought up to date, with accounts, taken down from direct narration, of the celebrated voyages of Ohthere to the White Sea, and Wulfstan to the Baltic. (5) ' The Consolation of Philosophy ' of Boethius. Of this work Chaucer also made a translation.

One of the most important pieces of work due to Alfred's inspiration, and of which some portion was probably written by himself, is the Anglo-Saxon Chronicle. This became a contemporary document giving a summary account of the historical events of each year, and it continued until 1154. It is not only an historical document of the highest importance, but it is of great value to the philologist in showing the continuous development of the language from the accounts of fighting between Alfred and the Danes to the story of the deplorable state of England at the end of Stephen's reign. It is, indeed, a national possession without parallel, and should be a source of pride to every Englishman.

It is difficult to overrate the importance of Alfred's work for English literature and scholarship. He was, in truth, not only King of Wessex, but King of English Letters as well.

During the tenth century the most important writer was the scholarly monk Ælfric, who wrote vigorous homilies in a flexible prose. Apart from his work and some notable translations from the Bible, there is no outstanding prose before the Norman Conquest.

To the development of Old English a period is placed covering the Danish and Norman conquests and on through the years 1150–1350. During the first of these two centuries the old inflections were broken up, and in the second, numerous French words were incorporated in the English language. Middle English, of which Chaucer was the great literary artificer, flourished from 1350 to 1500, and since the latter date our language and literature are classed as Modern English.

Language differed somewhat then, as it does now, according to the part of England in which it was spoken. A Yorkshireman today still speaks a dialect markedly different from that of his Cockney relative, both in pronunciation and in idiom. In those more distant days the dialects spoken by those who lived north of the Humber, in the Midlands, in East Anglia, in Kent, in the South, and in Wessex, showed still greater divergences. It was the East Midland dialect which finally triumphed. The Universities of Oxford and Cambridge, and the growing city of London, came within its influence, and in Chaucer's day it became the literary language of England.

Middle English Prose. As was the case with the Anglo-Saxon and Early English writers, their successors of the fourteenth century concerned themselves chiefly with the work of translation. Several of Chaucer's works are of this nature—two of the famous 'Canterbury Tales': 'The Tale of Melibeus,' borrowed from Albertano of Brescia, and 'The Persones (Parson's) Tale,' a sermon

derived from Frere Lorens ; the unfinished 'Treatise on the Astrolabe'; and his 'Boethius.'

The prose of this period is neither distinguished nor extensive. 'The Ayenbite of Inwit,' or 'Remorse of Conscience,' is a translation from the French by Dan Michel, a monk of Canterbury. Richard Rolle of Hampole, a hermit, wrote prose on religious matters. Some of this has been considered of such value as to justify the recent publication of a modernized version of a portion of his theological essays. 'The Wohunge of Ure Lauerd' ('The Wooing of our Lord') and 'The Ureisun (Orison) of God Almihti' show more than usual merit. But, without doubt, the most widely popular religious work in prose was 'Ancren Riwle (or 'Anchoresses' Rule') which by its homeliness and fervour makes a very direct appeal. As an example of its style, here is a very brief extract (in modernized spelling) from the address of Christ to the Soul :

If thy love be sold, I have bought it with love above all other. And if thou sayest that thou wilt not value it so cheaply, but thou wilt have yet more, name what it shall be : set a price upon thy love. Thou shalt not say so much that I will not give thee much more for thy love. Wilt thou have castles and kingdoms ? Wilt thou rule the world ? I will do better for thee, I will make thee, with all this, queen of heaven.

By this time Paris had become famous as a University, and its influence was widespread. Later it was to link up with Oxford. Latin was the *lingua franca* of the learned world, and the language of instruction used at the Universities. Thus, to whatever University a student went, a knowledge of Latin opened the door for him in the subject he wished to study. Naturally, too, through the work of the Universities and the influence of the Church, which conducted its services in Latin, a considerable number of books were written in that language. We are not here concerned with their literary aspects ; but their subject-matter had an important influence on the medieval mind.

It was the time, too, when men were beginning to make European reputations as scholars. One such example was Peter Abelard (1079–1142), a lecturer at the University of Paris. Helen Waddell's novel, 'Peter Abelard,' gives a most moving picture of this unhappy man, and a brilliant description of medieval France. Among his English pupils was John of Salisbury, who was in the service of Thomas à Becket, and is said to have been with the archbishop when he was murdered. John became Bishop of Chartres, and wrote a number of learned treatises in Latin.

That the French influence was by no means a negligible quantity is evident if we examine the work of Chaucer alone. Following upon the death of Chaucer, however, the French wars and the Wars of the Roses once more set back the clock of English literary activity, and there is but little of interest to chronicle, save the introduction of the printing press by William Caxton (c. 1422–91), till we reach the age of the Tudors, whence may be dated the beginning of Modern English.

Early Masters of English Prose

ONE example of the manner in which the English appropriated French literature is to be found in the anonymous translation of 'The Voyage and Travels of Sir John Mandeville,' who assumed the name of Jehan de Bourgogne, a work which is still read on account of its naïve descriptions of the marvellous. This book is a remarkable literary forgery and may possibly be the work of Jean d'Oultremouse, a writer of history and fables. But especially interesting is it to ponder the influence of the romantic legends of the Norman poets known as the trouvères. These deal with Alexander the Great, King Arthur and the Knights of the Round Table, Charlemagne, and the Crusaders.

Malory. The origin of the Arthurian legends (*see* also Lesson 6) is Celtic—partly Welsh and partly Breton. 'Morte d'Arthur,' by Sir Thomas Malory, (1470), so delighted the heart of Sir Walter Scott that he described it as being indisputably the best prose romance of which the English language can boast. Many writers of the 19th century, Tennyson among them, are the eternal debtors of Malory, whose work, as printed with all the affection of a great and sympathetic craftsman by William Caxton, played no small part in the making of Elizabethan prose.

For his black-letter folio of this work—of which only two copies are known to exist, though a number of reprints are obtainable—Caxton wrote a preface, in which he said, in language that indicates the rapidity of the change from Chaucer's :

I have after the symple connyng that God hath sente to me, under the favour and correctyon of al noble lordes and gentylmen, enprysed to enprynte a book of the noble hystoryes of the said kynge Arthur, and of certeyn of his knyghtes, after a copye unto me delyvered, whyche copye syr Thomas Malorye dyd take oute of certeyn bookes of Frensshe and reduced it into Englysshe. And I, accordyng to my copye, have doon sette it

in enprynte, to the entente that noblemen may see and lerne the noble acts of chyvalrye, the jentyl and vertuous dedes, that somme knyghtes used in tho dayes, by whyche they came to honour, and how they that were vycious were punysshed, and often put to shame and rebuke, humbly bysechying al noble lordes and ladyes, wyth al other estates, of what estate or degree they been of, that shal see and rede in this sayd book and werke, that they take the good and honest actes in their remembrance, and to folowe the same.

A favourite passage from Malory's own text is his account of the passing of Arthur. How English it is, apart from the spelling, may be seen from the following modernized extract :

And when they were at the water-side, even fast by the bank hoved a little barge with many fair ladies in it, and among them all was a Queen, and they all had black hoods, and they all wept and shrieked when they saw King Arthur. ' Now put me into the barge,' said the King ; and so they did softly. And there received him three Queens, and in one of their laps King Arthur laid his head, and then that Queen said, 'Ah, dear brother ! why have ye tarried so long from me ? Alas, this wound on your head hath caught overmuch cold.' . . . Then Sir Bedivere cried, 'Ah, my lord Arthur, what shall become of me now ye go from me, and leave me here alone among mine enemies?' 'Comfort thyself,' said the King, 'and do as well as thou mayst; for in me is no trust to trust in. For I will go into the Vale of Avillon, to heal me of my grievous wound. And if thou hear never more of me, pray for my soul.'

Froissart. Malory's monumental work, following that of Chaucer and Gower, gave to English literature something of the glamour of chivalry and romance ; and this influence was followed in its turn by the translation of Froissart's 'Chronicles' by Lord Berners (1467–1533), who also translated 'The Golden Book of Marcus Aurelius.'

Jean Froissart, like one of his own heroes, set out on his travels in quest of adventure. He visited England twice, in the reigns of

Edward III—when he was secretary to Queen Philippa for some years—and of Richard II; he was the guest of David Bruce in Scotland; he journeyed in Aquitaine with the Black Prince, and was in Italy, possibly with Chaucer and Petrarch. Ten years before his death he settled in Flanders. His 'Chronicles' deal with the period between 1326 and 1400, and are drawn from his travels and experiences. They are among the most vivid and picturesque things in European literature. Sir Walter Scott considered his history had less the air 'of a narrative than of a dramatic representation.'

Paston Letters. The student of fifteenth-century England should not omit to pay some attention to the 'Paston Letters' (1422–1509). These documents, which are about a thousand in number and were not printed in full until the present century, were written during the reigns of Henry VI, Edward IV, Richard III, and Henry VII, by members of an East Anglian family. They not only throw a flood of light on the social customs of fifteenth-century England, but serve to indicate that the civil strife of the Wars of the Roses which then divided families did not altogether crush out either the desire for, or the means of, learning.

Sir Thomas More (1478–1535) was a man whose thoughts were far in advance of his time. His theories were essentially those of a humane man and a philosopher; his practice, as Chancellor of Henry VIII, was at variance with his avowed sympathies, but undoubtedly he was bound by the legal conventions of his period. He was beheaded for refusing to acknowledge any other head of the Church than the Pope. His best known work, the 'Utopia,' a political satire, was written in Latin, and translated into English by Ralph Robynson thirty-five years later. It deals with the social defects of English life, and pictures an imaginary island where communism is the rule, education common to the sexes, and religious toleration general. The title is derived from two Greek words, meaning 'Nowhere.' More also wrote a number of English works of which the most notable are his 'Historie of Richard the Third' and his 'Dialogue' against Lutherans.

Ascham. As our Anglo-Saxon forebears fought against the influence of Norman-French, so Roger Ascham (1515–68), the tutor of Queen Elizabeth and afterwards her secretary, reflected the native English spirit in his vigorous prose and his antagonism to the 'Italianate Englishman,' who modelled his conduct and his studies on what he or others brought back from Italy in those early days of Continental intercourse and travel. Ascham was devoted to the old English pastime of archery, and wrote a defence of it in English, 'Toxophilus,' which he dedicated to Henry VIII, adding an address to the gentlemen and yeomen of England, in which occurs a passage that forms at once an apology for and a defence of his native tongue:

> As for the Latin or Greek tongue, everything is so excellently done in them that none can do better; in the English tongue, on the contrary, everything is in a manner so meanly, both for the matter and handling, that no man can do worse. . . .
>
> He that will write well in any tongue must follow this counsel of Aristotle, to speak as the common people do, to think as wise men do.

There are several important works on education which belong to the sixteenth century, but Ascham's 'Scholemaster' is the first in point of time, and contains not a little advice the value of which is of a permanent character. One of the truths that he urges is being propagated in our own day: namely, the need of awakening in the mind of the pupil a real interest in his work.

In this connexion the following excerpt from the 'Toxophilus' has interest, and serves also as an illustration of Ascham's easy and pointed style:

> If men would go about matters which they should do and be fit for, and not such things which wilfully they desire, and yet be unfit for, verily greater matters in the commonwealth than shooting should be in better case than they be. . . . This perverse judgment of men hindereth nothing so much as learning, because commonly those that be unfitted for learning be chiefly set to learning. As if a man nowadays have two sons, the one impotent, weak, sickly, lisping, stuttering, and stammering, or having any mis-shape in his body, what does the father of such one commonly say? This boy is fit for nothing else but to set to learning and make a priest of. . . . This fault, and many such like, might be soon wiped away if fathers would bestow their children always on that thing whereunto nature hath ordained them most apt and fit.

Henry VIII, who encouraged Ascham, must have it placed to his credit also that he gave similar aid to Sir Thomas Elyot (c. 1490–1546), who wrote 'The Governour,' the first book on the subject of education written and printed in English. The first Latin-English dictionary was compiled in this reign.

LESSON 31

Religion's Part in the Shaping of English Prose

As poetry, in a chronological sense, takes precedence of prose in the history of English literature, so religious works precede secular in influencing the growth of English prose. The services of the early translators of the Bible cannot be overestimated. First among these translators was John Wycliffe (c. 1325–84). It is important to remember, however, that neither the 'Wycliffe Bible' nor any of its successors was the work of one man, although 'Wycliffe's Bible,' 'Tyndale's Bible' and 'Coverdale's Bible' are common terms. According to Cardinal Gasquet, Wycliffe's Bible was the work of the English bishops.

Wycliffe. Before Wycliffe's time only portions of the Scripture had been translated into English. Wycliffe—to follow the accepted story—set himself a few years before his death to the task of producing the first complete English Bible. By 1382 he had completed the New Testament. His friend, Nicholas of Hereford, translated most of the Old Testament and the Apocrypha. John Purvey, a pupil of the Reformer, revised the work four years after Wycliffe's death. The translation (or paraphrase), which was made from the Vulgate (or Latin version) was originally issued in manuscript form ; of this 150 copies are still extant. Written as it was for the common people, it is remarkable to find with how much ease 'Wycliffe's Bible' can still be read. Wycliffe was a Yorkshireman, and we are told that when, some years ago, several long passages were read to a congregation in his native county, not only were they understood by the hearers, but almost every word was found to be still in use.

Tyndale. The work of Wycliffe was carried on and improved by William Tyndale (c. 1492–1536), a pupil of Erasmus, the great co-worker with Martin Luther in the Reformation. When Erasmus published his Latin version of the New Testament in 1516 he declared :

I long that the husbandman should sing portions of them (the Gospels) as he follows the plough, that the weaver should hum them to the tune of his shuttle, that the traveller should beguile with their stories the tedium of his journey.

Tyndale, who was a good Greek scholar, studied Hebrew for the purpose in hand, and,

while consulting the Vulgate, went back to the originals as the basis of his version. He was helped in his task by a fugitive friar named Roy and others. It was 'Tyndale's Bible' which, revised by Miles Coverdale (c. 1488–1568)—the first complete printed English Bible—and edited and re-edited as 'Cromwell's Bible' (1539), and 'Cranmer's Bible' or 'The Great Bible' (1540), was set up in every parish church in England, in some cases being chained to the lectern—hence the term 'Chain Bible.'

The Bible, to quote Stopford Brooke, 'got north into Scotland and made the Lowland English more like the London English. It passed over to the Protestant settlements in Ireland.' After its revision in 1611, it went as the Authorized Version with the Puritan Fathers to New England and fixed the standard of English in America. There had been printed meanwhile the 'Geneva Bible,' sometimes referred to as the 'Breeches Bible' from the rendering of 'aprons' as 'breeches' in Gen. iii. 7. It was a work handier in size than its predecessors, in Roman type and with the text divided into verses pithily annotated.

In Edward VI's reign Thomas Cranmer (1489–1556) edited the English Prayer Book (1549–52). 'Its English,' Stopford Brooke notes, 'is a good deal mixed with Latin words, and its style is sometimes weak or heavy, but on the whole it is a fine example of stately prose. It also steadied our speech.'

Religious and Philosophic Writers. The development of English rhetoric and English philosophic and religious thought during the 16th and 17th centuries may be studied in the writings of Hugh Latimer (c. 1485–1555), Bishop of Worcester, whose sermons well sustain the homely and direct character of his native tongue ; John Knox (c.1505–72), the Scottish reformer and historian ; John Foxe (1516–87), whose 'Actes and Monuments,' commonly known as 'Foxe's Book of Martyrs,' 'gave to the people of all over England a book which, by its simple style, the ease of its story-telling, and its popular charm, made the very peasants who heard it read feel what is meant by literature'; Richard Hooker (c. 1553–1600), author of 'The Laws of Ecclesiasticall Politie,' a great theologian whose memory is enshrined in 'Walton's Lives,' and whose character is fitly indicated on his monument at Bishopsbourne, Kent, as 'judicious'; and Jeremy Taylor (1613–67), Bishop of Down and Connor, the author of 'Holy Living' and 'Holy Dying,' and a voluminous writer who, in the words of his friend Bishop Rust, of Dromore, 'had the good humour of a gentleman, the eloquence of an orator, the fancy of a poet, the acuteness of a schoolman, the profoundness of a philosopher, the wisdom of a chancellor, the reason of an angel, and the piety of a saint.'

Equally important to the student of English literature are the writings of Thomas Hobbes (1588–1679), a philosopher who applied the principles of geometry to the judgement of human conduct and in his 'Leviathan,' 'De Cive,' 'Treatise on Human Nature,' and other works, showed himself to be 'the first of all our prose writers whose style may be said to be uniform and correct and adapted carefully to the subjects on which he wrote.' Thomas Fuller (1608–61), in his best-known work, 'Worthies of England,' shows admirable narrative faculty, 'with a nervous brevity and point almost new to English, and a homely directness ever shrewd and never vulgar.' The jurist John Selden (1584–1654), a distinguished scholar, is memorable for his 'Table Talk.'

Sir Thomas Browne (1605–82) was a Norwich physician of whom Sir Edmund Gosse said: 'among English prose writers of the highest merit there are few who have more consciously, more successfully, aimed at the translation of temperament by style.' His 'Religio Medici' shows profound spiritual insight, expressed in glowing imaginative prose. 'Hydriotaphia, or Urn Burial' is a discussion of burial customs, rich in imagery; and 'Vulgar Errors' an entertaining account of contemporary beliefs, in which shrewdness and credulity are happily blended.

John Bunyan (1628–88), the inspired tinker, most zealous of Puritans and author of some sixty books, is chiefly famous for his masterpiece 'The Pilgrim's Progress,' in which Man tests all the delights of the world and all the resources of the intellect, rejects them as dangerous or inadequate, and finds religion the only sure road through life, even though beset with doctrinal dangers. The book sprang at once into fame, 100,000 copies being sold during the author's life-time. The first part of it was written in Bedford gaol, where he had been imprisoned as a Nonconformist preacher under the Conventicle Act. Next to 'The Pilgrim's Progress,' Bunyan's most famous books are 'The Holy War' and 'Grace Abounding'; the former contains variations on the theme of his masterpiece, while the latter is an intimate autobiography, in which his deeply religious experiences are vividly described.

Another eminent Puritan writer is Richard Baxter (1615–91); his life is an example of self-help, and his writings are among the finest specimens extant of vigorous English. Of greater value to the general reader is John Locke (1632–1704), author of 'Two Treatises on Civil Government,' 'An Essay Concerning Toleration,' 'An Essay Concerning Human Understanding,' and a work especially to be commended to students on 'The Conduct of the Understanding'; he is considered to be the unquestioned founder of the analytic philosophy of mind.

Gilbert Burnet (1643–1715), bishop of Salisbury, was author of a 'History of the Reformation' and 'History of My Own Times,' written from the Whig standpoint.

Discovered in manuscript form in the early years of the present century, the mystic Thomas Traherne (c. 1636–74) is remarkable as a poet and even more remarkable as a prose-writer. We give a passage from 'Centuries of Meditation':

The corn was orient and immortal wheat which never should be reaped nor was ever sown. I thought it had stood from everlasting to everlasting. The dust and stones of the street were as precious as gold; the gates were at first the end of the world. The green trees when I saw them first through one of the gates transported and ravished me; their sweetness and unusual beauty made my heart to leap, and almost mad with ecstasy, they were such strange and wonderful things. The Men! O what venerable and reverend creatures did the aged seem! Immortal Cherubims! And young men glittering and sparkling angels, and maids strange seraphic pieces of life and beauty! Boys and girls tumbling in the street were moving jewels: I knew not that they were born or should die. But all things abided eternally as they were in their proper places. Eternity was manifest in the Light of the Day, and something infinite behind everything appeared, which talked with my expectation and moved my desire. The City seemed to stand in Eden or to be built in Heaven. The streets were mine, and so were the sun and moon and stars, and all the world was mine; and I the only spectator and enjoyer of it.

Everyone who aspires to a sound appreciation of our literature should have firsthand knowledge of these writers, not only because of what they have to teach of philosophy and theology, but because of their charm of style, their wisdom, their vision, and their humanity.

English Prose in the 17th Century

BOTH Spenser and Shakespeare wrote some prose. Spenser's 'View of the Present State of Ireland' is written in a most pleasing style. Shakespeare's prose has been the theme of many commentators. The student is recommended to study the 'men in buckram' section of 'Henry IV.' The 'Arcadia' and the 'Defence of Poesie' of Sir Philip Sidney (1554–86) should also be studied in this connexion.

Historians. The first popular English history in the language is 'The History of England to the Time of Edward III' of the poet Samuel Daniel (1562–1619). After Daniel's work may be considered the 'History of the World,' written in the Tower by Sir Walter Raleigh (1552–1618), and to be read for its human and personal interest more than on account of its intrinsic value as history. Edward Hyde, first Earl of Clarendon (1609–74), friend of poets like Jonson and Waller, wrote a 'History of the Rebellion.' This was modelled on the style of the Roman historian Tacitus, and is notable for its biographical value.

The 'Life of Colonel Hutchinson,' the Puritan, by his widow, Lucy Hutchinson (b. 1620), is one of the most delightful of biographies, with a historical character for subject, and, taken up as a study, will be read through for the charm and simplicity of the narrative.

To the domain of history and antiquarian study belong the writings of William Camden (1551–1623), John Selden (1584–1654), John Stow (c. 1525–1605), Raphael Holinshed (c. 1520–80), from whom Shakespeare drew much of his history, and William Harrison (1534–93). Mention must also be made here of the invaluable diaries of Samuel Pepys (1633–1703) and John Evelyn (1620–1706). Pepys's diary in the original, comprehending six volumes, was closely written in shorthand by the author, and was included in the collection of books and pictures bequeathed by him to Magdalene College, Cambridge. The shorthand MS. was not deciphered till early in the 19th century by the Rev. J. Smith, and first published in an abridged version in 1825. Besides throwing a brilliant light on the manners, personages and events of the Restoration period—the diary deals with the years 1659–1669—it presents an amazing, because absolutely honest, psychological study of Pepys himself.

John Evelyn's diary (first published in 1818) covers a period of seventy years; his intellect remained fresh and vigorous to the last. His pen was a busy one, describing Court life after the Restoration, travel scenes and the countryside.

The 'Familiar Letters' of James Howell (1593–1666) contain much contemporary history and display both brilliant wit and keen observation. They are the earliest written series of English letters which may be styled literary. We must mention, too, the exquisite epistles of Dorothy Osborne (1627–95), afterwards the wife of Sir William Temple, diplomatist and essayist.

Pamphlets and Essays. The meaning of the word essay is 'a testing.' As we understand it today, an essay is a valuation of a subject, usually of a literary or social nature, from the standpoint of the writer. The 'Essays of Montaigne,' the translation of which by John Florio (c. 1553–1625) preserves for us a vigorous and perennially delightful example of Elizabethan prose, hardly come within the limits of the essay as we understand the word.

The Elizabethan and Jacobean pamphlets were, in a sense, essays, but we see in them perhaps more distinctly the beginning of the modern newspaper, because they were published for controversial purposes. They form in themselves a somewhat absorbing branch of literary and historical study.

A number of the writers of these pamphlets also wrote tales, so that while the 'Euphues' of Lyly is sometimes regarded as the earliest English novel, it is not quite isolated as an example of English prose narrative. Even if we leave Sidney's 'Arcadia' out of the question, there are the tales as well as the pamphlets of Robert Greene; of Thomas Lodge (c. 1558–1625), whose 'Rosalynde' inspired Shakespeare's 'As You Like It'; and Thomas Nash (1567–1601), whose 'Jack Wilton' is said to have provided the prototype of Falstaff.

Londoners who wish to learn how their Elizabethan predecessors lived will find a world of entertainment in 'The Gull's Hornbook' of Thomas Dekker (1570–1637). The most interesting and permanent of all the pamphlets is the 'Areopagitica'

—so named after the Aeropagus, the open-air court of Athens in which matters of public concern were freely ventilated—a trenchant plea for the liberty of the printing press, by John Milton (1608–74). Another of the great poet's prose works was the 'Doctrine and Discipline of Divorce,' in which he attacked the sacramental view of marriage and argued that incompatibility of character or contrariety of mind should be constituted just grounds for divorce.

The first of the English essayists proper is Francis Bacon, Lord Verulam (1561–1626). The student can have no better guide than is provided in the fiftieth of Bacon's fifty-eight 'Essays'—the one entitled 'Of Studies' —full-charged with wise and practical advice, perfectly exemplifying Bacon's method and perspicuity of style :

> Histories make men wise ; poets witty ; the mathematics subtile ; natural philosophy deep ; moral grave ; logic and rhetoric able to contend.

Writing 'Of Death,' he says :

> Men fear death, as children fear to go into the dark : and as that natural fear in children is increased with tales, so is the other. Certainly the contemplation of death as the wages of sin and passage to another world is holy and religious ; but the fear of it as a tribute due unto nature is weak. . . . It is worthy the observing that there is no passion in the mind of man so weak but it mates and masters the fear of death ; and therefore death is no such terrible enemy, when a man hath so many attendants about him that can win the combat of him. Revenge triumphs over death ; love slights it ; honour aspireth to it ; grief flyeth to it ; fear pre-occupateth it ; nay, we read, after Otho the Emperor had slain himself, pity, which is the tenderest of affections, provoked many to die out of mere compassion to their sovereign, and as the truest sort of followers.

Of these 'Essays' Hallam rightly declared that it 'would be derogatory to any educated man to be unacquainted with them.' They deal with the essentials of life as recorded by a man of the acutest intellect ; they fail only where the intellectual predominates unduly over the emotions.

Next to Bacon's 'Essays' should be ranked the 'Discoveries' of Ben Jonson, which Swinburne prefers before them, and Professor Saintsbury describes as coming 'in character as in time midway between Hooker and Dryden.' Jonson's 'Discoveries' have been too long neglected. There is a great deal in them concerning education and study that will generously reward the most careful attention.

After Jonson, considered as an essayist, come Abraham Cowley (1618–67), whose language is at once simple and graceful ; and Sir William Temple (1628–99), whose essays (' Miscellanea') contain much sensible matter written in an easy style.

It is difficult to classify the 'Anatomy of Melancholy' of Robert Burton (1577–1640), but Johnson and Charles Lamb both greatly admired it ; it is full of quaint and curious learning, of a profound earnestness, irony, and somewhat bitter humour. Burton explains that he wrote of melancholy 'to comfort one sorrow with another . . . make an Antidote out of that which was the prime cause of my disease.' The 'Microcosmographie,' a collection of character sketches by John Earle, bishop of Salisbury (c. 1601–65), is at once of social and philosophical value, but stands, like the 'Anatomy,' by itself. Three other books that demand notice are the 'Lives' and 'Compleat Angler' of Izaak Walton (1593–1683), the first a gem of literary biography—containing the five lives of Donne, Wotton, Hooker, Herbert and Sanderson, and one of Dr. Johnson's favourite books—the second one of the first of 'country books' ; and the 'Autobiography' of Lord Herbert of Cherbury (1583–1648), which Swinburne placed among 'the hundred best books.'

Rise of Criticism. The place of honour as the first English critic belongs to John Dryden. In the view of Lowell, Dryden, more than any other single writer, contributed, as well by precept as example, to free English prose from 'the cloister of pedantry,' and by his masterly handling to give it 'suppleness of movement and the easier air of the modern world.'

> His style (Lowell continues) has the familiar dignity so hard to attain, perhaps unattainable except by one who feels that his own position is assured. Swift was as idiomatic, but not so elevated ; Burke more splendid, but not so equally luminous. That his style was no easy acquisition, though, of course, the aptitude was innate, he himself tells us, when he tells us that the Court, the College, and the Town must be joined in the perfect knowledge of a tongue.

The introductions to Dryden's works are specially worthy of study. The famous 'Essay on Dramatic Poesy' has already been commended. Nearly the whole of Dryden's criticisms were edited by W. P. Ker in his 'Essays of John Dryden.'

LESSON 33

Prose Masters of the Early 18th Century

WHAT the prose of the eighteenth century may lack in colour and warmth, as compared with the prose of the seventeenth century, it gains in general smoothness, perspicacity and correctness. It has been styled 'aristocratic,' and this description is in the main a true one. But at the period with which we are now to deal the 'aristocracy of intellect' was to a great extent employed in the furtherance of ends more practical, or at least more partisan, than literary. These ends were in part political, in part ecclesiastical, in part ethical. Thus the literature of the time must be studied in connexion with its political, religious and social history. Journalism, which had its rise in the controversial pamphlets of Elizabethan and Jacobean times, received in the eighteenth century a new impetus, and the novel assumed a more definite shape.

Defoe. Daniel Defoe (c. 1659–1731) is often regarded as the father of modern English journalism, and the forerunner of Richardson and Fielding. Today, except as the author of two or three books, one of them of world-wide repute, Defoe is half forgotten. In his lifetime, however, he played many parts, and over 250 distinct works bear his name. Numbers of pamphlets and treatises flowed from his pen. Educated as a Dissenter, he had the cause of Protestant Nonconformity at heart. As an able and vigorous controversial writer, he supported William III's Whig policy against the High Church Tories. In the famous treatise, 'The Shortest Way with Dissenters' (1702), Defoe with scathing satire advocated the complete extirpation of the dissenters, and this with such surface plausibility that his High Church opponents were at first deceived, and afterwards being the more enraged against him because of their deception, secured his committal for trial at the Old Bailey, where he was sentenced to be fined and imprisoned during the queen's pleasure, and to stand three days in the pillory. Viewing him there, the sympathetic crowd, instead of insulting him, drank his health.

'Robinson Crusoe,' and the 'Journal of the Plague Year' (fictitious but a masterpiece of reality) are enough to secure for Defoe pre-eminence as a master of the art of literary illusion. He had defects. He was curiously heedless of chronology ; he was weak, on the whole, as a delineator of character. But he was an essential 'realist,' with creative imagination ; immensely vigorous, clear-sighted and dramatic, he remains one of the greatest of English writers. Sir Walter Raleigh, the modern critic, says :

> With Defoe the art of fiction came to be the art of grave, imperturbable lying, in which art the best instructor is the truth. And it was to no reputed master of romance, but to recorders of fact, biographers, writers of voyages and travels, historians and annalists, that Defoe served his apprenticeship.

As the author of 'Captain Singleton,' ' Moll Flanders,' 'Colonel Jack' and other works of a kindred character, Defoe stood brilliant sponsor to the novel of crime. In 1704 he started a 'Review' which was the forerunner of 'The Tatler,' 'The Spectator' and 'The Rambler.' He has been called the typical journalist. His 'Robinson Crusoe,' written when he was fifty-eight, is as immortal as 'The Pilgrim's Progress' or 'Don Quixote.' Like these two works and one other that we shall have to mention almost immediately, 'Robinson Crusoe' may be read by the young on account of the narrative alone, and by older readers as an allegory. The sequel, less well known and inferior, possesses considerable interest.

Swift. As a pamphleteer Jonathan Swift (1667–1745) affords an interesting companion study to Defoe. Swift was, however, by far the greater man. His power as a pamphleteer may be gauged by a consideration of the famous 'Letters,' signed 'M. B. Drapier,' and familiarly known as 'The Drapier Letters ' (1724). In these compositions he attacked the iniquitous 'job' by which a certain William Wood, a hardware-man and a bankrupt, was granted a patent for supplying Ireland with copper coin. The 'Drapier Letters' defeated this project ; and though it is often said that the ensuing popularity of their author among the Irish people was unpalatable to him, his bequests to Irish charities seem to negative the idea that he had no sympathy for the people amid whom his lot was for a long time cast ; he always sympathized with sufferers from injustice and had 'a perfect hatred of tyranny and oppression,' wherever he found it.

'The Tale of a Tub' is the most comprehensive example of all that is characteristic of his prose style. As sailors were supposed to throw out a tub to a whale to prevent it from colliding with their ship, so Swift thought by his 'Tale' to afford such temporary diversion to the wits and free-thinkers of his day as to prevent them from injuring the State by the propagation of wild theories respecting religion and politics. But his satiric genius, his fiery imagination and his keen eye for 'the seamy side' imparted to 'The Tale of a Tub' qualities that disguised his avowed object, and at the very outset placed an insurmountable obstacle in the way of his ecclesiastical preferment.

'The Battle of the Books,' which, with 'The Tale of a Tub,' helped to make Swift famous, takes a witty part in a controversy that was raging amongst his literary contemporaries over the respective claims of modern and ancient literature.

Something like one-fourth of Swift's most remarkable work, 'Gulliver's Travels,' and a great part of his other writings are marred by coarseness. But of 'Gulliver's Travels' enough is so delightful as romance as to rival both 'Robinson Crusoe' and 'The Pilgrim's Progress.' Important as a satire, 'Gulliver's Travels' has a distinct value as an autobiography. While Defoe excelled in the art of making fiction read like fact, Swift, with the finest skill, cultivated a drastic simplicity and homeliness of style, the accumulated effect of which was so formidable as to afford a permanent object-lesson in the art that conceals art where the writing of nervous English prose is concerned. But with all its carefully calculated simplicity, the English of Jonathan Swift is never pedestrian or devoid of sparkle or variety.

Students of Swift's life will find in his work much that reflects his unhappy experiences. They will be especially indebted to the 'Journal to Stella' (Esther Johnson, whose tutor he was) for many valuable pages of autobiography and for many sidelights on the manners of the time. A staunch friend, in spite of his intermittent bitterness of spirit, his correspondence with Pope and Gay also affords biographical material.

Steele and Addison. Sir Richard Steele (1672–1729), the friend and schoolfellow of Joseph Addison (1672–1719), was, like Swift, born in Ireland, but in this fact lies the sole resemblance between the saturnine Dean of St. Patrick's and the genial 'scallywag' who originated 'The Tatler,' wrote part of 'The Spectator,' founded 'The Guardian' and worshipped Addison.

In 1709 Steele started '**The Tatler**,' anonymously. It was a small sheet, sold for a penny, appearing three times a week, and designed to expose 'the false arts of life, to pull off the disguises of cunning, vanity and affectation, and to recommend a general simplicity in our dress, our discourse, and our behaviour.' Part of 'The Tatler' was devoted to news. When his pen-name of Isaac Bickerstaff, which he borrowed from a diverting pamphlet by Swift, became useless as a disguise, Steele founded 'The Spectator.' 'The Tatler' extended to 271 numbers, of which Steele wrote 188 ; his friend Addison contributed 42, and they were jointly responsible for 36. 'The Spectator,' which was published daily, ran to 635 numbers, of which Addison wrote 274 and Steele 240.

Literature and Morals. The wholesome effect of these publications on the manners of the period can hardly be exaggerated. Both the style of writing and the tone of conversation were improved as a result of their influence. Contrary to the custom of the time, women were treated in Steele's pages with genuine respect. It is generally conceded that while Addison's style is the more finished, Steele's is more marked by liveliness of invention. Addison usually wrote at leisure, Steele often in a 'white heat.' The papers took the form sometimes of moral and critical discourses, sometimes of short stories of domestic life, in the writing of which, and as an essayist, Steele excelled.

The plan of 'The Spectator' was laid at a club, and in the second number, written by Steele, we are given the first sketches of the members. It is a remarkable testimony to the skill of Steele's work that the characters stand out so clearly before us. The immortal baronet Sir Roger de Coverley is understood to be Steele's invention. Steele, as Hazlitt remarked, seems to have gone into his study chiefly to set down what he observed out of doors. Addison, on the other hand, drew most of his inspiration from books.

Not the least of Addison's services to literature was the attention he gave in 'The Spectator' to Milton. These papers should be studied by all who desire to appreciate the style and value of literary criticism in Addison's time. On the whole we read Addison today not so much for the value of what he has to say as for the way in which he says it.

That his style is not without its defects goes without saying. He sacrificed everything to elegance, that is to rhythm or melody of phrase. He shows, too, a somewhat limited vocabulary at times, and is apt to repeat unnecessarily his ideas and his images. Occasional looseness of construction must also be attributed to him ; but in the essay this is not without its advantages, helping to lightness of touch, which is scarcely possible where the writer aims at rounded periods or stately, slow-moving sentences.

There are not wanting those who think that Addison has long been something of a fetish with writers on literary style—'read an essay of Addison's every day' has been the injunction of our literary mentors for generations—and that in the not very distant future his chief interest will be historical. But such authorities as Johnson and Macaulay have weight concerning the high qualities of Addison's limpid style. Addison's sentences, according to Johnson, have neither studied amplitude nor affected brevity ; his periods, though not diligently rounded, are voluble and easy. 'Never,' said Macaulay, 'had the English language been written with such sweetness, grace and facility.' And if in the future his influence on individuals is less immediate, its effect on 18th-century prose can never be gainsaid.

LESSON 34

Great Writers of the Johnsonian Age

THE autocrat before whom every 'quill-driver' quailed, **Samuel Johnson** (1709–84), poet, essayist, dramatist, biographer, critic, novelist, lexicographer, and the 'great Cham' of English literature, cannot be considered here in relation to his unrivalled position as a great and wise talker. The student should refer to James Boswell's 'Life of Samuel Johnson, LL.D.' as the only way of realizing Johnson's greatness. If one's leisure will not permit of reading the whole of its six hundred thousand words, an abridgement will serve.

As to Johnson's influence on prose literature, Macaulay says :

His constant practice of padding out a sentence with useless epithets till it became as stiff as the bust of an exquisite ; his antithetical forms of expression, constantly employed even where there is no opposition in the ideas expressed ; his big words wasted on little things ; his harsh inversions, so widely different from those graceful and easy inversions which give variety, spirit, and sweetness to the expression of our great old writers—all these peculiarities have been imitated by his admirers, and parodied by his assailants, till the public has become sick of the subject.

Gibbon, the historian of Roman decadence, lived to write ; Johnson, an infinitely greater man, wrote to live. Today, Johnson's 'Lives of the Poets' are read more, perhaps, than anything he wrote, but not for the accuracy of their data or their infallibility of judgement. They disclose to us not fine literary instinct so much as fine human sympathy.

His prose tale of 'Rasselas, Prince of Abyssinia,' written to defray the cost of his mother's funeral, has been aptly described as a prose version of his poem on 'The Vanity of Human Wishes.' According to Boswell, Johnson told his intimate friend, Sir Joshua Reynolds, that he composed 'Rasselas' in the evenings of one week, sent it to press as it was written, and had never since 'read it over.' His great 'Dictionary' was the first of its kind. It stands almost alone as the work of one man. Its value and influence have been great ; and even today, except for its weakness on the side of etymology, a weakness due to the fact that Johnson's Latin learning was not approached by his knowledge of Anglo-Saxon, it is a standard book of reference. The ordinary reader should have some acquaintance with the 'Lives of the Poets' ; and 'Rasselas' he is not likely to miss. For the rest, to know this grand old character in Boswell's biography is, as it was to love Sir Richard Steele's 'Aspasia,' 'a liberal education.'

Goldsmith. The friendship between Steele and Addison was not greater than that between Johnson and Oliver Goldsmith (1728–74). But no greater contrast could be imagined than that afforded by their writings. Sir Edmund Gosse says :

In prose style, as in poetic, it is noticeable that Goldsmith has little in common with his great contemporaries, with their splendid burst of rhetoric and Latin pomp of speech, but that he goes back to the perfect plainness and simple grace of the Queen Anne men. He aims at a straightforward effect of pathos or of humour, accompanied, as a rule, with a colloquial ease of expression, an apparent absence of all effort or calculation.

Goldsmith's prose approximates to that of Addison. The best examples of it are to be found in his 'Citizen of the World' and 'The Vicar of Wakefield.' The first-named work consists of a series of letters supposed to have been written by a China-man resident in London, who was jotting down his experiences for the benefit of his friends in the Far East. The idea was not original, and it has since been imitated by innumerable writers, but the delightful wit and humour of Goldsmith's work have never been excelled. 'The Vicar of Wake-field,' Goldsmith's chief prose work, is dealt with in another Lesson in this Course (*see* page 192), one of several concerned with the history of the English novel.

Three Philosophers. The period now under consideration, dominated as it was by humanism and intelligence, is naturally rich in historians and philosophers. George Berkeley, Bishop of Cloyne (1685–1753), was a man whose life, apart from his writings, is full of interest. As a philosopher he aimed at the overthrow of materialism (*see* Course in Philosophy, Volume v). He was an acute and original thinker; his style has great force and elegance, and he is one of our most accomplished writers of dialogue.

Joseph Butler, Bishop of Durham (1692–1752), was the author of a work on the 'Analogy of Religion, Natural and Revealed, to the Constitution and Course of Nature,' which won for him the name of 'the Bacon of Theology,' and remains a standard work in its own department. David Hume (1711–76) was distinguished as an essayist, a philosopher (*see* Course in Philosophy), and a historian. Possessing wonderful clearness of mental vision, his style is marked by exceptional lucidity. An opponent of popular government, he was yet the first of our writers to recognize the importance of the social and scientific as well as the constitutional and political factors in the making of history. His influence as a philosopher was most appreci-able in Scotland and Germany.

Gibbon. The greatest of English histor-ians, Edward Gibbon, the son of a Hamp-shire gentleman, was born April 27, 1737. After a preliminary education at West-minster, and fourteen 'unprofitable' months at Magdalen College, Oxford, a whim to join the Roman Church led to his banish-ment to Lausanne, where he spent five years, formed his taste for literary expres-sion, and settled his religious doubts in a profound scepticism. It was in 1764, while musing amid the ruins of the Capitol of Rome, that the idea of writing 'The Decline and Fall of the Roman Empire' first started into his mind. The vast work was com-pleted in 1787. 'A Study in Literature,' written in French, and his ' Miscellaneous Works,' published after his death, which include 'The Memoirs of his Life and Writings,' complete the list of his literary labours. He died on January 16, 1794.

The manner in which Gibbon contrived a literary style that fitted the magnitude of his theme remains one of the marvels of our literature. Much nonsense about its 'pom-posity' has been written : it moves with becoming gravity and produces a sense of formality which is impressive without be-coming wearisome, and must, by that token, be most ingeniously varied without any appearance of effort at variety. There is a wonderful illusion of continued progress in the narrative, even when the essence of it is associated with things that are static. One is impressed with the drama of history ; the historian seems by some subtle process of art to have fitted all the episodes of fourteen centuries into one congruous drama of humanity, and the multitudinous historic characters that tread his vast stage in a pageant beyond the dreams of imaginative poets, though shown in true historic per-spective, are all endowed with their dramatic values to the furtherance of the grandiose scheme of the arch-director, who summons them back with such a wonderful illusion of life to re-tread the stage of history. Some would say, however, that Gibbon, in an age of intellectual riches and spiritual poverty, and by reason of his temperamental lack of sympathy, forgot his customary impartiality in the famous 15th and 16th chapters, in which he gave his view of the rise and spread of Christianity.

In spite of this, 'The Decline and Fall' is one of the inevitable items in any list of books to read. Gibbon's 'Memoirs' is also one of the books that should be read and re-read ; it is held by some to be the best autobiography in English.

Burke. The Irishman, Edmund Burke (1729–97), was a statesman and orator as well as an author. Matthew Arnold has described Burke as the greatest master of English prose style that ever lived. Apart from his speeches, Burke's principal prose works are : 'A Vindication of Natural Society,' written to ridicule Bolingbroke's views on society and religion ; an 'Inquiry into the Sublime and the Beautiful,' and 'Reflections on the Revolution in France.'

Of all the eighteenth-century writers, perhaps Burke is the one whom the student can least afford to neglect. De Quincey, who was no hasty eulogist, considered him the supreme writer of his time. Whether that judgement can be entirely justified is not easy to show without entering into detailed comparisons between Burke and his contemporaries ; but the fact remains that for much that makes for true citizenship, as well as for the literary graces, the student must have recourse to the works of Edmund Burke—his speeches not less than his writings. He helps us marvellously to an understanding of the public life of our country, though he may not always convince us.

We must not be content, however, with knowing Burke in 'The Sublime and the Beautiful,' which, though somewhat crude, is a notable contribution to aesthetics ; his 'Reflections on the Revolution in France,' far less known to the ordinary reader, is even more worthy of study. It presents lucidly his horror of violence and his contention that liberty is only to be admired in the guise of order. His eloquent speeches present a rich field whence we may glean knowledge of life and wisdom.

Horace Walpole, fourth Earl of Orford (1717–97), set up a private press, whence he issued 'A Catalogue of Royal and Noble Authors.' He also wrote 'Anecdotes of Painting in England' ; a tragedy, 'The Mysterious Mother,' and a romance entitled 'The Castle of Otranto.' He left nearly 3,000 letters and a 'History of the Last Ten Years of the Reign of George II.' Walpole possessed a brilliant style, which will serve to keep his works alive and render his letters readable independently of their historical value.

Adam Smith (1723–90) wrote a work entitled 'The Wealth of Nations,' which originated the study of 'political economy' as a distinct branch of science, inspired a world-wide interest in the sources of wealth, and was responsible for the rise of the theory of Free Trade. 'The Wealth of Nations' is a book that may still be studied with pleasure and profit. It affords an example of the way in which a 'dry' subject may be treated so as to appeal to the popular mind.

LESSON 35

Some 18th Century Scholars and Stylists

ENOUGH has now been said to make it evident that the study of English prose must be pursued on lines different from those on which English poetry is to be studied. Whereas poetry is universally the voice of inspiration, prose in its development departs from the sphere of literature proper. Sometimes retaining but frequently losing its claim as literature, it becomes in turn the servant of theology, the handmaid of history, the medium of science, the channel of philosophy—essential alike to religious and atheistical propaganda, to practical and to theoretical ends.

At the beginning of the 18th century the student stands at a parting of the ways. He has to distinguish between what is prose literature and what is not. To a certain extent the answer will depend upon his own bent or humour, but he still has to ascertain why and when and by whom particular books were written. He must learn not only the history of those books, but become acquainted with their relationships—their position in regard to the treatment by others of the subjects with which they deal—before he is able to satisfy himself as to their value.

It is proper at this point to urge the advisability of some study of the political and social developments of which particular books were either a cause or an outcome. The extent of this study will depend largely upon the reader's desire to confine himself to, or to range beyond, the scope of belles-lettres. By belles-lettres is meant literature that is distinguished by the charm of its style or form, apart from its claim as a vehicle of instruction. It has to be borne in mind in this connexion that in the last resort prose lives because of its power, not for its prettiness.

Charm and distinction of style are peculiarly characteristic of our 18th-century prose. The century 'found English prose antiquated, amorphous, without a standard of form ; it left it a finished thing, the completed body for which,' as Sir Edmund Gosse says, 'subsequent ages could do no more than weave successive robes of ornament and fashion.' The wider our knowledge of the literature of this period grows,

JOHN BUNYAN, a tinker by trade, wrote his immortal allegory, 'The Pilgrim's Progress,' in Bedford Gaol, where he was imprisoned as a Dissenter. In 'Grace Abounding' is a moving record of his own conversion.
National Portrait Gallery

SAMUEL PEPYS wrote his famous Diary in cipher, and it was not decoded until some 150 years later, in 1819-22. It records his inmost thoughts and most trivial doings with the utmost frankness, and gives an entertaining record of the period.
Portrait by Hayls, National Portrait Gallery

JOHN EVELYN, another famous diarist, was an austere and penetrating observer of the contemporary scene and we owe much of our knowledge of it to him. He was an intimate friend of Pepys.
Portrait by Kneller, Royal Society

FRANCIS BACON, Lord Verulam, best known for his 'Essays,' was a philosopher, devoted to scientific research; he expounds his methods in 'The Advancement of Learning' and 'Novum Organum.'
National Portrait Gallery

161

F*

DANIEL DEFOE, famous as the author of 'Robinson Crusoe,' was one of the greatest masters of English prose. He wrote many brilliant and attractive novels and histories.

Frontispiece to his 'Jure Divino' (1706)

JONATHAN SWIFT was a master of irony, sometimes of the savagest kind. His greatest work is in 'A Tale of a Tub' and 'Gulliver's Travels,' and he is at his most attractive in the 'Journal to Stella.'

Portrait by Jervas, National Portrait Gallery

JOSEPH ADDISON, a delightful writer, composed many light discursive essays on the foibles of the day, developing the character of Sir Roger de Coverley who appeared in the 'Spectator.' He also wrote polished verse, a blank-verse tragedy ('Cato') and much literary criticism.

Portrait by Kneller

SIR RICHARD STEELE, essayist and dramatist, founded the 'Tatler,' to which Addison contributed, and later joined with him in founding the 'Spectator,' for which he wrote many pleasant essays. His plays are sentimental comedies, starting a new vogue.

Portrait by Richardson, National Portrait Gallery

HORACE WALPOLE, connoisseur and dilettante, wrote the romantic ' Castle of Otranto,' full of supernatural effects. Some 2,700 of his vivacious letters have been published.

Portrait by N. Hone. National Portrait Gallery

SAMUEL JOHNSON, after many years of hardship, was recognized as the leading man of letters in his period. Boswell's ' Life' brings him vividly before us. Here he is shown without his wig.

Portrait by Romney, National Portrait Gallery

EDMUND BURKE, statesman and orator, clothed his thoughts in sonorous language and rich imagery, yet was essentially a practical man. His ' Reflections on the French Revolution ' had considerable influence.

Portrait by Romney

EDWARD GIBBON spent 17 years in writing with wonderful power and judgement his monumental ' Decline and Fall of the Roman Empire,' which depicts in glowing colours the splendours of the past.

Portrait by Romney

FAMOUS LETTER-WRITERS. The gifted Lady Mary Wortley Montagu travelled widely and knew the most interesting people of her day. The Earl of Chesterfield's shrewd letters to his son are marred by cynicism.

Portrait of Lady M. W. Montagu by permission of the Earl of Wharncliffe; Chesterfield, by Gainsborough

Leigh Hunt

Charles Lamb

Robert Southey

William Hazlitt

POETS, ESSAYISTS AND CRITICS. Hunt's work is pleasant, though undistinguished. Lamb is dearly loved for his intensely individual 'Essays of Elia,' and for his verse and his letters. Southey had a prodigious output of verse and prose; his 'Life of Nelson' is a classic in simple vigorous style. Hazlitt was a penetrating critic, and De Quincey wrote superb imaginative prose.

Portrait of Lamb after Henry Mayer, De Quincey by Sir J. Watson Gordon (both in National Portrait Gallery); Southey after Robert Hancock; Hazlitt from a miniature by his brother, John Hazlitt

Thomas de Quincey

Walter Savage Landor

Sydney Smith

William Cobbett

Thomas Carlyle

Lord Macaulay

John Stuart Mill

HISTORIANS AND OTHERS.
Landor wrote stately prose and lyric verse, under classical influences. Sydney Smith was a witty and popular satirist, and Cobbett a generous reformer.   Most influential was Carlyle, historian and philosopher, whose dynamic force is seen in his ' French Revolution ' and much other work. Macaulay and Froude were accomplished historians, and Mill was famous as an economist.

Portrait of Landor by W. Fisher; Mill by G. F. Watts, Carlyle by Millais (both in National Portrait Gallery); Sydney Smith, engraved by E. O. Eddis after W. Greatbach; Cobbett from an engraving by Bartolozzi, after J. R. Smith; Macaulay by Sir F. Grant

J. A. Froude

165

John Ruskin   Sir Leslie Stephen   Walter Pater

George Saintsbury   Alice Meynell   Sir Edmund Gosse

G. K Chesterton   Hilaire Belloc   Lytton Strachey

*BELLES-LETTRES. Ruskin was one of the most important Victorians ; he gave the call to a higher life.
' The Stones of Venice ' and ' Modern Painters ' are among his greatest writings. Pater's principal gift to
literature was ' Marius the Epicurean.' Stephen, Saintsbury and Gosse were scholarly critics, Mrs. Meynell a
sensitive essayist, and Strachey an iconoclast. Chesterton and Belloc have written brilliant essays, critical
biographies, books of travel, stories and vigorous verse.*

Photos, Elliott & Fry, Russell and Hoppé

Aphra Behn

Samuel Richardson

Henry Fielding

Laurence Sterne

Fanny Burney

Tobias Smollett

Jane Austen

Sir Walter Scott

EARLY NOVELISTS. *Aphra Behn was the first professional woman writer. Richardson, Fielding, Sterne and Smollett are an important 18th century quartette. Fanny Burney wrote the delightful ' Evelina,' and Jane Austen did exquisite work within a limited scope. Scott is the first great novelist, with a very large output in verse as well ; much of his inspiration was drawn from his native Scotland.*

Portrait of Richardson by Joseph Highmore, Smollett by an unknown artist (both in National Portrait Gallery); Fielding by Hogarth, Sterne from an engraving by Fisher after Reynolds; Fanny Burney from an engraving after Edward W. Burney; Jane Austen after a drawing made of her at the age of fifteen; Scott from an engraving after Sir J. Watson Gordon

167

GREAT VICTORIANS. Thomas Love Peacock (top left) wrote in erudite but entertaining style. George Borrow (top right) is unique for his understanding of gipsy life. Thackeray (lower left) and Dickens (lower right) were the master novelists of their age. Thackeray's 'Henry Esmond' and 'Vanity Fair' are his finest work. Dickens won the heart of the people by his warm understanding and his exposure of social abuses.

Photograph of Peacock by Maull & Fox; portrait of Borrow by H. W. Phillips; crayon drawing of Thackeray by E. Goodwyn Lewis; portrait of Dickens by Scheffer (National Portrait Gallery) the more clearly shall we see the injustice of the common indictment of the age as one of shams and sentiment. Apart from Johnson, the age of Berkeley, Wesley and Whitefield cannot be described as devoid of enthusiasm.

It was the age of our great historians. It was adorned by some of our greatest philosophers and keenest critics. English writers of the time influenced Continental thought more, perhaps, than did the writers of any other period of our history. Eighteenth-century England, as we have already seen, discovered Shakespeare before the Germans. It standardized the essay, sowed the seeds of modern Nature study and modern chemistry, gave birth to our first great novel, laid the foundations of our periodical literature, stood sponsor to the beginnings of daily journalism, and crushed the system of literary patronage. It was the age, also, of political economy and of public eloquence.

Famous Letter-Writers. The 18th century is also rich in its letters. The correspondence of Horace Walpole has been already referred to. Philip Dormer Stanhope, fourth earl of Chesterfield (1694–1773), was a statesman and wit who is remembered today chiefly for his 'Letters to His Son.' Given to the world in 1774 by the son's widow, these letters were described by Johnson as displaying the morals of a courtesan and the manners of a dancing-master. They argue, nevertheless, despite their worldliness, a sincere solicitude for the welfare of the son to whom they were addressed. They furnish also an example of writing that is at once clear, simple, forcible and polished. The aim of the writer is apparent throughout. The means he adopts to further that aim are direct. He describes things that are desirable, and against them sets the means by which they are to be attained. If the chance that ambition may not be sufficiently stimulated is sometimes provided for by an appeal to fear—the fear of ridicule—the fact is not to be counted for affectation on the writer's part. To him the most important thing in life was to shine in the fashionable society of his period.

Among other letter-writers of the 18th century must be named the poets Cowper and Gray. The letters of Cowper afford, perhaps, the best argument against the effectiveness of ornamental diction when it is confronted with a style that is simple and sincere. Cowper's delightful letters describe in the most natural and most charming of language the surroundings and incidents

of the poet's life at Olney and Weston. Gray's letters possess the qualities of the bookman and the scholar, and represent a man who seems never to have permitted himself to appear in 'dressing gown and slippers.' The 'Letters' of Lady Mary Wortley Montagu (1689–1762) describe, in the simple and elegant style of an accomplished if worldly woman, her experiences of travel in Europe and the Near East between 1716 and 1718.

Natural History. The 'Natural History of Selborne,' by Gilbert White (1720–93), marks the beginning of popular Nature studies. Probably no book on natural history has been more widely read or more loved. With just sufficient formality to give it 18th-century charm, it is composed of letters to the writer's friends, written, it is believed, at the suggestion of the Hon. Daines Barrington (1727–1800), who was an antiquary and a naturalist as well as a lawyer. Thomas Pennant (1726–98) was another famous naturalist ; his 'British Zoology' and 'History of Quadrupeds' were for a long time classics.

Theology and Rationalism. Among the divines whose work continues to be read are William Law (1686–1761), whose 'Serious Call to a Devout and Holy Life' stands by the side of Jeremy Taylor's 'Rule and Exercises of Holy Living' as one of the most impressive devotional treatises in the language ; William Warburton, bishop of Gloucester (1698–1779), author of a voluminous work entitled 'The Divine Legation of Moses Demonstrated' ; and William Paley (1743–1805), whose 'Treatise on Natural Theology' and 'View of the Evidences of Christianity' are still read. His 'Horae Paulinae,' a defence of the genuineness of St. Paul's Epistles, is perhaps his most important work.

Conyers Middleton (1683–1750) wrote a remarkably rationalistic 'Free Inquiry' into the miraculous powers which were supposed to have existed in the Christian Church. His vigorous, direct style has many admirers. The 'Essay on Civil Society,' by Dr. Adam Ferguson (1723–1816), has been ranked as a companion to Adam Smith's 'Wealth of Nations.' Thomas Reid (1710–96), who wrote 'An Inquiry into the Human Mind on the Principles of Common Sense,' had a distinguished follower in the 'common-sense' philosophy of Dugald Stewart (1753–1828).

Following David Hartley (1705–57) and Abraham Tucker (1705–74) in adopting the theory of the association of ideas came

Joseph Priestley (1733–1804), a Unitarian divine and ardent Radical, who is best remembered as the father of modern chemistry, author of a 'History of Electricity,' and the man who discovered and named oxygen.

Thomas Paine (1737–1809) wrote an influential book on 'The Rights of Man' (1790), in answer to Burke, and 'The Age of Reason,' the Bible of rationalistic deism, in 1793, when a prisoner in Paris under the 'Terror.' A second part appeared in 1795.

Classical Scholarship. The Greek scholarship of Richard Porson and that of Elizabeth Carter, the translator of Epictetus ; the translation of Demosthenes by Dr. Thomas Leland ; the still unapproached translation of the Koran by George Sale ; the version of Plutarch's 'Lives' by J. and W. Langhorne ; the standard translation of Josephus's 'History of the Jews' by William Whiston ; the still popular version of 'Gil Blas' by Tobias Smollett, whose 'History of England' must also be noted ; the translation of the 'Satires' of Horace by Christopher Smart—all these testify to the 18th century's being an age of scholarship.

And even this list, long as it is, and irrespective of the fact that fiction is reserved for separate consideration, while poetry and drama have already been dealt with in this Course, is far from comprehensive. There yet remain to be noted for the student's due attention, Sir William Jones's translations from the Sanskrit, the scholarly 'Discourses' of Sir Joshua Reynolds, John Horne Tooke's valuable 'Diversions of Purley,' the histories and biographies of John Strype, the 'History of the Puritans Down to 1689' of Daniel Neal, Sir William Blackstone's authoritative 'Commentaries on the Laws of England,' the 'Anecdotes' of Joseph Spence, Mrs. Thrale's 'Anecdotes of Samuel Johnson,' the 'Travels' of Mungo

Park, the admirable Shakespearian studies of Farmer, Steevens and Dennis. Mary Wollstonecraft Godwin's 'Rights of Woman,' published in 1792, was the forerunner of the literature which helped to win the suffrage for women. T. R. Malthus's 'Essay on the Principle of Population' (1798) was afterwards to influence Darwin.

Eighteenth-Century Journalism. In the domain of journalism it is of interest to remember that *The Times*, first started as *The Daily Universal Register* in 1785, came out with its present title on January 1, 1788 ; that the 'Gentleman's Magazine' was originated in 1731 ; and that there was a 'London Magazine' in 1732, a 'Monthly Review' in 1749, a 'Literary Magazine' and a 'Critical Review' in 1756 ; while, in addition to other encyclopedias, the 'Encyclopædia Britannica' appeared in completed form in 1771, in three volumes.

At this point the great distinction has to be noted between the 18th century and our own time : that the term ' a man of letters' formerly stood for one who had ranged at will in all those fields of study represented in this review of 18th-century prose-writers—philosophy, travel, history, fiction, science, religion and so on. Unhappily, but perhaps inevitably, the 19th century saw a great change in the direction of 'specializing,' not only by writers, but also by readers. In the 18th century it was accounted no discredit to a writer that he expended his energies in many fields of thought. In our day such versatility is not always appreciated. That is the author's excuse, and it is perhaps a valid one ; but the reader who confines himself to only one class of reading has no excuse. The man who today would be well read should go for example to the 'men of letters' of the 18th century, who regarded the whole field of literature as their hunting-ground.

Short Review of 19th Century Prose

NINETEENTH-CENTURY prose, infinite in its variety of style, is distinguished by its rich complexity of matter and its widely contrasted points of view. Goethe's remark that there are many echoes but few voices is largely true of all literary periods ; but the voices of the nineteenth century will compare advantageously with those of any preceding period. Where

prose is concerned they are heard at their best, perhaps, in the novel. But they are hardly less resonant in the essay, the biography, the history, the book of theology, the narrative of travel, the scientific treatise, the studies of philosophy, art, education and economics. While a certain complacency, or easy optimism, was characteristic of some eminent writers, there was a greater number of eminent writers loudly protesting against self and national satisfaction, opposing such thought with a spirit of inquiry and unrest, with a passionate denunciation of social and human ills.

If the twentieth century opened for us with a wider mental outlook it is due largely to the work accomplished in the preceding century in the domain of English letters, when our great writers took to heart the aphorism of an eighteenth-century poet. They saw with Pope that 'the proper study of mankind is man.'

'**Renascence of Wonder.**' The literature of knowledge and the literature of power belonging to this period are alike marked by a dominating but informed interrogative ; for it was not only in imaginative writing that the last century witnessed what Watts-Dunton called 'the Renascence of Wonder,' but in all fields of literature—in criticism and science, not less than in poetry and romance—this re-birth of 'wonder' took place. The originator of the phrase thus explains it :

The Renascence of Wonder merely indicates that there are two great impulses governing man, and probably not man only, but the entire world of conscious life : the impulse of acceptance—the impulse to take unchallenged and for granted all the phenomena of the outer world as they are—and the impulse to confront these phenomena with eyes of inquiry and wonder.

Before studying the effects, let us glance at the causes of this change in the nation's literary life. The French Revolution shattered the scholastic formalism of English letters. Jean Jacques Rousseau stirred up a feeling for humanity such as England had never before acquired from French or Italian writers, much as she had been influenced previously by Continental models. The effects of the French Terror threw the thoughtful back for a time into the slough of despond. We have seen how Wordsworth, for example, was bowed down in this way. Then a Scottish teacher read Mme. de Staël's 'De l'Allemagne,' set himself to master the German language, put Jean Paul Richter in the place of Jean Jacques Rousseau, and by the exercise, on the one hand, of the extraordinary knowledge he acquired of German philosophy and German individualism, and his painstaking elucidation of the Cromwellian epoch, on the other, set aloft an ideal of manhood and patriotic duty which influenced materially the popular view of history, and the outlook on Nature and Life.

There were others, beside Carlyle, who drank deeply at the Teutonic spring. Wordsworth was one, Coleridge another, Byron a third ; Scott and De Quincey were of the company. Each was affected differently, but at the same time profoundly.

Had there been no 'Renascence of Wonder' we had seen few, if any, of the marvellous inventions which rubricate the nineteenth in the calendar of centuries. Thus romance was reborn ; metaphysics acquired a new meaning ; humour was reincarnated. Men longed to look at things as they were—to see them 'whole.' Carlyle entered as an iconoclast into the temple of 'the Gigmanities,' and of all the masterminds of the century Carlyle is the one who, both directly and indirectly, stirred most deeply the heart of the vast reading public called into being by the mechanical inventions of 'the Wonderful Century.'

The history of the essay, both critical and constructive, in the century we are considering, is bound up with the history of the periodical. Something of the same kind may be said of both poetry and the novel. The various periodicals having a political bias, if not basis, literature developed more or less under the aegis of politics. The writers made the reviews, and the reviews helped to make the writers.

Today much of the vital force which animated the work of earlier writers has been scattered, much of their 'thunder' has been stolen, the knowledge in the light of which they wrote has been found to be misleading. But the saving salt of an individual style preserves many an old and obsolete book from the blight of oblivion.

Creators of Style. Among the influences on later prose must be remembered the prose of the poets—the prefaces of Wordsworth, the miscellanies of Scott, the critical essays of Coleridge, the letters of Byron, Shelley and Keats. But the student has a wonderful variety of object lessons in style before him, apart from these great names. There are the Puritan fervour, the irony and grim humour of Carlyle, the gentle intimacy of Charles Lamb, the graceful confidences of Leigh Hunt, the aerial cadence of De Quincey, the emphatic, unmistakable vigour of Cobbett, the brilliant antitheses of the sometimes prejudiced, sometimes complacent, but always vitally interesting Macaulay, the incisive phrases of Hazlitt, the wit of Sydney Smith, the beautiful imagery and deeply penetrative criticism of Ruskin, the flowing sea-music of Swinburne, the classic beauty of Landor's dialogues, the perfect serenity and harmony of Newman, the scholarly prose of Matthew Arnold, the undecorated diction of Hallam and Freeman, the picturesque pages of Froude, the jewelled sentences of Walter Pater, the sparkle of Stevenson, and the austerely great prose of Charles Doughty, whose 'Travels in Arabia Deserta' was for long so little known. In the main the prose writer who aspires to style must be an artist just as the poet is an artist, but the secret of style is, ultimately, the harmony between the subject and its treatment.

For general purposes style has been considerably influenced by the usage of journalism. The Press is responsible for a marked lessening of the distinction between written and spoken language. There must always be some distinction between the two. The skilled writer must of necessity possess a close acquaintance with the meaning of words ; and it is perhaps a defective knowledge of the meaning of words that lies at the root of most failures in composition.

The speaker, by means of accent, emphasis, look, gesture, personality, can lend significance to a comparatively poor speech. The writer must find literary equivalents for the methods and circumstances of platform and pulpit. But the aim of the writer who addresses himself to a wide public should be directed to the perfection of a style that shall be distinctive—a copied styı is but a mask—clear and colloquial, yet avoiding baldness and vulgarity, and in which foreign words are used sparingly.

Biographers and Historians. While the essayists have done much to increase our knowledge of bygone literature, as well as to popularize various branches of scientific learning, the biographers have given to the prose of the period some of its greatest intellectual assets. Southey's 'Nelson,' Lockhart's 'Scott,' 'Burns' and 'Napoleon'; Lewes's 'Goethe,' Carlyle's 'Cromwell' and 'Sterling,' Froude's 'Carlyle,' Masson's 'Milton,' Spedding's 'Bacon,' Stanley's 'Arnold,' and Forster's 'Goldsmith', 'Landor,' and 'Dickens,' are classics.

The influence of English historical methods has been world-wide. The nineteenth-century historians—Hallam, Buckle, Macaulay, Lecky, Green, Froude and others —are worthy successors of Gibbon. They have determined the unity of history, and made it fascinating.

The output of books on various other subjects of general interest will be briefly discussed later. Meantime, two facts of special interest must be noted. One is the high literary value of much of the scientific literature of the time, as disclosed, for example, in Huxley's writings ; the other is the distinction attained by women writers.

LESSON 37

Some 19th Century Critics and Essayists

DUE attention has already been given to the poetical productions of Samuel Taylor Coleridge (1772–1834) and Robert Southey 1774–1843). With regard to their prose writings it has to be said that no serious student of English criticism can afford to neglect those of Coleridge. His 'Lectures and Notes on Shakespeare' are especially valuable both, on account of their great intrinsic worth and of the effects they had on later estimates of the national poet.

As for Southey, few men whose names are remembered in literature ever wrote more that has been forgotten than did he. His fertility of production was as amazing as its variety. He was a scholar and, considered as a stylist alone, claims a high place among his contemporaries. And yet, 'of what is called style,' he said, 'not a thought enters my head at any time. I only endeavour to write plain English, and put my thoughts in language which everyone can understand.' Herein lies the secret of his style, however. To think that academic prose need be great prose is to conjure up the fallacy that style can exist apart from matter. Southey's greatest prose work is the classic 'Life of Nelson.'

Sir Walter Scott (1771–1832) wrote almost as incessantly and as variously as Southey, but with greater success, independently of his greatest work as a novelist. His essays on chivalry, romance and the drama, and his letters on demonology and witchcraft are still eminently readable ; and he was a painstaking as well as a capable editor, especially of Swift and of the Border antiquities.

John Wilson (1785–1854), the 'Christopher North' of 'Blackwood's Magazine,' is chiefly remembered as the literary parent of De Quincey, as part author of that brilliant series of dialogues 'Noctes Ambrosianae,' and as author of 'Lights and Shadows of Scottish Life.'

John Gibson Lockhart (1794–1854), Scott's son-in-law, and Wilson's friend and colleague on 'Blackwood,' who succeeded Gifford as editor of the 'Quarterly,' gave to journalism much that by right should have been devoted to literature. His masterpiece is the 'Life of Scott.'

Charles Lamb. One of the greatest, as he is one of the least pretentious, of English prose writers is Charles Lamb (1775–1834). Master of as many styles as he possessed moods, he is full of elusive echoes of the old writers whom he loved. His is the art that conceals art, for seemingly he is as frank and as communicative as Montaigne. His character is written in his 'Essays'; his autobiography in his Letters. But Lamb was not only an essayist of unique charm; he was also a critic of rare insight and surprising accuracy. Nothing that he wrote, or that others wrote of him, should the student neglect. He dared to be original in criticism and forestalled George Bernard Shaw in the use of paradox.

The paradoxes of a critic as great as Lamb are aflame with the insight of genius, and he brought readers to see that conventional judgements may prove even wilder and more fallacious than the new and surprising point of view ('English Literature in the Nineteenth Century,' Laurie Magnus).

William Hazlitt (1778–1830) was indebted to Lamb, and acknowledged the indebtedness; but with a critical faculty as keen as that of Lamb he possessed not a scintilla of 'Elia's' human sympathy; hence, whereas the one is loved, the other is given the meed of almost frigid praise. Yet Hazlitt's is a name of first importance. He is the master of the apt and illuminating phrase. The student of Shakespeare owes much to Coleridge's 'Lectures,' he owes much also to Lamb's 'Critical Essays,' but he must also study, and study with attention, Hazlitt's 'Characters of Shakespeare's Plays'—a work dedicated to Lamb—and the 'Lectures on the Dramatic Literature of the Reign of Elizabeth.' Of equal note are the 'Lectures on the English Comic Writers' and 'Lectures on the English Poets.' There is, however, more venom than justice in the personal sketches he called 'The Spirit of the Age.'

Thomas De Quincey (1785–1859) stands sponsor to the school of 'prose poets,' of which Swinburne is the great exemplar. He has much to attract, but is dangerous to follow. He lacks a certain dignity, is normally without what we understand by the word 'reverence,' and is at times terribly discursive; but we must remember that the bulk of his work was anonymous journalism, and that the writer kept up a weak physique by the use of opium. The 'Confessions of an Opium-Eater,' 'Suspiria de Profundis,' the historical essays, and the 'Autobiographic Sketches' should be closely studied. De Quincey has been styled the 'Boswell of Essayism,' so intimate are his revelations of both himself and his associates. He possessed to an almost amazing degree an instinct for dramatic expression. Whatever some of whom he wrote may have thought of his character drawing, he was well liked personally. This great essayist was a rhapsodist, but he was, too, an inquirer, and his valuable influence was against cast-iron formality in prose.

William Cobbett (1762–1835) started life by scaring crows, but left a name which should be remembered. He may be said to personify the whole art of self-education. By self-denial and perseverance he acquired a considerable sum of varied knowledge, and wielded immense influence as a politician and journalist. Despite extraordinary difficulties, he learnt English and French so well as to be able to write grammars in both languages, and developed a literary style as natural as Defoe's, as vigorous as Swift's, brightened by humour and telling invective, and perhaps as characteristically Saxon as any that could be named.

Cobbett's 'English Grammar' and 'French Grammar' are written in the form of letters to his son, and are unsurpassed in the lucidity of their arrangement and their quality of genuine liveliness. The 'English Grammar' may be commended as vastly entertaining as well as instructive. His 'Weekly Political Register,' started in 1802, was continued, apart from one small break, until his death. In 1803 he began the 'Parliamentary Debates' whence developed our present 'Hansard.' He wrote a 'History of the Reformation,' which is still read, though chiefly by Roman Catholics. His 'Advice to Young Men' is full of practical common sense for men and women. Its vigour and frankness are as refreshing as the breath of the sea.

His best work is to be found in the picturesque accounts of his political tours on horseback, entitled 'Rural Rides.' Cobbett is not a great literary character; but his style is the best of models for all who aspire to write clearly and correctly.

Walter Savage Landor (1775–1864) has already been dealt with as a poet. His prose masterpiece is his 'Imaginary Conversations,' 125 in number, published between 1824 and 1853. Full of fine thought expressed in a highly finished, eloquent style, felicitous in imagery and diction, and bearing a clear impress of genius and cultivated taste, they range over a vast area of topics, discussing questions of statesmanship, philosophy, poetry, literature, life and manners, and reveal strong dramatic qualities which have caused many to wonder why their author failed to write a great play. Among the dialogues specially admired for their dramatic intensity are those between Peter the Great and Alexis, and Henry VIII and Anne Boleyn. By one studying Shakespeare's life, Landor's 'Citation of William Shakespeare' may be read as a charming piece of imaginative prose.

Isaac D'Israeli (1766–1848), the father of Lord Beaconsfield, wrote a number of anecdotal works which, though somewhat slipshod, offer evidence of much culture and wide reading, being chiefly notable for the entertainment they afford and the stimulus they give to further inquiry in the by-paths of literary history. 'The Curiosities of Literature' is the best of these; its companions are 'Calamities and Quarrels of Authors,' 'Amenities of Literature' and 'The Literary Character.'

William Hone (1780–1842) was a sort of minor Cobbett, with something of D'Israeli's feeling for letters. His 'Every-Day Book,' 'Table-Book,' and 'Year-Book' bear tribute to his industrious study of old manners and customs, but are chiefly valuable as works of reference to the literary man.

The 'Papers' of John Wilson Croker (1780–1857) and Thomas Creevey (1768–1838) supply much intimate detail of the Court, literary, and political life of their time, the one from a Tory, and the other from a Whig point of view. Croker was a frequent contributor to the 'Quarterly Review.' His chief work was an edition of Boswell which drew forth a remarkably bitter criticism from Macaulay.

Leigh Hunt. Another essayist of considerable charm and versatility is James Leigh Hunt (1784–1859), whose friendships secure for him a greater meed of recognition than his writings, though these are not unimportant. He introduced Shelley and Keats to one another and brought these poets before the public in 'The Examiner,' of which he was editor and part proprietor. The student of literature will find much profit in his 'Imagination and Fancy,' 'Wit and Humour,' and 'Men, Women and Books,' while his 'Autobiography' contains enough to secure for it the permanent interest of all bookmen. London and 'The Cockney School' found in him an energetic champion, and his gossipy volume on 'The Town: Its Memorable Characters and Events' retains a certain measure of popularity. His notes on the Restoration dramatists inspired one of Macaulay's essays.

Three other minor writers of the period call for mention here. Nassau William Senior (1790–1864) was an acute literary critic as well as a political economist. His 'Essays on Fiction,' contributed to the 'Quarterly,' 'Edinburgh,' and other reviews, were published in collected form in 1864. William Maginn (1793–1842), scholar, critic, humorist, was one of 'Blackwood's' most brilliant contributors, and as the conductor of 'Fraser's Magazine' he gathered round him some of the most distinguished of contemporary writers. Finally, Anna Brownell Jameson (1794–1860) wrote on art, sacred legends and 'The Characteristics of Shakespeare's Women.'

LESSON 38

Carlyle, Macaulay and Froude

THE literary career of Thomas Carlyle (1795–1881) began with contributions to 'The Edinburgh Encyclopædia,' for which, between 1820 and 1823, he wrote articles on Lady Mary Wortley Montagu, Montaigne, Montesquieu, Dr. John Moore, Sir John Moore, Necker, Nelson, Mungo Park, Lord Chatham, William Pitt, and several papers of a topographical character.

Only one of these—the paper on Sir John Moore—can be described as inadequate.

From the first Carlyle seldom spared himself. In 1824 he published two translations—one from the French (Legendre's 'Geometry') and one from the German (Goethe's 'Wilhelm Meister'). The latter work, praised by 'Blackwood's' and the 'Edinburgh,' was attacked by De Quincey in 'The London Magazine' to which Carlyle had been contributing his 'Life of Schiller,' the last chapters of which actually appeared simultaneously with the unjustifiable attack. Whatever pain may have been caused by De Quincey was more than assuaged by the commendation by Goethe, who wrote a eulogistic introduction to a translation of the Schiller volume which was published at Frankfort in 1830, three years after Carlyle's period of apprenticeship may be said to have been brought to a close with his studies of German Romance. Meanwhile, Carlyle had met Jeffrey and become a contributor to 'The Edinburgh Review.'

One of the real curiosities of literature is the distinction between the form of Carlyle's early writings and that known as 'Carlylese,' the undoubtedly powerful, but electrical, explosive, ejaculatory style whose beginning may be noted in his 'Sartor Resartus,' a work of autobiographical as well as of philosophical interest, which, originally published in 'Fraser's Magazine,' first won adequate recognition in America.

The reader who would study Carlyle should begin by digesting Professor Nichol's masterly monograph in the 'English Men of Letters' series ; Froude's contentious pages may be left for a later stage.

Carlyle's greatest works are those in history, sociology and politics. But there is a great deal in his miscellaneous essays—those on Burns, Johnson, Scott, Voltaire, Diderot and Mirabeau, for example—that must not be overlooked by any reader who desires to understand the man himself. Carlyle has been greatly misunderstood ; but his influence has been almost incalculable in Germany as well as in England. He was 'human, like ourselves' ; more, perhaps, of an iconoclast and a prophet than a constructive power ; but he looked to the 'foundations of society,' he had a genuine love of truth, and his striving after truth has left to posterity a standard of thought which must remain a permanent social as well as literary force.

Appreciations—and depreciations—of his labours there are in abundance, but perhaps Walt Whitman touched the reality :

As a representative author, a literary figure, no man else will bequeath to the future more significant hints of our stormy era, its fierce paradoxes, its din, and its struggling periods than Carlyle. He belongs to our own branch of the stock, too ; neither Latin nor Greek, but altogether Gothic. Rugged, mountainous, volcanic, he was himself more a French Revolution than any of his volumes. . . . As launching into the self-complacent atmosphere of our days a rasping. questioning, dislocating agitation and shock, is Carlyle's final value.

Carlyle began life, in a sense, by teaching mathematics in a Fifeshire school ; he remained a teacher to the end of the chapter. As a stylist he is the greatest 'free lance' in the language ; but the reader should beware lest he impute to the leader the sins of his would-be followers, as many a one has sought to thunder in Carlylean strain with the most unhappy results. Where Carlyle's style is concerned we must not judge him by the standard of any other writer ; he claims by right to be judged by the vivid (and vivifying) result. Of no great writer could it be said with more cogency that 'the style is the man.'

It is impossible in a few words to formulate any plan for the special study of Carlyle. From the wide range of his writings the general reader will take to such works as his fancy prompts, the student to those his studies suggest, and both may be left safely to come under the all-compelling influence of this virile and original thinker. Of Carlyle's works the general reader should at least be acquainted with 'The French Revolution,' 'Sartor Resartus,' 'Heroes and Hero Worship' and 'The Life of John Sterling.' If one begins with 'Heroes and Hero Worship,' the appetite is more likely to be whetted than by entering the Carlyle treasure-house through the gate of 'The French Revolution.'

Wellnigh as interesting as anything Carlyle wrote was the story of his own married life, which, indeed, has been fruitful of more controversy than any of his boldest assertions in the domain of philosophy. Jane Welsh Carlyle (1801–66) was almost as notable a personality as her husband, for her 'Letters and Memorials' prove her to have been one of the most accomplished women of her time, a shrewd critic, and fit to rank with the great letter-writers who have contributed no inconsiderable proportion of what we call our national literature. Mrs. Alexander Ireland wrote an excellent Life of Mrs. Carlyle.

Macaulay. Carlyle's greatest contemporary as an essayist and historian was Thomas Babington Macaulay (1800–59). Unlike Carlyle, Macaulay did not confine his labours to the desk. He was a public official and a member of Parliament as well as a man of letters. After a careful education he became famous at the age of twenty-five as the writer of an essay on Milton in 'The Edinburgh Review.' In this Review all his best-known essays appeared, if we except the biographies of Atterbury, Bunyan, Goldsmith, Johnson and Pitt, which were contributed to 'The Encyclopædia Britannica.' The Essays are rich in applied knowledge, drawn from the exceptionally retentive memory of an omnivorous reader. The judgements they contain, where these are not affected by the author's Whig sympathies, are usually sound. For a parallel to their diversity of subject-matter we must go to Landor's 'Conversations.'

Macaulay was essentially a popular writer, one whose purpose was to think for his reader and to leave nothing to chance. Whole generations may be said to have been nurtured on his writings. His influence will always be considerable both as a stylist and as an historian, though he needs careful editing.

His great quality is clearness of diction, which he shares with Cobbett, his great art that of detail-decorated abbreviation ; but his use of a succession of short sentences, while agreeable to the eye, is not invariably acceptable to the ear. His use of antithesis is responsible for much deplorably ineffective imitation. He remains, withal, a brilliant writer ; but, being brilliant, is hard. What he gains in glitter he misses in emotion ; he does not delve very deeply into the heart of things ; but without his aid many men and women of average insight and ability would never have been able to see so far or so well as they have seen. In this connexion the educative value of Macaulay's writings cannot easily be exaggerated ; it may be more easily satirized. In the realm of prose his relation to Carlyle is that of Tennyson to Browning in the realm of poetry, although Macaulay in his clear brilliance may better be compared with Pope. It is curious to note that, in judging Scott, both Carlyle and Macaulay erred, if at all, on the side of severity ; but it is useful to remember that neither had the Journal before him.

Macaulay has been infinitely happier in his biographer than was Carlyle in Froude ; the fine tribute of his nephew, Sir George Otto Trevelyan, to his memory reveals to us a family affection undisclosed in the Essays.

J. S. Mill. Perhaps the greatest of Carlyle's contemporaries was John Stuart Mill (1806–73), the philosopher whose 'System of Logic,' 'Principles of Political Economy,'

'On Liberty,' and 'Subjection of Women' will not be read for any literary graces if they do not attract the student in search of profitable mental exercise. It would be difficult to overestimate the influence of the 'Saint of Rationalism' (Gladstone's apt phrase) on contemporary thought in politics, logic and ethics.

A vigorous freedom of criticism, a display of conscience in judgement, and a certain earnestness in matters of the mind remained a worthy characteristic of the Victorian age, though tending to ponderosity and eventually declining into mere dullness. Many are the names that might be mentioned in this relation, but four only shall be alluded to here : Edward FitzGerald (1809–83), of Omar Khayyam fame, mainly for his wonderful letters—amongst others those to Fanny Kemble ; Dr. John Brown (1810–82), the essayist, almost comparable with Lamb in lucidity, for his exquisite 'Rab and His Friends' ; John Forster (1812–76) for his excellent 'Life of Dickens' and 'The Life and Times of Oliver Goldsmith,' one of the best biographies in English literature ; and George Eliot's friend, George Henry Lewes (1817–78), a most able encyclopedist with a great gift of popularizing the abstruse. His 'History of Philosophy' and 'Life of Goethe' are very competent works ; 'On Actors and the Art of Acting' is another of his books that will repay study. Lewes founded 'The Fortnightly Review,' which still exists—as a monthly.

Froude. The name of James Anthony Froude (1818–94) has been the centre of a veritable whirlwind of controversy, which relates to literary history rather than to the study of literature. The friend of Carlyle, whose literary executor he was, Froude had much of Carlyle's sincerity and he was not less able as a writer. Indeed, he stands with the supreme prose masters of the century, his thought often soaring to heights of true eloquence. But he rivalled Macaulay in partisanship when he wrote history, which was the main concern of his literary life. Froude's contentious character colours all he wrote, yet his 'Nemesis of Faith,' in which he reveals with deep sincerity his religious doubts, and 'Oceana'—a delightful account of a voyage to Australia—are fascinating books, and his 'Short Studies on Great Subjects' constitute one of the most brilliant and engaging series of essays and papers that ever emanated from one hand.

Sensitive Masters of the Art of Criticism

A GREAT social force, as well as a great critic, was **John Ruskin** (1819–1900). Among his paramount services to criticism were his early recognition of Turner's genius and his defence of the pre-Raphaelites (*see* Lesson 17 in our Course on Art). He was the most influential art-critic of the century ; but his authority, like that of many eminent Victorians, suffered diminution during the early years of this century. Today he is quoted by most writers on painting, sculpture and architecture, and his ideas are frequently in accordance with the deepest thought of our time. The centre of his artistic creed was belief in 'Truth to Nature,' but he upheld the structural artist who explained natural forms against the artist who gave a momentary impression of them. Thus he praised Holman Hunt and Turner and blamed Constable and Whistler.

He imparted an incalculable impetus to the raising of the standard of labour ; whatever nature of labour it may be, it can hardly be regarded without some respect by anyone who has come under the influence of Ruskin's teaching. Like Carlyle, and, in a lesser degree, like Froude, Ruskin gloried in the power of imparting and inspiring enthusiasm. He sought after the truth with all the ardour of Carlyle, and the student of his works will witness how, time after time, he was compelled by his own discoveries to relinquish positions he at one time thought to be unassailable. His was the scientific spirit of inquiry—even his drawings he regarded rather as of scientific than of artistic importance.

Ruskin was the embodiment of the spirit of reverence, and a high priest of the temple of beauty. He has opened our eyes to the infinite variety and charm of external Nature, and even the clouds have a different meaning to us since Ruskin wrote about them. His style glows with rich colour, and is full of musical sweetness. It is impregnated with the influence of Bible study, an influence which, however, can be realized only by those whose knowledge of the Bible corresponds in some measure to Ruskin's own intimate grasp of it. Everything he wrote is worth reading, from 'The Seven Lamps of Architecture' to 'Fors Clavigera.' A modern analysis of his life and work is contained in 'John Ruskin' by R. H. Wilenski ; the author, in summarizing, accepts Ruskin as a lawgiver, and acknowledges his vital contributions to the theories of sociology and aesthetics.

Matthew Arnold (1822–88), whose work as a poet has already been discussed (*see* page 137), combined social with literary criticism. He foretold the fall of the aristocracy, and distrusted the middle classes, but much that has been written and said concerning his 'contempt for unintellectual people' is unjustified, and caused him no small amount of disquiet, as his 'Letters' —especially the epistle written to his mother in 1868—testify. As a writer, he had much in common with Sainte-Beuve, perhaps the greatest literary critic of the nineteenth century, his standpoint in regard to art and letters being in many respects more French than English. First and foremost, he was a scholar and valued scholarship highly. His 'Essays in Criticism,' 'Culture and Anarchy,' 'Literature and Dogma,' and an earlier work 'On Translating Homer' are his most widely read books.

Another critic born in the same year as Arnold was **David Masson** (1822–1907). A Scottish author and editor of erudition and broad sympathies, he wrote much for encyclopedias, reviews, and the periodical press, and his contributions to our knowledge of the English novelists, and of De Quincey, Chatterton, Carlyle, Drummond of Hawthornden and—especially—Ben Jonson, are of value. His greatest work is his 'Life of John Milton, Narrated in Connection with the Political, Ecclesiastical and Literary History of his Time,' a work which has been described as the most complete biography of any Englishman. Masson held chairs of English Literature in University College, London, and (1865–95) at Edinburgh.

Goldwin Smith (1823–1910) had the true Carlylean independence and intolerance in his outlook on society, and although most that he wrote has a professional dryness of style, he could be attractive on purely literary subjects, as witness his books on Cowper and Jane Austen, and also his essays. But he was essentially an exponent of history and a controversialist. Another of that generation of thinkers was Alfred Russel Wallace (1823–1913)—famous also for his independent working out of the theory of natural selection chiefly associated with Charles Darwin—who wrote in good fluent style, especially in 'Travels on the Amazon' and 'The Malay Archipelago,' whilst Augustus Jessopp (1824–1914) had an attractive manner in such books as 'The Coming of the Friars' and 'Trials of a Country Parson.'

Victorian Journalism. Periodical journalism was now at its literary best in the weeklies like 'The Saturday Review,' 'The Examiner' and 'The Spectator' and in the monthlies like 'Blackwood's ' and 'The Cornhill,' and, of course, in the quarterlies. Their peculiar use was to give encouragement to good writers and also to produce men like Holt Hutton of 'The Spectator,' William Minto of 'The Examiner,' Henry Morley, who also edited that journal in the course of his wonderful career as a popularizer of good literature, and Walter Bagehot (1826–77), editor of 'The Economist,' who wrote authoritative works on ' The English Constitution ' and 'Lombard Street, ' and in 'Physics and Politics,' made an attempt to apply Darwinian ideas to political development.

Frederic Harrison (1831–1923) was a young man when Carlyle had his generation by the ears, and he profited accordingly. He was a true scholar, who found his chief delight in the study of history, on which he wrote much and wisely. His interest in the Byzantine period induced him to try his hand at historic romance with 'Theophano,' but he was essentially a biographer, a literary critic—his instructive volume ' On the Choice of Books' should be noted—and a writer on positivism, philosophy and religion.

Sir Leslie Stephen (1832–1904), brother and biographer of Sir James Fitzjames Stephen of 'The Saturday Review,' edited 'The Cornhill' and wrote much in biography. He was the original editor of 'The Dictionary of National Biography,' and in 'An Agnostic's Apology' made one of the most valuable additions to the literature of rationalism. His clear, unadorned style, just a trifle icy, is entirely suited to his clear argument. His 'Hours in a Library' should on no account be overlooked. Born in the same year as Stephen was the brilliant Irishman Stopford A. Brooke (1832–1916), who won renown as a Unitarian preacher as well as a critic. His 'Primer of English Literature' has been of great service to generations of young students, and his study of Tennyson is still unexcelled. On Early English, he is especially valuable.

Watts-Dunton and Swinburne. A particularly sensitive critic of literature—especially poetry—and one of the most potent critical forces of the last century, was Theodore Watts-Dunton (1832–1914). His 'Studies of Shakespeare' and 'The Renascence of Wonder' are notable productions, but for some of his most remarkable work the student must turn to 'The Encyclopædia Britannica' and the leading reviews. For some forty years he was the close friend and companion of Algernon Charles Swinburne (1837–1909), whose poetry has already received attention (Lesson 27). As a critic Swinburne had the faults of over-statement and passionate praise, which anyone would expect who first met him as a poet. His prose was the fine, vibrant prose of a poet, and his biographical and critical studies, ranging from the Elizabethans to the Victorians, offer unusual opportunities for the awakening of enthusiasms. If the reader is careful not to place himself too completely at the critic's disposition he will have considerable increase of literary understanding. Philip Gilbert Hamerton (1834–94) wrote a series of letters on 'The Intellectual Life,' which literary aspirants should not neglect.

Carlyle had written nearly everything of his that mattered by the time **John, Lord Morley** (1838–1923) was twenty-one, but although we know that Morley was the pupil of John Stuart Mill—whence the austerity of his literary style—there are few whose names occur in this Lesson that gave more evidence of having been influenced by the liberal ideas which the Sage of Chelsea set himself to implant in the mind of his generation. His 'Life of Gladstone' is his magnum opus, but before it appeared in 1903 he had won a European reputation by his studies of Burke, Voltaire, Rousseau, Diderot, Cobden, Cromwell and Machiavelli.

Two other eminent men of affairs born in the same year as Lord Morley, and whose literary work also entitles them to rank among the prose masters of the century, are Sir George Trevelyan (1838–1928), whose 'Life of Lord Macaulay' is one of the great biographies, and Lord Bryce (1838–1922), whose principal productions, 'The Holy Roman Empire' and 'The American Commonwealth,' are standard works.

Pater and Symonds. Eminent among the other critics who lent distinction to English letters in the latter part of the nineteenth century was Walter Horatio Pater (1839–94), whose exclusiveness was akin to that which so long kept Matthew Arnold aloof from the average reader, and whose 'Sketches in the History of the Renaissance,' 'Imaginary Portraits' and 'Appreciations' are marked by an exotic beauty of style, refinement of taste, breadth of culture, and keenness of insight. Into the point of view of Walter Pater it is not here necessary to enter, but this must come into consideration where the permanent value of his literary work is under appraisement.

A similar remark is called for in regard to the writings of another hedonist, John Addington Symonds (1840–93), who also helped to bring the bright side of the Renaissance, as well as that of Elizabethan England, before English readers. The splendid selfishness of these writers, however, cannot compensate for all the problems they left untouched. To them, engrossed in their introspection, it mattered not that the times were out of joint—as the times of their aesthetic movement, culminating in Oscar Wilde's writings, undoubtedly were.

LESSON 40

Versatile Prose Writers of the Late 19th Century

IT has already been frankly admitted that mere chronological order in the survey of a long and rich literature is almost as arbitrary a method of treatment as alphabetical order, but for the purpose of these Lessons it has advantages that cannot be denied. In the present Lesson it has the further justification that, of the critics, essayists and prose writers who figured most prominently in the literary activities of the second half of the nineteenth century, and in their own individual ways represented the later Victorian stream of thought, at least a dozen were born in the decade 1840–50 and had established their reputations before the century ended, although the majority of them were alive and still industrious when the twentieth century was well under way.

Critics and Essayists. First of these was Austin Dobson (1840–1921), not a great prose writer but still a moderately good one. While he was elegant and charming in verse, he was somewhat self-conscious in prose, for, avoiding the ornate, he tended at times towards the bald. His 'Eighteenth Century Vignettes' are, however, full of an old-world charm.

William John Courthope (1842–1917), sometime professor of English poetry at Oxford, published an exhaustive 'History of English Poetry' in six volumes which ranks as his chief work, but his 'Life of Pope,' written for his standard edition of Pope's works, and his 'Life of Addison' are also of value.

Edward Dowden (1843–1913), the gifted Irish critic, was a student of French and English literature, and his works on Shelley and on Shakespeare in particular have become classic. Every student should own Dowden's 'Introduction to Shakespeare.'

In his own day Andrew Lang (1844–1912) was the recipient of a more generous measure of adulation than he is likely to receive from posterity. A ripe scholar and exceptionally versatile man, he produced some first-rate translations from the Greek, and was poet, critic, philosopher, biographer, essayist, novelist, historian. In truth, there was not much in a literary way that he did not try his hand at, with a temporary degree of success. He was the brightest literary journalist of his age, but his historical work abounds in error ; his literary judgements, always delivered in the most engaging phrases, are not free from asperity and prejudice ; and in matters where he was no sort of authority he spoke with a cocksureness that fortunately did not always persuade his readers. But the literary student will enjoy Andrew Lang's critical works, such as 'Books and Bookmen,' 'Letters to Dead Authors,' 'Letters on Literature' and 'Essays in Little.'

John Churton Collins (1848–1908) was a skilled professional critic of literature. His knowledge of English literature prior to his own day was as profound and accurate as his knowledge of contemporary letters was slight and perfunctory. His most competent works, such as 'Studies in Shakespeare,' 'Greek Influence on English Poetry' and 'Voltaire, Montesquieu and Rousseau in England,' should be read for their scholarship.

In Sir Edmund Gosse (1849–1928) urbanity and literary scholarship were happily combined. Although he wrote much he seldom wrote hastily, his judgements are usually convincing, and his work is as assured of permanence as any modern criticism of letters can be. Either in critical biography or in pure criticism, the student has a wide choice among his works. 'Gossip in a Library,' 'French Profiles' and his 'Life of Congreve' are representative works, and in 'Father and Son' he gave a fine and dignified study in the intimacies of biography.

Lord Rosebery (1847–1929) must be declared a might-have-been in literature as he was in politics. But his literary achievement is the more lasting ; it is, indeed, so substantial that it is regrettable that he did not devote himself to the life of letters, where the highest success as a master of prose was easily within his attainment. Everything that he wrote is informed with the subtle charm of a winning personality and the magical contact of a true bookman. There is some excellent criticism of letters in his 'Appreciations and Addresses,' and also in his later work, 'Miscellanies, Literary and Historical,' while such studies as 'Pitt,' 'Napoleon : the Last Phase' and 'Oliver Cromwell' prove that he could have stood with the best of his age.

William Hurrell Mallock (1849–1923), a nephew of Froude, was the master of a very brilliant and incisive prose style, which he used with great effect in his many writings on philosophy and fiction. He was greatly concerned all his life with religious and political questions, but although 'The New Republic' and 'The New Paul and Virginia,' which appeared about the beginning of his literary career, have both had a vogue and may still find readers, the stuff of immortality is not in his work.

Writers on Nature. Thirty-nine years, and three or four of them years of pain and hardship, were all that were measured out to Richard Jefferies (1848–87). He was thirty before he made a real success with 'The Gamekeeper at Home.' Nine years later he was dead, yet a whole shelf-ful of memorable books forms his legacy to us : novels, descriptive essays, autobiography. The reader will not regret whatever time he gives to Jefferies, and he will find in him how his native tongue can be written with a joyous expressiveness which on analysis seems to be so simple that it might be thought to be entirely effortless, though writers know that the greatest pains have often been exerted where there is least evidence of any. Jefferies was a conscious artist in words, just as he was a conscious philosopher in his reading of earth's secrets. His acquaintance with the teeming life of the hedgerow was accurate, not sentimental, penetrative, not superficial. 'The Story of My Heart' is one of the most engrossing books of confession in our language.

William Henry Hudson (1841–1922) must be placed with the best of the prose masters of his age and in the very forefront of writers about Nature. His style, which is so perfectly contrived for the forthright expression of his observations and opinions that it seems to make use of the only possible words, and those the simplest, has that rare and tenuous charm which pleases continuously without ever making us conscious of the art that is the source of our pleasure. He has no sort of resemblance to Stevenson, and yet in this matter of pure prose he is his peer. Everything of Hudson's will repay reading : no man in our time looked upon wild Nature with a more understanding eye or depicted it with a more friendly pen. 'The Naturalist in La Plata' and 'Far Away and Long Ago' may be singled out from his many books for particular commendation, and 'The Purple Land' and 'Green Mansions'— this last containing his wonderful creation Rima—are notable rather for their style than for their stories. Many of his writings are devoted to birds, though in 'A Shepherd's Life,' one of his finest Nature books, the descriptions of countryside characters, of sheep-dogs, foxes and rabbits and of the wide grasslands of Salisbury Plain, are all lovely things grouped round the central figure of an old Wiltshire shepherd from whom Hudson got much of his material.

Ernest Thompson Seton (b. 1860) wrote 'Wild Animals I Have Known' and much else in similar vein, illustrated by himself. Edward Grey, Viscount Grey of Fallodon (1862–1933), showed unusual gifts in 'Fly Fishing' (1899) and 'The Charm of Birds' (1925).

R.L.S. The name that rubricates the two closing decades of the nineteenth century is that of Robert Louis Stevenson (1850–94) ; and that because Stevenson was the true herald of a return to literary style in an age when slovenliness was common. Stevenson realized with Lowell that the true preservative of literature is style. He never wrote a careless or ill-considered phrase. Thus 'Kidnapped' and 'Treasure Island' were originally written for a boy's paper, in which disregard of literary grace might have been excused if due respect were paid to the laws of grammar. Yet they were written with all that sensitive feeling for the rhythm of prose, with all that savour of the right and just word which marked his finest work.

Stevenson has been described as 'the happiest master of vagabond discourse in the whole of the nineteenth century.' He began as an essayist, and his chief prose works, apart from fiction, are 'An Inland Voyage,' 'Travels with a Donkey in the Cevennes,' 'Virginibus Puerisque,' 'Familiar Studies of Men and Books,' 'Memories and Portraits,' and 'Across the Plains.'

He won fame as a writer of romance, and then in his intimate prose essays revealed to the public a most winning personality. Some of his best prose is to be found in his short stories, wherein he excelled all his contemporaries.

LESSON 41

Critics and Essayists at the Turn of the Century

IT is when the end of a century looms near that the weakness of the system of 'thinking in centuries' becomes manifest. There is then a tendency to indulge in a kind of intellectual stock-taking and in an assessment of values, heedless of the fact that, in respect of literature particularly, the perspective of time is all-important to the forming of a lasting estimate. The defects of this system are all the more manifest when the end of a century coincides so exactly with the end of an age as that of the nineteenth century did with the close of the Victorian age. Actually, of course, in matters of the mind, change is no more abrupt between one century and another than between any one year and another, and the current of literature flows on in one unbroken stream. Thus many of the writers—Samuel Butler, Hardy and H. G. Wells, for instance—who were prominent in the latter part of the nineteenth century, were emerging from Victorian ideas of permanency and of belief in the perfection of present civilization, while many have done the more important part of their work in the lifetime of the present generation.

A leading critic for many years was Professor George Saintsbury (1845–1933), a veritable storehouse of literary knowledge, with a range wellnigh universal and a fine humanity in his interests. His works are numerous—'A History of Criticism' is especially valuable—and their scholarship is unassailable ; their critical content is distinguished by knowledge and acute perception, but is expressed in phrases oddly rugged and often unkempt.

Almost coeval with Professor Saintsbury was Augustine Birrell (1850–1933), widely known as the author of 'Obiter Dicta,' 'Res Judicatae,' 'Men, Women and Books,' and a collected edition of suave and charming 'Essays' prefaced by a characteristically frank and revealing introduction. Pleasure and profit are to be gathered from everything he wrote. Birrell belonged to the amateurs of the pen, as literature was never more than a walking-stick to him ; the law and politics were his crutches. But it is a very elegant walking-stick.

Alice Meynell (1850–1922) wrote profoundly meditative and beautiful essays possessing exceptional grace of diction. Her literary criticism was penetrating and sympathetic, revealing her acquaintance with life. The student of lovely and living prose should on no account miss 'The Collected Essays of Alice Meynell' (1914). Her touch is sure, and her severely disciplined emotions permitted clarity of vision.

Sir William Robertson Nicoll (1851–1923) played a most important part in the literary world of his time, exercising great influence through the medium of 'The British Weekly.' He was a critic of the utmost catholicity, nearly always right in his opinions, as his taste in letters was delicate and true. Though not to be classed among the prose masters, he had a style that was supple and pleasing ; and he failed of a high and permanent place among the great critics of literature only because he was too much of a journalist to take the excessive pains that literature demands.

Clement K. Shorter (1857–1926) was still another journalist who was also a distinguished man of letters. Both from a literary and a pictorial standpoint he introduced a new spirit into English illustrated journalism, and through his weekly Literary Letter in 'The Sphere,' which he founded in 1900, he acquired an influence hardly less than that of Sir William Robertson Nicoll. As a critic and biographer Shorter specialized in the Brontës, George Borrow and Napoleon, and his 'Handbook of Victorian Literature' should be noted by the student.

Sir Walter Raleigh (1861–1922), professor of English literature at Glasgow during 1890–1904 and then at Oxford from 1904 until his death, gave us much important literary criticism in his monographs on 'The English Novel' and on 'Style,' and in his studies of Milton, Wordsworth and Shakespeare.

Arthur Christopher Benson (1862–1925) was the eldest of the three sons of Archbishop Benson, all of whom achieved some distinction in the world of letters. His best critical work is contained in his monographs on Rossetti, Edward FitzGerald and Walter Pater, but he is noteworthy also for having won for the essay a popularity rivalling that of the successful novel. Beginning with 'The Upton Letters,' published anonymously in 1905, he produced a number of volumes of essays, 'From a College Window,' 'The Gate of Death,' and others, weakened by his habit of playing for safety with the provision of alternatives, and by a too easy fluency, but with a mellow surface of culture that greatly pleased a wide public.

Sir Arthur Quiller-Couch (1863–1944) first made a reputation as a novelist, and in that capacity is the subject of further attention in Lesson 51, but has made a later and perhaps more enduring name as a critic of literature. 'The Oxford Book of English Verse,' which he edited in 1900, ranks with the very best anthologies, and equally scholarly discrimination is manifested in later anthologies of Ballads, Victorian Verse, and Prose. Appointed King Edward VII Professor of English Literature at Cambridge in 1912, he attracted large audiences to his lectures, which, collected under the titles 'On the Art of Writing ' and 'On the Art of Reading,' have since had very wide distribution in volume form. No student should fail to make the acquaintance of these works. Quiller-Couch's 'Studies in Literature,' 'Charles Dickens and other Victorians,' and ' Shakespeare's Workmanship ' should also be read.

Other writers whom we must mention briefly here are Arthur Machen (b. 1863), who in 'The Hill of Dreams,' 'The House of Souls,' ' Far Off Things,' and other rare and individual works, has shown himself almost too much of an artist in words, but still an adept at suggesting colour and atmosphere, a master of the short story and the essay ; Arthur Symons (b. 1865), a real prose master, author of numerous works in criticism, interpretative biography, description and the spirit of place ; and Richard Le Gallienne (b. 1866), who has written with distinction on many literary subjects since he produced his brilliant study of Meredith in 1890. C. E. Montague (1867–1928), a journalist of distinction and author of 'A Hind Let Loose,' wrote a fine volume of essays, 'The Right Place '; and E. V. Lucas (1868–1938) won great popularity by essays and travel sketches in facile vein.

Bennett and Wells. There yet remain two men born in this same decade who must be mentioned in this Lesson, although they, too, will receive fuller consideration in the Lessons dealing with English fiction. Arnold Bennett (1867–1931) is an outstanding example of a man who went into the writing business in the same spirit as others go into stockbroking, engineering, or the brewing trade. From the first he set out to write, and to make money by writing, fiction, both in what may be called the 'grand manner' and also in the more popular style, critical essays, reviews, daily journalism, plays—almost everything in the domain of general literature save poetry. He was a noteworthy product of the changes in time by which the essay has become the article and the prose writer finds in the columns of the newspapers an opportunity of addressing audiences incalculably larger than he can ever hope to reach through the medium of the bound book. Arnold Bennett's weekly notes on books in an evening newspaper had an influence that was almost incredible and has been acquired by no other writer of the time. Into much of this ephemeral criticism he also put an amount of personality that presents him as a far more engaging figure than he appears in much of his fiction. His 'Journals' will almost certainly rank as one of the most revealing self-portraits by any literary man.

The other notable figure is Herbert George Wells (b. 1866), the most astonishing figure in the English world of letters today. His intellectual vitality is inexhaustible, his range of interests immensely wide. Profoundly curious about life and its meaning, Wells is, indeed, more an intelligence than a personality. During both the World Wars no writer of established reputation so considerably extended his influence, the direct discussion of old and new problems partly taking the place of the fictional appeal. He was, too, author of the encyclopædic ' Outline of History,' 'Science of Life,' and ' Work, Wealth and Happiness of Mankind.'

Hilaire Belloc (b. 1870) is one of the most accomplished and versatile of English men of letters. An essayist of lightest touch, deft artist in descriptive narrative, an engaging novelist, brilliant biographer, a writer of verse, learned exponent of French history, authoritative critic of military affairs, a student of politics—he is one of the few who, in an age of narrow specialization, have maintained the larger tradition of the finest periods of literature by displaying a wide range of interest and confident power in many branches of the art. As an historian he identifies himself intimately with the period on which he happens to be writing. 'A traveller in time,' he returns in creative imagination to an age that is gone. But, first and last, he is an essayist with a notable gift of humour, at once urbane and hearty, which lights up most of his writing. 'The Path to Rome' is one of his most characteristic works.

Gilbert Keith Chesterton (1874–1936) was pre-eminent among recent critics and miscellaneous writers. No man ever ventilated his opinion on social and religious matters with more engaging frankness. Whether his use of paradox as a literary device did or did not sometimes lead him whither he had not intended to go is perhaps arguable ; but he was always interesting, and probably most interesting when the reader least agrees with his opinions. Assuredly the Chestertonian slogan was 'To be Interesting is Everything.' Nevertheless, you cannot read him in such works as his 'Dickens,' 'George Bernard Shaw,' or 'The Victorian Age in Literature,' without stimulation, and his numerous collections of essays, like 'All

Things Considered' and 'Tremendous Trifles,' are unfailing sources of entertainment. His literary style, though always nervous and bright, lacked that agreeable touch of courtliness which gives distinction to the prose of his friend and sometime collaborator, Hilaire Belloc. As historians of England, they both took the standpoint that the Reformation was a criminal blunder which destroyed the golden age of medieval faith ; both were engaged in controversies which centred round their advocacy of Roman Catholicism. G. K. C.'s Autobiography appeared in 1936.

R. B. Cunninghame Graham (1852–1936) was a romantic literary figure. The eldest son of a Scottish laird, he became at various periods in his life a strike leader, an anarchist, a great traveller, a Member of Parliament, a Justice of the Peace, and a Deputy Lieutenant. From his 'Mogreb-el-Acksa' (Morocco the Most Holy) Bernard Shaw took most of the local colour for 'Captain Brassbound's Conversion,' acknowledging the theft in a vividly descriptive sketch of Cunninghame Graham appended to the play. Other vigorous and fascinating writings include 'Progress,' 'His People' and 'Scottish Stories.'

LESSON 42

Some Notable Writers of Today

THE twentieth-century prose writers carry forward the literary tradition on lines somewhat different from those that were followed by the writers of even the later part of the previous century. We have seen how the newspaper and the magazine diverted the great eighteenth-century talent for letter-writing from private into public channels. What now becomes noticeable is how the changes in the newspapers and magazines themselves have modified the style and, to a considerable extent, the point of view of those whom we call the writers of today. In the main the essay has become the 'article,' and the article, as a rule, has a very definite character foreign to the essay proper. This is due in its turn to the progress of that popular movement inaugurated by the first Reform Act, and the rise of the newspaper press. The article is, in other words, the answer to the demand of the people for concise information on subjects which they have had no special opportunity to study.

With the widespread development of education, the specialized power of the pen passed from the hands of an exclusive 'literary' class ; the men of letters ceased to be a sort of priesthood. There is no literary 'class' today, although vastly more men and women make their livelihood by the pen than in any previous age. There is no literary class, because so many are potentially literary who are content to remain readers. Then, again, those who write for a livelihood must address themselves to the interpretation and solution of what are called 'questions of the day,' because it is 'journalistic interest' that rules. These 'questions,' it is true, are often literary in a sense, but every writer who now secures any considerable hold upon the public is compelled to recognize that life is greater than literature.

It was in journalism that George Bernard Shaw (b. 1856) began his career, as a dramatic critic and then, after joining the Fabian Society, became the champion of socialism, 'not'—in the words of G. K. Chesterton—'as a matter of sentiment but as a matter of common sense. The realism that he applied to the industrial problem he proceeded to apply with mordant wit and infinite zest to many other things, including vegetarianism and anti-vaccination.' Detailed reference has already been made to his distinctively individual genius in Lesson 19 (page 121), dealing with his plays, and here it suffices to name two of his more recent non-dramatic works, ' The Intelligent Woman's Guide to Socialism and Capitalism,' and 'Adventures of a Black Girl in Search of God.'

The twentieth century has witnessed a great increase in the output and circulation of books other than fiction. In the years between the two Great Wars a hundred books by essayists and descriptive writers seemingly found readers where formerly not more than five would have interested a publisher. This is a healthy sign, and so, too, is the increasing interest in history, in critical and biographical studies and in personal reminiscences and autobiography.

Scientific Books. That there is also a considerable public intelligently interested in scientific subjects lucidly presented is evidenced by the large sale enjoyed by such works as Sir James Jeans's 'The Mysterious Universe'; 'An Outline of Modern Knowledge,' edited by Dr. William Rose ; and Professor Lancelot Hogben's 'Mathematics for the Million' and 'Science for the Citizen.' Julian Huxley (b. 1887), a biologist of repute, is another writer whose scientific works, written alone or in collaboration with other such eminent men as Professor J. B. S. Haldane and H. G. Wells, have a very considerable circulation. Havelock Ellis (1859–1939) gathered a large audience for his psychological and philosophical studies ; and Bertrand (3rd earl) Russell (b. 1872) holds a foremost place among mathematicians and philosophers, and provokes wide interest by his keenly intellectual lucubrations on a variety of scientific, philosophic, ethical, economic and social problems.

History and Biography. Among the writers who have devoted themselves to history and biography, a prominent place must be accorded to the Right Hon. Winston Churchill (b. 1874), who has crowded into his life a quite extraordinary number and variety of activities and adventures. His first book, 'The Story of the Malakand Field Force,' was published in 1898, when he was only twenty-four, and

it was followed in 1899 by 'The River War.' His Life of his father, Lord Randolph Churchill, published in 1906, is an addition to the small number of first-rate biographies in our literature, and the same tribute may be paid with even greater justice to his biography of his great ancestor, the first duke of Marlborough. His most important contribution to history in the grand manner is 'The World Crisis,' published in four volumes between 1923 and 1929 ; Mr. Churchill may be confidently expected to retain a high place among historians. In 1941 and 1942 collections of his speeches appeared under the titles 'Into Battle ' and 'The Unrelenting Struggle.'

Lytton Strachey (1880–1932) introduced a new style into biography of which the preface to his 'Eminent Victorians' is the manifesto. He declined to treat his subjects as models for academy portraits or memorial statues, and presented them instead on the human level as men and women. Read without prejudice, he neither shocks nor depreciates. 'Eminent Victorians,' 'Queen Victoria' and 'Elizabeth and Essex' are the books by which he will be remembered.

Other biographers who may be singled out for mention are Philip Guedalla (b. 1889), who, with his 'Palmerston,' 'Gladstone and Palmerston,' 'The Duke,' 'Mr. Churchill : a Portrait' and other studies, shares the principles of writing created by Lytton Strachey ; Lord David Cecil, who began his distinguished literary career with 'The Stricken Deer,' a noteworthy life of Cowper ; Percy Lubbock, with his 'Samuel Pepys' and, more importantly, his 'Earlham,' a charmingly fragrant Quaker family history ; Lascelles Abercrombie, with his 'Thomas Hardy,' though his critical works, 'The Theory of Poetry' and 'The Idea of Great Poetry,' are more valuable to the student ; Charles Williams, who has illuminated the Tudor and Stuart periods with his 'Henry VII,' 'Elizabeth,' James I,' 'Bacon' and 'Rochester,' and his play 'Thomas Cranmer of Canterbury,' and is also a distinguished poet and literary critic and author of 'The Vision of Beatrice,' and other esoteric works. Edith Sitwell, a writer of entirely delightful English prose, whose 'Alexander Pope' is of first-rate quality, both as biography and as criticism ; with her must be named her brothers, Osbert Sitwell (b. 1892), author of, among many other books, 'Before the Bombardment,' with its sequel 'Those were the Days,' and in a different genre 'Winters of Content' ; and Sacheverell Sitwell (b. 1897),

Anthony Trollope

Charlotte Brontë

Charles Reade

George Eliot

Charles Kingsley

S. Baring-Gould

VICTORIAN NOVELISTS. Trollope is beloved for his 'Barsetshire' novels, Charlotte Brontë for 'Jane Eyre' and Reade for 'The Cloister and the Hearth.' George Eliot (Marian Evans) showed unusual perception and emotional power. Kingsley's vigour and sympathy are seen in his historical and sociological novels and his immortal 'Water Babies' and 'Heroes.' Baring-Gould wrote West Country tales and Wilkie Collins the thrilling novels 'The Woman in White' and 'The Moonstone.'

Portrait of George Eliot after F. D'Albret Durade; portrait of Wilkie Collins after Millais

Wilkie Collins

LESSON 47

G

GEORGE MEREDITH, novelist and poet, applied his keen intellect to the serious problems of life, showing remarkable psychological insight. His brilliant epigrammatic style is too complex to be generally appreciated.

From the etching by Mortimer Menpes

THOMAS HARDY stands by himself as novelist and poet. The Wessex scene and the Wessex peasantry are vividly depicted in his novels. ' The Dynasts ' is epic drama of terrific force, dealing with the Napoleonic Wars.

Photo, Walter Thomas

SAMUEL BUTLER showed himself to be a penetrating critic of modern society, notably in ' Erewhon ' (an anagram for ' Nowhere '), his conception of a Utopia. ' The Way of All Flesh ' is his finest novel.
Cogin, National Portrait Gallery

ROBERT LOUIS STEVENSON is much beloved, whether as essayist, novelist, short story writer or poet. A Scot, he travelled widely and finally made his home in the South Seas, where he died.
Photo, Notman, Boston, U.S.A.

William De Morgan	George Moore	George Gissing
Mrs. Humphry Ward	Sir Rider Haggard	John Oliver Hobbes
Maurice Hewlett	Eden Phillpotts	Henry James

NOVELISTS OF YESTERYEAR. *William De Morgan's Dickensian novels and Gissing's gloomy sociological tales have lost much of their popularity ; Mrs. Humphry Ward and Mrs. Craigie (John Oliver Hobbes) are likewise neglected. George Moore, originally a realist, did his most remarkable work in ' The Brook Kerith ' and 'Abélard and Héloise.' Rider Haggard's romances were, and still are, immensely popular, and the historical romances of Maurice Hewlett have also had great success. Eden Phillpotts is one of the most versatile and interesting of writers. Henry James, who was of American birth, excelled in the analytical treatment of his characters ; he is too subtle for most readers.*

Photos, Russell, Beresford and Hoppé

H. G. WELLS won an enormous public for his novels, of which some are realistic, with 'the little man' as hero, while others are imaginative scientific romances.

ARNOLD BENNETT is also a realistic novelist. His 'Clayhanger' trilogy has for background his native Potteries. In 'The Old Wives' Tale' he achieved real greatness.

RUDYARD KIPLING has had a tremendous vogue as novelist, short-story writer, and poet. Apart from the two 'Jungle Books' and 'Kim,' his vigorous poems represent his highest achievement.

JOSEPH CONRAD, a Pole, became such a master of the English language that his novels, especially his sea stories, are in the front rank, creating atmosphere and character with extraordinary skill.

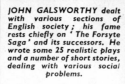

JOHN GALSWORTHY dealt with various sections of English society; his fame rests chiefly on ' The Forsyte Saga ' and its successors. He wrote some 25 realistic plays and a number of short stories, dealing with various social problems.

Photos, Russell, Beresford, Hoppé and Clive Edis

whose 'Life of Mozart' is a really competent piece of work. Arthur Bryant (b. 1899) wrote several admirable biographies, notably those on Charles II and Pepys.

Present-day historians include G. M. Trevelyan (b. 1876), who has written three great works on the growth of modern Italy, in addition to many brilliant studies in English history, including 'England under Queen Anne' and a short 'History of England.' The influence of that stupendous anthropological work, 'The Golden Bough' (1890) by Sir James Frazer (1854–1941), has been profound. Outstanding, too, are 'Human Personality,' by Sir F. W. H. Myers (1843–1901), and 'Mysticism,' by Evelyn Underhill (b. 1875).

Writers of noteworthy books that fall into other categories are H. M. Tomlinson (b. 1873) with his vivid travel books, such as 'The Sea and the Jungle,' and 'London River'; Peter Fleming (b. 1907), also a traveller, whose unconventional 'Brazilian Adventure' won immediate recognition;

Francis Yeats-Brown (b. 1886), author of 'Bengal Lancer' and 'Indian Pageant'; Siegfried Sassoon (b. 1886), who wrote 'Memoirs of a Fox-hunting Man,' 'Memoirs of an Infantry Officer,' 'Sherston's Progress' and 'The Weald of Youth'; Arthur Bryant who, in addition to the biographies already noted, wrote 'English Saga,' a brilliant economic and sociological study of the years 1840–1940; C. E. M. Joad (b. 1891), a prolific writer on philosophy and religion; C. S. Lewis (b. 1898), author of 'The Problem of Pain' and 'The Screwtape Letters,' two books which attracted wide notice in 1940 and 1942; and G. D. H. Cole (b. 1889), who ranges from sociology to crime stories.

New books are normally issued at the rate of something like 13,000 a year (in 1937 it was over 17,000), and hence the writers named in this Lesson are only singled out as representative types from the host of men and women who are carrying the banner of our national literature forward today.

LESSON 43

The English Novel and its Creators

ONE could betray no greater ignorance of literature than to suggest that prose fiction was unworthy of serious study on the ground that 'mere fiction' can be of no use to anyone. It may, indeed, be the very essence of truth; in the hands of the master-writers it is truth. An historical novel may, by re-creating scene and character, present a picture closer to life than a factual chronicle would be.

Cut out the romance, the novel, and the short story from English literature, and it would be small comfort to protest that there still remained to us the history, the essay, the poem, and the drama; yes, even though these preserved a Carlyle, a Lamb, a Keats and a Shakespeare! Our prose fiction must be accounted one of our greatest national treasures.

The great novel is, in a word, one of the indispensable means of modern culture. Jane Austen's description of the novel, as it should be, can hardly be improved upon. A novel, according to this peerless exponent of one phase of the art of fiction, is a work in which the greatest powers of the mind are displayed, in which the most thorough knowledge of human nature, the happiest delineation of its different types, the liveliest

varieties of wit and humour are conveyed to the world in the best chosen words.

It is too frequently forgotten that novels, as a form of art, must be regarded as critically as we regard dramas and poems. Drama is composed of two main divisions, comedy and tragedy, but each of these divisions has many subdivisions; and the quality of a play is to be judged by its relation to the standard of its particular division. This is true of the poem and its relation to what we understand by the epic, the narrative, and the lyrical standards. What is true of the play and the poem is true of the novel; with the further point that the novel is susceptible of innumerable gradations and of classification infinitely more intricate.

It was due to the first English translators of those Italian and Spanish works of genius—'The Decameron' by Boccaccio, 'Lazarillo de Tormes' (that earliest known picaresque novel which was long ascribed to Hurtado de Mendoza, though now the attribution is commonly regarded as doubtful), 'Don Quixote' by Cervantes—and other foreign imaginative works, that the novel of adventure and gallantry, the pastoral romance, and the picaresque novel (or novel

G*

of roguery, of Spanish origin) had become naturalized in Britain by the beginning of the seventeenth century.

16th Century Fiction. Meanwhile, England had produced a form of prose fiction which was indigenous. The outstanding examples were the Latin allegories of More ('Utopia,' 1516), Barclay ('Argenis,' 1621), and Bacon ('New Atlantis,' 1627). In 1579–80 appeared 'Euphues,' which some regard as the first original prose novel written in English. The author of this work was John Lyly (1553–1606), to whom, as a dramatist, attention has been previously given. The story, though received in Elizabethan Court circles with much delight, is less interesting to the modern reader, but the style in which it was written suggested a new word, 'euphuism,' and promoted a form of popular 'polite' dialogue, the influence of which is traceable in Shakespeare (Adriano de Armado in 'Love's Labour's Lost,' and Malvolio in 'Twelfth Night') ; Ben Jonson (Puntarvolo in 'Every Man out of His Humour') and Sir Walter Scott (Sir Piercy Shafton, in 'The Monastery'). Lyly has been unduly despised and much misrepresented. His importance as one of the first writers of witty prose dialogue in English and his lyrical gift are the chief facts to bear in mind in regard to him.

Next to Lyly's 'Euphues,' the posthumous 'Arcadia' (1590) of Sir Philip Sidney (1554–86) claims attention. Indebted as Sidney was to foreign influence, and particularly to the Italian Sannazaro and the Portuguese Montemayor—both disciples of Boccaccio —his pastoral romance enshrines true passion and has a ring of chivalrous sincerity that is absent from 'Euphues.' Sidney borrowed, but gave also. French and English writers felt his influence. Shakespeare is one of his debtors, and Sir Walter Raleigh points out that Richardson is the 'direct inheritor' of the analytic and sentimental method in romance which Sidney developed. In Raleigh's words :

The 'Arcadia' is in some sort a half-way house between the older romances of chivalry and the long-winded 'heroic' romances of the seventeenth century. Action and adventure are already giving way to the description of sentiment, or are remaining merely as a frame on which the diverse-coloured flowers of sentiment may be broidered.

'The Pilgrim's Progress,' written by John Bunyan and published in 1678 (*see* Lesson 31, page 153), is the first great popular allegorical narrative in the language. Twenty years after its appearance, the novel

of contemporary life may be said to have begun with 'The Fair Jilt' and 'Oroonoko,' two works of that romantic literary figure Mrs. Aphra Behn (1640–89), spy, brilliant conversationalist scintillating amongst the Restoration wits, and first English professional authoress. She was also the first writer to advocate the abolition of slavery. 'Oroonoko,' dealing with an enslaved African prince, influenced Chateaubriand and J. J. Rousseau. In her day Mrs. Behn enjoyed great popularity as a dramatist.

Defoe and Swift. Realism in fiction reached immediate perfection in the hands of Daniel Defoe, whose 'Robinson Crusoe,' published in 1719, remains unsurpassed in this respect. It provides an imaginative contrast to that immortal and wonderful story book, the satire 'Gulliver's Travels' of Jonathan Swift, which appeared in 1726. In neither work is any great appeal made to the emotions. The influence of both these writers on the development of English prose is considered in Lesson 33 (page 156).

Richardson. The 'literature of the drawing-room,' which Lyly began, was humanized by Samuel Richardson (1689–1761), who may be called the father of the domestic novel. As a lad he was the confidant of the young women in the neighbourhood of his home in Derbyshire. He read and wrote their love-letters for them, which accounts in some measure for his extraordinary success as a writer, chiefly for women, in his later years. At the age of fifty, when he was a printer in Salisbury Court, Fleet Street, he was induced by two bookseller friends to take up the task of writing a book of 'Familiar Letters on the Useful Concerns in Common Life.' He was doubtless engaged in this work when he became acquainted with the story which inspired his first novel, 'Pamela ; or, Virtue Rewarded' (1740), although the latter was published several months before the 'Familiar Letters.' His masterpiece, 'Clarissa Harlowe,' followed in 1747–48, and 'Sir Charles Grandison,' in 1753. These three works form a kind of trilogy, dealing respectively with humble, middle-class and high life ; they were extremely popular.

Richardson's adoption of the epistolary style was burlesqued and condemned by Fielding, but, though Fielding's protest was well grounded, the method had its advantages, and is still sometimes adopted. Even Fielding admired the penetration displayed by Richardson in his characterization of 'Clarissa Harlowe,' and the novel had a vogue in France. Perhaps the greatest obstacle in the way of a popular appreciation of Richardson today is his prolixity ; and other drawbacks are his passion for moralizing and stagnant sentimentality. For the student of eighteenth-century life, however, the novels of Richardson contain much that is invaluable.

Fielding. Two years after 'Pamela' was issued there appeared 'The History of the Adventures of Joseph Andrews and his Friend Mr. Abraham Adams, Written in Imitation of the Manner of Cervantes, Author of "Don Quixote."' In this work Henry Fielding (1707–54), barrister, journalist and playwright, essayed a satire and achieved a masterpiece just as Cervantes himself had done. The Parson Adams of the story takes rank in the gallery of the heroes of English fiction with Goldsmith's Dr. Primrose—just as Sophie Western sits with the daughter of the Vicar of Wakefield. 'The History of Tom Jones, a Foundling,' appeared in 1749 ; 'Amelia,' in 1751. The ' History of the Late Mr. Jonathan Wild the Great' was published among his 'Miscellanies' in 1743.

Fielding's knowledge of the law marks all his writings. Full of odd passages containing permanent beauties, 'Amelia' shows Fielding in his aspects of reformer and lawyer rather than of novelist. It is on this account none the less interesting to the modern reader. As a literary artist Fielding has a place above Richardson, and Sir Walter Scott styled him the 'Father of the English Novel.' He is a humorist, which Richardson is not. His knowledge of life is wide, his sympathies are catholic, his humour is of the rarest vintage, his style is like the vigour of a spring morning, and his constructive faculty is classical ; his novels are as charged with life today as when they first won the admiration of his contemporaries. Dr. Johnson considered 'Tom Jones' vicious, though he was fascinated by '.Amelia' ; but if the former great novel is too indulgent to the frailties of man, it is an open question whether it may not be so and yet remain a work of sounder morality than Richardson's 'Pamela,' in which we are supposed to witness 'virtue rewarded,' but a brand of 'virtue' that will not bear analysis. Fielding is securely a classic ; he has, moreover, created a crowded gallery of memorable characters, and this is the true test of the novelist.

LESSON 44

Some 18th Century Humorists and Romantics

IN addition to Fielding, three other novelists, Sterne, Smollett and Goldsmith, are included amongst Thackeray's representative humorists of the eighteenth century. Concerning **Laurence Sterne** (1713–68), however, a distinction is made with which most modern readers will agree. The distinction is that Sterne is a great jester rather than a great humorist. 'He is always looking in my face, watching his effect, uncertain whether I think him an impostor or not ; posture-making, coaxing, and imploring me.' The author of 'The Life and Opinions of Tristram Shandy, Gent.' and 'A Sentimental Journey through France and Italy' owed much, doubtless, to an acquaintance with the works of Rabelais and Cervantes and Burton's 'Anatomy of Melancholy,' but, as Augustine Birrell has said, 'Sterne is our best example of the plagiarist whom none dare make ashamed.' In Corporal Trim and 'My Uncle Toby,' he has created immortal types of character ; they would raise 'Tristram Shandy' to a place among the classics of English prose fiction even without the spirit of inimitable drollery which rattles through its pages. Among his defects are indecency and mawkish sentimentality, to which the age was prone.

Careless, usually, of his grammar, Sterne can on occasion find the 'only word.' His slipshod method cannot be held up to admiration, but it adds to the care-free and exuberant expression of his jests.

Smollett. The 'Hogarth of English Letters' is a phrase applied to Tobias Smollett (1721–71). Masson includes 'The Adventures of Roderick Random,' 'The Adventures of Peregrine Pickle' and 'The Expedition of Humphrey Clinker' with 'Joseph Andrews' and 'Tom Jones' among the most amusing novels in the language. In them, he says, 'for the first time British literature possessed compositions making any approach, in breadth, bustle and variety of interest, to that form of literature, always theoretically possible, and of which other countries had already had specimens in 'Don Quixote' and 'Gil Blas'—the comic prose epic of contemporary life.' Fielding and Smollett present the kaleidoscope of life, whereas Richardson focuses attention upon his chief characters.

Goldsmith and Johnson. Of Oliver Goldsmith (1728–74), to whose masterly and delightful achievements in other domains of literature attention has been drawn in earlier lessons, it has been said that *Virginibus puerisque* might have been his appropriate and uncontested motto. His one novel, 'The Vicar of Wakefield,' which appeared in 1766, was written with a moral motive akin to that which induced Richardson to write 'Pamela.' 'There are a hundred faults in the thing,' says the author in his preface, but, as it has been wittily observed, a hundred things might plausibly be said to prove them beauties.

Some seven years earlier, the novel having come well to the fore in literature, Samuel Johnson (1709–84) essayed his 'Rasselas,' writing it during the evenings of a single week. It is a prose narrative embodying the views expressed in his poem, 'The Vanity of Human Wishes,' and has been compared with Voltaire's 'Candide,' with which it has something in common. Dr. Johnson's genius, however, lay in other directions (*see* Lesson 34, page 158).

Although Fielding had set up a definite and adaptable form for the novel of character, and despite the sentimental romance of Richardson and the fresh naturalness of 'The Vicar of Wakefield,' the tendency was to tickle the palate of the common reader with tales of so-called 'Gothic romance,' a euphemism for fantastically conceived stories of adventures in remote and gloomy castles. Horace Walpole, in 'The Castle of Otranto,' produced in 1764 one of the best of the supernatural type. There were, however, many other meritorious works of fiction and some that have endured in reputation at least until our own day; Henry Mackenzie's 'The Man of Feeling,' for example; 'The Monk,' an excellent 'thriller' by Matthew Gregory Lewis; 'Vathek,' a powerfully imaginative conception by William Beckford; and Charles Robert Maturin's 'Melmoth the Wanderer.'

Women Novelists. The number of women writers who came forward in response to the demand for interesting and sensational novels is very noteworthy. Sarah Fielding, the sister of the author of 'Tom Jones'; Clara Reeve, highly popular with romantic fiction like 'The Old English Baron'; Mrs. Inchbald, who wrote 'A Simple Story,' which still finds readers; Charlotte Smith,

Mrs. Opie, Regina Marie Roche and the ultra-romantic Mrs. Ann Radcliffe, who, in 'The Mysteries of Udolpho' and several other novels, showed herself to be an incomparable adept at the art of exciting narration; these were excelled by two famous women novelists.

Fanny Burney, Madame d'Arblay (1752–1840), is one of the most attractive literary figures of her day. When she was twenty-six she published 'Evelina, or a Young Lady's Entrance into the World,' which, according to Macaulay, 'was the first tale written by a woman, and purporting to be a picture of life and manners, that lived or deserved to live. It took away reproach from the novel.' Written in the epistolary manner, it was issued anonymously by a firm that did not know the name of the writer, and attained an immediate and immense success, which gave the author a foremost place in the literary world of her day.

Fanny Burney, who was the second daughter of Dr. Burney, had picked up an education at home, without any tuition whatever, but had the advantage of browsing in her father's large miscellaneous library, and observing his brilliant circle of friends. She knew something of the Johnson circle before she wrote 'Evelina,' and became the doctor's pet. Later, Fanny Burney wrote 'Cecilia,' longer and more complex than 'Evelina,' and for this she received £250 (Macaulay wrongly says two thousand pounds). 'Camilla' brought her over £2,000. The appearance of 'Evelina' was a real event in the annals of fiction, for Fanny Burney had caught the secret of the quiet charm of entirely credible events imagined as taking place in the course of everyday domestic life. She was the precursor of a greater than herself—Jane Austen.

The second woman novelist of classic measure to arrive at this period was Maria Edgeworth (1767–1849), whose delightful character finds eloquent expression in her first novel, 'Castle Rackrent,' published anonymously in 1800. This is in many respects her best work. Later came 'The Absentee,' 'Belinda,' 'Helen,' 'Tales from Fashionable Life' and 'Moral Tales.' Sir Walter Scott confessed that reading these stories of Irish peasant life made him feel 'that something might be attempted for my own country of the same kind as that which Miss Edgeworth so fortunately achieved for Ireland'; something that would procure for his own countrymen 'sympathies for their virtues and indulgence for their foibles.'

LESSON 45

Novels of Scott and Jane Austen

TWO figures of supreme importance in the history of the English novel dominate the earlier years of the nineteenth century—Jane Austen and Sir Walter Scott—and both remain unexcelled in their own spheres.

Jane Austen (1775–1817) wrote six novels: 'Sense and Sensibility' (1811), 'Pride and Prejudice' (1812), 'Mansfield Park' (1814), 'Emma' (1816), 'Northanger Abbey' (1818), and 'Persuasion' (1818)—all of which were written in her father's house, the Rectory at Steventon, near Basingstoke, or, after his death, in the house at Chawton where she lived with her mother and sister. Her close intimacy with the latter enabled her exquisitely to express sisterly relationships in her novels. Though slow to publish, Jane Austen began writing at a very early age. 'Pride and Prejudice' she started in 1796; 'Northanger Abbey,' which, like 'Persuasion,' was published posthumously, was begun about 1798.

Macaulay suggested that Jane Austen among writers most nearly approached Shakespeare in the genius for character drawing which she displays in her novels; also that there were in the world no compositions 'which approach nearer to perfection.' She wrote in direct opposition to the 'Gothic' romances in vogue at the end of the eighteenth century. 'Northanger Abbey,' indeed, is in part a parody of Mrs. Radcliffe's 'Mysteries of Udolpho' and other blood-curdling fiction, best sellers of the day. A notable feature is the impersonal nature of her works. She tells us nothing about herself, and is unconscious of the happenings beyond her own circle. She is a satirist minus indignation; hers is the quiet irony of the cultured mind. Her stories are developments of character; they are neither emotional nor sentimental. To study her books is to know what went on in English parsonage, villa, town and country house at the beginning of the century.

Jane Austen's method was appreciated by Scott. After the third reading of 'Pride and Prejudice' he wrote:

The big bow-wow strain I can do myself, like any now going, but the exquisite touch which renders ordinary commonplace things and characters interesting from the truth of the description and sentiment is denied me. What a pity such a gifted creature died so early!

She has been compared to the miniature painter, but few have possessed her distinctive touch—a touch which enabled her to portray the scenes of quiet contemporary life with precision of detail and yet to maintain in the pattern of her novels a true relation with humanity at large.

Sir Walter Scott (1771–1832) is easily first of the great writers of English historical romance. His career illustrates the renewal and decision of the old battle between verse and prose for the prerogative of handling romantic themes. Scott 'took the bread out of the mouths of the novelists' by his metrical romances, 'The Lay of the Last Minstrel' (1805), 'Marmion' (1808), 'The Lady of the Lake' (1810), to which reference was made in Lesson 25; then, turning to prose, he proved that the historical and romantic interests need not be imperilled by the admixture of qualities that are known only to prose. In his works the novel proper and the romance were at last wedded.

Scott's genius was stirred by several factors—among them being the French Revolution, the Napoleonic wars, Percy's 'Reliques of Ancient English Poetry,' the songs of Burns, the ballads of Bürger, and the early poems of Goethe. Nor must the example of Fielding be discounted. But the Irish novels of Maria Edgeworth first inspired in him the thought which found such eloquent expression in that vast treasure-house, the 'Waverley' novels.

As a preliminary to their reading one should study the 'General Preface,' written by Scott in 1829, which will be found in the first volume of all good editions; and also the 'Epistle Introductory to the Fortunes of Nigel,' written in 1822. He explains, in the Epistle, that he was quite aware of the aims of Fielding, Smollett, Le Sage, and others, as writers of novels, but he goes on to say that it was enough for him to—

write with sense and spirit a few scenes, unlaboured and loosely put together, but which had sufficient interest in them to amuse in one corner the pain of body; in another to relieve anxiety of mind; in a third place to unwrinkle a brow bent with the furrows of daily toil; in another to fill the place of bad thoughts, or to suggest better; in yet another to induce the idler to study the history of his country; in all, save where the perusal interrupted the discharge of serious duties, to furnish harmless amusement.

Others before Scott had attempted the historical novel, 'but wholly without his knowledge of history and of the actual way of living and thinking in various periods of the past.' He it was who first 'made the dry bones of history live.' The casual reader needs to be reminded of the stores of varied and accurate learning which were garnered in Scott's capacious mind. This man was a student from his youth upwards. It is important also to secure at the outset of a study of his romances a knowledge of his methods of dealing with history. Scott's plan was never to make a famous character of history the central personage of his tale. He never coped with the records of actual events. But he achieved effects which were altogether denied to some of the most painstaking among historians. In all that he wrote we breathe the free mountain air.

Scott's novels, it must be remembered, do not finally depend for their popularity upon their plots. Taking time to arrange a story was a sore point with Scott. He confesses that 'the regular mansion' he always strove to build 'turned out a Gothic anomaly.' But it is questionable whether we should have been so long held captive by the spell of the Wizard if he had achieved those trim-built mansions he set out to construct, instead of the crazy, gargoyled edifices his rich and vigorous imagination reared for us. In their very irregularity of plot and style lie half their charm and all their vitality. It has to be remembered, also, that much which was new when Scott wrote has now become hackneyed, and as we do not base our claim for him on the excellence of his plots, haphazardly constructed, so we do not fall back upon his style, of which the best that can be said is that it is a free and easy medium wherewith he brings his scenes and persons vividly before us. His merit is so gigantic that he can be made the subject of the severest criticism in details, concerning which he was often slovenly—owing in part to pressure of external circumstances under which he was constrained to work—without detracting from the mighty mass of his achievement.

By taking up the novels in the order in which they were published rather than as fancy or other reasons may dictate, the student will be able to discern the workings of the author's mind when dealing successively with special phases of character and particular situations in human life. The introductions and notes may be reserved for consideration till each story has

been read. The following table gives the date of publication of the novels and an indication of the period of each.

A glance at the list below will serve to show that with few exceptions Scott, with all his love of the Gothic, preferred to deal in his novels with periods not far remote from his own time ; but he did for Scottish romance what Cervantes did for Spanish chivalry. Delightfully entertaining as are 'Ivanhoe,' 'Quentin Durward' and 'Anne of Geierstein,' it is in the Scottish stories that he excels.

'Waverley' was published in 1814, and thenceforward, for sixteen years, says Herford in his 'Age of Wordsworth,' 'the wonderful series of the 'Waverley novels,' as they were called, issued from the Ballantynes' press without a pause ; and for the last ten, at least, their appearance was watched for as eagerly in Paris and Weimar as in London. The poems had thrown the British world into a passing excitement ; the novels enlarged the intellectual horizon of all Europe, created in half a dozen nations the novel of national life, and opened a new epoch in the study of history.'

Chronological List of the Waverley Novels

Date	Title	Period
1814	Waverley ; or 'Tis Sixty Years Since ..	1745
1815	Guy Mannering ..	1760
1816	The Antiquary ..	1798
1816	Old Mortality* ..	1679
1816	The Black Dwarf* ..	1708
1818	Rob Roy ..	1715
1818	The Heart of Midlothian*	1736
1819	A Legend of Montrose* ..	1644
1819	The Bride of Lammermoor*	1700
1819	Ivanhoe..	1194
1820	The Monastery ..	1559
1820	The Abbot ..	1570
1821	The Pirate ..	1700
1822	Kenilworth ..	1575
1822	The Fortunes of Nigel ..	1620
1823	Quentin Durward ..	1470
1823	Peveril of the Peak ..	1660
1824	St. Ronan's Well ..	1804
1824	Redgauntlet ..	1770
1825	The Betrothed ..	1187
1825	The Talisman ..	1193
1826	Woodstock ..	1651
1827	The Surgeon's Daughter† ..	1765
1827	The Two Drovers† ..	1765
1827	The Highland Widow† ..	1755
1828	My Aunt Margaret's Mirror ..	1700
1828	The Tapestried Chamber ..	1780
1828	The Laird's Jock..	1600
1828	The Fair Maid of Perth† ..	1402
1829	Anne of Geierstein ..	1474
1828 } 1830 }	Tales of a Grandfather ..	{ 1707 { 1788
1831	Count Robert of Paris* ..	1090
1831	Castle Dangerous* ..	1307

* Tales of My Landlord.
† Chronicles of the Canongate.

Scott's Successors in the Field of Fiction

ONE of Scott's contemporaries and followers in fiction was John Galt (1779–1839), who wrote a long series of Scottish tales and was the real progenitor of the so-called ' Kailyard School,' revived with so much clatter in the 'nineties. 'Annals of the Parish,' 'The Entail,' 'The Provost,' and 'Sir Andrew Wylie' are among the best of Galt's novels.

In 'The Adventures of Hajji Baba,' by James Justinian Morier (c. 1780–1849), intimate knowledge of Persian life is displayed, and there is some of the real stuff of romance in 'Salathiel,' by George Croly (1780–1860).

Minor Novelists. Thomas Love Peacock (1785–1866) poured no little wit and knowledge of character—chiefly his own, with its hedonism, worldly virtues and venial sins—into the novels which stand to his name : 'Headlong Hall,' ' Melincourt,' 'Nightmare Abbey,' 'Maid Marian,' 'The Misfortunes of Elphin,' 'Crotchet Castle' and 'Gryll Grange.' These works, like those of Landor, caviare to the general reader, but their erudite satire should not deter the student. Lightened by whimsical humour, their charm is further enhanced by the lyrics scattered throughout their pages.

Frances Trollope (1780–1863), the mother of Anthony Trollope, wrote many novels, of which 'The Vicar of Wrexhill' and 'The Widow Barnaby' are her best.

Susan Edmondstone Ferrier (1782–1854) was a caustic but kindly-hearted delineator of old maids, pretty inanities, gauche doctors, and mock heroes. Like Maria Edgeworth and Fanny Burney, Miss Ferrier, in 'Marriage,' 'The Inheritance,' and 'Destiny,' laid bare the 'humours' of her time. A gifted satirist of her sex, she found a wealth of material in the society amidst which she moved in Edinburgh.

Mary Russell Mitford (1787–1855) wrote 'Our Village,' a series of delightful sketches which enshrine the life of the little hamlet of Three Mile Cross, near Reading, with a fancy, brightness, and pleasant humour all her own.

Mary Wollstonecraft Shelley (1797–1851), the second wife of the poet, and daughter of William Godwin and Mary Wollstonecraft, wrote in 'Frankenstein' a novel which, despite its horrible theme—the creation by a student of a semi-human monster— possesses sufficient of the elements of human interest and of imaginative vitality to preserve it from oblivion.

With William Nugent Glascock (1787–1847) began the novel of the sea, based on his experiences as a captain in the Navy. Contemporary with him was Michael Scott (1789–1835), author of 'Tom Cringle's Log' and 'The Cruise of the Midge,' two of the breeziest sea stories ever written.

Better known is Captain Frederick Marryat (1792–1848), who served with distinction until his retirement in 1830. Of his many novels, none is without a lively and sustained interest. The best known are 'Peter Simple,' 'Mr. Midshipman Easy,' 'Japhet in Search of a Father,' 'Snarleyyow,' and his excellent tales for children, 'Masterman Ready' and 'The Children of the New Forest.' He wrote in an easy, vigorous style, taking his scenes and characters from real life. In similar vein are the popular stories of Robert Michael Ballantyne (1815–94)—'The Coral Island,' ' Martin Rattler,' 'The Dog Crusoe,' and others.

Irish Novelists of the period include William Carleton (1794–1869), a peasant writer, who received his education in a 'hedge school,' and wrote, from what in his day was an unaccustomed angle, some very notable accounts of Irish peasant life ; he is perhaps best represented by the collection of sketches entitled 'Traits and Stories of the Irish Peasantry,' but his novel 'Fardorougha the Miser' is a powerful tale ; Samuel Lover (1779–1868), writer of songs, dramas, and high-spirited, rollicking stories of conventionally acceptable Irish humour, who achieved great popularity with 'Rory O'More,' later to be eclipsed by his 'Handy Andy' ; and Charles James Lever (1806–72), author of 'Charles O'Malley' and some three dozen other stories. Lever's brilliant caricatures, however, must not be taken as forming a real picture of Irish life.

The historical novels of George Payne Rainsford James (1799–1860) possess little interest today, and with those of the more popular William Harrison Ainsworth (1805–82) show the sharp decline of romance from the heights of the Waverley Novels, though Ainsworth may be considered the father of the novel which depends upon a succession of exciting incidents for its popularity. There is undeniably some exhilaration to be derived from his 'Old Saint Paul's ' and 'The Tower of London.'

Borrow. A much more important and attractive figure is George Henry Borrow (1803–81). There is a sort of cult of Borrow which glorifies the gipsy life, the foaming tankard and the swagger of vagabond scholarship. One may have little sympathy with this and yet owe many happy hours to 'Lavengro' and 'The Romany Rye,' as well as to his inimitable travel books, such as the 'Bible in Spain.' Borrow is only a novelist in the picaresque sense ; his fictional works lack form and are rambling records of imaginary experiences.

Lord Lytton. We encounter a novelist in a large way of business, as distinguished from one who might be called an inspired amateur, when we turned from Borrow to Edward George Earle Lytton-Bulwer, first Baron Lytton (1803–73). One of the most prominent and, during his lifetime, one of the most popular of the Victorian novelists, he played a part in fiction similar to that played by Byron in poetry. He posed as the man of the world in 'Pelham,' as the man of feeling in 'Ernest Maltravers,' and as the man of mystery in 'Zanoni.' The novel of horrors has in 'A Strange Story' a supreme example ; than 'The Haunted and the Haunters,' no better ghost story has been written. Lytton, with high success, too, essayed the historical romance in 'The Last Days of Pompeii,' 'The Last of the Barons,' 'Rienzi,' and 'Harold'; the criminal novel, in 'Paul Clifford' and 'Eugene Aram' ; and the novel of domestic life and ambition, in 'The Caxtons,' 'My Novel,' and 'What Will He Do With It ?'

Disraeli. A writer who, with Ainsworth and Lytton, came under the lash of Thackeray's satire, was Benjamin Disraeli, later Lord Beaconsfield (1804–81). He won greater distinction as a statesman than as a novelist, but his 'Coningsby,' 'Sybil,' 'Tancred,' 'Lothair,' and 'Endymion' possess permanent interest for the student of politics and social conditions.

A novelist of very different type was Elizabeth Cleghorn Gaskell (1810–65). Her fictional writings form a real link between the work of Jane Austen and that of Charlotte Brontë, whose biographer she was. 'Mary Barton' is a passionate tale of the sorrows of the Manchester poor, and a book of live power. But Mrs. Gaskell's supreme achievement and perpetual memorial is 'Cranford,' that classic picture of life in a small country town (Knutsford, in Cheshire).

LESSON 47

Thackeray, Dickens and Other Victorian Novelists

WITHIN a few months of each other, in the beginning of the second decade of the nineteenth century, were born two great men of English letters, masters in the art of fiction, who commanded a warmth of personal interest accorded to no other English writers before or since, and who still retain a secure place in the admiration and affection of a vast number of readers. To a certain extent complementary, Dickens and Thackeray confirm each other's views of a particular era in the history of England, though depicting phases of life widely apart.

William Makepeace Thackeray was born at Calcutta, July 18, 1811, son of an Indian Civil Servant, and was sent to England when he was six years old. From private schools he passed on to Charterhouse and thence to Trinity College, Cambridge. In 1831 he entered the Middle Temple, but abandoned law for journalism, becoming a principal contributor to 'Fraser's Magazine,' a lead-ing member of the 'Punch' staff, and, in 1860, the first editor of 'The Cornhill Magazine.' He died on Christmas Eve, 1863. A confirmed clubman, Thackeray mingled freely in the best society of his time, and found the right subjects for his art in the world of rank and fashion and wealth, and the brighter side of life in England. Versatile and cultured, he wrote some delightful light verse, some of the best parodies in the language, some charming whimsicalities—notably 'The Rose and the Ring'—and some first-rate criticism in 'The English Humorists of the 18th Century' and in 'The Four Georges,' delivered as lectures in England and the United States. 'The Book of Snobs' and the humorous 'Yellowplush' memoirs of life below stairs were contributed to 'Punch.'

But it is on his imaginative and romantic novels that his fame securely rests. Chief among these are 'Vanity Fair' (1848), 'Pendennis' (1850), 'Henry Esmond' (1852),

'The Newcomes' (1853), and 'The Virginians' (1859). He was writing 'Denis Duval' when he died. He was a student of 18th-century England, and his books fall into two groups—those dealing with contemporary life and manners, of which 'Vanity Fair' is the supreme example, and to which 'The Newcomes' and 'Pendennis' also belong, and those dealing with the 18th century, of which 'Henry Esmond,' that perfect picture of life in the reign of Queen Anne, with its sequel 'The Virginians,' is the predominant romance.

The final test of a great novel is that it teaches certain truths of human life and conduct, that it adds to the reader's store of knowledge and wisdom. This test can be applied to Thackeray's fiction. Of 'Vanity Fair' it may be said that it admirably exemplifies Thackeray's creed, which is that goodness, however scorned, is its own sufficient reward ; at the same time no one can read this splendid novel without sympathy for and understanding of that attractive adventuress, Becky Sharp.

Thackeray has been lightly called a cynic. The word, applied to him, is misused, yet there is undoubtedly force in the contention that while Thackeray saw, loved, felt and makes us love the higher, brighter, purer side of life, he had a surer hand when depicting what was base and artificial. For explanation of this we must look to the political and social circumstances of the time in which he lived and wrote, and to his peculiar sensitiveness to all around him. Thackeray was no cynic, but he is the greatest of all English satirists, a man who gibbeted snobbery for all time.

Dickens. Very different from those of Thackeray were the early environment and experiences of Charles Dickens, who on February 7, 1812, first opened his eyes upon the world which his genius was to do so much to make happier and better. No summary of his career is needed here ; the whole story is told in the Life of Dickens by his friend and confidant, John Forster—itself a classic, ample in its information, intimate in its knowledge, and wonderfully stimulating to read.

It is beyond all computation how many have been helped to smile through their tears and to take their courage in both hands under the influence of the inimitable, imperishable humour of Charles Dickens. Dickens saw the soul of goodness in ordinary things ; his was the saving grace of humour enriching those novels, too familiar by name to require setting forth

here. He has not only enshrined in his wonderful portrait gallery the tragic and comic annals of the poor of a period happily now no more, but he has shown us the possibilities of goodness and of happiness even in the most unlikely circumstances and characters. What Dickens stood for in a social sense has been largely attained ; and the pose that affects to find his writings crude or antiquated is an unworthy affectation to be pitied, perhaps, as much as condemned. Dickens was 'self-educated' ; he had obvious limitations, but his absolute genius is even more pronounced than that of Thackeray, of whose pictures of high life Dickens's transcripts from humble life may be said to form a necessary counterpart. Mawkish and sentimental sometimes, melodramatic and unreal on occasion, failing to inspire certain characters in fashionable society with life, Dickens's gallery contains portraits such as Micawber, Pickwick, Pecksniff, Sam Weller, the Marchioness, Mrs. Gamp, Betsey Trotwood, Uriah Heep, Squeers, the Wilfers, the Boffins, and the rest—too many to count—sure of immortality while the English language lasts.

Charles Reade. A novelist who, like Charles Dickens, 'wrote with a purpose,' but who, unlike Dickens, was a scholar of no mean attainments rather than a genius, was Charles Reade (1814–84). He attacked prison scandals in 'It is Never Too Late to Mend,' private lunatic asylums in 'Hard Cash,' and 'coffin ships' in "Foul Play.' He has left us a vivid picture of industrial life in 'Put Yourself in His Place,' but his greatest book is indubitably 'The Cloister and the Hearth,' a medieval romance based on the 'Colloquies' of Erasmus. He also wrote 'The Lyons Mail' and other plays.

Joseph Sheridan Le Fanu (1814–73), an Irish novelist with a strong bent towards the 'uncanny,' wrote some sixteen books in all ; 'Uncle Silas' is perhaps the best.

Anthony Trollope (1815–82) should be approached first of all in his 'Autobiography.' His series of Barchester novels—'The Warden,' 'Barchester Towers,' 'Dr.Thorne,' 'Framley Parsonage,' 'The Small House at Allington,' and 'The Last Chronicle of Barset'—represent very faithfully English clerical life in the 'fifties and 'sixties. The same people recur in the various books, including that masterpiece of comedy characterization, the redoubtable Mrs. Proudie. Trollope's studies of life in a cathedral town (Barchester is a thinly disguised Winchester) and diocese are invaluable to the student of the Victorian era, and will almost certainly enjoy in the future far greater popularity than they have had since Trollope passed away.

The Brontës. Charlotte Brontë (1816–55) struck, in 'Jane Eyre,' 'Shirley,' and 'Villette,' the first clear bell-note of English womanhood in fiction, describing love for the first time from an average woman's point of view. Her work is part of her own pathetic life-story, her combined passionate energy and glow of expression breaking through the enforced self-suppression of her shadowed life. Emily Jane Brontë (1818–48) also displayed exceptional if morbid power in 'Wuthering Heights'; and Charlotte's youngest sister, Anne Brontë (1820–49), wrote two novels, 'Agnes Grey' and 'The Tenant of Wildfell Hall,' which, while they gain in interest from their personal associations, vividly picturing moorland scenery and the life of a governess, possess none of the power of her sisters' work. Before taking up the books of the three sisters, the student should read Mrs. Gaskell's classic 'Life' of Charlotte Brontë and Clement Shorter's 'Charlotte Brontë and Her Sisters.'

'Jane Eyre' is essentially melodramatic in detail, but there is artistry in the faithful observation and sympathetic portrayal of character in 'Villette,' which is largely auto-biographical. On the whole, though it is the custom to credit Charlotte with the honours of this remarkable trio of sisters, Emily, in both her prose and her poetry, 'so terribly strong, so exquisitely subtle,' was the most gifted of them. But there is probably no more humanly moving story in the annals of literature than that of these three shy, quiet and intensely courageous women, away there in the bleak and dismal surroundings of Haworth, transferring to paper their emotional and unconventional spiritual experiences.

Charles Kingsley (1819–75) was a follower of Frederick Denison Maurice and Thomas Carlyle, and a manly exponent of 'muscular Christianity,' or 'Christian Socialism.' His books possess the prime quality of stimulus, 'Alton Locke' and 'Yeast' in particular. 'Westward Ho!' and 'Hereward the Wake,' fine historical romances, will always have a warm place in the hero-loving, adventure-seeking heart of youth. 'The Heroes' and 'The Water Babies' are children's classics. His brother, Henry Kingsley (1830–76), was in some respects a better novelist. 'Ravenshoe' is a finer piece of romantic fiction than 'Westward Ho!' which might be named as the fine flower of Charles Kingsley's story-telling powers.

In George Eliot (Marian Evans) (1819–80), we have a great English novelist. Like Charlotte Brontë, George Eliot put herself and her actual experiences into what she wrote. Her books are, for the most part, real, sincere, vigorous. Her genius flowered late; some of her writings have the effect of finished buildings from which all the scaffolding has not been taken down. With her the writing of fiction was the art of thinking aloud, the novel was a form of philosophy; but in the forefront of her philosophy—which, like Carlyle's, was devotion to duty—her characters stand out with life-like fidelity. She was influenced by foreign—especially German—studies.

A remarkable thing about George Eliot was that her undoubted scholastic attainments in no way fettered her power of objective imagination. The 'Scenes of Clerical Life,' 'Adam Bede,' 'The Mill on the Floss,' 'Silas Marner,' and, perhaps her greatest work, 'Middlemarch,' display her genius at its best. 'Romola,' a story of the Italian Renaissance, will always have its admirers. It betrays scholarship of no ordinary kind, but it was brilliant taskwork, and its author said afterwards that she was a young woman when she began the book and an old one when she finished it. 'Daniel Deronda,' another piece of taskwork, should be studied with Disraeli's 'Tancred' by those interested in the mysteries of the Hebrew character. But it is on her studies of lower middle-class town and country life, pictured with humour and vivacity, understanding and solidity, that her fame securely rests.

William Wilkie Collins (1824–89) wrote two classic stories, 'The Woman in White' and 'The Moonstone'; the latter is one of the greatest detective stories in literature.

Lesser Novelists. The novel had now become a definite art form in the hands of numerous brilliant exponents, among whom were many women. The names of Mrs. Henry Wood, Mrs. Lynn Linton, Charlotte M. Yonge, Dinah Maria Mulock (Mrs. Craik), Mrs. Oliphant, Ada Ellen Bayly ('Edna Lyall'), G. J. Whyte-Melville, Sir Walter Besant (often collaborating with James Rice), Thomas Mayne Reid, 'Ouida,' Thomas Hughes, George Macdonald and James Payn—each stands for novels which are still finding admiring readers.

None of them wrote such a classic of romance as 'Lorna Doone,' by Richard Doddridge Blackmore (1825–1900). It is on record that its original success in 1869 was due to a confusion in the public mind between the Lorna of the tale and the Lorne which became Princess Louise's name on marrying the Marquess of Lorne. The fictional Lady Lorna is the heiress of the Earl of Lorne, and on this most adventitious interest a masterpiece of romantic fiction, which was else sinking into oblivion, enjoyed a blaze of popularity. Blackmore has depicted heroines equal in charm to Lorna in 'Cradock Nowell,' 'Alice Lorraine,' and 'The Maid of Sker,' but his construction in these stories is weak.

Abiding popularity has been won by 'Alice's Adventures in Wonderland' (1865) and its successor, 'Through the Looking-Glass,' the work of an Oxford mathematical don, Charles Lutwidge Dodgson (1832-98), better known as Lewis Carroll.

No novelist has been made the object of more frequent or less availing efforts to 'log-roll' him into fame than William Hale White (1831-1913). There are critics who acclaim him one of the greatest writers of English, and put him, in respect of style, even before George Meredith. His best-known books, 'The Autobiography of Mark Rutherford,' 'Mark Rutherford's Deliverance,' and 'The Revolution in Tanner's Lane,' have never won any great measure of popularity, for, despite all the truth of 'Mark Rutherford's' observation and wisdom of reflection, there is in his style a coolness, an intellectual detachment, that does not make for warmth of appreciation in the ordinary reader of novels. He lacks neither humour nor pathos, but is too continuously, and always somewhat sadly, concerned about immortality and the sectarian creeds that seek to confine it to their own narrow borders, to awaken the real glow of affection in his readers.

Theodore Watts-Dunton (1832-1914) was the author of only one romance, 'Aylwin,' which he did not allow to leave his fastidious pen until he was sixty-six, but that beautiful story of Romany life ranks quite easily among our modern classics.

If we except the prolific hack-work of Percy Fitzgerald, probably no author of his time wrote so much as Sabine Baring-Gould (1834-1924); 'John Herring' and 'Mehalah' were his best novels. Perhaps his most interesting book is 'The Vicar of Morwenstow,' a romantic semi-biography of the solitary and eccentric Cornish parson, Robert S. Hawker, the author of 'Cornish Ballads and other Poems,' lover of birds, beasts, the soil, his chapel and glebe in the wild and lovely country near Tintagel. Joseph Henry Shorthouse (1834-1903) wrote his 'John Inglesant' in exquisite English; this is a historical romance, imbued with religious fervour. It was published in 1881 and won instant success.

LESSON 48

Meredith, Hardy and Stevenson

IT was the good fortune of **George Meredith** (1828-1909) to become the most eminent figure of his later days in the English world of letters, sharing with Hardy the sunset glories of the 'last of the great Victorians.' His first book, a small volume of exquisite poems, was published in 1851. A series of powerful and original novels won the regard of discriminating critics, but it was not until the appearance of 'Diana of the Crossways' (1885) that he stirred the interest of a wider public. Meredith, though he has not the depth or the breadth of wisdom possessed by Thackeray, or the humanity of Dickens, is more than a popular writer. He has been for two generations a great influence.

There are various reasons for the power he exerted over contemporaries. The chief is that he chose to look at life with his own eyes, and to depict it in his own words. He described his people as 'actual, yet uncommon.' But his characters all talk Meredith—even his fools are epigrammatic. His novels are analytical, not perceptive. He delights in analysing traits of character, in presenting a study of temperament rather than in building up concrete human beings. Meredith is thought-compelling. He gives exercise to the mind.

None of his novels can be thoroughly appreciated at a first reading. Knowledge, as well as industry, is essential. His style is admittedly difficult; it is like a river with many tortuous windings, but with noble reaches. But his English, at its best, is the best English of the time. He is to be studied, not imitated; and the study should result in a disregard for toil-worn phrases.

The best of Meredith's novels to begin with is 'The Ordeal of Richard Feverel.' If we ask 'What is education?' we have here an answer equivalent to many debates in Parliament and many speeches on political platforms. We have education not merely described, but seen in action. If we ask 'What are love and passion ?' we have but to take up 'Richard Feverel' to see these dominating attributes of our common human nature set forth with a freshness, a vigour, a reverence, a sympathy, a feeling for external nature—with a temperamental knowledge, in short—unrivalled by any other writer of contemporary fiction. If we seek the analysis of motive, of a particular trait of character, we cannot do better than study the dissection of Sir Willoughby Patterne in 'The Egoist.' 'Beauchamp's Career,' 'Diana of the Crossways' and 'Harry Richmond' are the best of Meredith's other novels ; 'The Shaving of Shagpat' is the most imaginative.

Samuel Butler. As 'reader' for Chapman and Hall, Meredith turned down 'Erewhon,' the first book written by Samuel Butler (1835-1902). With regard to its rejection by these publishers, the author writes in his preface to the revised edition : 'I believe their reader advised them quite wisely. They told me he reported that it was a philosophical work, little likely to be popular with a large circle of readers.' There was certainly little to link the philosophy of 'the first of the moderns' with that of the last but one of the great Victorian novelists.

Most thinkers of today owe something to Butler's ideas ; indeed, so penetrating have they been that it is difficult to realize—unless one is acquainted with 'The Notebooks of Samuel Butler,' in which his views are set forth in detail—how subversive they were in the writer's own period. 'Erewhon' and its sequel, 'Erewhon Revisited,' stand in the highest rank of that class of fiction to which 'Gulliver's Travels' belongs. The sequel, published thirty years after 'Erewhon,' is the finer work of art and contains the ripened Butlerian conclusions ; both books are attacks on the civilization of his day presented with irony, vivid flashes of humour and genuine satire. His great novel, 'The Way of All Flesh,' was published posthumously in 1902.

Sir Walter Besant (1836-1901) was a good, but not a great novelist. He wrote to some purpose, however ; his 'All Sorts and Conditions of Men' gave a real impetus to social work in the East End of London. Besant was not an inspiring figure of romance—he was too eminently respectable ; but he never did a really poor piece of work. 'Ready-Money Mortiboy' and 'The Golden Butterfly,' written in collaboration with James Rice (1843-82), are first-rate stories.

Thomas Hardy. The note of paganism sounds in the writings of Thomas Hardy (1840-1928), as in Meredith, and yet it cannot be said that the novels of Meredith and those of Hardy have any noteworthy qualities in common. Meredith's earth-worship makes him in some sort a chastened optimist, while Hardy's reading of earth, with all his merry humour and brave fronting to fate, leaves him rather an unquerulous pessimist, resigned, uncomplaining, thrilling with pity for his fellows. To a far greater degree .than we find it in Meredith, Hardy has dramatic power. But his voice—it is his novels only that are now being considered—is that of the countryside, of the countryside that is far removed from town. To him the greenwood tree suggests no merriment, but destiny ; a pair of blue eyes not heaven, but fate. Life is a tragedy with a few interludes. Yet the philosophy of this old Dorset seer is stern, not weeping. The words of religion are quoted freely in his novels, but in the spirit of the sooth-sayer and son of the soil.

The peasants he introduces to us belong to a part of England whose exclusiveness has now been broken into. Their ways and modes of thought are depicted with a realism that is pitiless, though the novelist lightens his narratives with many a flash of genuine humour. Hardy is a writer who must be approached with an understanding of his own environment, which is the environment of the characters of his novels. His art may be locally circumscribed, but it is great art, nevertheless. His characters are conceived grandly.

His best works appeared in the following order : 'Under the Greenwood Tree' (1872), 'A Pair of Blue Eyes' (1873), 'Far From the Madding Crowd' (1874), 'The Return of the Native' (1878), 'The Mayor of Caster-bridge' (1886), 'The Woodlanders' (1887), 'Tess of the D'Urbervilles'—his greatest novel—(1891), and 'Jude the Obscure' (1895). The student would do well to take up his novels in this sequence ; but 'Far From the Madding Crowd' may be mentioned as thoroughly representative of his art. The hostile reception of 'Jude the Obscure' finished his career as a novelist, and he then turned to building up his second great reputation—that of a poet—as a preface to his crowning achievement 'The Dynasts,' 1904-8.

R. L. S. Robert Louis Stevenson (1850-94), as a predominant influence in nineteenth-century prose, has already been dealt with (*see* page 180) ; here it is his fiction, especially his novels, in which we are interested. There are many competent critics who avow a warmer admiration for Stevenson the traveller, the essayist, the writer of short stories, than for Stevenson the novelist. His best writing is to be found in his short stories, his travels and his essays, and his main service to contemporary letters was concerned with style.

Yet it was as a novelist that he brought the greatest influence to bear upon contemporary literature. He brought to the novel a keener sense of form, and, the world being still young for him, he set about furthering the revival of the latent spirit of romance, which Blackmore a decade earlier had awakened in 'Lorna Doone.' 'Treasure Island' and 'Kidnapped' restored to literature a story material that had been long worked only by crude writers for young uncritical readers. 'Catriona,' written seven years later, as a sequel to 'Kidnapped,' should suffice to silence those critics who talk of Stevenson's inability to draw feminine character, though, like most sequels, it suffers by comparison.

'The Master of Ballantrae' and 'Prince Otto' are good examples of Stevenson's skill as a novelist. His 'Dr. Jekyll and Mr. Hyde' is a grim study of dual personality. 'The Black Arrow' is a romance of the Wars of the Roses. The three books he wrote with his stepson, Lloyd Osbourne (b. 1868) —'The Wrong Box,' 'The Wrecker' and 'The Ebb Tide'—deserve notice. 'The Ebb Tide' is particularly powerful.

Stevenson was too good a critic of himself to attempt to fill the great canvases which the genius of Scott could so easily crowd with unforgettable figures of romance : his was a smaller, more fastidious talent. He was as much above Scott in the difficult art of the short story as Scott excelled him in sustained narrative. His best short stories are in 'The New Arabian Nights,' 'The Dynamiter' and 'The Merry Men.'

LESSON 49

Novelists of Recent Yesterdays

ONE of the curious phenomena of literature is seen in **William de Morgan** (1839–1917), a novelist who makes his first try at the art when he is sixty-five, and in the brief remainder of his days produces another half-dozen novels of such unusual length that they would equal in size a dozen of any modern novelist—and all are good ! 'Joseph Vance' (1906), with which he made an immediate success, is typical, and is like nothing else written in the twentieth century. As a story it is formless and inert, but it is a veritable portrait gallery of Victorian character, charged with the most agreeable humour and a happy sort of philosophy, the lesson of which would seem to be that life, despite all its sadness and sorrows, is so spiced with interest that it is worth living. 'Alice-for-Short,' which followed in 1907, is a sort of female Joseph Vance, and is well-nigh the equal of the first book in every respect. De Morgan has nothing to tell the hasty reader ; you must take him at your ease and your reward in pleasure will be great.

Of English novelists born in the forties and early fifties of last century, who loomed rather large in the literary world of their day, very few call for more than nominal mention here. There was Robert Buchanan (1841–1901), for example, a restless soul who wielded the pen of poet, playwright, novelist and critic with varying success. 'God and the Man' is his best novel. But of the twenty or so that he wrote, few, if any, retain vitality today. Highly successful in his lifetime, again, but not greatly read today, was William Black (1841–98), author of 'A Daughter of Heth' and many a pleasantly competent tale in which Scottish scenery, 'complete with trout stream,' formed the background.

William Clark Russell (1844–1911), a sailor for seven years, had the real sense of the sea and was no indifferent successor to Marryat, though he never just managed to achieve that last unmistakable touch which carries a good story into the category of the great. 'The Wreck of the Grosvenor' established him as a novelist and remains his most memorable achievement. David Christie Murray (1847–1907) is another instance. Of his numerous long novels, 'Despair's Last Journey,' written near the end of his somewhat clouded and unhappy life, might be ranked with the finest fiction published in the last decade of the nineteenth century.

With these novelists, distinguished in their day, mention may also be made of

Flora Annie Steel (1847–1929). In 1867 she married an officer in the Bengal Civil Service, and lived for many years in India, obtaining a profound knowledge of the country and people. Her novels include a really fine romance of the Indian Mutiny, 'On the Face of the Waters,' which was followed by another Indian story of great power, 'The Hosts of the Lord.'

Mrs. Humphry Ward (1851–1920) concerned herself with the interpretation of social life. Her novel 'Robert Elsmere,' published in 1888, created a tremendous stir at the time, but lies quite peacefully in its grave today. This is less the fault of the book than of the age ; its chief use in the future will be to illustrate a social phase that has passed. 'Marcella,' 'History of David Grieve' and 'Eleanor' are later novels ; these also are limited in subject and by Mrs. Ward's didactic style.

Another popular woman writer was Mrs. St. Leger Harrison (1852–1931), who, as 'Lucas Malet,' wrote powerful novels, notably 'The Wages of Sin' and 'Sir Richard Calmady,' which have fine qualities and enjoyed a considerable success. She may have derived much of her literary talent from her father, Charles Kingsley.

A name which some people might expect to find included among those of great novelists is that of Sir Hall Caine (1853–1931). As a novelist he attracted notice first by 'The Deemster,' published in 1887, which was followed by 'The Bondman' in 1890, 'The Scapegoat,' 1891, and 'The Manxman,' 1894, all books which throw light on Manx customs and superstitions. That his work is not important from the literary point of view is due to the assiduous manner in which he sought with large subjects and grandiose effect to impress the multitude in such novels as 'The Christian,' 'The Eternal City' and 'The Prodigal Son.' In all these flamboyant and highly-coloured romances the dramatic becomes overstrained and melodramatic.

Henry James. Among novelists born in the 'forties and 'fifties who remain figures of importance in English literature are Henry James, George Moore and George Gissing. Although born in New York, Henry James (1843–1916) was an Englishman by adoption, and most of his work was done in England, where he had lived from early manhood. He was never 'popular,' but he became a cult, and to admire Henry James was a touchstone of literary percipience. Some of his short stories, such as 'The Turn of the Screw,' are likely to outlive all his long novels. He had great charm and some obscurity of style, and he was a sound critic, especially of French literature. Henry James must certainly be ranked among great novelists, a leader of the analytical school, and although the fastidiousness of his language, amounting often to mannerism, lends itself to parody, it undoubtedly exercised a wholesome influence upon literary style.

George Moore (1852–1933) occupies an eminent niche in the gallery of modern novelists. Like Henry James, a fastidious stylist, George Moore had an unshakable belief in his own immortality. As a novelist he began with 'A Mummer's Wife' (1885), which, like 'Esther Waters' (1894), showed the influence of the French realists. He might be chosen as our outstanding representative of the realist school, but, being an Irishman of a various talent and an exponent of the Celtic revival, he is not so easily 'placed.' Renouncing the Irish movement and Roman Catholicism, he recorded his disillusionment in ' Memoirs of My Dead Life' (1906) and ' Hail and Farewell.' Of his other works, ' The Brook Kereth,' 'Heloise and Abelard' and 'Avowals' are important. In his novel ' The Lake' he first created the last and most beautiful of his three styles. His short stories of Irish character, under the title of 'The Untilled Field,' are among his finest writings.

George Gissing (1857–1903) should presumably be classed with the French-inspired realists, but that is rather from the Zolaesque nature of his subject-matter than his manner. He is capable of wonderful graces of style, and the astonishing thing is to find so much pessimism and stark despair, such pictures of poverty and sordid distress, penned in such admirable prose. We need not turn to him if entertainment be our desire ; but if we would understand the lower, sombre side of social life in the latter years of the nineteenth century we could not read more impressive studies than his ' New Grub Street ' and 'Odd Women.' Of striking interest also—in a different vein —is his 'Charles Dickens : a Critical Study.' Gissing's thinly-veiled autobiography in fictional form, 'The Private Papers of Henry Ryecroft,' has all the importance of a human document.

As novelist, essayist and poet, Maurice Hewlett (1861–1923) was a literary artist of rare distinction. He made his reputation in 1898 with ' The Forest Lovers,' a romance of the kind of nebulous medievalism which was initiated by William Morris, and he followed this initial success—with which he himself was none too elated—with 'Richard Yea and Nay,' 'New Canterbury Tales,' 'The Queen's Quair,' 'The Fool Errant,' 'Brazenhead the Great,' 'A Lover's Tale,' and 'Mainwaring.' In these he gave modern English fiction a high place in the realm of romance, winning wide popularity as a teller of stories without departing from the very high standard required by his own fastidious taste. It may be added that some of Maurice Hewlett's most lovely work is embodied in his essays, collected into four volumes, 'In a Green Shade,' 'Wiltshire Essays,' 'Extemporary Essays,' and 'Last Essays.' He also wrote some beautiful verse, including 'Pan and the Young Shepherd' and 'The Song of the Plow.'

Eden Phillpotts (b. 1862) was author of many good novels, the majority of them—in which the best are included—being identified with Devonshire and, more particularly, with the Dartmoor country and people. 'Sons of the Morning' and 'Children of the Mist' were among the earliest of these intimate studies and vivid presentations of Devonshire life, and these were followed by a long sequence of West Country novels, notably by 'The Secret Woman' and 'The Mother,' revealing a steady growth of dramatic power and fine technique. A man of great versatility, he also made some notable contributions to humorous literature and published verse of real merit. Mention has been made of his plays in Lesson 20 (page 123).

LESSON 50

Five Novelists of Enduring Fame

WITHIN the compass of the decade 1857 to 1867 were born those distinguished leading writers of fiction, Joseph Conrad, Rudyard Kipling, John Galsworthy, H. G. Wells and Arnold Bennett. Each in his own way has added to the prestige of the English novel ; their work retains significance and will survive.

Joseph Conrad (1857–1924) wrote a rich and characteristic English, although he was a Pole (his full name was Theodor Jozef Konrad Korzeniowski) and, so far as can be judged by his fiction, never quite grew into the English habit of mind. Perhaps in some subtle exoticism partly lies the secret of his charm ; also it lies in his philosophy of loyalty, in his recurrent themes of the universal brotherhood of the sea and the integrity of human relationship, in his appeal to the hearts of a seafaring nation by his powerful expression of the terror and fascination of the sea. At one time he seemed to suffer from the kindly-intentioned efforts of well-meaning friends, something like a Conrad cabal among the critics appearing to be bent on forcing this Polish writer of English stories, with his wide, unconventional outlook, upon a half-reluctant British public. But all who began to read him, in however hyper-critical a mood, were soon so caught by his splendid powers of descriptive narrative and characterization that they went on eagerly from story to story—all held by his strange mixture of the painful and

beautiful, powerful and gloomy, squalid and graceful, romantic and realistic.

'The Nigger of the Narcissus,' for all the abounding merits of his later books, is his most characteristic piece of work, his finest plotless novel—the story was always secondary to his artistic delight in the creation of people—just as 'The Arrow of Gold,' written a quarter of a century later, is his least successful. But what a choice of delightful reading he has left for the generations arriving !—'Almayer's Folly,' 'An Outcast of the Islands,' 'Lord Jim,' 'Typhoon,' 'Nostromo,' 'Chance,' 'Victory,' and his volumes of short stories. 'The Secret Agent' was a novel of the underworld, and it was through this wider sweep of subject that he began to earn financial success. His final book, 'The Rover,' appeared in 1923. Particularly Joseph Conrad excelled in his creation of atmosphere and emotional tension, in his psychological penetration and ironic power.

As a fiction writer, **Rudyard Kipling** (1865–1936) is not so great in the novel as in the short story form, in which many competent critics have regarded him as supreme, but it would be difficult to name a better novel than 'Kim,' written within the early years of the present century. Excelling, however, as a teller of stories, it is in his Jungle Books, in his 'Plain Tales from the Hills,' 'Under the Deodars,' 'Many Inventions,' and other collections of short stories—mostly dealing with an

Anglo-Indian day that is past—that Kipling achieved and retains success. While he continues to be widely read, reaction against his aggressive imperialism set in with disillusionment after the disintegrating experiences of the First Great War. This reaction has sometimes caused literary criticism to be warped by an overwhelming prejudice from which the rising generation may happily be free.

In John Galsworthy (1867–1933), already dealt with as a dramatist (*see* page 122), we have a writer of great importance to English letters. His rise to fame and authority was deliberate and steady, in plays, novels and stories. No novelist of fame ever took his work more seriously than Galsworthy ; in the sense, that is, of feeling deep responsibility for the possible influence of his novels. He chronicled the fortunes of his Forsyte family with something of the care and minuteness of concern which Zola gave to his much more ambitious record of the Rougon-Macquart family. His seriousness of purpose was most happily reinforced by the highest literary gifts and the saving grace of humour, the absence of which might have produced merely boredom where we have sustained an approving interest. At times he was not above resort to melodrama, as in the death of Bosinney in 'The Man of Property,' which seems to be dictated by no purpose other than the needs of a dénouement ; it is arbitrary, not inevitable. And if he has a fault of attitude, it is that he assumes a virtue if the clothes are shabby and a vice if they are modish.

But withal Galsworthy was a great novelist, and 'The Man of Property' is a great novel. It is the first of a trilogy, the others being 'In Chancery' and 'To Let,' which, with two 'interludes,' 'Indian Summer of a Forsyte' and 'Awakening,' make up that noble volume 'The Forsyte Saga.' A second Forsyte trilogy, carrying on the story of the younger generation, contained 'The White Monkey,' 'The Silver Spoon' and 'Swan Song.' A volume of short stories, 'On Forsyte 'Change,' dealt with the same rich, upper-middle-class family. During the course of this long succession of novels, Forsytes were to die and to be born, to marry and to break their marriages, and gradually to enter the speech and thought of England as no characters had done since the creations of Charles Dickens.

Others of Galsworthy's novels were 'The Country House,' 'Fraternity,' 'The

Patrician,' and 'The Dark Flower.' His last book, 'Over the River,' was published posthumously.

Both **H. G. Wells** (b. 1866) and Arnold Bennett (1867–1931) have received consideration in Lesson 41, page 182. Wells stands in the very foremost rank of contemporary English authors. More subjective than objective in style, his books are not, to him, ends in themselves. All his novels, stories, philosophic and miscellaneous writings are expressions of a mind profoundly curious about life and its meaning. 'The Time Machine' was the forerunner of a memorable succession of scientific romances which includes 'The Island of Dr. Moreau,' 'The Sleeper Awakes,' 'The First Men in the Moon,' and 'The Food of the Gods,' while 'Kipps' and 'Tono-Bungay' are good examples of his skill in the novel of character, afterwards developed with even more intimacy of analysis in 'Ann Veronica' and 'The New Machiavelli,' and, best of all, in his immortal 'History of Mr. Polly.'

Largely as the result of his intellectual activities during the period of the First Great War, Wells emerged as the most prominent figure in the post-war literary world, and his novel 'Mr. Britling Sees It Through' seems destined to remain one of the works of fiction of really prime importance that owe their origin directly to that War. In the course of the next twenty years or so, Wells published several novels, including 'Christina Alberta's Father,' 'The World of William Clissold' and 'The Bulpington of Blup.'

The Second World War inspired 'Babes in the Darkling Wood,' a novel of ideas in which he hammers away again at his doctrines of Internationalism and the World State. In 'You Can't Be Too Careful,' published in 1941, he sets out to give 'a complete and veracious study of a sample contemporary man.' The result is a very unflattering picture of present-day humanity, and the book ends with a fierce denunciation of the social system which produces it.

Arnold Bennett possessed hardly any quality in common with Wells, although the two men's names were at one time commonly bracketed together. In the realm of fiction, Bennett's masterpiece is 'The Old Wives' Tale,' a really great novel, in which the genius of the author fuses into a living work of art the most ordinary and, indeed, unpromising material. That is his most worthy characteristic : the ability to take the commonest appurtenances of life in a group of smoke-wreathed pottery towns and to present them to us with such a persuasive air that we find ourselves as interested in his narrative as if it had been woven out of the time-approved stuff of romance. Only a great novelist can do that, and Arnold Bennett, who wrote also quite ordinary novels, schooled himself to the doing of it by the will to achieve great fiction rather than by any heaven-born gift of narrative power. 'Clayhanger,'

'Hilda Lessways' and 'These Twain' are a trilogy which show the novelist at his best ; and of his later work, when he had abandoned the Five Towns for a wider field, 'Riceyman Steps' is as good as anything he ever did ; character, atmosphere, story, humour and sympathy are all exemplified in this moving tale of mean streets. 'Buried Alive,' afterwards successfully dramatized as 'The Great Adventure,' and 'Mr. Prohack,' both show Arnold Bennett's humour at its best.

LESSON 51

Modern Novelists and Humorists

IN a brief survey of the remaining modern novelists, many writers of real merit must unavoidably be omitted. We can merely indicate some of the outstanding figures who throng the scene.

Sir Henry Rider Haggard (1856–1925) is the most familiar of those who won popularity in the later years of the 19th century. He made a tremendous hit with 'King Solomon's Mines' and 'She', and followed it up with many stories of adventure and romance, savouring of the weird, against a savage background, usually Africa, where lost civilizations were encountered.

Stanley Weyman (1855–1928) produced many stirring historical novels, of which 'A Gentleman of France' and 'Under the Red Robe' are best known. In the same vein Sir Arthur Quiller-Couch (1862–1944) wrote 'The Splendid Spur,' under the pen-name 'Q'; he was also the author of 'Dead Man's Rock,' 'Troy Town' and other Cornish tales. His work as a critic has been noted in Lesson 41, page 182.

Sir Anthony Hope Hawkins (1863–1933), as 'Anthony Hope,' started the school of Ruritanian romance with his 'Prisoner of Zenda' and 'Rupert of Hentzau,' the scene being an imaginary Balkan state.

Henry Seton Merriman (1862–1903), whose real name was Hugh Stowell Scott, happily combined romance and realism in 'The Sowers,' 'Barlasch of the Guard' and other popular novels. The American-born Mrs. Craigie (1867–1906), under the pseudonym 'John Oliver Hobbes,' had a tremendous success with her first novel, 'Some Emotions and a Moral.'

Skilful writers, each with a long list of popular novels to his credit, are W. J. Locke (1863–1930), who wrote 'The Beloved

Vagabond'; Robert Hichens (b. 1864), whose 'Garden of Allah' and 'Bella Donna' are best known ; A. E. W. Mason (b. 1865), whose 'Four Feathers' was a favourite ; J. D. Beresford (b. 1873), whose highwater-mark was 'The Early History of Jacob Stahl' and 'The Hampdenshire Wonder'; and W. B. Maxwell (1876–1938), whose best work may be found in 'Vivien' and 'The Guarded Flame.'

Signs that fiction was going to take itself more seriously could be discovered in Richard Whiteing's 'Number Five John-street,' in which extremes of wealth and poverty were picturesquely contrasted. 'The Ragged-trousered Philanthropists' is a study of the mass mind which has permanent value, written by a house-painter and decorator, who never wrote anything else and died unknown in 1911, three years before his book saw the light. His name was Noonan, but he used the pen-name of Robert Tressell.

The first World War, by turning public attention to social as well as international problems, deepened the channel of seriousness which novels had begun to navigate. The period between 1918 and 1939 was one in which a high level of novel-writing was reached by a large number of authors.

Controversy raged around the Irish writer James Joyce (1882–1941), who, plunging into the depths of the subconscious, abandoned the usual methods of expression and wrote in a style which, at first sight, is mere gibberish, but actually is most appropriate to the subject-matter. His 'Ulysses' explores, during twenty hours, the minds of a middle-aged Jewish commercial traveller and a young student, and others linked with them in Dublin. 'Finnegan's Wake' is a similar record of the night's sleep of a working man in the same city.

Joyce was trained at a Jesuit college for the Roman Catholic priesthood. His first work reproduced the seminary atmosphere, but was not otherwise remarkable. 'Portrait of the Artist as a Young Man' gave no hint of what was to follow. ' Ulysses,' published in 1922, came as a surprise, even to those few who had seen promise in the earlier work ; it was also something of a shock. It appeared in Paris, where Joyce lived ; the British booksellers refused to handle it for fear that it might be banned as indecent literature ; only smuggled copies were brought into this country. But it was not so much the occasional obscene passages that shocked Joyce's former admirers ; it was the astonishing and, to them, perverse method in which he wrote. What he aimed at was to carry further the process favoured by Dorothy Richardson and Virginia Woolf, by which a running stream of thoughts flowing through the mind of a character was followed as a means of telling a story and building up personality.

Joyce tried to intensify this process by hastening the flow, mixing words up and telescoping them, mis-spelling and mangling them, as they might be mixed up in the mind of an Irish Jew in the course of a day's happenings. A few critics eager to be in at the birth of any novelty declared that Joyce was destined to revolutionize English prose ; others waved him aside as a freak writer. Upon the reading public in general he made no impression. If they picked up one of his books, they found such writing as this :

Well, arundgirond in a waveney lyne aringarouma she pattered and swung and sidled, dribbling her boulder through narrowa mosses, the diliskydrear on our drier side and the vilde vetchvine agin us, curara here, careero there, not knowing which medway or weser to strike it, edereider, making chatta-hoochee all to her ain chichiu, like Santa Claus at the cree of the pale and puny, nistling to hear for their tiny hearties, her arms encircling Isolabella, then running with reconciled Romas and Reims, on like a lech to be off like a dart, then bathing Dirty Hans' spatters with spittle, with a Christmas box apiece for aisch and iverone of her childer, the birthday gifts they dreamt they gabe her, the spoiled she fleetly laid at our door !

That is taken, not from 'Ulysses,' but from the later work, 'Finnegan's Wake.' As he grew older, Joyce's eccentricity deepened. Whether the future will rate him as a great novelist or forget him as a man of some talent with a very large bee in his bonnet, cannot be foretold.

The obscurities of Dorothy Richardson left little mark. Virginia Woolf (1882-1941) was more influential. Boldly experimental in technique, 'Jacob's Room' and Mrs. Dalloway' showed her to be a writer of distinction. Later books, 'To The Lighthouse,' 'The Waves,' 'A Room of One's Own' and 'Orlando' were more complex.

D. H. Lawrence (1885-1930) is sometimes bracketed with Joyce as if they fell into the same category ; this is by no means the case. They were alike in one respect only : both suffered from a deep-seated pathological obsession. Lawrence came of Nottinghamshire mining stock and began as a school teacher. He wrote excellent English of the ordinary kind, and 'Sons and Lovers,' the autobiographical novel which made his reputation, is pretty certain to be kept alive both by its vivid portraits—especially that of the author's mother, a magnificent study—and by its satisfying artistry. No other book of Lawrence's quite came up to this high standard he had set himself, though they were all above the average, and clearly the product of a powerful, though restless and rebellious, intellect.

Conan Doyle (1859-1930) was the forerunner of numberless detective-story writers who carried on the tradition he started with Sherlock Holmes. Very few of them approached him either in ingenuity of plot or picturesqueness of character. Sherlock Holmes made a hit with a large public —the public of the 'Strand Magazine.' Doyle owed something to his French predecessors of the de Boisgobey school, but his amateur detective, who had worked out his own original methods and relied very much on his close observation of small details, was a creation entirely his own. It was clever to provide a foil to Holmes's shrewdness in the not-very-quick Dr. Watson who accompanied him on his investigations. Doyle afterwards wrote some fine historical novels, the best being 'The White Company.'

Though Conan Doyle had many imitators, it was not till Edgar Wallace (1875-1932) came into the field with 'The Four Just Men' that the surprising boom in detective fiction began. Wallace was a London newspaper reporter. As a boy he had sold papers and got little education. He had a knack of turning out tales and plays at high speed and they caught the public fancy, selling literally by the million. There was a strong family likeness between his plots which gave rise to the saying :

'I have read all Wallace's 56 stories and like them both.' His style was crude, his characterization slapdash, his invention not very fertile, but his vigour and rapidity carried all before it. He made a large fortune, but when he died, in Hollywood, he had run through all his available assets.

His vogue kindled the ambition of countless authors. The craze for writing crime stories attacked serious novelists and writers in more studious branches of literature, as well as those who wrote merely to hit a passing caprice and make money. Dorothy Sayers (b. 1893) was a woman of letters in addition to being the creator of Lord Peter Wimsey ; G. D. H. Cole (b. 1889), who produced, with his wife, a number of thrillers, was a leading economist ; J. S. Fletcher (1863-1935), the Yorkshireman who adroitly mingled character-drawing with intricate plots and so made his stories more readable than most, had been a historical novelist.

Of war novels, the most important were 'The Spanish Farm' trilogy, by R. H. Mottram (b. 1883). A. S. M. Hutchinson (b. 1880) caught the post-war mood when he wrote 'If Winter Comes' ; C. E. Montague (1867-1928) gave vent to his feelings of frustration, shared by so many, in 'Disenchantment' and 'Fiery Particles.'

Sir Hugh Walpole (1884-1941) had a versatile talent. His London novels, grouped round certain families in Mayfair, are interlinked with each other and with his Russian novels, 'The Dark Forest' and 'The Secret City.' The 'Jeremy' books trace the development of a small boy onwards through adolescence. A monumental achievement was his 'Rogue Herries' series, which followed the history of a Lakeland family from the 17th century down to modern times, with a wealth of thrilling episodes and characters. In 'The Cathedral' he challenged comparison with Trollope. Of all his work, perhaps the most vivid were the two books of eccentric and rather frightening personalities, 'Mr. Perrin and Mr. Traill' and 'The Old Ladies.' The first, a study of schoolmasters' nerves, won the praise of Henry James. Other thrillers were 'Portrait of a Man with Red Hair' and 'Above the Dark Circus.'

Frank Swinnerton (b. 1884) has been a prolific writer of good popular novels. His 'Nocturne' was enthusiastically praised by H. G. Wells and Arnold Bennett. He is a sound and interesting critic.

J. B. Priestley (b. 1894) made a popular success with 'The Good Companions,' a picaresque tale of a group of travelling players. This created a wide public for his other novels and miscellaneous work. He is a successful playwright.

Of the many novels of W. Somerset Maugham (b. 1874), 'Of Human Bondage' has sold by the hundred thousand. 'The Moon and Sixpence,' a study of a painter who, like Gauguin, 'went native' in the South Seas, almost touched greatness.

The careful, supremely conscientious work of E. M. Forster (b. 1879) was divided by long intervals. He has written solely with the aim of expressing his view of life and human nature. 'A Passage to India' will probably live longer than his earlier novels because of its bearing on the relations between Indians and the British in their country, and its subtle analysis of the causes that kept them apart. But everything he wrote bore the impress of a vivid imagination and keen intellect.

Compton Mackenzie (b. 1883) made his first hit with 'Carnival,' which showed him to have the makings of a great novelist. 'Sinister Street,' based in part on his schooldays at St. Paul's in London, added considerably to his reputation and had many sequels.

John Buchan (1875-1940), later 1st Lord Tweedsmuir, wrote many exciting novels of various types ; his 'Greenmantle' stories are his best known. Robert Graves, the poet (b. 1895), made some excellent reconstructions of Roman history in 'I, Claudius,' 'Claudius the God' and 'Count Belisarius.'

Charles Morgan (b. 1894) saw Naval service, then became dramatic critic to 'The Times.' His third novel 'The Fountain' was the most talked-of book during the year of its appearance (1932). It was an examination of the minds of officers in an internment camp and appealed to a large number of readers by reason of its blend of mysticism and intellect.

Aldous Huxley (b. 1894) in 'Brave New World' wrote one of the few remarkable novels with which everyone desirous of keeping up with the thought of the time must be acquainted. It was a coldly furious satire on the scientific advances which fifty years earlier his famous grandfather, Thomas Henry Huxley, held up to admiration as leading to progress in every direction. Before this, Aldous Huxley's novels had made a limited appeal to those who enjoy studies in morbidity. Afterwards, in 'Eyeless in Gaza,' he pointed to a method of 'saving the world' which would be more efficacious than giving science free rein.

Appealing, like Huxley, mainly to the sophisticated intellectual are Richard Aldington (b. 1892), author of 'Death of a Hero,' and Evelyn Waugh (b. 1903), whose brilliantly satirical 'Decline and Fall,' 'Vile Bodies,' and 'Black Mischief' won many admirers. His brother Alec (b. 1898) came into notice, while still in his teens, with 'The Loom of Youth.'

In 'The Edwardians,' V. Sackville-West (the Hon. Mrs. Harold Nicolson, b. 1892) described rather than satirized the aristocracy in the first decade of the 20th century. She did the same, perhaps more effectively, in 'Heritage'; and in 'All Passion Spent' she drew a touchingly beautiful portrait of an aristocratic old lady in whom the fire of youth had been gently quenched.

Rose Macaulay's brilliant observation, irony and wit are embodied in many novels, of which 'Told by an Idiot,' 'Orphan Island' and 'Going Abroad' are typical.

Among other notable women novelists were Rebecca West (b. 1892), 'The Judge' and 'Harriet Hume'; G. B. Stern (b. 1890), 'The Rakonitz Chronicles'; Margaret Irwin, 'Royal Flush,' 'The Proud Servant'; F. Tennyson Jesse, 'The Secret Bread,' 'Moonraker,' and, with H. M. Harwood, her husband, 'London Frost' and 'While London Burns'; Margaret Kennedy, 'The Constant Nymph' and 'Escape Me Never'; Rosamund Lehmann, 'Dusty Answer' and 'Invitation to the Waltz'; Naomi Mitchison (b. 1897), 'Cloud Cuckoo Land' and 'Black Sparta'; Sylvia Townsend Warner (born 1893), 'Lolly Willowes.'

Warwick Deeping (b. 1877) is an example of the persevering author who at last finds a large public for his work. He was a doctor and wrote many novels before he swam into the best-seller class with an after-the-war story, 'Sorrell and Son' (1925).

Two other doctors who made their names as novelists were Francis Brett Young (b. 1884), author of 'Portrait of Clare' and many other fine novels; and A. J. Cronin (b. 1896), who caught the popular fancy with 'Hatter's Castle,' a study of a tyrannical old Scot, reminiscent of a more distinguished work of the same nature, 'The House with Green Shutters,' by George Douglas (1869–1902). Dr. Cronin also interested a large public in 'The Stars Look Down,' with its vivid pictures of life in a small Welsh mining town, and in 'The Citadel,' an attack on the get-rich-quick members of the medical profession.

'Ian Hay'—in real life, Major John Hay Beith (b. 1876)—is the author of many popular novels, such as 'Tilly of Bloomsbury,' 'The Safety Match' and 'The Middle Watch,' equally successful in dramatized form. Another versatile writer is A. P. Herbert (b. 1890), whose most memorable novels are 'The Secret Battle,' 'The Water Gipsies' and 'Holy Deadlock.'

Locality Novelists. Of those who may be called locality novelists, Sheila Kaye-Smith took a high place with 'Sussex Gorse,' 'Green Apple Harvest,' and other stories of the South country. Mary Webb (1881–1927) had a well-merited vogue, her district being Shropshire and the Welsh marches. 'Precious Bane' was one of the first and best. The author's descriptive talent outweighed her skill in character-drawing and knack of telling a story, but she wrote well enough to please a public 'few though fit.' Hilda Vaughan, wife of Charles Morgan (mentioned above), helped readers of 'The Invader,' 'The Soldier and the Gentlewoman,' and other books about Wales, to understand the Welsh character.

E. H. Young took Bristol and the country round about it for her province. Her delicate gift of making everyday life interesting set 'The Misses Mallett,' 'The Vicar's Daughter,' 'Miss Mole,' and 'William,' far above the average of 20th century fiction. Phyllis Bentley (b. 1894) wrote of Yorkshire, whose inhabitants were with somewhat laborious accuracy shown as they are, or were in the between-wars period: 'A Modern Tragedy' and 'Inheritance' were typical of this writer.

J. L. Hodson (b. 1892), a distinguished journalist, took his native Lancashire as the scene of his powerful 'Harvest in the North,' 'Jonathan North' and other novels. Norah Hoult and Kate O'Brien specialized in 'Holy Ireland'; St. John Ervine wrote, in 'Changing Winds,' a novel of Ulster life that made a sharp impression.

Another dramatist, Laurence Housman, also wrote novels; his 'John of Jingalo' was a shrewd and entertaining political satire, though not up to the level of Hilaire Belloc's 'Change in the Cabinet' and 'Mr. Clutterbuck's Election,' written with a close knowledge of the political scene as well as with flashing wit. H. M. Tomlinson's 'Gallion's Reach' placed its author in the front rank of British writers. Henry Williamson's nature stories, especially 'Tarka the Otter,' are outstanding.

In a niche of his own is Algernon Blackwood (b. 1869), a student of the occult, whose beautifully written tales, notably 'The Centaur' and 'John Silence,' were lit with mysticism. Claude Houghton wrote well and had many admirers for 'I am Jonathan Scrivener' and 'Chaos is Come Again,' but his addiction to fantasy narrowed the field of his appeal.

David Garnett (b. 1892) wrote in delightfully original vein; his 'Lady into Fox,' 'The Sailor's Return,' 'The Grasshoppers Come,' 'Beany Eye' and 'Pocahontas' have all made their mark.

Some English Humorists. No humorous writer during the past half-century has been so widely popular as Jerome K. Jerome (1859–1927). His fun was in the Mark Twain tradition, which consisted mostly of comic exaggeration, but he introduced a strong personal note, sentimental and mildly satirical, with a dash of commonsense that made his essays, 'The Idle Thoughts of an Idle Fellow,' seem to most of his readers profound rather than fantastic comments on life and human nature. 'Three Men in a Boat,' the record of a Thames trip, had this quality also.

Neil Lyons (1880–1940) had a more original gift of humour. His 'Sixpenny Pieces,' sketches of the patients who came to a 'sixpenny doctor' in the East-end of London, with sidelights on their lives and his, can be regarded as a social document as well as being very funny. 'Arthur's,' which describes the customers at an all-night coffee-stall in London, has the same merits, and Lyons's tales of soldiers at home ('Kitchener Chaps') and abroad ('A Kiss from France') were irresistibly laughter-provoking. Taking what may be called the lower middle class for the object of his humour, Pett Ridge (1860–1930) produced a series of amusing and at the same time truthful studies of Cockney types such as 'Mord Em'ly' and 'The Wickhamses.' He wrote of these with sympathy, even affection, and made a real contribution to the understanding of Londoners and their lives. There was not much sociological value in W. W. Jacobs' (1863–1943) stories of Thames-side bargees and lightermen and dock watchmen and captains of little ships, but they were extremely amusing in a broadly comic manner, which the author never varied through all his many volumes, though he did now and then try his hand at a tragic theme, as in 'The Monkey's Paw.'

For sheer high-spirited fun of the uproarious kind, H. G. Wells beat everybody with his fight in 'Mr. Polly.' In the power to compel mirth of a quieter order, Barry Pain (1864–1928) was unrivalled. 'Eliza' and 'Eliza's Husband' were illuminating presentments of the lower middle-class mind worthy to be set alongside that masterpiece of George and Weedon Grossmith, 'The Diary of a Nobody.' Of this, Lord Rosebery (Liberal Prime Minister) said he had 'given away more copies than any living man' and 'regarded any bedroom he occupied as unfurnished without a copy of it.' Charles Pooter, the immortal diarist, was ranked by Augustine Birrell with Don Quixote—not entirely as a joke. He and his friends represented the clerkly type of the latter part of the 19th century, with typical wife and employer.

Stella Gibbons (b. 1902) very nearly achieved a masterpiece of parody in 'Cold Comfort Farm,' making capital fun of the rural novel. By far the best parodies of the age were contained in Max Beerbohm's (b. 1872) 'Christmas Garland,' a delightful collection in which both the merits and defects of prominent authors were ridiculed with discreet impertinence. As criticism, they were scarcely less apt than they were conceded to be as satire. In this line F. Anstey, whose real name was Anstey Guthrie (1856–1933), had a great success with 'Vice Versa,' the story of a father who changed places with his schoolboy son, and underwent tortures at the hands of boys and masters, while his office was turned upside down by the antics of the thirteen-year-old at its head. There was in most of his tales a magical element which, along with the humour, went down well.

The lady who came before the public with the delightful 'Elizabeth and her German Garden' was first a German baroness by marriage and then the wife of Earl Russell. She made fun of both her husbands and of everything and everyone else. Her novels were most of them sheer delight. In long involved sentences she drew the most absurd characters, the most preposterous incidents, yet never seemed to be going outside the bounds of possibility. She gained the warm admiring gratitude of all who care for artistry.

Also in mock-serious vein, E. M. Delafield (1890–1943), in real life Mrs. Dashwood, won fame with her 'Diary of a Provincial Lady' and its sequels. She wrote a great many serious novels and some plays.

P. G. Wodehouse (b. 1881) relied largely on verbal humour, traded in the fantastic, and created a new type of social imbecile in Bertie Wooster and an ideal butler in Jeeves. He became a steady producer of popular novels and short stories.

LESSON 52

The Earlier American Writers

THE earliest English colonists were much too preoccupied with their own needs to produce, at first, any literature of their own. Moreover, they were nearly all English-born, and there was need for a new generation to grow up in fresh surroundings before American literature could arise. Indeed, it may be stated that not till about the middle of the eighteenth century was anything of real importance written in America.

Then began this new branch of literature which was to endeavour to supply the intellectual needs of a country whose inhabitants are nearly three times as numerous as those of Great Britain, using the same language as our own, though with a slightly differing idiom, and having certain democratic ideals in common with us.

Seventeenth - Century Literature. The books produced in the 17th century dealt mainly with travel, sermons and poems. They were written by men and women, English-born, living in a foreign country which they were colonizing. Hence their work was British in form and outlook. Time would have to pass before the first book written by a writer born in America was to be published in that country. Captain John Smith, who related the story of Pocahontas, was an adult when he joined the expedition to Virginia in 1605. Moreover, he spent but little of his time in America, and died in London. Nevertheless, his 'True Relation of Occurrences in Virginia,' published in 1608, is considered to be the first book in American literature, though it is generally agreed that the literary standard attained is not a high one. 'The Bay Psalm Book,' printed in Cambridge, Massachusetts, was the first book in English to be published in America. It was mainly the work of John Eliot, 'the apostle of the Indians,' who arrived in America in 1631 at the age of 30, and of Richard Mather, a Lancashire Puritan who reached America in 1635. He was the father of Increase Mather, and grandfather of Cotton Mather (*see* below), each of whom played a part of some importance in the development of American letters.

To Anne Bradstreet (1612–1672) falls the distinction of being the first poetess of New England. She was, however, a grown woman before she left England, and her works were sent to her native land to be published. The most popular of all the early poems was, however, Michael Wigglesworth's 'The Day of Doom, or a Poetical Description of the Great and Last Judgement' (1662). The literary quality of this work is not high, but for more than a century it remained the classic religious poem of the American Puritans. Indeed, the first preoccupation in their early books was mainly religious, and although their arrival in America was due to their search for religious freedom, they were strongly disinclined to grant much latitude to those who disagreed with them in theological matters. Travel and history also occupied some of the energies of the early writers who are of interest mainly as pioneers. Of what is termed 'polite literature,' there was practically none at first.

Two writers of outstanding power survive from this period which might be termed that of ecclesiastical disputation—Cotton Mather and Jonathan Edwards.

Cotton Mather (1663–1728) is credited with having written some four hundred books and pamphlets. His *magnum opus* was the 'Magnalia Christi Americana, or the Ecclesiastical History of New England from its First Planting, in the Year of our Lord 1620, unto the Year of our Lord 1698.' This is a work of much learning and colossal size. Mather seems to have suffered from a verbosity he inherited from his father, Increase Mather, a graduate both of Harvard and Trinity College, Dublin, who was the author of 136 works, mostly sermons. But as an example of his extraordinary qualities it should be noted that, while, well in advance of his time, Cotton Mather advocated the practice of inoculation for smallpox, he was nevertheless notorious for his prosecution of alleged witches. It is worth while drawing attention to the fact that these early colonists seem much concerned with the matter of witchcraft. Indeed one of Cotton Mather's more important works bore the title 'Late Memorable Providences relating to Witchcraft and Possession.'

Jonathan Edwards (1702–58) was a graduate of Yale, a Church pastor for 23 years, for eight years a missionary to the Indians, and for a very brief time President of Princeton, where he died of smallpox.

He was a man of fine intellect and stern moral character. His three great books, all theological, were 'Treatise Concerning the Religious Affections,' 'On the Freedom of the Will,' and 'Treatise on Original Sin.' Such works, although they had a vogue in their own day among the religiously disputatious Puritans of New England, can hardly be regarded now as more than museum specimens.

Benjamin Franklin (1706–90) is primarily important as a great citizen. There is one outstanding work to his credit. This is his 'Autobiography,' written in a clear and attractive prose. John Woolman (1720–72), an itinerant preacher among the Quakers, has left in his 'Journal ' an interesting and well written account of his travels. The book was much admired by both Charles Lamb and J. G. Whittier. George Washington can in no way be described as a literary man, but some of his public declarations are expressed in a prose which has imperishable qualities. Thus his 'Farewell Address' has a dignity and beauty of expression which places it in the same immortal class as Lincoln's speech at Gettysburg.

Charles Brockden Brown (1771–1810) is of interest as the first American to choose literature deliberately as his career. He also claimed to be the first American novelist, but his works are not read today, and with the coming of Fenimore Cooper his vogue passed, although he had anticipated his rival in writing of the forest life of the American continent. James Kirke Paulding (1779–1860) was a writer of some gifts, who produced both prose and verse of readable quality. His chief claim to fame, however, is probably his association with Washington Irving in the popular semi-monthly magazine, 'Salmagundi,' an imitation of the well-known 'Spectator.'

William Ellery Channing (1780–1842) was a miscellaneous writer who by his books and strong personal influence became one of the intellectual leaders of New England in the early part of the nineteenth century. He wrote on such varied subjects as Milton, Fénelon, slavery, and self-culture. Daniel Webster (1782–1852) takes his place in American literature as a very distinguished orator. An advocate, a Senator, and afterwards a Secretary of State, his best speeches were collected and published, and are fine examples of oratory.

Washington Irving (1783–1859), essayist and historian, was one of the most successful writers of the New World. He soon obtained a reputation which extended far beyond the bounds of America. He was a member of the American Bar and travelled widely in Europe, on one occasion not returning to his native land for 17 years. In 1807 he first attracted notice by his amusing miscellany 'Salmagundi,' which after 20 numbers stopped, for no apparent reason, when it was highly successful. In 1809 there appeared 'A History of New York, by Diedrich Knickerbocker,' a burlesque upon the Dutch settlers. It has become a classic in America, where everybody knows the little man in the knee breeches and the cocked hat. In 1819 Irving published on both sides of the Atlantic his 'Sketch Book.' Sir Walter Scott was warm in its praises, and the book was a great success. It is written with much charm, and three of the sketches are outstanding. They are 'Rip van Winkle,' 'The Legend of Sleepy Hollow,' and 'Westminster Abbey.' Rip van Winkle is one of those creations of genius which are assured of immortality. In 1822 Irving brought out ' Bracebridge Hall,' followed two years later by ' Tales of a Traveller,' works which maintained his reputation.

In 1826 Everett, the American Minister at Madrid, asked him to come to Spain to assist in making translations of historical matter dealing with Columbus. The result of this visit was a series of most interesting and well written books : 'History of the Life and Voyages of Columbus,' 'The Conquest of Granada,' 'Voyages of the Companions of Columbus,' 'The Alhambra,' 'Legends of the Conquest of Spain,' and 'Mahomet and his Successors.' All these were written between 1828 and 1849. At one time he contemplated writing a history of the conquest of Mexico, for which he had collected much material, but, hearing that W. H. Prescott was engaged in a similar task, with great generosity he left the field open for the younger man.

In 1842 Irving was appointed Minister to Spain, and finally returned to America in 1846. In that year he published his 'Life of Goldsmith,' and brought out his most ambitious work, a life of Washington, in five volumes, between 1855 and 1859. Irving's high character and kindliness of disposition, his charming style and his ability to win and retain interest, all help to make him an author whose reputation has withstood the test of time.

George Ticknor (1791–1871) was a historian and biographer. After being a Professor at Harvard from 1819 to 1835, he went to Europe, where he spent some time in collecting material for his 'History of Spanish Literature.' He is also the author of lives of Lafayette and of W. H. Prescott, the historian. His 'Letters and Journals,' published after his death, make most interesting reading. Nathaniel Parker Wills (1806–67), who came of a family of journalists, was himself a highly successful journalist, and the author of much poetry which was read in his own time but has not the qualities which defy the passage of the years. He established the 'American Monthly Magazine.' His best known collection of stories is 'The Slingsby Papers,' and his best poem 'Unseen Spirits.'

James Fenimore Cooper (1789–1851), after three years at Yale, shipped as an ordinary seaman in the merchant service, and two years later entered the United States navy, in which he served for three years. His experience was invaluable to him when he began to write tales of high adventure. He was not regarded in America primarily as a writer for boys, as he is in England. Altogether he wrote some 30 novels, of which 'The Last of the Mohicans,' 'The Pathfinder,' and 'The Deerslayer' still find enthusiastic readers among boys. Cooper also wrote a 'Naval History of the United States,' and 'Lives of Distinguished American Naval Officers.' Fenimore Cooper possessed remarkable powers of narrative and description, though he was somewhat less successful in the delineation of character.

William Gilmore Simms (1806–1870) was the first Southerner to gain any reputation as a writer. He began his literary career as a journalist, and then tried poetry without any great success except in his 'Southern Passages and Pictures.' As a novelist, however, he was the most capable of the imitators of Fenimore Cooper. 'The Yemassee' is generally considered to be the best of his novels. Richard Henry Dana Junior (1815–82), son of Richard Henry Dana (1787–1879), a successful critic and editor of the 'North American Review,' won immortality by a book which is probably the best of its kind. This is 'Two Years Before the Mast,' written as the fruits of his own experience, when, in a break in his college career, he had shipped as an ordinary seaman, and had sailed round Cape Horn to California and back.

William Cullen Bryant (1794–1878) occupies an honoured position in the history of American literature, and justly takes his place among the more important authors of his country. His blank verse poem 'Than-

atopsis,' published in 1817, was acclaimed as the finest poem so far produced in America. He was a lawyer for some time, and then changed over to journalism, becoming in 1829 editor-in-chief of the 'New York Evening Post.' By his fine character and high principles he did much to improve the tone of the daily newspapers. In the bitter controversies over the slavery question, Bryant's paper took the anti-slavery side, and helped to found the Republican party.

But it is as a poet that Bryant made his greatest claim on the gratitude of his countrymen. Apart from his longer blank verse poems, he was the author of a number of short lyrics which became very popular. In spirit and substance these lyrics showed literary kinship with Gray and Cowper. Among the best known favourites were 'The Fringed Gentian,' 'Lines to a Waterfowl,' 'Oh, Mother of a Mighty Race,' 'The Rivulet,' and 'The Battlefield.' When he was over seventy he translated the 'Iliad' and 'Odyssey' into blank verse, but in this he was no more successful than a number of writers before him.

George Bancroft (1800–91), scholar, diplomat, and historian, spent some forty years in writing a 'History of the United States' from the discovery of the continent to the end of the revolutionary war in 1782. His other great work was 'The History of the Formation of the Constitution of the United States.' His writings were long and diffuse, and it is reckoned that had he carried on his History to his own day, on the same large scale, it would have occupied between seventy and eighty volumes. He had a high ideal of his responsibilities as a historian, and in his own day was popular.

Lydia Huntley Sigourney (1791–1865) is of interest chiefly as showing the change of taste which occurs in literary matters. An exceptionally copious writer of smooth sentimental verse, she had at one time a very large public, and was widely read. Her most ambitious work was a blank verse poem called 'Traits of the Aborigines of America.' She is little read now.

Sarah Margaret Fuller (1810–1850) injured her health by overworking when she was young, but succeeded in becoming a very proficient linguist, reading the literatures of France, Spain and Italy, and German philosophy in the original languages. She was one of the leaders of the movement of revolt against Puritanism, and conducted for two years the important paper 'The Dial,' the organ of New England

Transcendentalism. She made some translations of German works, was literary critic to the 'Tribune,' and her 'Papers on Literature and Art,' republished as a book, form her most important contribution to American literature.

Louisa May Alcott (1832–88) became famous for her charming book for children, 'Little Women,' which still continues to be read over here and in America. In no other of her thirty publications did she produce anything of lasting value.

Ralph Waldo Emerson (1803–1882) will always be regarded as one of the literary giants of America. The son of a Unitarian clergyman who died when the boy was only eight, leaving his widow with but scanty support to bring up a family of six, Emerson owes a great debt to his mother. Resolved that her children should have a good education, she took in boarders in order to earn enough for their schooling. But more than this, she encouraged her children to read in their spare time, and so the family was brought up in an atmosphere where the reading of Shakespeare, Milton, Addison and Pope, and translations of Plato and Plutarch, were regarded as normal intellectual occupations. In his essay on 'Domestic Life' Emerson refers to this, though in quite an impersonal way.

After going to Harvard in 1817 (the College in its early days was little more than a boys' school to which pupils went at about the same age as they now enter Public Schools) and graduating, Emerson taught for a few years. But he abandoned this calling for the ministry, and after some specialized training he was ordained as colleague of the Rev. Henry Ware, minister of the Second Church in Boston. Soon afterwards, on the resignation of Mr. Ware, he was appointed pastor of this important church. In 1832, feeling that he had travelled some distance from the orthodoxy of his congregation, Emerson in turn resigned.

All these events, and especially his changed outlook on religious matters, were to have considerable effect on Emerson's life and writings. His health not proving satisfactory, and being much affected by the death of his young wife, a victim of consumption, Emerson sought relief in a voyage to Europe. On Christmas Day, 1832, he left Boston in a brig bound for the Mediterranean, and visited Sicily, Italy, France and Great Britain. He saw Coleridge, Wordsworth, Landor and Carlyle, with the last of whom he began a life-long friendship. An interesting record of this

is to be found in their correspondence, which began with Emerson's first letter in 1834, and ended with Carlyle's last letter in 1872; it was collected and edited by Charles Eliot Norton.

On his return from Europe Emerson settled in Concord and devoted his time to lecturing and writing. He married again very happily and spent the rest of his life in work of his own choice, and in reading, meditating and conversing with friends and visitors. He was still much concerned with his religious outlook, about which he both lectured and wrote. He evolved his own form of belief which it is difficult to classify; it has leanings towards Pantheism.

In 1847 Emerson sailed to Europe on his second visit. He spent a week with Carlyle and then gave a number of lectures in England and Scotland, afterwards publishing some of them in 'Representative Men.' Another volume, 'English Traits,' was a further product of his experiences during this European visit. In 1857 he began to write for 'The Atlantic Monthly,' to which he contributed a number of poems.

Emerson's works have been collected in 12 volumes. His reputation rests upon his Essays and Discourses, based upon the large variety of subjects dealt with in his lectures, which were the main source of his income. He was a man of singularly fine character, and the general esteem in which he was held added to the influence of his writings.

William Hickling Prescott (1796–1859), the historian, was educated at Harvard, where he met with the unhappy incident which was to handicap him all his life. During rough play by some of his fellow students, he was hit full in the eye by a piece of hard bread. He completely lost the sight of that eye. Later on, when he had entered his father's office to be trained as a lawyer, the other eye became seriously affected, and he had to abandon all thoughts of a legal career. He trained himself to use a writing frame for the blind, and learned to listen intently to anything that was read or told to him.

He resolved to devote himself to literature, and after ten years of study and preparation he published in 1837 his 'History of Ferdinand and Isabella,' which at once won for him a high place among historians. This book was followed six years later by his 'History of the Conquest of Mexico,' which the unselfish withdrawal of Washington Irving gave him the opportunity to write. 'The History of the Conquest of Peru' came four years later. He had completed three volumes of the 'History of Philip II' when he died.

Prescott showed in all his work much painstaking research, impartiality, and vivid narrative power. The fact that he was not always sound in Ethnology—a science then in its early beginnings—detracts little from the value of his work as a competent historian exploring new and interesting ground.

Henry Wadsworth Longfellow (1807–1882), the most popular of America's poets, and for long the best known of them abroad, went to Bowdoin College, in Brunswick, Maine, where he had Nathaniel Hawthorne as a classmate. After graduation he was sent abroad by the college authorities to prepare himself for their new chair in modern languages, and visited France, Italy and Spain. He returned in 1829 to take up his new duties, and began to write in the 'North American Review.' In 1833 he published his first books, some translations from the Spanish, and the first part of his 'Outre Mer,' an account of his travels overseas. At the end of this year Longfellow was offered the Professorship of Modern Languages at Harvard, and gladly accepted. He paid a second visit to Europe, accompanied this time by his wife, who died at Amsterdam. He returned to Harvard in 1836, and in 1838 published his 'Voices of the Night,' which included 'Excelsior.' This was followed by 'Ballads and Poems,' which contained 'The Wreck of the Hesperus' and 'The Village Blacksmith.' These three poems were highly popular in England, and found a warm welcome in anthologies.

It was very hard on Longfellow that his reputation as a poet should be linked over here with such thoroughly third-rate stuff. He accomplished much of worth, was a master of metre, and in his three longest poems—'Evangeline' (1847), 'Hiawatha' (1855), and 'The Courtship of Miles Standish' (1858)—he produced work on which a solid reputation might rest. In 1861 he lost his second wife, who was fatally burned. Longfellow sustained himself in this terrible calamity by translating Dante's 'Divina Commedia.' This was a very useful and competent piece of work, even if it lacked, of necessity, some of the fire and brilliance of the original. Later there followed 'Tales of a Wayside Inn,' and a trilogy called 'Christus' consisting of 'The New England Tragedies,' 'The Divine Tragedy,' and 'The Golden Legend.' In 1868 he paid his last visit to England,

where much honour was accorded him. After his return to America he wrote nothing which increased his reputation.

Longfellow lacked the intensity of feeling and the high imaginative power which are necessary for the production of really great poetry. But if he failed to reach the heights, he knew how to appeal to the hearts of his readers and his fine chivalrous character is revealed in his writing.

John Greenleaf Whittier (1807–92) came of a Quaker family, and had little formal education. When very young he worked on a farm, and in later life divided his time between journalism, farming and local political work. He was an ardent supporter of the anti-slavery party, and by his writings he did much to stimulate the movement for emancipation. Some of his best-known poems are to be found in the collections entitled : 'In War Time,' 'Snow Bound,' 'The Tent on the Beach,' and 'Ballads of New England.' In his early writings Whittier showed clearly the influence of Burns. He was a poet of nature, and one who sang also of faith and the love of liberty. His want of early education was, however, a heavy handicap, and made his work at times faulty in form and grammar. But in his own day he had a large following among his country folk.

Nathaniel Hawthorne (1804–64), a distinguished writer of American fiction, early showed his love of reading. In 1821 he entered Bowdoin College, where Longfellow was also a student. After his college career he went into complete seclusion for a period of nearly twelve years, spending his time in reading and meditation, and even doing most of his walking at night. He held posts in the Custom-Houses at Boston and Salem, but he gave them up and resolved to live by his pen. After some early failures he had his short tales and sketches accepted by periodicals, and his first successful book was a collection of these published in 1837, in one volume, as 'Twice-told Tales.' A second volume followed five years later.

Hawthorne married in 1842, and set up house in Concord in an old manse where Emerson had once lived. There he wrote 'Mosses from an Old Manse,' followed by 'The Snow Image' and 'The Scarlet Letter,' by far his greatest book, and the novel which fully established his reputation. This powerful and tragic story still has a wide public today. Hawthorne's books for children are 'The Wonder Book' and 'The Tanglewood Tales,' both of which have considerable merit. In 1853 he was appointed United States Consul at Liverpool, where he remained four years. The last book published in his lifetime was 'Our Old Home,' consisting of notes on England and the English. Hawthorne's style was graceful and charming, and he takes his place among the most imaginative writers the United States have so far produced.

Abraham Lincoln (1809–65), though in no way a literary man, takes a high place among the writers of first-class English prose. His official documents and proclamations, and in particular his immortal address at Gettysburg, have a quality of diction which it would be difficult to excel.

Charles Godfrey Leland (1824–1903) was a lawyer who turned to journalism. He is remembered for his amusing 'Hans Breitmann Ballads,' written in the mixture of German and American-English known as Pennsylvania Dutch. They were extraordinarily popular both in America and Britain, and at one time were constantly quoted. His more serious work is now forgotten, but he was also a student of gypsy life and lore, on which he wrote much of value.

Edgar Allan Poe (1809–49), poet, critic and short story writer, was an author of quite outstanding ability. Left destitute as an orphan, he was adopted by a Mr. Allan of Virginia and ill requited his benefactor for all his kindness. Poe spent five years in England, where he received his early education, and after his return to America he went to the University of Virginia, where he distinguished himself as a student, but ran deeply into debt through gambling and had to be removed.

Poe began his literary career with three volumes of poems, 1827, 1829, and 1831, and in 1833 was successful in a competition for a prize poem and a prize tale. The poem was 'The Coliseum,' the tale 'The MS. found in a Bottle.' The following year Mr. Allan died without making any provision for Poe, who, having to rely on himself for a livelihood, took up literature as a career and wrote for various periodicals. His drinking habits were a great handicap to him and later in his life he became addicted to opium. In 1839 he became editor of the 'Gentleman's Magazine,' in which he published, as 'Tales of the Arabesque and Grotesque,' many of his best stories. In 1845 his best-known poem, 'The Raven,' appeared. In 1849, after a violent drinking bout, he was taken to hospital in Baltimore, where he died.

Poe's literary output was not at all large and his range was distinctly limited, but there is no doubt that he was an original genius. His poetry, at its best, has a charm and attractiveness quite its own. His best stories, most of which are to be found in the collection, 'Tales of Mystery and Imagination,' are remarkable both for their ingenuity and for the skill of their construction. At times Poe's imagination rises to great heights, as in 'The Murders in the Rue Morgue,' 'The Purloined Letter,' 'The Mystery of Marie Roget,' and 'The Fall of the House of Usher.' He was the pioneer of the modern detective story which is so extremely popular today.

LESSON 53

American Writers of the 19th Century

OF good Dutch and English descent, Oliver Wendell Holmes (1809–94) graduated at Harvard and studied medicine, practising first at home, and later in Paris. On his return to America he practised for a short time in his native town of Cambridge, Massachusetts. In 1838 he became Professor of Anatomy and Physiology first at Dartmouth College, and nine years later at Harvard University.

Until 1857 Holmes had done little in literature beyond publishing a small volume of poems which included 'The Last Leaf.' When, however, the 'Atlantic Monthly' was started, with Lowell as editor, Dr. Holmes was engaged as one of the principal regular contributors. For this magazine he wrote the three books by which he is best known: 'The Autocrat of the Breakfast Table,' 'The Professor at the Breakfast Table,' and 'The Poet at the Breakfast Table.' These books, charming, allusive and frankly self-revealing, had wide popularity on both sides of the Atlantic. He also wrote 'Elsie Venner,' described as 'with the exception of the story of Eve, par excellence the snake story of literature.' His other novel, 'The Guardian Angel,' was not so successful. Some people like his poems, often inserted in his prose works, better than his essays or novels. Among his verses which gained wide popularity are 'The Chambered Nautilus,' 'The Last Leaf,' 'Homesick in Heaven,' 'The Boys' and 'The One-Hoss Shay.' Holmes had a delightful sense of humour, and all his work is illuminated by a kindly urbanity.

Susan Warner (1819–1885), who wrote under the name of Elizabeth Wetherell, published in 1851 'The Wide, Wide World,' which, in its own time, was second only to 'Uncle Tom's Cabin' in popularity. Her 'Queechy' also had a very wide circle of readers. Her books are somewhat marred by over-sentimentality.

Henry David Thoreau (1817–1862) came from Concord, Massachusetts, and was educated at Harvard. For ten years after leaving college he followed no regular form of employment, preferring to do odd jobs in the open air, such as boat-building, farm and garden work and surveying, in order to obtain the essential necessities for his simple mode of life. This enabled him to have that silent communion with nature which he so much desired, and to train himself as an accurate observer and recorder of life in the wilds. In 1837 he began noting his observations in diaries and in ten years filled 30 volumes. In 1845 he published his first book, 'A Week on the Concord and Merrimac Rivers.' In 1847 he went to live with the Emerson household, where he stayed a couple of years. Later he wrote ' Walden,' his best known work ; this was followed after a long interval by ' The Maine Woods' and 'Cape Cod.'

Thoreau aimed at living a life of simplicity as nearly as possible under quite natural conditions. Hence his cult of the open air and solitude. In his writings he has the fine quality of conveying to his reader, in clear and admirable prose, and occasionally in pleasant verse, the results of his painstaking and solitary observation.

James Russell Lowell (1819–1891), poet and essayist, was educated at Harvard. He abandoned a legal career for literature, and was a strong advocate for the anti-slavery party. In 1841 he published his first book, a volume of poems called 'A Year's Life,' which was followed by more poems : 'A Fable for Critics,' 'The Biglow Papers,' and 'The Vision of Sir Launfal.' The best of his critical work is to be found in his two series of 'Among my Books.' Lowell was a man of many gifts, a scholar with a pleasant touch of humour, a poet, and one of the most discerning critics that the United States has so far produced.

Walt Whitman (1819–1892), the poet, is noted as a rebel against all convention, and the publication of 'Leaves of Grass' in 1855 was the beginning of a movement for writing *vers libre.* The fact that he was not only an iconoclast in the matter of verse forms, but also in his devastatingly frank methods of handling sexual relationships in his writings, made him the centre of long and bitter controversy. During the Civil War Whitman acted as a nurse for two years at Washington. He incorporated his experiences in two volumes of verse— 'Drum Taps ' and 'The Wound Dresser'— and in one prose work, 'Specimen Days.' Shortly after this he was appointed to a Government clerkship, from which, however, he was soon removed for having written books of an immoral tendency. A controversy of some violence then arose, as a result of which Whitman shortly afterwards received another Government appointment, which he held until a paralytic seizure in 1873 made his retirement necessary.

Revolt against all convention seemed to Whitman his self-appointed task, both in his versification and in his treatment of the elemental appetites of human beings. But in spite of very real faults, his writings, at their best, showed genuine poetic insight and power.

Harriet Beecher Stowe (1811–1896) was the daughter of a well-known clergyman and sister of Henry Ward Beecher (1813–1887), one of the most popular preachers America ever produced, and the writer of a number of books of sermons and addresses and of a volume of 'Autobiographical Reminiscences.' After some years as a teacher Harriet Beecher married the Rev. Calvin E. Stowe. Up to 1852 she had written only a small volume of stories which had attracted little attention. In that year, acting on the suggestion of her sister-in-law, she decided to write something against slavery, and so produced 'Uncle Tom's Cabin.' This book, written with difficulty in time snatched from household chores and the task of bringing up a family of some size, first appeared, in serial form, in 'The National Era.' It did not then attract much attention, but on being issued in book form it was an overwhelming success. The sales in Britain alone have exceeded a million and half copies. It has been translated into numerous foreign languages. But what was best of all, it hastened the day of emancipation. Of her later works, the most meritorious are 'Dred' and 'Old Town Folks.' Although in a literary sense they are superior to 'Uncle Tom's Cabin,' they in no other way rivalled its success.

Julia Ward Howe (1819–1910), poet and lecturer on social reform, is best known as the author of 'The Battle Hymn of the Republic,' first published in 'The Atlantic Monthly' in February, 1862. It was written to the tune of 'John Brown's Body.' Mrs. Howe's poems are to be found in 'Passion Flowers' and 'Later Lyrics.'

John Lothrop Motley (1814–1877), the historian, was educated at Harvard, where he had Oliver Wendell Holmes, afterwards to be his biographer, as a classmate. He went to Europe and studied at the University of Göttingen, where he formed a friendship with Bismarck. Later he went to Berlin University. Having published two novels without much success, he turned to history, and, deciding to write a historical work on Holland, went to that country in 1851 to collect material. He published the result of these researches in 1856 in 'The Rise of the Dutch Republic.' This work was very favourably received by the critics, and in 1860 it was followed by the first two volumes of 'The United Netherlands,' with the further addition of two more volumes eight years later. Two volumes on 'The Life and Death of John of Barneveld' were the result of more researches, but were not very favourably received by Dutch scholars, who alleged bias. Motley holds a high place among historians for the diligence of his researches and his fine vivid style, but his lack of a judicial impartiality detracts from the lasting value of his work.

Francis Parkman (1823–1893) is also one of the outstanding historians of America, specializing in the history of the conflict between France and England. As the documents dealing with this subject often exhibited hatred between French and English and strong prejudice between Catholic and Protestant, much care was needed in arriving at a true picture of the actual events. But Parkman produced a fine succession of works, amongst which were 'The Conspiracy of Pontiac,' 'The Pioneers of France in the New World,' 'The Jesuits in North America,' 'Count Frontenac and New France,' ' Montcalm and Wolfe,' and 'Half a Century of Conflict.' Parkman, who spared no trouble in collecting and sifting his material and in visiting places mentioned in his narratives, made a most valuable contribution to the history of the struggle between England and France in their fight for Canada. His style is clear and vivid.

Herman Melville (1819–1891) will be remembered for his capital sea story 'Moby Dick,' or the White Whale,' which was deservedly popular. He also wrote 'Typee,' an account of his adventures among the cannibals of the Marquesas Islands, and 'Omoo,' but these two books did not gain him the same measure of success as 'Moby Dick.' He was a competent short story writer and his best collection was 'The Piazza Tales.' His writings were neglected for some time, but about 1920 he was 'rediscovered' and assigned a place more in accord with his intrinsic merit.

Bayard Taylor (1825–1878), poet, essayist, novelist, diplomat, and traveller, was a versatile writer. His best work is perhaps the translation of Goethe's 'Faust' in the original metres. He was apprenticed to a printer, but, finding the job uncongenial, he purchased his indentures and went on a walking tour in Europe, giving an account of his experiences in ' Views Afoot.' He later went to California in the gold rush, and set down his adventures in 'El Dorado.' His wide travels in many other parts of the world are described in numerous other books. Among his novels the most successful are 'Hannah Thurston,' 'John Godfrey's Fortunes' (in part autobiographical), and 'The Story of Kenneth.'

Stephen Collins Foster (1826–1864), song writer and composer, wrote over 100 songs, many of which gained the widest popularity. They included 'The Old Folks at Home,' 'Massa's in de Cold, Cold Ground,' 'Nelly Bly,' 'Old Kentucky Home,' 'Poor Old Joe,' 'Come where my Love Lies Dreaming.' They were not poetry of a high order, but few other writers have made such a wide appeal to ordinary folk.

General Lew Wallace (1827–1905) became famous for his very popular religious novel ' Ben Hur.' Over two million copies were sold, and it was translated into many foreign languages.

The recluse Emily Dickinson (1830–86) wrote poems which are worthy to rank with the world's greatest. Most of them are brief lyrics, exquisitely composed, with a poignant introspective quality. Miss Dickinson was a mystic. Her work was published posthumously, and has been an inspiration to many.

Thomas Bailey Aldrich (1836–1906) wrote some charming verses and stories. His work was often characterized by a most pleasant touch of humour. His verse may be found in 'Cloth of Gold' and 'Mercedes and Later Lyrics' ; his best novel is probably 'Prudence Palfrey,' and his best known short stories are to be found in the collections 'Marjorie Daw and Other People' and 'Two Bites at a Cherry, with Other Tales.'

Francis Richard Stockton (1834–1902) made a reputation for humorous books and short stories. Among the latter 'The Lady or the Tiger?' is outstanding. Of his novels 'Rudder Grange' is best remembered.

Artemus Ward was the pseudonym of Charles Farrar Browne (1834–1867). He worked first as a compositor and reporter, and became widely popular as a humorist, writing a series of 'Artemus Ward's Sayings,' a record of the imaginary adventures of a wandering showman. He attracted attention by comic misspellings, a technique frequently copied afterwards. He was a very successful lecturer both in the States and over here, and was lecturing in London and contributing to 'Punch' when he died of tuberculosis.

Mark Twain. Samuel Langhorne Clemens (1835–1910), better known as Mark Twain, was in turn journeyman printer and Mississippi pilot before he became a journalist. His 'Innocents Abroad' had an immediate and enormous success and established his reputation as a humorist. Other highly successful works were 'Adventures of Tom Sawyer,' 'A Tramp Abroad,' 'Life on the Mississippi,' 'Huckleberry Finn,' 'Pudd'nhead Wilson,' 'The Prince and the Pauper,' and 'The £1,000,000 Bank Note.' In the midst of his success he was faced with bankruptcy through the failure of the publishing firm with which he was connected. Like Scott before him, he shouldered this burden, and worked his way to solvency by writing and lecturing. He possessed an exuberant sense of humour, but underneath all his fun there was a very genuine desire for social justice. So highly was he thought of in Great Britain that Oxford conferred on him an honorary LL.D.

Ambrose Bierce (1838–1914?) was a writer of short stories comparable with those of Poe. They have been collected, with some verse, into twelve volumes.

Rear-Admiral A. T. Mahan (1840–1914), at one time lecturer on naval history and tactics at Newport War College, collected his lectures and published them as 'The Influence of Sea Power upon History (1660–1783)' and 'The Influence of Sea Power upon the French Revolution and Empire (1793–1812).' These lectures, admirably written, and of great value to naval men, have very largely influenced the policies of the great sea powers.

Francis Bret Harte (1839–1902) was in turn teacher, miner, and journalist. It is as the chronicler of the Californian gold fields that he first attracted notice. His original sense of humour is shown in his 'Condensed Novels,' a most amusing collection of parodies. He was a skilled writer of the short story and 'The Luck of Roaring Camp,' 'The Outcasts of Poker Flat,' 'Miggles,' and 'The Idyll of Red Gulch,' as well as his highly amusing piece of verse 'The Heathen Chinee,' made him very popular. Within his limited range Bret Harte was a fine writer. His poetry could be humorous, delicate, and patriotic, and his picture of the Californian miners is often tender without false sentimentality.

William Dean Howells (1837–1920) was a copious writer of novels, verse, and criticism. He was recognized as leader of the realistic school of fiction in the States. Three volumes of his poems were published, and among his novels typical examples are 'The Rise of Silas Lapham,' 'Indian Summer,' 'A Hazard of New Fortunes,' 'The Quality of Mercy,' 'The Landlord at the Lion's Head,' and 'The Leatherwood God.' His own critical belief is summed up in 'Criticism and Fiction,' while 'My Literary Passions' and 'Literature and Life' throw further light on his standards.

Joel Chandler Harris (1848–1908) was in turn printer, lawyer, and journalist. He is noted for his delightful stories of animal life, written in a southern Negro dialect. They were very popular with both children and adults, and also attracted students of folk-lore and anthropology. The background of the plantation and the well worked-out dialogue of the animals are excellent. The best collections in book form are 'Uncle Remus : His Songs and his Sayings,' 'Nights with Uncle Remus,' ' Uncle Remus and His Friends,' 'Mr. Rabbit at Home,' 'The Tar-Baby and Other Rhymes of Uncle Remus,' and 'Uncle Remus and Brer Rabbit.' They may be considered the greatest works in the school of Negro folk literature.

Francis Marion Crawford (1854–1909) was the son of an American sculptor. He was born in Italy, and educated in America, Cambridge, and Germany. He settled in Rome and became a very proficient and popular novelist, being the author of between 30 and 40 well written and well constructed novels, of which good examples are : 'Mr. Isaacs,' 'A Roman Singer,' 'Marzio's

Crucifix,' 'Greifenstein,' 'A Cigarette-Maker's Romance,' 'Dr. Claudius,' and 'In the Palace of the King.'

Harold Frederic (1856–98) was first a newspaper reporter before he came a competent novelist. 'The Copperhead' was his first real success. This was followed by 'The Damnation of Theron Ware' (published in England under the title 'Illumination,') and 'Gloria Mundi.' 'In the Market-place' and 'The New Exodus,' a realistic study of Russian anti-semitism, were both published posthumously. Frederic was a novelist of more than usual gifts, and his early death was a real loss to American letters.

Richard Harding Davis (1864–1916) made a reputation for himself as the greatest American reporter and war correspondent of his day. He wrote numerous books describing his experiences, and among them were 'With Both Armies in South Africa,' 'With the Allies' (1914), and 'With the French in France and Salonika.' He was a copious writer of short stories, which he published in 11 volumes. Typical of these are 'Gallegher and Other Stories,' 'Van Bibber and Others,' and 'The Exiles.' He also wrote a large number of vivid but slight novels, of which 'Soldiers of Fortune,' 'Captain Macklin,' and 'The Bar Sinister' are good examples.

Robert William Chambers (1865–1933) began as a painter and illustrator, but found his real calling as a writer of historical romances. He won his first success with 'The Red Republic.' Later he wrote 'Lorraine,' 'Ashes of Empire,' and 'The Fighting Chance.' He was also the author of a large number of short stories. Stephen Crane (1871–1900), reporter and war correspondent, first made his name as a novelist with 'The Red Badge of Courage,' a realistic study of the reactions of an inexperienced soldier caught up in the turmoil of battle. This book, a real triumph of the imagination, for it was written before Crane had any experience of warfare, actually led to his being employed as a war correspondent. During his time of war reporting in Cuba his ship was sunk, and he was struggling in the water for 50 hours. This experience prompted his best known short story, 'The Open Boat.' He wrote some free verse, and a number of short stories, but his hardships caused his health to break down, and he died of tuberculosis.

O. Henry. William Sydney Porter (1862–1910), who wrote under the name of O. Henry, worked in a drug store, and did some journalistic work. Later he was appointed clerk in a bank at Austin. Accused of embezzlement, he fled to Honduras, returning when his wife was dying. After her death he was tried for his alleged offence, and was sentenced to three years imprisonment. He took no interest in his trial, and was not properly defended, and it is quite probable that he was not actually guilty of the offence for which he was sentenced. But in the penitentiary he assumed the name of O. Henry, and began that long series of short stories which won for him wide fame.

He was a master of both humour and pathos, and specialized in the technique of the surprise ending, sometimes, as in 'Jeff Peters as a Personal Magnet,' bringing off a double surprise. A warm humanity is to be found in O. Henry's work, and he was ever the champion of the underdog. There are many collections of his stories.

LESSON 54

Later American Literature: The Novelists

THE volume of American literature has increased very considerably of late years and it will be possible to deal in this brief Lesson only with the most important authors, omitting many minor writers of interest. The leading novelists will be examined, and an attempt will be made to arrange them in groups. It is by no means a simple task to arrange and classify the novelists, for the Americans are very individual and there is also a good deal of overlapping. Many Americans are most versatile, and it is no uncommon thing to find a novelist successful also as poet, playwright, essayist, and short story writer. Indeed, in no country in the world is the short story more popular. One reason for this is the very large number of magazines published throughout the United States which provide a constant market for the short story. An author who is popular and has established a reputation in some other branch of literature may well affect the circulation of a magazine favourably.

The first group of writers are those belonging to the older tradition. Edward Noyes Westcott (1846–98), a banker, wrote an excellent novel, 'David Harum : A Story of American Life.' Well written, very human, and most amusing, it was published posthumously, and was widely read both in the States and in Great Britain. Frances Hodgson Burnett (1849–1924) was the author of some very successful stories for children, of which the best known is 'Little Lord Fauntleroy,' later dramatized with great success. Some pleasant novels for more mature readers include 'The Making of a Marchioness,' 'A Fair Barbarian,' and 'T. Tembaron.' Gertrude Atherton (born 1857) is a Californian novelist who has written a series of novels depicting life in her home state and others of a sociological tendency. Well known among them are 'The Californians' (re-written 1935), 'The Conqueror,' 'Tower of Ivory' and 'American Wives and English Husbands.' Alice Brown (born 1857) made a sound reputation as a delineator of New England character. Among her carefully written books are 'Fools of Nature,' 'The Prisoner,' and 'Dear Old Templeton.' Kate Douglas Wiggin (1856–1923), a kindergarten teacher and a capable musician, wrote primarily for children, but her 'Timothy's Quest' and 'Rebecca of Sunnybrook Farm' were read with pleasure by a host of older readers.

Owen Wister (1860–1938), although the author of eleven volumes, will be remembered chiefly for his tale of the Wyoming cattle country, 'The Virginian.' A well written story of the 1870's, it was popular on both sides of the Atlantic. Mary Hunter Austin (1868–1934) made a special study of Indian life in the desert, showed her sympathetic understanding of conditions in the West, and emphasized her insistence on the individual's right to freedom. 'The Basket Woman,' 'A Woman of Genius,' 'The Lovely Lady,' and her fine autobiography, 'Easter Horizon,' are good examples of her work. Alice Hegan Rice (born 1870) is, like Kate Douglas Wiggin, chiefly a writer for children. Her charming 'Mrs. Wiggs of the Cabbage Patch' has had a world-wide circle of readers.

The next five writers are of more importance, as they are outstanding novelists who have established their reputations since 1900. They are Mrs. Edith Wharton, Theodore Dreiser, Willa Cather, Sherwood Anderson, and J. B. Cabell.

Edith Wharton (1862–1937), a disciple of Henry James, is rightly regarded as an American novelist whose fame is unlikely to be lessened by the passage of time. She travelled extensively, and lived for most of her later years in France. Her main themes were concerned with the easily broken moral standards of high society, the background of the first World War, the sordidness of middle-class life in New York in the 19th century, and the supernatural. In 'The Writing of Fiction' she expresses her own literary ideals when she writes :

Every great novel must first of all be based on a profound sense of moral values, and then constructed with a classical unity and economy of means.

Mrs. Wharton was also a successful writer of short stories (some of them dealing with ghosts), and the author of two volumes of verse, and of an autobiography, 'A Backward Glance.' Representative of her well-constructed novels are 'House of Mirth,' 'Ethan Frome' (her greatest tragic story), 'The Age of Innocence' (awarded the Pulitzer Prize), 'The Children,' 'Hudson River Bracketed,' and 'The Gods Arrive.'

Theodore Dreiser (b. 1871) is an example of a writer who has triumphed over the clumsiness of a very awkward style by the power and honesty of his purpose. His finest work, 'The American Tragedy,' created a great impression, despite its prolixity, by its power and the tragic nature of its theme. It is the author's ardent desire to portray the truth that holds the interest of the reader, and encourages him to wrestle with difficulties of style and poorness of diction. In his books Dreiser draws largely on his wide experience as a journalist. His other chief novels are 'Sister Carrie,' 'Jennie Gerhardt,' 'The Financier' and 'The Genius.' He is also the author of short stories, poems, essays, and plays.

Willa S. Cather (b. 1876) has a very individual and charming style which makes her work a delight to the reader. She is not concerned with the conventional form of the novel, but in some of her most successful books (as in 'Death Comes to the Archbishop' and 'Shadows on the Rock') she presents a series of incidents linked together by the interlocking of actions of charming characters. Her special field is the pioneer life of immigrants to the Middle West. In 'O Pioneers !' she used the Nebraska prairies as her background. 'My Antonia' is the story of an immigrant girl's life on the frontier. 'One of Ours' (awarded the

James Joyce   Aldous Huxley   D. H. Lawrence

Virginia Woolf   Rose Macaulay   Mary Webb

J. B. Priestley   Sir Hugh Walpole   Charles Morgan

MODERN NOVELISTS. Most prolific, varied and popular has been the work of the late Sir Hugh Walpole. J. B. Priestley is successful both as novelist and as dramatist. Mary Webb's novels still have their posthumous vogue, and Rose Macaulay's wit has won many admirers. Joyce, D. H. Lawrence and Virginia Woolf were intellectuals whose work had a more limited appeal. Huxley stands in the forefront of the younger moderns, and the thoughtful novels of Charles Morgan are in a niche of their own.

BENJAMIN FRANKLIN, famous as a scientist, wrote an excellent 'Autobiography.' Washington Irving (top right) is at his best in his 'Sketch Book,' which contains the immortal 'Rip van Winkle,' and Oliver Wendell Holmes (lower right) in his 'Breakfast Table' series.
Portrait of Franklin by M. Chamberlain, from Seidlitz, Porträtwerke: Irving from a contemporary engraving; Holmes after A. Schoff

AMERICAN MEN OF LETTERS. Best loved of American poets is Longfellow (left) ; his ' Courtship of Miles Standish,' 'Evangeline' and 'Hiawatha' are his greatest achievement, and many of his minor poems are household words. Emerson (centre) was a profound and influential thinker, who is usually regarded as the greatest and most stimulating of American men of letters ; and Poe is a masterly short story writer, with a gift for evoking eeriness.

Mark Twain   Harriet Beecher Stowe   Walt Whitman

Herman Melville   J. Lothrop Motley   Bret Harte

Theodore Dreiser   Ernest Hemingway   Eugene O'Neill

FAMOUS WRITERS OF AMERICA. *Greatest of American humorists was S. L. Clemens (Mark Twain). Mrs. Harriet Beecher Stowe won fame with ' Uncle Tom's Cabin.' Walt Whitman is one of the giants of literature; his splendid poems, mainly in vers libre, are a spiritual experience. Herman Melville's books of travel, Motley's historical studies and Bret Harte's short stories are all excellent of their kind. Prominent among modern novelists are Theodore Dreiser, and, of the younger generation, the vital Hemingway; while Eugene O'Neill is perhaps the most exciting and original American playwright.*

Photograph of Mark Twain by H. J. Barratt; portrait of Walt Whitman by J. W. Alexander (Met. Mus. of Art. New York); drawing of Melville from a photograph

Sir Gilbert Parker	**Mazo de la Roche**	**Stephen Leacock**

Helen Simpson	**Adam Lindsay Gordon**	**Henry Handel Richardson**

Olive Schreiner	**Roy Campbell**	**Katherine Mansfield**

WRITERS FROM THE DOMINIONS. *From Canada, we have Sir Gilbert Parker's historical romances, Mrs. Mazo de la Roche's 'Whiteoaks' stories, and Professor Leacock's popular humour. Australia has given us, in Adam Lindsay Gordon, one of the most vital poets, and in Miss Helen Simpson and Henry Handel Richardson (Mrs. J. G. Robertson), two fine novelists. Katherine Mansfield, a New Zealander, won the applause of discriminating readers by her sensitive short stories. Mrs. Schreiner's 'Story of an African Farm' appeared in 1883. Roy Campbell is South Africa's notable addition to the modern poets.*
Photograph of Mazo de la Roche by Pearl Freeman, by courtesy of Macmillan & Co.; bust of Adam Lindsay Gordon by Lady Kennet, in Westminster Abbey

Pulitzer Prize for the best novel of 1922) tells of the vitalizing influence of the first World War in France on a young man from a Mid-western farm. 'The Professor's House,' with its discoveries in New Mexico, points the way to the setting of what many consider her best book, 'Death Comes to the Archbishop,' a beautiful account of the pioneer work of the Catholic Church in New Mexico. 'Shadows on the Rock' is a vivid picture of 17th century Quebec. A more recent success is 'Sapphira.'

Sherwood Anderson (1876–1941) is equally important as short story writer and novelist. In both he strikes the same note. As a craftsman he shows indifference to traditional methods. He emphasizes the importance of individual life, however insignificant, and is largely concerned with the aspirations of industrial America. He first attracted attention by a volume of short stories of life in a small town, 'Winesburg, Ohio.' Of his novels, 'Poor White' tells how machinery came to a town and destroyed its beauty and significance, 'Many Marriages' relates the story of a business man's attempt to escape from routine, and 'Dark Laughter' contrasts the happiness of free negroes with the lack of spirituality of the whites.

Writers of Romance. James Branch Cabell (b. 1879) considers that fiction should be allegorical in interpreting the drama of life as it should be, not as it is. He states that it is false for a writer to be true to life because 'facts out of relation to the rest of life become lies.' Cabell's fiction falls into two types : (1) romances of the middle ages set in the imaginary French province of Poictesme, a caustically satirical series of novels; (2) comedies of present-day Virginia. Books which belong to the pseudo-erudite series include 'The Soul of Melicent' (revised later as 'Domnei'), 'Jurgen' (considered by many Cabell's greatest book, and one which at any rate added to his notoriety, since it was banned), 'Figures of Earth,' 'The High Place' and 'The Silver Stallion.' Among the books with Virginian settings are 'The Cords of Vanity,' 'The Rivet in Grandfather's Neck,' and 'The Cream of the Jest.'

Booth Tarkington (b. 1869) wrote a very successful romance in 'Monsieur Beaucaire' (which made a popular play), and a series of realistic novels about the Middle West, two of which, 'The Magnificent Ambersons' and 'Alice Adams,' gained Pulitzer Prizes. He is noted for his 'Penrod' studies of boys and adolescents.

Winston Churchill (b. 1871) wrote both historical romance and the regional novel.

In 'The Celebrity,' 'Richard Carvel,' 'The Crisis,' 'The Crossing' (usually considered to be his finest work), 'Coniston,' 'Mr. Crewe's Career,' 'A Far Country,' and 'A Modern Chronicle,' we have a group of particularly well-written novels.

Ellen Glasgow (b. 1874) produced a long series of novels about her native state of Virginia. She endeavoured to break down the romantic glamour of the South by showing its reaction to the new industrial revolution in 'The Voice of the People,' 'The Battleground,' 'The Ancient Law,' and 'Life and Gabriella.' Saying that 'what the South needs now is blood and irony,' she wrote three satirical books, 'The Romantic Comedians,' 'They Stooped to Folly,' and 'The Sheltered Life.'

The best book of **Joseph Hergesheimer** (b. 1880) is probably 'Java Head,' which handles the theme of the tragic results of miscegenation. Other successful books are 'The Three Black Pennys' (the story of a family engaged in the Pennsylvanian iron industry), 'The Limestone Tree,' 'The Party Dress' and 'Tampico.'

Sinclair Lewis (b. 1885) is the satirist of American middle-class society. 'The Job,' dealing with life in New York City, was his first important work of fiction, and with the publication of 'Main Street' he won a wide circle of readers. But 'Babbitt,' a picture of the average American business man, complacent and intellectually stagnant, and 'Arrowsmith,' which describes the career of a man of science, contain much of the author's best work. For 'Arrowsmith,' Lewis was awarded the Pulitzer Prize, but refused it. 'Elmer Gantry' is a bitter novel about religious shams in the States, and 'The Man Who Knew Coolidge' is a malicious picture of a man in a small way of business. 'Dodsworth' followed next, and in 1930 Lewis was the first American writer to be awarded the Nobel Literature Prize. Among his later books are 'Ann Vickers,' 'Work of Art,' and 'It Can't Happen Here.'

Susan Glaspell (b. 1882) has written thoughtful and well-constructed novels, notably 'The Glory of the Conquered' and 'Alison's House.' The latter was a Pulitzer Prize-winner. She is also the author of two outstanding plays, 'The Verge' and 'Bernice,' besides one-act plays. She depends less upon incident than upon the inner drama of her characters' minds.

Christopher Morley (b. 1890) is extremely popular in America as an essayist. He is author of the remarkable novel

'Thunder on the Left' and others, and is also a poet and playwright.

Pearl Buck (b. 1892), wife of a missionary in China, wrote some excellent novels on Chinese life, beginning with 'The Good Earth.' She won the Nobel Prize in 1938.

Thornton Wilder (b. 1897) will be remembered for his delightfully written book 'The Bridge of San Luis Rey,' which won an international reputation, and was awarded the Pulitzer Prize. Other novels of his are 'The Cabala,' 'The Woman of Andros,' and 'Heaven's My Destination.' Wilder obtained success also as a playwright and won another Pulitzer Prize for his play 'Our Town,' a picture of life in a small New England town, which was later filmed.

The two great exponents of what may be termed the sentimental novel are Gene Stratton Porter (1868–1924), whose 'Freckles,' 'A Girl of the Limberlost,' and 'The Harvester' gained a vast circle of readers, and Harold Bell Wright (b. 1872), author of 'The Shepherd of the Hills' and 'The Winning of Barbara Worth.'

American Realists. There are a considerable number of highly competent American writers who belong to the school of realism. Of the realists, Stephen Crane (*see* page 219) exercised much influence by his work. Robert Herrick (1868–1938) tackles the problem of the conflict between the desire for personal success and personal integrity. Among his powerfully written books are 'The Common Lot,' 'The Memoirs of an American Citizen,' 'A Life for a Life,' 'Clark's Field,' 'Chimes' (a satirical novel about the introduction of big business into University life) and 'Sometime,' a Utopian story. Frank Norris (1870–1902), a war correspondent, became concerned about social and economic forces, and planned a trilogy on the epic of wheat. Unhappily, he lived long enough to complete only two of the books: 'The Octopus,' which describes the raising of wheat in California, and 'The Pit,' a story of speculation on the Chicago wheat exchange.

Jack London (1876–1916) wrote many short stories and novels dealing with the brutal and vigorous life in the far North. The most popular of his novels are 'The Call of the Wild,' 'The Sea-Wolf,' and 'White Fang.'

Upton Sinclair (b. 1878), the author of some hundred books, created a sensation with his 'The Jungle,' which revealed the scandal of the Chicago stockyards. Other important novels dealing with undesirable social conditions are 'The Metropolis,' 'King Coal,' 'Oil,' 'World's End' and 'Between Two Worlds.' Sinclair uses his novels to attack different sides of contemporary American life and exposes their abuses.

John Cournos (b. 1881) was born in Russia, but has lived in the U.S.A. since 1891. He made a reputation for realistic stories of immigrant life, 'The Mask' and 'The Wall.' His 'New Candide' is an outspoken attack on American foibles.

John Dos Passos (b. 1896) is one of the important younger writers preoccupied with the social evils arising from big business and exploitation. In 'Three Soldiers' he wrote a powerful novel of disillusion about the first World War. But more ambitious is his trilogy 'The 42nd Parallel,' '1919' and 'The Big Money,' having as its theme the demoralizing effect of modern commercialism and exploitation.

Ernest Hemingway (b. 1898), considered by many one of the foremost of recent American novelists, developed a prose style which had considerable influence on other writers. He described incidents of violence and emotional crises with a studied simplicity from which the dramatic was carefully eliminated. Examples are his celebrated books 'A Farewell to Arms' and 'Winner Take Nothing.' 'For Whom the Bell Tolls' is concerned with an incident in the Spanish Civil War, and its main theme is that loss of liberty in one country is bound to have its inevitable reactions all the world over.

William Faulkner (b. 1897) is the most outstanding of the younger realists, author of 'Pylon,' which depicts the mentality of an airman, and 'Absalom! Absalom!', a passionate story of the Civil War period.

John Steinbeck (b. 1902) combines romance with realism. He is largely concerned with the problem of the landless farm labourer. 'The Grapes of Wrath' won the Pulitzer Prize. Other important novels are 'In Dubious Battle,' 'Of Mice and Men,' and 'The Moon is Down.'

Women Realists. A number of women writers have distinguished themselves in the school of realism. Margaret Deland (b. 1857) is the author of many books of great charm. 'John Ward, Preacher,' the story of a 19th-century Calvinist minister whose doctrines are at variance with those of his more liberally minded wife, was founded on actual experience, for Mrs. Deland's father was a Presbyterian and her mother an Episcopalian.

Anne Douglas Sedgwick (1873–1935) gave ironic portrayals of feminine character in her 'Valerie Upton,' 'Tante,' 'The Little French Girl' and 'The Old Countess.'

Mary Wilkins Freeman (1862–1930) has New England for the background of her compact and well-written stories, full of local colour and dialect.

Zona Gale (1874–1938) is also noted for the local colour in her Wisconsin books. 'Miss Lulu Brett' and 'Birth' (dramatized as 'Mr. Pitt') contain much of her best work.

Evelyn Scott (b. 1893) belongs to the post-war school of disillusion. In her first two books, 'The Narrow House' and 'Narcissus,' she attacked middle-class morality. Marjorie Rawlings (b. 1896) made the hummock country of Florida her background. She won the Pulitzer Prize in 1938 with her charming story 'The Yearling,' which tells the moving tale of a young boy's love for his pet fawn.

Margaret Mitchell spent ten years in writing 'Gone With the Wind,' a long realistic novel of Georgia during the Civil War and the early days of reconstruction. The characters are brilliantly drawn, especially those of Scarlett O'Hara and Rhett Butler. This, her only book, won the Pulitzer Prize in 1936, and has beaten every record for the extent of its sales. By the end of May, 1941, 3,368,000 copies in English had been sold, the book had been translated into 18 languages, and over half a million copies had been sold in Germany. This remarkable first novel has also been filmed with immense success.

LESSON 55

Later American Literature: Poets and Miscellaneous Writers

THE new American poetry came to the fore about 1910 with a strongly marked reaction against the Victorian tradition in verse, and with new experiments in poetic form. This gave rise to much critical controversy as to what exactly was the distinction between prose and verse, and how far the school of free verse was justified in going. James Whitcomb Riley (1849–1916), Richard Hovey (1864–1900), and William Vaughn Moody (1869–1910) were pioneer rebels, and the revival of interest in Walt Whitman, the writings of Amy Lowell, and the foundation of 'Poetry : A Magazine of Verse,' by Harriet Monroe, in 1912, and of several other important magazines devoted to verse a little later, gave the new poetic movement much impetus. It was felt that poetry should touch every aspect of life and should not be confined to the conventional subjects of the past.

The poets are best examined in groups, and the two leading rebels against the old conventions are Edwin Arlington Robinson (1869–1935) and Robert Frost (b. 1875). They were both winners of the Pulitzer Prize for Poetry on three occasions, and some critics hold that Robinson is the greatest poet that America has so far produced. He was oppressed by the sense of tragedy in the world, but had an unfaltering faith in the glimmer of light that lies beyond.

He excelled in character studies such as 'The Children of the Night' and 'Captain Craig,' and wrote his own version of the Arthurian legend in his trilogy, 'Merlin,' 'Lancelot,' and 'Tristram,' in which he removes the supernatural element, and makes the characters act according to their particular passions. His native town of Gardiner, Maine, is the prototype of his 'Tilbury,' characters from which appear in several of his collections. 'The Man Against the Sky,' 'The Three Taverns,' 'Avon's Harvest,' 'The Man Who Died Twice' (the tragic story of a musician's dissipation of his genius), 'Cavender's House, 'The Glory of the Nightingale,' 'Nicodemus,' 'King Jasper,' and 'Sonnets' include most of the poet's best work. Robinson used blank verse largely in his longer narrative poems.

Robert Frost is of considerable importance for his delineation of New England characters. After a restless youth and a long period of farming, he published his first book of poems, 'A Boy's Will.' 'North of Boston' made secure his reputation as an important American poet, which was enhanced by 'Mountain Interval,' 'New Hampshire,' 'West-Running Brook,' 'Collected Poems,' and 'A Further Range.' He is restrained both in emotion and diction, and employs colloquial New England speech. He spent the years 1912–1915 in England, and during that period published his first book.

Mid-Western Poets. These include Edgar Lee Masters (b. 1869), Carl Sandburg (b. 1878), and Vachel Lindsay (1879–1931). Masters gained fame by his 'Spoon River Anthology,' in which, in free verse, he makes the village dead in the churchyard pronounce the truth about themselves, very different from the epitaphs upon their tombstones. The verse used by the writer in this iconoclastic work is so free as to be indistinguishable from prose, though it has a cadenced quality. 'The Domesday Book' and its sequel, 'The Fate of the Jury,' are considered the best of his later poetry, to which belongs his 'New Spoon River Anthology,' with its bitter attack on the urban standards of America. Masters wrote a good deal of prose ; this was iconoclastic also, especially his violent attack in ' Lincoln, the Man.'

Carl Sandburg (b. 1878) deals with the brutal aspects of life, especially among the stevedores and lorry drivers of the Middle West. He wrote vigorous free verse with much colloquial language, but it is in his gentler mood, when enchanted by the loveliness of the prairies and the nobility of character shown sometimes by quite ordinary people, that he is at his best. 'Chicago Poems,' 'Cornhuskers' (special Pulitzer Award), 'Smoke and Steel,' 'Slabs of the Sunburnt West,' and 'Good Morning, America' contain much of his best verse.

It is the earlier poetry of Vachel Lindsay that is of importance. In his later writings he became less self-critical and more careless and diffuse. He was at first an itinerant poet who bartered his verses for board and lodging—surely a dangerous occupation ! He included some of these in 'Rhymes to be Traded for Bread.' It was his first book, 'General Booth Enters into Heaven,' that displayed his talents for an original kind of verse writing and captured the public's approval. 'The Congo and Other Poems' and 'The Chinese Nightingale and Other Poems ' contain his best work. He wrote much doggerel, and at times a kind of poetic jazz.

Gertrude Stein (b. 1874) explores the unconscious mind, expressing herself in word-patterns which bear little relation to ordinary speech. Her 'Autobiography of Alice B. Toklas' (1933) influenced some of the recent writers in America.

The Imagists. A group called the Imagists was launched by Ezra Pound, and afterwards abandoned by him. Amy Lowell published 'Some Imagist Poets,' in which their principles were stated. These included (1) the production of an image, and avoidance of any vagueness ; (2) complete freedom in the choice of subject ; (3) new rhythms to be employed to express new moods ; and (4) the language of everyday speech, but moulded with great exactness and concentration of meaning. This movement gave rise to much controversy, and the reader has much difficulty at times in convincing himself that he is actually dealing with poetry, and not with some new form of polyphonic prose. The leading exponents of this school are Amy Lowell (1874–1925), regarded, after the defection of Ezra Pound, as the leader of this group, and awarded, posthumously, the Pulitzer Prize, John Gould Fletcher (b. 1886), and Conrad Aiken (b. 1889) (both awarded the Pulitzer Prize on publication of their 'Collected Poems'), and H. D. (Hilda Doolittle, b. 1886), the writer who has consistently kept to the Imagist creed.

Alfred Kreymborg (b. 1883) issued the first anthology of free verse. He experimented in poetic drama in 'Plays for Poem-Mimes,' 'Plays for Merry-Andrews,' and in 'Puppet Plays.' He also made some bold experiments with the sonnet.

Ezra Pound (b. 1885) was considered a very important figure in modern American literature, but his Fascist sympathies and anti-Ally broadcasts from Rome in 1941–42 overshadowed his achievements as a poet. An experimenter in verse forms, Ezra Pound possesses much erudition and has translated troubadour ballads and ' The Sonnets and Ballate of Guido Cavalcante.' He has also made verse translations from the Chinese from notes left by his friend Ernest Francisco Fenollosa (1853–1908).

In 'Quia Pauper Amavi' he started the series of Cantos of which he planned to write a hundred, and up to the end of 1940 had published 71. This very ambitious scheme was to have a structure similar to Dante's 'Divina Commedia.' The idea was to present a poetic human comedy divided into three periods—ancient history, the Renaissance, and present time—and to show how history repeats itself. Unfortunately there is much obscurity in these Cantos which make them very difficult, and sometimes impossible, for the ordinary reader to understand. Pound wrote :

Poetry is a sort of inspired mathematics, which gives us equations, not for abstract figures, triangles, spheres and the like, but equations for the human emotions. . . .

A much more readable poet was Stephen Vincent Benét (1898–1943). 'John Brown's Body' won him the Pulitzer Prize in 1928. It breathes the spirit of freedom and the sense of spiritual values that are so notable in his speeches, collected and published as 'A Summons to the Free,' in which he called upon America to rally in defence of democracy during the Second World War.

Benét was the son of a colonel and was himself educated at a military academy in California and at Yale. He wrote many notable novels, short stories and poems.

Edna St. Vincent Millay (b. 1892) is one of the finest of America's lyric poets. She also writes poetic plays and short stories.

Of special interest, in a class of its own, is the work of coloured poets, as shown in 'American Negro Poetry,' edited by James Weldon Johnson, and 'Caroling Dusk,' edited by Countee Cullen.

Internationally famed is George Santayana (b. 1863), a Spaniard who was educated at Harvard and became Professor of Philosophy there in 1907. His great work, 'The Life of Reason,' 1906, won him a high place among contemporary philosophers. 'The Realms of Being' was completed in 1940.

Biographical Writers. In biography American authors have done some useful work. Gamaliel Bradford (1863–1932) is regarded as the father of American biography. He described his method as 'Psychography,' that is, the extraction of the essential, permanent, and characteristic qualities which make up a person's life. 'Lee, the American,' 'Confederate Portraits,' 'Union Portraits,' and 'Damaged Lives' contain much of his best work.

The British writer Lytton Strachey, with his iconoclastic 'Eminent Victorians,' had an important influence on American biographers. In the past, biographies had sometimes been studies in hero-worship rather than pictures of fallible human beings. The Strachey tendency was to underline the faults and foibles, and thus to give a picture as misleading as before.

Among important biographies is 'George Washington,' by Rupert Hughes (b. 1872), an attempt to give an honest picture of a great man without the myths that had grown up round him. W. E. Woodward (b. 1874), in 'George Washington—the Image and the Man,' and 'Meet General Grant,' wrote the Strachey type of biography. Carl Sandburg, in 'Abraham Lincoln: The Prairie Years' (2 vols.), and 'Abraham Lincoln : The War Years' (4 vols., awarded the Pulitzer Prize), produced a monumental

biography. In 1943 he wrote 'Storm over Land,' presenting military operations in the last years of Lincoln's life.

Constance Rourke (1885–1941) wrote 'Trumpets of Jubilee,' in which she dealt with the Beechers and Barnum the showman ; Thomas Beer (1889–1940) chose as his subject Stephen Crane ; Joseph Wood Krutch (b. 1893) is the author of 'Edgar Allan Poe : A Study in Genius,' and Hervey Allen (b. 1889), the author of the highly successful long novel 'Anthony Adverse,' wrote about the same unhappy author in his book 'Israfel.' Morris Werner (b. 1897) gave frank biographies in 'Barnum' and 'Brigham Young.'

Criticism. Of the leading writers, James Gibbons Huneker (1860–1921) was recognized as an authority on music, art, literature and drama. Irving Babbitt (1865–1933) was a strong critic against romanticism, and pleaded eloquently for the humanities.

H. L. Mencken (b. 1880) has had the widest influence as a literary critic and gave great encouragement to Dreiser, Cabell, Lewis, and Sherwood Anderson. Being very outspoken in his views, his writings have often been the object of much controversy. He wrote verses and plays as well as criticism, and his most scholarly piece of work is 'The American Language,' a discussion of English as spoken and written in America. George Jean Nathan (b. 1882) is mainly a theatrical critic, and was one of the earliest to champion Eugene O'Neill. Nathan's views are expressed in numerous volumes, notably the 'Encyclopaedia of the Theatre.'

The American Theatre. Foremost of the new generation of dramatists is Eugene O'Neill (b. 1888), whose first full-length play, 'Beyond the Horizon,' had a great success in 1919. Two years later appeared 'The Emperor Jones,' a tremendously impressive short play with a negro as chief actor, and the poignant 'Diff'rent.' His other important plays are 'Anna Christie,' 'The Hairy Ape,' 'All God's Chillun Got Wings,' 'Desire Under the Elms,' 'The Great God Brown,' 'Marco Millions,' 'Strange Interlude,' 'Mourning Becomes Electra,' and 'Ah Wilderness.' Some of his one-act plays are collected with 'The Moon of the Caribbees.' His work is marked with dynamic vigour and emotional intensity, combined with a powerful and original intellect. He won the Pulitzer Prize several times, and the Nobel Prize in 1936. Another highly original dramatist is Elmer Rice (b. 1892), whose 'Adding

Machine,' an Expressionistic play, made his reputation in 1923. It is the story of Mr. Zero, ' the little man ' who is merely a cog in the wheel of modern civilization. Of quite another type is ' See Naples and Die,' an uproarious extravaganza. Rice's most popular play is ' Street Scene '; it won him the Pulitzer Prize in 1929.

Paul Green (b. 1894) has written a great number of remarkable plays, most of them in one act; perhaps the most effective are his negro plays. His full-length plays

' Tread the Green Grass,' ' The House of Connelly ' and ' Potter's Field ' are strangely beautiful tragedies.

Marc Connelly (b. 1890), in his famous play 'The Green Pastures,' gave a brilliant rendering of Bible history as seen through the mind of a negro.

Of the remaining American dramatists, we can do no more than mention Sidney Howard, Maxwell Anderson, Robert E. Sherwood, George F. Kaufmann and Clifford Odets.

LESSON 56

Dominion Literature

WRITERS of Canada, Australia, New Zealand, and South Africa naturally started late. The distant countries, members of what was to become the British commonwealth of nations, were fully occupied with their pioneering problems. They looked to their mother country, in the first instance, as the source of their literature, and shared with her in their common inheritance of Chaucer, Shakespeare, Milton, and other giants of the past. They were content to import their books ; thus individual literatures have taken some time in emerging.

A further difficulty arose from the fact that some Dominion writers were born in the home country, and yet became, by the choice and treatment of their matter, essentially writers belonging to the lands of their adoption. Sometimes the process worked the other way. Some writers, born in the Dominions, left their homes at an early age, came to Europe for their training and education, and remained there, contributing directly to English literature. Thus Goldwin Smith, a former Oxford Professor of Modern History, did not settle in Canada until he was in his fiftieth year. Although he did much literary work after his arrival in his new home, it was all essentially English. Prof. Gilbert Murray (b. 1866), on the other hand, though born in Australia, came early to the home country. His brilliant verse translations from Euripides, Aeschylus, Sophocles, and Aristophanes succeeded in putting the Greek drama on the English stage. These, together with his technical work on Greek literature and religion, and his writings on international affairs, are a direct contribution to English literature.

Canada. The first of the Canadian writers in English was Thomas Chandler Haliburton (1796–1865), who was born at Windsor, Nova Scotia. He had a highly successful career as a barrister, became a member of the House of Assembly, Chief Justice of the Common Pleas, and Judge of the Supreme Court. He retired in 1856, came to England, and from 1859 to 1863 sat as Conservative M.P. for Launceston. In British American literature he is known chiefly as the creator of 'Sam Slick,' a Yankee pedlar and clockmaker, whose quaint humour and knowledge of human nature made him a real character. The sketches, first published anonymously in a newspaper, were collected together in book form and brought out in 1837–1840 as 'The Clockmaker, or Sayings and Doings of Samuel Slick of Slickville.' Haliburton wrote an authoritative historical work on Nova Scotia, and one of the most interesting of his serious books is 'The Old Judge, or Life in a Colony.'

Joseph Howe (1804–73) wrote 'Poems and Essays,' and took a distinguished part in the politics of Nova Scotia. He was the proprietor-editor of 'The Nova Scotian,' and it was in his paper that Haliburton first published his 'Sam Slick' stories. Isabella Valancy Crawford (1850–87), though born in Ireland, was the first to write what was genuine Canadian poetry. Her lyric verse, of which 'Love's Forget-Me-Not' is an outstanding example, shows fine qualities. She also wrote a number of dialect poems, of which 'Old Spookses' Pass ' is probably the best known.

William Henry Drummond (1854–1907) was born in Ireland, but all his writing bears the authentic Canadian touch. He found his great interest in depicting the lives of the French settlers. In his youth he sought the company of *habitant* and *voyageur*, and made their quaint French-English a charming poetical medium in such collections as 'The Habitant,' 'Johnny Courteau' and 'The Voyageur.' Archibald Lampman (1861-1899), a Canadian-born poet, wrote pleasant and musical verse in 'Among the Millet,' and 'Lyrics of Earth.' **Sir Charles G. D.** Roberts (1860-1943), hailed in Canada as 'Father of Canadian literature,' has written distinguished verse in the traditional manner, ranging through a wide variety of topic and mood. His other work, besides miscellaneous journalism, includes novels and nature stories; it is by the latter that he is best known in England.

In later Canadian poetry the most important figure is William Bliss Carman (1861-1929), whose principal works are 'Low Tide on Grand Pré,' 'Songs from Vagabondia' (in collaboration with Richard Hovey), 'Ballads of Lost Haven,' and 'Pipes of Pan.' He edited 'The Oxford Book of American Verse' in 1927. Ernest Thompson Seton (born 1860) started his career as a writer of distinguished Nature books in Canada (*see* page 180).

Charles William Gordon (1860-1937), a Canadian clergyman who wrote under the pseudonym of Ralph Connor, was the author of a number of novels, the scenes of which were set among the mining regions and lumber districts of West Canada. A fine writer, his books were deservedly popular. Among them are 'Beyond the Marshes,' 'The Sky Pilot,' and 'The Prospector.' Ralph Connor's interesting autobiography, 'Postscript to Adventure,' was published posthumously. W. W. Campbell (1861-1918), and Duncan Campbell Scott (born 1862), whose collected works were published in 1926, both made a useful contribution to Canadian poetry.

Sir Gilbert Parker (1862-1932) was for some time on the staff of the Sydney Morning Herald. Turning novelist, he drew largely upon various aspects of Canadian life for his material. 'Pierre and his People' was published in 1892. 'The Seats of the Mighty,' later dramatized by the author, 'The Pomp of the Lavilettes' and 'The Right of Way' were among his most successful novels. Parker wrote an excellent history of Old Quebec, and was also a poet of merit.

Quite one of the best-known Canadian writers was Stephen Leacock (1869-1944). He was born in England, but his long association with the Dominion places him definitely among Canadian writers. Head of the Department of Economics and Social Science in the McGill University, he has written several technical books on Economics, and biographies of Dickens and Mark Twain. It is as a writer of subtle and original humour that he is best known, and he has caused much pleasant laughter in his lighter books, among which are 'Literary Lapses' and 'Moonbeams from the Larger Lunacy.' John M'Crae (1872-1918) will be remembered for his imperishable lyric, 'In Flanders Fields,' originally contributed to 'Punch.'

Robert William Service (born 1874) attracted much attention in 1907 by the publication of 'The Songs of a Sourdough,' followed by 'Rhymes of a Rolling Stone,' and other poems, which describe with much vividness the hard life in the wild North West. His 'Rhymes of a Red-Cross Man' were based on experiences in the First Great War. Service has been called the Canadian Kipling. His collected works were published in 1930. Marjorie Pickthall (1883-1922) wrote more than usually good verse in 'Drift of Pinions,' 'Little Hearts' and 'Little Songs.'

A representative 'Anthology of Canadian Verse' was published at the end of the nineteenth century, and contained the names of no fewer than 135 writers, and the best collection of more recent Canadian poetry is to be found in 'The Oxford Book of Canadian Verse.'

One of the best-known Canadian novelists of today is Mrs. Mazo de la Roche (b. 1885), who, in a sequence of novels beginning with 'Jalna' (1927), developed the history of a Canadian family through several generations. 'Whiteoaks,' one of this series, was dramatized in 1936 and had a long run in London.

Australia and New Zealand. There are four main divisions in the story of Australia, the periods being those of (1) the penal settlements, (2) pastoral development, (3) gold exploitation, and (4) democracy of industry and labour. Its literature reflects all these activities. New Zealand, on the other hand, was never used as a penal settlement. Her literature is naturally on a somewhat small scale, and deals, in part, with the traditions and customs of the Maoris, one of the finest of all native races.

The earliest Australian poetry was published in 1819 by Barron Field, Judge of the Supreme Court of New South Wales, when he brought out his 'First Fruits of

Australian Poetry.' The book was favourably reviewed by Charles Lamb, whose friend Field was. Other early poems were Charles Tompson's 'Wild Notes from the Lyre of a Nature Minstrel' (1826), and John Dunmore Lang's 'Aurora Australis,' published the same year.

The development of New South Wales caused more newspapers to be published, and Sir Henry Parks, who made a high reputation as a Liberal politician, and wrote five volumes of verse himself—the best known being 'Murmurs of the Stream'— encouraged others to write. Among the writers just before the gold rush, the most promising were Daniel Henry Deniehy, Richard P. L. Rowe, a journalist who wrote under the pen name of 'Peter Possum,' Henry Halloran, and J. Sheridan Moore.

The poet of the Maoris was Alfred Domett (1811–87), the friend of Robert Browning, and the inspirer of his poem 'Waring.' Domett lived in New Zealand for thirty years. He describes the scenery of New Zealand in a fine variety of lyric metres. His longest poem is 'Ranolf and Amohia.' The first distinctively Australian poet is Charles Harpur (1817–68), and 'The Creek of the Four Graves' is his most typical poem.

Adam Lindsay Gordon (1833–70) was born in the Azores, and was educated in England. He did not go to Australia until he was twenty. There he spent his life among horses, being in turn mounted trooper, horse-breaker, and steeplechase rider. His poetry appeals to Australians so strongly because it deals with adventure and gallant fighting against odds. It breathes the very essence of the spirit of Australia, and describes in vivid language the excitement of race meetings. Gordon's best work is in 'Sea Spray and Smoke Drift,' 'Ashtaroth' and 'Bush Ballads and Galloping Rhymes.'

James Brunton Stephens (1835–1902) is regarded especially as the poet of Queensland, but his popularity is largely due to his comic poems 'To a Black Gin,' and 'Universally Respected.' Henry Clarence Kendall (1841–82) is one of the most important Australian poets. Some of his poems were published in the 'Athenaeum,' the first English critical periodical of high standing to take notice of Australian poetry. Kendall's best work is contained in his 'Leaves from Australian Forests' and 'Songs from the Mountains.'

History and Travel. It is not easy to make a concise representative selection of the many Australian writers who have dealt with travel, discovery and history. Of importance are 'The History of Discovery in Australia, Tasmania and New Zealand,' by William Howitt (1792–1879), who spent only two years in Australia. 'Australian Facts and Prospects' and 'Australian Autobiography,' by R. H. Horne (1803–1884), are both sound and amusing. George William Rusden (1819–1903) wrote a 'History of Australia' and a 'History of New Zealand,' both important works and both published in England. Charles Edward Woodrow Bean (b. 1879) was the official historian of Australia's important part in the First World War of 1914–1918, and is also the author of two well-known books, 'On the Wool Track' and 'The Dreadnought of the Darling.' William Pember Reeves (b. 1860) in 'The Long White Cloud'—the Maori name for the Dominion—wrote the standard work on New Zealand.

Australian Fiction. 'A Boy's Adventures in the Wilds of Australia,' by William Howitt, and 'Tales of the Colonies' and 'The Bushranger of Van Dieman's Land,' published between 1843 and 1846, are among the earliest Australian novels of merit. Thomas Alexander Browne (1826–1915), a police magistrate who wrote under the name of 'Rolf Boldrewood,' was the author of 'The Squatter's Dream,' 'A Colonial Reformer' and 'Robbery Under Arms.' It was this last book which established his reputation, and had a large sale in the mother country. It tells the story of Captain Starlight, the notorious bushranger.

Henry Kingsley (1830–76), brother of the more famous Charles, spent five years in Australia in the early 'fifties. He was for a time a trooper in the Sydney mounted police. Two of his novels enjoyed a wide popularity in Australia, and reflect his own experiences in that country. They are 'Geoffrey Hamlyn' and 'The Hillyars and the Burtons.' The lives of the early settlers are well described, and there are exciting incidents of struggles with bush fires and bushrangers. Benjamin Leopold Farjeon (1838–1903) was born in London, but went straight from school to the Australian goldfields. Later he went to New Zealand, where he became manager and part proprietor of the first daily paper to be published in that country. He returned to London in 1868. His best known novel is 'Grif.' He also wrote 'Blade o' Grass,' 'Joshua Marvel,' and 'The Mesmerists.'

Ada Cambridge (b. 1844) sailed for Victoria in 1870. Her chief novels are 'The

Three Miss Kings'—the story of three girls bred in the bush—'A Masked Man,' 'A Little Minx,' 'Materfamilias' and 'Path and Goal.' Her good, clear, natural style gave her a measure of popularity. Marcus Clarke (1846–81) wrote several novels, of which the best is 'For the Term of his Natural Life,' a book which gave a moving and vivid picture of life in a penal settlement. Louis Becke (1848–1913) was a successful writer of stories of the southern seas, of which the most representative collection is 'By Reef and Palm.'

Mrs. Campbell Praed (1851–1935) wrote some 30 novels. In 'Policy and Passion' she pictured some phases of Australian life. Other well-known novels are 'Nadine' and 'The Romance of a Station.' 'Tasma' (Miss Huybers) was born in London about 1860, and went to Hobart in infancy, but in 1879 she returned to live in France. Her novels enjoyed a wide popularity in Australia. Her best known book is 'Uncle Piper of Piper's Hill.' Henry Hertzberg Lawson (1867–1922) is well known as the author of 'While the Billy Boils' (in prose) and 'In the Days when the World was Wide' (in verse). Helen Simpson (1897–1940) wrote many powerful novels, one of which, 'Boomerang' (1932), was awarded the James Tait Memorial Prize. Others included 'The Desolate House' (1930) and 'Saraband for Dead Lovers' (1935). Henry Handel Richardson (Mrs. J. G. Robertson) wrote outstanding novels in 'Maurice Guest' and 'The Young Cosima,' and accomplished a long continuous story in a trilogy of novels, 'The Fortunes of Richard Mahony.' She possesses a vigorous and virile style, and for years her work was thought to be that of a man.

The fame of Katherine Mansfield (1888–1923) rests mainly on her superb short stories, written in the manner of Tchekhov and remarkable for their spare clear-cut lines, their penetrating analysis of motive and their lively appreciation of Nature's beauties. 'Bliss,' 'The Garden Party' and 'The Dove's Nest,' dealing with the author's childhood in New Zealand, are the most effective volumes. Katherine Mansfield was the wife of J. Middleton Murry. Her 'Journal' and 'Letters' were published posthumously.

Among the most versatile of recent Australian authors is Jack Lindsay (born 1900), the son of Norman Lindsay (b. 1879), the Australian cartoonist, essayist and story writer. The younger Lindsay has written poems, plays, and novels. He has made extensive translations from the Greek and Latin classics, and has edited many medieval texts. A number of his novels reflect his classical researches— 'Cressida's First Lover,' 'Rome for Sale,' 'Caesar is Dead,' and 'Last Days with Cleopatra.' He is an accomplished poet.

Xavier Herbert has producd one of the most remarkable Australian novels of recent years. This is ' Capricornia,' awarded the Commonwealth Literary prize for the best novel of 1937. It deals with conditions in Northern Australia some forty years ago. It is a brutal story of evil-doers and one which presents an immense contrast with the civilized conditions of today. Xavier Herbert has accomplished his task with great skill, for although the story may disgust the reader by its brutality, his interest is retained throughout.

South Africa. The father of South African poetry was Thomas Pringle (1789–1834), a Scotsman by birth. He was a distinguished writer when he settled in Cape Town in 1819, where he was appointed government librarian. His most artistic long poem was ' The Bechuana Boy.' He also wrote in prose a ' Narrative of a Residence in South Africa.' Pringle gives a most vivid description of life in South Africa at the beginning of the 19th century.

A good early anthology of South African poetry is ' The Treasury of South African Poetry and Verse,' edited by Edward Heath Crouch, and published in 1907. But a more representative collection was published in 1925. This is ' The Centenary Book of South African Verse,' edited by Francis Carey Slater, himself the author of 'The Sunburnt South' and 'The Karoo.'

E. B. Watermayer (1824–67) was a characteristic South African poet, whose best-known poem is ' After a Storm.' Alfred Henry Haynes Bell shows more variety in his writing, and his poem, ' The Last Stand,' is of interest as an example of an early empire poem.

Among later poets Roy Campbell (b. 1902) is remarkable. In ' The Flaming Terrapin ' (1924), ' Adamastor ' (1930), ' The Georgiad ' (1931), a satire, and ' The Flowering Rifle' (1939), he shows a considerable measure of originality. He is also the author of some vigorous prose. Arthur Shearly Cripps, who was a missionary, has made an interesting contribution to South African verse in ' The Pilgrimage of Grace,' ' Lake and War,' and ' Africa ' (published in 1939). He has also written excellent prose in ' Faery Lands Forlorn' and ' Lion Man.'

South Africa has not been rich in outstanding novelists, though one novel, Olive Schreiner's ' The Story of an African Farm,' published in 1883, aroused worldwide interest. It shows real genius, and the heroine, surrounded by all sorts of conventions and struggling to attain independence, is [convincingly drawn. Gertrude Page (d. 1922) depicted in many popular novels life on the farm in Rhodesia. Pauline Smith, in ' The Little Karoo ' (1925) and ' The Beadle,' wrote two South African novels of quite unusual charm. Sarah Gertrude Millin, in ' God's Step-Children ' (1924), dealt with the treatment of native races.

The contribution of the Dominions is important, though there has been, as yet, no outstanding genius worthy of comparison with the literary giants of the homeland. As time.goes on, no doubt the Dominions will continue to add much of real value to the treasures of English Literature.

BOOK LIST

General : 'Cambridge History of English Literature ' (15 vols.) and 'Concise Cambridge History of English Literature (one vol.) ; 'Chambers's Cyclopaedia of English Literature (three vols.) ; 'History of English Literature,' Legouis and Cazamian (Dent) ; 'Short History of English Literature,' G. Saintsbury (Macmillan) ; 'The Background of English Literature,' H. J. C. Grierson (Chatto) ; 'The Sources of English Literature,' A. Esdaile (Camb. Univ. P.) ; 'Oxford Companion to English Literature ' ; 'English Men of Letters' series (Macmillan).

Verse and Prose : 'Oxford Book of English Verse' ; 'Oxford Book of English Prose' ; 'The Art of Poetry,' W. P. Ker (Oxford) ; 'Poetry and the Ordinary Reader,' M. R. Ridley (Dent) ; 'The English Poetic Mind,' Charles Williams (Oxford) ; 'A Study of Metre,' T. S. Omond (Moring) ; 'An Historical Manual of English Prosody,' G. Saintsbury (Macmillan) ; 'British Drama,' Allardyce Nicoll (Harrap) ; 'The English Novel,' W. Raleigh (Murray) ; 'Aspects of the Novel,' E. M. Forster (Arnold) ; 'English Prose Style,' Herbert Read (Bell).

Old and Middle English : 'English Literature from Widsith to the Death of Chaucer,' A. R. Benham (Oxford) ; 'English Literature from the Norman Conquest to Chaucer,' W. H. Schofield ; 'Chaucer Primer,' A. W. Pollard (Macmillan) ; 'Chaucer and his England,' G. G. Coulton (Methuen) ; 'English Literature : Medieval,' W. P. Ker ; 'The Medieval Stage,' E. K. Chambers ; 'English Miracle Plays,' A. W. Pollard (Oxford) ; 'The Age of Alfred,' 'Age of Chaucer,' 'Age of Transition,' F. J. Snell (Bell).

Sixteenth Century : 'Oxford Book of Sixteenth-Century Verse' ; 'Early Tudor Poetry, 1485-1547,' J. M. Berdan (Macmillan) ; 'Introduction to Tudor Drama,' F. S. Boas (Oxford) ; 'Shakespeare's Predecessors in the English Drama,' J. A. Symonds (Smith, Elder) ; 'Elizabethan Literature,' G. Saintsbury (Macmillan) ; 'Elizabethan Essays,' T. S. Eliot (Faber) ; 'The Elizabethan Theatre,' E. K. Chambers (Oxford) ; ' The Age of Shakespeare,' Seccombe and Allen (Bell).

Shakespeare : 'Introduction to the Reading of Shakespeare,' F. S. Boas (Oxford) ; 'The Essential Shakespeare,' J. Dover Wilson (Camb. Univ. Press) ; 'Prefaces to Shakespeare,' Granville Barker (Sidgwick) ; 'Shakespeare Primer,' E. Dowden, ' Shakespeare,' W. Raleigh, 'Shakespearean Tragedy,' A. C. Bradley (Macmillan) ; 'Essays and Lectures on Shakespeare,' S. T. Coleridge ; 'Characters of Shakespeare's Plays,' W. Hazlitt (Dent) ; 'Shakespeare's Workmanship' (Camb. Univ. Press) ; 'Shakespeare at Work,' G. B. Harrison (Routledge).

Seventeenth Century : 'Oxford Book of Seventeenth-Century Verse' ; 'Jacobean Poets,' Edmund Gosse ; 'Jacobean Drama,' U. Ellis-Fermor (Methuen) ; 'Milton,' John Bailey (Oxford) ; 'The Age of Milton,' J. H. B. Masterman (Bell) ; 'The Metaphysical Poets,' J. B. Leishman (Oxford) ; 'History of Restoration Drama,' Allardyce Nicoll ; 'The Age of Dryden,' R. Garnett (Bell).

Eighteenth Century : 'Oxford Book of 18th-Century Verse ' ; ' 18th-Century Literature,' Edmund Gosse (Macmillan) ; 'History of 18th-Century Drama,' Allardyce Nicoll (Camb. Press) ; 'The Age of Pope,' J. Dennis (Bell) ; 'Poetry of Pope,' A. Tillotson (Oxford) ; 'The Age of Johnson,' T. Seccombe (Bell).

Nineteenth Century : 'Oxford Book of Regency Verse' ; 'Oxford Book of Victorian Verse ' ; 'History of 19th-Century Literature,' G. Saintsbury (Macmillan) ; 'The Age of Wordsworth,' C. H. Herford (Bell) ; 'The Victorian Age in Literature,' G. K. Chesterton (Oxford) ; 'The Age of Tennyson,' H. Walker (Bell) ; 'Ten Victorian Poets,' F. L. Lucas (Camb. Univ. Press) ; 'Early Victorian Novelists,' David Cecil (Constable).

Twentieth Century : 'Oxford Book of Modern Verse' ; 'Twentieth - Century Literature, 1901-1940,' A. C. Ward (Methuen) ; 'The Present Age, from 1914,' Edwin Muir (Cresset Press) ; 'Poetry at Present,' Charles Williams (Oxford) ; 'The Twentieth-Century Novel,' J. W. Beach (Appleton) ; 'Poems of Today' (Sidgwick) ; 'Selections from Modern Poets,' ed. J. C. Squire (Secker) ; 'Twentieth-Century Poetry,' ed. H. Monro (Chatto) ; 'Anthology of Modern Verse, 1920-1940' (Methuen).

American and Dominions Literature : 'Oxford Book of American Verse' ; 'Oxford Book of Canadian Verse' ; 'Great Writers of America,' Erskine and Trent (Butterworth) ; ' The American Novel,' C. van Doren (Macmillan) ; 'Cambridge History of American Literature.'

ASTRONOMY

THIS *Course is our first in the group of the Natural Sciences. Beginning with a sketch of the history and progress of Astronomy, it covers the whole field of astronomical discovery and knowledge, including modern work on the computation of the Sun's distance from the Earth, the Moon, the planets, comets and meteorites, the stellar system and the nebulae. It is necessarily associated in some degree with the Course that follows it on* PHYSICS.

32 LESSONS

First Steps in the Study of the Heavens

ASTRONOMY is the science which tells of the heavens, of worlds beyond our own, of conditions strange, weird, and wonderful that exist upon vast rolling spheres, many of them hundreds of times greater than the earth. It tells of fiery suns to be numbered by hundreds of millions, and reveals radiant marvels in the depths of space, where may be found the original ' stuff ' or matter from which all things are made.

Worlds in the making, worlds dead and arid, whirling fragments of worlds—all pass above us from night to night. There in those glittering heavens may be seen suns in myriads, ascending through successive states of stellar evolution, from youth to old age. There through interminable aeons they waste away.

All these things and more astronomy explains, and tells us where we may see them for ourselves. It unravels the celestial tangle of mysterious forces which fill space with energy, and like a vast though invisible mechanism hold together each fractional part, no matter how small, of our universe, notwithstanding the tremendous speed with which each unit is travelling through an infinity in which nothing is lost and a void has no existence.

What the Telescope Reveals. To the naked eye of an observer on a clear, starlit night some 2,000 objects may be seen bespangling the heavens ; a good pair of field glasses will increase the number visible about ten-fold, but a powerful telescope will reveal the existence of several thousand where but one is visible to the unaided vision. The number increases with each improvement in the powers of the telescope, so while about 2,000 million suns are at present known to enter into the composition of our universe, there can be no doubt that they are actually very much more numerous.

With the exception of the sun, moon, and an occasional comet, meteor, or nebula, all celestial objects appear to the naked eye as points of light. This is because of their enormous distance, which, notwithstanding the immensity of the objects, reduces them to an apparent width that is immeasurable to the eye.

That splendid instrument the telescope, and its valuable accessories, the spectroscope and interferometer, together with astrographic photography, have enlarged Man's vision so greatly that the astronomer is now equipped with the equivalent of an eye 25 feet in diameter. Vastly remote suns may now be measured, and the analysing ' eye ' of the spectroscope reveals so much about them that we are enabled accurately to visualize these giant, pulsating and otherwise disturbed stellar monsters, capable of enveloping not only our sun but the earth and its orbit as well.

With such instruments at his disposal the astronomer experiences no difficulty in accurately distinguishing between suns and worlds, for although both shine and appear to the naked eye as stars, only the suns, like colossal furnaces, shine by their own light. Worlds, on the other hand, shine by reflected light from the suns round which they revolve. They are always very much smaller spheres, more or less resembling the earth. Known worlds are usually very much nearer to us than the suns, because, worlds being considerably smaller bodies and radiating much less light, they are imperceptible—even through powerful telescopes—at the vast distances of the starry suns. The existence of worlds revolving round many of these distant luminaries is, however, revealed indirectly and will be discussed in due course.

With those worlds which revolve round our sun we are, of course, much better acquainted, our knowledge being derived from direct observation, mathematical deduction, and inference based on theoretical considerations of known analogies—in other words, when we see smoke we infer fire. It is by these means that we have learnt so much about enormously distant worlds and suns without ever having visited them.

Astronomy has thus been built up through the ages so as to become one of the most exact of sciences—so exact that numerous celestial events that will not occur until many years hence can be foretold to a minute—sometimes, as in the case of eclipses of the sun, to a second or so. Still more marvellous is the fact that there are celestial events which we know took place many years ago but which have yet to be observed by us or our descendants.

Classes of Worlds. The worlds that revolve round the sun are divided into planets and satellites, the latter being worlds that revolve round some of the planets. None of the satellites is visible to the naked eye except the earth's satellite, the moon. Good field glasses will, however, reveal two of Jupiter's satellites, while a comparatively small astronomical telescope will reveal several more. So many most interesting celestial objects are only just beyond naked-eye visibility that an ordinary telescope will help in identifying them.

Were many of these ' points of light,' as they appear to our unaided vision, only as near to us as the moon, spectacles of unexampled grandeur would be presented. Saturn, for instance, a world 734 times the size of the earth, would appear to us at times as shown in the illustration in p. 241, if it were only 238,840 miles away, which is the average distance of the moon.

The Milky Way. In many large areas of the sky the stars are numerous but so far away that only a dim light is seen with the naked eye. Such a region is the great belt constituting what is popularly known as the Milky Way. The illustration in p. 241 (top, right) shows a small portion of this Milky Way as revealed by photography through a powerful telescope. Every dot in this photograph represents one of the two thousand million suns known to astronomers. The space beyond seems literally hidden by their numbers, yet the individual suns are relatively as far apart from one another as our sun is distant from the nearest stars or suns in our region. Beyond them again are vast systems, galaxies, such as that illustrated in page 248.

Were we not so familiar with it from our earliest years, and were it presented unexpectedly to our eyes for the first time and for only a brief space of time, we should probably account the sight of the heavens on a starlit night as among the most wonderful experiences of our lives. On any cloudless and moonless night one may see between 1,500 and 2,000 points of light collectively known as stars, spread over what appears to be a great dome or hemisphere. The ancient astronomers originally regarded the latter as solid—hence its name firmament. But it is now known to be illimitable space extending to unfathomed depths, the stars being, with few exceptions, suns at various and immense distances.

They all appear to the naked eye to be still, and to remain in the same relative position to one another from night to night ; they, therefore, received the name of fixed stars at a time when very much less was known

about them than now. The student must remember that they are not actually fixed, though the term is still used conventionally to distinguish them from the planets.

The planets may be regarded as worlds ; they shine by the reflected light from our sun, and are very much nearer to us than any of the other stars, which are suns far more distant than our own. Only five planets are ordinarily visible to the naked eye, i.e. without optical aid, though two more that are very faint may be seen if their position is known, and more still with an astronomical telescope.

The student will soon be able to distinguish the planets or worlds from the stars or suns by their movements. The four planets, Venus, Jupiter, Mars, and Saturn, are the most readily identified by their brilliance ; the three former appear to be brighter than any of the other stars. Other aids to identification are their steady, continuous light and the comparative absence of the scintillation, or twinkling, so characteristic of the starry suns.

The largest number of stars that may be observed by the naked eye on the clearest night is about 2,000. This represents the number visible at one time, when we see only the hemisphere or one-half of the entire heavens. But there is another half which reveals approximately another 2,000 stars.

Stars of the Night Sky. In the British Isles persons may see most of these in the following circumstances. If the student faces south at, say, 8 o'clock in the evening, and takes note of the positions of many of the more prominent stars, which are arranged in easily remembered geometrical patterns, and then again looks for those same stars about midnight, it will be obvious that the whole concourse of stars has moved from east to west to the extent of about one-third of the whole expanse ; the actual amount will vary according to the altitude of the star, being greatest for those farther south. Those stars that were near the eastern horizon will, by midnight, be high up and approaching due south, while those that were in the south will be seen to be descending to the west, and in the course of another four hours will have vanished below the horizon. Thus, the whole celestial sphere will appear to be revolving from east to west, with the result that, if the student takes note of all the stars that are visible to the east, south, and west of him at 6 o'clock on a winter's evening, and then compares them with all those that occupy the same sections of sky at 6 o'clock on a winter's morning, he will see that they are totally different. Fresh groupings will have taken the place of those present in the evening sky, while those that were in the north-west portion of the sky will have changed places with those that were in the north-east portion. The star-maps in p. 242 present a picture of the chief stars to be seen on each occasion in January.

There are approximately another 1,000 stars which remain for ever out of sight of the observer in Britain and can be observed only by travelling to a place south of the equator. All the stars that pass near the zenith or overhead point, however, together with all those to the north of it, are always visible on any fine night; it is only their position relative to the northern horizon that changes. The stars within this region are said to be within the *circle of perpetual apparition.*

The heavens as revealed to the naked eye were all that was known to the astronomers of Chaldea and Egypt of 5,000 years ago. This is why the constellations, particularly those of the zodiac, that is, the twelve constellations through which the sun appears to pass in the course of a year, constitute the basis of the most ancient astronomy.

The chief constellations consist mostly of conventional star groupings associated with imaginary figures of mythological beings, both animal and human. In ancient times they had an impressive symbolical meaning, and represented some deity or annual event concerned with the sun god or moon god. Thus it was that astronomy was intimately connected with the religions of most ancient peoples. So it has continued to the present day. Easter, for instance, is fixed by the occurrence of the first full moon after March 21.

Not until the time of the Greeks did astronomy begin to emerge from the realm of myth and mysticism, though for long the earth was still regarded as an enormous flat disk encircled by an ocean that lost itself in mystery just as did the sky above. The solid firmament conception gradually gave way to more scientific reasoning. The ideas of Empedocles (450 B.C.) and Plato (427-347 B.C.) led to the belief that the earth might be a sphere in space. Pythagoras in the 6th century B.C. has been credited with a similar, but very fanciful, idea in connexion with his famous theory of the 'harmony of the spheres.'

In the time of Aristarchus of Samos (310-230 B.C.) a true conception of the earth's place in the heavens was first produced. From Aristarchus' one surviving work it appears that he held the opinion that the earth was a sphere in motion round the sun. Succeeding ages would not accept his scientific reasoning, and for eighteen hundred years mankind followed the erroneous idea that the earth was the centre and all-important pivot of the universe, around which everything else revolved.

LESSON TWO

Ancient Astronomy and the Pioneers of the New

IN the preceding Lesson we learnt that Aristarchus arrived at the conclusion that the earth was a sphere revolving about the sun. Despite his reasoning, however, men still persisted in believing that the reverse held true—that it was the sun that revolved daily round the earth.

Even Hipparchus, the greatest astronomer of antiquity, who flourished in Rhodes in the second century B.C., adhered to the idea of a fixed earth, although by careful and prolonged observation he decided that sun and moon moved at varying speeds, and that at certain times the latter was nearer the earth than at others. As the result of his discoveries, astronomers were enabled to predict when eclipses of the sun would take place—a matter of considerable moment in those days, when eclipses were viewed with apprehension as presages of dire misfortune.

Ptolemaic System. The astronomy of the ancients was consolidated by Claudius Ptolemaeus, or Ptolemy as he is more usually called, about A.D. 150, in the book known to us as the 'Almagest.' For 1,400 years the 'Almagest' was the textbook of astronomy, and hence the system described therein goes under the name of the Ptolemaic, although Ptolemy was a compiler rather than an original thinker and observer. The Ptolemaic conception of the universe is shown in p. 239; we see the earth fixed in the centre, with the other heavenly bodies moving around it in circular orbits. The sun, moon, and planets were supposed to be each attached to rotating crystal spheres, which in turn, together with the earth, were contained within an immensely larger sphere to whose inner surface were fixed the outermost stars. The eccentric motions of the planets (Gr. *planetes*, wanderer) were accounted for by supposing them to move in small circles whose centres themselves revolved about the earth. This epicyclic motion, as it is called, is explained in the diagram below.

This ingenious and complicated system became somewhat modified in the course

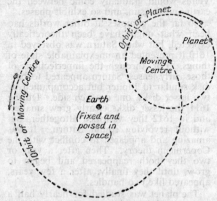

DIAGRAM OF ' EPICYCLIC MOTION.' *According to this theory, planets revolve round a point which itself revolves round the earth.*

of centuries, as observation revealed its inaccuracies and inadequacy; but, generally speaking, it endured until the sixteenth century, when it received its deathblow. As early as 1440 Nicolas of Cusa, a cardinal of the Church, wrote: ' I have long considered that the earth is not fixed, but moves as do the other stars '; but it was not until 1543 that Nicolaus Copernicus (*see* page 244) published his great work, ' De Revolutionibus Orbium Coelestium ' (Concerning the Revolutions of Celestial Orbs), in which he demonstrated that the sun is the central body in our universe, and that round it revolve the earth and the other planets.

Theory of Brahe. Tycho Brahe (1546-1601) refused to accept the Copernican theory. He had made very exact measurements of the motions of the sun, moon and planets; his instruments were far more accurate than any used before, and he considered that if the

Copernican system was correct, the wide arc produced by the earth's motion round the sun should have made the apparent places of the stars change annually, whereas they did not appear to do so. We have learned since that their positions do change, but so slightly, owing to their distance, that a telescope is needed to reveal it.

But so much in the Copernican theory was obviously incontestable that Tycho Brahe devised a theory which still left the earth as the all-important centre of the universe, while the sun, which he regarded as at a very great distance, revolved round the earth. The moon did likewise. The planets, however, he considered to revolve round the sun. This was the Tychonic system, which was intermediate between the Ptolemaic and Copernican systems. It was not generally accepted, but Brahe's numerous accurate measurements and observations led directly to the discovery of the fundamental laws of the universe, and of the reason why the planets travel as they do with varying speeds round the sun.

Kepler's Laws. This great discovery was due to the genius of a pupil of Tycho Brahe, John Kepler (1571-1630), who undertook to calculate from the above observations how the planets ought to move round the sun in order at all times to be in the positions in which they were found. The difficulties and the amount of work were enormous—comparing each hypothesis with the observations of Tycho Brahe; then if it were found wrong over some detail of one or other of the planets, laboriously having to prepare another.

These famous laws of Kepler are three in number:

1. The orbit of each planet is an ellipse having the sun in one of the foci.
2. As a planet moves round the sun the areas (P_1P_2S, P_3P_4S, etc.), shown in the accompanying diagram) described by its radius vector, i.e. the space enclosed between lines drawn from the focus (S) to two successive points (P_1, P_2, etc.) in the planet's path, are proportional to the time taken in describing them; or, to put it in other words, its radius vector sweeps over equal areas in equal times.
3. The square of the time in which each planet completes its orbit is proportional to the cube of its mean distance from the sun.

This third law shows that there is a definite numerical relation between the motions

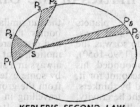

KEPLER'S SECOND LAW

of all the planets, and that the time which each of them takes to complete its orbit depends upon its distance from the sun. Why the planets should obey these so-called laws was not known as yet owing to the fact that the mighty force of gravitation had not then been discovered, but nevertheless these laws propounded by Kepler enabled astronomers to predict where a planet would be at a stated time.

Galileo's Discoveries. About the same time Galileo Galilei (1564-1642), a native of Pisa, heard that a Dutch instrument-maker had discovered the principle of the telescope for magnifying objects, an elaboration of the magnifying glass discovered by Roger Bacon. Galileo conceived the idea of applying the principle to magnifying the stars. By experimenting with a convex lens and a concave lens fitted into a tube he succeeded, in 1609, in constructing the first astronomical telescope (*see* p. 244). It magnified only three times, so he ground and polished other lenses and made a much more powerful telescope, magnifying eight times.

The planets were then found to be perceptibly different from the stars, and instead of points of light tiny disks were revealed. Then Galileo constructed his large telescope, which magnified about thirty times. He turned it on Jupiter on January 7, 1610, and saw, instead of a point of light, a world with a disk almost as large as the moon appears to the naked eye. This was anticipated from his preceding observations, but there on the left side were two brilliant points of light and another on the right. This was astounding. A few days later a fourth appeared, and from evening to evening they changed places around the large disk of Jupiter. Galileo called them the Medicean stars, but later it was realized that they were moons, and though Jupiter is now known to have seven other,

though much smaller, moons, the first four are known as the Galilean moons.

When Venus was first observed by Galileo in September, 1610, it appeared like a half-moon, and then during succeeding weeks gradually changed into a crescent. Thus it was seen that Venus exhibited phases similar to the moon, a fact which confirmed the Copernican theory. For since this claimed that Venus revolved round the sun in an orbit within that of the earth, therefore Venus would gradually come between the earth and the sun, and so exhibit phases.

So far the glimpses at other worlds had been what might have been theoretically expected, but when Saturn was observed in 1610 it presented an unexplainable state of things. For, through the imperfections of those early lenses, Saturn appeared to be a disk similar to Jupiter but accompanied by two lesser disks, one on each side. During 1611 the lesser disks clearly grew smaller, and in 1612 they vanished altogether, but without revolving round Saturn. It was amazing and appeared to conflict with the Copernican theory. Then after a year or two they both reappeared and began to grow, until they finally, after a few years, appeared like two handles.

The planet was studied for nearly half a century and through better telescopes before Christian Huygens (1629-1695), a Dutch astronomer and physicist, thought out the true explanation in 1655. This was that Saturn was surrounded by a thin flat ring suspended from the body of the planet by intervening space.

Thus was another objection to the Copernican theory swept away. Mars and Mercury, together with Venus and Jupiter, had been found to substantiate it further ; but the question, what invisible power held all these bodies together in such orderly paths, remained to be answered.

LESSON THREE

Mathematics of the Universe

KEPLER had shown how the planets moved according to the three laws, but what made them do so was the problem. At first Descartes (1596-1650), the French philosopher, propounded his theory of ethereal vortices to account for it, and this was generally accepted by thinkers. Then the idea arose that it might be gravity, or the weight of the planets falling toward

the sun similar to the way in which propelled bodies fall toward the ground. Galileo had discovered, long before, the first law of motion, that a body will continue to move always in a straight line unless it is deflected by some external force. A body propelled from the ground always returned to it after travelling in a tangent—a thrown ball, for instance. It was supposed that some force

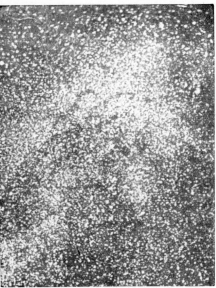

WONDERS OF THE HEAVENS. *Saturn is nearly 800 million miles distant from our earth ; were it as near as the moon it would present to us the magnificent spectacle depicted above on the left. Right, a few of the 30 thousand million stars contained in the Milky Way ; this remarkable photograph, taken by the famous French astronomer, M. Lucien Rudaux, shows part of the constellation of Cygnus, The Swan. (See page 237.)*

THE MILKY WAY AS IT WOULD APPEAR FROM OUTER SPACE

STAR CLUSTER IN WHICH
OUR EARTH IS HIDDEN

*THE MILKY WAY.
As seen by the naked
eye, the Milky Way
appears as a luminous
belt of faint light
stretching across the
sky at night. Could this
belt with its curious
structure be viewed
from outer space, it
would be seen to be
composed of streams
of innumerable stars,
condensed clusters and
star-clouds; the whole
arranged in the form
of a revolving spiral.
In one of the clusters
our Solar System is
considered to be situ-
ated, as indicated at A.
(See page 237.)*

241

H*

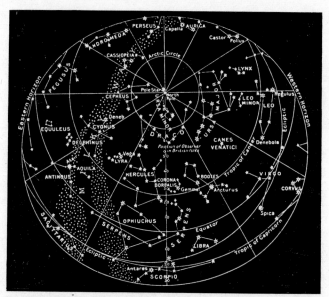

This star map shows the constellations visible at 6 a.m. on February 18 or at 7 a.m. on January 31. The position of an observer in the British Isles is marked both in this and in the map below, a little below the Arctic Circle.

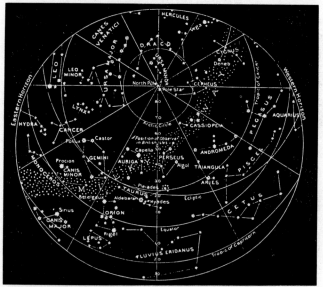

MORNING AND EVENING SKY IN WINTER. In the map immediately above are charted the principal stars visible at 6 p.m. on February 18 or at 7 p.m. on January 31. The Milky Way, vertical in the early morning (see top map), now stretches horizontally across the sky. (See pages 237 and 319.)

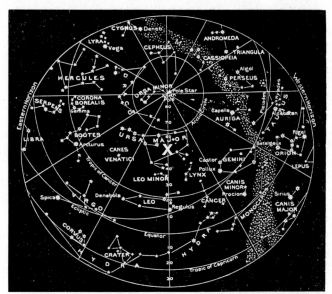

In this map are shown the positions of the principal stars visible at 10 p.m. on March 21 or at 8 p.m. on April 22. In all four of these maps the stars of each constellation have been joined by lines to facilitate their recognition.

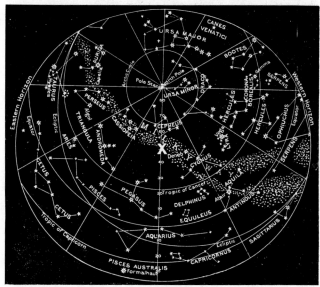

THE HEAVENS IN SPRING AND AUTUMN. Here is a map of the sky as an observer would see it at 10 p.m. on September 21 or at 8 p.m. on October 22. The Ecliptic indicates the annual path of the sun and the approximate paths of the moon and planets. X indicates overhead point. (See page 319.)

Copernicus   Tycho Brahe   Galileo

Johann Kepler   Sir Isaac Newton   John Flamsteed

Edmund Halley   Marquis de Laplace   Sir John Herschel

FAMOUS ASTRONOMERS. Copernicus (1473–1543) proved that the sun, and not the earth, was the centre round which the other planets revolved. Tycho Brahe (1546–1601) by his accurate calculations paved the way for Kepler (1571–1630) and Galileo (1564–1642). Kepler was the first to discover that a planet's orbit is elliptical. Galileo established the Copernican theory and, like Kepler, enunciated the principles on which Newton (1642–1727) based his tremendous exposition of the laws of gravity. Flamsteed (1646–1719), first Astronomer Royal, catalogued the fixed stars, and Halley (1656–1742), his successor, observed the comet that bears his name and predicted the date of its return. Laplace (1749–1827) was the greatest mathematician of his time. Herschel (1792–1871) did brilliant work in mapping the heavens; his father and aunt were also notable astronomers.

244

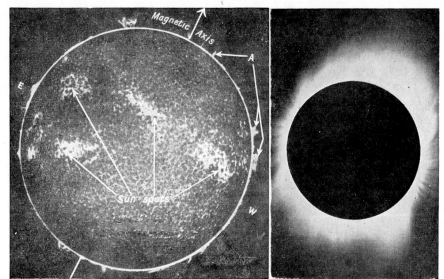

SUN SPOTS AND A TOTAL ECLIPSE. Left, spectroscopic photograph at a time of maximum sun-spot activity. The light patches which surround the apparently dark sun-spot vortices are violently disturbed eruptive areas of cyclonic activity. These break through the clouds of glowing calcium vapour which covers the sun beneath the enveloping helium and hydrogen. Note the solar prominences (A) erupted from the chromosphere. Note, too, that the solar East and West, seen through the telescope, are reversed. Right photograph of the magnificent spectacle afforded by the mysterious Corona which surrounds the sun, as it appeared in the total solar eclipse of May 28, 1900. (See text pages 251-52.)

Photos, Dr. J. Evershed and Dr. A. A. Barnard

WHEN THE MOON BLOTS OUT THE SUN. Diagram representing the solar eclipse of January 24, 1925. It will be seen that the track of the shadow of solar eclipse, extending from western Canada to the N. of the British Isles, is very narrow compared with the oval area embraced by the partial eclipse.

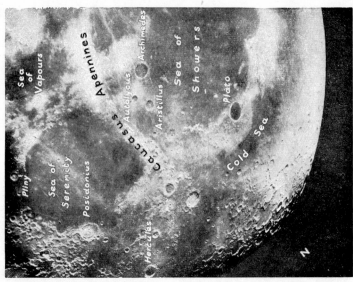

FEATURES OF THE MOON'S FACE. Left, photograph, taken at Lick Observatory, of the moon when 14 days and 8 hours old. The principal seas are shown as follows: B, Mare Nubium; C, Mare Nectaris; D, Mare Fecunditatis; E, Mare Tranquillitatis; G, Mare Vaporum; J, Oceanus Procellarum; K, Mare Crisium; L, Mare Serenitatis; O, Mare Imbrium. Craters seen are: A, Tycho; F, Ptolemy; H, Copernicus; N, Archimedes; P, Aristarchus; Q, Plato. Two of the great mountain ranges, the Apennines and the Alps, are shown at M and R. Right, view of the northern section of the lunar disk. It must be borne in mind that photographs of the moon's surface are represented as viewed through a telescope-reversed, and consequently the north polar region is at the bottom here. The dark areas, to which the name of Seas has been given, are probably vast plains of solid lava. The volcanic craters vary in size from immense walled plains to small craterlets. This photograph was taken at Mount Wilson Observatory in 1925. (See pages 259-260.)

246

MERCURY'S ORBIT. This planet presents all the phases of the moon and its apparent changes are seen in the diagram on the left. Mercury takes the same time to complete its journey round the sun as it does to rotate once on its own axis.

VENUS, MERCURY AND THE EARTH. The orbits of the three planets which keep nearest to the sun are shown in the diagram on the right, with their positions at aphelion (point farthest from the sun) and perihelion (nearest the sun) respectively. All planetary orbits are elliptical, but that of Venus approaches most nearly to a circle. Because Mercury is so near the sun observation of this planet is at all times difficult. Mercury also moves faster than any other planet, the speed at which it travels varying from about 24 miles a second when at aphelion, to about 36 miles a second at perihelion. This last figure is twice the speed of the earth's circuit round the sun. (See text, page 261.)

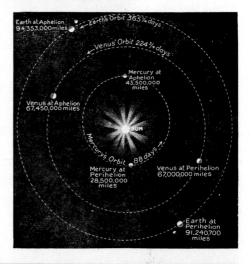

ECLIPSE OF THE MOON. A lunar eclipse, shown partial above, is caused when the earth comes between the moon and the sun, so its shadow falls upon the moon, as explained in page 258. The penumbra is the faint partial shadow produced when only part of the sun is hidden from the moon's surface by the earth. The figures given are average, for they vary in accordance with the varying distance of the earth from the sun and of the moon from the earth. Thus, while the diameter of the earth's cone of shadow, or umbra, where the moon may cross it, averages 5,700 miles, it may be some 200 miles more or less than this figure.

247

HORSE'S HEAD IN ORION NEBULA. Some of the vast spaces between the stars are occupied by nebulous matter, which in parts is illuminated by the stars; the intervention of dark non-illuminated nebulous masses is strikingly shown in the photograph (above) of the so-called horse's head region of the great Orion Nebula. For a discussion of dark nebulae see page 324.

Photos, courtesy of the Royal Astronomical Society (left) and Mount Wilson Observatory

ANDROMEDA 'NEBULA.' The great spiral nebula of Andromeda is not actually a nebula, but another universe similar to our galaxy and composed of some thousands of millions of suns together with numerous masses of nebulae and doubtless myriads of worlds, the whole at a distance of about 680 light-years, or 210,000 parsecs. (See pages 302 and 325.)

at the centre of the earth caused this, for the law of gravitation had not yet been discovered.

Now, it could be mathematically shown that if only the ball could be propelled fast enough it would remain suspended and continue travelling round the earth, provided that it met no air or other resistance. Huygens, in 1671, propounded the laws which govern a body travelling in a circle, showing that it was subject to a force similar to gravity. Robert Hooke (1635-1703) had already conceived the true idea of universal gravitation, but from lack of mathematical ability he was unable to frame a law to prove it. Other astronomers and mathematicians had similar ideas. Chief among them were Sir Christopher Wren (1632-1723), Edmund Halley (1656-1742), and Sir Isaac Newton (1642-1727).

It had already been learned that it was possible to account for the orbital motion of our world and the planets by supposing them to be subject to a force which attracted them to the centre of the sun, just as it was known that the earth attracted bodies to its centre as if a gigantic loadstone were there. This pulling to earth which gave bodies their weight was known as gravity ; we see, therefore, that gravitation as an idea was not discovered by Sir Isaac Newton.

Law of Gravity. The idea needed defining mathematically, so that it could be proved experimentally in any test case. This Newton set himself to do in 1665. He knew the rate at which a body will fall to the ground at the earth's surface, and he decided to find out the rate at which the moon should fall toward the earth if the same force, that is, gravity, was the cause of it. It was most important that the distance of the moon should be known accurately. Newton based his calculations upon the accepted distance of 30 times the earth's diameter. Thus far it was correct, but unfortunately the earth's diameter was considered to be 6,900 miles instead of 7,927, an error which threw all Newton's calculations out, and he concluded that the moon was not pulled by gravity toward the earth. He, therefore, abandoned the problem for 16 years, after which, becoming aware that Picard, a French astronomer, had, in 1679, found that the earth's diameter was nearly 8,000 miles, he recomputed his former figures and discovered that after all the moon did fall towards the earth and was subject to the force of gravity. Then he arrived at the fundamental law that holds the universe together, that ' every particle of matter in the universe attracts every other particle with a force varying inversely as the square of the distance between them, and directly as the mass of the attracting particle.'

To understand how, in accordance with the above law, the moon continues to fall towards, and yet never reaches the earth, we must remember that the earth is a sphere and the moon distant from it on an average 238,840 miles. Now, while a body will fall to the earth at the rate of about $16\frac{1}{10}$th feet in a second when near the earth's surface, it will fall at the rate of only $\frac{16}{3600}$ths of a foot at the distance of the moon, because, owing to the force of gravitation decreasing inversely as the square of the distance, the force will be only $\frac{1}{3600}$th of what it is at the earth's surface. Being a sphere, this surface is everywhere curved downward relative to the moon ; therefore, since the moon is travelling as a projectile tangentially toward the earth, on account of the latter's gravitational pull, for every few feet the moon falls, the earth's curved surface also curves away from it. The moon's velocity is so nicely balanced to this pull that, apart from minor variations due to other gravitational pulls and subject to the laws of Kepler, it never reaches the earth but perpetually encircles it.

The student may thus learn, as Newton did, that the force which keeps the moon always falling to the earth also keeps the planets always falling toward the sun in the same manner. It must, however, be remembered that the fall takes the form of a tangential curve which is a compound of the body's initial velocity and the gravitational pull from the centre of attraction, with the result that the body moves in a closed orbit.

The story that it was the fall of an apple which resulted in Newton's discovery of the law of gravitation may perhaps be true, but it is inherently improbable, because the apple's perpendicular fall was totally different from the tangential fall of celestial bodies ; moreover, the cause of the apple's fall was regarded as already satisfactorily explained by gravity from the earth's centre.

The question was not whether the earth's gravity attracted terrestrial things, but whether gravitation caused celestial bodies to travel as they are observed to do. Newton discovered the law concerning the latter, and it was incorporated with other discoveries in his great work, ' Philosophiae Naturalis Principia Mathematica.' This, generally known as the ' Principia,' was printed and published at the expense of Halley in 1686-7.

The work has provided the basis for all calculations of the movements, not only of the planets, satellites and other bodies of the solar system, but also of the distant stars and remote universes far beyond our own, where just the same laws are found to operate. So exact are their movements in accord with Newton's laws that ever since it has been possible to foretell, by means of a few observations, the positions of the celestial bodies at different times far ahead. Thus the tables of the sun, moon and planets are prepared years in advance for the ' Nautical Almanac ' at the Greenwich Observatory. This tells the navigator exactly where the sun, moon and planets are to be found at a certain time, thus enabling him to find his position at sea.

The improved mathematics of the 20th century have accounted for some unexplained discrepancies revealed in matters unknown in Newton's day and only to be perceived by the extreme accuracy of present-day observation. They are too small, however, to affect ordinary mathematical calculations appreciably. They have been satisfactorily accounted for in Einstein's theories of relativity.

LESSON FOUR

What We Know About the Sun

BY far the most important member of the solar system is the sun, not only, as we saw in the preceding Lesson, on account of its immensity and enormous mass, with its resultant gravitational pull which keeps all the planets in their paths, but also on account of its all-importance to Man, for no life would be possible without its continuous light and heat.

As seen by the naked eye, the sun appears as a flat disk, but through an astronomical telescope suitably fitted with a sun prism, it is seen to be an immense globe. So immense is this globe that, were it hollow, it could enclose the material of 1,300,000 bodies the size of the earth. So huge is it that, were the earth at its centre, the sun's surface would be nearly 430,000 miles above us, and since the average distance of the moon is 238,840 miles from the earth, it follows that the moon would revolve far down within the sun.

The sun's diameter is about 864,000 miles. If this were represented by a globe a foot in diameter, then the earth would, by comparison, be represented by a tiny sphere less than an eighth of an inch in diameter ; by placing this nearly 108 feet away from the globe representing the sun, we should then have the proportionate distance of the earth from the sun. This amounts to an average of 93,005,000 miles, which is usually described as the mean distance, for since the distance of the earth from the sun is continually changing from day to day between two extremes, the average, or mean, is stated for purposes of comparison. This applies to all other celestial bodies, unless the maximum and minimum are given. These distances are given as from the centre of the sun to the centre of the earth. Celestial distances are always given from centre to centre of spheres. This figure of 93,005,000 miles, the most accurate yet obtained, having a possible uncertainty either way of only 9,000 miles, was determined by 1942 by the Astronomer Royal, Sir H. Spencer Jones, from data based on the co-operative work of 24 observatories all over the world in 1931, the year in which the tiny asteroid, Eros, achieved its latest near approach to the earth (*see* Lesson 5).

Sun's Rotation. That the sun rotates on its own axis is not obvious to the eye, but observed telescopically it is seen that striking details on its surface travelled across its disk from east to west. Exact measurements have shown that different parts of the sun's surface travel at different rates and that the rotation period varies according to latitude. This is greatest at the sun's equator, where it amounts to 25 days 1 hour. At latitude 30 degrees north or south, the rate of the sun's rotation is about 26 days 6 hours. In latitude 40 degrees it has been found to average about 27 days 12 hours, nearly 31 days for latitude 60 degrees, and about 34 days in polar regions. From this it will be seen that the sun's surface must be far from solid.

This surface is known as the photosphere, or sphere of light, and consists of incandescent clouds floating in a less luminous but fiery atmosphere. It is intensely brilliant owing to the very high temperature, amounting to between 5,500 and 6,000 degrees Centigrade ; the most brilliant electric light appears black by comparison when projected against the sun's photosphere. Observed through a powerful telescope this is seen to be covered with still more intensely bright patches resembling luminous granules, which are usually about 500 miles in length. They are in places assembled together in long streaks known as filaments and resembling willow leaves ; actually they are incandescent cloud formations produced by metals in a state of vapour, changing rapidly in shape and position.

Sun Spots. The sun's surface is mottled with very bright streaks and patches called *faculae* : these are less apparent toward the centre of the disk, but very much in evidence around what are known as sun spots (*see* page 245). These, the most interesting objects on the solar surface, are actually storm centres and cyclones of incandescent vapours. They vary greatly in diameter, from less than 500 miles to occasionally 50,000 miles ; obviously the whole earth could be lost in one of these storm areas. They appear and sometimes disappear in a few days ; others persist for months—on one occasion, in 1840–1841, for eighteen months. It is partly by these persistent sun spots that the sun's rotation in various latitudes has been so accurately measured.

In appearance, sun spots consist of a relatively dark central part, called the nucleus, surrounded by a border relatively less dark, but it should be mentioned that actually these apparently dark areas are brighter than almost any illuminant we can produce on earth. The sun has to be artificially darkened both for observation and photography. The shaded area surrounding a group of spots, which is the disturbed storm area, is sometimes as much as 150,000 miles across. These spots, which are solar storms or cyclones, can be seen to develop by a gathering of brilliant faculae ; then small dark spots appear ; these rapidly develop, coalesce, and the brilliant granules become changed into filaments and converge inwards towards the centre, and take on a more or less rotary movement. This is the cyclonic motion, which is usually concentrated in two leading spots, one following the other, while a train of spotlets follow on. Speeds of a thousand miles an hour are often witnessed, and the changes are considerable, even in half an hour, although these terrific cyclones may persist for weeks.

Sun spots show that the sun has a stormy period followed by a quiescent one. For it was discovered by Schwabe of Dessau in 1843 that the spots periodically increased and then decreased over a period of between 11 and 12 years from maximum to maximum. The last occurred in 1938–1939, and the next is expected in 1949. Usually minima occur four years preceding the maxima, but the last were in 1933 and the next are due about 1944. Then all spots may vanish for weeks or longer. When they reappear these solar storms begin in high latitudes, and in the course of the next three or four years they increase towards the equator, and at the time of maximum as many as a hundred may be seen stretching across the equatorial belt of the sun.

Above the photosphere of the sun is another atmosphere, called the chromosphere, which is composed mainly of flaming calcium, hydrogen, and helium vapour, extending above the photosphere to a height of between 10,000 and 12,000 miles and in eruptive outbursts for hundreds of thousands of miles. This is the region of scarlet light, hence its name chromosphere, or sphere of colour. Hydrogen predominates in the higher levels of this fiery atmosphere. The lower portion is known as the reversing layer because, when at the moment of totality during an eclipse of the sun a spectroscope is analysing its light, a transformation takes place. All the dark lines which normally are in the solar spectrum suddenly flash out in brilliant colour against the dark background which has replaced the normal spectrum band. This reversing layer is a region of denser atmosphere than the chromosphere, extending probably not more than 500 miles above the photosphere. The spectral lines show it to be composed of the vapours of numerous elements.

Among the most important elements discovered in the sun are silver, tin, lead, sodium, potassium, silicon, zinc, magnesium, iron, aluminium, nickel, oxygen, titanium, manganese, chromium, cobalt, zirconium, vanadium, cerium, neodymium, lanthanum, scandium, carbon, yttrium, strontium, barium, gallium, lithium, copper and many others, including the calcium, helium and hydrogen present in the higher atmospheric layers. Altogether over 40 elements are known to be present in the sun.

Eclipses. We have seen that much may be learnt about the sun when the human eye is supplemented by certain instruments. Much more may be discovered during an eclipse, total or partial, when the moon's dark body is interposed between the earth and the sun, so that a greater or lesser portion of the latter is hidden from our world (*see* illus: in page 245).

If the earth, sun and moon moved in the same plane, then it is obvious there would be an eclipse whenever the three were in a straight line. As it is, however, the moon moves in an orbit inclined at an angle of a little more than five degrees to the plane of the sun's path, or the ecliptic as it is called, and so there can only be an eclipse when the three bodies are approximately in a straight line at the moment when the moon crosses the plane of the ecliptic. The points where the moon crosses the ecliptic are called nodes, and there is an eclipse of the sun each time the new moon happens to be at one of these nodes.

Partial eclipses take place when the new moon is not quite at the node. Annular eclipses are observed when the moon is too far from the earth to hide the sun completely. (The distance of the moon from the earth varies from 221,614 miles to 252,972 miles.)

Total eclipses of the sun are eagerly looked forward to by astronomers, but unfortunately they are of but short duration, lasting only from one second up to 6½ minutes. In the latter case the shadow band cast by the moon covers a belt 167 miles wide and sweeps across the earth from west to east with great rapidity. Total eclipse is only visible from places swept by the shadow, but beyond the belt, for a distance reaching to as much as 2,000 miles, the sun is seen in a state of partial eclipse.

Rare Total Eclipses. There must be at least two solar eclipses in a year. There may be five. Total eclipses are much rarer for any given place than partial eclipses. The last observable in London was in 1715, and the next visible from London will not take place until June 4, 2151. England was in the shadow zone of a total eclipse on June 29, 1927; and will be so again on August 11, 1999, when in Devon and Cornwall the shadow will last for two minutes. On June 30, 1954, however, two minutes of totality may be observed in the northern Shetlands.

On the all too short occasions when the sun has been completely eclipsed some remarkable scientific discoveries have been made. The corona and prominences which puzzled the observers of the 1706 and 1715 eclipses were proved by the Spanish eclipse of 1860 to be definitely solar. During the total eclipse of 1868 the spectroscope was applied to the prominences, with the result

that these were proved to consist of glowing gases, one of which was hydrogen; and a bright yellow line in their spectrum was found by Sir Norman Lockyer to belong to a different element, to which the name of helium was given. It was not until 189- that this element was found by Sir William Ramsay to exist also on the earth. The- the eclipse of May 29, 1919, provided an opportunity for testing Einstein's prediction based wholly on theoretical reasoning, that light is subjected to deflection by gravity.

Two parties of observers left England one going to North Brazil and one to Principe Island off the African coast, and in both cases the observations tended to confirm the Einsteinian theory.

The Corona. During a total eclipse the solar prominences—great tongues of vivid flame rising sometimes to a height of 400,000 miles above the sun's surface, with a velocity of 250 miles a second—may be clearly observed (*see* Colour Plate facing page 264). The corona, too, appears there most clearly as a halo of light extending into outer space for two or three times the diameter of the sun. Through the spectroscope, it is revealed as consisting of glowing gas of an extreme tenuosity, now called coronium.

During the total solar eclipse of June 8, 1937, the existence of a hitherto unknown 'halo,' or globular corona, extending beyond the visible corona and streamers was said to have been revealed by photographs taken from a flying-boat, 25,000 feet above Peru, by a member of the Hayden Planetarium-Grace Eclipse Expedition. This globular atmosphere, calculated to be more than 1,000,000 miles in depth, enveloped the whole sun.

Sun spot phenomena are often followed by electrical disturbances and violent magnetic storms on earth, due apparently to electro-magnetic radiations from the sun spot regions. A twenty-seven-day recurrence of magnetic disturbances has been frequently noted, corresponding to the time taken by the sun in its rotation; and it has also been observed that magnetic storms increase and decrease in correspondence with the eleven-year cycle of sun spots.

Solar Energy. Light and heat are the most obvious forms of solar energy, without which the earth would be a sterile globe with a temperature approaching absolute zero—a globe on which not only water but even the air would be frozen solid. The quantity of heat which the earth receives from the sun in a year is sufficient to melt a heet of ice 200 feet thick over its whole surface. Every square foot receives annually enough energy from the sun to raise a weight of 100 tons to the height of a mile.

According to Sir James Jeans, the sun is losing weight through radiation at a rate of about 250 million tons a minute. ' It is a wasting structure,' he writes (' The Mysterious Universe '), ' gradually disappearing before our eyes ; it is melting away like an iceberg in the Gulf Stream '— although he comfortingly adds that it will require millions of millions of years for the sun to lose the greater part of its weight.

As regards the source of this colossal display of solar energy, most astronomers today seem to find it in the annihilation of matter. To quote Sir James Jeans again— this time from 'The Universe Around Us' :

According to this hypothesis all the energy which makes life possible on earth, the light and heat which keep the earth warm and grow our food, and the stored up sunlight in the coal and wood we burn, if traced far enough back, are found to originate out of the annihilation of electrons and protons in the sun. The sun is destroying its substance in order that we may live, or, perhaps we should rather say,

with the consequence that we are able to live. The atoms in the sun and stars are, in effect, bottles of energy, each capable of being broken and having its energy spilled throughout the universe in the form of light and heat. Most of the atoms with which the sun and stars started their lives have already met this fate ; the remainder are doubtless destined to meet it in time. Scientific writers of half a century ago delighted in the picturesque description of coal as ' bottled sunshine ' ; they asked us to think of the sunshine as being bottled up as it fell on the vegetation of the primeval jungle, and stored for use in our fireplaces after millions of years. On the modern view we must think of it as re-bottled sunshine, or rather re-bottled energy. The first bottling took place millions of millions of years ago, before either sun or earth was in being, when the energy was first penned up in protons and electrons. Instead of thinking prosaically of our sun as a mere collection of atoms, let us think of it for a moment as a vast storehouse of bottles of energy which have already lain in storage for millions of millions of years. So enormous is the sun's supply of these bottles, and so great the amount of energy stored in each that, even after radiating light and heat for 7 or 8 million-million years, it still has enough left to provide light and heat for millions of millions of years yet to come.

LESSON FIVE

Finding the Sun's Distance

ALL celestial distances are based upon one measured standard known as the astronomical unit. This consists of the distance of the sun from the earth, the sun being the most important star for us and the earth the most important world to us ; their distance apart has therefore been made the all-important ' foot-rule,' so to speak, of astronomical measurements.

Once the distance of the sun is known it becomes possible not only to determine the relative distances of all other celestial objects but also their relative sizes. Their size or volume follows owing to the fact that the *absolute magnitude* of a body is arrived at, by calculation, from its observed *apparent magnitude* at a certain distance. This distance, if known, plus certain other considerations involved in the body's appearance, enables its absolute or real magnitude to be calculated, with a very close approximation to the actual size, even of remote stars. The veracity of the method has been proved in certain instances by interferometer measurements (*see* page 308).

It will be realized, therefore, how essential

it is that the accuracy of the sun's distance be known, for an accurate conception of the magnitude of the whole heavens depends upon it. So for centuries astronomers have endeavoured to measure, by various means, the space between earth and sun.

It was evident from the first that trigonometry and geometrical methods offered the best prospect of a solution. But the earth provides a base line of not more than 7,927 miles. This is not sufficient to reveal with any degree of accuracy the sun's parallax, or apparent shift in the sky, when viewed simultaneously from opposite sides of the earth.

However, the famous astronomer Halley (1656-1742) pointed out in 1716 the possibility and advantages of using Venus, when in transit across the sun's disk, for finding the parallax of the sun and therefore its distance. These transits are very rare, but two occurred, one in 1761 and the other in 1769, when great efforts were made and world-wide expeditions fitted up.

The transit of 1761 was not very successful, but the 1769 transit of Venus, made famous by Captain Cook's expedition to Otaheite in the far Pacific for the purpose of obtaining expert observations from that remote spot, was generally a success. A great deal of valuable data was collected from the various world-wide expeditions, but it was very involved and precise photographs were naturally absent, so that it was not until the year 1824 that the data were all finally reduced by Encke to a definite determination, by computing the average distance of the sun to be 95,000,000 miles.

This value remained the universally adopted standard for half a century, until in 1874, and again in 1882, two more transits of Venus occurred, and again still more elaborate expeditions went to far-off regions for observations, this time with photography as an aid. Doubts had arisen as regards the accuracy of Encke's determination of 95,000,000 miles, and it became evident that this was too great. In the meantime other methods and sources for finding the solar parallax had been discovered, as follows :—

1. By geometrical methods of direct angular measurement of the parallax of Mars, or preferably some asteroids which approach much nearer to the earth than does the sun, and which are presented as sharply defined points of light, and therefore admirably suited for fine measurement.
2. By gravitational perturbations which follow from Newton's famous Law (*see* page 249), in particular those based on the parallax variations in the moon's motion.
3. By the velocity of light.

The general averages of all these methods are in very close accord and reveal a parallax of 8″ 80 (seconds of arc) as the mean apparent shift of the sun. This corresponds to an average distance of 92,900,000 miles, and has been adopted by international agreement since 1900 and in the Nautical Almanac for nearly half a century.

The distance of 92,874,000 miles obtained as the result of Sir David Gill's parallax of 8″ 802 derived from observation of the asteroids Victoria, Iris and Sappho, in the year 1889, was the nearest to this ultimately accepted value.

Then came the discovery of Eros in 1898, and its near approach to the earth in 1900–1901 provided an ideal opportunity. The visual observations by Hinks gave an average for the sun's parallax as 8″ 806. Thus the possibility of improving on the accepted value of the sun's distance became apparent, but the investigation had to be postponed.

In 1931 Eros approached to as near as 16,200,000 miles of the earth, less than half

the nearest approach of Mars and much nearer than any other asteroid had previously been known to do. This was an exceptional opportunity, so in the mean time Sir H. Spencer Jones, the Astronomer Royal, organized a world-wide cooperation with 25 of the leading observatories in widely separated areas in each continent In these areas 32 of the largest and best equipped telescopes were to be concentrated upon Eros, more particularly when it reached its best position between the nights of Jan. 27 and Feb. 5, 1931.

Very precise measurements were obtained of its parallax, or apparent shift in position relative to adjacent stars which, on account of their very much greater distance, appear fixed. The procedure was to photograph the field of view at the same time from widely separated places on the earth, and, or alternatively, from the same observatory but at widely separated times of the night as near 12 hours apart as possible. By these means the longest possible base lines were secured for obtaining the parallax of Eros

Several thousands of photographs were taken in which Eros appeared as a dot ; but when the various photographs are compared each dot is in a slightly different position relative to the other dots which represent distant stars. Either nearly 8,000 miles or at least 12 hours in time will have intervened Eros, however, may appear as a short trail or as a succession of dots due to repeated exposures at intervals while it travels ; this is sometimes done to neutralize possibilities of error which might result from peculiarities in the shape of Eros.

Some idea of this may be obtained by inferring that Eros presents something of a dumb-bell shape, for it has appeared elongated and, as described by Van den Bos and Finsen of the Union Observatory, Johannesburg, it resembles a figure-of-eight. Now, as this rotates boomerang fashion, once in every period of 5 hours, 17 minutes, there occurs not only a change of brightness to a minimum at intervals of about 2 hours 38 minutes, but an apparent change of position results which might affect the parallax.

Once taken, all these photographs entailed many years of study and computation to reduce them to their true value by comparison. The mass of evidence had to be analysed, measured and correlated, one observatory's work with another, times corrected and errors eliminated as far as possible, and discrepancies accounted for ; this was the work of several years from 1931.

Ultimately the exact positions of Eros relative to the earth at various times were obtained, and so the orbit of Eros could be constructed mathematically with great precision. This was the essential thing, and the goal was reached for calculating the sun's distance therefrom with equal precision.

Now if the orbit of Eros was a perfect circle with the sun in the centre, this would be a very simple matter, but its orbit is an ellipse, with considerable eccentricity, and it has two foci, or centres. However, if the size and shape of the ellipse are accurately known, then it becomes easy for a mathematician to find the sun's distance, simply because the sun is always at one of the foci. If the student refers back to page 239, and consults the three famous Keplerian Laws governing ellipses, this will be seen stated and made clear.

The third of these Laws, generally known as the ' Harmonic Law,' states that ' the square of the time in which each planet completes its orbit is *proportional* to the cube of its mean distance from the sun.' It will be noted that the word proportional has been italicized, because proportional is not sufficient without a precise example by which to measure the proportion. One planet might be twice the distance of another, but twice ' what ? ' is the problem. Eros has provided the precise example. Its elliptical orbit, because of its close approach to the earth, has become known in shape, size and period to within a few seconds ; therefore the position of the sun in the foci of that ellipse could be known to within 9,000 miles at the most.

So now we have a still more accurate measurement of the sun's distance and therefore of everything else in the heavens ; present accepted values will need minor corrections when the new value is adopted internationally for the astronomical unit. This remains to be done, and until this celestial ' foot-rule ' of 93,005,000 miles is accepted as final, the old standard of 92,900,000 miles will continue to be used.

LESSON SIX

The Sun's Family of Worlds

THE student will hardly need to be told that we live on a world that is but one of many that travel round the sun. These, together with their moons and satellites, numerous comets and innumerable meteoric bodies, are all assembled like a celestial archipelago in a vast ocean of space, and situated at an enormous distance from the stars and their systems.

This assemblage constitutes the solar system, and is in reality the sun's family. It may be divided into four distinct classes—planets, satellites, periodic comets and meteoric bodies. The planets consist of major planets, of which there are nine, and minor planets, of which there are about 1,200 already known, while more are discovered every year.

Nine Major Planets. The major planets in order outwards from the sun are : Mercury, Venus, Earth, Mars, Jupiter, Saturn, Uranus, Neptune, and Pluto, discovered in 1930. The minor planets occupy the wide space between Mars and Jupiter, a few of their orbits extending to beyond that of Jupiter and within close proximity to the orbit of the earth. None of the minor planets possesses satellites, nor does Mercury, Venus or Pluto of the major planets.

Of the others, the earth has one, the moon ; Mars two ; Jupiter eleven ; Saturn nine ; Uranus four, and Neptune one.

All the planets travel round the sun in elliptical orbits and in a direction contrary to that of the hands of a clock, Mercury travelling fastest and Pluto slowest, their speed being in proportion to their distance, in exact accordance with the laws of Kepler. But the ellipticity of their orbits varies considerably, the orbits of Venus and Neptune being almost circular, whereas those of Mercury, Mars and Pluto are relatively very elliptical, or eccentric, as it is called—the eccentricity of Pluto's orbit is so great that it is an oval almost twice as long as it is broad ; consequently there are great differences in the speeds at which these planets travel in different parts of their orbits round the sun. This is in accordance with Kepler's second law.

The satellites also travel in ellipses round their respective planets, and these likewise vary in eccentricity and speed ; it is the rule for the satellites also to move in an anti-clockwise direction, like the planets. There are, however, a few exceptions due to special causes. The orbits of the periodic comets and meteors are in many cases of such great eccentricity that their length is many times greater than their breadth.

So immense is the sun, the central orb of the system, that it outweighs all the planets put together over 700 times ; it is this massiveness, or great weight of material described as mass, which provides the gravitational pull that keeps the planets in their observed orbits. The sun possesses 9,000,000 times the mass of Mercury, 403,490 times that of Venus, 329,390 times that of the earth, 3,093,500 times that of Mars, 1,047 times that of Jupiter, 3,502 times that of Saturn, 22,869 times that of Uranus, and 19,314 times that of Neptune.

When we come to consider the comparative diameters of the planets in relation to that of the sun the differences are seen to be also very great, for the sun has a mean diameter of 864,000 miles. The mean diameters of the major planets can be seen for comparison from the first column in the accompanying table.

THE MAJOR PLANETS

Planet	Diameter in miles	Mass (Earth = 1)	Mean solar distance in millions of miles	Periodical time in years
Mercury	3,030	0·037	36·0	0·24
Venus ..	7,700	0·826	67·2	0·62
Earth ..	7,927	1·0	93·0	1·00
Mars ..	4,230	0·108	141·5	1·88
Jupiter..	85,750	318·4	483·3	11·86
Saturn ..	73,000	95·2	886·1	29·46
Uranus..	31,900	14·6	1,783	84·02
Neptune	33,000	17·3	2,793	164·79
Pluto ..	4,000	?	3,666	247·70

Now, when their mass is considered, a surprising state of things is revealed. The earth is, in proportion to its size, very heavy ; it is, in fact, the densest of all the planets, and is, moreover, bulk for bulk, about four times heavier than the sun. That is, every average cubic foot of the earth is four times denser than every average cubic foot of the sun. A good idea of the relative densities of the sun and planets, that is, the average weight of the materials composing them as compared with their present size, or volume as it is called, may be obtained by comparing them with the density of water.

The earth is found to be 5·52 times as dense, Venus 5·21 times, Mars 3·94 times, Mercury 3·73 times ; these are all the heavy planets and the smallest, as can be seen from the table. They are the worlds which have parted with most of their original heat

by radiation, and are much more advanced in planetary evolution than the outer and greater planets, except, perhaps, Pluto.

The density of the other outer planets is similar to that of the sun, which is only 1·41 times that of water. Jupiter is 1·34 times; Uranus 1·36 times, and Neptune 1·32 times, while Saturn is, taken as a whole, lighter than water, being only about ·69 that of water. This low density of the great outer planets, although near to that of the sun, does not mean that they are in a similar condition to this very hot and radiant luminary, but that they are, like the sun, composed very largely of gases. The difference is that, whereas the sun's superficial gases are incandescent and at an enormous temperature, the superficial gases of these planets are for a considerable depth below freezing point, as indeed is known to be the case with the earth. The evidence, both telescopic and spectroscopic, indicates that these great outer planets have atmospheres of great depth ; they are always seen to be cloud-laden and so completely covered that it is probable that we never see any of the solid or liquid surfaces of either Jupiter, Saturn, Uranus or Neptune.

An interesting consequence of the size of the sun and the planets, considered together with their relative densities and mass, is the mean average surface gravity that results. This may be compared with that known at the surface of the earth and the extent estimated as to how much the same body would weigh, more or less, were it transferred to the surface of the sun or any one of the above planets. As might be expected, owing to its enormous mass, a body would weight about 27·89 times more at the sun's surface than it would at the surface of the earth ; only ·27, or little more than a quarter, on Mercury ; about ·85 on Venus ; and only ·38 on Mars. A pound weight would, therefore, amount to so many ounces if tested by a spring balance on either of these planets, although its size and mass would remain the same. We see that a pound weight would be transformed to nearly 28 pounds at the surface of the sun, notwithstanding its gaseous condition. On Jupiter it would average about 2·65 times as much as on earth, and on Saturn about 1·14, notwithstanding its immensity, while on Uranus a pound would weigh about the same as on earth, although its mass is 14·60 times greater. This apparent anomaly is explained by gravity, or weight, becoming less the farther the object is from the centre of the planet, in accordance with Newton's laws. In the case of Uranus, its surface is nearly four times farther from its centre than is the surface of the earth. On Neptune a pound would weigh exactly the same as on earth.

The student will see from all this that the weight of a body is the force with which the particular planet attracts it; the extent of this force depends upon the mass, or the amount of matter composing the planet, and also its density, for the force acts as if it were all concentrated at the centre of the planet. Consequently the farther a body, or, say, our pound weight, is from the centre of the planet, the less will be its weight as defined by Newton's law. Now while the mass of a planet is a fixed quantity, since it possesses so much material and no more, it is otherwise with the planet's density, for this depends upon the amount of

space which the aforesaid matter occupies, that is, the planet's volume, or size. Density, therefore, varies with time, place and circumstances. For instance, loss of heat by radiation will increase density.

It is mass which produces weight, but what that weight will be depends upon how far the planet's surface is from the centre of the mass ; and since this depends upon the planet's volume, we see why planets like Uranus and Neptune, which possess a much greater mass than the earth, exert no greater gravitational pull at their surfaces. This also partly accounts for bodies not weighing exactly the same at all parts of a planet's surface. It is always less at the equatorial regions as compared with the polar, one reason for this being that the polar areas are nearer to the planet's centre owing to the planet's oblateness.

LESSON SEVEN

The Moon and its Influence on Tides

AFTER the sun, the moon is the most important of the celestial bodies— at least, from our point of view. Our calendar is to a great extent based upon its phases, and the tides are largely due to lunar influence.

The moon, in effect, is a small world with a diameter of 2,160 miles, as compared with the earth's 7,927 miles. Its surface is only ·074 and its mass ·0123 of that of the earth. In other words, the earth possesses about 81½ times more material in its composition than does the moon. The latter's density is only about three-fifths that of the earth, or 3·34 times that of water.

The moon's volume or size is only ·0203, or about 1/49th, that of the earth. Hence it follows that gravity at its surface is only about one-sixth of what it is on our world. This leads to some curious results. For instance, an article six pounds in weight would, if weighed by a spring balance on the moon, weigh only one pound. A ball would travel six times higher on the moon than on the earth, if thrown with the same amount of energy ; and anyone who could jump five feet on the earth could jump over thirty feet on the moon.

The moon's distance from the centre of the earth varies between 252,710 miles when it is in apogee, or at its farthest, and 221,463 miles when it is in perigee, or at its nearest ; but, situated as we are on the earth's surface,

the moon really comes nearly 4,000 miles nearer. It is at its nearest when it is due south and high in the sky—just how near depends upon latitude. Its mean distance is 238,857 miles, or about 30 times the earth's diameter.

Lunar Phases. The moon takes, on an average, 27 days 7 hours 43 minutes to revolve round the earth. This is the sidereal month, which varies, however, sometimes as much as seven hours. Since the moon is travelling with the earth round the sun, it follows that the moon must travel a little farther each month in order to reach the same relative position with regard to the earth and the sun. Consequently, the average time from one full moon to another is 29 days 12 hours 44 minutes. This con-stitutes the synodic month, and this, too, varies sometimes by nearly 13 hours.

These lunar phases depend upon the place which the moon occupies with regard to the sun as seen from the earth. When the moon is between the earth and the sun, its dark side is turned to us and we say the moon is new. When the earth lies between the moon and the sun we see the moon fully illuminated. Every night the moon wears a different appearance, waxing through the first half of the month and waning through the next half.

If its orbit lay in the same plane as that of the earth it would pass directly between us and the sun once every month at the time of new moon and would then eclipse the sun. As a matter of fact, this does occasionally happen. Then, too, when the moon was full the earth would lie in a straight line between it and the sun, with the result that the earth's shadow would be cast upon the moon, depriving it of the sunlight. This also happens occasionally, i.e. we have a lunar eclipse (*see* illus. p. 247).

The moon's orbit does not lie in the same plane as that of the earth, but is inclined at an angle of 5° 8½′ (i.e. about ten times the moon's apparent diameter—about half a degree). Consequently the moon, when passing between the earth and the sun, is usually a little above or below the latter, and there is no eclipse. Hence in some years there may be no lunar eclipse, e.g. 1944 ; but usually there are two, and even three.

From the computed motions of the earth and moon, we find that the relative positions of these bodies in regard to the sun repeat themselves with great exactness after a period of about 18 years 11 days, causing a recurrence of eclipses. This cycle period, known as the Saros, was observed by the Chaldeans, who were thus enabled to predict coming eclipses. It applies to both solar and lunar eclipses.

There is a great difference between eclipses of the sun, which are described in Lesson 4 (page 251), and those of the moon, for the moon is obscured only by the shadow of the earth—not by an opaque body, as is the case in a solar eclipse. Consequently, the moon never quite vanishes, even at a so-called total eclipse. This is because a certain amount of the solar light that penetrates the earth's encircling atmosphere gets refracted on to the moon, thus dimly illuminating its surface. Were we on the moon, we should see a brilliant ring of light encircling the great dark disk of the earth, the earth's disk seen from the moon appearing nearly four times wider than the moon appears to us.

Lunar Influence on the Tides. While the earth pulls the moon continually towards itself, the moon also pulls the earth towards its surface. The extent of this pull is somewhat less than the radius of the earth, and it results in the earth performing a small monthly orbit, with a diameter of about 5,760 miles, relative to the moon, in addition to its other motions. This orbital motion is not visually perceptible to us, as the earth as a whole is lifted toward the moon. The oceans of the world, on the other hand, being fluid, are free to move, and become

piled up on that side of the earth which, at the moment in question, is facing the moon. At the same time the solid body of the earth is pulled away from the waters at the opposite side of its sphere, so the water there seems to us as if it, too, were heaped up. Thus we have two simultaneous high tides culminating in two areas of the earth, immediately beneath the moon, as it were, and in direct line with it ; but owing to the inequalities of the earth's surface, continents, channels, ocean currents and the influence of winds, together with minor influences (to say nothing of the sun's tide-raising force, which twice every month acts at right angles to that of the moon), we get high tides that are by no means in direct line with the moon. Moreover, low tides—which theoretically should occur at places 90° east and west of the high-tide line—are similarly complicated and the low water delayed. In some places, e.g. Southampton, where the tide water enters by two channels, four high tides may occur in a day instead of the two actually engendered by the moon.

If the earth did not rotate and the moon were fixed, the water would remain permanently high at one set of places and permanently low in another ; but as the earth rotates in 24 hours the tide-wave sweeps round the earth in the wake of the moon. As the moon, however, in the course of a day has travelled farther round in its orbit, high-water occurs about 24 hours 51 minutes after its predecessor, and successive high tides occur at intervals of nearly 12½ hours. Thus it is that tides get later every day.

Since the sun also exerts a tide-raising force (about two-fifths of that of the moon),

SPRING TIDES　　　　NEAP TIDES

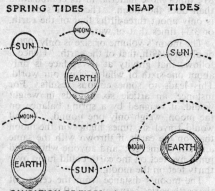

CAUSATION OF TIDES. As the earth rotates on its axis, its waters are piled up on the side facing the moon, and at the same time it is pulled away from the waters on the opposite side of the globe.

it happens that twice a month, when the moon is full and new, the sun and moon are nearly in line, with the result that the solar pull is added to the lunar. Then we have extra high tides, or spring tides as they are called. If these occur when the moon is near perigee we get extra high spring tides. When the sun and moon lie at right angles to one another with regard to the earth, and the moon is in its first or last quarter, their tidal forces are opposed—with the result that we have moderate or neap tides. Allowing for all these factors, the average height of a spring tide may be regarded as rather more than double that of a neap tide at any particular place. In the open ocean the average range of the tides is only about 2½ feet, but in shallow waters and narrowing channels, bays and gulfs, it is greatly increased, sometimes to 40 and 50 feet.

One interesting effect of the tides has been to act as a brake upon the rotation of the earth, and so to lengthen the day. In the early days of the earth this braking effect was much greater than at present, and Sir George Darwin has shown that tidal friction has had the effect of lengthening the day from about three hours to twenty-four.

LESSON EIGHT

Is the Moon a Dead World?

WE have now to consider the moon as it appears to us—its surface, scenery and conditions—in the light of all that has been discovered telescopically. To the naked eye certain distinct markings are perceptible, which are successively lit up as the sunlight extends across the moon's face from the thin crescent phase to full. The darker parts were in the early days of telescopic observation regarded as seas. They were named as indicated by the following letters in the photograph in page 246 (*mare* = Latin, sea): B, Mare Nubium ; C, Mare Nectaris ; D, Mare Fecunditatis ; E, Mare Tranquillitatis ; G, Mare Vaporum ; J, Oceanus Procellarum ; K, Mare Crisium ; L, Mare Serenitatis ; O, Mare Imbrium. All these may once have been watery wastes on this side of the moon, but not for long ages. There are many indications, such as cliffs, bays, and a relatively smooth and less broken surface, which suggest the action of water, or molten matter, long ago. If water was present it has long been absorbed by the rocks as the body of the moon cooled.

All these features are easily discerned with binoculars or good sight. Moreover, during the progress of the phases it will be seen that the line dividing the bright from the dark part of the lunar disk is uneven, and that its details change from evening to evening, at times resembling the profile of a human face. This dividing line between night and day on the moon is known as the terminator. When the phases are progressing from new moon to full it represents the region where the sun is rising, but when the phases are passing from full moon to new the terminator represents the region of sunset. The horns, or cusps, of the crescent are always facing away from the sun, and a straight line joining their tips is always at right angles to a line from the moon to the sun. The smooth edge or circumference of the moon's disk is known as the *limb*.

Since the familiar details on the moon's disk are seen to be always there, it is obvious that we never see the other side. That is because the moon rotates on its axis in precisely the same time that it takes to revolve round the earth ; this is the moon's sidereal day, which lasts for nearly 27¼ of our days. The moon consequently always presents almost exactly the same face, but owing to libration (that is, a certain oscillation of our satellite relative to the earth), and to the fact that we are on occasions, such as rising and setting, able to see a little farther round the edge, as it were, of the moon, altogether about 59% of the surface is observed.

If the moon be observed with binoculars, or field-glasses, the serrated edge of the terminator between the night and day regions is at once obvious. Bright portions will be seen to project into the dark area and sometimes be observed detached from the bright area ; these are the lofty eminences, the mountain ranges and high crater walls lit up first by the rising sun. They will be seen in the course of a few hours to merge into the rest of the sunlit portion, and then others will appear ; thus it becomes possible with little magnification to perceive the larger craters and ranges.

The chief lunar mountain ranges attain great heights ; these can be measured with great accuracy by means of the shadows they cast. The following is a list of the chief of these ranges, together with the heights they attain in feet : Alps, 14,000 feet, and Apennines, 18,000–21,000 feet, shown at R and M respectively, in the photograph in p. 246. Altai, 13,000 feet ; Caucasus, 18,500 feet ; Pyrenees, 12,000 feet ; Doerfel Mountains, 26,000 feet ; Leibnitz Mountains, 30,000 feet ; Mount Taurus, 10,000 feet.

The photograph in page 246 of the northern section also shows the Apennines and the Caucasus, as well as some of the craters.

The Moon's Craters. The most notable features are, however, the craters and the so-called walled plains. Many of these are perceptible with binoculars if observed when near the terminator dividing line, for there long shadows are cast by the sun, which is rising or setting over that area.

The lunar craters may vary in size from a mile or less in diameter to 50 or 60 miles, the small craterlets often encircling the larger ones and forming a very striking feature of their terraced walls. The crater of Copernicus (marked H in the photograph), which may be taken as typical, is 56 miles in diameter, so it would occupy all the space between, say, London and Eastbourne, or York and Manchester. The terraces rise to peaks which reach a height of 13,500 feet and average about 11,000 feet above the bottom of the crater. In the centre of the floor rises a six-headed central mountain to a height of about 2,400 feet.

These central peaks are a feature of the craters, being generally present. They would appear to be the remains of a central cone of eruption, but there are still some diverse opinions among experts as to how these craters came to be formed, since some have ascribed to them a meteoric origin instead of a volcanic, as in the case of terrestrial volcanoes, the craters of which never exceed seven miles across. The moon having no appreciable atmosphere, its surface would, therefore, be much exposed to meteoric bombardment, and it has been claimed that huge meteors, striking the semi-plastic crust of the moon long ages ago, would have produced just this effect. This theory is, however, fraught with some difficulties, so that, as a rule, the volcanic theory of their origin is most generally accepted.

As regards the enormous walled plains, these are more difficult to explain upon the volcanic theory, particularly since the central peaks are usually absent. Instead, a vast level plain generally studded with craterlets exists, while a more or less circular range of distant mountains forms a remarkable ring, which may be over 100 miles in diameter, and is composed of lofty peaks and numerous craters, which form a circle, as in the case of Clavius. This has a diameter of 142 miles, with an encircling wall of mountains reaching to a height of 17,300 feet and including many minor craters. Plato, shown at Q in the photograph in p. 246, is another of these walled plains. It resembles a vast crater that has enclosed, in the distant past, a lake of lava 2,700 square miles in extent. The terraced mountains attain a height of 9,000 feet.

Tycho, shown at A, is by far the most striking of all the hundreds of craters present, particularly at full moon. The remarkable series of bright rays or streaks that will be observed extending for many hundreds of miles in every direction constitutes a singular formation that is best seen then. They pass across valleys and mountains, craters and rifts, at an average width of about five miles, and remain one of the mysteries of the moon. Tycho itself is a superb crater 54 miles in diameter and 17,000 feet deep ; from this floor rises a central mountain to a height between 5,000 and 6,000 feet.

Lunar 'Seas.' Numerous craters and other formations are partially broken down, particularly round the so-called seas, or *maria*, as if these had been seas of molten lava that had melted them, or water had been capable of washing away their walls. Other features are deep clefts that extend for hundreds of miles, and also deep valleys called rills ; but everywhere are ruin and desolation. It is certain that the moon is a dead world with no perceptible atmosphere. Such air and water as the moon may once have possessed must have been absorbed into its substance, or have flown away into space ; therefore its surface must undergo extremes of heat and cold far beyond anything experienced on earth, attaining a midday temperature of about 280 degrees Fahrenheit and a night temperature of about 140 degrees below zero. In some deep craters and clefts, sheltered from such extremes of temperature, lowly forms of life have been suspected to exist, the evidence being changes of colouring.

The moon is now regarded as an immense fragment of the earth that became detached through tidal strain when they were both molten ; it is, therefore, probably composed of materials similar to the earth's.

Mercury, the Planet Nearest the Sun

O F all the five planets known since ancient times, Mercury is the one most rarely seen in these latitudes. Owing to its proximity to the sun, it never appears more than from 18 to 28 degrees east or west of the latter, and in consequence has always to be observed against a twilight sky and at a low altitude, where the mists and cloud near the horizon often obscure it. Many people, therefore, never see Mercury, although it is oftentimes quite easy to observe if its locality is known. It shines as a bright first-magnitude star with a slight golden hue, and always appears either as an 'evening star,' east of the sun, or as a 'morning star,' west of the sun. The ancients regarded these two apparitions of the planet as different objects, the 'morning star' being known as Apollo. It never appears at night.

Mercury is best seen in the evening in March or April, between one and two hours after sunset ; or in the morning, between one and two hours before sunrise, in September or October.

It is usually easier to find Mercury when the crescent moon, Venus, or Jupiter appears in the vicinity, as they become guiding objects to the less obvious Mercury. These occasions, together with planetary phenomena in general, may be found by consulting the Nautical Almanac or astronomical columns of the Press.

Orbital Eccentricity. Mercury on favourable occasions approaches the earth to within 50,000,000 miles, but on others it will not come nearer than 65,000,000 miles. This is because of the great eccentricity of its orbit—0.206 : at aphelion it is 43,350,000 miles from the sun, but only 28,550,000 miles at perihelion. This subjects Mercury to great variations of solar heat and light, since the sun's disk, which at aphelion appears over twice the width that it appears to us, will appear three-and-a-half times the width at Mercury's perihelion (*see* illus. in page 247).

Another consequence of the great eccentricity of Mercury's orbit is that the speed at which it travels varies from about 24 miles a second when at aphelion to about 36 miles a second at perihelion. This latter, by the way, is just twice the speed of the earth—which is about 18 miles a second on an average.

Mercury takes only 88 days to complete its journey round the sun, or sidereal period, but it takes 116 days (synodic period) to come back to the same relative position to the earth and sun. The plane of its orbit is inclined at an angle of 7 degrees to the ecliptic or the plane of the earth's orbit ; this is more than the inclination of any other major planet's orbit, except that of Pluto. Being very much less in evidence than the brilliant Venus, the motions of Mercury are not obvious, but the orbits of Mercury and Venus are within that of the earth (*see* illus. in page 247).

Both Mercury and Venus present all the phases of the moon, although these differ in detail. When the planet is approximately between the earth and the sun its unilluminated side is presented toward us, and although it is then at its nearest we do not see it.

Visibility. When either Mercury or Venus is placed between us and the sun it is said, at the moment when either planet is exactly north or south of that luminary, to be in *inferior conjunction* with the sun. When, on the other hand, either Mercury or Venus passes beyond the sun, whether above, below or behind the solar disk, it is said to be in *superior conjunction*. It is then that they present a full disk (which, however, the brilliance of the sun obscures) and, moreover, are at their greatest distance from the earth. For Mercury this may amount to about 136,000,000 miles.

We see Mercury and Venus when they appear to swing left or right—that is, east or west of the sun. If, when they are beginning to be visible as ' evening stars' (though they are not actually stars), they are observed through a telescope, they will appear small, almost circular, and near the sun. In the course of a few days in the case of Mercury, or a few weeks in the case of Venus, they will appear to travel eastward away from the sun, become larger (or to the naked eye, brighter) and gradually assume the shape of a half-moon—*quadrature*, it is called. They will then be near the extremity of their eastern swing or *elongation*. Next the crescent phases supervene, the planet appearing to grow larger until, when about midway between quadrature and inferior conjunction, Mercury or Venus, as the case may be, arrives at its greatest brilliancy. Although the planet approaches still closer, the crescent will continue to grow thinner and less brilliant as it seems to get nearer to the sun and inferior conjunction.

When this occurs, it occasionally happens, if Mercury is near its node, that it comes directly between the earth and the sun ; then the planet appears as a small black disk in transit across the sun's disk. Transits of Mercury always occur on or near May 7 or November 9, which represent the two nodes of its orbit. The last took place on Nov. 11–12, 1940.

With a diameter of only 3,030 miles, not much more than one-third that of the earth, Mercury has a surface barely one-seventh as extensive. Owing to its proximity to the sun, observation of any details on its disk is difficult, but from time to time sufficient dark permanent markings have been noted to indicate that Mercury revolves but once in the course of a revolution round the sun. Consequently its days must be about 88 of our days in length ; and just as our moon always presents the same face to the earth, so Mercury has ever the same hemisphere facing the sun. There is no evidence of an atmosphere on the planet ; low *albedo*, or light reflection—0.07—suggests that its light is reflected from a dark and broken solid surface, similar to that of the moon, and not from clouds. Moreover, the force of gravity on Mercury would be insufficient to enable it to retain atmosphere over a very long period of time.

Conditions on Mercury must, therefore, be vastly different from what we experience on the earth or even from those on the moon. For while the immense solar disk would, as seen from over the greater part of one hemisphere of Mercury, appear permanently in the sky, from the other the sun would never be seen, except possibly from the polar regions and a narrow belt, a hundred miles or so in width, bordering the dividing line between night and day. Over this latter region the sun would rise a little way above the horizon and then set again in the course of about 44 of our days. The frigid conditions of Mercury's night hemisphere must be intense, while its hemisphere of perpetual day would be hot enough to melt lead.

The existence of a world between Mercury and the sun—an intra-Mercurial planet— was for long conjectured, owing to a perceptible acceleration of Mercury in its orbit which could not be otherwise accounted for. This acceleration is known as the advance of Mercury's perihelion. Several times during the last century the discovery of such a planet was claimed, the most noteworthy being in 1859, when the supposed planet was named Vulcan. Its existence has never been established, however, and the advance of Mercury's perihelion has since been accounted for by Einstein's theory of General Relativity.

LESSON TEN

Venus, Sister Planet to the Earth

VENUS is the sister planet to the earth and the most brilliant and easily recognized of all the sun's family of planets. It is familiarly known as the 'evening star' when it appears in the western sky, and, alternatively, as the 'morning star,' when it is in the eastern sky. As in the case of Mercury, the ancient astronomers regarded its two appearances as separate luminaries ; the Greeks named them Hesperus and Phosphorus respectively.

Venus will remain for seven or eight months at a time the most striking object in the evening sky, shining with a pearly lustre far exceeding any other star or planet. Then it will vanish and reappear in less than a month in the morning sky, having in the interval passed between the earth and the sun. Venus passes through a complete series of phases as seen from the earth (p. 261). The planet takes about 584 days to complete a series from one inferior conjunction to another. This *synodic period*, as it is called, represents the time occupied by Venus after passing the earth at, say, inferior conjunction, until it again returns to a similar position relative to the earth and sun. The synodic period is exceptionally long because Venus is travelling at about 22 miles a second, whereas the earth travels at nearly 4 miles a second slower, and hence takes time to catch up to the synodic point of Venus.

Visibility and Brilliancy. It takes Venus 224.7 days to perform its revolution round the sun ; this is its 'sidereal period' and constitutes the length of the planet's year. Its distance from the sun averages 67,200,000 miles and varies to the extent of about 500,000 miles each way to aphelion and perihelion ; thus the orbit of Venus approaches to a circle than any other planet. It approaches the earth to within about 25,000,000 miles, and so comes nearer to us than any other world except the moon ; but on such occasions Venus is usually invisible, owing to the fact that, between us and the sun, its dark hemisphere is turned towards us. As in the case of Mercury, Venus is best observed when near eastern or western elongation, as then it appears to swing to its greatest angular distance from the sun, as seen from the earth, and sets between four and five hours after the sun. On these occasions it appears high in the south-west sky and is well placed for observation. Its greatest brilliancy is attained about five weeks later, when it appears as a broad crescent similar to that of the moon two days before the first quarter. In the early morning sky Venus attains greatest brilliancy about five weeks after inferior conjunction. So brilliant is it at these times that it will cast a distinct shadow on a dark moonless night and, if its position be known, can be seen in daylight while the sun is shining.

Size of Venus. The diameter of Venus is about 7,700 miles, as compared with the earth's equatorial diameter of 7,927 miles ; its surface is, therefore, nearly (0.95) as large as the earth's. It appears to be generally enveloped in clouds, whose great reflective power has the very high albedo of 0.60 —the degree of albedo being the proportion of light reflected of that which is received from the sun. This brilliance, while making Venus a splendid object visually, causes it to be disappointing telescopically, because so little detail is perceptible on its intensely luminous surface.

That it has a dense atmosphere is proved by the prolongation of the cusps of the crescent. Then, too, when Venus is about to transit across the sun's disk, a brilliant ring of refracted light is seen to surround the planet's black disk as it enters upon the sun. This is produced by the sunlight passing through the atmospheric envelope of the planet. Spectroscopic tests confirm the existence of this atmosphere, but it is difficult to decide its composition, as the lines in the Venus spectrum are involved with those of the spectra of the sun and earth. Moreover, since nearly all, or perhaps all, of the light from Venus is reflected from the lofty surfaces of the cloud envelope, spectroscopic evidence of what lies below must obviously be difficult to obtain. Expert investigation has found less than 0.1 per cent of oxygen in that part of the atmosphere of Venus that is above the clouds by comparison with that of the earth, and hence some authorities claim that Venus cannot possess any vegetation or higher forms of life. It should be borne in mind, however, that the higher layers of the earth's atmosphere would also give very little evidence of the oxygen present in the lower layers to, say, an investigator on Mars, if it were covered with clouds.

Is There Life on Venus ? Owing to its greater proximity to the sun, the latter appears nearly half as wide again as seen from Venus compared with the earth, while it pours down upon the planet about twice as much light and heat as it does upon our world. Moreover, the fact that heat has been found radiating from the dark night side of Venus suggests a fairly equable temperature maintained by a cloud-laden atmosphere of considerable density. An important addition to our knowledge of conditions on Venus was made in 1932, when at Mount Wilson Observatory Dr. W. S. Adams and Dr. Theodore Dunham discovered that there was sufficient carbon dioxide for the maintenance of vegetable life on Venus, and from this it might be inferred that animal life, too, may exist.

Such questions cannot be settled, however, until the period of the planet's rotation on its axis, i.e. the length of its day, has been decided. At present there are wide differences in the estimates put forward, as these include 23 hours, 20 minutes ; 68 hours ; and 224.7 *days*. The last is also the period of its rotation about the sun, and if it be correct, then the same hemisphere would be always facing the sun and life would be impossible over most of the planet.

More recently visual observation and spectroscopic evidence have been supplemented by photography by infra-red rays. These penetrate the brilliant white radiance of the cloud surface sufficiently to obtain more definite markings, and evidence has been obtained of rapid motion that would seem to be incompatible with the 225-day period. The confusing factor is the great tilt of the planet's axis, but, taking into account all that has so far been discovered, it seems likely that Venus rotates in a period amounting to between 24 and 30 of our days. These long days of Venus are theoretically what might be expected in a world which has through the ages been subject to much greater tidal retardation from the sun than has our world. The remarkable absence of polar flattening may be accounted for by the planet's slow rotation. Another line of speculation suggests that Venus is entirely covered by ocean. This seems to be in keeping with a planet devoid of vegetation, covered by cloud, and containing carbon dioxide in its atmosphere.

Transits. The transits of Venus, i.e. when the planet passes so exactly in between the earth and the sun that it is presented to terrestrial observation as a black disk—provided astronomers with a welcome opportunity of accurately measuring the earth's distance from the sun by means of a simple trigonometrical process. Two observers, A and B, stationed one at each end of a measured base line on the earth, see the disk of Venus projected on the sun at a and b. The length of the line joining a and b on the sun represents the parallax —in the case exceedingly small. As the exact length of the base line on the earth is known, it is possible to calculate how long it would appear as seen from the sun. Then, as the apparent sizes of objects are known to diminish in a certain ratio in proportion to their distance, it is a simple matter to calculate the distance in the case in point, i.e. the distance between the sun and the earth. It should be added that corrections have to be made for light and atmospheric effects. The astronomer, Edmund Halley, was the first to suggest this method in 1716, the results of which are described in pages 253–4.

Transits of Venus across the sun always occur on or about June 7 and December 8, and always come in pairs, e.g. the transit of June, 1761, and June, 1769. These were followed by the transits of December, 1874, and December, 1882. The latter was the last, and the next pair will not occur until June 8, 2004, and June 6, 2012. The transit of Venus was first observed by the English astronomer, Jeremiah Horrocks, in 1639.

LESSON 11

Astronomical Basis of the Calendar

WE have now to consider the third planet of the solar system, the earth —which is, as it were, the moving platform from which we observe all other celestial bodies. The student has learnt how, as the result of the earth's motion, the stars appear to move in one vast body from east to west, and complete the circuit of the heavens in nearly 24 hours ; this is the Apparent Diurnal Rotation of the heavens due to the earth's rotation. In addition, there is the Apparent Annual Rotation of the heavens due to the earth's revolution round the sun ; in this an additional rotation of the heavens occurs, so that they appear to rotate 366 times in 365 days. Then there are the apparent paths of the sun, moon and planets.

We now know that most of this movement is only as it appears from our point of view, that it is continually changing and highly involved owing to the motions of the celestial bodies themselves. There is, however, a general movement of the sun, moon and planets in addition to their apparent diurnal motion across the sky from east to west ; this is their apparent path through the heavens from west to east in the case of all except the inner planets, Mercury and Venus, which, as we have seen, exhibit motions due to perspective, peculiar to themselves. Nevertheless, they all, except Pluto, follow paths which are contained within a belt of the sky 18 degrees wide and 9 degrees each side of the ecliptic, which is the sun's apparent path.

Sections of the Zodiac. This belt or zone, known as the zodiac, is divided into twelve sections, each 30 degrees wide and constituting one of the signs of the zodiac. Each sign has a symbol and is named after a constellation—which, however, does not correspond to the area represented by the sign ; the reason for this will be explained later. The names of the signs from first to last are :

Aries (♈) Leo (♌) Sagittarius (♐)
Taurus (♉) Virgo (♍) Capricornus (♑)
Gemini (♊) Libra (♎) Aquarius (♒)
Cancer (♋) Scorpio (♏) Pisces (♓)

Each of these signs represents the arc of the heavens traversed by the sun in a twelfth part of the year. Beginning with the first

TOTAL ECLIPSE OF THE SUN

Based on a photograph taken at Giggleswick, Yorkshire, on June 29, 1927, the first obtained which showed the corona, this Plate also displays the solar prominences. Only a total eclipse enables these immense tongues of vivid flame to be directly photographed. One of them, viewed through the spectroscope, is seen on the other side of this Plate.

Courtesy of the Astronomer Royal, Greenwich Observatory

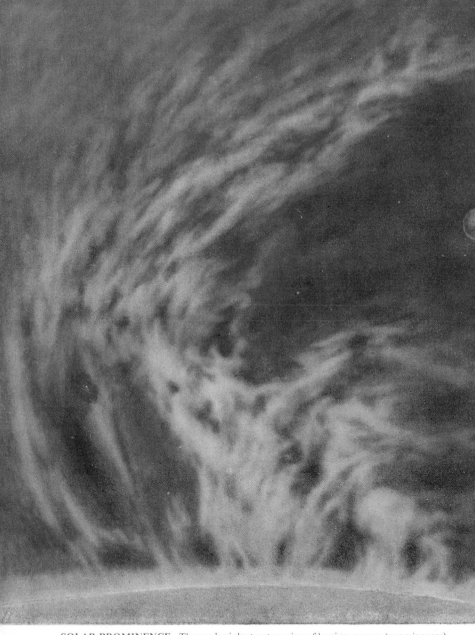

SOLAR PROMINENCE. The sun's violent outpouring of luminous gases (prominences) is well seen in this calcium prominence, 140,000 miles high, taken from a photograph through the spectroscope at two positions in the violet region. The small green sphere represents the earth on the same scale. *See also* preceding Plate.

Mount Wilson Observatory

point of Aries on March 21 (March 20 in leap years), the sun passes through the first three signs in spring ; the next three during summer, which begins on June 21, when the sun enters the sign of Cancer ; the next three signs are passed through during autumn, which begins when the sun enters the sign of Libra—usually on September 23 ; finally, the last three signs are passed through in winter, after the sun enters Capricornus on December 22. This apparent movement of the sun through the signs of the zodiac represents the earth's motion round the sun, together with the plane of the earth's orbit ; it is known as the tropical year, or year of the seasons, being 365 days 5 hours 48 minutes and 46 seconds in length. Since each successive year is nearly 6 hours longer than the normal year of 365 days, every fourth year (leap year) a day is added to the normal year to adjust it to the tropical year as represented by the sun.

This was the chief feature of the Julian calendar as ordained by Julius Caesar, in accordance with the plans of the astronomer Sosigenes of Alexandria, in 45 B.C., with the object of adjusting the extensive errors which had crept into the civil year, as compared with that represented by the sun. At the same time the beginning of the year was changed from March to January 1—an arrangement which was not in accord with the tropical year, which begins on March 21.

Pope Gregory's Calendar. The Gregorian calendar was introduced in A.D. 1582 further to adjust the calendar to the tropical year, since the Julian calendar had left 11 minutes 14 seconds to be disposed of, and this had resulted in an error of 10 days since its adoption. Pope Gregory, therefore, in accordance with the suggestions of the astronomer Clavius, ordered these 10 days to be omitted ; that in future all century years, which would otherwise have been leap years, such as 1700, 1800 and so forth, should be regarded as normal years, with the exception of such century years as 1600 and 2000, which are divisible by 400.

It was not until the year 1752 that the Gregorian calendar was adopted in Britain by regarding September 3 of that year as September 14—11 days being thus sacrificed to bring the calendar into approximate conformity with the tropical year and the position of the sun. The Gregorian calendar was only gradually adopted : by Italy, France, Spain and Portugal in 1582 ; by Switzerland, Holland and Flanders, Prussia and the German Catholic states in 1583 ; Poland in 1586 ; Hungary in 1587 ; Denmark, the Netherlands and the German Protestant states in 1700 ; Sweden between 1700 and 1740, by omitting leap-year days ; the British colonies in 1752 ; Japan in 1872 ; China in 1912 ; Bulgaria in 1915 ; Russia and Turkey in 1917 ; Yugoslavia and Rumania in 1919 ; Greece in 1923—by which time the difference between the so-called Old Style and New Style was about 13 days. Recent leap years have been 1932, 1936, 1940 and 1944, and they will recur every four years. This plan of adding and subtracting days to adjust the discrepancies between the earth's Diurnal Rotation period and the period of its revolution round the sun, or tropical year, still leaves some minor discrepancies, which, however, will not be appreciable for many thousands of years.

The period of the earth's annual revolution, relative to the stars, known as the sidereal year, is 365 days 6 hours 9 minutes $9\frac{1}{2}$ seconds. Inasmuch as this completes the earth's orbit in space, it is the true year ; but as it does not conform to the sun's apparent motion from season to season, it cannot be used as an accurate basis for the calendar year.

We have learnt that what appears to be the sun's path through the zodiac is really the earth's path projected against the stars in the depths of space beyond. This path is known as the ecliptic, and it represents the plane of the earth's orbit. Now, since the paths of the moon and all the principal planets, except Pluto, are contained within 9 degrees of each side of this ecliptic or plane of the earth's orbit, the planes of

PLANETARY PATHS. With the exception of that of Pluto, the paths of all the principal planets are contained within nine degrees of the ecliptic. This diagram shows the inclination of each planet's orbit compared with that of the earth.

I

each of their orbits can depart but little from the level of that of the earth.

Sidereal Days. In calculating the length of the year the normal day of 24 hours is taken as the basis of the measurement of time ; it is further subdivided into 60 minutes and each minute into 60 seconds. This artificial division is based upon the average time which the sun appears to take to return to its highest point in the sky. It occurs approximately at noon, and hence from noon to noon constitutes a solar day ; but actually the 24 hours of the solar day represent the time that the earth has taken to turn once on its axis so as to bring us round directly to face the sun again, which occurs about noon. This constitutes one rotation of the earth relative to the sun, but not to the heavens generally. If the student were to note the exact minute at which a star, high up in the south, reached a certain point relative to, say, a church spire or a tree-top, and then watched for the same star to reach the same position on the next night, he would find that it arrived there nearly 4 minutes earlier.

These sidereal days, as they are called, represent the time taken for the earth to turn on its axis to bring us round to face a certain star again ; since this amounts to about 23 hours and 56 minutes, therefore, while there are nearly 365¼ days of 24 hours each, i.e. solar days, in a year, there are about 366¼ sidereal days. The precise

length of the sidereal day is 3 minutes 55.91 seconds less than the solar day. Now the earth's motion round the sun is not, on account of its varying distance from the sun, quite uniform or always at the same rate ; consequently the sun does not always precisely represent noon at twelve o'clock. Apparent solar days vary, therefore, in length ; to get over this difficulty an exact equalization of the variations has been made, known as the equation of time, and the result is the mean solar day of 24 hours as indicated by all clocks and watches that are in proper accord with chronometers. This 'mean time' is artificial, but the only practicable scheme in the circumstances. If we set our clocks by sundials we should find that 24 hours would vary in length by several minutes at certain times of the year. The most regular of all movements is the earth's rotation ; and, though not absolutely exact, its variations are inappreciable in a century. This rotation occupies 23 hours 56 minutes 4.09 seconds out of a solar day of 24 hours of mean time, and constitutes a sidereal day.

The sidereal day is used by astronomers as the basis of exact time, but it is impracticable for daily use, inasmuch as, being shorter by nearly four minutes, all clocks would need to be corrected by this amount every day to keep them in accord with the sun and, for instance, to prevent noon occurring at all hours of the day and night.

LESSON 12

The Six Superior Planets

THE outer or superior planets are those whose orbits lie outside that of the earth relative to the sun. They are Mars, Jupiter, Saturn, Uranus, Neptune, and Pluto, and their respective distances and order outwards from the sun, together with their relative sizes, are given in the table in page 256. Mars, Jupiter and Saturn appear as brilliant objects of the night sky, one or other being usually present ; Uranus is only just perceptible to the unaided vision : to see Neptune and Pluto requires a telescope.

All the orbits of these outer planets traverse the zodiac, except that of Pluto, which during part of its course extends beyond the limits of the zodiac.

While sharing the common diurnal motion from east to west of all celestial

bodies, the six planets also participate in the annual sidereal motion of the heavens, which causes them to appear first in the east and then gradually, in the course of several months, to descend into the west, setting earlier each evening. In addition, there is each planet's own orbital motion, perceived partly as direct, toward the east, and partly as retrograde, toward the west. Actually the planet's motion is always toward the east, i.e. anti-clockwise ; but since the earth travels faster than any of the outer planets, there comes a point— when the earth and the planet in question are approaching their nearest-—when the overtaking earth causes the planet to appear to move backward among the stars. This illusion is precisely similar in effect to that produced upon a passenger in a fast-moving train as it passes one that is moving less quickly ; the latter appears to move backward in relation to the landscape beyond.

Course of Planetary Movements. The entire course of an outer planet's movements, as observed from our rapidly moving world, may be concisely summarized. Beginning with conjunction with the sun— that is, when the planet passes through the point of its orbit which lies directly behind and beyond the sun—the sun, and the particular planet are in a straight line ; the planet is then invisible, being lost in the solar radiance. In the course of three or four weeks after conjunction the planet will begin to be seen in the dawn. As the more rapid motion of the earth brings the planet more and more into view, so it will rise earlier—ultimately, before midnight. Gradually, as the earth catches it up, so to speak, the planet becomes b r i g h t e r and apparently larger as observed telescopically. Now, as it approaches nearer, its apparent motion will diminish, until it appears to become stationary in the heavens ; then, in a day or so, movement may be detected, but now it seems as if it is moving in the opposite direction, i.e. it is retrograding. This is merely due to perspective and to the fact that the earth is travelling faster and along a track within that of the other planet. The planet will continue to retrograde for some weeks, the length of time being in proportion to its distance and the speed at which it is travelling. Mars, the planet which comes nearest, will take, on an average, 70 days ; Jupiter, travelling slower, about four months.

Meanwhile, the distance separating the earth from the planet will now rapidly diminish, and the planet will appear higher in the sky, toward midnight, until it will reach its highest point and be due south at midnight. The planet will then be at the opposite point of the heavens to the sun and in what is called opposition. This is usually the most important stage of an outer planet's path through the heavens as observed from the earth, because then it is at about its nearest to us, at its greatest altitude above the horizon, most extensively illuminated, and, therefore, best situated for telescopic study.

After opposition the planet becomes a prominent object high in the south of the evening sky between sunset and midnight. It is now receding from the earth, becoming less bright, and its motion becoming slower, until finally the planet becomes stationary again. It then resumes its direct motion eastward. Usually the retrograde motion combined with the direct takes the form of a loop, or a returning curve above or below the direct path ; this is due to the planet's orbit being on a slightly different plane from that of the earth. Now, travelling rapidly eastward among the stars, and at the same time setting earlier each evening, the planet will consequently sink gradually toward the west, until it is ultimately lost

COURSE OF A PLANET, showing how the retrograde and direct movements combine to form a loop. This diagram illustrates the path of Mars among the stars of Cancer from October, 1930, to May, 1931.

in the sunset glow. It is now far beyond the sun and will soon be back in conjunction again. Thus ends each successive apparition —an apparition being one entire course of an outer planet from the time it is first seen in the dawn after conjunction until it is finally lost in the evening twilight several months later.

The entire series from one opposition to another, or between two conjunctions, constitutes the synodic period of the planet, and represents the interval between the occasions when it is in the same relative position to the sun as seen from the earth. The synodic period is longest in the case of Mars, amounting to two years and about 50 days ; it amounts to 399 days in the case of Jupiter, 378 days for Saturn, 369 days for Uranus, and only $367\frac{1}{2}$ days in the case of Neptune. It is most for Mars because this planet's speed is greatest (15 miles a second), and also because the orbit of Mars is the smallest relative to that of the earth.

The sidereal period is the true period representing the time the planet takes to revolve around the sun relative to the stars, but the synodic period represents the time the planet takes to revolve round the sun relative to the earth. For instance, if we imagine ourselves situated in space so that we see the sun, the earth and, say, Mars in a line, with Mars at the opposite end of the line to the sun ; watching them from that moment, we should see that the earth, after passing Mars at the time of opposition, when it was in line with the sun, would perform more than two journeys round the sun before it is again in line with Mars and the sun.

Mathematics of Planetary Orbits. The actual path of a planet may be obtained from its apparent path by means of what are known as the Elements of its Orbit. These are certain arithmetical quantities which not only describe the particular planet's orbit precisely, but also enable the planet's position to be found at any time. There are eight elements ordinarily used, each one being designated by a letter or sign. The elements may be briefly described as follows :

1. The Semi-major Axis, or Mean Distance from the sun, denoted by a ; this is usually expressed in astronomical units, the earth's distance from the sun constituting one such unit. The Semi-major Axis is equal to half the longer diameter of the ellipse forming the orbit of the planet, and enables the size of the orbit to be calculated.

2. Eccentricity, describing the ellipticity of the orbit, is denoted by the letter e, and is obtained by dividing the distance between the centre of the orbit and the sun by the Semi-major Axis.

3. Inclination of its orbit to the ecliptic, denoted by the letter i, and expressed by the angle between the plane of the planet's orbit relative to the plane of that of the earth.

4. The Longitude of the Ascending Node. This is denoted by the sign Ω, and repre-sents the distance in degrees, minutes and seconds from the Vernal Equinox, or First Point of Aries, eastward to the point where the orbit of the planet crosses the ecliptic from south to north.

5. The Longitude of the Perihelion, denoted by the sign ω. This defines the direction in which the Major Axis of the elliptical orbit lies, and is represented by the longitude of the point on the orbit where the planet approaches nearest to the sun, i.e. the nearest end of its Major Axis to the sun. It is measured from the First Point of Aries, i.e. the Vernal Equinoctial Point.

6. The Mean Longitude at the Epoch, expressed by the letter L. This represents the mean longitude of the planet as seen from the sun at some precise moment.

7. The Period of the planet's revolution in its orbit, denoted by the letter P, when it is expressed as the Sidereal Period in Tropical Years, in terms of the earth's period as unity. It is denoted by the sign n, when it is expressed as the Sidereal Mean Daily Motion in degrees of arc. In addition, the Mean Synodic Period and Period of Axial Rotation are sometimes used. These will be found in the Planet Lessons.

The elements a, P and n are fixed, whereas the others change with the Epoch, although in some cases only slightly with the lapse of centuries. They are all given in the accompanying table compiled by the British Astronomical Association and including Mercury, Venus and the Earth, as well as the six superior planets. It is for the year 1943 and calculated for the beginning of January.

ELEMENTS OF THE PLANETARY ORBITS

Planet	Mean Distance in Astronomical Units a	Eccentricity e	Inclination to the Ecliptic i	Mean Longitude of the Ascending Node Ω	Mean Longitude of the Perihelion ω	Mean Longitude at the Epoch L	Sidereal Period in Tropical Years P	Sidereal Mean Daily Motion n
			° ′ ″	° ′ ″	° ′ ″	° ′ ″		°
Mercury	0·387099	0·205 6230	7 00 13·3	47 39 20·1	76 34 06·9	8 57 37·03	0·24085	4·092338
Venus	0·723331	0·006 8002	3 23 38·6	76 09 59·9	130 46 08·7	304 49 35·78	0·61521	1·602131
Earth	1·000000	0·016 7330	. .	. .	101 57 36·5	99 17 17·29	1·00004	0·985609
Mars	1·523688	0·093 3525	1 51 00·2	49 07 04·6	335 00 35·0	244 17 07·13	1·88089	0·524033
Jupiter	5·202803	0·048 4075	1 18 22·7	99 52 21·2	13 24 15·5	103 35 50·58	11·86223	0·083091
Saturn	9·538843	0·055 7406	2 29 26·2	113 09 32·5	91 55 52·8	72 38 58·18	29·45772	0·033460
Uranus	19·190978	0·047 1647	0 46 22·6	73 42 17·7	169 44 18·5	68 12 43·53	84·01529	0·011732
Neptune	30·070672	0·008 5631	1 46 30·5	131 09 05·2	44 06 05·1	179 33 39·17	164·78829	0·005981
Pluto	39·45743	0·248 5200	17 08 35·5	109 32 19·2	223 25 28·6	155 19 47·2	247·6968	0·003979

Mars as Revealed by the Telescope

MARS, the fourth planet outwards from the sun, comes nearer to the earth than any of the planets save Venus. Its mean distance from the sun is 141,500,000 miles, but the eccentricity of its orbit (which amounts to 0.0933—greater than that of any other planet except Mercury and Pluto) causes its distance to vary to the extent of about 13,000,000 miles each way. Hence, at aphelion it is about 154,500,000 miles from the sun, but at perihelion only 128,500,000 miles. When Mars is in opposition, or nearest the earth, at about the time of perihelion, its distance from the earth is only about 34,637,000 miles ; whereas when the opposition of Mars occurs when it is near aphelion, then its distance from the earth may be as much as 62,680,000 miles.

The planet's sidereal period, which represents the Martian year, is 687 of our days, the inclination of its orbit to the ecliptic being only 1° 51′. Its synodic period is 780 days—the longest of any planet. The diameter of Mars is only about 4,230 miles ; its surface is, therefore, little more than a quarter that of the earth, while its volume is rather less than one-seventh (0.150) the size of our world. Its mass amounts to 0.108 of that of the earth ; while its density is 0.71 of our world, and its surface gravity 0.38.

When Mars is studied through a telescope certain details on its disk are seen to be present at the same hour for several evenings in succession, but they then tend to drop backward, and finally vanish at the *limb* or edge of the planet's disk. Others are seen to appear at the western side, for Mars rotates from west to east, as does the earth. The cycle, as observed from the earth, occupies about 40 days. The length of day on Mars is 24 hours, 37 minutes, 23 seconds.

The tilt of the axis of Mars is very little different from that of the earth, being about 24½ degrees to its orbital plane. There is very little polar flattening perceptible—only 1/190th, in fact.

Geographical Features. In a sense we know more of this planet than we do of the moon, for we see both sides of its sphere and obtain more complete views over its polar regions. The brilliant whiteness of the latter makes them a most striking feature ; usually only one is present, according to whether the north or south pole is tilted toward the earth. The size of the polar caps is found to vary with the Martian seasons, decreasing with the advance of spring and summer ; the south polar cap occasionally vanishes altogether, as in 1894 and 1911. This seems to suggest that they are composed of ice and snow, and the fact that there is usually a darkening of the area encircling the pole immediately following the polar cap's diminution suggests the formation of water and flooding in consequence of the periodical melting of the snow.

Seen through the telescope when conditions for observation are good, what may be called the ' geographical ' features of Mars—continents and seas, estuaries, bays, isthmuses and islands—are revealed in impressive grandeur ; these, together with the varied tints, suggest that the planet's surface is composed of land and water.

The large orange-tinted masses which give Mars, as seen with the naked eye, its rosy hue, are believed to be great desert areas. As regards the greenish-grey and bluish areas which cover about one-third of the planet's surface, the darkest portions, possessing sharply defined and permanent outlines, would appear to be shallow water

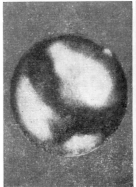 

MARS. These photographs of Mars, taken by Dr. Hale at Mount Wilson Observatory, California, show the varying appearance of the planet on a single night in October, 1909.

areas or seas. The lighter greenish-grey regions vary considerably in colour and extent with the changes of the Martian seasons, e.g. the bright greenish tints of spring give place to yellowish and brown tones in the autumn. Areas thus appear and disappear amid the prevailing orange of the desert belts ; where they are visible in these belts as greenish-grey spots they are known as oases and lakes, the latter being fairly permanent. It is believed that these regions are areas of vegetation, the changing tints representing the cycle of growth and decay through the long Martian year. The ' seas ' called Syrtis Major, Sinus Sabaeus and Mare Acidalium or Mare Tyrrhenum are always present.

All the definite features of Mars have been mapped and are generally known by the names given them by G. V. Schiaparelli (1835-1910 ; pron. Skyapparelly), a well-known Italian astronomer. There are also indefinite features — held to be clouds and mists — which temporarily obscure permanent areas by substituting a blurred patch, extending over the greater part of the planet's disk. Whitish areas that occasionally appear and disappear with the progress of the Martian day are ascribed to hoar frost.

Mars possesses two moons, named Phobos and Deimos, discovered by Asaph Hall at Washington in August, 1877. The outermost of these satellites, Deimos, is estimated to be only 5 miles in diameter; it revolves around Mars in 30 hours, 18 minutes, at an average distance of 12,535 miles above the planet's surface. To an observer on Mars its disk would appear to be only 1/20th the width of our moon. Phobos,

estimated to be about 10 miles in diameter, revolves in the short period of 7 hours, 39 minutes, in an orbit which is only 3,715 miles above the planet's surface. Phobos and Deimos, it may be noted, are the smallest satellites known.

It is a remarkable fact that Dean Swift in ' Gulliver's Travels ' states that the astronomers of Laputa ' have likewise discovered two lesser stars, or satellites, which revolve about Mars '—an anticipation of a scientific discovery that was not actually made until 150 years later.

Is There Life on Mars ? As to the possibility of life in other worlds, it is usual to look to Mars as offering the best opportunities for a solution of the problem. Its comparative proximity and the favourable conditions under which it may be observed suggest that it is on Mars that we should be able to recognize any signs of life.

Mars possesses water and an atmosphere, two essentials of life. The former has been

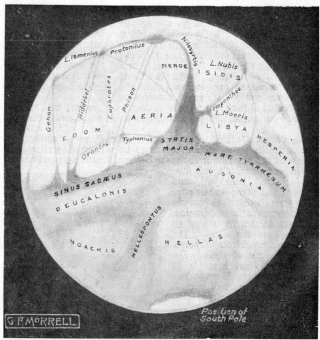

MARS: SOME OF ITS PRINCIPAL FEATURES. Seen through a telescope, Mars presents a series of impressive geographical features—continents and seas, estuaries, bays, isthmuses and islands, desert areas and regions believed to be covered with vegetation. All these phenomena have been mapped and are generally known by the names given them by the nineteenth-century Italian astronomer Schiaparelli, who was a pioneer observer of the surface of Mars.

proved to exist by visual observation and spectroscopic analysis, although the amount of water in the atmosphere of Mars is apparently only about 5 per cent of that existing in our own atmosphere. This conclusion is in accord with the scarcity of clouds observed and the extreme rarity of the Martian atmosphere. As regards the latter, it is probable that it contains an excess of oxygen and nitrogen and heavier gases, but a minimum of hydrogen, helium and the lighter gases, because, the planet's mass being relatively so small compared with the earth, its power to retain the atoms of the lighter gases would be much less and they would, in the course of ages, be lost in space. Air may be plentiful, then, near the surface of Mars, even though water be scarce. That this is so is evidenced by the planet's shaded terminator—the line dividing night from day—seen when Mars is so placed in its orbit that its disk appears gibbous, like that of the moon two days from the full. On these occasions the terminator is not sharp and hard as in the case of our moon, but softened, and it extends for some eight degrees in what is known as the twilight arc beyond the true sunlit portion of Mars. This appearance is produced by the diffused and refracted sunlight in the planet's atmosphere, indicating that this is certainly more than half as dense as that of the earth. This is a very important point to establish as suggesting the probability of life on that small world.

Temperature and Atmosphere. Temperature is the next essential consideration, and here the evidence is not so conclusive. As seen from Mars, the sun's disk appears, on an average, rather less than five-eighths of its width as seen from the earth ; while Mars receives, on an average, only 0.43 of the light and heat received by our world. Its day differs but little from ours, but Mars experiences seasonal changes which, though similar, are yet far more rigorous and prolonged than those of the earth. These changes are particularly great owing to the fact that when the southern hemisphere of the planet is tilted towards the sun, Mars is about 26,000,000 miles nearer than when its northern hemisphere is so turned. The same consideration applies to the earth, too, but only so as to cause the comparatively small difference of 3,000,000 miles.

Moreover, the rarefied atmosphere of Mars is less able to retain through the Martian night the heat received by day ; this would result in intensely cold nights, unless the atmosphere be sufficiently dense near the surface to prevent rapid radiation. Radiometer tests have indicated that, while the temperature may reach over 50 degrees Fahrenheit about midday in the equatorial regions, it drops far below freezing at night, and is freezing at sunset, even in midsummer. If these radiometer observations are to be accepted as indicative of the temperatures at the planet's surface rather than the higher reaches of its atmospheric envelope, then the conditions for life on Mars are not promising. The chief objections to their acceptance are : first, that visual observation does not indicate any such rigorous frosty conditions ; and secondly, why should the polar ice or snow caps vanish so much more completely than the terrestrial ones ? Even though, as has been suggested, the layer be comparatively thin as compared with the thick masses at the earth's poles, it would seem impossible for the caps to melt so completely and quickly over such vast areas, upwards of 3,000 miles in diameter.

Another objection to a rigorous frost-ridden Martian climate is the visual evidences of vegetation and seasonal changes, as described in the preceding page. If not due to vegetation, how are these regular variations of tint and cycle of colour to be explained ? Finally, we have the so-called 'canals' of Mars to consider, both as to their objective reality and as to whether they are evidence of the existence, not only of life but of sentient beings—more or less similar to ourselves.

The Canals of Mars. The 'canals' of Mars were first discovered in 1877 by the Italian astronomer, Schiaparelli. They appeared to him as straight, greenish-grey streaks, exceedingly narrow and faint, extending across the reddish desert areas, and he called them 'canali' (Italian for channels). They appeared to stretch from certain estuaries, bays, and 'coast lines,' as they might be called, to other similar markings and greenish-grey patches termed oases and lakes (or lacus), where several 'canali' were recorded as meeting and crossing. They extended in some cases for over 3,000 miles, and were singularly straight. In 1881–82, when Mars was again favourably placed for observation, Schiaparelli again saw the 'canali,' and in many cases found that for considerable distances they were double. They appeared to develop rapidly with the progress of the Martian seasons, particularly spring.

Though many observers failed to perceive these markings, their existence was confirmed by numbers of expert astronomers who were suitably equipped with telescopes well placed for observation. Among these were W. H. Pickering and Percival Lowell in America, and Perrotin, Thollon, and Flammarion in France. In England, where observation is generally poor, the existence of the 'canals' has been generally questioned, from the time of Maunder over 40 years ago to Jeans at the present day.

According to Percival Lowell, who represents a very large number of expert observers, the 'canals' appear as perfectly straight dark lines forming a network, geometrically arranged over the reddish, and even crossing the dark greenish, regions of the planet's disk ; in width they are from 15 to 40 miles, and are up to 3,000 miles long ; as many as fourteen such 'canals' will meet at the oases and lakes and then continue across the apparent desert areas to other oases, or the extensive greenish-grey areas ; about 50 'canals' have been observed to be double, those constituting a pair being parallel and between 100 and 200 miles apart.

It is not claimed that the 'canals' are really watercourses, but that they are irrigated areas—that they are apparently the resulting belts of vegetation which develop, most probably by cultivation, for several miles on each side of much narrower watercourses, which are artificially constructed to convey water from the polar regions when the snow cap begins to melt. This melting, as we have seen, apparently floods the regions surrounding the poles ; and what more probable, therefore, than for reasoning beings to seek to make the best use of so valuable

and rare a commodity as water ? The geometrical arrangement of the cultivated tracks, so different from the courses rivers would take, strengthens the suggestion that the 'canals' are the work of reasoning beings. Lowell, who had his famous observatory erected in the ideal situation of Flagstaff, Arizona, delineated over 400 'canals' and some 200 'oases' and 'lakes.' Slipher and many other astronomers have independently confirmed most of the discoveries of Schiaparelli and Lowell, both of whom prepared a chart of Mars upon which the details are mapped.

Negative Evidence. The evidence against this theory and against the existence of life on Mars and the presence of belts of vegetation or 'canals' is negative. Its chief exponents are Barnard in America, Antoniadi in France, and Jeans in this country. Barnard, though using the most powerful telescopes, claims that he never saw what Lowell and so many others revealed ; Antoniadi has expressed like opinions, while Jeans states that

'so far no convincing evidence has been forthcoming. The supposed canals on Mars disappear when looked at through a really large telescope, and have not survived the test of being photographed. Seasonal changes necessarily occur on Mars as on the earth, and certain phenomena accompany these which many astronomers are inclined to ascribe to the growth and decline of vegetation, although they may represent nothing more than rains watering the desert. There is no definite evidence of life, and certainly no evidence of conscious life, on Mars—or, indeed, anywhere else in the universe.'

It will be seen, then, that there is a definite clash among astronomers as to the meanings of the markings on Mars, but those who favour the existence of life and the reality of the *canali* as belts of vegetation tend to increase.

LESSON 14

Miniature Worlds of the Solar System

ONE of the results of Kepler's study of the heavens was the recognition of what seemed to be an arithmetical relation between the distances of the planets from the sun. This relation was worked out by the astronomer Titius, but it is generally ascribed to the German astronomer, J. E. Bode (1747–1826). As subsequently amplified, it may be arrived at as

follows : First write down the numbers 0, 3, 6, 12, 24, 48, 96, 192, 384, and then add 4 to each. We then have 4, 7, 10, 16, 28, 52, 100, 196, 388 ; and these numbers are approximately proportional to the distances from the sun of Mercury, Venus, the earth, Mars, the asteroids, Jupiter, Saturn, Uranus and Neptune. Thus, if 10 be taken as the earth's distance from the sun, then the distance of Mercury is 4, that of Mars is 16, and so on. As a matter of fact, the actual distances, taking the earth as 10, are Mercury 3·9, Venus 7·2, the earth 10, Mars 15·2, the asteroids 27·4, Jupiter 52·9, Saturn 95·4, Uranus 192 and Neptune 300. To this sequence the name of Bode's Law is generally given, although it should be realized that up to the present it is merely an empirical rule.

Discovery of the Asteroids. When it was first framed the existence of the asteroids was unknown, and there was a gap between Mars and Jupiter. It was inferred, therefore, that another planet must exist, corresponding to the number 28, and in 1800 astronomers set to work to locate it.

On the night of January 1, 1801, the Italian astronomer Piazzi, at Palermo, discovered a hitherto unknown star; this was found to have a planetary orbit and was named Ceres after the mythical divinity of Sicily. Its mean distance from the sun was found to be 257 million miles (28·1 on the Bode scale), and corresponded, therefore, very closely with the missing number. What was almost as amazing was its exceeding smallness; later on it was found to be only 477 miles in diameter.

Then, on March 28, 1802, another planet was discovered by Olbers, who named it Pallas; this was found to be at an average distance of about 256 million miles and to be only 304 miles in diameter. On September 2, 1804, Harding discovered Juno, a third small planet, only 120 miles in diameter and at a mean distance of 248 million miles from the sun. Then, on March 29, 1807, Olbers discovered yet another, which he named Vesta. This is only about 250 miles in diameter, and at a mean distance of 219 million miles from the sun.

Thus, instead of the solitary planet whose existence had been suspected, there were found instead four little worlds. More were sought, but not until 1845 was another found—Astraea, discovered by Heneke, in the same group. In 1847 three more were discovered, and since then more have been added every year—all of them much smaller than the first four discovered.

Since the application of photography to astronomical research large numbers of these asteroids have made their existence known by way of small streaks on photographic plates—their motion while the plate was being exposed causing them to be presented in this way instead of dots, as are the 'fixed' stars. Telescopically, they appear as small stars; hence their name

asteroids, though planetoids or minor planets are more correct terms.

A Host of Planetoids. Altogether over 2,200 have been discovered to date; of these about 1,400 are permanently followed in recognized orbits. These have received names, chiefly from ancient mythology, together with numbers enclosed and prefixed to the name, thus: '(911) Agamemnon.' A large proportion are more recently discovered and very small planetoids are known at present only by numbers, and will be so known until their identity is established by successive revolutions.

Only about twenty of this host are estimated to possess diameters exceeding 100 miles; probably about 150 have diameters between 50 and 100 miles; while the remainder, judging from their relative faintness, are all below 50 miles in diameter. There are, in addition to these known planetoids with assigned orbits, a large number—probably a thousand—whose identities are so involved with one another that they become difficult to follow. Averaging between 5 and 10 miles in diameter, they are very faint, and can be glimpsed only when near opposition; and perturbations due to Jupiter's attraction still further complicate their orbits. There are certainly many more less than 5 miles in diameter and beyond the range of telescopic photography.

It might be supposed that from such numbers there might be sufficient material to form a planet at least as massive as the earth. This is far from being the case, however, for it is probable that the combined mass of all the planetoids known is between 1/500 and 1/1,000 of that of our world. At least 8,000 bodies similar to Ceres, the largest planetoid, would be required to constitute a world as massive as the earth.

As the force of gravity and, therefore, the velocity of escape are so low on even the largest of the planetoids, it is certain that they can have no atmospheres such as we are familiar with.

Several planetoids exhibit periodical variations of brightness, indicating that they rotate. It has been found that they take between 1·75 and 13·7 years to complete their revolutions round the sun, both revolutions and rotations (where known) being direct, as in the case of the earth and planets in general. The inclinations of their orbits average within about 9 degrees of the ecliptic, thus conforming to that of the major planets. There are some notable exceptions, however, the chief being Hidalgo, which is 43 degrees, and Pallas, which is nearly 35 degrees removed from the ecliptic.

Distance of Planetoids from the Sun. The eccentricity of the planetoid orbits varies considerably, for while some are nearly circular, others are elongated ellipses with eccentricity amounting to 0·65 in the case of Hidalgo, 0·55 for Reinmuth's 1932 planetoid, and 0·54 for Albert. Exceedingly great, therefore, is the range of some of the planetoids' distances from the sun. The distances of about seven-eighths range from 215 million miles to 310 million miles from the sun. The remainder include Hidalgo, which has an aphelion distance of about 880 million miles—as far as the orbit of Saturn—while its perihelion distance is only about 185 million miles. Its revolution period, the longest of the planetoids, is 13·7 years.

On the other hand, Eros, which at aphelion is 165,630,000 miles from the sun, is only 105,230,000 miles distant at perihelion; hence it may approach to within 13,840,000 miles of the earth, and in January, 1931, actually came within 16,200,000 miles. Eros was then found to be an elongated body, suspected to be almost divided in the centre, irregular in form, while the two sections rotated about 4½ times in the course of a day. Its greatest diameter has been variously estimated to be between 15 and 20 miles; the period of its revolution is 643 days, but its synodic period is 845 days (*see* Lesson 5).

Four other planetoids have since been found to approach the earth still closer. Amor, with an orbit which also crosses that of Mars, was discovered by M. Delporte on March 12, 1932; it came within 10,160,000 miles of the earth on March 23, 1932. Amor appears to be only about

3 miles in diameter; its revolution period is 2·76 years. The minimum distance of Apollo, a tiny planetoid discovered by Herr Reinmuth in 1932, is 3,000,000 miles. Four years later Delporte discovered and named Adonis, which at its nearest is only 1,500,000 miles away. But the smallest planetoid hitherto observed—it is probably less than one mile in diameter—has approached nearer to the earth than any other celestial body except the moon. Now known as Hermes, it was accidentally discovered by Reinmuth on October 28, 1937; two days later it was only 485,000 miles away, missing a collision with the earth by 5½ hours. It is possible for this planetoid to approach within 220,000 miles of the earth, which is less than the mean distance of the moon; its revolution period is rather more than 2 years.

Origin of the Planetoids. What of the origin of the planetoids? Are they, as has been suggested, fragments of an exploded world? Although they occupy such a wide belt between the orbits of Mars and Jupiter—and even beyond—yet it can be shown this could have been produced by the gravitational action of the planets, more particularly Jupiter. A remarkable circumstance is that all their orbits are so involved that it is not possible to disentangle one from the rest without breaking through others. It has been possible to trace back mathematically the perturbations until they are all equidistant from a point on a line which joins the sun with the *centre* of Jupiter's orbit. Thus there is decided evidence for the conclusion that all the planetoids once occupied a certain spot at a certain epoch, when they would have constituted a single world, instead of being, as now, fragments possibly of a world that met with catastrophe.

LESSON 15

Jupiter and Its Many Moons

THE greatest of the planets is Jupiter. Thirteen hundred and twelve times the size of the earth, it has an immense mass—318·4 times that of the earth and more than twice the amount of all the other planets put together. With the exception of Venus it is usually the brightest planet in our sky, and with its eleven satellites forms a miniature solar system of its own.

Its mean diameter is given as 85,750 miles, but the planet is so elliptical that its polar diameter is 82,800 miles, while its equatorial diameter is about 88,700. It is thus an oblate spheroid with a great equatorial bulge, and possesses a surface about 120 times greater than that of the earth. Its density is only 0·24 that of our world and 1·34 times that of water; this indicates that Jupiter is very largely

Jupiter

composed of gases, which descend doubtless for many thousands of miles below its visible surface as a colossal atmospheric envelope.

While the force of gravity on Jupiter *averages* about 2·65 times that of the earth, it varies considerably between the equator and the poles, the weight of bodies becoming greater as the poles are approached; therefore, superficial gravity, which is 2·64 at the equator, amounts to 2·67 at the poles of the planet. This is due in part to polar flattening and in part to rapid rotation of the equatorial regions.

Rotation Periods. Jupiter's rotation periods are remarkable. Not only does it rotate faster than any other planet,

but also at rates which vary for different latitudes and even for different objects at the same latitude. At the great equatorial belt, averaging about 12,000 miles in width, the speed amounts to a mean of 9 hours 50 minutes to complete a rotation; this is known as System I. In temperate latitudes the speed averages about 9 hours 55 minutes; this is System II. In high latitudes the speed of rotation amounts to about 9 hours 57 minutes. Thus there is a difference of 7 minutes, or approximately 1/85th of the entire period; in the course of 85 revolutions of the planet, therefore, the equatorial regions must gain a complete rotation on the rest of Jupiter's surface. Since the equatorial circumference is about 300,000 miles, objects at or near Jupiter's equator travel at the rate of some 30,000 miles an hour, and 350 miles an hour faster—more or less according to latitude—than in the north and south temperate zones. This may be compared with the speed of nearly 1,000 miles an hour at which bodies travel in terrestrial equatorial regions. Jupiter rotates in an almost upright position, since the inclination of its axis to the plane of its orbit is only 3°; it can have no appreciable seasons due to varying tilt relative to the sun.

Jupiter revolves at an average distance from the sun of 5·20 astronomical units, i.e. 483,300,000 miles; but this is subject to wide variation owing to the great eccentricity of the planet's orbit, which

JUPITER'S SURFACE FEATURES. *This planet is remarkable for its constantly changing 'belts' and spots. They vary in width, depth and tint, and these three drawings, made by members of the British Astronomical Association, show some of these differences of appearance. The first (top, left) records the surface of the planet on Sept. 3, 1929; the second (bottom, left), on Jan. 10, 1930, and the third on Jan. 20, 1931.*
Courtesy of the British Astronomical Association

amounts to one-twentieth. Therefore, while Jupiter is about 507,000,000 miles from the sun at aphelion, it is only about 460,000,000 miles away at perihelion. This makes a considerable difference in the apparent size and brightness of the planet as seen from the earth ; for when Jupiter is in opposition and at perihelion, i.e. in October, it is then only about 367,000,000 miles away and has an apparent diameter of about 50 seconds of arc. When opposition occurs at aphelion, i.e. in April, then Jupiter is about 414,000,000 miles distant and has an apparent diameter of 44 seconds of arc. It takes Jupiter 11 years, 314 days to complete one sidereal revolution ; about six years, therefore, intervene between aphelion and perihelion.

Varying Surface Features. The details on Jupiter's disk are varied, distinctly visible, and subject to constant change. Even a small telescope of 2-inch aperture will reveal two or three of the chief belts. The general arrangement of these belts is more or less uniform in character, but they change both in width and depth of tint in the course of Jupiter's long year. With the aid of powerful instruments we may see a mass of detail—the great reddish tropical belts bordering the bright yellowish equatorial band, while greyish and greenish belts indicate the temperate regions. Spots —some very bright, others quite dark— appear on these belts and change their positions relative to one another from time to time.

The most remarkable of these spots is the Great Red Spot, which first became prominent in 1878 below the South Tropical Belt. It was calculated to be about 30,000 miles long, parallel to the belt and 7,000 miles wide. Originally pinkish in tint, it became a deep red by the next year and has continued until the present time, gradually getting fainter and rounder, until now it is scarcely perceptible. But the great bay or hollow, 45,000 miles long, which it occupied still remains a very distinct feature of the South Tropical Belt and one of the most permanent markings on the planet ; it is known as the South Tropical Disturbance. The Great Red Spot cannot be attached to the planet's surface, because it travels at a different rate from that of the adjoining belts and appears to be floating, together with the belts and other details, in the atmosphere of Jupiter. The continual and rapid changes in the other surface details indicate that they are produced by currents and storms in a dense atmosphere, only the upper layers of which are ordinarily observable. These layers have been found by radiometric tests to be at a temperature far below zero. Probably thousands of miles below them is the actual and largely molten surface of the planet, at a terrific heat consistent with its low density and disturbed state.

This view, based upon the observed phenomena and the analogy of the earth, has been generally held until recent years, when it was found that the cloud surface of Jupiter averaged some 200° F. below zero. This appeared to rule out the possibility of the clouds being composed of water-vapour. Then analysis of Jupiter's spectrum indicated the presence of ammonia and methane in its atmosphere and therefore its extreme cold, for otherwise the ammonia would dissolve out in a temperature higher than 185°F. below zero. This, together with the theory of Dr. Harold Jeffreys, derived from the extreme lightness of Jupiter as compared with its bulk or volume, led him to assume that Jupiter has a solid core about 42,000 miles in diameter. Above this is an ice-layer some 16,000 miles thick, while enclosing the whole is the dense and very cold cloud-laden atmosphere about 6,000 miles in depth. This theory has therefore obtained some support from the discovery of ammonia and methane in Jupiter's atmosphere, as regards frigid conditions ; otherwise there is actually no evidence for Dr. Jeffreys' supposition of Jupiter's internal ice and rocky core.

There is no probability of life on such a world, any more than on a molten one.

Moons of Jupiter. Jupiter has eleven satellites. The four largest were first discerned by Galileo in January, 1610, and have been known since as the Galilean Moons. They have also individual names, as indicated below, but as a rule they, together with Jupiter's other satellites, are known by Roman numerals.

The first nine of these satellites revolve direct from west to east, but the motion of the two outermost is retrograde, i.e. clockwise. Until 1892 Jupiter was believed to possess only four moons. No. V was discovered by Barnard at the Lick Observatory in 1892. In 1904 Perrine discovered VI by photography at the same observatory, and VII in 1905. Then VIII was discovered by Melotte in 1908, and IX in 1914 by Nicholson, who also discovered X and XI in 1938.

Very little is known about these small bodies. In view of the great eccentricity of the orbits of the five outermost, their considerable inclination from the plane

MOONS OR SATELLITES OF JUPITER

Satellite	Diameter	Mean distance from Jupiter	Sidereal Period of Revolution		
	miles	miles	days	hours	mins.
V	100	112,500	—	11	57
	(about)				
I Io	2,109	261,000	1	18	28
II Europa ..	1,865	415,000	3	13	14
III Ganymede	3,273	664,000	7	3	43
XI	—	718,600	—	—	—
IV Callisto ..	3,142	1,167,000	16	16	32
VI	130	7,113,000	250	14	40
	(about)				
X	—	7,186,000	254	5	0
VII	40	7,390,000	260	1	24
	(about)				
VIII	25	14,600,000	738	21	36
	(about)				
IX	11–17	14,690,000	745	(about)	

of Jupiter's orbit, and also of the fact that two of the satellites have a retrograde motion, it seems probable that they are 'captured' planetoids.

The four large Galilean moons are of great interest, and would be perceptible to the naked eye were it not for their apparent close proximity to the radiant Jupiter. As it is, Ganymede and Callisto may be observed with good field glasses, appearing, at times, about one-twelfth and one-sixth of a degree respectively either to the right or the left of the planet. (A degree is approximately twice our moon's apparent width.)

Observed through powerful telescopes, these satellites present perceptible disks with distinct markings sufficient to indicate that each satellite keeps the same face turned towards Jupiter. The changes in their relative positions, and, more particularly, their eclipse and transit phenomena, provide a constant fund of entertainment to possessors of smaller telescopes. These changes occur several times a week, the orbits of the satellites being so nearly in the plane of Jupiter's equator that they all, except Callisto, pass through the planet's shadow and are eclipsed or occulted at every revolution. When they pass between us and Jupiter they are seen to travel in transit across the latter's disk.

The times of these occurrences are known today with great precision, but in the seventeenth century it was found that they seldom took place at the expected time— either they were too early, or too late, the difference often amounting to several minutes. Then, in 1675, Roemer, a Danish astronomer, explained the discrepancies as being due to the time light takes to travel across the space between us and the satellites. As we have seen, this distance varies, and Jupiter is, at times, over 200 million miles nearer than at others ; hence, as the distance of Jupiter increases so the satellite phenomena appear delayed, the reverse occurring as Jupiter draws nearer. It is now known that light travels at the rate of 186,325 miles per second, but Roemer's explanation was not accepted for more than fifty years, until it was confirmed by Bradley's discovery of the aberration of light.

LESSON 16

Saturn and Its System of Rings

SATURN, the second largest of the planets, is the most impressive of them on account of the ring system which encircles the planet ; this is seen from year to year at a different angle, and so provides an ever-varying spectacle. Now, while the sphere of Saturn is 95·2 times more massive than the earth, it is 763 times the size or volume ; this indicates how exceedingly light in density the planet must be. Its density is only 0·12 that of the earth and 0·69 that of water. Assuming Saturn to be of equal density throughout, it would float on water.

The planet's mean diameter is 73,000 miles, but, owing to its great oblateness or polar flattening, it is more elliptical than any other planet. This amounts to about 10 per cent, so while its equatorial diameter is 75,100 miles, its polar diameter amounts to only 67,200 miles. As a result of this difference bodies would weigh about 30 per cent less at the equatorial regions of Saturn, as compared with the polar. This oval shape of the planet is very obvious when the rings are presented edgewise, and, therefore, are almost invisible. This equatorial bulge, amounting to nearly 4,000 miles, is due to Saturn's very rapid rotation, which takes only 10 hours 14 minutes 24 seconds at the planet's equatorial regions, but from 20 to 25 minutes longer in the belts to the north and south. In this respect Saturn resembles Jupiter and the sun.

Since the axis of the planet is inclined 26° 45′ to the plane of its orbit, it has well defined seasons, but of immense length, the sidereal period of its revolution being 29 years 167 days. A season on Saturn is, therefore, between 7 and 8 of our years in length. Saturn revolves at an average distance from the sun of 9·54 astronomical units, or 886,000,000 miles, but, the eccentricity of its orbit amounting to 0·056, the planet's distance varies between 936,000,000 miles at aphelion and 836,000,000 at perihelion. Therefore, while Saturn may approach the earth to within 745,000,000 at its nearest opposition it will be about 100 million miles farther off at an aphelion opposition; consequently, this adds to the great variation in the apparent brightness of Saturn.

The planet's sphere, which, like Jupiter and the sun, appears brightest in the centre and fades off round the edges, has a very high albedo, amounting to 0·42. It is crossed by several belts, faint replicas of those of Jupiter, with the broad equatorial belt a brilliant yellow, the tropical and temperate belts greyish, and the polar caps of a greenish tint. On the belts appear occasionally white or dark spots, together with faint, indistinct shadings.

These belts represent clouds of vapour in an atmosphere of great depth, doubtless of many thousands of miles, the rapid rotation at different rates spreading the clouds out into belts which rush past one another at great speeds. A difference of over 750 miles an hour exists between the speed of the great equatorial belt and those of more temperate latitudes.

It has hitherto been considered probable that several thousands of miles beneath this visible cloud-laden surface a hot and possibly molten surface existed. Various considerations warranted this conclusion notwithstanding the lack of solar heat. But in recent years theories propounded by Dr. Jeffreys on Jupiter (*see* page 276) have credited Saturn, not only with an intensely cold atmosphere, but with an average depth of some 16,000 miles, enveloping a world covered with ice to a depth of 6,000 miles, this in turn enclosing a solid rocky core about 28,000 miles in diameter. This fanciful presentation is, of course, highly speculative, but, as in the case of Jupiter, it has obtained some credence owing to the atmosphere of Saturn being found to possess a large proportion of methane and a relatively greater proportion of ammonia, as compared with Jupiter, this being attributed to the much greater cold experienced by Saturn owing to its much greater distance from the sun.

System of Rings. Saturn's ring system is unique and, when wide open, exhibits a large area of the surfaces of the rings. It adds about one and two-third times to the brilliance of Saturn observed with the naked eye. In the year 1936 they almost vanished; then they began to open out, to reach their widest in July 1943. After this they will begin to close up until, in the year 1950, they will almost vanish again. During this time it will be the south side of the rings that will be presented to view.

SATURN AND ITS RINGS. *Discovered by Galileo in 1610, the ring system of Saturn was thought to be a solid body or bodies, but it is now held to be composed of an aggregation of small moonlets revolving about the planet with great rapidity.*

The successive phases they go through are indicated in the illustration in page 278, the dark equatorial band shown in the 1921 picture being the shadow produced by the invisble rings on the planet's surface. At intervals of nearly 15 years the rings go through all their phases, but alternately in the reverse direction presenting the north and then the south side of the rings to our view. When at their maximum they extend a little above the globe of the planet and possess an apparent diameter about one-sixth more than Saturn. Just before vanishing the rings appear as a thin line of light projecting from each side of the planet's disk, but when the rings are presented quite edgewise they entirely vanish, and in their place, as seen with most powerful telescopes, are a string of dots and streaks, suggesting that the rings are not more than 50 miles in thickness.

In extent the rings are enormous, resembling vast concentric disks, the outer one with a diameter of 171,500 miles. There are three main divisions of the ring system, known as A, B and C. The outer ring, A, being less bright and distinct, is about 10,000 miles wide. This is separated from B, which is much the brightest ring, by Cassini's division, which is between 2,000 and 3,000 miles in width. The ring B is about 16,000 miles wide, and has a diameter averaging 145,000 miles. These rings vary in width, together with the divisions between them, on account of perturbations caused by Saturn's satellites, to which are doubtless due the additional divisions occasionally seen, the ring A being sometimes divided by what is known as Encke's division.

Inside the bright ring B is a division probably about 1,000 miles wide separating it from the inner ring C, which is very faint and dusky. While permitting the ball of the planet to show through, it does not appear in the illustrations in page 278. It is usually known as the 'crape ring,' and is about 11,000 miles in width, the indistinct inner edge of which is between 6,000 and 7,000 miles from the planet's surface. While the rings produce a distinct shadow upon the planet, it will be seen that the globe of Saturn also casts a very dark shadow over the rings.

Composition of the Rings. The rings of Saturn have been proved to be composed of innumerable particles in steady but very rapid rotation round Saturn—'moonlets'

as we might say—each with its own orbit and travelling in the same direction, that is, counter-clockwise and almost in the same plane as the chief satellites. A few of these particles may approach 50 miles in diameter, judging by the appearance of the rings when seen edgewise, but the great majority must be of small dimensions, perhaps no larger than golf balls or small shot, because the total mass appears to be less than a quarter the mass of our moon. They revolve round Saturn at about 10 miles a second on the outer edge of the ring system, a particle thus taking nearly 140 hours to complete a revolution round that edge of the system. At the inner edge they attain a speed of about $12\frac{1}{2}$ miles a second, and so complete their revolution on this smaller circumference in about five hours.

In 1857 Clerk-Maxwell had shown from theoretical considerations that the rings must be composed of separate particles like swarms of meteorites. The fact that the planet and some of Saturn's satellites could be seen through the less dense parts of the rings confirmed this. Then, in 1895, Keeler proved conclusively, by spectroscopic observation, that the inner portions travelled faster than the outer, and exactly as they would if they were composed of particles, their light and other considerations leaving finally no doubt in the matter.

The Planet's Satellites. Saturn's satellites amount to nine, or, if the doubtful Themis be included, to ten. Their chief details are given in the accompanying table.

SATELLITES OF SATURN

Satellite	Diameter in miles	Mean Distance from Saturn	Sidereal Period of Revolution		
	(about)	miles	days	hours	min.
Mimas	370	115,300	—	22	37
Enceladus ..	460	148,000	1	8	53
Tethys	750	184,000	1	21	18
Dione	900	235,000	2	17	41
Rhea	1,150	327,500	4	12	25
Titan	3,550	760 000	15	22	41
Hyperion ..	300	920,000	21	6	38
Iapetus ..	1,000	2,220,000	79	7	56
Phoebe ..	200	7,996,000	550	10	35

Themis, whose supposed discovery was made by W. H. Pickering in 1905, has not been seen since, so its existence is discredited. Titan, first observed by Huygens in 1655, has a diameter greater than that of the planet Mercury, and appears to be the largest satellite in the solar system. It is above ninth magnitude, and can be seen with small telescopes of 2 to 3 inches aperture, while in large instruments it exhibits a disk with periodic variations in brilliance. Its mass is greater in proportion than that of our moon and about $3\frac{1}{2}$ times that of water, so Titan appears to be also the most massive of all the satellites of the solar system, so far as is known.

Tethys, Dione, Rhea and Iapetus were discovered by Cassini in 1700. The densities of the first three are very low, while their albedo is high, suggesting a gaseous condition quite unlike Titan. Mimas and Enceladus, discovered by Sir William Herschel in 1789, are the lightest in density, Mimas being over two thousand times less than the moon ; it, therefore, may be nothing but a mass of cloud. Hyperion was discovered by W. C. Bond in 1848, and has also a very low density. Phoebe was found photographically by W. H. Pickering in 1898, and is remarkable as being the only one with a retrograde motion round Saturn ; this, together with its great eccentricity of 0·166 and very great inclination of about 149° to the planet's equator, points to the satellite being a 'captured' planetoid.

The fact that sunlight is 90 times less (1/90) per unit area at the distance of Saturn, as compared with the earth, renders the satellites rather faint objects ; but regular variation in their brightness is perceptible, and from this it appears that they keep the same face toward Saturn as does our moon to the earth.

LESSON 17

Uranus, the Green Planet

URANUS, the next planet beyond Saturn, being about twice as far from the earth, presents therefore a much smaller disk and with but little detail perceptible. It is, however, of great interest, because Uranus was the first additional world to be discovered, and it led directly to the finding of Neptune. The discovery of Uranus was made by Sir William Herschel on March 13, 1781, with the 7-inch reflector telescope which he had made himself. At first the new body was regarded as a tailless comet, but by the following year it was found to be a planet moving in an orbit quite unlike that of a comet. Lalande and Continental astronomers gave it the name of Herschel ; then, later, Bode named it Uranus after the father of Saturn in Greek mythology. This gradually displaced the other name.

By referring to old star catalogues and previous observations it was found that Uranus had been recorded many times as a star, including an observation recorded by Flamsteed, the first Astronomer Royal, in 1690. Uranus appears as a star of the sixth magnitude, and is, therefore, just discernible to the naked eye, a good telescope being required to show its planetary disk. It may seem surprising that the keen-eyed ancient astronomers had not noticed Uranus in the clear air of Egypt and Chaldea, but the apparent movements of this planet are so slow, taking 84 years and six days to complete a circuit of the heavens (this being the planet's year), that its daily motion would, therefore, escape notice.

The mean distance of Uranus from the sun is 1,783,000,000 miles, but, the eccentricity of its orbit being 0·047, its actual distance therefore varies between about 1,866,000,000 when at aphelion and 1,698,000,000 at perihelion ; consequently there is very little difference in its apparent brightness or size as seen from the earth, its angular diameter averaging about 3·75″ (seconds of arc) and attaining about 4″ when at its nearest.

Uranus is 59 times the size of the earth ; but, though so much greater in volume, Uranus is only 14·6 times the mass, consequently its density is only 0·25 that of the earth or 1·36 times that of water. It therefore resembles Saturn and Jupiter in density, and also in possessing a very deep gaseous envelope. The mean diameter of Uranus according to the outer cloud surface of this atmospheric envelope is about 31,900 miles, but, as in the case of Saturn and Jupiter, its polar diameter is much less than the equatorial, amounting to about 1/14 less. The planet's ellipticity indicates a very rapid rotation, which has been found to amount to only 10 hours, 49 minutes ; this represents the length of a Uranian day, except so far as they are abnormally lengthened by the planet's remarkable arrangement of seasons.

Uranus rotates at the surprising angle of about 98 degrees to the plane of the planet's orbit. At this angle the greater part of the northern hemisphere and, alternately, the southern would remain continuously in the sunlight for 21 years ; this is the length of a season on Uranus, while a winter night of similar length would be experienced. On the other hand, the sun appears at that distance only as a very bright star with a scarcely perceptible disk and with a surface 368 times less, so Uranus must receive 368 times less light and heat than the earth. From this we see that twilight conditions must prevail on Uranus, providing that this feeble sunlight can penetrate the planet's dense cloud canopy. A

SYSTEM OF URANUS, showing the singular angles of the equatorial belts, planes of orbits and position of poles.

curious and unexplained circumstance is the greenish tint of the disk of Uranus, a feature which is shared by Neptune. It indicates the presence of an extremely rarefied and unknown gas ; the spectrum of Uranus, while consisting of reflected sunlight, contains absorption bands indicating that pure hydrogen is in the planet's upper atmosphere, and also a still greater quantity of methane than in the case of Jupiter and Saturn.

The surface of Uranus exhibits belts similar to those of Saturn, but much fainter and tilted at the remarkable angle that is almost perpendicular to the plane of the planet's orbit. This orbit has an inclination of only 46′ (minutes of arc) to the plane of the earth's orbit, and is, therefore, about the same. The albedo of Uranus is very high, amounting to 0·60, as would be expected from a cloud-laden atmosphere of great reflecting power.

Satellites. Uranus has four satellites, their chief details being shown below. They are all extremely faint. Titania and Oberon, appearing about 14½ magnitude,

were discovered by Sir William Herschel in 1787. Ariel, about 16 magnitude, and Umbriel, about 16½ magnitude, were discovered by Lassell in 1851. The most remarkable features about these satellites are that they all appear to travel in a retrograde direction round Uranus (that is, clockwise), a motion that is shared by the rotation of the planet itself, which is also retrograde ; also that the orbits of these satellites are at an extreme angle to the plane of the planet's orbit. This amounts apparently to 82° (degrees of arc), but is actually 98°, when theoretical considerations are taken into account.

These point to the conclusion that Uranus at some far-distant epoch turned over to this angle of 98° together with its satellites, or while the whole was in a gaseous state and before the birth of the satellites ; for since the planet rotates in the same plane and direction as the satellites, the inverting process must have been common to both. The most probable cause would appear to have been the near approach of some great body—another sun perhaps—which, by raising great tides on the plastic and possibly half-formed world of Uranus, was thus able to alter its axis of rotation long ages before the satellites came into existence.

Now the south pole of Uranus is actually on a higher level relative to the plane of its orbit than is its north pole as the result of inversion ; thus the effect is produced of the revolution of its moons being retrograde, whereas their motion is in reality direct. If the student experiments with a ball to imitate the rotation of Uranus and its satellites, it will be seen that, whereas normally they will appear to revolve, say, from left to right, if they are inverted they will appear to revolve from right to left, though still continuing in the same rotation.

Uranus was in 1942 in the constellation of Taurus, remaining in it for seven years, since the planet's annual motion through the heavens amounts to an average of only 4¼ degrees, though it is actually travelling at about 4¼ miles a second.

SATELLITES OF URANUS

Name	Diameter in miles	Mean Distance from Uranus	Sidereal Period of Revolution		
	(about)	miles	days	hours	mins.
Ariel	900	120,000	2	12	29
Umbriel	700	167,000	4	3	28
Titania	1,700	273,000	8	16	56
Oberon	1,500	365,000	13	11	7

The physical condition of the planet is generally regarded as being similar to that of Jupiter and Saturn, the actual surface being some thousands of miles below its atmospheric cloud surface. It may be at a great heat—probably molten, more or less— notwithstanding what must be a very frigid exterior. Nevertheless the possibility of a frigid and solid interior similar to those suggested for Jupiter and Saturn (*see* Lessons 15 and 16) would also apply to the planet Uranus.

LESSON 18

Discovery of Neptune and Pluto

NEPTUNE, for long regarded as the outermost planet of the solar system, is not visible to the naked eye, though it may be glimpsed with powerful field-glasses. Its discovery in 1846 was the result of one of the greatest triumphs of mathematical astronomy. The existence of a world beyond Uranus had been suspected as the cause of certain accelerations and retardations in its orbit, which amounted to nearly two minutes of arc. While Saturn and Jupiter accounted for part of this irregularity, the residue was suggested by the astronomer Bessel as due to a planet beyond Uranus.

Then, in 1845, the English astronomer J. C. Adams and, in 1846, the French astronomer Leverrier independently calculated where this supposed planet must be. Though Adams had computed the position first and informed the Astronomer Royal by letter, his communication was neglected, and he thus lost the honour of the discovery. It was not until July 19, 1846, that Professor Challis, of the Cambridge University Observatory, took up the search at the suggestion of G. B. Airy, the Astronomer Royal, as Leverrier's results had now been made known.

In August, 1846, Leverrier's elements of the planet's position, which were in accord with those already computed by Adams, were published. Subsequently, Leverrier wrote to the observatory at Berlin, on September 18, asking them to search for a 'new planet looking like a star of the ninth magnitude and having a perceptible disk,' indicating also where it was to be found. It was discovered within half an hour, and only 52 minutes of arc from the place predicted ; it possessed the apparent disk but was a magnitude brighter. This was a great achievement for Leverrier, and one in which Adams shares the honour, though at the time it caused much controversy, for Professor Challis at Cambridge had actually observed the planet weeks before, but in the absence of good star-charts had failed to identify its presence.

Neptune's mean distance from the sun is 30·06 astronomical units ; from this it departs relatively little, being at aphelion 2,816,000,000 miles, and at perihelion 2,768,000,000 miles from the sun. The eccentricity of Neptune's orbit is, therefore, only 0·0086, and its orbit the most circular of all the planets, except that of Venus. Moreover, the inclination of its orbit to the ecliptic is only 1° 47′.

While the mass of Neptune is 17 times that of the earth, its size or volume is 72 times ; therefore the planet's density is much less, being 0·24 that of the earth or 1·32 that of water. Neptune is, therefore, but little denser than Uranus, and is generally a replica of that planet, except that it exists under much more frigid conditions as regards solar heat. The sun would appear as a very bright star, and to the unaided eye would exhibit no perceptible disk. The heat and light received by Neptune are 900 times less, area for area, than are received by the earth ; although this solar light would far exceed our brightest moonlight, Neptune is a world of twilight.

It rotates very rapidly in about 15 hours 40 minutes on an axis inclined about 61 degrees to the planet's orbit. Since it takes 164 years 280 days to complete a revolution of the same, Neptune has very pronounced seasons of great length, amounting to about 41 of our years.

Telescopically, Neptune's disk appears to have an average diameter of only 2·3 seconds of arc. From this its real diameter has been calculated to be between 31,000 and 34,800 miles ; the difference is possibly the result of the planet's polar flattening being presented at different angles in the course of many years. Neptune has the high albedo of 0·52, indicating a cloud-covered surface. This, as in the case of Uranus, appears greenish, but without trace of belts or markings, the details so far ascertained being revealed spectroscopically. These indicate a very dense and deep atmosphere, and while its surface may be 220 degrees below zero (Centigrade), yet great heat doubtless exists in its depths, where, however, neither sunlight nor solar heat may ever penetrate. On the other hand, frigid conditions may exist similar to those now suggested for Jupiter, Saturn and Uranus.

Neptune's Only Satellite. Triton, the only known satellite of Neptune, revolves in a period of 5 days 21 hours 2½ minutes, at an average distance of 220,000 miles from Neptune's centre, and so almost as far as the moon is from the earth. Its orbit is retrograde and inclined at between 35° and 40° to that of Neptune. It appears to possess the remarkable property of a varying angle of inclination, which has been found to change in the course of many years to the extent of about 10°; this deflection of the path of the satellite has been ascribed to variations in the plane of Neptune's equator. Triton was discovered by Lassell in 1846. It is very faint, appearing about 13th magnitude, and is, therefore, estimated to be approximately the size of our moon.

Since the discovery of Neptune the existence of yet another world beyond this planet has been suspected for many years. Further unaccounted perturbations of Uranus, together with the fact that the aphelia of several comets might, therefore, be accounted for, stimulated the search by methods similar to those of Adams and Leverrier. The existence of 'families' of comets had long been regarded as indicating worlds beyond Neptune, because, while the comets had the sun at the perihelion end of their very elliptical orbits, they had one of the greater planets near the aphelion end. Now, since certain comets had their aphelia far beyond the orbit of Neptune, these were regarded as pointing to Trans-Neptunian planets, but they supplied no further data.

More definite were the small irregularities in the motion of Uranus, Neptune and even Saturn, which could not otherwise be accounted for. Dr. Percival Lowell, Professor W. H. Pickering and A. Gaillot, in particular, made elaborate mathematical calculations to locate the Trans-Neptunian world which they firmly believed existed. An immense amount of work was involved in these, Percival Lowell publishing his 'Memoir on Trans-Neptunian Planet' in 1915. This indicated the region where the body, which he termed Planet X, would be found. Professor W. H. Pickering also published his estimate of the approximate position of this unknown world as early as 1919.

Discovery of the Unknown Planet. Though an intermittent search was maintained after Lowell's death in 1916, it was not until January 21, 1930, that it was discovered. It had been the rule at the Lowell Observatory at Flagstaff, Arizona, to photograph those regions in some part of which, according to Lowell's elements, the planet might be situated, and then to scrutinize the plates to find any small dash in place of the multitude of dots which represented the so-called fixed stars. It was thus that the young assistant at the observatory, Clive W. Tombaugh, discovered the world beyond Neptune on one of the photographic plates. Dr. V. M. Slipher, chief of the observatory, closely studied the moving body; elements were calculated, and then, on March 13, the official announcement was made that the Trans-Neptunian planet

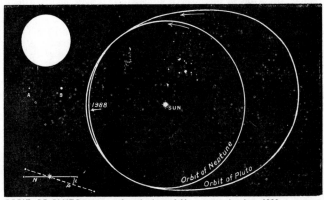

ORBIT OF PLUTO compared with that of Neptune ; the date 1988 represents the next perihelion of Pluto. Top left, the sun as seen from the earth ; A, sun as seen from Pluto at aphelion ; B, at perihelion. In the diagram, bottom left : N, diameter of Neptune's orbit ; P, greatest diameter of Pluto's orbit ; I, inclination of Pluto's orbit to Neptune's.

was actually discovered only 6 degrees away from the place assigned to it fifteen years earlier by Lowell's elements. It was subsequently found that Professor W. H. Pickering's predicted position was only about 10 degrees from where the planet was found, while some of his figures relating to it were closer than Lowell's.

Pluto is estimated from its brightness to be about half the diameter of the earth, or 4,000 miles, the period of its revolution round the sun being 248 years. Its orbit is the most elliptical of all the planets, ranging from about 50 astronomical units in aphelion, that is, 4,650,000,000 miles, to 29·6 units, or 2,753,000,000 miles, at perihelion. Then, it comes within the orbit of Neptune, but at the high inclination of its plane of 17 degrees to the ecliptic, so Neptune and Pluto can never meet.

At present Pluto is at a distance of about 3,700,000,000 miles, and it is gradually coming closer to us each year. Sunlight is there equivalent to our moonlight, while Pluto at present receives about 1,500 times less heat and light from the sun than the earth does.

The possibility of yet another world beyond Pluto is now seriously considered, and Professor W. H. Pickering, at the Mandeville Observatory, Jamaica, has made exhaustive computations by which he hopes with the increasing powers of great telescopes that it may be discovered.

LESSON 19

The Three Classes of Comets

THE name comet is derived from the Greek *kométés*, long-haired, a name that had its origin in the hairy appearance of the luminous mist which surrounds the celestial body known as a comet and which, in many, trails away into space ; this appearance forms the so-called tail, and obtained for comets their old title of *stellae comatae*, that is, 'hairy stars.' About 950 comets are known, the elements of whose orbits have been computed ; while, on an average, about five new ones are discovered each year. The greatest number observed in one year is fourteen, in 1932 ; of these eight were new comets. ·

The majority of comets have never been seen without telescopic aid ; as a rule, not more than about one in ten becomes easily visible to the naked eye. Occasionally, a splendid body appears, with a nucleus that may be as bright as Venus and with a tail that stretches half way from the horizon to the sky overhead ; but only about five of these great comets may be expected on an average in a century.

While a comet usually possesses a bright central nucleus or a perceptible condensation surrounded by a more or less spherical mass of fainter luminosity, called the coma, the radiant tail is frequently imperceptible or absent from the smaller comets, or it may develop as the comet approaches the sun. From the orbits of several hundred comets which have been defined the majority are found to be parabolic, a large number elliptical and a few bolic, a large number elliptical and a few hyperbolic ; but as only a small portion of a comet's orbit—i.e. that which is in the vicinity of the earth and the sun— is observable, it becomes a question as to whether the entire orbit may not be elliptical. If some are hyperbolic it appears certain that these comets, therefore, leave the solar system never to return. The orbits of nearly a hundred comets are definitely known to be elliptical, so that their return to the sun may be predicted ; these are known as periodic comets.

Such comets are better known than the others, since in many cases the return of the same comet has been observed several times, as in the case of Halley's famous comet, and of Encke's comet, observed for 33 returns. Thus it becomes possible to note the changes, both in the comet's period and its structure, which have occurred in the intervals of their return.

Generally, the eccentricity of these cometary orbits is much greater than that of the planets and most planetoids. Therefore, the comet approaches comparatively close to the sun at the perihelion end of its orbit, while the aphelion may be within the orbit of Jupiter or it may be far beyond that of Neptune ; so the period of its return may be anything between 3½ years and 10,000 years. These comets are divided into two classes : (1) the short-period comets ; (2) the long-period comets.

Short-Period Comets. About 50 comets are known with short-period orbits, requiring between three and nine years for

Comets

the comets to complete a revolution and return to perihelion. These comets are all faint objects, only a few being perceptible to the naked eye. They are usually known by the name of their discoverer, but their full title states also the year of discovery and the order of discovery relative to others, thus : Geddes' comet 1932 *g*, and Faye's comet 1932 *h*, the letters in italics indicating that these comets were the seventh and eighth discovered in 1932. There is another form of nomenclature used by astronomers, based upon the time the comet arrives at perihelion, when it passes closest the sun, and which, therefore, represents the major axis of its orbit. This affords greater precision than the order of discovery, since a comet may overtake another which was found earlier, and arrive at perihelion first. So in the case of comets discovered before the present year or two, this form of nomenclature is usually adopted ; it is expressed thus : Coggia's comet 1874 III, or Taylor's comet 1916 I. The Roman numerals replace the letters when the perihelion time is established.

All these short-period comets have their aphelion point not far from the orbit of Jupiter — some within it to the extent of about 90,000,000 miles, as in the case of Encke's comet, which is the least of all. A few have it about 100,000,000 miles beyond Jupiter's orbit, but, on an average, they are within 22,000,000 miles. A remarkable feature is that the inclination of their orbits to the ecliptic is within 30°, whereas, generally, comets' orbits are at all inclinations from 0° to 90°. Moreover, their motion is direct, that is, they travel round the sun in the same direction as Jupiter and the other planets. These are elements which indicate that these comets are an integral part of the solar system ; also that they are a great family of comets dominated by Jupiter, which somehow has caused them to possess these orbits ; for this reason they are known as the Jovian family of comets.

There are other very similar, though generally much larger comets, which have their aphelia

comparatively near to the orbits of the outer planets : Saturn has thus a 'family' of two comets, Uranus three, and Neptune six, while Pluto also appears to possess some. There are also other groups whose aphelion points are several times the distance of Neptune or even Pluto ; this seems to suggest the existence of other undiscovered worlds.

Halley's Comet. The best known member of these families of comets is Halley's, so named because Halley computed its orbit for the first time and, having identified it with several which had previously appeared, predicted its return to perihelion in March, 1759. He did not live to see this forecast verified, for he died before its return, but ever since it has been known as Halley's comet ; it returned as predicted, on March 13, and with a tail 50 degrees long, that is, about 100 times the apparent width of the moon. The discovery of Halley's comet is lost in the mists of antiquity. The historical records of its return go back through the years 1682, 1607, 1531, 1456, 1301, 1145, to 1066, the famous historical year commemorated on the Bayeux Tapestry, which depicts Halley's comet. Thence it has been traced to 240 B.C.

From the evidence it is found that the comet returns at an average interval of 75 to 76 years, with a variation of about 18 months each way, due to planetary accelerations and retardations, its motion being retrograde. Following Halley's predicted return, it again appeared to time in 1835, but with a tail only 10 degrees in length, which occasioned some anxiety as to the possible condition of the comet at its next return in 1910.

This was predicted with remarkable accuracy by the astronomers Cowell and Crommelin of Greenwich Observatory.

ENCKE'S COMET. Discovered by J. L. Pons of Marseilles in 1818, this short-period comet is named after the German astronomer, J. F. Encke (1791-1865), who first determined its orbit and demonstrated that it had been previously observed in 1786, 1795 and 1805. The period of its recurrence or revolution about the sun is approximately 1,200 days.

The comet returned to perihelion on April 20 and proved the most sensational astronomical event for many years, since it had regained all its old splendour and through coming so close to the earth surpassed itself as a celestial spectacle. The weather and conditions were not very favourable in this country, but the comet was very well observed farther south and in America and the tropics.

It appeared at its best as an early morning object in the early part of May, when its nucleus rivalled the brightest stars and its tail attained a length of 60 degrees. Later, when at its nearest to the earth and only 14,300,000 miles away, the tail had broadened out to a band of luminosity resembling the Milky Way; it was then about 120 degrees in length and stretched two-thirds across the sky, though the comet's head

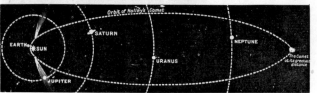

was not then visible. It is believed that the earth actually passed through the tail on May 21 of that year. This comet may be regarded as typical of this class of periodic comets—and a very good specimen, because it usually approaches close to our world.

Long-Period Comets. The comets of long period, of which there are not many with *known* elliptical orbits, are best exemplified in a well-known group, two of the most famous being the magnificent comets of 1843 and 1882. These are so similar as to be almost identical. Both passed through the sun's corona at perihelion and less than 300,000 miles above the sun's surface, so from the earth they would have appeared less than half the sun's diameter away. In their close approach to the sun they resembled the great long-period comets of 1668, 1880 and 1887. They had another common resemblance in approaching the sun from almost the same point in space—the direction of the brilliant star Sirius—and in possessing almost identical elements of their orbits. It was as if they were various apparitions of the same object, which was, however, impossible. The comets of 1843 and 1882 presented vastly different spectacles owing to the different distances and perspective from which they were viewed by observers.

The comet 1843 I was calculated to have a period of between 400 and 800 years, while that of the comet 1882 III was computed to be between 600 and 900 years. Now, it so happened that the 1882 comet—after its violent ordeal, when it passed so close to the terrific solar furnace—emerged as a 'broken comet' and split into four divisions, which gradually parted company and travelled away into the depths of space as four comets along slightly different paths. The astronomer Kreutz has calculated that they will return after a lapse of 664, 769, 875 and 959 years for each portion, when a great comet will be observed, which will be only a fourth part of the original comet 1882 III.

Thus the singular grouping of the five great comets, those of 1668, 1843, 1880, 1882 and 1887, may be accounted for as

HALLEY'S COMET. The photograph at top shows the famous comet in relation to the planet Venus. A periodic comet, returning at intervals of 75-76 years, it has been observed for more than 2,000 years. The diagram below shows its orbit.

Photo, Union Observatory, Johannesburg

being due to a still greater comet sub-
dividing, long ages ago, on one of its
visits to the sun, as did the 1882 comet.

Non-Periodic Comets. The comets with
parabolic orbits are the most numerous,
and, together with those possessing what
appear to be hyperbolic orbits, the most
mysterious. As these bodies usually only
become visible somewhere within a limit
of about 450 million miles, we may never
even know the existence of all those with
a perihelion distance beyond this. The
greater proportion of these comets, about
63 per cent, come within the earth's orbit,
and another 30 per cent between the orbits
of the earth and Mars to perihelion.

Now, since about 300 new comets
of this class (as distinct from the periodic
comets considered in pages 284–6) are discovered in a century, with a tendency to
increasing numbers, the total must amount
to several thousands. The all-important
question is whether they ever return. The
relatively small portions of their orbits
which are observable permit of the possibility that, instead of parabolas, they may
be extremely elongated ellipses, in which
their outward and return paths are almost
parallel. This is, of course, *relative to
the sun;* but since the sun, together with
the whole solar system, is travelling very
rapidly in a certain direction in space,
we realize that, *relative to space*, these
comets' orbits would be far from parabolic.
They might, therefore, be ellipses if they
return, or hyperbolas if they do not.

Now, it so happens that there are about
20 comets whose orbits are apparently
hyperbolic. When, however, account is
taken of the deviating attractions of the
greater planets, particularly Jupiter and
Saturn, it is found that the comets' paths,
which may have originally been ellipses,
have been distorted in approaching the
sun into hyperbolas, and into what appear
to be hyperbolas as they recede from the
sun, whereas actually the orbits are ellipses,
and so the comets will eventually return.

Thus, the evidence inclines toward all
comets being an integral part of the solar
system, and, consequently, the old belief
that the parabolic and hyperbolic comets
travel across space from star to star and
visit our sun but once, is improbable.

Comets Have Mass. That comets are
celestial bodies and not intangible phenomena is proved by their being governed
by the force of gravitation. Therefore,
they must have mass ; this has been found
to be very small in proportion to their

COMET'S STELLAR BACKGROUND. In this photograph of Morehouse's comet of 1908, the slanting
lines represent the images of stars, shown thus in
the photo owing to the movement of the telescope
in following the comet, which moves considerably
along its path during the long exposure—in this
case 30 minutes—that was necessary.

volume or bulk, and though it has not
been found possible to measure a comet's
mass definitely, it is certain that the largest
comets do not contain more material
in their composition than could be condensed into a sphere 10 miles in diameter.
This small mass has been proved by the
fact that comets exercise no perceptible
perturbing or deflecting force on the
planets, whereas the latter produce great
perturbations upon comets.

Nearly all the body of a comet is contained within its nucleus, that is, the bright
centre within its head or coma. Comets
shine partly by reflected sunlight, but are to
a certain extent self-luminous. Moreover,
while the coma and nucleus, if any, obey
the laws of gravitation, the tail does not.
This always curves and floats away into
space in a direction opposite to the sun's
attraction ; hence as a comet recedes from
the sun after perihelion, its tail always
precedes it. A comet may have more than
one tail—perhaps three or four extending
fan-shaped or as curved streamers, this effect
being produced by the comet's motion.

Composition of the Tail. The tail appears to be composed of exceedingly minute
particles of matter generated by the comet

in the form of highly rarefied gas. The particles are so small and light that the radiation pressure of the sun's light is greater than the sun's gravitational pull ; they are thus driven away into space, causing a continuous loss to the comet. The particles composing the tail are seen being produced in bright comets from the head as jets of light or as hollow luminous rings ; the processes are often well shown in photographs of comets. The tail is frequently absent from smaller comets—as if all the finer particles which might enter into its composition had been lost. On the other hand, a comet may develop a large tail and also a brilliant nucleus, originally absent, as it approaches the sun, the brightness of the comet continually increasing.

There is always a more or less globular head or coma, which, in a typical comet, contains a bright nucleus ; but in many instances, particularly in small comets, the nucleus may be absent and replaced by a more diffuse condensation, as shown in the picture of Encke's comet in page 285. Occasionally the condensation is absent, particularly when the comet is at a great distance from the sun ; then the comet will frequently develop a nucleus as it approaches the sun, and go through fluctuations of brilliancy with successive outbursts of material which expand the tail. In a few exceptional instances the nucleus has been seen to become double (and even quadruple in the case of the Great comet 1882 III), but in these cases the phenomenon precedes division of the comet.

Vast Size of Comets. The dimensions of comets impress us by their vastness. The head of Halley's comet had at one time during its last visit a diameter of 550,000 miles, two-thirds that of the sun ; but this had varied between 30,000 and 220,000 miles during most of its visibility while approaching and receding from the sun. The head of the Great comet 1811 I was over a million miles in diameter—that is, it was much larger than the sun. On an average the heads of comets are between 10,000 and 150,000 miles in diameter.

The nucleus within the head or coma is much smaller, often not more than 100 miles in diameter. The nucleus of the Great comet 1811 I was only 428 miles at one time, while that of Halley's comet was only about 500 miles across. The nucleus of the Great comet 1882 III, before it divided, was 1,800 miles in diameter—one of the largest known. Donati's famous comet 1858 VI had a nucleus only about 630 miles across at a time when its tail was 45,000,000 miles in length. As with other parts of a comet, the nucleus varies considerably in size as it progresses in its path toward the sun. The nucleus of Donati's comet, for instance, varied between 5,000 miles and only 400 in width, shrinking as it neared the sun, but at the same time greatly increasing in brilliancy. The tail, on the other hand, expanded enormously. This comet had an elliptical orbit ; it is expected to return in about 2,000 years. We see that the dimensions of comets vary considerably. The Great comet 1811 I had a tail over 100,000,000 miles long, so it would have stretched farther than from the earth to the sun. The tails of the Great comet 1822 III were 60,000,000 miles long, with a diameter reaching to 15,000,000 miles. Their volume must have been colossal, yet stars will shine through all this cometary material with undiminished lustre; from this we gain some idea of their tenuity. Schwarzschild calculated that there could not have been more material in 2,000 cubic miles of the tail of Halley's comet than there is in a cubic inch of ordinary air.

Composition of the Nucleus. The nucleus is much more substantial, spectroscopy revealing the presence of nitrogen, cyanogen, hydrocarbons, carbon monoxide and radiations of sodium and iron when the comet is nearer the sun. These gases do not represent all the materials composing the nucleus, but only the radiant product of the commotion, friction or combustion taking place in the nucleus. There is good reason for regarding most of the elements with which we are familiar as entering into the composition of comets. This will be explained when we deal with meteors, and also why the nucleus of comets is now regarded as composed of innumerable discrete particles ranging from the size of grains and pebbles to masses a hundred feet or more in diameter. How close all these particles are together or what is the nature and speed of their movements, to produce the intense luminosity when near the sun, the emission of gases and the material for their gigantic luminous tail, can only be inferred from the meteoric matter into which comets disintegrate.

Division and Dissolution. There is no doubt that comets gradually waste away ; they also part asunder and thus deteriorate ; this process was witnessed in the case of the Great comet 1882 III, also in that of Taylor's comet 1916 I, a Jovian comet of short period, and of Brooks' comet 1889

V, which passed so close to Jupiter that it became divided, the two parts separating and following short 7-year orbits between Jupiter and the sun instead of the previous 27-year orbit. This was a clear case of 'capture,' as it is called, by Jupiter, which may account for all the Jovian 'family' of comets. There are other instances of comets dividing and even vanishing in consequence. The most noteworthy is Biela's comet, which was seen to become double in 1846 ; it returned in two parts in 1852 and then vanished. Its period was about $6\frac{3}{4}$ years. It should, therefore, have appeared several times since, but, instead, a brilliant meteoric display was witnessed when the earth crossed its path. Remnants of this comet are thus still met with as meteors, and destroyed in the earth's atmosphere each November.

While comets thus dissolve and vanish their origin is still a problem. One theory is that the material of comets originated in a meteoric or cosmic dust cloud a million or so years ago, and that the solar system in its journey through space passed through such a cloud. Another more probable theory is that comets represent material ejected from the sun and planets millions of years ago, when their eruptive activity was far more violent than now. Yet another suggested solution is that comets originate in a vast quantity of exceedingly rarefied material encircling the outer periphery of the solar system, many times beyond the orbit of Neptune, to include the orbits of comets with periods approaching 10,000 years. At such distances the speed of a comet would amount to only a few yards a second ; this would slowly increase, until a speed approaching 30 miles a second would be attained as it passed the earth's orbit. On nearing the sun this would rapidly increase in proportion to the nearness of the comet's perihelion to the sun's surface. Comet 1882 III sped round the sun with a velocity of 300 miles a second.

The possibility of a comet's nucleus striking the earth must be admitted, but from elaborate calculations the chances would appear to be one in many millions of years. Then such collision would amount to no more than a local and dense fall of meteorites. There are evidences of such falls having occurred ; these will be discussed in the next Lesson.

LESSON 20

Meteors or Shooting Stars and Meteorites

METEORS produce the streaks of light occasionally to be observed shooting across the night sky, and are therefore popularly known as 'shooting stars.' They are not stars, however, and in reality they do not shoot but fall. Sometimes one or more of these bodies will reach the earth's surface before being completely destroyed. Such bodies are known as meteorites or aerolites.

It is possible to see an occasional meteor on any dark, starlit night when the moon or artificial lights are absent, but on more rare occasions a meteor will appear as bright as Venus or Jupiter and last for 2 or 3 seconds, leaving a luminous train, which will remain sometimes for a minute or two. Still more rare are those splendid meteors which light up the landscape and have even been seen in daylight ; these are usually known as *fire-balls*, a term which must not be confused with the electric phenomena associated with thunderstorms.

These different types of meteors have not the same origin, though they are all individual bodies travelling freely through space and from distances amounting to many hundred of millions of miles—in some cases, thousands of millions—far beyond the orbit of Neptune. Consequently, there is a great interest attaching to bodies which have travelled so far and arrived in such numbers, to become part of the earth.

While speeding through interplanetary space, meteors are invisible on account of their small size ; they only appear after penetrating the earth's atmosphere, and when they are at a height of between 80 and 100 miles above the earth's surface. Then they become visible through ignition, in consequence of the heat generated by friction against the air, which is intense at the speed with which they are travelling— and, as a rule, the meteor is consumed.

Speed of Meteors. The average speed at which the meteors travel when near the earth is about 26 miles a second, but this, as observed by us, may be increased relatively, owing to the fact that the earth travels at about $18\frac{1}{2}$ miles a second.

Consequently, if our world and the meteors are approaching head on, as it were, the observed speed may amount to over 40 miles a second. On the other hand, the speed of meteors approaching the earth obliquely, or from the rear, will seem relatively much slower, their apparent velocity being only a few miles a second. Such meteors are more likely to reach the earth's surface, since their combustion is slower ; they usually appear reddish and less bright. The meteors which do not reach the ground may disappear at any height ; since most of them are very small they vanish when between 50 and 30 miles above the surface, after travelling along a path which, though it averages only 30 miles through the air, may, in the case of large meteors, be over 200 miles long.

While the number of meteors counted by a single observer on a fine dark night may amount to between 6 and 8 an hour, on some nights this may be increased, until at certain well-known times it can exceed 60 meteors an hour. Though the arrival of the large individual meteors cannot be predicted, yet there are many meteor swarms or showers which appear with a periodicity that can be foretold to within a day or two.

Meteor Radiants. The meteor swarm of a particular period will be seen to come from a certain spot in the sky if the meteors be traced back to their first appearance. This point is called the *radiant ;* it is the same for all observers, and represents the direction from which the meteors approach the earth before they enter its atmosphere. Therefore, each swarm of meteors has its own particular radiant, the meteors from which are named after the constellation in which the radiant is situated—as, for

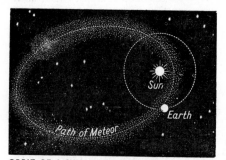

ORBIT OF A SWARM OF METEORS. *Swarms of meteors travel in orbits around the sun, becoming incandescent when they encounter the earth's atmosphere. A swarm may be only a few hundred miles thick, but its length may amount to hundreds of millions of miles.*

instance, the Leonids, from Leo. Sometimes, when more than one radiant is known to be in a constellation, it is named after a particular star which appears near by, such as the Alpha Leonids, which are distinct from the above. The stars have no connexion whatever with the meteors.

The meteor radiant is defined according to degrees in right ascension and declination on the celestial sphere. These are the imaginary lines which correspond to those of longitude and latitude respectively on the terrestrial sphere. The whole of the meteors from a particular radiant are known as a meteor swarm, and each swarm has its peculiarities in addition to the date of appearance ; some are swift meteors, those from other radiants slow, while some swarms are reddish, others bluish. The most notable meteor swarms, together with the dates about when they appear and the radiant point of each, are listed in a table in the next page. The Greek letters indicate the star after which the radiant is named.

The dates of the radiants given in the table may vary by as much as a day—this is usual in leap years ; moreover, the position of the radiant in some cases is known to move slightly during the display. Altogether, about 1,200 radiants are known.

If any one swarm or *shower* (as it is called when the display takes place) be watched throughout the night, the number of meteors seen usually increases towards the morning hours ; the observer is at that time nearer the *apex* or direction of the earth's motion in her orbit. He is, as it were, then at the front of the earth, whereas in the evening he is at the rear, and the effect is comparable to the greater number of raindrops caught in front by a person advancing against a downpour.

Meteor Showers. Quite the most remarkable among the meteor swarms are the Perseids, Leonids, Andromedids, Lyrids, γ Aquarids, η Draconids and α Capricornids. These have on many occasions provided superb displays. The Perseids, once known as the Tears of St. Lawrence, are to be seen from midnight, when their radiant is low in the north-east, throughout the night until between 3 and 4 a.m., when the radiant is almost overhead and the meteors appear to fall from the zenith. They are very swift, usually small and their paths short, an average of 60 an hour being often counted at their annual display, while at times this will be doubled. Although the maximum occurs at some time between August 10 and

12, some of these meteors are to be seen 3 or 4 weeks beforehand. The position of the radiant, which changes from night to night, is given in the table below for the date of maximum display.

NOTABLE METEOR SWARMS

Date	Meteor Swarm	Right Asc.	Declination
Jan. 2–4 ..	Quadrantids ..	231°	51° N.
Jan. 29 ..	α Coronids ..	236°	25° N.
Feb. 10–13	λ Hydrids ..	147°	11° S.
Feb. 22–28	α Leonids ..	155°	14° N.
Mar. 1–4 ..	τ Leonids ..	166°	4° N.
Mar. 11–12	ζ Boötids ..	218°	12° N.
Mar. 24 ..	β Ursids Major	161°	58° N.
Apr. 10–13	ζ Boötids ..	219°	13° N.
Apr. 20–22	Lyrids	271°	33° N.
Apr. 21. ..	Herculids ..	274°	25° N.
May 2–6 ..	γ Aquarids ..	337°	1° S.
May 11–18	α Coronids ..	231°	27° S.
May 30 ..	η Pegasids ..	333°	27° N.
Jun. 3–7 ..	α Scorpiids ..	252°	22° S.
Jun. 27–30	η Draconids..	245°	64° N.
Jun. 27–30	Pons-Winneckeids	213°	53° N.
Jul. 7–11 ..	α Pegasids ..	343°	12° N.
Jul. 24–26	α Capricornids	305°	12° S.
Jul. 27–31	δ Aquarids ..	339°	11° S.
Jul. 30–Aug. 3	γ Andromedids	23°	42° N.
Aug. 10–12	Perseids	46°	57° N.
Aug. 11 ..	μ Perseids ..	61°	48° N.
Aug. 10–16	θ Cygnids ..	293°	53° N.
Aug. 16 ..	α Lyrids ..	284°	44° N.
Aug. 21–25	o Draconids..	291°	60° N.
Aug. 21–25	γ Pegasids ..	6°	11° N.
Sep. 3–4 ..	α Cygnids ..	315°	48° N.
Sep. 4 ..	γ Piscids ..	348°	2° N.
Sep. 6 ..	ε Perseids ..	61°	36° N.
Sep. 21–22	η Aurigids ..	75°	41° N.
Sep. 22 ..	μ Perseids ..	61°	48° N.
Sep. 27 ..	ε Piscids ..	14°	6° N.
Oct. 8 ..	ι Aurigids ..	77°	33° N.
Oct. 9 ..	β Draconids..	264°	55° N.
Oct. 15–16	ξ Arietids ..	31°	9° N.
Oct. 17–22	Orionids ..	92°	15° N.
Oct. 21–23	α Cetids ..	45°	6° N.
Oct. 29–Nov. 2	ε Arietids ..	43°	22° N.
Nov. 5 ..	ε Perseids ..	61°	35° N.
Nov. 15–16	Leonids	152°	22° N.
Nov. 17–23	Andromedids	25°	43° N.
Nov. 26–28	μ Ursids Major	155°	36° N.
Nov. 28 ..	κ Taurids ..	63°	22° N.
Dec. 7–9 ..	ζ Taurids ..	81°	23° N.
Dec. 11–14	Geminids ..	113°	32° N.
Dec. 22–23	δ Cancrids ..	130°	19° N.
Dec. 31 ..	θ Geminids ..	104°	33° N.

Leonid Swarms. The Leonids have provided the most famous of all meteor showers. The first record of their having been observed is in A.D. 902, and records since then show that the shower came in greater brilliancy and profusion thrice a century. Every year a few of the swarms are to be seen ; they are low in the east about midnight, their numbers considerably increasing afterwards until they attain their maxima about 5 a.m. Then they appear high up in the south. These meteors have not been very numerous in recent years, but on some historic occasions the display has been superb. In the year 1799 they resembled fireworks from a celestial fountain, pouring from the radiant and spreading out over the sky. This appearance is the effect of perspective, for actually the meteors travel in parallel paths. In 1833 this grand shower was repeated, 200,000 an hour being the estimate of some observers. The display lasted about six hours.

An expert investigator, H. A. Newton, predicted in 1864, from a study of past records, yet another return of this Leonid swarm to take place on November 13 or 14, 1866. It came true to time, and was in a lesser degree repeated in the following year. Then J. C. Adams, of Neptune fame, computed the orbit of this meteor swarm, and found that the meteors travelled in a long stream over a very elliptical orbit, a more concentrated mass of the meteors constituting the grand swarm. These cross the earth's path every 33 to 34 years, when our world is in their vicinity, the meteor shower being the effect of numbers of them colliding with the earth's atmosphere.

It was expected that the shower would be repeated in 1899 or 1900, but the results were disappointing, except that early on the morning of November 15, 1901, many thousands of the meteors were observed in the western States of North America. It is feared that the main swarm has been deflected by Jupiter and other planets. More recently fifty Leonids an hour were counted, the normal annual display.

Meteorites or Aerolites. Meteorites or, as the larger specimens are often called, aerolites are those fragments of meteoric material which survive entire combustion and reach the earth's surface more or less intact ; in many cases they are subsequently found deeply embedded in the ground. Large luminous bodies of this class, while travelling through the sky, are sometimes called bolides and fireballs. The meteorites are always the remains of these large

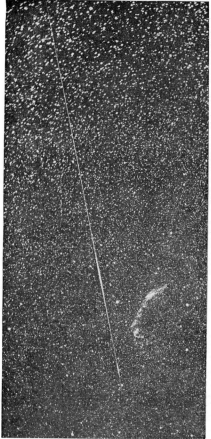

METEOR'S JOURNEY through the earth's atmo-sphere. In this telescopic photograph the white line reveals the second-long passage of a meteor, rendered incandescent by friction with the air. The white body to the right is a nebula.
Yerkes Observatory

the less combustible elements is left, which accounts for meteorites being such heavy bodies. Much of the vaporized material enters into the composition of the earth's atmosphere as gas, while a proportion sub-sequently falls as meteoric dust ; in Arctic regions this dust is perceptible and may be collected from the snow. Thus it will be seen that there is a constant accretion by the earth of meteoric matter.

Fireballs. In the case of the large spec-tacular meteorites commonly called fireballs, the period of incandescence is too short to consume more than an outer layer, the interior being unaffected if the fireball remains intact. Fireballs have even been found quite cold soon after reaching the ground. The length of time occupied by these solitary fireballs in their flight will often amount to several seconds, their paths frequently reaching to between 100 and 2,000 miles in length. Their progress is often irregular, while becoming percep-tibly slower owing to air resistance ; ulti-mately, it may be less than 10 miles a second. The spectacle is occasionally very fine, as the meteoric fireball strews its path with sparks of varied colours and lights up the landscape as brightly as the full moon ; sometimes fireballs rival the moon in apparent size. A roar or thunderous sound frequently follows their appearance, and, since some of them explode, they are known as detonating and bursting meteors. They usually leave a trail behind, produced by the hot luminous vapours given off in their flight ; this may last for several minutes, or longer in exceptional cases. Therefore, their paths may be measured with exactitude, and their height, vanishing point and size calculated from various observations at different points, by two or more observers of the same object.

Between four and five are to be observed annually in one locality ; from this it is to be inferred that the actual number of these large meteoric fireballs, which annually become part of the earth, must amount to thousands. The great majority will fall in the sea, as its area is so much larger than the land, while only a very few of those which are seen to fall are ever recovered ; nevertheless, many thousands have been collected and are in various museums and private collections of the world. These are chiefly the heavy metallic meteorites, some-times called siderites, which, owing to their weight and crystalline exterior, are more easily recognized, whereas the stony meteor-ites, which actually constitute the great

bodies ; a considerable portion of their material has become vaporized and entered the atmosphere as gases and dust during their swift incandescent passage to the ground. If their velocity is greater than about six miles a second the frictional resis-tance of the air will generate this incan-descence, and since the speed at which they enter the atmosphere usually far exceeds this—amounting in many instances to about forty miles a second—the heat generated and the consequent loss of material are considerable ; in this way, only a residue of majority of the recovered particles of the meteorites seen to fall, will, unless their position is noted, often get lost or overlooked because their appearance is that of common stones.

Notable Meteorites. The following are the most notable recent examples. An exceptionally fine meteorite was observed early in the morning of March 24, 1933, in Mexico, Texas, Kansas, Arizona and Colorado. It first appeared at a height of about 65 miles above Oklahoma State, and disappeared at a height of between 6 and 8 miles over a point in the State of New Mexico. Its detonations were heard in five States ; they were accompanied by a roar likened to artillery, rattling of windows and vibrations of the ground.

On October 9, 1933, a fine display of meteors followed the return of Giacobini's comet of 1900, which seems to indicate that meteor swarms accompany disrupted comets. On January 3, 1935, a brilliant fireball was seen at a height of 55 miles over the English Channel, 23 miles south of Christchurch, passing 20 miles above Wotton-under-Edge, Glos. It was described as being brighter and larger than the full moon and producing a chain of sparks visible for nearly three seconds. As during this time it travelled 92 miles, it was a slow fireball ; it changed colour and finally broke into two pieces. A detonation was heard at Bradford-on-Avon due to the meteor's rush giving rise to shock waves sounding like thunder. A shower of brilliant meteorites was seen in Southern Sweden during the evening of May 27, 1938, together with two extraordinarily bright fireballs. As will be seen from the table of radiants there is no shower known for this day. But it may be that this display was due to a stream which had been perturbed and thus met the earth's orbit. On October 2, 1938, a fireball was seen for 30 seconds from Brittany, about the size of the full moon and with a red trail.

Metallic and Stony Meteors. The meteorites or aerolites have very often, after cooling, a crystalline exterior, and are covered with what appears to be a black carbonized glaze ; this is the result of surface fusion and subsequent rapid cooling. There are two characteristic varieties, the

A METEOR CRATER IN ARIZONA. *Countless ages ago a celestial projectile of vast dimensions fell in the desert of north-west Arizona, and Meteor Crater, near Winslow—here seen from the air—is the abiding memorial of the terrific collision. The cavity measures 1,500 yards in diameter, is 600 feet deep, and is surrounded by a ridge, 150 to 200 feet high, of matter thrown up by the impact. Scattered about the slopes and adjacent plain are fragments of meteoric iron, crushed rocks and boulders.*
Photo. H. J. Shepstone

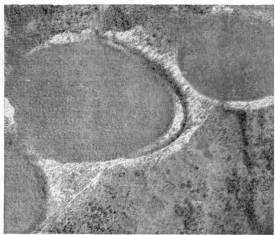

METEORIC SCARS. In South Carolina, U.S.A., there is an area of more than ten thousand square miles containing a large number of scars or ' bays '—elliptical depressions in the earth with features which suggest that they were caused by a vast shower of meteorites a million or so years ago.

Photo, Fairchild Aerial Surveys

metallic or ' iron ' meteorite, and the uranolith or ' stony ' meteorite. The metallic examples are usually composed of masses of iron, together with nickel, cobalt, magnesium and other elements. The stony examples are masses of crystalline rock, and these masses often possess peculiar crystals of familiar elements, such as limestone, magnesian and siliceous stone ; faulting, veins, fragmentation and re-cementation are frequently perceptible, serving as indications that the meteorites were composed of old rocks and material blown out of volcanoes, or were the particles of a disrupted world. Some possess a large admixture of iron. Altogether numerous elements have been found in meteorites ; these are chiefly iron, nickel, oxygen, silicon, magnesium, sulphur, calcium, cobalt, aluminium, sodium, and even argon and helium, while hydrogen, nitrogen, carbon monoxide, hydrocarbons and phosphide of iron are present in different chemical combinations.

Meteorites in History. The most notable meteoric masses are to be seen in museums. The South Kensington Museum, for instance, possesses a very fine collection ; one specimen weighing about 3½ tons was found at Cranbourne, near Melbourne, Australia, in 1854. One of the oldest meteorites of the fall of which there is an authentic record is in the parish church of Ensisheim, in Alsace, suspended by a chain. The record states

that on November 16, 1492, a crash of thunder and prolonged noise were heard, while a stone weighing 260 pounds was seen by a child to fall in a field, making a hole more than 5 feet deep.

The black stone of Mecca, in the sacred Kaaba, is another ancient meteorite. The primitive ' image ' of Diana at Ephesus, which was regarded as having fallen from the god Jupiter, was doubtless another meteorite. A Chinese record of 616 B.C. refers to a meteorite which killed 10 persons. Livy mentions a fall of meteorites as occurring about 650 B.C. This was accompanied by a ' mighty noise.' The astronomer Gassendi saw one fall in 1627 which weighed 59 pounds ; this was in Provence. A very large single mass was found in Greenland, and brought from Melville Bay by Peary for the Museum of Natural History in New York ; it weighs 37½ tons. Another large specimen was found in Brazil, weighing 6 tons ; while one still remains in the ground in Mexico weighing about 60 tons.

Multiple Fireballs. These bodies do not always travel singly. A fireball may consist of large numbers of smaller bodies, all massed together. Such a fall occurred at Pultusk, in Poland, on January 30, 1868, when over 100,000 were estimated to have fallen. In 1510 a large number fell near Padua, some weighing up to 100 lb. Between 2,000 and 3,000 aerolites fell at L'Aigle, in France, on April 26, 1803. At Mocs, in Hungary, on February 3, 1882, over 100,000 were estimated to have fallen. About 14,000 fell in Arizona on July 19, 1912. Most mysterious and devastating was the fall which apparently occurred on June 30, 1908 ; though the fall was not actually observed, a very brilliant light was seen in the sky from the east of Scotland and elsewhere in northern Europe. Even at Greenwich a strange glare was noted, resembling the dawn, while many places reported the period before midnight becoming as light as day. Subsequently, it was found that peasants in Siberia reported a great explosion, earth-shock and earthquake vibrations north of Irkutsk, where there was much destruction. Finally, the area was explored in 1927, and a group of meteor craters were found containing at least 130 tons of meteoric stones. The forests for 40 miles from the scene were destroyed, the trees being laid flat.

Most famous of all evidences of past meteoric falls is the great meteor crater in Arizona, situated near Winslow and the Cañon Diablo, far from all volcanic activity. It presents a depression 600 feet deep and about 4,500 feet in diameter; thousands of iron meteorites have been found, and doubtless large numbers remain buried beneath the crushed masses of rock. Another crater is known in Texas 530 feet in diameter, while a group at Henbury, in Australia, has one crater about 600 feet in diameter. In South Carolina there is an area of 10,000 sq. miles sown with meteoric scars. Craters are discovered annually in unfrequented areas of the earth, and are the subject of exploration.

LESSON 21

Unsolved Problems of the Solar System

IN the preceding survey of the various bodies that constitute the solar system, we have considered all those which are individually visible and may be studied as separate units of the grand whole ; but there remain certain phenomena which cannot be so studied. The most notable of these are the zodiacal light and the Gegenschein.

The zodiacal light may be observed in the west soon after twilight has vanished, and also in the east just before dawn. It produces a faint cone of light, appearing in these latitudes slightly tilted. This cone of light is best seen in the evenings in spring, when it slopes upwards toward the left from where the sun has set. In the mornings it is best seen in the early autumn, when it will slope towards the right from about where the sun will rise later. A clear and fairly dark moonless sky is necessary to reveal the cone of pearly zodiacal light. It is brightest near the horizon, and actually extends to about 45 degrees from the sun — which, however, has to be some distance below the horizon before the light becomes perceptible. Much depends upon the clearness of the atmosphere and the angle which the cone subtends to the horizon ; hence spring and autumn are best for observation, for then the cone of light is nearer to perpendicular than in summer or winter, since it follows the angle of the ecliptic, or zodiac.

Origin of Zodiacal Light. This singular light has been found, spectroscopically, to be the same as sunlight reflected from the moon and, like it, it is partially polarized. Thus it is evident that the zodiacal light is reflected from solid particles obviously too small to be perceptible, even through most

ZODIACAL LIGHT. *Drawing showing at its perfection the luminosity that appears in the west sky after twilight or in the east before dawn. Though best seen in the clear skies of the East, it may be observed from London and many other places. It is suggested that the light is caused by the reflection of sunlight from meteoric masses still in the original plane of the solar system.*

powerful telescopes. Close observation in tropical lands has shown that the light in a very faint degree extends across the sky to a small replica of the zodiacal light. The latter is the Gegenschein which appears in the opposite side of the sky and covers an area about 10 degrees in diameter. The centre of this Gegenschein, or ' counter-glow,' is directly opposite the sun.

Thus it becomes evident that there exists a large lenticular-shaped belt of small bodies or particles encircling the sun and extending to beyond the earth's orbit ; the zodiacal light is that which is reflected from the particles within the circumference of the orbit, while the light of the Gegenschein comes from particles outside its circumference. They must be exceedingly small, approximating to meteors in size, and on an average several miles apart—otherwise the combined mass would sensibly affect the motions of the earth, Venus and Mercury in their orbits.

Matter from Space. When we consider the myriads of these particles, together with the innumerable meteors which are speeding in some thousands of streams along their elliptical orbits to and from the sun, we realize that interplanetary space is far from being empty, although visually it appears so. It has been calculated by Professor Newton that 20,000,000 meteors large enough to be visible to the naked eye enter the earth's atmosphere every day and thus become part of our world. Hence there is a constant accretion of material, which must result in the gradual growth of this and other planets. This material has been calculated to amount to about 36,500 tons per annum on an average—that is, assuming that something like 100 tons fall to the earth every day from the 20,000,000 meteors. These estimates, though necessarily vague, are based upon observed facts, and we find that even the deposition of this amount of material would require, according to the calculations of Professor Young, about 1,000,000,000 years to accumulate a layer one inch thick over the earth's surface. Planetary growth is, therefore, by this means exceedingly slow nowadays, but it may not have been so in the distant past, when quite possibly meteoric matter was far more prolific than at present.

Origin of Meteors We are now at the threshold of the problem of the origin of the earth, planets and solar system generally. Have the planets grown by the accretion of meteoric matter through the long aeons

of time ? If they have, whence have come the meteors ? It has been found that some meteor swarms represent disintegrated comets, others the residue of known comets. For example, the residue of Tuttle's comet of 1862 produces the Perseid meteors of August 10–12 ; the Leonids of November 15–16 are the residue of Tempel's comet of 1866 ; the Andromedid meteors of November 17–23 proved to be the disintegrated Biela's comet, which was seen to part asunder and has since vanished. The Aquarids of May 2–6 are the residue of Halley's comet : while the Pons-Winnecke comet appears to be responsible for the Draconids of June 27–30, and the Comet 1881 V for the Capricornids of July 24–26. It appears that the nucleus in the head of a comet is composed of a great concentration of meteoric bodies or particles all probably in violent commotion, their concentration and consequent concussions increasing as the comet approaches the sun.

It may, therefore, be inferred that all meteor streams are the product of cometary disintegration. Now, if it could be proved that all comets originally entered the solar system along hyperbolic paths from outer space, paths which were subsequently transformed in many cases into elliptical paths, we should have a possible source of the meteoric material from which, in the course of ages, the planets have grown. This, in brief, is the meteoric theory of the growth of worlds and systems.

There are other theories which approach this problem from different standpoints of ascertained facts, and even to the extent of accounting for the origin of the planets and their remarkable series of similarities—such as their common direction of orbital motion, rotation, the closeness of the planes of their orbits, the singular sequence of their proportionate distances from the sun as represented by Bode's Law, together with the way in which the sun's equator and its rotation conform to those of the revolving planets.

Laplace's Nebular Hypothesis. The nebular hypothesis of Laplace is the oldest and best known of these theories, and may be described as follows. Suppose that we have a nebula or cloud of primordial luminous mist—say, some 6,000,000,000 miles in diameter. This nebula must be subjected to two distinct causes of change. First, all its material particles must attract one another by the law of gravitation, so that the nebula tends to condense towards the centre ; simultaneously, the luminous or incandescent particles composing the nebula would be constantly radiating heat out into space. Such a nebula could not for a moment remain at rest, even if it was originally in such a condition— which is practically impossible. For, as it gradually radiated its heat, it would contract ; and, having acquired a rotation about an axis, this would gradually become more rapid, to preserve its angular momentum. Finally, the speed near the edge of the rotating mass would overcome the pull of gravity sufficiently for this to resist further shrinkage, and a separate ring of matter would become detached and continue rotating under its own centrifugal force.

Subsequently, other rings would form in the same way at regular intervals. The material of the rings would under various gravitational perturbations tend to coalesce in masses, finally forming spherical bodies or planets, which would continue to revolve round the central nucleus that eventually condensed into the sun. Each of the revolving masses, while hot enough to preserve its nebulous condition, and having acquired a rotation from tidal attraction of the central mass, would, when rapid enough, also shed minor rings, which in time would form spheres or satellites (except in the case of part of Saturn which formed the rings). The asteroids or planetoids might also be regarded as an instance in which the nebu-

lous ring failed to coalesce into a planet. The theory has been found to have two objections : first, that the rings would not coalesce into single large bodies but into numerous very small ones ; secondly, that if the nebula was rotating at such a rate as to throw off the outer ring, the sun's present speed indicates that it is far too slow for it to have thrown off anything in that distant period.

Tidal Theory of the Solar System. The tidal theory or, as it is technically termed, the Hypothesis of Dynamic Encounter, is a more recent explanation, which has grown in favour during the past 30 years. It assumes that the sun was at one time without planets ; then another sun, or ' wandering star,' approached sufficiently near to raise enormous tides on our sun. These tides, reaching many thousands of miles in height, resulted in the material being finally drawn away from the sun into space.

The two illustrations below give a good idea of the suggested process and the ultimate evolving of the planets as a consequence. The ' wandering star's ' attraction would tend to impart a motion to the original mass in a direction similar to that in which the star was travelling, and thus the ' embryo ' planets would begin travelling in what was later to become their orbits. This hypothesis thus explains the angular momentum or speed possessed by the planets in their orbits, and also accounts for the sun's rotation in harmony therewith.

But an assumed ' wandering star ' fails to account for the many satellite systems such as those presented by Jupiter and Saturn which on this ' wandering star ' hypothesis would need other ' wandering stars ' for their production ; all in a similar plane as well, which is most improbable. Recent discoveries among stellar ' solar systems ' have tended to show that the disturbing pull of a ' wandering star ' is unnecessary.

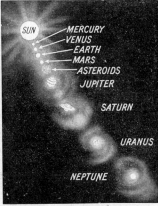

TIDAL THEORY OF THE SOLAR SYSTEM'S ORIGIN. *A theory at one time widely accepted concerning the origin of the solar system of sun and circling planets was that at some inconceivably remote date a ' wandering star ' came so near to the as yet planetless sun as to cause tremendous waves on its surface and ultimately the drawing away into space of vast ' blobs ' of matter which settled down into planets.*

K

Ancient and Modern Star Groupings

THE nature and constitution of the stars are, more or less, similar to our sun, which, however, is a star far advanced in stellar evolution, and therefore much smaller than most other stars. About 2,000 can be seen at one time over the half of the heavens visible on a very clear and dark night, but haze and the presence of artificial lights normally reduce this number to less than half ; field-glasses will increase the number to twenty or thirty thousand ; to these must be added about half as many again, which are below the horizon and will come into view in due course. There are also about 25 per cent more which are for ever out of sight in Britain, but which may be observed from southern latitudes. The telescope greatly increases the number visible with each increase of power, until about a thousand million are revealed by the most powerful instruments, and many more are known to exist in masses in which the individual stars are indistinguishable. The total number has been estimated at fifty to a hundred thousand millions.

The stars are grouped by astronomers in certain constellations of which there are 89 now in general use (*see* Table) ; 48 have continued from the time of Ptolemy, including the Zodiac and the larger constellations containing bright stars visible from the northern hemisphere. Most of these date from early Chaldean times and were placed in the sky by the astronomer-priests of the Euphrates valley, for it appears evident that they were not Egyptian, Hindu or Chinese in their origin, because there are neither elephant, crocodile, tiger, hippopotamus, nor cat among the numerous animals represented — some of which creatures would have doubtless been introduced had the constellations originated in any of those countries. Nevertheless, there were Egyptian, Greek and Roman changes at a later date. Deities famous in Greek and Egyptian mythology were introduced, and names have in many cases been Latinized, as, for instance, Hercules, Leo, Virgo.

Those Chaldean constellations originally typified the annual succession of ordinary events in the lives of those ancient peoples — events which were believed to be presided over by their sun-god and moon-god, whose position relative to the various groups of stars signified the seedtime,

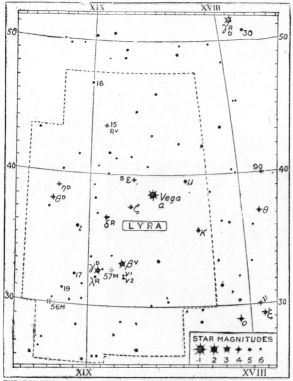

TYPICAL STAR MAP. *The perpendicular lines are those of right ascension, divided into hours. The horizontal lines are those of declination, divided into degrees. The dotted lines indicate the constellation of Lyra.*

CONSTELLATIONS AS DEFINED BY THE INTERNATIONAL ASTRONOMICAL UNION IN 1922

(List arranged in alphabetical order of Latin names)

English Name	Latin Name	Genitive Form	Abbreviation	English Name	Latin Name	Genitive Form	Abbreviation
Chained Lady	Andromeda	Andromedae	And.	Lizard*	Lacerta	Lacertae	Lac.
Air Pump*	Antlia	Antliae	Ant.	Lion	Leo	Leonis	Leo.
Bird of Paradise*	Apus	Apodis	Aps.	Lesser Lion*	Leo Minor	Leonis Minoris	LMi.
Water Bearer	Aquarius	Aquarii	Aqr.	Hare	Lepus	Leporis	Lep.
Eagle	Aquila	Aquilae	Aqi.	Balance	Libra	Librae	Lib.
Altar	Ara	Arae	Ara.	Wolf	Lupus	Lupi	Lup.
Ship Argo	Argo	Argūs	Arg.	Lynx*	Lynx	Lyncis	Lyn.
Ram	Aries	Arietis	Ari.	Lyre	Lyra	Lyrae	Lyr.
Wagoner	Auriga	Aurigae	Aur.	Mast* (of Argo)	Malus or Pyxis	Mali	Pyx.
Herdsman	Boötes	Boötis	Boo.	Table Mountain*	Mensa	Mensae	Men.
Sculptor's Tool*	Caelum	Caeli	Cae.	Microscope*	Microscopium	Microscopii	Mic.
Giraffe*	Camelopardus	Camelopardi	Cam.	Unicorn*	Monoceros	Monocerotis	Mon.
Crab	Cancer	Cancri	Cnc.	Bee*	Musca (Apis)	Muscae	Mus.
Hunting Dogs*	Canes Venatici	Canum Venaticorum	CVn.	Rule*	Norma	Normae	Nor.
Dog	Canis Major	Canis Majoris	CMa.	Octant*	Octans	Octantis	Oct.
Lesser Dog	Canis Minor	Canis Minoris	CMi.	Serpent-Bearer	Ophiuchus	Ophiuchi	Oph.
Sea-Goat	Capricornus	Capricorni	Cap.	Giant-Hunter	Orion	Orionis	Ori.
Lady in the Chair	Cassiopeia	Cassiopeiae	Cas.	Peacock*	Pavo	Pavonis	Pav.
Keel* (of Argo)	Carina	Carinae	Car.	Winged Horse	Pegasus	Pegasi	Peg.
Centaur	Centaurus	Centauri	Cen.	Rescuer	Perseus	Persei	Per.
Monarch	Cepheus	Cephei	Cep.	Phoenix*	Phoenix	Phoenicis	Phe.
Sea-Monster	Cetus	Ceti	Cet.	Painter's Easel*	Pictor	Pictoris	Pic.
Chameleon	Chamaeleon	Chamaeleontis	Cha.	Fishes	Pisces	Piscium	Psc.
Compasses*	Circinus	Circini	Cir.	Southern Fish	Piscis Australis	Piscis Australis	PsA.
Dove*	Columba	Columbae	Col.	Poop* (of Argo)	Puppis	Puppis	Pup.
Berenice's Hair*	Coma Berenices	Comae Berenices	Com.	Net*	Reticulum	Reticuli	Ret.
Southern Crown	Corona Australis	Coronae Australis	CrA.	Arrow	Sagitta	Sagittae	Sge.
Northern Crown	Corona Borealis	Coronae Borealis	CrB.	Archer	Sagittarius	Sagittarii	Sgr.
Crow	Corvus	Corvi	Crv.	Scorpion	Scorpius	Scorpii	Sco.
Cup	Crater	Crateris	Crt.	Sculptor's Workshop	Sculptor	Sculptoris	Scl.
Cross (Southern)*	Crux	Crucis	Cru.	Serpent	Serpens	Serpentis	Ser.
Swan	Cygnus	Cygni	Cyg.	Sextant*	Sextans	Sextantis	Sex.
Dolphin	Delphinus	Delphini	Del.	Bull	Taurus	Tauri	Tau.
Sword-Fish*	Dorado	Doradūs	Dor.	Telescope*	Telescopium	Telescopii	Tel.
Dragon	Draco	Draconis	Dra.	Toucan*	Tucana	Tucanae	Tuc.
Little Horse	Equuleus	Equulei	Equ.	Triangle	Triangulum	Trianguli	Tri.
River Eridanus	Eridanus	Eridani	Eri.	Triangle (South)*	Triangulum Aust.	Trianguli Aust.	TrA.
Furnace*	Fornax	Fornacis	For.	Bear	Ursa Major	Ursae Majoris	UMa.
Twins	Gemini	Geminorum	Gem.	Lesser Bear	Ursa Minor	Ursae Minoris	UMi.
Crane*	Grus	Gruis	Gru.	Sails* (of Argo)	Vela	Velorum	Vel.
Hercules	Hercules	Herculis	Her.	Virgin	Virgo	Virginis	Vir.
Clock*	Horologium	Horologii	Hor.	Flying Fish*	Volans	Volantis	Vol.
Sea Serpent	Hydra	Hydrae	Hya.	Fox*	Vulpecula	Vulpeculae	Vul.
Water-Snake*	Hydrus	Hydri	Hyi.	Sobieski's Shield*	Scutum Sobieski	Scuti	Sct.
Indian*	Indus	Indi	Ind.				

NOTES. The asterisk in the list indicates that the constellation is a modern grouping, since 1600.

The great constellation of Argo has been divided into Carina, Puppis, Vela and Malus ; the last is now usually called Pyxis.

In these divisions Argo, the Ship, is most generally known.

Sobieski's Shield has only recently been generally recognized ; Taurus Poniatowski, Sceptrum Brandenburgium, Harpa Georgii, Globus Aethereus (Balloon), Avis Solitaria vel Noctua, Machina Electrica, Officina Tipographica, Telescopium Herschelii and Honores Frederici, insignificant groups of faint stars with ponderous titles, have been discarded by the International Astronomical Union.

harvesting, hunting period, rainy season, midwinter, midsummer, and the like. The story of the Flood has also been traced in the arrangement of some of the constellations, while the Argonautic Expedition of the ancient Greeks was undoubtedly thus symbolized. In addition to these ancient groups there are about 40 constellations, invented since 1600, chiefly by Hevelius and Bayer, to fill in gaps between the older constellations and also to include the stars surrounding the south celestial pole. Most of these added constellations are insignificant ; while some have been discarded.

Star Maps. The boundaries of the constellations originally followed irregular curves, in some cases vaguely suggesting the object represented. In 1930 the International Astronomical Union adopted a plan in which the boundaries follow the lines of right ascension and declination corresponding to terrestrial longitude and latitude ; the resulting angular arrangement suggests the boundaries of many American states. The student should study the four star maps reproduced in pages 242–243, and should also acquire a star atlas in order to become acquainted with the position of the thousands of objects visible in the celestial dome. The stars are presented according to magnitudes with either their proper names, Greek alphabetical designation, that of Roman numerals or some famous catalogue nomenclature, together with other abbreviated information, such as V for variable star,

R for red ; while Novae or new stars, star clusters, and nebulae are also indicated.

The name of the constellation follows the Greek letter or the numeral, as β Lyrae, ζ Virginis, 81 Ursae Majoris or 26 Geminorum. The genitive case is always used. The list in the Table in page 299 gives (1) the English name of the constellation ; (2) its Latin equivalent ; (3) the genitive case in which each is expressed ; (4) the abbreviated form in which each constellation is now usually written.

About 140 of the brighter stars possess names ; these are of great antiquity, usually Greek, Latin, or Arabic. Only about 60 are in general use, the technical nomenclature according to the letters of the Greek alphabet being preferred, particularly since they give some impression of the relative brightness of the brighter stars in a constellation, α usually being brighter than β, and so on until ω is reached, when the Roman numerals are resorted to. The stars are then much fainter and approaching the limit of naked-eye visibility.

The brighter stars will, therefore, have two titles, as, for example, Sirius, which is also α Canis Majoris or, as it would be written, α CMa. Castor is also α Geminorum, Pollux is also β Geminorum, otherwise α Gem. and β Gem. But in this particular instance β is brighter than α, possibly owing to a change of relative brilliance in the course of centuries since Bayer, in 1603, first instituted this method of designating noteworthy stars.

LESSON 23

Stellar Magnitudes and Distances

THE visible stars are classified according to their apparent brightness in a series of magnitudes which have no relation to their real, or, as it is called, *absolute* magnitude. Thus a faint star of the fifth magnitude may actually be larger and brighter than one of the first magnitude, its apparent faintness being due to its much greater distance. The apparent magnitudes visible to the naked eye range from first down to sixth. The latter are the faintest to be perceived on a clear, dark night, in the absence of any artificial aid. Each magnitude is about 2½ times brighter than the next. This *light ratio*, precisely calculated to be 2·512 times that of the magnitude below it, shows

that a difference of five magnitudes represents a ratio of brightness of about 100 to 1. Below the sixth are the telescopic magnitudes ; these now extend down to the 20th magnitude for stars observed visually and 21st for stars perceptible photographically.

Visual and Photographic Magnitudes. As distinct from photographic magnitudes, visual magnitudes are based on the above *light-ratio* scale, and the extent to which a star's light is below either of the standard magnitudes is indicated by decimals—as, for instance, Antares, which is 1·22, a little more than one-fifth, below the standard first magnitude. On the other hand, there are a few stars brighter than this standard ; they are measured from zero, as, for example, Capella, which is 0·21 magnitude or just over four-fifths brighter than the standard first. Then, again, there are two stars brighter than even zero ; these are Sirius and Canopus, which have a negative magnitude rendered thus : Sirius —1·58 and Canopus —0·86, the figures being preceded by the minus sign. On this scale, the sun is a star of magnitude —26·7, while the moon's magnitude is —11·2.

Photographic methods of determining magnitudes have produced a somewhat different scale from the visual. Stars of different brightness produce dots of different size on the photographic plates, and this is used to determine the magnitude. Moreover, by lengthening the exposure, the light of very faint stars, invisible to the eye through even the highest powers of the telescope, becomes imprinted on the photographic plate as a result of the accumulation of the star's light. Again, since the photographic plate is relatively more sensitive to the blue end of the spectrum, if a blue star and a red star of equal visual magnitude be photographed, the blue will appear much brighter on the plate. The difference of the photographic, minus the visual, is known as the *colour-index*. By using a yellow filter with isochromatic plates, a magnitude scale corresponding very closely with the visual has been obtained ; such magnitudes are called *photo-visual*.

The table below gives the number of stars between each standard magnitude ; those below sixth magnitude are according

STARS OF STANDARD MAGNITUDES

Standard Magnitude		Number of stars calculated according to	
		Photographic magnitude	Visual magnitude
Above 1·5		20	20
From 1·5 to	2·5	38	41
2·5 to	3·5	111	138
3·5 to	4·5	300	454
4·5 to	5·5	950	1,480
5·5 to	6·5	3,150	4,750
6·5 to	7·5	8,200	14,300
7·5 to	8·5	22,800	41,000
8·5 to	9·5	62,000	117,000
9·5 to	10·5	166,000	324,000
10·5 to	11·5	431,000	870,000
11·5 to	12·5	1,100,000	2,270,000
12·5 to	13·5	2,720,000	5,700,000
13·5 to	14·5	6,500,000	13,800,000
14·5 to	15·5	15,000,000	32,000,000
15·5 to	16·5	33,000,000	71,000,000
16·5 to	17·5	70,000,000	150,000,000
17·5 to	18·5	143,000,000	296,000,000
18·5 to	19·5	275,000,000	560,000,000
19·5 to	20·5	505,000,000	1,000,000,000

to the estimates of Seares and van Rhijn. The brighter magnitudes are subject to different estimates owing to the number of stars whose brightness varies, while the number of the telescopic stars is calculated from counts over certain areas.

It is usual to include in a given magnitude all stars with ·5 above or below the standard magnitude, as indicated in the table. There are, in addition to this estimated number of visible stars, immense numbers more, which will be revealed as higher powers of the telescope are effected. It has been estimated by Seares and van Rhijn from several considerations that the total number of stars reaches the colossal figure of about 30,000,000,000.

The tremendous distances of the stars afford the next most astounding fact. The remoteness of even the nearest is arrived at by means of their *annual parallax* ; that is, the apparent position of the nearest stars changes relatively to that of the more distant ones in consequence of the earth's annual change of position in its orbit round the sun. The difference in the star's apparent position is very slight, and depends upon the side of the earth's orbit from which we are looking. This represents an annual translation of about 186,000,000 miles, say, between mid-summer and mid-winter, and produces a different perspective in the apparent relation of one star to another ; the difference is much less for the more distant stars, until a point is reached at which any change is imperceptible. The limit at present is ·001 of a second of arc. Thus only a limited number of stars can have their distance measured by this method, in spite of the immense length of the base-line subtended by the earth's orbit.

The annual parallax of a star is, therefore, equal to the angle which would be subtended at that star by the diameter of the earth's orbit ; but there is no star in whose case this parallax would amount to as much as a single second of arc. The great difficulty of measuring quantities of this nature, and which also are much involved, is obvious. The most delicate instruments and refined handling are necessary, together with numerous most accurately measured observations, the parallax shift having to be disentangled from the star's own *proper motion* through space.

Units of Stellar Measurement. Stellar distances are so gigantic that we are forced to represent them in terms of some different unit from that ordinarily used. Miles become meaningless, for the nearest star is about 270,000 times farther away than the earth is from the sun, which means that it is about 25,110,000,000,000 miles away. On the other hand, suppose we take the sun's distance, which is the *astronomical unit* of 92·9 million miles, and represent this by a foot, the sun would then be, in proportion, a tiny sphere ⅛ of an inch in diameter, the earth a scarcely perceptible speck of dust, while the nearest star on this scale would be about fifty miles away.

To represent the distance of a star in terms of parallax, this would have always to be expressed in small fractions of a second, which would vary inversely as to the parallax. This inconvenient method has been overcome by the institution of the *parsec*. This represents the distance at which the diameter of the earth's orbit would subtend an angle of one second of arc, expressed as 1″. Thus the *par*allax and one *sec*ond make the standard *parsec*, which is 206,265 times the sun's distance, the astronomical unit, and represents about 20,000,000,000,000 miles. A *kiloparsec* represents 1,000 parsecs and a *megaparsec* a million parsecs.

An older and more popular unit of measurement is the *light-year*, which represents the distance light travels in vacuo at 186,271 miles per second, according to the accepted standard of Michelson.

Light travels from the sun in a little over 8 minutes, or 499 seconds; it travels 63,290 times the sun's distance (i.e. astronomical units) in a year; thus we get a most convenient standard, easily grasped, hence its extensive use. There are 3·26 light-years in a parsec or, more precisely, a light-year is 0·3069 of a parsec. Another rarely used unit is the *siriometer*, representing a million astronomical units.

From the above we see that if a star were at a distance that caused its apparent annual shift or parallax to amount to 1″, or one parsec, this would equal 3·26 light-years; so to find the distance of any star from its parallax this simple formula may be used:

$$d = \frac{3.26}{p} \text{ where } d \text{ is the distance in light-years}$$

and p is the parallax in seconds.

The necessary observations had originally to be taken visually, and it was thus that Bessel in 1838 measured for the first time the distance of a star. This was 61 Cygni, a small double star which, from its relatively rapid *proper motion*, led him to suspect that it was one of the nearest; it proved to be 10 light-years distant. Soon after Bessel's discovery Henderson, at the Cape of Good Hope observatory, found that the bright star Alpha Centauri was (as was thought

MEASURING THE DISTANCE OF THE STARS. These diagrams show an accurate method of determining star distances. A photograph (left) of a portion of the heavens is taken through a powerful telescope at the beginning of a six-month period. A second photograph taken at the end of the period, when the telescope has been carried by the earth to a point 186 million miles distant, shows an apparent movement of the star marked X relative to those marked A and B and the fainter stars in the background. Calculations based on this difference give the star's distance in parsecs. Note that the star pattern in the background remains unaltered, so remotely distant are its components.

then) at 3 light-years' distance ; it is now known to be about 4¼ light-years.

Parallaxes by Photographs. The photographic method of obtaining parallaxes was introduced by Professor Pritchard of Oxford in 1886, and, instead of laborious observations, photographic plates were exposed when the earth was at opposite sides of its orbit. The observations have to be made at the same hour-angle to avoid varying effects of refraction and atmospheric dispersion. Over a dozen plates are now taken, the comparison stars having to be measured too for proper motion, and in case any of them are near enough to have an appreciable parallax.

Stars showing a parallax of only ·005 of a second, which represents about 650 light-years, can now be measured with a fair degree of accuracy, while less sure measurements may be taken down to ·001", which represents about 1,000 light-years.

Stellar Motions. Although the stars are apparently fixed, they have a real motion of their own in addition to the apparent diurnal motion due to the earth's rotation, and the apparent annual motion across the sky, as a body, due to the earth's revolution round the sun. This latter, as we have seen in page 301, produces yet another motion, only apparent in stars sufficiently near—the minute circle which they appear to perform relative to the more distant stars.

In addition to these apparent motions the stars change their positions slightly from year to year ; this is known as their *proper motion.* It is imperceptible to the naked eye, even during a lifetime, but is very apparent in modern instruments of precision. There are two ways in which this motion can be measured. One is by the actual displacement of the star on the celestial sphere—but most of this is found to be due to *precession, nutation* and *aberration,* which are also due to terrestrial influences and are shared by all the stars in any particular section of the sky.

After all these minute quantities have been allowed for, there remains the gradual shift of each star relative to the others. Not many more than a hundred stars are known which thus move a second of arc or more in a year. So small an amount is

'PROPER MOTION' OF THE STARS. *A way of determining 'proper motion' of an individual star is shown in these diagrams prepared by Dr. Smart. The star at A, in the photo on the left, taken at Cambridge Observatory in 1903, is 'Groombridge 34,' a double star with a large proper motion. From photographs taken 23 years later, this proper motion was accurately determined, so that it is possible (right) to estimate the position (B) the star will occupy 500 years hence. The proper motions of the other stars are relatively small.*

this that it would take about 2,000 years for a star with such a proper motion to move over a distance equal to the apparent diameter of the full moon. It was discovered by Halley, 200 years ago, that Sirius had travelled southward to about this extent, that is, half a degree, since the time of Ptolemy.

A large proper motion is generally an indication that the star is among the nearest to us and, therefore, likely to reveal a parallax when measured. If we know the distance of such a star from the earth or, as is usually reckoned, from the sun, then it becomes possible to calculate the star's actual velocity. It is, however, necessary to know also its radial velocity, to be obtained from the angle at which the star is travelling relative to the line of sight. Thus a distinction must be drawn between the star's apparent angular rate of motion and its actual velocity, since a star travelling direct towards us in the line of sight would possess no perceptible proper motion.

Döppler's Principle. The spectroscope has enabled astronomers to solve this problem, to measure a star's motion in the line of sight and decide whether it is approaching or receding, with remarkable accuracy. This is in virtue of *Dòppler's principle*, which briefly is as follows :

Each of the series of lines in the spectrum has a precisely defined space according to the gas from which it originates ; this is due to the fact that light of any particular wave-length is refracted to a certain definite extent. Now suppose the source of the light is a star travelling towards the spectroscope, the light which it emits will reach the spectroscope with its own speed added to that of the star. Consequently, a greater number of light waves will reach the refracting prism of the spectroscope in a second than would be the case if the star were at rest, while a lesser number of light waves will arrive if the star be receding. Thus there is revealed a shift in the lines in the spectrum through a distance which, though very minute, is capable of being measured with sufficient accuracy to show the direction and extent of stellar velocity. If the star is receding, the lines will be shifted toward the red end of the spectrum ; if it is approaching, the lines will be shifted toward the violet end. Thus is the *radial velocity* obtained.

Measuring Speed. The speed of stars was thus obtained, visually at first, by Huggins in 1867 ; but for the last 50 years photographic records of the star's spectrum have replaced the visual, and the *radial velocity* of several thousand stars is now known. This, together with the star's angular *proper motion*, which gives us by a simple calculation the star's *tangential velocity*, enables its actual speed to be calculated and also the direction in which it is travelling. It is found that the stars generally appear to be speeding in different directions, though there are some which form groups and travel like a vast flock all in one direction. There is no such thing as rest in the universe, for all the bodies within it are travelling at immense speeds. Our own sun is moving at the rate of about 12½ miles per second towards a certain point, called the solar apex, in the constellation of Hercules at approximately right ascension 270°, or 18 hours, and declination +31°.

An effect of this motion is to cause the stars to open out in the direction of the sun's motion and to close in toward the *antapex* or opposite point. Sir William Herschel noticed this effect, and concluded that it was caused by the motion of the sun and, of course, the whole solar system, which is travelling through this never-ending stellar vista.

Absolute and Apparent Magnitude. The *absolute magnitude* of a star may now be arrived at, since its parallax, i.e. distance and *apparent magnitude*, is known. It thus becomes possible to deduce the brightness and real magnitude a star would present if it were removed to a standard distance. For if all stars were at this standard distance, their apparent magnitude would represent their absolute magnitude ; but they are, in fact, at vastly different distances.

While a star's absolute magnitude may be computed from its apparent magnitude, it is necessary to have some standard of comparison. The sun used to serve this purpose as magnitude 0·0, but since 1922 the standard has been defined by the International Astronomical Union as the magnitude a star would have if it were at a distance of 10 parsecs, which corresponds to a parallax of 0·1″ and represents about 33 light-years. The absolute magnitude M is, therefore, expressed in terms of the apparent magnitude m, and parallax p, in seconds of arc thus : $M = m + 5 + 5 \log p$.

We may thus visualize our sun, which is the nearest star and has an apparent magnitude of $-26·6$; but at a distance of 10 parsecs or 33 light-years this would be reduced to $+5·0$ of apparent magnitude. In other words, it would be classed as about fifth magnitude and be only visible as a faint star. Now, since Vega, for example, at a distance of 8·1 parsecs, and Capella, at 13·5 parsecs, appear as brilliant first magnitude stars at this distance, it becomes obvious how much greater their absolute magnitude must be as compared with the sun, Vega being 0·6 and Capella much greater, with $-0·4$. The minus sign indicates that it is above the standard 0·0, and, therefore, the greater the $-$ magnitude the greater the luminosity ; on the other hand, the greater the $+$ sign the less is the luminosity and the smaller the absolute magnitude.

Magnitude Without Parallax. It has of late years been found possible to determine the absolute magnitude of a star without taking into account its parallax. Differences in the intensities of certain lines of the spectra of dwarf stars, as compared with corresponding intensities of certain lines of giant stars' spectra, had long been noticed ; it was ultimately found, from an investigation of individual stars whose parallax, and therefore absolute magnitude, was known, that there was a relation between the intensities of the lines and the absolute magnitude of the stars. A calibration curve of intensities was eventually constructed from numerous stars of known parallax and absolute magnitude, and from this it became possible to deduce the absolute magnitude of numerous stars of *unknown* parallax simply by comparing the relative intensity of the particular lines in their spectrum with those of the standardized curve of spectroscopic intensities for various absolute magnitudes. This done, it became possible to determine a star's parallax from the absolute magnitude thus obtained. Parallaxes obtained by this method are termed *spectroscopic*.

LESSON 24

The Light of Stars and their Spectra

MOST of our knowledge concerning the stars has been obtained by analysing the light they emit. This light varies enormously both in quantity and character. Luminosity as observed visually is no absolute criterion of the particular star's mass or immensity, since a relatively small mass may accompany an immense volume and a surface of comparatively poor luminosity—in which case a relatively small star of great luminosity will far outshine and radiate more light than its much greater rival. These differences are found to be associated with their surface temperatures.

The luminosity of the stars has been very precisely ascertained from their distances and absolute magnitudes. This luminosity is usually expressed in terms of the sun by the symbol ⊙. The differences are tremendous, the most luminous, as far as is known, being Canopus, which has been calculated to radiate 91,000 times the light of the sun, but from a distance of 652 light-years. On the other hand, Proxima Centauri, which happens to be the nearest known sun to our own and which is invisible except through powerful telescopes, radiates 11,000 times *less* light than our sun. It is a small sun which appears to have nearly 'burnt itself out' or, in other words, exhausted its luminous radiation.

We find that Canopus has the greatest absolute magnitude of —7·4 ; Rigel, a brilliant star which radiates 18,000 times the light of the sun, follows with —5·8. Sirius, which owing to its proximity appears the brightest star in the heavens, with an *apparent* magnitude of —1·58, actually radiates only 30 times more light than our sun ; its *absolute* magnitude is + 1·3.

It is obvious to the naked eye that the stars exhibit different colours, from the reddish Antares and Betelgeuse to the orange Arcturus, the pale yellowish Capella, brilliant white Sirius and Vega, the bluish Rigel and many other Orion stars. Spectro-scopic study of these differences in light has revealed astonishing differences in the surface conditions and in the constitution of the stars. The various tints indicate different spectra.

Classification of Stellar Spectra. A spectroscopic analysis has now been made of about 250,000 stars. The spectra have been arranged in *classes*, each designated by a letter ; O, B, A, F, G, K, M, N, R, and S. They were originally in alphabetical order, but subsequent discoveries have necessitated the changed sequence. Since these types blend one into another, various subdivisions by decimal numbers are used, such as B2 and B5, the latter indicating a star of spectral *type* midway between the *classes* B and A. Subdivisions are indicated by letters, as Oa, Ob, Ma, and so on.

This classification, while indicating a spectral type, reveals at the same time a period in the life of a star or sun when it is at about a certain surface-temperature and in a definite known physical condition associated with either youth or age. The light when analysed is seen to consist of a continuous emission spectrum, upon which appear different lines of absorption characteristic of the various spectral classes. The lines of hydrogen appear in all, but the lines of other elements appear with different intensities in each spectral class, and are variously absent in certain classes.

Class O spectra consist of bright bands superimposed upon a faint continuous background. This class represents the Wolf-Rayet stars. New or temporary stars which suddenly blaze up and then die down to faintness also frequently belong to it, when they are expressed as either Oa, Ob or Oc. The subdivisions Od and Oe represent spectra which contain dark lines chiefly of hydrogen, ionized helium and ionized calcium. The star λ Cephei is typical of these. The surface temperatures of stars of Class O are considered to range between 35,000° and 40,000° Centigrade ; Novae (new) or temporary stars doubtless reach much higher temperatures. Thus the greenish-white Class O represents the hottest type of star known.

Class B spectra contain only dark lines, chiefly of helium. Stars in this class are called helium stars, being largely enveloped in incandescent helium, together with ionized oxygen and nitrogen. Surface temperatures range from about 23,000° C. for class Bo to about 15,000° C. for sub-class B5. Several of the stars of Orion, including δ, ε and ζ of the 'Belt,' are of class Bo. Achernar .and δ Persei are notable examples of B5 sub-class.

Class A spectra consist of very intense hydrogen and increased calcium lines ; magnesium and numerous lines of ionized metals appear in A5. Surface temperatures range from about 11,000° C. for Ao to about 8,500° C. for A5. Sirius and Vega are good examples of Ao stars and Altair of the A5 sub-class. All are white.

Class F spectra display a great increase in the intensity of the metallic lines and a decrease in those of hydrogen. Surface temperatures of about 7,500° C. are attained for Fo, to which class Canopus belongs. The temperature declines to about 6,500° C. for F5. Procyon is a good example.

Class G spectra have numerous metallic lines present, together with reduced hydrogen lines. Those of iron and ionized calcium are very strong, and there is a band representing a carbon compound. Surface temperatures are about 6,000° C. for class Go, to which our sun and Capella belong. For the intermediate class G5 the surface temperature declines to about 5,500° C. The stars μ Cassiopeiae and κ Geminorum are of this class. All G types stars are yellowish owing to the greater absorption at the violet end of the spectrum.

Class K spectra are noteworthy for bands due to the presence of hydrocarbons ; surface temperatures are about 4,200° C. Arcturus is a good example of 'giants' of this type. In the intermediate class K5 bands due to titanium oxide appear, and there is a reduction of temperature to about 3,400° C. K stars are orange, deepening to K5.

Class M spectra exhibit broad absorption bands with low temperature metallic lines intense, and solar lines faint and few in number ; titanium oxide bands become strong and increase towards the intermediate classes M5 and M8. Surface temperatures range from about 3,000° C. for Mo to about 2,700° C. for M5. Betelgeuse and Antares are typical examples of Mo class.

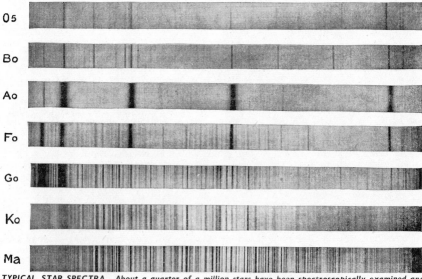

TYPICAL STAR SPECTRA. *About a quarter of a million stars have been spectroscopically examined and their spectra arranged in classes. These classes are fully described in the accompanying text.*

Photos taken by Curtiss at Michigan, with 37½″ Reflector

This type have a reddish-orange tint. The subdivision class M8e have spectra similar to M8 but with *bright* hydrogen emission lines, a remarkable feature peculiar to long-period variable stars ; Mira or o Ceti is a notable example. Temperatures vary between 2,300° C. and 1,700° C.

Class N spectra have broad absorption bands very intense at the red end of the spectrum ; these are chiefly caused by the presence of carbon monoxide and cyanogen. All stars of this class are small and very red, owing to the absence of violet in the spectrum. They are apparently 'dying suns,' and the surface temperatures are low —about 2,600° C. The star 19 Piscium is typical of this class.

Class R spectra are similar to class N, but with the cyanogen line very intense. These stars, though very faint, are not so red as N, and have surface temperatures of about 2,300° C.

Class S spectra exhibit bands of zirconium oxide and strong low temperature lines, indicating that they are not much above 2,000° C. They are faint and red, being all telescopic, and mostly variable stars of long period.

Stages of Stellar Decay. It will be seen from this short survey that the stars decrease in temperature through a well-defined series of gradations indicated by their spectra.

That the details of the spectrum reveal the temperatures and, therefore, the conditions existing on each star or sun has been proved from laboratory experiments in physics. It is, however, not to be supposed, because, for instance, B stars exhibit a spectrum rich in helium lines and A stars one well supplied with hydrogen that, therefore, these elements are exceptionally plentiful in such stars. It means that these stars are in that degree of incandescence which causes these elements, helium and hydrogen, to be in such a condition as to produce the effect recorded in the star's spectrum.

Every star goes through most of the stages indicated by the above classes during successive periods of its existence. Long ages ago our sun was an F star ; before that it was an A, in still more distant aeons a brilliant B, and possibly even an O5 type of star at the apex of heat and light radiation ; still more remotely it was a *giant* K star, and from thence to near its birth stage a super-*giant* M star like Betelgeuse. On the other hand, long ages hence our sun will dwindle to a *dwarf* M type, and thence probably pass through the N stage, or through R to N, ultimately to its final extinction, when its radiant energy is expended. Such is the accepted theory of the normal life of a star—barring collisions, convulsions, or stellar conflagrations.

LESSON 25

Calculating the Size of Stars

WE have seen how the distance, magnitude and temperature or colour index of a star are arrived at, and how a fairly accurate conception of its size may be estimated as a consequence. Where it has subsequently been possible to measure giant stars, the calculated dimensions have been found remarkably in accord with the measured diameters. It is obvious that when the intrinsic brilliance of a star's surface is known, its total output of luminous energy will depend upon the area of surface presented, a large surface pouring out a much greater volume than a small one. This can be measured mathematically ; thus, when it and the star's distance, colour index and temperature are taken into account, the star's size may be calculated.

We know that our sun, whose size has been precisely measured, possesses a certain absolute magnitude, and from this its

apparent magnitude at certain distances can be calculated ; therefore any other star possessing a similar spectrum and absolute magnitude, at the same assumed distance, will be of similar proportions to the sun. Any variations therefrom, either as to spectra, absolute magnitude and distance, become a sure indication of the size of a star by comparison with the sun. It is, therefore, usual to express a star's radius in *radii* of the sun—the sun's radius is 432,000 miles—easily converted into diameter by doubling the figures.

Stellar Interferometer. Measurement of the angular diameter of the larger stars, if not too distant, has of late years become possible by means of the stellar interferometer. This is a most ingenious appliance —developed by Michelson, originally conceived by Fizeau in 1868—which may be attached to great telescopes, such as the

100-inch telescope at Mount Wilson Obser-vatory in California. Its principle is dis-cussed in Physics, page 369.

By means of four plane mirrors placed at M1, M2, M3, and M4 in the illustration below, the capacity of the telescope be-comes greatly increased by the two outer mirrors, M1 and M4, which are placed at an angle of 45° to the horizontal, reflecting the light of the star to the two inner mirrors, M2 and M3, which are also at an angle of 45° and which are so placed that the star's light is thence sent down the tube of the telescope to its great concave mirror. Thus two beams or 'pencils' of light from the star reach the magnifying mirror, which passes them on to the focal plane of the eye-piece. The effect is to produce a series of interference fringes, which at a certain but varying distance apart of the plane mirrors, M1 and M4, will cause the interference fringes to disappear. Now the *distance apart of these two plane mirrors bears a definite and measurable relationship to the angular diameter* of the particular star under consideration.

The smaller the angular diameter of the star to be measured the greater is the tele-scopic aperture necessary ; to effect this, the two outer plane mirrors M1 and M4 are placed farther apart, the two inner ones M2 and M3 remaining at a distance of four feet, and each pair of mirrors being equi-distant from the long axis of the telescope.

Changes in the distance are effected by a long girder (G), which is placed across the end of the open tube of the telescope ; along this the plane mirrors M1 and M4 can be moved to its full extent. Thus it be-comes possible to have the equivalent of a telescope over 20 feet in diameter for the production of the interference bands, which is all that matters in this case, but not, of course, for normal observation.

When Betelgeuse had this interferometer applied, it was found that the interference fringes produced by the two beams of light vanished when the plane mirrors were 10 feet apart. Mathematical calculations based upon a standard derived from the known angular distances apart of certain double stars, notably Capella, gave for Betelgeuse the angular diameter of 0·047 of a second of arc, an amount quite beyond the possibility of measurement by direct vision on account of the minute spurious disks presented by the stars when observed telescopically.

Giant Suns. At the distance of Betel-geuse, that is, 58·80 parsecs or nearly 192 light-years, this angular diameter of 0·047″ would represent an actual diameter of 300 times that of the sun, or 259,200,000 miles. Thus Betelgeuse was found to be a colossal sun with a diameter much larger than the earth's orbit ; if the earth were as near to the centre of Betelgeuse as it is to the centre of our sun it would be 123,000,000 miles below the surface of that giant sun. It has long been known to vary irregularly in its brightness, and the above measurement was taken near its maximum. Since then, the star having become less brilliant, it was remeasured ; it required a spacing of 14 feet between the plane mirrors M1 and M4. This proved that Betelgeuse now had an angular diameter of 0·034″, and had therefore shrunk to 210 times the sun's diameter, or 181,440,000 miles. Thus the irregular variations in the light of the 'pulsating suns' was proved to be due to expansion and contraction of the bodies in question.

Arcturus, another giant sun, required an extension of the interferometer to 24 feet

INTERFEROMETER FOR MEASURING STARS. *In this combined photograph and diagram the star's light, as shown by the arrows, reaches the plane mirrors M1 and M4 direct from the star ; it is then reflected on to plane mirrors M2 and M3. From these it is projected down the long open tube of the telescope in two slender beams to the great 100-inch mirror, whence the beams are passed to the focus of the eyepiece in the usual manner of a reflecting telescope.*

before the interference fringes vanished. This spacing indicated an angular diameter of 0·020″, which at the distance of Arcturus, that is, 12·50 parsecs, represented a diameter 27 times greater than that of our sun, or 23,382,000 miles. Aldebaran also gave an angular diameter of 0·020″, but owing to its

ε Pegasi, or Enif, is another more recently measured *giant* sun and found to have a diameter of 86 million miles. It is at a distance of 53 parsecs and radiates about 235 times the light of our sun.

α Ceti, or Menkar, with a diameter of 97 million miles, radiates about 75 times the radiance of our sun and from a distance of 33½ parsecs.

γ Aquilae, or Tarazed, with a diameter of 43 million miles, radiates only about 125 times the light of our sun and from a distance of 43½ parsecs.

Dwarf Stars. The dwarf type of star, to which our sun, Sirius, Vega, Altair, Procyon, and most stars belong, is much farther advanced in stellar evolution, and much more massive in proportion to its volume. Though usually of greater intrinsic brilliance and greater apparent magnitude, yet owing to the smallness of their angular diameter it will not be possible to measure most dwarf stars until the spacing of the interferometer plane mirrors can be greatly extended.

CHARACTERISTICS OF THE MOST IMPORTANT STARS

Name of Star	Apparent Magnitude	Absolute Magnitude	Distance in Parsecs	Spectral Class	Light radiated	Proper Motion in Seconds
Sirius	—1·58	+1·3	2·7	A0	30	1·315
Canopus ..	—0·86	—7·4	200·0	gF0	91,000	0·022
Vega	0·14	0·6	8·1	A0	50	0·348
Arcturus ..	0·24	—0·2	12·5	gK0	130	2·287
Rigel	0·34	—5·8	167·0	B8	18,000	0·005
Procyon ..	0·48	3·0	3·2	F5	6·5	1·242
Achernar ..	0·60	—0·9	20·4	B5	240	0·093
β Centauri ..	0·86	—1·36	27·8	B1	340	0·039
Altair	0·89	2·4	4·9	A5	11	0·659
Betelgeuse ..	0·90	—2·9	58·8	gM0	1,500	0·032
Aldebaran ..	1·06	—0·2	17·5	gK5	112	0·205
Pollux	1·21	1·2	9·9	K0	28	0·623
Spica	1·21	—4·0	111·0	B2	4,100	0·051
Antares ..	1·22	—1·7	38·5	gM2	3,400	0·032
Fomalhaut ..	1·29	2·0	7·3	A3	16·3	0·367
α Cygni ..	1·33	—5·2	200·0	A2	12,000	0·004
Regulus ..	1·34	0·2	17·2	B8	86·7	0·244
β Crucis ..	1·50	—3·98	125·0	B1	3,930	0·054
Barnard's Star	9·70	13·4	1·86	M5	0·0005	10·250
van Maanen's Star	12·30	14·3	3·92	F0	0·0002	3·010

much greater distance of 17·54 parsecs this represented an actual diameter 38 times that of the sun, or 32,928,000 miles.

Aldebaran belongs to the gK5 class, while Arcturus is gK0 ; the letter g prefixed to the class signifies 'giant,' to distinguish them from the 'dwarf' types, which, exhibiting similar spectra, are in a much later stage of stellar evolution.

Antares is another of these colossal giant suns which have already been thus measured. It required a spacing of 12 feet between the plane mirrors ; from this was calculated an angular diameter of 0·040″, actually less than Betelgeuse. But Antares is much farther off, and at a distance of about 38·5 parsecs ; therefore this angular diameter represented the stupendous actual diameter of about 232 times that of the sun, or nearly 200,000,000 miles.

Subsequent measurements revealed that α Herculis, also known as Ras Algethi, was still more stupendous, with a diameter of about 346 million miles, or nearly 400 times the diameter of our sun. Great though this is, it is probable that Canopus far exceeds it, for Canopus radiates 91,000 times more light than our sun as compared with a maximum of but 620 times for α Herculis.

of their angular diameter it will not be possible to measure most dwarf stars until the spacing of the interferometer plane mirrors can be greatly extended.

There remains, however, the method of *calculating* diameters which was described above. Now, in the case of those stars which it was subsequently found possible to measure, it was seen that the calculated diameters were remarkably in accord with the measured diameters; Arcturus e.g., calculated to have an angular diameter of 0·023″, was found by interferometer measurement to be 0·020″. Betelgeuse was calculated to be 0·048″, while the interferometer revealed it as 0·047″, and Antares, calculated as 0·042″, proved to be 0·040″.

The calculated diameters are as follows for the most prominent stars, in proportion to the sun—Sirius, 1·8 times ; Vega, 2·4 ; Altair, 1·4 ; Procyon, 1·9 ; Barnard's Star, 0·16 ; van Maanen's Star, 0·007 ; β Centauri, 11·0.

The last two stars in the table are introduced for comparison from the other end of the scale. Betelgeuse is variable.

The table above applies the facts elucidated in the three previous Lessons to the most noteworthy stars. The column of 'Light radiated' is in terms of our sun.

LESSON 26

Double Stars and Binary Systems

DOUBLE stars when viewed telescopically are found to consist of two suns with an angular separation of usually not more than 30″ ; a few exceptions, however, have been discovered in which such stars have a physical connexion at distances greater than this. · The first star found to be double was Mizar or ζ Ursae Majoris, when Riccioli noted it in 1650. In 1874 Sir William Herschel, who had for some years been giving close scrutiny to the subject, produced a catalogue with about 700 double stars, describing their relative positions. Now about 21,000 have been catalogued and more are being added every year. This includes many triple and some multiple stars.

It will be obvious that because two stars appear close together they may, in some instances, be thus seen in the line of sight only and one component may actually be nearer to us than to the other. When there is thus no physical connexion they are described as *optical doubles*. When, instead, they are connected by gravitational attraction or common proper motion they are known as *physical doubles* or pairs. This is a further and important distinction which originated with Sir William Herschel. By the beginning of the last century he had noted changes in the relative positions of the components of some of the double stars which he had catalogued many years before. The fact was consequently revealed that several pairs were sufficiently close to influence one another gravitationally and so produce orbital motions. To such a star he gave the name of *binary*.

The probability of two stars being binaries when appearing very close together is much greater than that they are merely optical doubles ; this is particularly the case when they are both of similar brilliance, or if the brighter component is yellowish and the fainter either greenish, blue or purplish in tint. These complementary colours prevail in binary systems and are the direct consequence of their stellar evolution.

Interferometer Detection of Binaries. A few binaries or double stars are perceptible with good field glasses, and these are examples which are much more than 30″ apart. Nearly all require telescopic aid and usually high powers, since so many appear not more than a second or two apart.

A great telescope will reveal double stars down to 0.2″ of separation, but the interferometer, the instrument described in page 308, which has been such a valuable aid in measuring the diameters of stars, has been useful in proving suspected stars to be · double. It was, in fact, first used upon the star Capella, which Greenwich observations had indicated as appearing elongated in its spurious disk, thus suggesting that the star might be double ; the interferometer not only proved it to be so, but also gave the angular distance apart of the components. As a consequence it has become possible to measure the angular distance of separation between stars down to 0.08″.

At the distance of many double stars this small amount represents thousands of millions of miles, and even in the case of the nearest it will mean hundreds of millions, but numbers of binaries are much nearer together even than the earth is to the sun. This has been found out by means of spectroscopy ; for instance, if two stars close together and of similar brightness are revolving in an orbit appearing more or less edgewise, as seen from the earth, then at certain times one of the stars will be moving along the line of sight towards the observer, while the other star at the opposite side of this stellar orbit will be moving away from the observer. The result will be that the lines of the spectra of each component star will be displaced, upon the same principle, i.e. Döppler's (*see* Lesson 23, page 303), as obtained in the case of stars advancing and receding from us.

There will also be the additional peculiarity that the spectral lines will appear doubled. This appearance is greatest when the perspective presents the stars widest apart, while, when both stars are together in the line of sight, the duplicated spectral lines close up and appear single. If there are great differences in the respective magnitudes of the components, or if they are of different spectral types, the problem becomes more complex, but can nevertheless be accurately solved. The variations are always periodic and repeat themselves at intervals of perhaps a few hours, a few days or, occasionally, after the lapse of several years.

Spectroscopic Binaries. In the case of orbits presented more or less circular, other methods, involving the orientation of the spectroscope to the stars, have to be adopted; thus precision may be attained even as to the position of *periastron* and *apastron*; in the instances of stars which are also visually double, additional data become available, while one method may be used to check the accuracy of the other.

These stars are known as *spectroscopic binaries*; over a thousand are known, and from the number tested about one star in five proves to be a spectroscopic binary, on an average, though in some spectral classes the proportion is greater, notably the B type of star. From this calculation we see what a large number of stars must be spectroscopic binaries. The details are obtained photographically from five, or preferably more, spectrograms taken at different times in order to record various positions of the component stars and thus compute their orbit.

With their parallax known it subsequently becomes possible to calculate their mass, luminosity, distance apart, and even their actual dimensions in miles. Thus it is found that many spectroscopic binaries are composed of suns only a few million miles apart. Curiously enough, the first to be discovered, as in the case of double stars, was again Mizar of Ursa Major, when Pickering, in 1889, found that the spectrum of the brighter of these two stars possessed lines that were doubled at regular periods of $20\frac{1}{2}$ days. Subsequent research explained the cause, and showed this star to be composed of two suns, 25,300,000 miles apart, with an average orbital velocity of 43 miles a second and revolving in a period of 20·54 days; their united mass being 1·67 of the sun's with an absolute magnitude of 1·4 at a distance of 22·22 parsecs, or nearly $72\frac{1}{2}$ light-years. It has been calculated that about 56 per cent of spectroscopic binaries have periods of less than 20 days, and 26 per cent between 20 and 100 days, the remainder being longer. Of these the most noteworthy is Capella, one of whose visual components, as revealed by the interferometer, is a spectroscopic binary, whose suns have a period of 104 days, and a mass somewhat larger than our sun. The star β Arietis

is a spectroscopic binary whose suns average about 29,000,000 miles apart, and the period of their revolution 107 days. The brighter star of ξ Ursae Majoris is composed of two suns averaging 36,500,000 miles apart, with a period of revolution amounting to 665 days, their orbital motion averaging only $4\frac{1}{2}$ miles a second. An exceptionally long period is that of β Capricorni, its two suns taking $1,375\frac{1}{4}$ days to complete the revolution of their immense orbit, the diameter of which averages no less than 470,000,000 miles.

Noteworthy examples of close spectroscopic binaries with very short periods are the following: Spica Virginis, a brilliant star of the first magnitude, being composed of two suns whose mass is 9·6 and 5·8 that of our sun, and whose distance apart of their centres averages only 7,000,000 miles; from this we see that their surfaces must be almost in contact, consequently their period of revolution is only 4 days, the smaller sun travelling over the larger orbit at the terrific average rate of 130 miles a second. ψ Orionis has a period of only 3 days, while the components of μ Scorpii revolve in only $1\frac{3}{4}$ days, speeding round their common centre of gravity at the terrific rate of about 300 miles a second. The centres of these suns being only about 7,000,000 miles apart, their surfaces must be close together.

Visual Binaries. Similar details have been obtained regarding *visual binaries*, in which some components have been found to be themselves spectroscopic binaries. Thus stellar systems are gradually revealed to be composed of several suns, some with pairs of almost equal mass and

VISUAL BINARIES OR DOUBLE STARS

Name	Distance in Parsecs	Period of Revolution in years	Apparent Distance apart in secs.	Actual Distance apart in astro. units	Mass of each Component
α Centauri ..	1·32	78·8	17″·65	23·3	1·10 and 0·94
' Proxima ' ..	1·30	—	131′·0″·00	—	Very small
Sirius ..	2·70	50·0	7·57	20·4	2·44 and 0·96
Procyon .	3·21	39·0	4·05	13·0	1·10 and 0·40
Capella ..	13·30	0·285	0·054	0·85	4·20 and 3·40
Castor ..	13·16	340·00	6·06	80·0	Spectro. bin.
εHydrae .	50·00	15·3	0·23	11·5	3·50 and 3·0
ζHerculis ..	9·00	34·5	1·35	12·2	1·10 and 0·5
ξUrsae Majoris ..	7·00	59·8	2·51	17·0	0·7 and 0·7
γCoronae Borealis ..	45·45	87·8	0·73	33·0	4·7 (combined mass of both)
ηCassiopeiae	5·60	478·7	10·10	55·0	0·8 and 0·6

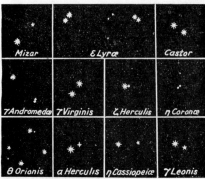

VISUAL BINARIES. *Famous examples of visual double, triple, quadruple and multiple stars such as are described in the text.*

volume like ε Lyrae, with two pairs of visual suns and one spectroscopic companion to the brightest of the four ; their periods are hundreds of years in duration. Again, Castor is a splendid example of a multiple system of suns. It is a visual binary (particulars of which are given in the table in p. 311) ; these components,

known, as is usual with double stars, as A and B, according to their relative brightness, have a distant companion star known as C. Now all three, A, B, and C, are spectroscopic binaries with short periods of revolution, thus providing six suns to this system of Castor.

Other binaries consist of a large primary with one or more lesser suns revolving round it, usually in elliptical orbits ; they are probably 'glowing worlds in the making,' such as were once Jupiter, Saturn, and our earth, when their volume and radiance were much greater than now.

The table in page 311 shows the brightest and most noteworthy visual binaries. The period of revolution is given in years and decimal fractions of the same. The apparent angular mean distance apart is given in seconds of arc, while the actual mean or average distance is in terms of the sun's distance or astronomical units, as, for example, the companion of Sirius, which is nearly 20½ times 93,000,000 miles. The mass of each component is given in terms of the sun's mass ; for example, one component of α Centauri has a slightly greater mass than the sun.

LESSON 27

Principal Classes of Variable Stars

ALTHOUGH the great majority of stars shine with a luminosity apparently steady and without perceptible variations, there are between 5,000 and 6,000 known stars whose fluctuations are a characteristic and very instructive feature as to stellar conditions. These are termed *variable stars*. There are many types, the different variations in their light being due to different causes. The various peculiarities, in their periods, in their light curves or intensities and in their spectra, have been closely studied. As a result, distinct varieties and classes, with characteristics common to each class, have been revealed, with minor differences in each class.

The four classes are : eclipsing variables ; short-period variables ; irregular variables ; and long-period variables. To these are added by some a fifth class, the *Novae* or so-called new stars.

Variable stars are designated by a Roman letter, one from R to Z, which is placed in front of the name of the constellation. Thus we get S Persei for Algol, Z Herculis and

Y Cygni. When all the letters down to Z have been applied and there are still more variables in the constellation to be designated, the letters are doubled progressively, from RR, RS, RT, and so on to ZZ. This has been reached in some constellations and so is now followed by AA. Thus are obtained TV Cassiopeiae, RT Persei, TX Herculis and RZ Ophiuchi. No letters above R are used for this purpose, and no methods are at present adopted to distinguish the four classes.

Eclipsing Variables. This class consists of *binary* stars whose components revolve at such an angle relative to the earth that the planes of their orbits are presented edgewise or almost so ; consequently, one or other periodically passes in front of its companion, and there occurs an observed diminution of the light during the time that one is being eclipsed. The resulting variations in magnitude differ according to the relative brightness of the two components and the inclination of the planes of their orbits. When this reaches 90° the orbits appear as straight lines, and one star passes centrally across the other in eclipse.

Between 200 and 300 eclipsing variables are known. More are discovered each year, mainly through photography of their spectra, because none of the separate components is perceptible visually — even through the most powerful telescopes, in which they always appear as one star ; but through the spectroscope their binary character is proved.

The most noteworthy and easily observed eclipsing variable is Algol or β Persei, also known under its variable star title of S Persei. Algol decreases from 2·3 to 3·7 magnitude in about $4\frac{1}{2}$ hours, during which time a large and much less luminous body passes in front of Algol until the minimum is reached, when only one-sixth the light of the star reaches us. After a few minutes it is perceived to be brightening up, until after another $4\frac{1}{2}$ hours Algol has resumed its normal brilliance and the obscuring body has passed. The whole process is repeated after an interval of 2 days 20 hours and 49 minutes, but about midway between each minimum there occurs a slight diminution of Algol's light ; this happens when the bright orb of Algol passes in front of the much less luminous disk of its companion. This is known as the secondary minimum and is a frequently observed feature of eclipsing variables, as is theoretically to be expected. The above phenomena, together with spectroscopic and mathematical considerations, indicate that Algol consists of two bodies, one very brilliant and radiating about 200 times the light of the sun, while the other is much less luminous and, though nearly as large, or perhaps larger, possesses far less mass. Algol is a B type of star, and the distance of its centre from that of its faint companion is, according to Vogel, about 3,250,000 miles.

Another type of eclipsing variable is represented in a bright star by β Lyrae ; in this case the secondary minima are much more pronounced, each being separated by two equal maxima. The whole cycle of change takes 12 days 21 hours 47 minutes, and ranges from 3·4 to 4·5 magnitude at greatest minima, and to 3·8 at secondary minima, which occurs exactly midway between the greatest minima. Spectroscopic investigation into this curious variation has shown that it is due to two very ellipsoidal bodies, one much brighter than the other, revolving round a central point of gravity, between two centres, and with their surfaces almost touching. The result-

ant tidal effect of such proximity is sufficient to account for their oval shape. The brightness of one is about $9\frac{1}{2}$ times greater than that of the other, so when it is the turn of the brighter one to pass in front of the fainter, the secondary minima occur. Another bright variant is that of β Aurigae, in which both stars are of nearly equal brightness and size ; in this case the minima are of equal intensity and the whole cycle of variation 3 days 23 hours $2\frac{1}{2}$ minutes. Most other eclipsing variables are very faint or telescopic.

Short-Period Variables. This class of variable star consists of those whose brightness varies in consequence of periodical physical changes in the star itself ; they are therefore true variables and are now usually referred to as *Cepheid* variables, from the star δ Cephei, which typically represents them. This star varies between 3·7 and 4·6 magnitude in a period of 5 days 8 hours 48 minutes, so it is easily observable, It is of type gF8, with a mass 10·5 times that of our sun, but with the very low density of only 0·0006 that of our sun. With a mean absolute magnitude of 2·2 it becomes obvious that δ Cephei is a sun of enormous size. This has been calculated to amount to an average diameter of 22,500,000 miles, or about $26\frac{1}{2}$ times that of our sun.

Now spectroscopic and mathematical research has established the fact that the great variations in the light of this star are due to a periodic change in its diameter amounting to about 1,600,000 miles. At maximum this huge gaseous sun has risen to a great increase of surface temperature amounting to about a thousand degrees Centigrade, resulting in an immense increase in light and heat radiation. After this terrific expansion, which occupies little more than a day, it shrinks less rapidly during the course of the next four days to minimum, in preparation for the next outburst of energy. As distinct from the eclipsing variables, the increase from minima to maxima is always much more rapid with Cepheids than is the decrease.

While δ Cephei is typical of short-period variable stars, of which several hundred are known and are being added to every year, there are the following differences. The periods of pulsation range from a few hours to about 36 days, though the average is about 7 days. While the light variation usually amounts to about 1 magnitude it may be nearly half a magnitude more or less. The Cepheids are all giant suns, some attaining 5 or 6 times the diameter of δ

Cephei, but they are all of very low density, which is lower in proportion to the increase in the star's diameter and in its absolute magnitude.

A most remarkable ' law ' has been recently discovered in regard to Cepheid variables. It is that there is a definite relationship between the star's luminosity and the period of the star's pulsations— the greater the luminosity the longer the pulsation is the rule. Therefore, when the length of the pulsation is ascertained, an easy matter, then the star's luminosity or absolute magnitude becomes known in consequence. Now by comparing the star's *absolute* magnitude with its *apparent* magnitude, its distance may be calculated (*see* Lesson 23, p. 304). In consequence of this most valuable discovery it has become possible to measure colossal distances far beyond the possibilities of trigonometry and spectroscopy. It applies more particularly to finding the distances of those remote star clusters and spiral nebulae, now known to be far distant universes, in which Cepheid variables have been found, their observed length of pulsation as compared with their faintness recording their distance and therefore that of the particular star cluster or spiral nebula in which they are placed.

Certain varieties of short-period variables, such as RV Tauri, possess light curves which suggest, according to Jeans, that they may be composed of two bodies very close together or in a state approaching fission, in which the variations in their light would be produced largely by their rotation and tidal oscillations, thus accounting for the complicated light curves.

Long-Period Variables. This class exhibits periods of variation ranging from about 150 days to 400, though a few of the stars belonging to it extend to 600 days ; rarely are they less than 150. There is thus a wide separation from the Cepheids and eclipsing variables. In the long-period variables the variation is very great, often amounting to a difference of 9 magnitudes.

A typical example is the easily observed o Ceti, popularly termed Mira, the ' Wonderful.' While known from ancient times, Fabricius, in 1596, first noted its periodic variations. These take a cycle of between 320 and 370 days to complete ; at maxima it will reach magnitude 2 on occasions, but is usually about magnitude 3, less frequently 4, and more rarely only 5. At minima it usually descends to magnitude 9, and has reached 9·6. As this star is most of

the time below 6th magnitude its absence from the sky is readily noted. It is also perceptible for between 80 and 90 days after maxima, from which it will be seen that, like the Cepheids, the decrease is not so rapid as the increase ; but the ascending light curve is not so steep and much less regular than in those of the Cepheids, thus suggesting spasmodic and explosive outbursts, which are spectroscopically shown to be chiefly incandescent hydrogen ; these produce the colossal eruptions, which may amount on occasion at maximum to 10,000 times the star's luminosity at minimum.

The star χ Cygni is another notable example, in which the light has been known to increase 35,000 times, from a minimum of 13·7 to a maximum of magnitude 4·8, in about 8 months. Its light curve shows varying maxima and minima, and with the ascent nearly twice as rapid as the descent, or decline in brilliancy.

Over 1,000 of these long-period variables are known, and it has been found impossible to formulate any theory fully to explain all their variations and to ascribe them to any one cause. Some undoubtedly pulsate. Two famous giant variables, Betelgeuse (*see* Lesson 25) and α Herculis, have been measured by interferometer. Thus a good idea is obtained of the immensity of the change that must take place in the star's volume, as well as its brilliance. α Herculis, while at the maxima of its pulsations, will radiate about 620 times more light than our sun ; whereas at minima, which occurs at intervals of only 120 days, it radiates only about 300 times more.

A probable solution in other instances is that clouds of less luminous material envelop these giant gaseous M stars, increase during quiescent minima, are then subsequently rent and temporarily dispersed by the great uprush of super-heated gases from below in which hydrogen chiefly figures. Then the star appears as a great blaze of light, like o Ceti (described above).

Irregular Variables. One type of this class is the U Geminorum type. These are faint stars which have periodic outbursts at irregular intervals of a month or two lasting but a few days. In the case of U Geminorum two different maxima occur at intervals of between 40 and 150 days, when it will increase from magnitude 13½ to nearly 9 in 3 to 4 days, then diminishing like a Cepheid, and later, after a varying interval, rise to perhaps magnitude 8·8. The stars SS Cygni vary similarly from magnitude 12 to 8·5, and SS Aurigae from 14·7 to 10·5.

Another singular type of irregular variable is that of R Coronae Borealis. While normally of magnitude 5·5, at irregular intervals its light decreases to 7 or, maybe, down to magnitude 15; it then remains so for a few months or several years, subject to slight variations.

Finally there are a number of generally faint and red stars, chiefly of the types Me, N and S, whose variations are less than 2 magnitudes. With but few exceptions they appear to be suns approaching the end of their luminous radiation. Normally they are very faint, of 13 magnitude or below; then at irregular and usually long intervals they will temporarily brighten up by 1 or 2 magnitudes, and then revert to their former faintness. Their temperatures are low, about 2,000° Centigrade. The explanation of their variability would appear to be that more or less solid surfaces are forming which get periodically broken up by outbursts of incandescent material from below these less luminous molten or solid surfaces. The star U Hydrae is a notable example of this type, varying from magnitude 4·5 to 6·1–6·3, and with an Nb spectrum devoid of violet light.

LESSON 28

Novae or New Stars

THE novae or 'new stars' are new only in the sense that they blaze up and present the spectacle of a brilliant star where nothing before was perceptible to the naked eye. By means, however, of the higher telescope powers and the more complete methods of stellar photography now available it has been found that a faint star originally existed where the outburst occurred, and that what was observed was not actually a new star, but an old one which had become subject to some celestial catastrophe. The brilliance rapidly fades and the star slowly dwindles to a faint telescopic visibility again, after sundry oscillations in brightness. Such is the normal life of so-called novae.

The method of nomenclature adopted is the word Nova, followed by the name of the constellation in which it appeared and the year, as indicated in the following list. This includes only the prominent novae visible to the naked eye which have appeared during the present century.

PRINCIPAL NOVAE

Nova Persei 1901	inc. from mag.		13·5 to	−0·8
Nova Lacertae 1910	,,	,,	13·5 to	5·0
Nova Geminorum 1912	,,	,,	15·0 to	3·7
Nova Aquilae 1918	,,	,,	11·0 to	−1·0
Nova Cygni 1920	,, below ,,		15·0 to	1·8
Nova Pictoris 1925	,, from ,,		12·7 to	1·2
Nova Herculis 1934	,, ,, below		15·0 to	1·3
Nova Lacertae 1936	,, ,, ,,		15·0 to	2·2
Nova Sagittarii 1936			faint to	4·5
Nova Aquilae 1936	,, ,, below		15·0 to	5·0
Nova Puppis 1942	,, ,, very faint to			2·0

In addition to these novae a number of faint and telescopic stars of this type have been discovered, largely by photography, chiefly in the Milky Way and in star clusters, but of these little is known.

Nova Persei 1901 was discovered by Anderson on February 22 of that year. It was the first to provide visual evidence through powerful telescopes of what had happened. This star increased over eight magnitudes in 28 hours, finally exceeding Capella in brilliance. So colossal was the outburst that in four days its light had increased 20,000 times. It soon diminished; after 24 hours its brilliance had decreased by one-third, and in about a year it had dwindled to twelfth magnitude.

Stellar Conflagrations. In the meantime the ordeal of the star had been revealed, for a cloud of faint light was subsequently seen to be enveloping Nova Persei; later it was found to be expanding at a great rate. This continued until, after about 8 months, it had attained the enormous apparent distance of about a minute of arc from the star. When the distance of Nova Persei from us—about 111 parsecs—was taken into account, it became obvious that the luminous clouds, if they were travelling, were doing so with the speed of light. Since this was an impossibility, the true solution appeared to be that what was observed was the light of the colossal conflagration on Nova Persei travelling outwards and illuminating clouds of nebulous matter in its path long after the outburst itself had died down.

The importance of the revelation was great, because the phenomenon proved the truth of one of the supposed causes of these outbursts, namely that they were due to a faint and relatively small sun rushing into a nebula or cloud of dark matter and consequently blazing up into a terrific incandescence, on much the same principle that causes a great meteor to blaze on entering the earth's atmosphere—though with this difference, that in the star the conflagration is relatively only superficial, for after passing through the nebula it again settles down to the condition of an apparently faint star, but at a higher temperature and magnitude than it was before. In some cases, as with Nova Persei, for instance, the star is later on found to be surrounded by a vast nebulous envelope or gaseous shell as the result of the outburst ; this is revealed both visually and spectroscopically.

Vast Star Convulsions. Nova Aquilae 1918 was the brightest nova of modern times, exceeding all stars in apparent brilliance except Sirius and Canopus. Its rise from eleventh magnitude to — 1·0 took only about four days, from June 5 to 9, during which time its luminosity had increased about 3,000 times. Having attained maximum, it immediately began to diminish, and a fortnight later was of only third magnitude, while six months afterwards it had diminished to sixth magnitude.

It was one of the most exhaustively studied of all novae, particularly its spectroscopic changes. By a fortunate chance it was photographed on June 5 at Heidelberg, when the star was of only 10·5 magnitude, and at the beginning of its stellar conflagration. Another fortunate chance provided a photograph of this celestial region on June 7, when Nova Aquilae had attained sixth magnitude ; by the next evening it was of first magnitude and its true character was realized.

Meanwhile many spectrograms had been obtained indicating the terrific convulsions the star was undergoing, far exceeding in magnitude and velocity any other known celestial phenomena. The absorption lines of the spectra indicated immense radial velocities of approach, reaching to over 1,400 miles per second, thus revealing the explosive force of the gases which expanded in all directions outward from the star. This subsequently became *visible* as a vast shell of luminous vapour or nebulosity, and then became a luminous disk, which continued to expand for several years until it attained the immense diameter of 16″. While the light curve was very similar to that of Nova Persei, and exhibited minor fluctuations as it decreased, there was no evidence that Nova Aquilae had become immersed in a dark nebula (as had happened to Nova Persei), which could be accounted a possible cause of the outburst. The evidence rather suggests that the luminous nebulosity was due to a colossal explosion of Nova Aquilae itself.

Nova Cygni 1920 was discovered by the veteran astronomer Denning, on August 20, when its magnitude had increased to about 3·5. By August 22 it had reached magnitude 2·8, and on August 24 it attained 1·8. Its total increase of luminosity must have been far greater than that of Nova Persei or Nova Aquilae, since photographs taken before the outburst and registering stars down to 15 magnitude show no trace of the star ; therefore the increase must have been stupendous, and the catastrophe the greatest known. The decrease was most rapid, the nova declining to

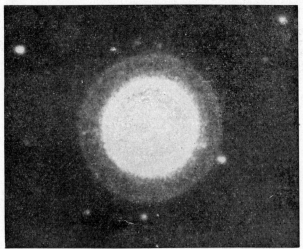

NOVA PICTORIS. First observed in May, 1925, this star suddenly attained to an extraordinary degree of brilliance (as seen in this photo) and then slowly waned, until in January, 1928, observers noticed the appearance of a nebulous ring. This continued to expand until in March, 1928, two stars were seen where one had been before. It has been suggested, therefore, that in 1925 Nova Pictoris was split in two, as the result either of an internal convulsion or of the impact of another star.

Courtesy of H E. Wood. Union Astronomer, Johannesburg

magnitude 4 in a week and magnitude 9 in a couple of months. It appears to have been originally a small star at a distance of 38½ parsecs, and much nearer than the other novae. Though no shell or disk of expansive gases was observed, yet its spectrum indicated terrific radial velocities, amounting to as much as 1,100 miles a second ; so, apparently, Nova Cygni 1920 was of the same type as Nova Aquilae 1918.

Mystery of Nova Pictoris. Nova Pictoris 1925 provided a somewhat different spectacle and a unique problem. This star, which was only observable from southern latitudes, blazed up to about 60,000 times its original brilliance, being first noticed in May of that year. Its increase took several days, and it also remained bright for a longer period than is usual with novae, being still of third magnitude in the following September and remaining visible to the naked eye for over three years.

A singular feature of this outburst — which was obviously a different convulsion from those already considered—was the appearance of a nebulous ring, not seen until January, 1928, which continued to expand ; then in March, 1928, the unprecedented spectacle was revealed that Nova Pictoris had apparently divided into two separating stars. Bearing in mind the immense distance and date of the convulsion, it would have taken quite three years for the separation to have become perceptible even in powerful telescopes, that is, supposing the stars to have divided with speeds of several hundred miles a second.

The nebulosity had by this time attained a diameter of about 6′ and exhibited condensations similar to those of Nova Persei 1901. In view of the stupendous diameter represented by this nebulous ring, and the presence of two inner rings, it became obvious that what was being witnessed was the progress of the light of three successive outbursts through a vast and otherwise invisible nebula. Whether this stellar catastrophe was actually caused by a star

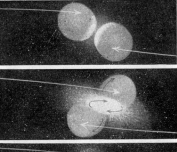

WHEN A STAR SPLITS. These diagrams, prepared by Professor A. W. Bickerton, purport to show how two stars colliding with one another may split and produce a third.

being rent asunder by some terrific explosive force within itself, or through becoming immersed in the dark nebulous matter, it is impossible to say. Or the conflagration might have been caused by two suns or a sun and a dark world colliding. This theory is generally discounted because of the immensity of space between independent stars. In Nova Pictoris it would not account for the presence of the vast nebula. It is possible that the two stars of Nova Pictoris were originally there, that one of them was becoming a dark world, and that the whole was rejuvenated by the nebulous immersion.

Nova Herculis 1934 proved to be another most interesting example, similar in some ways to and yet different from Nova Pictoris. The outburst, which appears to have been stupendous, happened at a distance of some 1,500 light-years. The outburst was unquestionably on the decline when discovered, but in view of the star's original faintness it was estimated that it had increased in luminosity by at least 400,000 times. Its light fluctuated considerably during the first six months of observation. This suggested subsequent outbursts of vast extent, since, after declining to 13 magnitude, it brightened up again to 7½ magnitude.

A surprising sequel was the eventual discovery, some six months after the outburst, that two stars had apparently come into being. This was closely studied, particularly with the great 40-inch refractor at the Yerkes Observatory, where the two stars were found to be separating. Close measurements of their rate of motion revealed that they were separating at the uniform rate of about 380 miles a second

It was found that at this rate the two stars would have about covered the distance between them, from the time of the outburst. Observation continuing showed that in 1937, three years afterwards, the distance between the stars had increased uniformly from about 2″ to 6″ and was continuing.

Records of novae go back for over 2,000 years. The first was noted in Scorpius in

134 B.C. and another in Ophiuchus in 123 B.C. ; one in Centaurus in A.D. 173, and the next in Aquila in A.D. 389. All these were of about first magnitude, and, as is usual with novae, in or near the Milky Way. Scorpius again had novae in A.D. 827, 1006 and 1203, all about first magnitude ; while Ophiuchus had another nova in A.D. 1230.

The famous nova of 1572 was the most brilliant known ; it appeared in Cassiopeia, and was generally known as Tycho's star. It was brighter than Venus at her greatest brilliance and reached −4 magnitude, being visible during the day. After 16 months it became invisible. Another very bright nova appeared in Ophiuchus during 1604, and has been known as Kepler's star ; it reached −2 magnitude.

Novae usually appear in constellations of the Milky Way, and in the nebulous areas within 10° of the galactic equator, the medium line of the Milky Way. Numbers of the fainter telescopic novae occur in Scorpius and Sagittarius, while Aquila, Perseus, Cygnus, Ophiuchus and Gemini follow closely in the occurrence of these stellar outbursts.

LESSON 29

The Study of Star Maps

So as to facilitate the recognition of any particular star or constellation, the apparent sphere of the sky is divided by imaginary lines of right ascension and declination, corresponding respectively to terrestrial meridians and parallels of longitude and latitude. The imaginary lines of right ascension—great circles or meridians —pass through the imaginary celestial sphere's two poles. These poles are situated where the axis of the earth, if indefinitely prolonged in both directions, would intersect the celestial sphere, and so they occupy the *zenith of the terrestrial poles*—'zenith' being the astronomical term for the point vertically above the observer's head. The *celestial equator* is a great circle drawn round the imaginary sphere midway between the poles, and is situated above the earth's equator.

Every place has its own celestial meridian circle, and the rotation of the earth causes this meridian to make a complete revolution of the sky in 24 hours. In the course of this revolution it passes over every visible star, but it is usual to speak of the stars as 'crossing the meridian.' This occurs when they are due south of the North Celestial Pole (as seen from these latitudes), and are therefore at their highest altitude above the horizon. The horizon is usually regarded as the limit of our vision at any particular place, but astronomically it consists of the great circle 90° distant from the zenith of the observer ; consequently observers at different latitudes on earth are bounded by different celestial horizons. The farther south the latitude, the higher the altitude attained by the stars, and therefore the greater the number to come within observation. A star's altitude, then, depends upon the observer's standpoint on the earth and also upon the time of observation.

There is one star upon which the time of observation makes very little difference— the Pole Star, which is nearly above the terrestrial pole and always remains almost at the same altitude according to the latitude of the observer. It is always practically in the same position, since it revolves in a small circle round the exact celestial pole at a distance of only 1° 3½′ from it. All the other stars will be seen to bear a permanent relationship to this star, and only differ relatively to the horizon and observer because of their diurnal revolution and annual progression westwards. But

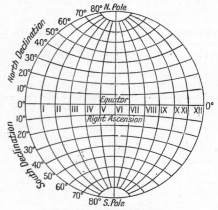

STELLAR MEASUREMENTS

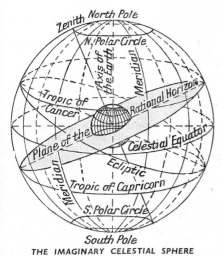

THE IMAGINARY CELESTIAL SPHERE

those which are *circumpolar* and revolve N. of the zenith point are within the *circle of perpetual apparition* (*see* page 238).

The most famous and familiar of these are the seven bright stars of Ursa Major, known popularly as the Plough or Charles's Wain. Two of these stars, α and β, will be seen to point almost directly to the Pole Star or *Polaris*—hence their name of the Pointers. Five of these stars, β, γ, δ, ε and ζ, together with several smaller ones, constitute a group of suns which are all travelling in the same direction in space, apparently more or less toward Arcturus ; on the other hand, α and η are travelling in different directions, with the result that in 50,000 years' time the familiar figure of the Plough will have changed. The Plough is about overhead in the spring evenings and low down in the north below the Pole Star in the autumn (*see* star maps in pages 242-43).

On the opposite side of the Pole Star to the Plough are the five familiar stars of Cassiopeia, arranged somewhat in the form of a W, which, with a fainter sixth star κ added, constitute the popular Cassiopeia's Chair. While these constellations occupy two quadrants of this circumpolar area, two very bright stars, together with several easily remembered of lesser brilliance, comprise the constellations of Auriga and Lyra. The brilliant Capella and β Aurigae of the former are almost overhead in the winter evenings, and Vega and the two stars β and γ Lyrae below it are nearly

overhead late in the summer evenings. On the other hand, Vega is low down in the north in winter evenings, while Capella occupies this position in summer evenings.

Among the less prominent stars is the constellation of Draco, the celestial Dragon, which is between the zenith and the Pole Star on summer evenings ; Cepheus is in this position on autumn evenings, with the brilliant Deneb of Cygnus, the Swan, but popularly known as the Northern Cross, nearly overhead. Deneb is also within the circle of perpetual visibility, although the 'Cross' is not ; it is a sun of exceptional intrinsic brilliance, radiating 10,000 times the light of our sun, but from a distance 41,140,000 times as great, and possessing an absolute magnitude of −5·2. It is the most brilliant sun of the northern heavens.

As if they were swinging round the north celestial pole are the seven stars of Ursa Minor, the Little Bear. These remotely resemble in arrangement the seven stars of Ursa Major, but only Polaris and the ' Leaders ' are bright—Polaris at the tip of the Bear's tail, β and γ between it and the 'Plough Handle.' They are north of Polaris in winter evenings, east in spring, south in summer, and west in autumn.

Procession of the Stars. Apart from these circumpolar, always visible stars, most of the starry host appear to pass before us as a diurnal procession from east to west between the zenith and the southern horizon ; all, that is, except those perpetually hidden because they encircle the south celestial pole.

As the earth's rotation successively brings into view all these stars in 24 hours, it would be possible to see the entire concourse were it not that the sunlight obscures

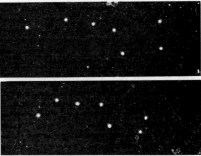

MOTION OF THE ' PLOUGH.' *The stars have not only an apparent but a ' proper ' motion. Thus the familiar constellation of the ' Plough ' or ' Great Bear,' seen as it is today, in the upper diagram, will have changed in 50,000 years from now to the shape shown in the lower diagram.*

about one-half of them during daylight hours. As the earth revolves, however, in its annual orbit, the other half of the starry heavens comes into view. In the sky stars appear as if projected upon a dome, but star maps, such as those in pages 242–43, present them on a flat surface with resultant distortion of relative positions. There the lines of right ascension have to appear as if radiating from the pole in straight lines instead of arcs of great circles. Those of declination are indicated by the degrees close to the central meridian.

The right ascension of a star is the angular distance between the great circle which passes through that star and the pole, and another great circle passing through the pole and a fixed point on the celestial equator known as the vernal equinox or the First Point of Aries. Right ascension is always reckoned from this equinox in an easterly direction round the equator, which is divided into 360°. As the celestial sphere appears to make one complete revolution in 24 hours, a meridian passes over 15° in every hour. It is usual, therefore, to reckon right ascension not in degrees but in hours, minutes and seconds. One hour of time or right ascension is equal to 15°, one minute of time to 15 minutes of angular measurement, and one second of time to 15 seconds of angular measurement. ⁄This is expressed in symbols thus : 1 hr. = 15°, 1 min. = 15′, 1 sec. = 15″. As the position of a geographical place is stated as being situated in, say, latitude 51° 30′ and longitude 10° 15′, so the position of a star—Sirius, e.g.—is stated as right ascension 6h. 40 m. 42 sec., and declination −16° 35′ (the minus sign indicates south declination, and + north declination).

LESSON 30

Open and Globular Star Clusters and Star Clouds

STAR clusters are those aggregations in which groups of stars are physically associated, and are quite distinct from artificially grouped constellations (*see* Lesson 22, page 298). They are divided into *open clusters* and *globular clusters.* The first variety, of which about 200 are known, consists of clusters in which large numbers of stars are apparently massed together in an irregular manner with many outlying members, as in the cases of the well-known Pleiades and Hyades clusters, which are two of the few open clusters visible to the naked eye. It is usual for the members of the cluster to possess a similar proper motion and to average about the same distance from the earth. Thus it comes about that in some cases there are numbers of bright stars apparently not close together, or clustered, which nevertheless are found to form a cluster ; the individual members appear far apart on account of their comparative nearness to our planet. Nearly all the stars of Orion and most of those in the 'Plough' area of Ursa Major thus form two open clusters, while our sun is found to be a member of a cluster with Sirius, Procyon, Alpha Centauri, Altair and many lesser luminaries.

We see, therefore, that the thousands of millions of stars composing our universe are not distributed evenly or at haphazard throughout the heavens, but are arranged in obvious groups—in clustered masses like eddies in a vast swirl of waters. Though apparently massed together, the stars are nevertheless separated from each other by distances usually to be measured in light-years and approximating to the distances of the nearest stars to our sun.

Open Clusters. The Hyades are the nearest of these open clusters and averages about 40 parsecs distant. In this are calculated to be about 100 stars, 40 of them larger and brighter than our sun. The whole forms a cluster between 30 and 40 light-years in diameter, and all travelling in a similar direction, towards the east, as observed from our latitudes. This cluster, therefore, contains approximately a similar number of stars to that contained in the same cubic space of our solar cluster. Some of the stars—for instance, Aldebaran—lie between us and the Hyades, while many faint ones are beyond it ; stars which are not members of the cluster may usually be distinguished by their different parallax and proper motion.

The Pleiades is the best known open cluster and is interesting as a sight test. Seven stars are to be perceived by sharp eyes. These were known to the ancients under the names of Alcyone, the brightest, of 3rd magnitude ; Electra and Atlas, of the 4th ;

Merope, Maia and Taygeta, of the 5th ; and Pleione, of the 6th magnitude ; very good sight could perceive Asterope and also glimpse its companion, Celaeno, under very favourable conditions. A field-glass will increase the number to between 30 and 40, while a powerful telescope will reveal over 2,000 stars in this field, a large number of which are members of the Pleiades cluster. Its average distance is about 100 parsecs, a singular feature being the radiant nebulosity surrounding the brighter stars, which are of the B Class. This nebulous matter apparently fills most of the space between the stars ; it is now believed that its radiance is derived from the intense luminosity of these helium suns.

The greater the distance of these known agglomerations of stars the more they help us to gain some idea of the structure of the universe. Many of these open clusters are between 2,000 and 3,000 parsecs distant. The density of the stars in the various clusters differs immensely, but it is usually much greater toward the centre. In some cases the number of stars is a thousand times greater than in our solar cluster.

Spectroscopic examination of the members of star clusters shows that every type of star is represented, but in some clusters certain types predominate. For instance, in the Hyades and Praesepe the A Class predominates in the brighter stars ; in the Pleiades and Orion clusters the B Class stars are by far the most numerous and brightest.

Star Clouds. Numerous nebulous patches of light in various regions of the heavens are found on telescopic examination to be composed of innumerable stars ; two such are in Perseus, and known as H.VI.33,34, but in this famous double cluster many of the stars are revealed by field-glasses. Other impressive areas, most of them much more extensive, require powerful telescopes to resolve them into stars ; they are then found to amount to many millions, and are usually designated *star clouds*.

The nomenclature adopted is that of the following generally accepted Catalogues. The first and most famous was that of Messier, made in 1784. This contained nomenclature for all the brighter objects then observable, and is still most generally used for those objects, which included nebulae as well as star clusters, the essential differences between the two being then unknown ; altogether 103 items were catalogued, and they are now referred to as, for instance, M.44 for the Praesepe, or

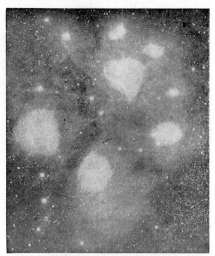

THE PLEIADES. One of the most familiar objects in the winter sky, the Pleiades cluster consists of more than two thousand stars, although only six or seven are visible to the naked eye. The brighter stars are of the helium type, and many are surrounded by a vast nebulosity.

Professor G. W. Ritchey, Yerkes Observatory

M.35 for the splendid cluster in Gemini. Subsequently, Sir John Herschel compiled some lists which were gathered into a General Catalogue. Thus the above double cluster in Perseus has come to be known as H.VI.33,34. By the year 1887 Dreyer's New General Catalogue, containing 7,840 objects, was produced ; in this, for example, the Praesepe M.44 becomes N.G.C.2632. Dreyer's catalogue refers mostly to the fainter objects, chiefly nebulae which had been revealed by the higher powers of the telescope, and a supplement is the Index Catalogue, I.C., which adds about 6,000 more objects, chiefly faint nebulae.

Globular Clusters. The globular clusters, included in the above catalogue nomenclature, are totally different from open clusters; about 70 are known, and they constitute most remarkable agglomerations of suns into what would seem to be small island universes apart. The number of stars each cluster contains must average at least 50,000, probably many more, since, owing to their great distance, suns the size of ours would not be perceptible. Moreover, toward the centre these clusters appear so condensed that individual stars are indistinguishable. Every type of star ranging from Class B to Class M is present, the latter being

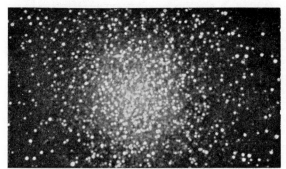

A STARRY MAZE. This photograph is of M.13 in Hercules, a typical globular cluster which is so far removed from us in space that Sirius, the apparently brightest star in the heavens, would be quite invisible to us if it were situated at the same distance. Each one of the stars in the cluster must, therefore, have an actual luminosity greater than that of Sirius.

Courtesy of Royal Astronomical Society

obviously the largest. They contain numerous variable stars, proved by taking photographs at short intervals ; thus both short-period Cepheids and long-period variables are revealed. The presence of Cepheids has proved to be a valuable aid for estimating the distances of these clusters. This has been ascertained by means of the period-luminosity curve, which provides mathematically the absolute magnitude of the particular star (*see* Lesson 27, page 314). The difference between the absolute and the apparent magnitude gives the distance, by the same method as already described in Lesson 23 (page 304) as applied to the stars.

The distance of the clusters being thus obtained, their size is but a matter of calculation, and so it is found that the diameters of these clusters must approximate to at least 30 parsecs. The condensation of stars toward the centre will therefore be very great ; there must be over a thousand stars in some cubic regions of these clusters, where there is but one in a similar cube of space in our part of the universe.

The nearest of all these star clusters is the grand spectacle of ω Centauri. It was so titled because to the eye without telescopic aid it appears as a hazy 4th magnitude star and its true character was not then known. Now it is seen to be a still vaster cluster than M.13 and about 6,500 parsecs away. The farthest clusters are over 70,000 parsecs distant.

The arrangement of these singular clusters in space takes the form of an ellipsoidal area some 75,000 parsecs in diameter, according to the exhaustive researches of Shapley. The solar system is situated on one side of this vast area, thus accounting for the clusters being almost exclusively found in the half of the celestial sphere that is within 90° of the constellation of Sagittarius, which is regarded by many as the centre of 'our universe.'

Principal Types of Nebulae

NEBULAE are faint ill-defined areas of light usually of small apparent extent and resembling wisps of luminous mist. They present every conceivable form and are generalized into four classes : (1) irregular nebulae ; (2) planetary nebulae ; (3) dark nebulae ; (4) spiral nebulae. Between 2,000,000 and 3,000,000 such areas are now known, most of them through the application of long-exposure photography, in conjunction with very high telescopic powers.

Some of these hazy spots of light having been revealed by increases in the powers of the telescope as clusters of stars, the opinion was formed that all were simply

star clusters so far away that their light merged into the impression of nebulous light as does that of the Milky Way. This assumption was destroyed by the spectroscope, which distinguishes with certainty between the light sent to us from a solid star and that emitted by a gas. When this instrument was applied to the nebulae it showed that, whereas some were composed of groups of stars, others were, beyond doubt, masses of luminous gas. The so-called nebulae were therefore divided into two groups, the gaseous and non-gaseous.

It was soon noticed that whereas the gaseous variety shone with a bluish light, the other radiated a white light, this being due to the above differences in their sources. Fortunately there are a few examples of both types just perceptible to the naked eye.

Irregular Nebulae. These are essentially gaseous, bluish in tint and occasionally associated with highly incandescent stars of very great temperatures. Such, for example, is the great nebula of Orion, which may be perceived on any dark and clear night below the 'belt' of Orion, and extending for a considerable apparent distance from the multiple star θ Orionis. Various portions of this nebula are in motion in different directions, amounting to as much as 6 or 7 miles a second, and suggesting a rotary motion which indicates a period of about 300,000 years. Actually this nebula extends as a diffuse nebulosity for about 45° to 30° over an area much larger than the constellation of Orion, and enveloping most of its stars, including the three stars of the 'belt.'

Other nebulae of this first class visible in the low powers of the telescope are the 'dumb-bell' nebula in Vulpecula and the 'crab' nebula in Taurus, which has also been found to have a rotary motion with an observed tendency to expansion. The extensive nebulosities surrounding many of the Pleiades are also of the irregular class, while there are numerous areas in Scorpius, Sagittarius and Cygnus ; the 'looped' nebula in Dorado is, however, the largest known irregular nebula, with a diameter calculated by Shapley at 130 light-years.

The spectra of these irregular nebulae consist of a faint continuous spectrum upon which is superimposed a line emission spectrum ; lines of hydrogen and helium are pronounced, together with two green lines, supposed to be derived from an unidentified element named *nebulium*.

The densities of these nebulae are exceedingly low, estimated to be many billions of times less than the earth's atmosphere—therefore far less than can be attained in an artificial vacuum. For such rarefied matter in space to be incandescent and produce the spectra of hydrogen and helium seems out of the question.

Now since these gases in a state of incandescence are most prominent in the stars which are enveloped or associated with these vast areas of diffuse nebulae, it appears, according to Hubble, that these stars cause the luminosity observed in the nebulae. This circumstance is singularly well displayed in the way in which the Pleiades light up the surrounding nebulous masses. These masses are obviously in

motion and the light has been observed to change with the movement. When we come to consider dark nebulae this solution would appear to be true.

Planetary Nebulae. In this second class the nebulae are smaller than in the first ; they are also denser, more massive, and appear approximately regular in outline, presenting under low magnification a disk which looks somewhat like that of a planet seen out of focus.

Though a few of these nebulae have a diameter approaching 12′, most of them are much smaller. About 150 are known, and of these the 'owl' nebula in Ursa Major— so named from the fancied resemblance of its disk to the face of an owl—known astronomically as N.G.C.3587, is one of the most easily observed. Another is the so-called 'ring' nebula in Lyra—N.G.C. 6720 in the Catalogue nomenclature, which is the same as for star clusters (*see* Lesson 30, page 321). This nebula is situated almost midway between β and γ Lyrae, and has an apparent diameter of 1′ 23″ at its widest ; it appears as a ring under low magnification, but, photographed with high telescopic powers, it is seen to be filled with nebulous detail together with a star in the centre. Most of the disks of planetary nebulae are found, when photographed through powerful telescopes, to exhibit a mass of detail which suggests the rotation of the whole round a central star, nucleus or condensation. This rotation may take from 5,000 to 15,000 years to complete.

Other noteworthy examples are N.G.C. 7662 in Andromeda, H.IV.27 in Hydra, and, largest of all, N.G.C.7293 in Aquarius,

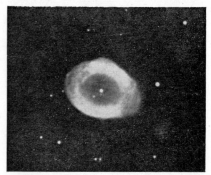

PLANETARY NEBULA. *Planetary, ring, or disk nebulae apparently consist of vast luminous atmospheres, surrounding a comparatively faint star. This photo is of the nebula in Lyra, one of the best known of the 150 disk nebulae so far observed.*

which, with a diameter of 12', is at a distance of about 80 light-years and is the nearest known planetary nebula. These nebulae are more numerous in the neighbourhood of the Milky Way, especially in the region of Sagittarius, and are as a rule apparently smaller than those in regions distant from the Milky Way. This is explained as due to the fact that those situated near the galactic plane (the central line of the Milky Way) are farthest from the earth.

The spectra of this class of nebulae are similar to those of the class O and Wolf–Rayet stars. Some of these so strikingly resemble planetary nebulae that it might be inferred that many of them represent one-time novae, which in distant ages blazed up and have been left in nebulous condition, slowly to die down into star again.

Dark Nebulae. These were first suspected to exist as many dark patches in the heavens, conspicuous for being destitute of distant stars, in regions—such as certain parts of the Milky Way—where the adjoining areas are dense with stellar luminosity. At one time it was thought that these dark areas were regions destitute of stars ; but since Cowper Ranyard drew attention to their singular shape in many of the smaller patches revealed in the early days of celestial photography, it has been found that they are due to the intervention of opaque cosmic material. Barnard catalogued nearly 200 of these remarkable objects ;

more have been added by the continued application of photography, particularly in the vicinity of the luminous nebulae, one of the most impressive being the mass of dark nebulous material which encroaches upon the bright portions of the Orion nebula below ζ Orionis, the easternmost star of the famous 'belt' illustrated in page 248. These are doubtless dark portions of the nebula itself which more or less obscure the illuminated regions.

Other remarkable examples are the 'coal sack' in Crux (the Southern Cross), and the dark nebulae in Ophiuchus, Scorpius, Taurus and Cygnus. Their distances are found to vary from 100 parsecs to the limits of the Milky Way ; they are also associated with many of the open clusters, e.g. the Pleiades and Orion.

The great cleft in Cygnus, perceptible on any dark night in summer and autumn, extends through Aquila to Ophiuchus. It is undoubtedly caused by the intervention of a belt of opaque nebulous matter which obscures part of the Milky Way with its numerous stars beyond, while only those which are between us and the obscuring clouds are perceived. The material is believed to consist of cosmic particles which may be, in size, anything from a molecule to a planetoid, and spread through areas to be measured by hundreds or even thousands of parsecs, as we shall now see in considering the spiral nebulae.

LESSON 32

Spiral Nebulae and Problems of the Cosmos

SPIRAL nebulae were at one time regarded as masses of gaseous nebulosity which ultimately evolved into suns and solar systems ; but spectroscopic analysis of their light, together with photography applied with greatly increased powers of the telescope, has revealed them to be of stellar composition, only slightly gaseous, possessing many features which distinguish them entirely from every other class of celestial object, and nebulae only in appearance. Though more numerous than the true or galactic nebulae, these so-called nebulae are spread over the sky on a totally different plan, their numbers apparently increasing towards the *galactic poles*, particularly the northern, and there being only very few within 20° of the *galactic equator*, that is, the median line of the Milky Way.

The spectroscope, with the aid of long exposure photographs, shows the spectra of spiral nebulae to be continuous and crossed by numbers of dark absorption lines—just such spectra as are obtained from the sun and the stars. Thus it has been ascertained that these so-called nebulae are actually composed of suns more or less similar to our own, and since lines of nebulium are also present in certain localized areas, gaseous nebulae are also present as in our *galactic system*.

The fact is therefore revealed that they are galaxies apart from the galaxy or universe of which the solar system is a constituent. They are in consequence often referred to as extra-galactic nebulae.

Photographs taken by long exposure for several hours have revealed the dim patches of misty light (which is all that even telescopes exhibit to the eye) to be composed of star clouds, clustered masses of suns, the larger of which are individually perceived in the nearer of the 'nebulae.' The whole usually appears arranged as a vast spiral, the arms composed of streaming star clouds intermingled with nebulosity and frequently more bluish at the outer than the central regions. In some cases there are belts of dark nebulous matter, generally extending round the outer regions of the spiral, which partially hide the stellar radiance beyond, as in our galaxy. The centre of a typical spiral consists of a massed condensation of stellar radiance in which the individual suns appear clustered and require still higher powers of the telescope to resolve.

The spirals exhibit every variety of form ; variations are increased by perspective. They appear to be somewhat flattened lens-shaped agglomerations of thousands of millions of suns and doubtless numerous worlds, together with star clusters and nebulae proper, such as enter into the composition of our galaxy. In a small proportion the spiral form is less obvious owing to various irregular star clouds and streams of nebulosity disguising the structure ; these are known as *irregular spirals*. Others are so distant, or in such an early stage, that the spiral form is not obvious.

In the larger and nearer of the so-called spiral nebulae both variable stars, particularly Cepheids, and novae are found. The Cepheids have proved to be most important as a means for calculating the distance and immensity of the extra-galactic nebulae. For since it was possible to estimate the absolute magnitude of the Cepheid variables from the period-luminosity curve, their distance could be calculated from the difference between their absolute and apparent magnitudes (*see* Lesson 27, page 314). These extra-galactic universes are the most distant objects known.

Nebula of Andromeda. One of the nearest is the great nebula of Andromeda, at a distance of about 210,000 parsecs, and therefore far beyond the extreme limits of our galaxy, which are probably from 20,000 to 50,000 parsecs distant. This grand spiral, shown almost edgewise in the photograph given on page 248, may be seen with the naked eye almost overhead in the autumn evenings, when it appears as an oval area of faint misty light somewhat greater than the moon's apparent width. The study of this far-off galaxy has proved instructive, and we have gained therefrom some conception of what our own galaxy appears like *from the outside*, as it were. Considerations such as the arrangement of the star clouds of the Milky Way, spectroscopic parallaxes and Cepheid distances, have combined to give experts fairly accurate grounds for the hypothesis that our galaxy has the form of a spiral and that the solar system is situated somewhere within it, at about 10,000 parsecs from one side and between 20,000 and 50,000 parsecs from the farther and vaguer side. The centre of the system is estimated to be in the dense star clouds of Sagittarius and Scorpius at approximately some 10,000 parsecs distant, and the greatest diameter of the whole galactic system is between 40,000 and 60,000 parsecs. Owing to the obvious difficulty of estimating the *depth* of the star clouds, considerable latitude must be allowed in estimates. Professor Kapteyn, the late leading expert authority upon the galaxy, considered the diameter of this lens-shaped spiral system to be about five times its thickness ; this is well in accord with the observed proportions of many extra-galactic universes. Kapteyn estimated our galaxy to contain a total of about 47,000,000,000 stars ; Seares and Van Rhijn, about 30,000,000,000. Of these something like 2,000,000,000 may be regarded as dimly observable, the others being hidden in the star clouds of the Milky Way.

Magellanic Clouds (Nebecula). There are two other galactic systems that are known to be nearer than the great nebula of Andromeda, but they are only to be seen from more southern latitudes. Visible to the naked eye as large, faintly luminous areas, resembling detached portions of the Milky Way, they are popularly known as the Magellanic Clouds, but astronomically as Nebecula Major and Nebecula Minor. They are far apart, the former chiefly in Dorado, the latter in Toucan. Belonging to the irregular class of spirals, they are of great interest, since they represent small galaxies adjacent to our own. Nebecula Minor was found by Shapley to be at a distance of about 32,000 parsecs, and Nebecula Major at one of about 34,500.

The total number of these extra-galactic universes represented by these spiral nebulae approaches 2,000,000, and it is certain that further increase of telescopic power will add to the number. The speed at which they are travelling relative to our galaxy is terrific, ranging from 200 to 1,000 miles a second. Now, a most remarkable circumstance of supreme importance to our conception of the Cosmos is the fact that about 80 per cent of these galaxies appear to be receding from our galaxy. From this it is inferred by certain authorities, particularly those who accept the mathematical concepts of Relativity, that the Cosmos or entire 'Universe of Galaxies' is expanding.

Relativity of Space and Time. Our galaxy is doubtless travelling at a speed comparable with the above, and in a direction which has no meaning except one *relative* to the others. The time taken has likewise no meaning except that it is *relative* to the speeds of other objects through what we call space. When mathematically considered as an essential part of the Cosmos, space and time are found to be indissolubly linked ; thus the mathematical investigation, begun by Lorentz and elaborated by Minkowski, may be summed up in the latter's words :

The views of space and time which I have set forth have their foundation in experimental physics. . . From henceforth space in itself and time in itself sink into mere shadows, and only a kind of union of the two preserves an independent existence.

Moreover, none of these extra-galactic universes is where it appears to be ; neither are the stellar denizens of our own galaxy ; the *space* separating us from each, and the *time* that light takes in transit across those spaces, vary with the different distances. Indeed, it has even been conceived that a galaxy which now appears in one region of the heavens may actually be in the opposite region, owing to the lapse of time the light has taken to reach us, 140 million light-years being taken by the light of the farthest galaxy known.

The Theory of Relativity. Dr. Albert Einstein carried on the work of his predecessors and, in particular, corrected and adapted the famous laws of Newton adequately to explain by mathematical formulae certain observed phenomena in physics, optics and astronomy. This he presented in his Special Theory of Relativity in 1905. His General Theory of Relativity (1915) chiefly deals with optical and electrical phenomena and accelerated motion, even to the extent of predicting certain results. These were, first, the forward motion of the perihelion of Mercury, which amounts to $40''\cdot1$ per century ; Einstein's hypothesis requires it to be $42''\cdot9$ per century and is the only adequate explanation.

The second was the bending of light rays when passing near a large gravitational mass such as our sun ; this was proved to occur by the Greenwich Eclipse Expedition to Brazil in 1919, when the photographs, taken with great precision, showed that the light from certain stars passing near the sun at the time of total eclipse was bent towards it to the observed extent of $1''\cdot98$, whereas Einstein predicted $1''\cdot75$. A subsequent expedition to the Australian total eclipse of 1922 gave the observed bending as $1''\cdot78$; thus, after allowing for unavoidable observational errors, Einstein was proved correct.

The third was the displacement of spectral lines so that they shift towards the red end of the spectrum, as the result of the vibrations becoming slower when the light is emitted from the sun or any other massive body ; this was also finally proved to occur in the case of the massive companion to Sirius. (*See* further in our Course on Physics, Vol. I, Lesson 19.)

The Expanding Universe. Already, however, Einstein's concept of a cosmic universe of fixed and limited extent has had to give place to one conceived by Dr. de Sitter, in 1917, which presents an expanding cosmic universe. This at present is most in accord with the observed receding galaxies. Other concepts are : warped space in gravitational fields ; the possibility of curved space and a spherical cosmos in which light travels in a curved path and may return upon itself, as does the surface of a sphere ; even gravitation as a force is questioned by the new theories. These are largely subjects of mathematical discussion, in which the names of Sir H. Spencer Jones (Astronomer Royal), Dr. de Sitter, Sir James Jeans, Sir Arthur Eddington, Professor E. A. Milne, and the Abbé G. Lemaître are in the forefront. Their writings should be referred to for a presentation of the various aspects of the problems. Meanwhile, this outstanding fact remains beyond question : that there is no known limit to *that which is*, i.e. existence, in either time, space or spacetime ; therefore we must infer its infinity and eternity.

BOOK LIST

'The Sun, the Stars and the Universe,' W. M. Smart (Longmans) ; 'Story of the Stars,' A. C. Crommelin (Collins) ; 'Worlds Without End,' Sir H. Spencer Jones (English Univ. Press) ; 'General Astronomy,' Sir H. Spencer Jones (Arnold) ; 'Present-day Astronomy,' J. W. N. Sullivan (Newnes) ; 'The Stars in Their Courses,' 'The Mysterious Universe,' 'Through Space and Time,' all Sir James Jeans (C.U.P.) ; 'The Expanding Universe,' Sir A. Eddington (C.U.P.) ; 'The Realm of the Nebulae,' Edwin Hubble (O.U.P.) ; 'Makers of Astronomy,' H. Macpherson (O.U.P.) ; 'Star Atlas,' A. P. Norton (Gall and Inglis).

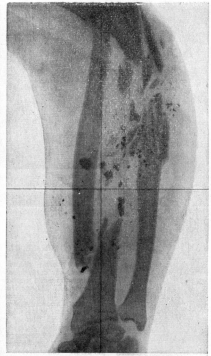

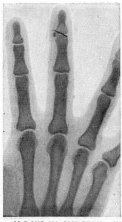

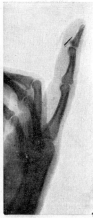

X-RAYS IN SURGERY. When the electron stream in a cathode ray tube is checked by an obstacle (metal cathode) part of the energy is changed into X-rays, a radiation which penetrates solid objects. This radiation has a wavelength of 12 Angstrom units. An early use of radiation (see Lesson 17) was the diagnosis of fracture and other conditions (left, a radiograph of leg bones fractured by a bullet) and of foreign bodies (above, a needle in a finger with consequent bony growth). Below, examples of X-ray crystallography. At A, concentric circles of paraffin; at B, crystals patterns shown in a radiograph of a diamond.

Courtesy, Sir Wm. Bragg, Royal Institution

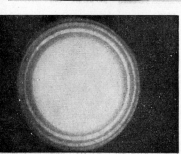

A
X-ray of paraffin

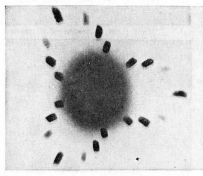

B
X-ray of crystal structure of diamond

FRA RED	a	B	c		D		E	b	F			
		RED		ORANGE		· YELLOW	GREEN		BLUE INDIGO VIOLET		ULTRA VIOLET	

| | 8000 | 7700 | 7000 | 6900 | | 6400 | 6000 | 5900 | 5500 | 5000 | 4000 | 3900 | 3000 | 2000 | 1000 |

eat Rays ⟵ - - - - - - - - Visible - - - - - - - - - - - ⟶ Chemical Rays

THE SPECTRUM. A beam of light is split up by a prism into its constituent colours. Outside the red are longer rays, the infra-red (radiant heat), and beyond the violet the ultra-violet. (See Lesson 11, p. 364). The position of any colour in the spectrum is determined by its wave-length stated in Ångström units, each of which represents one ten-millionth part of a millimetre. The reference letters at the top of the diagram are Fraunhöfer's lines. (See also p. 366 where the spectrum is extended diagrammatically.)

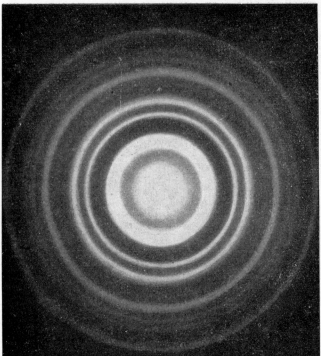

Wave form of motion of electrons shown photographically.

Alpha rays (helium atoms) made visible.

Cloud condensation photo by Dr. P. M. S. Blackett

BEHAVIOUR OF ELEC TRONS. Although th electron theory treats electrons as corpuscles c particles, the wave mechanic theory of Schroedinge treats the moving electro as waves. Experimental wor shows that when passe through a thin film of go (left) electrons behave c waves; passed through gas (below) they behave c particles. (See Lesson 20

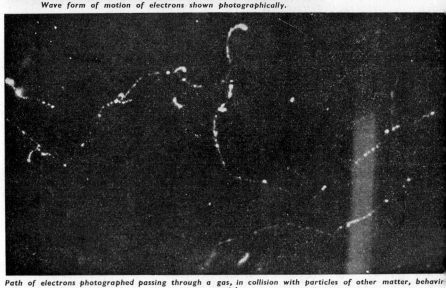

Path of electrons photographed passing through a gas, in collision with particles of other matter, behavir as particles.

Photos by Prof. C. T. R. Wilson and Prof. G. P. Thomson, Cambridge University Press

PHYSICS

*H*EREIN *we study the bases of Physical Science—the nature and the behaviour of matter in all its forms, the so-called 'Laws' by which the great men of science, philosophers and discoverers, have deduced the manner of operation of the natural forces—gravity, heat, light, sound, electricity, magnetism, radiation.*

The student who has studied this Course carefully and with understanding will have covered in a general way, yet with considerable precision, the whole field of Physics from gravity to relativity. He should pursue certain branches of the subject in other Courses : CHEMISTRY *in Vol. III for physical chemistry ;* ENGINEERING *in Vol. III for the practical applications of heat and electromagnetism ;* MECHANICS *in Vol. IV for Newton's Laws and their theoretical developments and applications.* MATHEMATICS *in Vol. V will provide him with some of the tools for further studies.*

20 LESSONS

Foundations of Science

THE scope of Physics is really the study of nature ; in some universities, indeed, the subject is termed natural philosophy. The study of all natural phenomena covers a very wide field. The biologists take over that part which has to do with animal and plant life, and, apart from the help which is looked for in the development of these subjects, the main work of the physicist is to study the inanimate, to formulate laws, and seek explanation of the events which take place in nature.

In general, the experimental physicist makes careful observations of the events which take place freely in nature, or which he causes to take place in apparatus designed for this purpose. As a result of these observations laws are formulated and theories are developed to account for the events. Then, perhaps, the theoretical physicist is able to make deductions as to what might happen under another set of conditions. These speculations are then tested by experiment, the results of which may give material for further deduction.

This kind of development has gone on in the different parts of physics, and in these parts theories have been formulated. It has then been found that there is a similarity in the theories which have been suggested in various cases, and so correlation has been made possible between facts which otherwise seemed entirely disconnected. Then a wider theory has grown and embraced the many similar local theories, and a large group of phenomena have been welded together in this way.

During the growth of the subject as outlined above, certain developments, from time to time, have led to the establishing of very definite methods of research, which have gradually formed parallel lines of study. These have apparently kept entirely apart from the parent subject. In this way chemistry has been evolved. However, examination of modern chemical methods shows a very strong family resemblance to the parent subject ; the research methods of the chemist are rapidly reverting to the experimental methods of the physicist.

Another factor has been operative in the formation of new sciences as a result of the developments in physics. Some discoveries have been found to have a direct practical application, and so the practical sciences of mechanical, civil and, more recently, electrical engineering have grown up. A recent example is seen in the rapidly developing science popularly called Wireless.

This has grown from what was regarded as a very effective laboratory experiment to a universally employed practical science as a result of the research work of physicists, who first of all discovered the basic facts and then tested them experimentally. The modern development of the principle discovered by Professor O. W. Richardson, that a hot wire emits electrons, is, of course, the thermionic valve ; engineers as well as physicists have not been slow to realize the importance of the discovery. The practical development is the work of the engineer, but the investigation of the transmission of the radio waves from transmitter to receiver is very definitely the province of the physicist, as we shall see later.

Before the tremendous activity of the present century began, it was often said that the physicist had no more to do than to measure known properties to 'one more decimal place.' Now the measurement to extreme accuracy is left to metrologists, the physicists being fully occupied in coping with new discoveries.

The syllabus of a university course in physics is usually subdivided into the following parts : (1) mechanics, (2) general properties of solids, liquids, and gases, (3) heat, (4) sound, (5) light, (6) magnetism and electricity. Most of these subdivisions are more or less self-explanatory ; the first of them, however, is not quite so obvious as the rest. It is dealt with at proper length in its own Course, and here it is only necessary to consider it as a foundation of the science of physics.

Galileo's Experiment. If a body, a stone for instance, is allowed to fall freely to the earth, it does so with ever-increasing velocity. We say that it falls because the earth pulls it towards itself, and we know that wherever we are on the earth's surface the direction of fall is towards the centre of the earth. Up to the time of Galileo, Aristotle's teaching, that the heavier the body the quicker it will fall freely to the earth, was apparently accepted without question. Galileo devised a simple experiment to test the truth of this statement, and carried out the test in the presence of a distinguished but sceptical audience. A heavy and a light body were released at the same instant from the top of the leaning tower of Pisa. The noise of impact of the bodies as they hit the ground was heard at the same time for both bodies, showing that the time of fall was the same in each case. This simple experiment shows Galileo to be a true physicist, and illustrates the importance of testing all theoretical speculations by direct experiment.

Gravity and the Feather. A question which arises from this experiment is : If all bodies are supposed to fall over the same distance in the same time, how does one account for the vast time difference in the fall of, say, a feather and a piece of lead ? The explanation of the apparent contradiction is to be had from a consideration of another experiment. A feather and a guinea were placed in a long tube which was airtight, and the air was withdrawn from the tube by means of a suction pump. When most of the air had been withdrawn, the tube was placed in an upright position and then quickly inverted ; the guinea and the feather fell down the tube in the same time. So the observations of Galileo were confirmed even with such a light article as a feather.

In ordinary air the feather is resisted by the air itself ; in other words, the feather is not falling freely, and we are not observing the effects of the earth's attraction only. We say that there are two forces acting on the feather, the one due to gravity and the other due to the air resistance, but the air resistance is very small, so that in the case of heavy bodies the effect of the attraction of the earth alone governs their motion.

Acceleration Due to Gravity. Now if we consider the fall of the different bodies again, we see that they start together from rest and take the same time to fall the same distance, and therefore we may say that they acquire the same velocity, i.e., they travel at the same number of feet per second or the same number of centimetres per second. Since the bodies started from rest it follows that the increase in velocity has been at the same rate for each body. Now the increase in velocity per second is called the acceleration of the body, and so we may summarize the experiment by saying that all bodies falling freely to the earth do so with a constant acceleration, which is called the acceleration due to gravity. This has the value of about 32 feet per second per second, or 981 cm. per second per second, i.e. a gain in velocity of 32 ft. per second in

one second, hence the phrase per second per second or, as it is usually written, 32/ft.sec./sec. It is often referred to as g.

When it is stated that the acceleration due to gravity (g) is a constant, reference is made to the value obtained at one position on the earth's surface for all bodies falling there. As a matter of fact, the acceleration due to gravity is found by careful experiment to have a value which depends on the location in which it is determined.

For example, at the equator its value at sea level is 978·03 cm./sec./sec., and at sea level near the north pole its value is 983·216 cm./sec./sec. A sufficiently refined method of measuring g would show that its value at the bottom of a very deep mine is greater than the value at the surface, or, again, that the value taken at the summit of a high mountain peak is less than the corresponding value at sea level. Over ordinary ranges of fall it might be considered as constant, but in the type of refined measurement to which reference has been made it does, in fact, vary. The farther the point where g is measured is from the centre of the earth, the less its value, and, of course, the north pole is nearer the centre of the earth than is the equator, since the earth is not a perfect sphere, but is flattened at the poles, being what is called an oblate spheroid. Some idea of the changes in g may be obtained from the following table :

Value of 'G' at Different Places

Place	Latitude	Value of 'g'
Pole	90° N.	983·216 cm./sec./sec.
Aberdeen	57° 8' N.	981·68 ,,
London	51° 25' N.	981·190 ,,
Portsmouth	50° 48' N.	981·136 ,,
Chicago	41° 47' N.	980·283 ,,
Equator	00	978·030 ,,
Capetown	33° 56' S.	979·659 ,,

From these variations interesting results emerge, which we can best appreciate if we first consider certain definitions and terms.

Mass and Matter. We are every day in contact with matter ; it is the very world in which we live. Matter has been described as that which occupies space, but really this only introduces another undefined term. All solids, liquids and gases are made of different forms of matter. The amount of matter in a body is determined by the nature of the body itself. For example, equal volumes of lead and cork do not have the same amount of matter. The lead seems to have more stuffing in it than the cork—it contains a greater amount of matter. Associated with the amount of matter in a body is what we call mass. (Do not, however, confuse it with the weight of the body, which is really the attraction of the earth.) If we were able to eliminate the attraction of the earth on bodies we should find that they behaved differently in response to applied forces.

For example, if we were able to reproduce, at will, a kick of a fixed amount and apply the kick in turn, for the same time, to a volume of lead which is resting on a smooth horizontal sheet of ice, and to a similar-sized piece of cork, we should find that the cork would travel much farther than the lead. We recognize that there is some inherent quality in the two substances which decides what will happen in a case such as the one described.

We say that the substance has mass, and we associate the larger mass with the lead, which goes the shorter distance on applying the force of the kick ; or, to put the same thing another way, we would find that to send the lead as far as the cork a much bigger force is required than for the cork. The larger the mass the larger is the force required to produce a definite motion in the body. This quality of mass is something which remains constant wherever the body is. If the matter could be transplanted to the moon it would still have the same mass. We regard it as an axiom that mass is indestructible and invariable.

Some students may have knowledge of new theories which seem to make these statements appear untrue. The popular accounts make a great point of the new features, and do not always state clearly the basic conditions which limit them; but so long as we can deal with large-scale quantities of matter which are not moving at prodigious speeds, the new theories and the consequent modification which they suggest have no meaning for us at all.

Newton's Laws of Motion. Newton, who was born in the year of Galileo's death, developed the work which he had begun, and formulated the laws of motion which are still the basic laws of our mechanics. These laws may be stated as under :

1. *Every body continues in its state of rest or uniform motion in a straight line, unless acted upon by impressed forces.*

2. *When acted upon by an impressed force, the rate of change of the quantity of motion is proportional to the impressed force, and takes place in the direction of the impressed force.*

3. *To every action there is an equal and opposite reaction.*

Law I indicates that force is that which tends to alter the state of rest or motion of a body. The law itself seems to be the statement of the obvious. Dozens of illustrations will occur to the student at once. As he sits reading he notices that a cloud of tobacco smoke has suddenly taken up a movement across the room : its state of rest has been disturbed. He instantly turns round to see who has opened the door and allowed the air to act on the smoke.

As an illustration of the other part of the law, in which a body continues in the state of uniform motion unless acted upon by an impressed force, one might quote the experience of most persons at one time or another. In a railway carriage facing the engine which is travelling at a fair speed, one moves at the speed of the train. Should the train suddenly stop it is perfectly well known that the traveller continues with his uniform velocity, and, if caught unawares, might very well be deposited at that speed on the person opposite.

Force and its Unit of Measurement. The **Second Law** is very important, giving us as it does a precise definition of force. The term *quantity of motion* is an old form of the present term *momentum*. It really involves both the mass and the velocity with which the body is moving. The momentum is defined as the product of the mass (m) and the velocity (v), viz. momentum $= m \times v$. Now, the second Law says that force (F) is proportional to the rate of change of momentum, i.e. F is proportional to rate of change of ($m\,v$), and since m is constant, and rate of change means the change in unit time, or one second, we may write

$$F \propto m \times \text{change of } v \text{ per second.}$$

But we have seen that the acceleration, which we will denote by f, is the change of velocity per second, therefore we have, F is proportional to $m \times f$. Incidentally, we actually define unit force as 'that force which, when acting on unit mass, produces unit acceleration,' i.e. we may write

$$F = mf.$$

If we use British measurements (i.e. foot, pound), the unit force is called the *poundal*, and it produces in a mass of 1 lb. an acceleration of 1 ft. per sec. per sec.

In many of the calculations and in most theoretical deductions, however, the units used are centimetres, grammes, and seconds. This system of units is called the C.G.S. system. Here the unit of force is the *dyne*, and is such that, when acting on a mass of

1 gm., produces an acceleration of 1 cm. per sec. per sec.

We might just reconsider for a moment the illustration used in an earlier paragraph in which we compared the effect of kicking a body made of lead and one made of cork. We were really thinking of the application of the same force to each mass for the same time. The resulting acceleration and consequent velocity may be had from the above equation, viz.

$$F = mf \text{ or } f = F/m,$$

i.e. the bigger the mass the smaller the acceleration imparted, and hence the less the distance traversed or, alternatively, the bigger the mass, the greater must F be to produce the same acceleration.

Another point which emerges from the law is that we associate a direction both with the force and the movement which results in its application. Quantities like these, which require the statement of the direction as well as the size or magnitude, are called vectors, as distinct from such things as temperature, volume, etc., which are specified by their size only. These latter are called scalars.

LESSON TWO

Gravitation Law in the Universe

IT has been shown that a force is measured by the product of the mass of the body on which it acts, and the acceleration it produces in that body. For example, a force of 200 × 40 = 8,000 dynes is required to produce an acceleration of 40 cm./sec./sec. in a mass of 200 gm.

Since all matter has mass and is attracted to the earth with an acceleration g cm./sec./sec., it follows that the earth attracts a body with a force which is g times its mass (m). This force is called the weight of the body, and may be written as mg. Since g varies according to the position on the earth, the weight of a body varies similarly although its mass remains constant.

We should, strictly, measure the weight of a body in dynes, or in poundals, which are units of force. However, we usually say, wrongly, the weight of a body is so many pounds or grammes, when we should say pounds weight or grammes weight.

In the ordinary method of weighing, using a common balance, we compare the weight of standard masses (lb. or gm.) with the weight of the unknown mass. The earth pulls each side of the balance down, and adjustment is made of the weight until balance is attained. Here g is the same on both sides, wherever the weighing is performed. If, however, we use a spring balance, the force of attraction of the earth on an unknown mass extends the spring a certain extent and we measure the weight by the amount of extension. If we were to take this spring balance to another place where g had a different value, the extension of the spring would be different—the body would have a different weight.

If we refer to the value of g given in the table in page 331, it will be seen that an object of mass m grammes would weigh 981·19 × m dynes in London and 980·28 × m dynes in Chicago. If, therefore, we could buy material weighed by a spring balance in Chicago and sell it by weight (as measured by spring balance) in London, we should have a greater weight to sell in London. The gain so obtained is not big, but it is definite.

Newton's Third Law. According to Newton's third Law of motion, action and reaction are equal and opposite. Therefore, if the earth attracts a body of mass m with a force mg, it follows that the body attracts the earth with the same force. This is, in fact, a particular case of the law of gravitation. All masses attract each other with a force of attraction which is proportional to the product of the masses (m and m^1) and inversely proportional to the square of the distance between the centres of the masses (d).

This force (F) may be written :

$$F = G \frac{m\,m^1}{d^2}$$

G is called the constant of gravitation. The law holds equally well for large bodies the size of the earth and moon and for small particles. So that if in an experiment it is possible to find the value of G for one set of masses, we can use it for others of all magnitudes.

Thomas Cavendish, in 1798, made an experimental investigation of the attraction between bodies and was able to estimate G. Prof. Poynting also carried out tests of this kind. A spherical mass of lead of about 20 kilogrammes (about 50 lb.) was counterpoised on a large sensitive balance, and a large sphere of lead of mass 150 kilogrammes (350 lb.) was placed just under the 20 kilogrammes : the attraction between the two caused a measurable increase in weight, F, which was found by adding weights to the other side. Since $m = 20,000$, $m^1 = 150,000$, and d the distance between their centres was also known, G was calculated from the equation above.

Weighing the Earth. Now, if we consider the attraction between the mass m on the balance and the earth, we see that if r is the distance between the centre of the earth and the centre of the mass m (i.e. r is equal to the radius of the earth), and if E is the mass of the earth, the force of attraction between m and E is the weight of m.

$$mg = G\frac{mE}{r^2}$$

$$\text{or } \frac{GE}{r^2} = g$$

Now g can be accurately found by many methods, e.g. the compound pendulum. Hence, since G is known by the experiment described above, and since $r = 6.37 \times 10^8$ c.m., E was found to be about 6×10^{27} g.m. ($10^2 = 100$, $10^3 = 1000$, etc., so that 10^8 means 100,000,000, 10^{27} means 1 and 27 0's.)

The attraction which was measured in the experiment described above is also operative between all the members of the solar system. In particular, the moon is attracted towards the earth with a force which is given by the equation quoted above. Fortunately the rotation of the moon round the earth causes a force which tends to send it away from the earth. This force and the gravitational attraction just balance at the particular distance away at which the moon is located. If the rotation stopped, then, of course, the moon and the earth would fall together. From a knowledge of the value of G, and the velocity of the moon, and the mass of the earth, it is a simple matter to calculate approximately the distance between the moon and the earth. Indeed, all paths of the heavenly bodies are known very largely from an application of the law of gravitation and other general laws.

The variations of g in different parts of the earth have been discussed. Now it is also an observed fact that g varies according to the nature of the immediate strata under the place at which the determination is made. The Eötvös balance is an instrument which is extremely sensitive to such changes. It records the change by means of the twist produced in a thin fibre which balances small masses on two levels, one about 2 ft. 4 in. above the other. Using this instrument, it has been possible to detect changes of one-thousand-millionth part of a dyne. Local changes of gravitation have been mapped out by the instrument in such countries as Persia, where oil deposits occur, and it has been found possible to predict the presence of oil as a result of such surveys.

Work and Energy. To conclude these remarks, which have dealt with fundamental ideas in mechanics, two more terms must be considered. These are *work* and *energy*. In physics, work is said to be performed only when a force moves its point of application. If a force (F) when applied to a body moves it a distance s in the direction of the force, the work (W) is given as the product of the force × distance moved :

$$W = Fs$$

Work is therefore measured in units called foot-pounds.

If one tries to move a heavy box by pushing at it with all the force one can command, no work is said to be done on the box unless it moves. If by some means a heavy boulder is brought to the edge of a cliff, it is apparent that, owing to the position it occupies, the boulder could do work if allowed to fall over the cliff. We express this by saying that the boulder has *potential energy*. Once the boulder is released, it acquires velocity and now can do work in virtue of the motion it possesses. The boulder is now said to have *kinetic energy*. This latter is actually measured by $\frac{1}{2}$ the product of the mass (m) and the square of the velocity (v) :

i.e. kinetic energy $= \frac{1}{2} mv^2$.

It will be seen that the definition of energy implied in the above is the 'capability of doing work.' In the one case it is capable of doing work because of its position, and in the other in virtue of its movement. When the boulder is at the bottom of the cliff it can fall no lower, its potential energy is then zero, but at that instant the velocity is greatest—all the energy is now kinetic and is found to be exactly equal to the potential energy it had at the top of the cliff. This is a particular example of a general law that if the energy changes its form, it does so without loss. At all times there is a conservation of energy ; i.e., if the sum of the potential and kinetic energies is measured at any one time, this sum will equal the initial and also the final energy.

It would appear that, in the case quoted, there seems to be an end of the energy when the boulder hits the ground. It certainly has no potential energy, and since it is at rest it has no kinetic energy. It is found, however, that the equivalent of the energy appears in the form of heat. Always the last stage of such transformations is the appearance of the equivalent amount of heat. The earth has exactly the initial amount of energy at the end of the changes, but it is now expressed in another form.

LESSON THREE

The Science of Hydrostatics

THE branch of Physics called hydrostatics deals with the general properties of fluids, that is, of liquids and gases, both of which have the essential property of fluids in that they flow, and must be placed in a containing vessel to prevent the flow. Like any other form of matter fluids have density, i.e. each cubic foot has a definite weight in lb. weight, or each cubic centimetre weighs a definite number of grammes. Since they possess weight it follows that any surface within a fluid supports a weight, equal, in fact, to the weight of the column of fluid above the surface. Of course, the bigger the area of the surface the bigger is the cross-section of the column of liquid supported and hence the bigger the weight supported. It is customary to express the effect in terms of the pressure that the fluid exerts. The term pressure is applied in all cases where we refer to the force acting on unit area.

Take, for example, the case of a man skating on ice. His whole weight is supported on two small areas which represent the runners of the skates. The pressure, or force per unit area, is the weight of the man (expressed, say, in dynes, i.e. mass $\times g$) divided by the area of the skates. Similarly, if we consider a submarine under water, the pressure on the submarine, due to the water only, is the weight of the column of water on one square foot, or on one square centimetre. This is, of course, dependent on the depth below the surface of the water. Actually, it is equal to $g \times d \times h$, where g is the acceleration due to gravity, d is the density of the liquid, and h is the depth below the free surface of the liquid. (This is but another way of saying the weight of the column of liquid on unit area.) The total pressure in the above case is due to the liquid plus the pressure arising from the air above the liquid, for the air, having density, has also weight and will make a definite contribution towards the pressure.

Atmospheric Pressure. Air seems a light enough substance, and yet the pressure it exerts is really great. Living as we do in the atmosphere of air we are subjected to a tremendous pressure, but fortunately, the pressure inside and outside our bodies is the same—otherwise we should collapse.

A simple experiment can be performed to show this. Take a cylindrical tin oil can of the form shown in Fig. 1 and place a little water inside. Boil the water on a gas ring, and when it has boiled vigorously for a minute or so turn out the gas, and cork immediately. The air has been expelled by the steam, and as the can cools down the steam condenses and leaves no air within. The pressure of the external air will cause the can to collapse in a crumpled heap.

Fig. 1. Experiment on atmospheric pressure.

A less destructive method of showing that air exerts a pressure is as follows. Fill a tumbler with water to the brim ; place a card on the top and, holding the card in position, invert the tumbler. It will be found that, when the hand is removed, the card remains in position apparently holding the water in the tumbler. What is actually happening is that the air is pressing on the card, upwards, to the extent of the atmospheric pressure, i.e. each square centimetre has a very large force acting on it upwards —sufficient, in fact, to hold up a column of mercury 30 inches long—whereas on the other side there is the pressure of the water downwards. This is only about a six-inch column of water, so that the card keeps in position and the water remains in the glass.

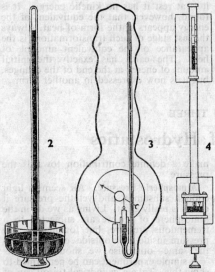

BAROMETER TYPES. Fig. 2. Mercury bowl. Fig. 3. Siphon. Fig. 4. Fortin barometer.

Theory of the Barometer. To measure atmospheric pressure use is made of a barometer. In its simplest form the barometer consists of a glass tube about a yard long and half an inch in diameter. This tube is sealed at one end and is filled with mercury (quicksilver). The thumb is placed on the open end and the tube inverted into a bowl of mercury, the thumb being then released (Fig. 2). The mercury runs down the tube a certain distance, but on an average day the column left in the tube is about 30 inches or 76 centimetres long above the surface of the mercury in the bowl. In the tube above the mercury there is no air, simply the vapour of mercury that exerts minute pressure.

The reason the mercury stays up is that, on the outside, the air is exerting a pressure on the surface of the mercury in the bowl. On the same level within the tube the mercury exerts a pressure which is equal to the outside pressure; in

fact, the height of the column adjusts itself until its pressure is equal to that due to the air. Any change of the atmospheric pressure results in a change of the level of the mercury column, and we say the barometer falls or rises. It is found that fine weather is often associated with a high barometer, and rain, etc., with a low barometer. But this is not universally true.

To avoid the use of a bowl of mercury the siphon barometer, shown in Fig. 3, is often employed. From the diagram we see the method used to indicate the barometer reading. An iron ball floats on the wide tube and the rise or fall of this makes a thread rotate a wheel which moves a pointer over a scale graduated in inches in the diagram. Often the scale carries the legend *very dry* at the 31-inch mark, and so on round the scale to *stormy* at the 28-inch mark. The accurate measurement of the atmospheric pressure as recorded by the Meteorological Office is brought about by a modified form of the instrument illustrated in Fig. 2, called the Fortin barometer, Fig. 4.

The aneroid barometer, shown in Fig. 5, does not give the same accuracy, but is employed very rarely as a portable instrument. Its construction is evident from the diagram. The essential feature is a corrugated metal box, which is exhausted of air and the upper surface of which is attached to a gearing which rotates a pointer for any movement of the top of the box. Increase of atmospheric pressure squashes the box inwards, and low pressure allows the box to move outwards.

If the pressure of the air is measured on such an instrument at the foot of a mountain and again by the same instrument at the top of the mountain, it is found that

ANEROID BAROMETER. Fig 5. 1. Hand turning on pivot. 2. Hair spring. 3. Chain that turns the hand. 4. Lever fixed to pivot. 5. Lever. 6. Lever rod from spring. 7. Spring pulling against the air pressure on box. 8. Rod. 9. Part of round metal vacuum box. 10. Box pressed in by increased air pressure. 11. Spring pulled down by lowered top of box. 12. Lever rod lowered. 13. Levers lowered. 14. Chain unwound by levers. 15. Hand pivot pulled round by chain.

there is a marked decrease in the pressure. This is obviously due to the fact that there is a shorter column of air at the summit—a difference exactly that of the height of ascent. In this way one could weigh the column of air or, alternatively, if one knew the way in which the pressure dropped for increase in altitude, the instrument could be used as an altitude measurer. The drawback to its use in this way is the fact that change in the barometer due to weather conditions makes an error in estimating height. For example, if the pressure of air, due to movement of a cyclone, caused a drop in the barometer at ground level, it would give a fictitious increase in height as recorded on a barometer used as a height measurer.

Properties of Fluid Pressure. We may now summarize the more important properties of fluid pressure.

(1) In the C.G.S. units, pressure is measured in dynes/sq. cm. : it is equal to

$g \times d \times h$ where $g = 981$ cm./sec.^{2}, d is measured in grammes/cubic cm. (gm./c.c.), and h is the depth below the free surface of the fluid, measured in cms.

In the case of liquids it is obvious where the surface is, but for gases, such as the atmosphere, we cannot say where the surface is, so we use the device called the barometer, which gives us a kind of weighing machine, and we say the pressure of the atmosphere is equal to that of the column of mercury supported in the barometer by it. If the column of mercury is 76 cm. we either say that the atmospheric pressure is 76 cm. of mercury, or 76 × 981 × 13·6 dynes/sq. cm., since the density of mercury is 13·6 gm./c.c.

(2) The pressure in a fluid always acts at right angles to an area placed in it. At any point in the fluid the pressure acts equally in all directions. We know, for example, that if we make a hole in a tank of water the water is forced out at right angles to the tank, not straight down.

(3) The pressure in one level of a liquid at rest is always the same.

The Hydrostatic Press. Consider a U-tube containing water, as in Fig. 6, with one wide tube A and one narrow tube B. Suppose that A is 1 sq. ft. (144 sq. in.) in cross section, and that B is 1 sq. in. in cross section. If we

Fig. 6. Hydrostatic press.

place on a tight-fitting piston in B a weight of 1 cwt., the pressure is 1 cwt./sq. in. Now under another tight-fitting piston in A the same pressure will be exerted at right angles to the area of the piston ; therefore the force on the piston in A is

144×1 cwt. upwards—i.e. $\dfrac{144}{20} = 7$ tons 4 cwt.

and this load could be supported without descending—i.e. it could be held up by the 1 cwt. in B ! This is the principle of the hydrostatic press. It is often called the hydrostatic paradox, because it appears as if we were getting more out of the machine than we put in. But if we move A upwards by the addition of an extra load on B, we find that B has to descend a distance 144 times as great as the rise in A. The work done is the same ; we do not obtain an exception to the principle of conservation of energy.

Buoyancy. When an object is placed in a liquid it either floats or sinks. If it floats we say that the buoyancy is greater than the weight of the body. The buoyancy is the upward force on the body due to the pressure of the liquid on the under side of the body.

All bodies when placed in liquid appear to lose weight by an amount which is exactly equal to the weight of the liquid displaced by the body. This is usually called the principle of Archimedes. For example, a steel battleship floats in water because the weight of the water displaced by the ship is equal to the weight of the ship itself. The size of a ship is usually expressed as so many tons displacement, which means the weight of water displaced is so many tons. Of course, when a ship is loaded it weighs more and so sinks farther into the water, thereby displacing more water, until the extra weight of water displaced is equal to the load taken on board. The Plimsoll line on a ship marks the lowest limit to which a ship may sink in the water and yet be safe.

The same object placed in different liquid sinks to an extent which depends on the weight of the body and the density of the liquid. For example, if the density of paraffin oil is 0·8 gm./c.c., then each cubic cm. of the body immersed will displace only 0·8 gm. of liquid. If the body weighs 80 gm., it will mean that

$$\dfrac{80}{\cdot 8} = 100 \text{ c.c.}$$

must be immersed in order that the body may float.

In water (density = 1 gm. per c.c.), on the other hand, the body will sink until 80 c.c. are displaced. The ordinary hydrometer is an instrument which is used to find densities, and works on these lines. It consists of a glass tube loaded by placing a little mercury in one end to make it float upright ; the depth to which it sinks is read on a scale within the glass stem, and this is graduated in densities. The lighter the liquid the more the hydrometer sinks. The little glass balls in some wireless accumulators are simply balls of the same volume but of different weight. When the density of the acid gets less than one of the balls this sinks, and we know that the acid is getting lighter and so the accumulator needs recharging.

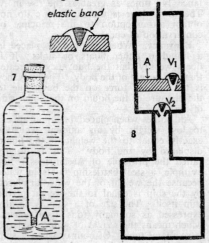

Fig. 7. Effect of pressure on a gas. Fig. 8. Sectional view showing principle of a simple exhaust pump ; inset, detail of valve in pump.

The upward force called buoyancy acts when a body is in any *fluid*. In a balloon a large volume is filled with hydrogen or coal gas. This envelope displaces air, and the balloon is acted on by an upward force equal to the weight of the air displaced. If this is greater than the weight of the balloon and gaseous contents, then the balloon will ascend. To lower the balloon the size is decreased by allowing gas to escape, thereby decreasing the buoyancy.

Boyle's Law. Gases very easily change in volume when acted upon by pressure. Robert Boyle, in 1662, found that if the pressure (P) acting on a gas be doubled, then the volume of the gas (V) is halved,

or, saying this in a general way, $P \times V =$ constant. The law applies to a fixed mass of gas kept at a constant temperature.

For example, if a glass tube of the shape shown in Fig. 7 containing air be placed under water in a closed bottle, a little water enters, as shown at A. If we press the cork, the increase in pressure is communicated through the liquid and the gas decreases in volume, and so there is less water displaced. The buoyancy is less, and so the tube sinks if properly adjusted. If we release the pressure from the cork, the volume of the air at once increases ; the buoyancy also increases and the tube rises.

Boyle's law also applies in the case of a simple exhaust pump, Fig. 8. A represents a piston moving freely in a cylinder and containing a valve V_1. The cylinder has a valve V_2. When the piston moves upwards the volume of the apparatus is increased by the volume of the cylinder, and so the pressure gets less. No air enters during this process, as V_1 closes owing to the great pressure above it. When the piston returns V_2 closes and the air in the cylinder is compressed, V_1 opens and this air is expelled ; then we start the whole motion again with a reduced mass of gas at a reduced pressure.

In a compression pump, such as that used to pump up tires, the valves work the other way—i.e. they are again cones, but with the points upwards. At the top of the stroke a volume of air is in the cylinder. When the piston is pushed down the increase of pressure within the cylinder closes V_1 and opens V_2. The air is pushed into the tire. On the upward stroke V_2 closes as a result of the pressure within the tire being greater than the partial vacuum in the cylinder, and V_1 opens. Air again fills the cylinder and the process is repeated. The ordinary water pump is designed on the lines of Fig. 8. The tube from the cylinder goes down to the water supply, and the reduction in pressure causes the water to rise up in it. This water is expelled from a side tube through another valve.

Now it is obvious that when the pump is working it creates a vacuum in the space above the water. Therefore, at the best, the greatest height, H, to which the water may be raised is that of a water barometer— i.e. when the column of water raised has a pressure on the underground water supply equal to the atmospheric pressure. This is given by the equation :

$$g \times H \times 1 = g \times 76 \times 13.6 :$$
$$H = 76 \times 13.6 = 1,033.6 \text{ cm., or about } 40 \text{ ft.}$$

On the Properties of Liquids

IF one watches the formation of a drop of water at the end of a tap which is very slowly dripping, it will be observed that the water collects as a drop in well-defined stages, making it appear as though an invisible elastic bag were attached to the tap. In fact, if a large thin sheet of rubber be stretched and water allowed to accumulate within it, the bag so formed will alter its shape in exactly the same way as the drop of water on the tap. This suggests that at the surface of the water there is some effect similar to an invisible membrane. Such a membrane does not actually exist, but, as we shall see later, there is a surface effect in all cases of separation of liquid from gas.

If water is allowed to drop on a clean wooden table, it spreads over the surface of the wood. We say that the water wets the table. Technically speaking, a liquid wets a solid when it spreads over it. There seems to be none of that invisible skin effect we found in this simple experiment.

However, it is equally well known that if water is dropped on to a greasy wooden surface, the water does not wet the surface, but piles up into globules. Very small quantities of water seem to make perfect spheres of water on the surface ; large quantities of water make flattened spheres. In this case there is once more evidence of the surface behaving as though constrained by some invisible outer cover. Many examples of this effect could be quoted. For instance, if we consider an ordinary canvas tent which has been waterproofed, we have a material in which the texture is really one mass of regularly spaced holes. On a rainy evening the light of the lamp within the tent reveals hundreds of glistening globules of rain water. What happens is that the rain water does not wet the threads and so does not spread over them : the water, therefore, piles up as little globules over the holes in the canvas, and the excess of water runs down the tent.

Here, again, it appears that under the correct conditions, i.e. when the material is not wetted by the water, the latter behaves as though there were this strong invisible membrane to support it. If, in the example we have just considered, we were to break the surface of the water globules, then the water would run through and the part so

treated would not keep out the water until the canvas had dried and once more acquired the rainproof property, with sealing globules of water over the holes.

Surface Tension. The ordinary rainproof coat keeps out the water simply as a result of a waterproofing process which aims at making each thread in such a state that it is not wetted by the water. As is well known, even the best waterproofing will not stand up against constant rubbing, as such rubbing breaks the surface of the water globules which are formed over the minute holes in the fabric. We use the term *surface tension* to describe the properties of liquid surfaces which the above simple experiments illustrate.

If we imagine that in a liquid surface there is a definite pull parallel to the surface, we can account for these and other surface phenomena. A very simple experiment can be performed to show that the pull is present, and enables us to get some idea of its value. A piece of clean iron or copper wire is bent into the shape of a goal post (about 4 in. long and 2 in. tall). The two ends are pushed into a piece of wood in order to hold the posts upright. A movable crossbar, AB, is attached freely to the

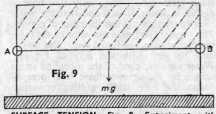

Fig. 9

mg

SURFACE TENSION. *Fig. 9. Experiment with soap solution.*

uprights, so that in the ordinary way it will slide down the posts by its own weight, when released at the top. A saturated soap solution is now made and the frame is placed in the solution so that a film of soap solution is formed, as shown in the shaded part of Fig. 9. It will be found that the soap film pulls the rod AB up the post, i.e. there is a pull in each surface of the film co-planar with (in the same plane) and towards the centre of the film. We actually define surface tension as the force, in dynes, acting on each centimetre of length on the rod AB, parallel to the surface, e.g. if we load up the rod until it just remains stationary, and find that the loaded rod has a mass m, there is a pull down of $g \times m$. The pull upwards is $T \times 1$ on each surface, making a total force of 2T1, where 1 is the length of AB in centimetres and T is the surface tension. So we can estimate T.

In the ordinary way it is clear that a fairly dense substance like steel will sink in water, yet under suitable conditions we can make steel 'float.' Place a steel sewing needle on a thin piece of blotting paper which is on the surface of clean water. In time the blotting paper will sink and leave the sewing needle 'floating' on the water. What happens is not flotation really, but the effect of surface tension. The water will not wet a sewing needle, especially if it has been slightly greased by rubbing it between the fingers. The result is seen in Fig. 10, which shows the section of the needle depressing the water and thereby causing two surface tension pulls in the directions of the arrows. If the needle is not too heavy it will be held to the surface by these two forces. It will be found that if the needle is made to break through the water surface, it will immediately sink.

Fig. 10. The floating needle.

Capillary Effects. One interesting result of the surface tension of liquid is the phenomenon often termed *capillarity*. If a clean glass tube with a very fine bore is placed in water, it is found that the water rises up the tube against the effect of gravity. The smaller the inside diameter of the tube, the higher does the liquid rise. The reason may be seen with the help of Fig. 11. Water wets the glass of the tube, and so, as shown by the arrows, there is a force all round the tube walls, pulling upwards; the result is that the water goes up until the water thus raised weighs exactly as much as the surface tension pull. The *meniscus* —the cup-shaped surface at the top of the water—is a result of the surface tension. If the liquid did

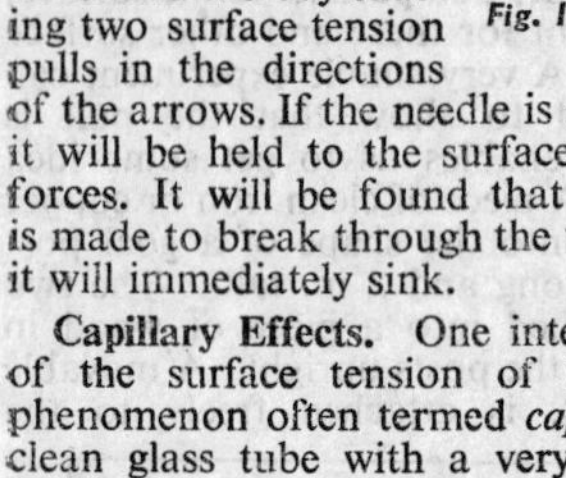

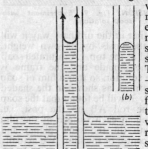

Fig. 11. Capillarity effect of water or mercury (b), in tubes.

not wet the surface the meniscus would be as in Fig. 11*b*, where the surface tension depresses the liquid. This will be recognized as the shape of the mercury meniscus in a barometer tube. A rise similar to that in a tube takes place between two plates; e.g. if two photographic plates are placed together and stood upright in ink, the rise of the ink between them will be obvious. Further, if a thin wedge be introduced between the plates at one side the result will be as shown in Fig. 12, the rise at the wedge side being much lower than the rise at the other side.

There are many practical applications of these effects. The rise of oil up a wick against gravity is one of the best known examples; also the flow of blood in the narrow capillaries and veins is governed partly by the surface tension effect. In many cases the effect of surface tension is a nuisance. In reading a hydrometer floated in a liquid whose specific gravity is to be measured, the extra pull due to surface tension must be allowed for.

Blowing Bubbles. Probably the first experiment on surface tension we all meet is the well-known bubble blowing experiment. The formation of ordinary soap bubbles is governed entirely by the effect of

Wedge→

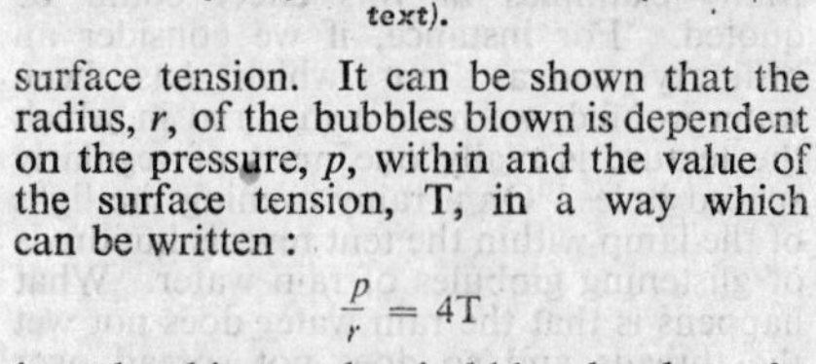

Fig. 12. Capillary attraction between plates (see text).

surface tension. It can be shown that the radius, r, of the bubbles blown is dependent on the pressure, p, within and the value of the surface tension, T, in a way which can be written:

$$\frac{p}{r} = 4T$$

i.e. the bigger the bubble the less the pressure. This seems wrong when we remember the extra blowing required to produce the big bubbles, but it can be shown to be quite a true statement, for if we join two bubbles together—a big one and a little one—we find that the little one, having a greater pressure within it, blows the big bubble up farther and gradually disappears itself.

The value of surface tension rapidly decreases when the liquid is contaminated with grease or dissolved impurity. If we scatter a little dusting powder over the surface of water and then touch the surface at a point with a greasy pencil, or with a rod of caustic soda or camphor, it will be found that the surface is pulled away from the point of contact, showing that the surface tension of the contaminated region is less than the rest. Exactly the same thing happens with a rubber balloon if we weaken the rubber at one point. The parts surrounding it would pull away from that point and the balloon would burst.

If we make a paper boat, attach a piece of camphor to one end and place it on water, it will be found that the boat moves forward, just as if the camphor were pushing it. What is really happening is that the camphor is dissolving. It is making a solution which has a less surface tension, and it is the strong surface tension of the pure water which pulls the boat forward. In time, when all the water is contaminated, i.e. when there is a uniform solution, the movement will cease. Just as instructive is the simple experiment using camphor only. If small scrapings of camphor are placed on water they will be seen to move over the surfaces in frantic rushes, always moving away from the places where the shape of the camphor has caused the most rapid solution.

Applications of Surface Tension. A very well-known example of the reduction of the surface tension by solution is to be had in the case of the oil treatment of water surfaces to suppress mosquito breeding. The larvae of mosquitoes suspend themselves on the surface of water by hair-like feelers which are not wetted by the water. A thin film of oil on the water reduces the surface tension value, so that the larvae are no longer supported. They sink and, being unable to breathe, expire : the direct effect of the paraffin oil doubtless assisting in their destruction.

We have all heard of ' pouring oil on troubled waters,' to reduce the waves. The calming effect of this is a real one. The oil blown forward by the wind makes a clear water area behind it. This clear water will pull back the oily region due to the greater surface tension, and so reduce movement. This effect, in addition to a direct lessening in the wave production, undoubtedly adds a scientific background to another well-established statement.

LESSON FIVE

Introduction to the Molecular Theory of Matter

IF we release a small volume of ammonia in one corner of a large room, it is only a matter of a few minutes before the smell of the gas reaches the opposite corner. This transference of the gas takes place when the air of the room appears to be quite still, so that it is not brought about by a regular movement of the air. We say that the gas has *diffused* through the air. A similar process takes place when the gas is separated by a porous membrane. For example, if we take a porous pot, such as is used in electric cells, and fill it with coal-gas and cork it up, we find that the gas escapes through the pores at a quicker rate than the air enters, and consequently the pressure inside is reduced.

Diffusion in Liquids and Solids. The process of diffusion is not confined to gases only, as may easily be shown by a simple experiment. A clean glass jar is half filled with water and, by means of a funnel which leads to the bottom of the water, a concentrated solution of blue copper sulphate, which is heavier than water, is poured gently to the bottom of the jar. If this is done carefully, we have in the jar two distinct layers. The lower one is blue and the upper one colourless. If the jar is again examined after some days it is found that the surface of separation has become indistinct and has moved upwards. The penetration of the blue copper sulphate upwards has been brought about against gravity, so that the possible explanation in terms of gravitation is eliminated. This is an example of diffusion in liquids. Eventually the copper sulphate is diffused throughout the whole liquid.

In solids, diffusion takes place at a very slow rate. Lead and gold blocks, which were resting together for some years, were found at the Mint to have inter-diffused. More recently, some experiments of this kind were discovered to work at a quicker rate. Thus we see that diffusion takes place in all forms of matter, the distinguishing feature being the time taken. In gases it is usually a matter of minutes, but the heavier the gas, the longer the time ; in liquids, it is a matter of days, and in solids years, to produce a small measurable effect.

Osmosis. This is the tendency of fluids separated by a membrane, or other porous substance, to percolate through that substance and mix. It is a most important phenomenon and can be best explained in terms of a simple experiment. A long glass tube is taken and at one end, which widens out, a sheet of parchment is stretched and fastened to the rim of the tube, to make a drum-like seal to it. A thistle tube serves well for this purpose. Holding the tube vertically with the parchment at the bottom, the container so formed is filled with a strong sugar solution, so that the surface of the solution in the tube can be marked. When the parchment end of this tube is immersed in a glass of clean water it is found that the level of the liquid in the tube gradually rises. This is due to osmosis. What happens is that water enters through the membrane, making the solution weaker, of course, but definitely raising the column against the effect of gravity, and so producing an increasing pressure on the membrane.

If the tube is long enough it will be found that in time the liquid within the tube comes to a level at which it remains constant. The pressure so created is called *osmotic pressure*. In some cases it may happen that the pressure becomes so large as to break the parchment. This can be well seen if, instead of the glass tube, we take a pig's bladder, fill it with a strong sugar solution, and immerse the tied-up bladder in clean water. The bladder will increase in size and may burst. This is due to the water entering at a quicker rate than the water of the solution inside leaves the bladder.

Referring again to the glass tube experiment, it is a fact that, if we use two sugar solutions of different strengths, the solution inside will rise if it is stronger than that outside. There is always the movement of the water tending to equalize the strength of the solutions, and thereby increasing the pressure opposing further change.

Biological Importance of Osmosis. Incidentally, this process of osmosis is of extreme importance to all living cells. It accounts for the movement of sap in the cells of a plant, and is one of the important factors in the rise of sap up very tall trees against the pull of gravity.

If dried currants are placed in water it is found that they swell and become rounded ;

this is due to water entering by the process of osmosis. In human beings, too, osmosis plays a most important role. The alimentary tract and the blood stream are contained in membranes which allow the passage through their walls of solution when the difference in concentration is suitably arranged. The administration of salines after operations and numerous other examples could be quoted of the most vital importance of the process of osmosis to our daily routine. The laws to which osmosis conforms have been studied at length by physicists, and many important theoretical as well as practical discoveries have been evolved.

Osmosis is also dealt with in Lesson 12 in Botany (Volume II) and in Lesson 9 in Biology (Volume II).

During the review of the properties of matter which has been given in these Lessons since dealing with definitions, the writer has had a strong desire to explain the phenomena described in terms of the accepted theories, and it is hoped that the student has also had a desire to know *why* this or that happens in the experiments described. Speculations as to the nature of matter began long before the Christian era, and are still being made. The theories can now be tested because we have a large mass of experimental data against which to check them.

Atoms and Molecules. Two theories concerning matter alternated in favour. According to the first, matter is infinitely divisible, that is to say, however small a piece of it is taken it retains its individuality. If, for instance, we take a piece of iron and cut it into small pieces, however small we make the pieces, they have the properties of iron. In answer to the question, 'What happens in the limit when we are dealing with ultra-microscopic particles ?' the upholders of this theory maintained that we should still have iron, and the process could go on indefinitely . According to the other school of thought, this process of division would lead us to a unit which is the smallest portion of that kind of matter which could exist as such.

This unit is regarded as differing from element to element, and is called the *atom*. It has the property of not being divisible and yet retaining the property of the element concerned. In compounds the unit is the *molecule*, which is made of a group of different atoms, just as the molecule of an element is made of one, two or more atoms. When the molecule repeats itself many times the accumulation is the matter we see. This theory is the one which seems to fit the observed experimental fact to the nearest degree of approximation. The old idea was to regard the molecules as solid elastic spheres, but, as we shall see later, this has been considerably modified in recent years. For the moment we will not concern ourselves with the structure of the atoms or molecules, but just regard them as extremely minute particles. They are so small, in fact, that it would need one hundred million of them in a row to measure 1 cm. In the same way we will not consider a possible shape for them, but regard them as being located by their centres.

The number of molecules in a cubic centimetre of a gas at normal pressure and at 0°C. is assessed at about 3×10^{19}, or thirty million million million. This number is too large to mean much to us, but when we remember the size of the molecule is 10^{-8} cm. in diameter we see that there is plenty of room between the molecules.

Since we saw, when discussing gravitation in Lesson 2 (page 333), that all matter attracts matter with a force that can be calculated from the equation given in that page it is clear that, if this attraction were the only force acting, all the molecules would gravitate together and, in spite of their number, would form a solid mass in the space.

Molecular Motion. Now actually we know this is not so. The experiment on diffusion in gases which we quoted earlier in this Lesson definitely disposes of this. The extra factor which is introduced is a *random velocity*. All the molecules move about in a haphazard manner with a velocity which is really great. If we confine our attention to a single molecule we shall see that it will fly off in a definite direction until it hits a second molecule, which will cause it to change its direction. This process will be repeated at every collision. Now at any given pressure the average distance a molecule will go without having a collision is constant. It is called the *mean free path*. When the pressure is reduced, as inside an ordinary valve, the mean free path might be as long as 10 to 25 cms., but at atmospheric pressure it is a fraction of a centimetre. Now we know further that each cubic centimetre of gas has a definite mass, so that if the number of molecules in that centimetre is known, the mass per molecule may be found.

When a gas is turned to liquid its volume becomes very much smaller, and so the molecules do not have the same freedom of movement—they have a greater influence on each other. In the change to solid state we find that the molecules are usually packed closer together, and now their mutual attractions become a very important factor. For example, if we think of a steel wire holding up a 2-ton load we realize that the attraction between molecules in the wire is at least equal to the pull of the earth on the 2-ton load, otherwise the molecules would separate, or, in commoner language, the wire would break.

We see, therefore, that according to the accepted molecular theory, the molecules have a random velocity which is great ; that in spite of the very large number of molecules per cubic centimetre (c.c.) of a gas at normal pressure and 0°C., there is a large space between them as they are so very small. The average distance between successive impacts, the 'mean free path,' depends on the pressure of the gas.

Now it seems clear that, if the molecule has a mass and moves with a velocity, it also possesses momentum (mv). If we consider a gas kept in a closed space it follows that the molecules will hit against the walls of the space and so have their momentum changed. The rate of change of momentum is force, so that on each unit of wall area of the containing vessel there will be a pressure which is equal to the change in momentum on that area per second.

If the volume is halved, there will be twice the number of molecules per c.c., and consequently twice as many hits per second, and consequently twice the pressure. This is what we saw to be the case, and it is stated in so many words in Boyle's Law.

The molecules of one sort—say, oxygen—all have the same mass (with the exceptions to be described later when considering isotopes), and if the temperature remains constant they have an average velocity which has a definite value. In spite of this being true, the individual molecules may have vastly varying velocities, just as a form in a school containing a number of boys of the (alleged) same intellectual level (corresponding to temperature) is said to have an average age of 16 ; whereas individual members may vary from 14¾ to 17 years.

Molecular Behaviour in Liquids. If the temperature is raised the result is an increase in the average velocity of the random movement of the molecules. The same applies in liquids. The closer associated molecules have an average random speed which depends on the temperature ; the velocity of individual molecules may be much greater or less.

When a molecule moves in a liquid it also has collisions, and, as in gases, the result is a rebound in another direction, or a spin is given to it as well as a movement in a straight line. The attractions between the molecules balance out, as there is a pull equally in all directions. When the molecule approaches the surface, however, the attractions no longer balance out. If we imagine that an instantaneous picture of one molecule shows it just on the surface, it seems clear that there is a big pull from the molecules under it, which is not compensated by a pull from above, where there is no liquid. The result is a pull back into the liquid. In fact, it makes the surface appear to behave as if it were a membrane. If a small drop of water be suspended, then the pull on the surface molecules is inward, directed to the centre, and the water forms a drop of spherical shape in consequence. These will be recognized as two of the effects discussed in dealing with surface tension. Most of the surface tension effects can be similarly explained.

Now if we return to consider the water surface, it is clear that if a molecule could arrive at the surface with sufficient speed it could overcome the attraction of the remaining liquid and break through the surface. Once away, it is free moving, and is said to form a vapour. It is a common experience, and it is what actually takes place in evaporation. One thing which should follow, since it is the quickly-moving molecules which are able to get out of the liquid, is that the remaining liquid should have a lower average velocity—or the liquid should be cooler, since the temperature depends on the average speed. This effect is very noticeable if a little ether or petrol is placed on the hand. The rapid evaporation produces a very marked cooling effect.

In solutions, the molecules of the solids intermix with those of the liquids, which are usually smaller. Now, if a solution is against a wall containing very minute holes, the chance of a water molecule getting through a small hole is hindered by the presence of the larger solid molecule. Therefore, if on two sides of such a partition we have pure water and solution respectively, it is clear that there is a better chance of pure water passing to the solution than of water of solution passing the other way. In fact, osmosis is to be expected.

'Brownian Movement.' These examples of the way in which the molecular theory fits the observed facts could be multiplied

considerably. But perhaps the most convincing experiments are those which Perrin developed from the simple observations of Robert Brown, an English botanist.

If a solution of ordinary gamboge water colour be viewed by a high-power microscope it will be found that the granules or particles of gamboge in suspension move about in a most erratic manner. This movement is called *Brownian movement*. The same kind of thing can be observed with gum arabic and other substances. After eliminating all possible explanations of the curious movement it was established that it was due to the liquid itself and not to any outside cause.

It is definitely established that what we see is simply due to the uneven bombardment of the gamboge granule by the molecules of the liquid. The granule happens to be hit on one side only by a molecule and moves away. Then another molecule hits the granule and causes it to move in some other direction, and so on.

If the granule is very large the chance of this erratic movement being imparted to it by molecular bombardment is much smaller. This is due to the fact that, as the granule becomes larger, it receives a greater number of direct hits by molecules coming from all directions, and the result is no net force on it in any direction. Of course, even with a large granule, an occasional chance of an unbalanced impact occurs. When we consider large objects, this chance of Brownian movement becomes very small.

Mathematical Tests of Molecular Movements. Perrin made a careful experimental study of Brownian movements and was able, by applying relatively simple mathematical treatment, to calculate from his observations the number of molecules per cubic centimetre, the mean free path, etc. Einstein, who is better known through his theory of relativity, also made it possible to find molecular constants from observations of the *positions* of the granule after measured times. The mathematics there is similar to the problem of finding how far a drunken man would go if he started in a given direction and then fell. After each fall he gets up and starts again in a random direction and has a 'mean free path' between falls. It can be shown how far he will go from his starting point by calculation analogous to that used for the random-moving granules. The granules are *seen*, their movement is measured, and molecular constant calculated. It is small wonder we always think of the phrase 'Molecular

Reality' when thinking of the Brownian movement, and we feel that—at any rate, in broad outline—the molecular theory must be very near the truth.

If at one temperature the average velocity of the molecules is fixed, it is clear that the average kinetic energy ($\frac{1}{2}mv^2$) is also fixed. If, therefore, we wish to raise the temperature of the substance, we must increase the kinetic energy of this random movement. The only way of doing this is by supplying the equivalent of the energy gained. In other words, we must do work equal to that gained. We say that we supply heat. We, therefore, implicitly state that heat is a form of energy.

In the old days heat was thought to be a massless fluid called *caloric*, which passed from the fire to the body, whose temperature was raised. But we know that by doing work we can produce heat. For example, if we rub a piece of wood on a table we impart a regular movement to the molecules of the wood ; we overcome the friction between them, and the work so done converts the regular movement into random movement of the molecules, and the temperature goes up. From an experimental side this was verified in the classical experiments of Dr. Joule, of Manchester, who showed that every 42 million ergs of work, if all converted to heat, produced one unit of heat, called the *calorie*. The calorie is the unit used to measure heat, and is the amount of heat which will raise the temperature of 1 gramme of water through 1°C. We usually call the relation 'the mechanical equivalent of heat,' or 'Joule's equivalent,' and write it in the form $4 \cdot 2 \times 10^7$ ergs per calorie.

LESSON SIX

Heat as the Physicist Studies It

OUR considerations of the molecular theory in the preceding Lesson led us to associate with the temperature of a body the mean kinetic energy of the molecules of that body, but this does not lead to a very ready method for the measurement of temperature. Defined as the 'degree of hotness' of a body, temperature is usually measured by means of a thermometer. Quantities of heat are measured in terms of the calorie ; temperature, or heat level, is measured in terms of an arbitrary scale of temperature. The Fahrenheit scale serves in everyday use, engineering and medicine, and the Centigrade scale is used for scientific purposes. The estimation of temperature by the sense of touch is a simple, but very unreliable method, which does not enable us to measure in a quantitative manner.

Measurement of Temperature. To establish a true scale of measurement of temperature we take any physical property which varies regularly with temperature ; we then find the magnitude at two fixed points, and subdivide the change into a convenient number of divisions. To make this clear, let us see how the Centigrade scale is actually defined in the case of a mercury thermometer. We select the expansion of mercury in glass as the physical property—we know quite well that substances increase in size as the temperature rises. When the thermometer is placed in melting ice, the mercury remains at one volume so long as any ice is left ; the level in the thermometer stem is noted and is taken as the lower fixed point. When the water and ice mixture is heated the mercury expands and rises up the stem as soon as all the ice is melted ; this goes on until the water boils, when again no further increase in volume and consequent rise occurs. This level of the mercury in the stem is taken as the second fixed point. Actually the stem of the thermometer should be in the *steam* from the boiling water, and the pressure should be 76 cms. of mercury.

The distance on the stem of the uniform bore tube of the thermometer between these points is then divided into 100 parts, and each division is called a degree Centigrade. It is merely a matter of agreement—any subdivision could have been taken. For example, the Fahrenheit scale is made by calling the melting ice level 32° F. and the boiling water level 212° F. ; there are thus 180° F. between melting ice and boiling water, corresponding to the 100° on the Centigrade scale.

The thermometers we have considered are suitable for the measurement of temperatures from near the freezing point of mercury to near the boiling point of that liquid. For accurate work the expansion of air is used in the 'air thermometer,' and for high temperatures the variation of other physical properties is utilized.

346

Physics 6

Clinical Thermometers. For special cases, where accurate measurement is required over a limited range, special forms are used. A well-known example is the clinical thermometer, which is used to measure a range of only 15° F. The normal temperature of the human body is 98·4° F., and variations from this form a most useful indication to the medical practitioner in diagnosis. This range is obtained by using a very fine bore tube, so that expansion in volume of the mercury takes up a large length of stem. The bulb of the thermometer is not fully filled, so that expansion taking place up to 94° F. merely fills the bulb. When the temperature reaches 95° F. the mercury comes to the first graduation on the stem, and so the further rises of temperature up to a maximum of 110° F. may be measured.

To prevent the mercury slipping back when the instrument is taken from the mouth there is a constriction in the bore, and the mercury must be shaken past this constriction. It is obvious that the instrument must not be put into boiling water to clean it, otherwise the mercury will expand sufficiently to burst the thermometer.

The Physical Units of Heat. In Lesson 5 we learnt that heat is a form of energy ; that if mechanical work be all converted to heat we can calculate the heat produced by making use of the 'mechanical equivalent' as found by Joule in his classical experiments, viz. $4\cdot2 \times 10^7$ ergs per calorie. In such calculations, as we shall see later, we deal with large numbers, and so we must often use a larger unit of work than the erg, called the *joule*, which is 10^7 ergs. In this unit we say that the mechanical equivalent is $4\cdot2$ joules per calorie.

To form some idea of the amount of work required to produce one calorie, let us consider a pan containing about $1\frac{3}{4}$ pints of water at room temperature, 20° C. Heat is supplied by a gas ring, and the water is gradually brought to the boiling point (100° C.). Now $1\frac{3}{4}$ pints are approximately equal to 1,000 c.cs. (1 litre), so we may readily find the heat taken from the gas flame to be $1,000 \times$ rise in temperature = $1,000 \times 80$ calories. This is equivalent to 80,000 $\times$ $4\cdot2$ joules, or $33\cdot6 \times 10^{11}$ ergs. To realize what this means, let us consider what mechanical task could be accomplished by the work. For example, suppose we apply it to lifting a 3-ton rock. The work would be used in giving the rock a potential energy $m\,g\,h$, where h is the number of feet the rock is raised, i.e. since

1 ton = 1,016,000 gm. and 1 ft. = 30 cms., we may say :
$$(3 \times 1,016,000) \times 981 \times (h \times 30)$$
$$= 33\cdot6 \times 10^{11} \text{ or } h \text{ is just over 37 ft.}$$

It seems rather astounding that the energy required in such a commonplace operation as boiling $1\frac{3}{4}$ pints of water could, if suitably applied, lift 3 tons from the ground to the top of a tall wireless mast, but such is the case.

Specific Heat. If we consider substances other than water we find that the heat required to raise the temperature of 1 gm. 1 degree Centigrade is not 1 calorie. For copper it is about 1/10 cal., for paraffin oil about 1/2 cal., and so on. We say that the *specific heat* of water is 1, of copper is 1/10, of paraffin oil is 1/2, etc. This is well exemplified in sand and sea water. When both are exposed to the intense heat of the sun for the same time the sand, being of low specific heat, becomes much warmer than the sea water, a fact we verify when bathing on a summer's day.

For large-scale phenomena, where mass is measured in pounds and temperature in degrees Fahrenheit, a larger heat unit is employed called the British Thermal Unit (B.Th.U.). This is the amount of heat required to raise the temperature of 1 lb. of water 1° F. For example, on the reverse side of many gas bills the heating power of the gas supplied is expressed as so many, say x, B.Th.U. per cubic foot. This means that if 1 cu. ft. of the gas were burnt under conditions of complete combustion x B.Th.U. would be obtained. As we have seen, this is equivalent to a definite amount of energy. The therm, which in 1933 began to be used in the Press to create an interest in gas, is the name given to the unit of supply of gas in terms of the B.Th.U., and is equal to 100,000 B.Th.U. ; so that if the consumption of gas is 1,000 cu. ft., and each cu. ft. happens to be equivalent to 470 B.Th.U. under the conditions stated, the number of therms is

$$\frac{470 \times 1000}{100,000} = 4\cdot7 \text{ therms.}$$

The excellence of this method of gas supply is that, if the calorific power of gas varies, the payment is still for the thermal equivalent of the energy, as the number 470 is adjusted by the company to be equivalent to the actual heating value of the gas supplied.

Latent Heat. If we put a thermometer into a pan containing ice and water we find that it reads 0° C., and if the pan is placed on a gas flame the temperature remains the same until all the ice is melted. Then there is a rise in temperature until the water boils, when again the temperature remains constant until all the water is boiled away. Now it is clear that the gas flame supplies heat all the time, and the question arises, what becomes of the heat when the thermometer stands at 0° C. and at 100° C.? In terms of the molecular theory the answer is not far to seek. The molecules of ice, changing to water, are split apart to be more free-moving, and there must be a certain amount of work done to overcome the attraction of the molecules to each other. The mechanical equivalent of the heat is used on this separation.

So work is done tearing the water molecules apart to make steam, only more work is required, because in the gaseous state the molecules are free entirely. We say the heat supplied is *latent* or *hidden*. Each gramme of ice at 0° C. changing to water at 0° C. requires 80 calories (approx.).

In the same way, if 1 gm. of water at 0° C. changes to ice at 0° C. there is a liberation of 80 calories. We say that the *latent heat of fusion of ice* is 80 cals. per gm. In the change from water to steam each gramme of water at 100° C. requires 540 cals. (approx.) to convert it to steam, and in the reverse operation each gramme of steam gives up 540 cals. on condensing to boiling water. The *latent heat of evaporation of water* is said to be 540 cals. per gm.

High Latent Heat of Steam. The high value of the latent heat of evaporation of water is seen in the intense scalding which takes place if the hand is placed in steam. The condensation of the steam on the hand is brought about with a consequent liberation of 540 calories for each gramme condensed to boiling water. If a gramme is condensed and cools to 20° C. the number of calories is 540 + (100 − 20) = 620, whereas if the hand had only 1 gramme of boiling water poured on it, the heat received would be only 100 − 20 = 80 cals.

Whenever a change to vapour from liquid takes place it is always necessary to supply heat equivalent to the latent heat. The lower the temperature at which the change takes place, the smaller is the latent heat ; but in all cases, as we saw in Lesson 5, we could anticipate the existence of latent heat from the molecular theory.

Linear Expansion. When we considered the construction of a mercury thermometer we assumed that there is an expansion of

the mercury when the temperature rises. We know as a matter of common observation that most substances do indeed change in size under these conditions of temperature change. The gap left between lengths of railway lines to allow for expansion in hot weather is a simple application.

The exact increase in length of a substance is usually expressed in terms of what is called the *coefficient of linear expansion* (a), which is defined as the increase in length of l cm. when heated through 1° C. For example, the coefficient of linear expansion of iron is 0·000012 per degree Centigrade. That is, the fractional increase per degree Centigrade rise is 0·000012. If the length of metal rod is l_0 at 0° C., the increase in length at $t°$ C. is $a\, l_0\, t$, and therefore the new length, l, at $t°$ C. is $l_0 + a\, l_t = l_0\,(1 + at)$. We thus see that, if the value of a is known, we can calculate the changes in length when the temperature changes. To facilitate such calculations, tables of constants are available, in which are tabulated the coefficients of linear expansion of different substances. Each figure in the table has been found by a set of careful experiments on the substances.

A Practical Application. At ordinary temperatures it is not necessary to use the formula above, to refer strictly to lengths initially measured at 0° C., if an approximate answer is required. For example, if a steel bridge is a quarter of a mile long at 10° C.

$$\left(= 32° + \frac{9}{5} \times 10 = 50° \text{ F.}\right)$$

we can see what the expansion is when the temperature rises to 40° C.

$$\left(= 32° + \frac{9}{5} \times 40 = 104° \text{F.}\right),$$

if we take l_0 to be the original length (i.e. not at 0°C. but at 10°C.), and take t to be the *rise* in temperature, viz. 40 − 10 = 30°C.

The expansion in feet then becomes (440 × 3) × 0·000014 × 30, since a for steel is 0·000014 and l_0 is 440 × 3 ft., i.e. the expansion or increase in length is 0·554 ft. = 6·65 inches. For ordinary small values of temperature, therefore, we write :—

$$l_2 = l_1 \left\{ l + a\,(t_2 - t_1) \right\}$$

where l_1 and t_1 refer to the lower temperature, and l_2 and t_2 refer to the higher temperature.

It is seen that the increase of length in $\frac{1}{4}$ mile in the above case is $6\frac{1}{2}$ inches, and provision must be made in construction to allow for this length change. In the same way, in the example quoted, the expansion in a long length of railway line would lead to serious warping of the line if it were all laid as a continuous length for, say, 100 miles, for here the expansion, of over 2 ft. per mile, would be 200 ft. In our conditions of climatic variation of temperature a bigger range has to be catered for.

Expansion in the Pendulum. Another application of this kind of expansion is seen in the pendulum of a clock. The time of swing, T of a simple pendulum, is the time for a complete swing—there and back again—and is equal to

$$2\pi \sqrt{\frac{l}{g}} \text{ where } \pi = 3\tfrac{1}{7} \text{ (approx.)}$$

and g is the acceleration due to gravity, and l is the length of the pendulum.

Obviously, in summer the length l increases and so T increases, and therefore the clock does not make as many swings in a day as in cold weather—in other words, we say the clock loses in summer. Now in most clocks the pendulum is not a simple one—i.e. a heavy very small mass on a light cord —but is compound : there is a *rod* which carries a massive bob. The same type of change occurs in its time of swing, however, and it is often corrected against temperature changes by allowing the bob to be free moving against an end stop on the rod (Fig. 13). When the rod expands, the centre of mass of the bob is lowered, but, at the same time the bob, which is made of a substance having a large coefficient of expansion, expands upwards to a greater extent, and is arranged so

that the centre of gravity just keeps the same distance from the point of support, and thus keeps the same time of swing however the temperature changes.

Varying Expansion of Metals. There are many devices in common use which make use of the differences in the linear coefficient of expansion of metals in other ways. If we take a strip of iron ($a = 0.000012$ per ° C.) and a strip of brass ($a = 0.000018$ per ° C.) of the same dimensions and rivet them together, it will be found that at a higher temperature the compound strip takes up a curved form : the brass, expanding more than the iron, is on the outer side of the curve.

This principle is made use of in such things as fire alarms, where the rise in temperature causes a double strip to bend and close an electric circuit and so cause an alarm bell to ring. The same principle, using other metals, is employed in the compensation of balance wheels of watches and clocks against temperature changes (Fig. 14). The rim which contains the bulk of the mass is divided and made of a compound strip whose more expansible component is on the outer side. For a rise in temperature the rim moves inward, and thus the mass moves nearer the axis of oscillation. Offset against this is the outward expansion of the spokes. It is adjusted to secure complete compensation.

In making the early form of electric lamps the difference in the coefficient of expansion of glass and the material of the filament cracked the glass as it had not expanded to the same extent as the filament. This was overcome by using short lengths of platinum wire to 'seal in' the filament, since, over ordinary ranges, the expansions of glass and platinum are the same.

There is always a bigger risk of breaking when the heated substance is a bad conductor of heat. When boiling water is poured into a tumbler the glass is heated locally and expands ; if the expansion is too local it breaks.

If a tumbler is made of fused silica it is possible to heat it up to dull red heat and then pour in cold water without any fracture taking place ; this is because the coefficient of expansion of the silica is so very small. In metals an alloy called invar has such a small coefficient of expansion that changes in length over ordinary ranges of temperature are negligible. It is, therefore, ideal for pendulums.

Cubical Expansion. Liquids and gases expand to a greater extent than solids, and

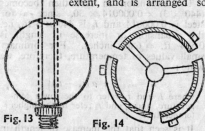

Fig. 13   Fig. 14

EXPANSION OF METAL. Fig. 13. Pendulum safeguarded against rise of temperature by free-moving bob. Fig. 14. Balance wheel of watch with expansible rim.

in their case there is a new feature, viz. they must be contained in a vessel made of some substance which also expands. The measurement of the expansion is, therefore, not as straightforward as in solids.

For example, if we observe an expansion of a liquid in a glass vessel there is the expansion of the vessel, tending to make the liquid appear to take up less space, and then the expansion of the liquid increases its size. So if we observe the net result, it is the real expansion of the liquid minus the expansion of the vessel.

In volume changes we express the expansion by means of a coefficient called the *coefficient of cubical expansion*. This is the volume change per unit volume for 1° C. rise in temperature, e.g. if a volume V increases by an amount v when the temperature is raised by $t°$ C., the coefficient of cubical expansion is $\dfrac{v}{Vt}$

For the liquid we have just considered there are two coefficients of cubical expansion ; the first is the *real coefficient of expansion*. When we measure the rise of a liquid in a vessel, we have seen that the observed amount is less than this, and the corresponding coefficient is called the *coefficient of apparent expansion*. The vessel expands as though it were solid, and the coefficient of cubical expansion for the solid material is very nearly three times the linear coefficient.

We have, therefore : The coefficient of real expansion = coefficient of apparent expansion + coefficient of cubic expansion of the glass of the vessel.

To see the difference in these two coefficients, consider water in a glass vessel. The real coefficient is 0.00015 between $10° - 20°$ C. ; for glass the linear coefficient is about 0.000007 ; the apparent coefficient for water in glass is $0.00015 - 3 \times 0.0000017 = 0.0001449$ per ° C.

LESSON SEVEN

Reaction of Gases to Temperature Changes

IN the case of gases the expansion due to a rise in temperature is so large that it is customary to neglect the effect of the containing vessel. This will be appreciated if we consider the order of the expansion : air has a coefficient of expansion ('cubical' is implied as this is the only possible case for gases) of 0.00366, and if we take away the cubical expansion of the glass vessel, viz. 0.0000051, it is only a matter of 5 in 3,600, or approximately 0.1 per cent. There is, however, a more serious complication. We have seen that the volume of a gas changes with pressure, so that a change in volume which takes place on heating will be related to the possible pressure conditions as well as temperature.

To make things clear, it is customary to deal with rises in temperature of a gas under two headings :

(1) At constant volume, and
(2) At constant pressure.

In the first case the result of a temperature rise is an increase in pressure ; in the second, in volume.

Taking the first case, we consider the volume of the gas as constrained to be constant, when common experience leads us to anticipate that there will be a rise in the pressure. In a careful experiment, it is possible to measure the pressure of a fixed volume of gas under different conditions of temperature, and so find the relation between pressure and temperature ' at constant volume.'

Pressure-Temperature Relation. The graphical method perhaps shows the results of these experiments to the best advantage, as seen in Fig. 15. It is clear that the relation may be expressed as a straight line. Actually, if

P_0 be the pressure at 0° C.
P_t be the pressure at $t°$ C.,
the relation between these is
$$P_t = P_0 (1 + \beta t),$$
where β is a constant which is equal to
$$\frac{P_t - P_0}{P_0 t}.$$

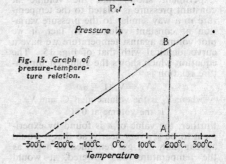

Pressure

Fig. 15. Graph of pressure-temperature relation.

Temperature
-300°C. -200°C. -100°C. 0°C. 100°C. 200°C. 300°C.

In such instances, therefore, β is called the *coefficient of increase of pressure at constant volume*. Experiment shows that this is a constant, having a value of about $\frac{1}{273}$ (·00366). Examination of the curve shows that it would intersect the axis of temperature at $-273°$ C. approximately. This is also seen if we consider the equation. For example—

when $t = -10°$ C., $P_t = P_0 (1 - \frac{10}{273})$,

and when $t = -273$, $P_t = P_0 (1 - \frac{273}{273}) = 0$.

The temperature of $-273°$ C. seems to be one at which gases, *if they remained gases*, would have no pressure. More of this is said in the next section. Before we leave this ' pressure-temperature ' relation, however, there is a point which will be apparent. If we enclose a volume of gas and always maintain its volume constant, we can use the pressure-temperature curve to measure unknown temperatures. This is the principle underlying the *constant volume gas thermometer*. The pressure at melting ice temperature and the pressure at boiling water temperature (boiling at a pressure of 76 cms. of mercury) are taken as the ' fixed points.' The size of the degree is $\frac{1}{100}$ of this ' fundamental interval,' and is very rarely the same as the ordinary Centigrade mercury thermometer unit. If the bulb which contains the gas is placed in an unknown temperature enclosure, and the pressure to maintain the volume constant corresponds to, say, AB (Fig. 15), the temperature can be read off the curve to be about 185° C. This type of constant volume thermometer has been used in the past to measure high temperatures.

Constant Pressure. The second method of studying the effect of temperature on gases is to maintain them at constant pressure and examine the change which takes place in the volume of the gas. Experiment shows that the volume at constant pressure is related to the temperature in a way similar to the pressure variation at constant volume. In fact, if we plot volume against temperature we have a curve identical with that of Fig. 15. The equation which shows the volume-temperature relation is

$$V_t = V_0 (1 + \alpha t)$$

where V_t is the volume at $t°$ C. and V_0 is the volume at $0°$ C.

Further, the value of α is found by experiment to be $\frac{1}{273}$ very nearly, so that it would appear that, if a gas remained as a gas as the temperature was lowered, it would

have no volume at all at $-273°$ C. This temperature is, therefore, called the absolute zero ; and a scale of temperature, called the *gas scale* or *absolute scale* ($A°$), is used. This has its zero at $-273°$ C., and the size of degree is the same as on the Centigrade gas scale. Thus $0°$ C. is 273° A. (absolute) ; again, $100°$ C. $= 273 + 100 = 373°$ A. ; $t°$ C. $= (273 + t)°$ A., and may be written $T°$. (It is customary to use capital letters to indicate absolute temperatures, i.e., temperatures on the absolute scale). Considering only the constant pressure changes, we have :

$$V_t = V_0 (1 + \frac{1}{273} t)$$

$$= V_0 \left(\frac{273 + t}{273}\right) = V_0 \frac{T}{T_0}$$

where $T = 273 + t$ and is the equivalent of $t°$ C. on the absolute scale ; T_0 is the equivalent of $0°$ C. on the absolute scale.

This is often written :

$$\frac{V_t}{T} = \frac{V_0}{T_0}, \text{ or } \frac{V}{T} \text{ is a constant,}$$

which is another way of saying that V is proportional to the absolute temperature.

This is called *Charles' Law*, and is also discussed in the Course on Chemistry, Volume III, Lesson 7, as it is always used when dealing with the volume changes with temperature. We must now, of course, remember that at low temperature gases are liable to change to liquids, and that the above relations do not apply when we have a change of state of this kind.

Liquids and Vapours. When water boils it changes to steam, a gaseous form of water. Even at ordinary room temperatures water evaporates and forms a vapour, as we know from the fact that water in an open vessel gradually disappears. If we have a closed space and introduce a small drop of water into it, we have a vapour which is *unsaturated*. This obeys Boyle's Law and Charles' Law. If now we introduce more and more water, we finally come to a state when the water does not evaporate into the *closed* space any further. We say that the space is saturated with water vapour. We discussed this in terms of the molecular theory in Lesson 5 (p. 341), and saw that the unsaturated vapour is due to quickly moving molecules leaving the water. In the saturated state the molecules still leave the water, but as the closed space has as many molecules in it as it can contain at that temperature, we have as many returning to the liquid as leave it in a given time. Both saturated and unsaturated vapours exert a pressure, as may be shown by using the space above the mercury in a barometer tube as the 'closed space' referred to above. This is the Torricellian vacuum (discovered by Torricelli in 1643). If water is introduced, drop by drop, in the vacuum above the mercury, it is found that the mercury is depressed owing to the pressure of the water vapour.

Finally, when sufficient water has been introduced to saturate the space, as judged by the fact that a little water remains *as such* on the mercury surface, it is found that the water vapour— called the *saturated water vapour*— exerts a maximum pressure at the temperature of the experiment. This is called the saturated vapour pressure. It can be measured in the way indicated in Fig. 16, where the left-hand barometer

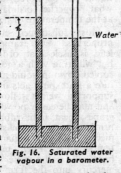

Fig. 16. Saturated water vapour in a barometer.

is an ordinary one and the right-hand tube contains free water over the mercury. The length h is the saturated water vapour pressure in cms. of mercury at the temperature of the experiment.

If the temperature rises the saturated vapour pressure gets bigger and, finally, for water, when the temperature is raised to 100° C., and the barometer reads 76, the water boils and the mercury in the tube is forced down to the level of the mercury outside. In other words, the saturated vapour pressure becomes equal to the outside pressure. If the barometer is low it is not necessary to heat the tube to 100° C. to bring this about. That is to say, the water boils at a lower temperature than 100° C. This is true in all cases. Take, for example, the case of water boiling up a high mountain, where the atmospheric pressure is always much less than 76 cms. of mercury ; the boiling point of water is correspondingly low—it might be as low as 94° C. On the other hand, if the pressure is increased the boiling point is raised. This is accomplished in boilers, 'digesters' and the like, where the steam is not allowed to escape until the pressure is high enough to open a valve at a set pressure. The tempera-

ture can, in this way, be raised to quite high values due to the steam pressure.

It will be seen now why we found it necessary to stipulate the atmospheric pressure when talking about the upper fixed points of a thermometer, as water boils at 100° C. only when the pressure is 76 cms.

Liquefaction of Gases. All the gases we have regarded in a general way as being the natural state of the element concerned, e.g. oxygen, nitrogen, etc., can be considered simply as unsaturated vapours of the corresponding liquid state. The so-called 'permanent gases' are no exception to this rule. We can, by proper means, convert them to saturated vapours and liquefy them.

Some gases respond to the same treatment as saturated vapour of water—simply cool them. Others can be liquefied by pressure only (e.g. sulphur dioxide), but in the latter case the gas must be below a temperature which is critical to the gas itself. At ordinary room temperatures, for example, sulphur dioxide may be liquefied by pressure only because it is below its *critical temperature.* Many early attempts at liquefaction of gases were carried out without success, despite the use of really large pressures, for the critical temperatures of the gases concerned were below the temperature of the room.

We realize nowadays that no pressure, however great, can bring about liquefaction, unless we first cool the gas below its critical temperature. The simple method of producing a small amount of cooling is to use a freezing mixture. Ordinary salt, calcium sulphate, etc., when mixed with ice, reduce the temperature below zero, but not *very* much below. However, this temperature (15° to 16° below zero) can be used to liquefy certain easily liquefied gases, and the liquids so formed may be used to produce cooling in other gases, and so on.

How Air is Liquefied. To produce a really appreciable drop in temperature the method which has been most utilized is the expansion of compressed gas. It is well known that if we compress a gas we produce a rise in temperature ; all who have pumped up a bicycle tire will have experienced this effect. Conversely, if we allow the compressed gas to expand suddenly it cools. So if we compress a gas—say, air—and cool it as low as possible by surrounding it with a low temperature bath (freezing mixture, liquefied carbon dioxide, etc.), and then allow it to expand, it will cool still further. This process is used to liquefy oxygen, nitrogen, the mixture called air, etc.

The gas is raised to a pressure of many times that of the normal atmosphere and is then cooled and led through a metal spiral tube contained within a second spiral tube. By means of a pin valve the highly compressed gas is allowed to expand and so become cooled. The cool gas passes into the space between the two tubes, and reduces the temperature of the oncoming compressed gas in the inner spiral tube. This cooled gas is then allowed to expand and cool still further. The process is repeated continuously until, finally, the expansion results in the liquefaction of the gas. This method is called the regenerative cooling process. At a temperature of — 183° C., air was liquefied (i.e. at 317° of frost on the Fahrenheit scale) and in turn the so-called permanent gases yielded to this form of treatment, and, finally, helium, the last, was converted to a liquid.

Laboratory Use of Very Low Temperatures. At Cambridge a large plant was installed for the production of supplies of liquid helium so that certain physical investigations could be made at the extremely low temperature of this liquid (— 269° C.)—at a temperature sufficiently low, in fact, to be approaching the absolute zero (it is actually about 4° A.). At these very low temperatures matter takes on very interesting properties. Electric resistance, for example, becomes exceedingly small, and the metals become 'super conductors' —a well-earned title in this case. If a ring of metal at the temperature of liquid helium has an electric current induced in it, the current goes on flowing for days. We shall return to this question later.

An interesting outcome of the production of these liquids at such low temperature was the fact that at ordinary temperature the liquids were well above their boiling point, and consequently they boiled away with extreme rapidity. Liquid air, for example, when placed on ice, behaves in the same way as would water placed on a dull red-hot metal. Dewar, who first produced liquid air, was faced with the problem of how to store the liquid ; he solved the problem by making the Dewar flask, also called the thermos flask (Fig. 17, p. 354). For the moment we can assume that the liquid can be stored, and briefly consider what properties ordinary matter has when at the temperature of liquid air.

Most substances change their elastic properties. For example, a bell made of lead is useless at ordinary temperatures, but will ring with a good clear note when cooled down in liquid air. At this temperature a lead spiral acts like a spring and will support a weight : flowers become brittle and may be easily powdered into fine dust ; grapes, meat, india-rubber, etc., all become brittle and may be smashed into a thousand pieces if hit by a hammer when at this temperature. Even mercury becomes a hard solid ; the writer has often moulded mercury into the form of a hammer, and used this hammer, made of mercury frozen solid in liquid air, to drive nails into wood. If these things happen at such a temperature as — 183° C., it is clear that we can 'expect the unexpected' at — 269°, the temperature of liquid helium ; and much useful information will be obtained by the experiments at these extremely low temperatures.

LESSON EIGHT

The Three Methods of Heat Conveyance

IN the previous Lesson we considered the production of very low temperatures and the liquefaction of so-called permanent gases. We found that, when air was liquefied, there was a great difficulty in storing it, as it so rapidly boiled away at ordinary temperatures. The thermos flask, which Dewar invented to overcome this difficulty, attains its object because in the design steps were taken to eliminate all gain of heat from the outside by the liquid kept within it. Most of us have used a thermos flask and know that we can keep hot liquids within it at a high temperature,

and cold liquids at a low temperature.

What Dewar really made in this flask is a good thermal insulator, i.e. he was able to cut down to a minimum all heat transference to or from the inside of the flask. To understand how this is brought about we must be acquainted, as he was, with the methods by which heat can pass from one place to another, and so see how to prevent its passage. We recognize three general methods by which heat is conveyed from point to point ; these are known as the methods of *conduction*, *convection*, and *radiation*.

Conduction. In conduction the random agitation ($\frac{1}{2}mv^2$) of the molecules of the substance conveying the heat passes from molecule to molecule through the mass of the substance; in consequence the temperature rises along the length of the conductor. A good example of conduction is to be had if a poker is left in a fire. The end remote from the fire becomes hot; we know also that the intermediate parts of the poker are hotter, i.e. there is a gradual drop in temperature along the length of the poker. In fact, the thermal agitation passes from molecule to molecule, and so the temperature rise spreads.

Substances behave differently in this respect. We have good conductors of heat (e.g. silver, copper, and the metals generally) and bad conductors of heat (paper, wood, etc.). As an example of a bad conductor perhaps the most obvious is the case of wood. An ordinary match when burning can be held until the flame is almost at the fingers, but no discomfort is felt, as the wood is a bad conductor of heat. Asbestos packing is used round hot-water pipes and some of the newer hot-water storage tanks, because it is such a poor conductor of heat, and so enables the hot water to be stored with very little loss. Glass is another bad conductor. Certain silver teapots are highly decorative, but, when provided with silver handles, are extremely unpleasant to hold, because silver is one of the best conductors of heat and so the handle becomes very hot.

On a cold day we again find common examples in the difference of *thermal conductivity* of different substances. If we touch a metal object it seems *very* cold, as heat is conducted from the hand by the metal; whereas, if we touch a wooden object, which we know is at the same temperature, it feels much warmer, because heat is not conducted away by the wood.

Convection. Liquids, generally speaking, are very poor conductors of heat. If we take a test tube and fill it with water, weight a piece of ice so that it sinks to the bottom, and then apply a flame to the upper part of the water in the tube, we can boil the upper layer vigorously without having any appreciable effect on the ice below.

In this experiment it will be noticed that the heat is applied to the *top* of the liquid and any thermal conductivity is downward. This was done deliberately, because, when heated from below, the temperature of the water is raised by another process called *convection*. This is the method whereby liquids and gases are most often heated.

The lower layers, when in contact with the supply of heat, naturally become hotter; they expand, and so, becoming less dense than the rest of the fluid, they rise within it and carry the hot portions bodily through the rest. To take the place of the hot fluid, cooler fluid sinks and, in turn, becomes heated, until the whole mass acquires a higher temperature. In convection it is seen that there is this bodily movement of the heated fluid. It is not a case of passing on the temperature rise from molecule to molecule, but rather a movement of the agitated molecules yielding place for the slower moving ones to come in contact with the heat source.

This process of convection is the cause of land and sea breezes, considering a large-scale case. In summer, when the sun shines on land and sea, the land, of low specific heat, becomes hotter than the sea. The air in contact with the land rises and colder air from over the sea comes in, as a sea breeze, to take its place. At night, when there is cooling, the land cools quicker than the sea, and so the reverse process takes place and causes a land breeze. If the circulation of the air is stopped this method of heat transference is eliminated. As an example of this, we notice how much quicker a pan of water boils when the lid is on than when the pan remains open and allows a continuous convection of the heat from the surface of the water.

Radiation. Both the methods of heat transference we have considered depend on the presence of some form of material substance. If the hot body could be supported by a fine thread of a very bad conducting material and be placed in a vacuum, the heat-loss by these two methods could be practically eliminated, and yet we should find that the temperature of the body would fall. The reason is that it loses heat by the process of radiation. It would appear from what has just been said that heat in the form of radiation may be transmitted without the help of any material medium; this is the case, and is the important distinguishing feature of the process.

Perhaps the best example of radiation, and certainly the most important to us, is the passage of the heat from the sun to the earth. We know that there is no material in the vast interstellar space through which the heat in the sun's rays passes on its long journey to us. Further, it is common observation that when material media do intervene, the amount of heat received is appreciably diminished—for example, when a cloud intercepts the sun's rays there is a marked drop in temperature.

During an eclipse of the sun another piece of information about radiation of heat may be obtained. It is most noticeable that the instant the light of the sun is cut off there is a pronounced drop in temperature. This suggests that the heat from the sun comes to us at the same speed as the light, and that it does so in a straight-line path. On a small scale, we have ample evidence of the fact that heat travelling in the form of radiation does so in straight lines if we consider the radiation from an open fire. The moment a solid object is placed between the fire and ourselves all radiation is cut off, and we recognize in the question, 'Can you *see* the fire ?' that this is so, and also that the radiation from it follows the same laws as light in this respect.

A simple experiment which many of us have performed shows that the heat which is radiated obeys other laws which are followed by light. A lens is used to 'focus the sun' on to a piece of dry tissue paper or dry leaves ; after a little time the dry object commences to smoulder and finally takes fire. This shows that the light and the heat are equally bent by the lens, or, as is said, the *refraction* of the two is the same. Moreover, many fires have been accidentally started by the sun's rays passing through a tumbler of water or pieces of broken bottle, and producing the same effect as the ' burning glass' in the example. There is no doubt, therefore, that radiation obeys almost all the laws applicable to light.

Loss of Heat by Radiation. An important consideration in the loss of heat by radiation is the nature of the surface of the hot body. If the surface is black and matt in character the loss of heat by radiation in a given time

is great compared with the loss from a similar body with a brightly polished surface. If we take two copper balls of the same size and at the same temperature and polish one brightly and deposit soot on the other and then hang them in front of a fire by a thin thread, it will be found that the black one absorbs most heat and is, therefore, hotter after a given time. It is a general law that good absorbers are good radiators, and good reflectors are bad radiators and bad absorbers, as they reflect the radiation instead of allowing it to pass through the outer surface.

Fig. 17. Thermos flask.

We can now summarize the three processes by considering the example of the thermos flask, which first drew our attention to this subject. A section of a thermos flask is shown in Fig. 17. It consists of a double-walled vessel of thin glass which is a bad conductor of heat. The air between the walls is pumped out and the tube is sealed. The 'vacuum' has no appreciable gas left in it, and so convection is stopped. The inner faces of the walls on the flask are silvered, and so, if the liquid is hot, it is in a bad radiator. Any heat which is radiated is reflected back by the outer walls, and so radiation is practically eliminated. It is most important to have a cork to stop convection above the liquid, and, finally, the minute amount of heat conducted along the glass walls is the only other loss. This flask, therefore, embodies all the necessary steps to eliminate heat transference, so that the liquid remains hot or cold for very considerable periods.

LESSON NINE

Some Properties of Wave Motion

IN the preceding Lesson it was stated that the heat from the sun reaches us in the form of waves. These waves were said to be like light waves, and to follow the same laws. In physics we often meet with examples of energy being transmitted in a wave form, and it seems desirable at the outset to have a clear idea of what is implied in the term wave motion—how it travels, and the like.

The first reference to waves, no doubt, brings to our mind a picture of waves on the sea, where we have a very direct visual evidence of the up and down movement of the water and the bodily movement of the form which we call a wave. One thing which this example shows clearly is that, in the wave motion, any part of the water through which the wave travels is not moving with the wave. For example, if we watch a boat on the sea, it moves up and down as the wave passes it, but it does not move bodily with the wave. In our early days we were a long time in learning this lesson. We all have recollections of sailing toy boats, and our attempts to bring them to shore by throwing stones. All that results in this : the stone produces waves, and the toy boat rides up and down on the water surface without making any attempt to move to the shore with the wave motion. Most of us, on occasions, have repeated the attempt to reclaim our becalmed craft by this impossible method.

How Waves Travel. Let us examine the simplest form of wave of the type referred to, and see if we can find out how it is produced and propagated (Fig. 18). We will think of a case simpler than water waves : for example, waves on a stretched cord or string. If we tap a stretched string (e.g. a long clothes-line) the tapping produces a depression in the string which travels as a wave along the length of the string until it reaches the other end, where it is reflected back again. The tapped part of the string comes back to the original position in time ; i.e. the string, like the water waves, moves up and down. The depressed part does not go along the length of the string, although the wave motion does so. If, instead of tapping the cord, we move one end up and down, the wave continues to travel along the length of the string. We have, no doubt, performed this experiment with a skipping rope, 'making snakes' with the rope. When one end of the rope moves up and down, this causes the next piece of the rope to move in a similar manner, and the movement, if maintained at the first end, continues the length of the rope. The beginning of the wave, therefore, is the up and down movement of the 'medium' in which the wave is transmitted.

The best known movement of this type is called *simple harmonic motion.* The bob of a pendulum is a good example of this. The physicist's simplest illustration of the production of simple harmonic motion (S.H.M.) seems rather arbitrary, but is, nevertheless, worth considering, as it does give useful help in considering waves.

Simple Harmonic Motion. If we consider a point, P, to move round a circle with a constant speed (*see* Fig. 19), it will go from A to D, D to B, B to C and C to A in equal times. Now let us imagine that from P, at every point it occupies, a perpendicular PN is drawn on to the diameter AB. Then it is clear that as P moves round the circle,

the foot of the perpendicular, N, moves up and down the diagonal. If we start with P at A and let it go round the circle once, N will start at A and go down to B, and, in fact, will be at point B when P is there ; and as P goes along BC, N will move along BO and finally come back to A when P reaches this point. N will complete one 'there and back' movement whilst P makes one complete circuit. The time for this will be fixed, of course, if we know the speed of the point P : this time is called the *periodic time,* T, and is also the time for one complete 'there and back' movement of N. N is said to oscillate with simple harmonic motion.

This simple harmonic motion has an extreme *amplitude* OA or OB = a, say. The time taken for the point N to go from the position of rest O to A is T/4 : after a second T/4 the point N is back again at O : then, in a further T/4, it is at the other extreme at B, and so on. If we consider the example of S.H.M. as provided in the simple pendulum, we see in Fig. 20 that OA = OB is the amplitude, and the time taken whilst the bob goes from O to A, back through O to B, and finally to O again, is the periodic time T, which, incidentally, is equal to $2\pi \sqrt{l/g}$ (as stated in Lesson 6, page 348); the point to be noticed is that the bob passes through O twice, once in each direction, and we agree to call T the time taken from one transit to the next *in the same direction.*

Let us consider the motion in a little more detail. If we start with the position o for P the foot of the perpendicular N is at O, in Fig. 21. The circumference is divided into 12 equal parts ; therefore the time taken for

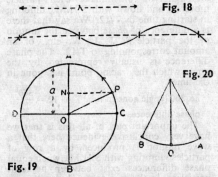

WAVE MOTION. Fig. 18. Simplest form of wave transmission. Figs. 19 and 20. Diagrams illustrating what is termed simple harmonic motion ; an explanation of the lettering is given in the text.

P to go from one of these points to the next is T/12. When P is at 1, N is at A ; when P is at 2, N is at B, and so on. It is clear that when P is at 3, N is at C (the same point), and is for the moment at rest whilst the direction of movement changes. At O, on the other hand, the velocity of N is greatest.

Particles in Simple Harmonic Motion. Now let us consider a row of particles, S, T, U, V, W, X, etc., all oscillating with simple harmonic motion of the same amplitude a and periodic time T. In fact, let the left-hand part of the diagram (Fig. 21, p. 357) be the key to give the positions of all the particles. If all start at rest and move upwards, they will all bodily advance to the first, then second, and then third dotted line position, and so on. If, on the other hand, they do not start together, but if we arrange that the particles each have a start of T/12 over their right-hand neighbour, we obtain the result we are requiring.

For example, S moves to position 1, and so gets T/12 start : when S moves to position 2, T moves to position 1 : when S moves to position 3 (i.e. $3\frac{T}{12}=\frac{T}{4}$), T moves to position 2 and U moves to position 1 : S now moves back to position 2, T moves to position 3, U moves to position 2 and V moves to position 1.

Finally, when S gets back to its original position at S, the other particles are in the positions shown in the wave line of Fig 21.

Draw a row of 12 equally spaced dots instead of S, T, etc., and carry on with this, moving each in distances as given by the key diagram, and you will find that the result is a wave which moves from left to right, although you only make each particle move up and down with S.H.M., differing in starting time by T/12. We say that there is a difference of *phase* between the motion of the particle S, T, U, V, etc., of an amount corresponding to T/12. The phase difference is usually represented by the angle which the tracing point has gone in the time,

i.e. 360 (angle gone in time T) $\div 12 = \dfrac{360°}{12}$

phase difference.

The important part of all this is that we have very conclusive evidence here that a wave motion is produced by a row of particles vibrating with S.H.M., when equal phase differences exist between adjacent particles. In the case taken in the illustration, the particles are vibrating in one direction and the wave is transmitted in a direction at right angles. This kind of wave is called a *transverse wave*. There are many examples of this type in addition to the obvious ones considered, e.g., waves on a stretched string, water waves, etc. There are the less obvious cases of light waves, wireless waves, radiant heat waves, etc.

If the particles S, T, U, V, etc., were made to vibrate in a direction parallel to SX, i.e. at right angles to the direction taken in Fig. 21, waves of a different character, called *longitudinal waves*, would be produced. The best example of this type of wave is the ordinary sound wave, and we will return to this problem later.

Transverse waves are easier to visualize and easier to illustrate by diagram, so we will continue in our investigation of wave properties with this type.

Interference of Waves. We will return to the illustration of the long skipping rope, fastened at one end and shaken at the other. For one sharp jerk we saw that the pulse or wave set up may be sent back or reflected from the fixed end. If we make the tension on the rope fairly large (i.e. pull on the rope), and continue to move the end up and down with sufficient speed, we find that the waves which we are sending along it and the waves which come back commence to act on each other, and in time, with suitable oscillation of the free end, the rope seems to take up a stationary form of one, two or more loops, and there is no longer a wave *progressing* along the rope. This is called a *stationary wave*. It is brought about by the interaction of the two wave trains— the incident and the reflected. This interaction is, of course, to be expected. For, suppose that the two sets of waves are so arranged that the crest and troughs of each fit together, the effect will be a double amplitude. If the crest of one comes with the trough of the other, the two waves just neutralize and there is no motion at all.

This is indicated in Fig. 22, which shows (*a*) two waves fitting crest to crest and trough to trough, and R shows the resultant with double amplitude. Fig. 22 (*b*) shows waves 1 and 2 with crest to trough, and R is the resultant. This shows that if two waves are sent in the same direction with equal amplitude, but with 180° phase difference, (*b*), the result is just as if no waves were present.

If the waves go in opposite directions, they are first as in Fig. 22 (*a*), then as in (*b*), then as in (*c*), then (*b*) and then (*a*), etc., i.e. they form stationary waves which are illustrated in Fig. 23.

Another way in which waves can react and produce what is called interference is illustrated if we take a flat dish and fill it with water. Two identical tuning forks have each a small bristle attached, so that when the forks vibrate the bristles set up little waves on the water surface. If one fork only vibrates there is set up a series of concentric water waves. When the other fork vibrates the waves,

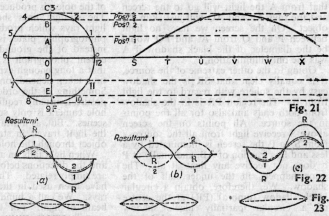

WAVE MOTION. Fig. 21. Detailed diagram illustrating simple harmonic motion. Figs. 22 and 23. Diagram showing production of interference of waves.

it sets up interference with the first set, and lines marking positions of no movement of the water can be seen. In fact, if at any place one wave causes a crest and the other a trough, there is no *net* movement, provided the amplitudes are the same.

When a wave approaches an obstacle it may behave in one of two ways ; either it will be stopped or reflected, or, if the obstacle is a small one, the wave can bend round it. If a sea is running towards a long breakwater, we notice that near the end of the breakwater wall there is a slight move-

ment, but within the 'shadow' of the wall there is no appreciable movement. On the other hand, if we watch a little farther from the shore, the same sea approaching a large rock, there is no appreciable shadow ; the waves appear to bend round the obstacle.

All these properties of waves will, of course, be expected in any wave motion. If light, 'waveless' waves, etc., are true waves, they must exhibit these properties ; and it will be seen in the last Lesson on light that, if we have the right conditions, we do, indeed, obtain analogous results with light.

LESSON TEN

Light and the Laws of Reflection & Refraction

BEFORE we proceed to discuss the physical nature of light, on the lines indicated in the preceding Lesson, we should consider certain simple properties of light. We shall be able to put into the form of laws, or rules of play, many facts which all appreciate in a general way already. Forgetting for the moment that we are later going to show that light travels as waves, the first thing which we notice is that light travels in a straight line path. If we have a very small bright light source, and we put an object between this and a white screen in a room where no other light can enter, we know very well that a shadow will be formed on the screen which has a shape identical with that of the

object casting the shadow. This is consistent with a straight line path for the light, or with 'rectilinear propagation' of light, as it is called. We have met this simple experiment in the amusing animal shadows cast by the hands.

If we use a large source of light we do not get this sharp outline ; there appears to be a double edge to the shadow, which has a black centre of the shape of the object, and this is edged with a half shadow, of the same outline. This is again consistent with rectilinear propagation of light. In Fig. 24 let AB be a large source of light illuminating a screen and let the object be a ball. If light travels in straight lines from every point in the source, then it is clear that from A the light will go to the screen and the rays AP and AQ will just skim the object. On the screen we have no light between P and Q from A, and PQ would be the diameter of the black shadow if A was the only illumination.

Going to the other extreme of the source, it is equally clear that SR is the shadow cast by the sphere with regard to the light from B. The region PR is in the shadow from both ends and also for all the points in the source. All points on the screen above S receive light from all the sources ; from S to P the screen is illuminated by a less and less fraction of AB, and finally at P it does not receive any light at all. The same happens in the under half of the shadow. We, therefore, obtain a circular black shadow (umbra) (PR) at the centre of a circular partially black shadow (penumbra). On a large scale, if AB is the sun, and the object casting the shadow is the moon, the resulting eclipse of the sun as seen from the earth is total if the earth happens to be within the region PR, or partial if in the region SP or RQ. From our present point of view the experiments referred to are only used to show that the light does travel in a straight line, i.e., the results obtained agree with the above explanation in terms of straight lines.

The Pin-hole Camera. Of the many simple experiments which may be quoted to add support to this is that of the simple pin-hole camera (Fig. 25). A pin-hole O is made in the centre of a light-tight box, and the other end has a ground glass end AB. When the box is pointed at a brightly illuminated object, represented in the diagram by the arrow XY, an inverted image of the object is produced on the glass screen. The straight lines show the path of the light rays which produce the image. If a photographic plate is placed in a box, instead of the ground glass sheet, an excellent photograph is produced, provided that a long enough exposure is given. The time taken depends on the size of the hole. Something of the order of two hours' exposure is usually required, so that the pin-hole camera is only suitable for stationary scenes. But, as indicated, it works because the light travels in straight lines from the object through the hole to the plate.

When light falls on a mirror it is reflected, and the directions before and after reflection are simply related. The straight lines which have been used in the diagram are called rays. We call a bundle of rays together a beam of light. For the simple treatment we will consider rays only.

If a ray of light falls on a mirror (Fig. 26) it is reflected from the mirror in a direction which depends on the angle at which the incoming light strikes the mirror. We call the incoming ray the incident ray, and the outgoing ray the reflected ray. We imagine a line drawn at right angles to the mirror at the point of incidence ; this line we call the normal at the point of incidence. The angle between the incident ray and the normal is called the *angle of incidence* : the angle between the normal and the reflected ray is called the *angle of reflection*.

Laws of Reflection. Experience shows the truth of the two Laws of Reflection:

(1) The incident ray, the normal at the point of incidence, and the reflected ray are all in one plane ;

(2) The angle of incidence is equal to the angle of reflection.

We all realize the truth of these laws, which are actually a statement of the results of many experiments. They really embody what we regard as common experience. For example, if you are in a train at night-time, when the windows act as mirrors, and you are at position A, in Fig. 27, which represents the plan of your carriage, and at X there is someone you

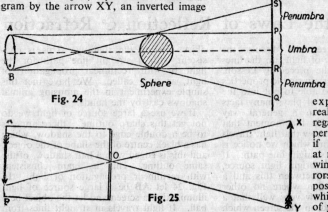

Fig. 24

Sphere

Penumbra

Umbra

Penumbra

Fig. 25

Figs. 24 and 25. Experiments to show that light travels in straight lines.

think you know, but there is an uncertainty which precludes direct observation, the obvious thing to do is to apply the Laws of Reflection. If you look out of the window so that the normal at the point of incidence is in a plane containing A and X, and the direction at which you appear to be examining the outer darkness is shown by the arrow, you are actually choosing a direction such that the dotted line and your direction are equally inclined to the window, and, of course, you see the person at X apparently outside the window.

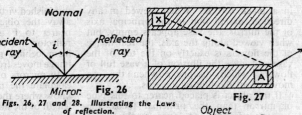

Fig. 26

Figs. 26, 27 and 28. Illustrating the Laws of reflection.

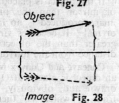

Fig. 27

Object

Image Fig. 28

Mirror Reflection. In all cases of reflection in plane mirrors the object we look at is reproduced as an image in the mirror. This image does not exist, but the eye takes in a beam of light that appears to diverge from an image, as far behind the mirror as the object is in front of it. This type of image is called a *virtual* image, and in a plane mirror it is the same size as the object. When we have a large object it produces a virtual image in a plane mirror (Fig. 28).

If we use curved mirrors we get other results. For example, if we take glasses which are parts of spheres and silver them, we can produce either concave mirrors (the inside of the spherical surface reflects), e.g. shaving mirrors ; or convex mirrors (the outside silvered and reflecting), e.g. motor-car reflector mirrors. In these cases the image is not always virtual and is not, in general, as far behind the mirror as the object is in front.

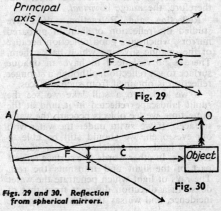

Figs. 29 and 30. Reflection from spherical mirrors.

We find the position of the image produced in either type of spherical mirror by applying the Laws of Reflection to the rays which leave the object. For example, in Fig. 29 the centre of the sphere of which the mirror is a part is at C and is called the centre of curvature. When a parallel set of rays falls on the mirror—say, from the sun—the normal in each case to the mirror is the radius, i.e. the line joining the point of incidence to C, and each ray is reflected at an equal angle on the other side of the normal. It is found that for small mirrors the reflected rays all pass through F, which is called the principal focus and is nearly half-way from C to the mirror. In the same way, if we reverse the rays we can see that all the rays passing through F, on their way to the mirror, after reflection go out parallel to each other and to the principal axis.

For example, if C is the centre of curvature and F the principal focus, an object placed at O, as in Fig. 30, will produce at I an image which is inverted and smaller than the image. The position of I is obtained by drawing a ray, parallel to the principal axis, to A ; after reflection it goes through F. A second ray incident through F after reflection comes out parallel to the principal axis and intersects the first ray at I, causing the brightness which is associated with the image. If we were to place a screen at I an image would be formed different from the virtual images formed by plane mirrors. This is called a *real* image because the rays of light do actually pass through it.

It is also clear that if an object were placed at I, its image would be at O : it would be inverted and real. This is exactly what happens in the optical illusion called the 'phantom bouquet.' A vase is placed at O, and a bunch of flowers is placed upside down at I and is illuminated on the mirror side. Everything except the vase is hidden in a black screen. When viewed in any direction, except that of the principal axis of the mirror, the vase appears empty, but when viewed along the axis, the real image of the flowers is exactly on the top of the vase and gives the illusion of a vase full of flowers, which disappear when the eye moves from the line of the axis.

If the object is placed nearer to this type of mirror than the principal focus, the image produced is no longer upside down or real. It becomes virtual, and of a size greater than the object depending on the distance from the mirror to the object.

Concave and Convex Mirrors. In Fig. 31 an object is placed at O : the two rays are drawn and, obviously, appear to diverge from I, which is, therefore, the virtual image of O. It is noticed that the image is bigger than the object. The concave mirror used as a shaving mirror acts in this manner, and the enlarged image produced is supposed to ensure a better view of the chin and so help to obtain a better result.

The convex mirror always produces virtual images of smaller size than the object and, therefore, allows a much larger field of view to be appreciated at once. This explains their use as reflecting mirrors in motor-cars. When light falls on this type of mirror parallel to the principal axis it reflects away and appears to come from the principal focus (e.g. in Fig. 32 OA incident reflects to AD). Here, again, a ray directed to F reflects away parallel to the axis. (OB, directed on F, reflects along BE.) Both rays appear to come from I, which is the

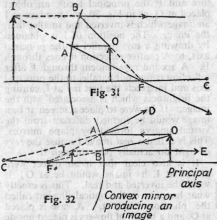

Fig. 31

Fig. 32 Convex mirror producing an image

Principal axis

VIRTUAL IMAGES, Figs. 31 and 32. As reflected from concave and convex mirrors.

diminished virtual image of O. The farther away the object is from the mirror, the nearer to F is the image. So in a car reflector mirror a second car approaching from behind gradually gets bigger as its image moves from near F to the mirror itself.

In mirrors of both kinds we are able to calculate the position of the image if we know where the object is, and also the focal length of the mirror (i.e. the distance from F to the mirror). We have not space to discuss this in detail, but we may take it that if the image distance is v, and the object distance u, and the focal length f, then

$$\frac{1}{f} = \frac{1}{v} + \frac{1}{u}$$

provided that we call distances on the object side of the mirror positive, and those on the other side negative.

Thus, suppose we have a concave mirror of focal length 15 cm. and an object is 40 cm. away, the image is produced a distance v away, such that

$$\frac{1}{15} = \frac{1}{40} + \frac{1}{v} \text{ or } \frac{1}{v} = \frac{1}{15} - \frac{1}{40} = \frac{8-3}{120} = \frac{5}{120}$$

$$\text{or } v = \frac{120}{5} = 24 \text{ cm.}$$

(i.e. on the same side as the object and, therefore, *real*).

For the same mirror an object 10 cm. away has an image v' away, which is given as before :

$$\frac{1}{15} = \frac{1}{10} + \frac{1}{v'} \therefore \frac{1}{v'} = \frac{1}{15} - \frac{1}{10} = \frac{2-3}{30} = \frac{-1}{30}$$

$$\text{or } v' = -30 ;$$

this means 30 cm. on the other side, and, therefore, the image is *virtual*.

Reflection and Refraction. We have studied the reflection of light at prepared mirrors, which give good reflection because of the opaque silvering which backs them. There is no real need to have an opaque surface to get reflection, although a stronger reflection is obtained from such surfaces.

If we look into a still lake we see the sunlit landscape reflected in it, and at the same time we see objects beneath the water surface. If we swim under the water with our eyes open, we should still be able to see the landscape which the water surface reflects. In other words, the surface reflects part of the light and transmits the rest. The rays of light which penetrate the water do so in a direction different from that of incidence, and we say the light is *refracted*.

COLOURS OF THE SPECTRUM

A beam of white light (sunlight) passed through a glass prism is separated into a band of visible colours—red, orange, yellow, green, blue and violet—shading off into the invisible infra-red at one end and the ultra-violet at the other. Newton called this the spectrum (*see* p. 364).

To face p. 360

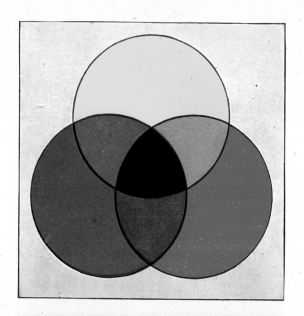

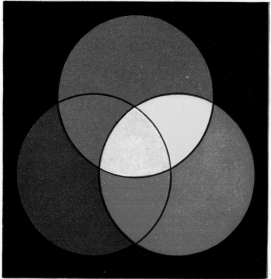

PRIMARY AND SECONDARY COLOURS

Above, on the outer parts of the three circles, red, blue and yellow are primary colours of pigments ; combined where they overlap, they produce secondary colours such as green, purple, orange. Secondary pigment colours combined in the centre give black. Below, light colour-primaries, blue-violet, yellow-green, red-orange (i.e. colours of the spectrum —*see* overleaf). Two overlapping produce light second-aries. If all three primaries combine white light is seen.

When an object which is under water is viewed from outside, the refraction of the rays makes the water depth appear less, and a submerged object appears nearer the surface than it really is. The student perhaps has met this case in early fishing expeditions, when the fish was invariably

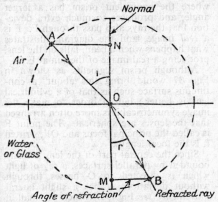

REFRACTIVE INDEX. Fig. 33. When light passes from air to a more dense medium such as water or glass, the refracted ray bends towards normal, making r less than i.

not in the place it appeared to occupy. The same effect is seen in the bath. One's toes always appear to be near the surface.

Laws of Refraction. By simple experiments the path of the rays from one medium to another can be traced out and the results agree with the following Laws of Refraction:

(i) The incident ray, the normal at the point of incidence, and the refracted ray are all in the same plane ;

(ii) There is always a constant relation between the sine of the angle of incidence and the sine of the angle of refraction for a given pair of media. The ratio

$$\frac{\sin i}{\sin r} = \text{constant},$$

is called the refractive index (μ) for the pair of media.

NOTE.—The sine of an angle is a convenient way of expressing the angle itself. For example, sin i (Fig. 33) = perpendicular AN ÷ hypotenuse OA ;

sine r (written sin r) = BM ÷ OB

$$\therefore \mu = \frac{AN}{OA} \div \frac{BM}{OB} = \frac{AN}{MB} \text{ and this is constant.}$$

The refractive index is always greater than unity when light goes from air to a more dense medium like water or glass, i.e. the ray from air always bends towards the

normal, making r less than i, as in Fig. 33. If we reverse the path of the rays the refractive index is less than unity.

Now we can see why the object under water always appears nearer to the surface when viewed from air. Let A (Fig. 34) be such an object. The ray AN, from A at right angles to the surface, suffers no bending ; any other ray is refracted as shown in the figure. The two rays drawn, AB and AD, are refracted along BC and DE respectively, and an eye placed to receive them is tricked into believing that the rays have come all along in the directions BC and DE—i.e. from I, which is the point where these rays meet if produced back. I is the image, and the object A appears to the eye to be at I, which is nearer the surface than A.

If we have a slab of glass with parallel faces, the refraction results in a ray of light being displaced, but the direction is still parallel to its original direction. For example, if a ray AB strikes the face of such a parallel-faced glass slab (Fig. 35) it is bent towards the normal *in the glass*, as along BC, and away along CD in air, where CD is parallel to AB. A appears to be at A[1].

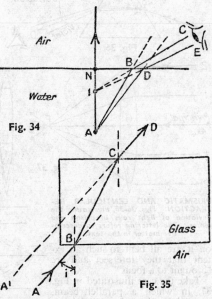

EFFECTS OF REFRACTION. Fig. 34. An object under water seems to be nearer the surface than it really is. **Fig. 35.** Displacement of an object seen in a mirror.

M

Prisms. If the glass is in the form of a prism we obtain a different result, which leads to rather important consequences. For example, in Fig. 36 we see the path of a ray ABCD, and notice that CD emerges in an entirely new direction. If the light AB is ordinary white light another additional fact is apparent. If we look in the direction DC we find that the beam which emerges is made up of the different colours of the rainbow. In other words, the incident white light AB becomes split up by the prism into these colours. We will return to this later ; the simple deviation of the ray in the prism as a result of refraction at two surfaces is our present interest. If the angle of the prism, marked x in Fig. 36, is big, the deviation is big ; if x becomes small, the deviation is small, as may be seen if different diagrams are drawn and a construction is used (as in Fig. 33) to find the path of the rays.

In a lens we have the equivalent of several prisms of different angles placed on top of each other, and the result is that rays falling

slab, and so goes through without deviation. Rays 1.1 each hit the lens at the same distance from the principal axis, and the parts of the lenses on which they fall may be regarded as prisms having an angle sufficient to make the rays pass through F. Rays 2.2 fall on the lens where the equivalent prism has a larger angle, and produces so much extra deviation that the rays also pass through F. F is a *real* image, and the diagram illustrates what happens when a beam falls on the lens, producing a real image of the sun at F.

Although prism segments as shown in Fig. 37 would bring this about, a continuous surface such as that of a cylindrical lens is better ; but in order to make the image symmetrical it is more often arranged that the lenses are spherical. The point F is called the principal focus and OF, written f, is the focal length.

Since the central part of the lens is really bounded by parallel surfaces, a ray of light which is directed to O passes through without deviation ; it has a slight lateral movement (*see* Fig. 35), which is small if the lens is thin. Another form of lens is called the *concave* lens, and the action of this type of lens on a parallel beam is seen in Fig. 38. The rays only appear to come from F—they do not actually do so—and, therefore, F is a virtual image of a distant object.

Images Produced by Lenses. That lenses are used in the camera, the projection lantern, the telescope and the microscope is well known, and it seems desirable to consider how simple lenses produce images, what arrangement of lenses is used in the instruments mentioned, and how this arrangement of lenses produces a final image.

Considering, first, the simple lens, we find that we may obtain graphically the position of images produced, if we consider rays of light starting at one point on the object and find where they intersect after passing through the lens. If the rays do not intersect to produce a real image, they will appear to come from a point which is the virtual image.

Three rays are sufficient, in general, to do this construction, as is

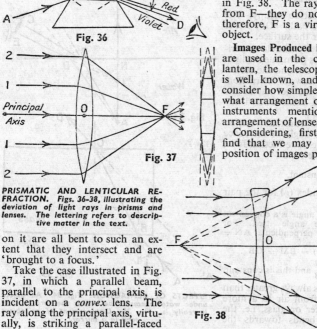

Fig. 36

Fig. 37

Fig. 38

PRISMATIC AND LENTICULAR REFRACTION. *Figs. 36-38, illustrating the deviation of light rays in prisms and lenses. The lettering refers to descriptive matter in the text.*

on it are all bent to such an extent that they intersect and are 'brought to a focus.'

Take the case illustrated in Fig. 37, in which a parallel beam, parallel to the principal axis, is incident on a *convex* lens. The ray along the principal axis, virtually, is striking a parallel-faced illustrated in Fig. 39 : (a) a ray from B parallel to the principal axis, after refraction goes through the focal point, F ; (b) a ray through F^1 after refraction goes out parallel to the principal axis, and (c) a ray through the centre goes straight through the lens. All these rays pass through B^1, which is the real image of B, and A^1B^1 is formed. So long as AB is farther away from the lens than F^1 there is a real image, which gets bigger and farther away as AB gets nearer F^1. The camera is in essence simply a lens or a group of lenses (Fig. 39), which is moved along the line AA^1, so that the inverted real image falls on the ground glass screen or on the photographic plate at A^1B^1.

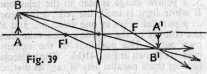

Fig. 39

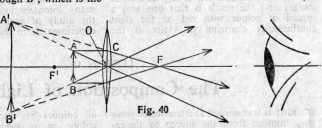

Fig. 40

PRODUCTION OF IMAGES BY LENSES. *Fig. 39, illustrating a simple lens. Fig. 40, showing how an enlarged image is produced (see text).*

When we use a convex lens of the kind shown in Fig. 39, as a 'magnifying glass,' we place the lens near the eye and then adjust the small object we wish to examine at a distance from the lens a little less than the focal length. This has the effect of producing a virtual image which is much enlarged. It is seen in Fig. 40 how this is produced. The rays appear to the eye to have come from A^1 and B^1, since they diverge after refraction. In principle, the astronomical telescope is a combination of the two cases. A lens of long focal length, called the object lens, is placed at one end of a tube which is pointed at the distant object, and a real image is produced in the tube. Then a second lens of shorter focal length is used to view the image. The second lens is arranged as in Fig. 40, e.g.

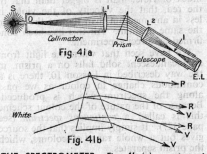

Fig. 41a

Collimator

Prism

Telescope

Fig. 41b

White

THE SPECTROMETER. *Fig. 41 (a), component parts. Fig. 41 (b), position of the extreme rays (red and violet) as bent by the prism.*

the real image is placed at AB and a virtual image of this, again magnified, is produced. There are many variations of this combination of lenses, which the student will find described in elementary books on light.

In the microscope, the small object to be viewed is well illuminated and the object glass, which is a lens of short focal length, is placed at a distance from the object a little greater than the focal length. A real magnified image is produced a relatively long distance from the lens. This real image is then viewed by the eye lens, which acts simply as a magnifying glass on the real image, and so produces a final virtual image, which is much magnified.

The Spectrometer. We will conclude this very brief survey of refraction by describing the spectrometer, which incorporates most of the points we have discussed.

The instrument is used to produce spectra. It consists of three parts : (i) a *collimator*, which is a tube having a slit O at one end, and a lens L^1 at the other. Since the slit is placed at the principal focus of the lens L^1, the light leaves as a parallel beam and falls on (ii) a *prism*, which is set to bend the light towards its base as already explained (*see* Fig. 36), and the light travels on as a parallel beam if it is of one colour, as seen in Fig. 41(a), and the third part (iii), the telescope, which is set in focus for distant vision, sees the image I of the slit as shown in Fig. 40 (the rays are left out in Fig. 41(b), for the sake of clearness). If a flame such as is given by a Bunsen burner or a gas ring heats a block of kitchen salt, the flame given is bright yellow. If this is used at

S, a yellow image is seen in the telescope. If white light is used, the red portion goes as a parallel beam in one direction, and all the colours of the rainbow each take their own path. The positions of the extreme rays are shown in Fig. 41(b). The telescope focuses these parallel sets of rays as distinct images and the result is that one sees a spread of colour with red on the right continuously changing to violet at the extreme left (most deviated). The general impression of this band of colour, which is called a *spectrum*, is seven main colour groups ; red, orange, yellow, green, blue, indigo and violet. These colours are always in the same relative position, and in the next Lesson we shall consider some of the many intensely interesting results which the study of such spectra yields to the experimenters in this branch of physics.

LESSON 11

The Composition of Light

LIGHT is transmitted as a transverse wave motion from the source to the receiver, as we have already stated. The fact is very well established as a result of many ingenious experiments, some of which are to be described in Lesson 12, where we shall see that it has been found possible to measure the length of the waves and obtain information as to the difference between the colours in this respect. Even the velocity of light has been found by special experiment. For many reasons it seems fairly certain that this velocity, which has the remarkably high value of 300,000,000 cms. per second (i.e. 186,000 miles per sec. or 669,600,000 miles per hour), is the highest speed attainable.

The Ether Theory. When we speak of the velocity of light, we must really be more specific and refer to the colour of light or refer to the velocity of light in empty space. We know, of course, that light can be transmitted through the tremendous distance between the distant stars and ourselves, that is, through a region in which no matter exists. The fact that this wave motion could be propagated through these empty regions led to the postulation of the ether. This purely hypothetical medium was, as has been said, invented 'to supply the subject of the verb to undulate.' Waves undulate or vibrate in something. In the cases known at the time of the commencement of the wave theory of light, as there was no material medium, an ether was postulated to give a more comfortable feeling to the theory. Once invented, its properties were deduced and a large field of research commenced.

Colour Velocities in a Medium. At the moment we cannot follow this line any farther ; our main concern is the vibration in it called light. In empty space, light of all colours has the same velocity. The colour of an extremely distant star is identical when viewed from the rise of the same to the going down thereof. If one colour travelled faster than another, that colour would tinge the first appearance of the star. From experience, however, it is found that this is not so.

When light enters a material medium, it is slowed down appreciably. In some glass, the velocity of light of all colours is reduced to about $\frac{2}{3}$ of the velocity in free space, and in water it is about $\frac{3}{4}$ of the free space value. Now, it is found that the different colours are not reduced in speed by exactly the same amount, although it is of the same order. The violet light is most reduced, and the red least reduced in speed in all straightforward cases.

The ratio we have called the refractive index is found to be equal to the ratio of

$$\frac{the \; velocity \; of \; light \; in \; free \; space}{the \; velocity \; of \; light \; in \; the \; medium.}$$

Now, as all the light has the same velocity in free space, it follows, since the refractive index of violet light is bigger than that of the red, that the velocity of the violet is less in any medium than that of the red in the same medium. All this has been confirmed by direct experiment.

We have seen that when the light from an incandescent solid falls on a prism, in the way described in Lesson 10, there is a continuous change in colour as we pass along the spectrum which is produced. Because of the nature of the colour scheme this is called a *continuous spectrum* (see page 327). It simply implies that the source gives out a whole range of colours, which the prism separates.

Now, the velocity (c) is equal to the product of wave length (λ) and frequency

(n), so that, for free space, we may calculate the frequency of each colour if we know λ and c.

This is constant for each colour, and is a much safer reference than an eye estimate of the actual colour itself. When the light enters a medium, since the value of n is constant, λ changes within the medium. We have also learnt that the deviation in the prism depends on the colour and, therefore, we must now associate the deviation with the more precise index, namely frequency.

For one prism, each frequency of light has its own deviation for a fixed angle of incidence. That is to say, the spectrum we see is a manifestation of a range of frequencies, which, when acting together, give the impression of white light.

Line Spectra. If we use as a source of light an electric arc which is struck between two rods of iron, we find that a continuous spectrum is not produced unless, by accident, we view the rods instead of the arc. In place of the continuous spectrum we have a set of lines each of definite colour. It is just as though a selection has been made of certain colours or frequencies which is found to be absolutely characteristic of the particular source of light chosen. Always with an iron arc we have the same lines (or frequencies) separated by black spaces where no light exists. These lines are so definite that, if we had lots of unknown rods of metals and used them to produce a line spectrum, we could tell beyond a doubt which rods were iron by the spectrum produced. Thus we have an infallible identification for the element.

Each element behaves in this way, i.e. each has its own line groupings. By careful use of the spectrum apparatus, an atlas showing the lines for each substance could be made, using photographs instead of visual identification, and this atlas would be a complete guide in an analysis of metals. If two metals are used, the spectra of the two would be superimposed and both could be recognized. This is the basis of a method of analysis by spectral means.

Band Spectra. Another characteristic form of spectrum is called the band spectrum. Here the lines are grouped together in the form of flutings or bands which are equally distinctive in analysis. More will be said of this when we discuss modern theories of atom and molecular structure, which can be supported by a study of the arrangement of the lines within the spectrum.

Absorption Spectra. When we discussed line spectra, an example of the line spectrum of iron was taken. This is really very complex. Perhaps the simplest common spectrum of this type is that given if a piece of common salt is placed in a Bunsen flame or on a gas ring. The flame looks yellow, and if analysed by means of a good spectrometer, it is found to be giving out two yellow lines in the visible region. These lines are very close together. Now, if white light from an incandescent source is sent into the spectrometer, but on its way is made to pass through a cooler flame containing salt, it is found that the continuous spectrum has two vacant places which show up as black lines. These occur in just the place where yellow lines appeared when the salt flame was used as a source.

The spectrum is called the *absorption spectrum*, and the absent lines are just as reliable a guide to the cooler vapour contents as are the emission lines of the glowing sodium chloride flame itself.

Fraunhöfer Lines. One very interesting conclusion was made on these lines, from a study of the spectrum of the sun. If an image of the sun is focused on the slit of the spectrometer and a camera is made to take the place of the telescope, the photograph so formed is in general appearance very like that produced by an incandescent solid. Closer examination, however, shows that it is crossed by a large number of black lines, called the Fraunhöfer lines (*see* p. 327).

They are explained by the fact that the light from the sun comes from the incandescent core, which is surrounded by a cooler gas. The light passing through the sun's atmosphere is, therefore, robbed of certain frequencies, which are consequently absent when the light reaches the earth. Examination of these black 'lines' led the physicist to a knowledge of the nature of these gases in the sun's atmosphere 93,000,000 miles away. Many well-known gases were identified. Some lines were still left over, and so new gases were discovered —at a considerable distance from the experimenters who found them. Helium has since been identified on the earth, and is now used in comparatively large quantities, but it was first found in the sun.

Ultra-Violet Radiations. When a continuous spectrum is produced and the frequency of the visible light waves is measured, it is found that the extreme visible violet has approximately double the frequency of the extreme red. Now, in sound, a note which has double the frequency of another is called the octave of that note. For this reason, we often refer, by analogy, to the 'visible octave' when speaking of the spectrum. These waves which give the sensation of light are but a small fraction of the radiations which are emitted by a source. If a photograph is taken of the spectrum of, say, an iron arc or an ordinary carbon arc, it is found that lines are produced well beyond the limit seen at the violet end of the visible region. These lines are said to be produced by the *ultra-violet* light. The ultra-violet light, whilst not affecting the retina, is very active in producing a photographic image. It has also the property of affecting the skin. In winter, when the rays of the sun have to penetrate the longer air path in their oblique track to the earth, the ultra-violet light is

of light are rich in ultra-violet light, e.g. iron and tungsten arcs, glowing mercury lamps (in quartz containers). Quartz prisms and lenses must be used in spectrometers to deviate and measure ultra-violet light.

Infra-Red Radiation. Beyond the red an invisible long wavelength radiation is given out. This is called *infra-red* radiation. This is very markedly strong in the heating effect it produces, and it is detected by sensitive heat recorders. Like ultra-violet light it has medical uses, but, unlike it, it can penetrate to a greater depth.

It will now be understood that the visible octave is only a small fraction of the energy sent out by a glowing solid. The 'light' extends to many octaves and affects different senses. We shall see later that the wave motions here discussed are themselves only

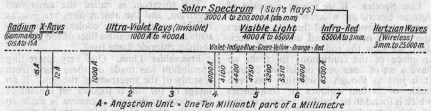

RADIATIONS. *Spectrum extended in diagram form (not to any scale) to indicate relations of visible and invisible rays and ultra-short radio active (gamma) rays to ultra-long wireless waves. See also page 327.*

largely cut off and, consequently, does not produce the same effect as in summer.

From this it will be gathered that ultra-violet light is very easily absorbed. Ordinary window glass cuts off most of it, and it requires quartz or special glasses to allow a free passage for these rays. Many sources

part of a very large family of similar radiations, which extend in wave length from several miles in length (wireless waves) down to one thousand millionth part of a centimetre (in radiation from radioactive bodies), and in all probability to a much more minute length in cosmic rays.

LESSON 12

The Wave Theory of Light

WE have seen that the visible octave which constitutes the range of electromagnetic waves that affect the retina of the eye only forms part of a large family of waves which may be detected because they affect one or more of the senses, or which may be detected by special apparatus (e.g. wireless waves). There is no doubt that the radiations are electromagnetic waves, and that their wave-lengths may be measured.

A source of white light sends out a band of wave-lengths from one value to double that value in all directions about the source ;

a monochromatic source sends out a very limited range of wave-lengths, which we might say has one value only, just as the modern wireless station sends out one wave-length only, whereas the old spark transmitting station used to send out a band of waves which affected a wireless receiver over a wide range of tuning. To study the wave nature itself it is much easier, in almost every case, to consider a 'monochromatic' source and see what happens, and then see how this is modified when we use white light. In Lesson 9, page 356, we saw that, when conditions were right, two sets of

waves act on each other, producing interference effects and diffraction or bending,
and we were led to anticipate similar results
with *any* wave motion.

Interference Effects. In strings and the
like, the conditions are easy to produce,
because, in the first place, it is relatively
easy to have two identical sources of vibration, and, again, the wave-motions produced
are readily visible. In light, even in a monochromatic source, we are dealing with a
complex thing. What happens is that any
particular point in the source sends out a
train of waves for a short interval of time
and then repeats this ; in other words,
the source is not giving a straightforward,
continuous output. To get interference we
must reproduce the same source in duplicate
and so get identical origins for two wave
trains, and in these circumstances we are able
to produce a large variety of interference
and allied effects.

Let us see how this was done by Fresnel.
A source of light illuminated a narrow slit
S, and the light was allowed to fall on
an arrangement (shown in Fig. 42) of two

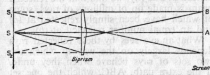

*Fig. 42. Fresnel's experiment with overlapping
light waves.*

identical prisms placed base to base. This
arrangement is called a biprism, and the
refracting angles of the prisms were equal
and very small. The light falling on the
prism was refracted as shown, and appeared
to come from S_1 and S_2, but in the region
AB the two beams overlapped. Considered
as waves, we have in the region AB two sets
of identical waves in the same space, and we
can, therefore, predict interference effects
in this region. Where the waves from the
two beams fit together, crest to crest and
trough to trough, we expect double the
amplitude and, in point of fact, four times
the brightness of the one beam ; but where
the waves emerge together with a crest of
the one joining a trough of the other, the
waves destructively interfere, and, although
the light beams are both there, the net result
is zero illumination. This experiment was
made, and the interference resulted in a set
of parallel fringes of alternately bright and
dark bands. (The experiment is made quite
easily with, say, sodium light.)

The distance apart of these bands can
be measured by viewing them through a
microscope, and if d and D (*see* Fig. 43) are
also measured, we can calculate quite easily
the wave-length of the light used. Fig. 43
shows the essentials of the optical paths.
S_1 and S_2 are the equivalent sources, and
OP is the screen or eye-piece of the microscope. It seems clear that rays of light from

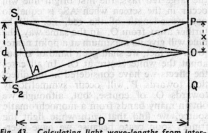

*Fig. 43. Calculating light wave-lengths from inter-
ference effects.*

S_1 and S_2 have the same length of path to O,
and, therefore, arrive in phase (i.e. crest to
crest) and so produce an addition of their
individual amplitudes. As we pass up the
screen to P, the illumination will depend
on the length of the path difference (S_2A
in Fig. 43). If S_2A is just half a wave-
length, the two rays will arrive half a wave-
length out of phase and will neutralize
each other, i.e. they will produce darkness.
As P moves out from O it is fairly clear
that AS_2 will gradually get bigger, and so
contain, in turn, a length equal to $\frac{1}{2}$, 1, $1\frac{1}{2}$, 2,
$2\frac{1}{2}$, etc. wave-lengths ; and so it is to be
expected that the illumination will be
alternately dark and light, as Fresnel found
to be the case. It can be shown quite simply
that when

$$x = \frac{D}{d} \cdot \frac{\lambda}{2} \text{ there is the first dark band,}$$

and when $x = \frac{D}{d} 2 \left(\frac{\lambda}{2}\right)$ there is the

first bright band, and so on.

Therefore, if D, d and x are measured
λ, the wave-length, can be calculated. In
this way the value is found to be $5\cdot89 \times$
10^{-5}. $= \cdot0000589$ cm. for the yellow
sodium light (actually this is composed of
two wave-lengths : $5\cdot8899 \times 10^{-5}$ and $5\cdot8959$
$\times 10^{-5}$cm.).

Interference Bands in White Light. In
all the above we have assumed a monochromatic source, but if we use white light,
which is a mixture of wave-lengths, to
illuminate the biprism, the maximum and

zero illumination produced by the yellow component will be precisely in the same place as when that colour only was used as source. But, in addition, each colour in the white light beam will produce its own effect, which is similar in nature, but differs in magnitude because of the difference in wave-length.

It seems obvious that, when we consider the large red rays, the first bright line will occur in the screen when AS_2 is equal to one wave-length of the red, i.e. will be farther away from O. In the same way, the blue will give its maximum at a point nearer to O. In fact, we shall get a band of colour about the white centre at O. In all cases the effects we have considered in the direction towards P will occur symmetrically towards O, of course, but, although we obtain many bands from a monochromatic source, we find that with white light the fringes soon cease because we have overlapping of the colours, producing a general white illumination, in a very small distance after the first set.

One might be rather tempted to suggest that these results seem very like those of ordinary refraction through a prism, as considered in Lesson 10, page 362, but the positions of these colours do not agree with such an explanation, and, further, the same scheme of things can be produced by other means without prisms, which, in this case, were simply used to obtain two similar sources. For example, in Fig. 44, another method of producing two identical sources is shown. Two mirrors OA and OB are slightly inclined to each other, and the source S is reproduced by reflection at S_1 and S_2 as far behind the mirrors as S is in front of them. At XY the two beams interfere and produce results similar to those described above.

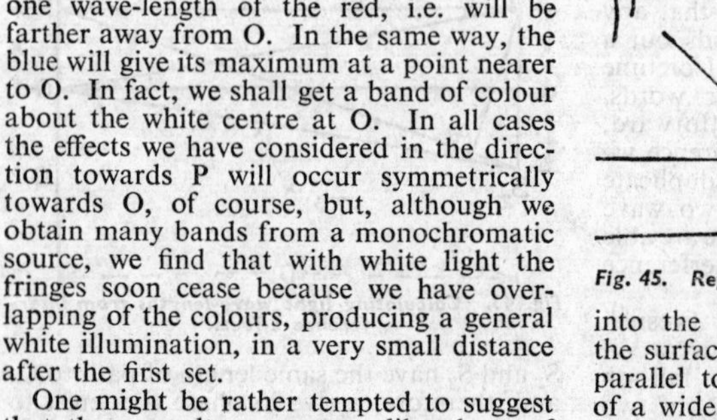

Colours on Soap Films. Perhaps the best-known example of the effects of the interference of light is the colour produced

Fig. 44. Identical light beams from two mirrors.

in soap films and soap bubbles. The magnificent hues seen on the bubbles blown from a pipe, or on the bubbly surface of soapy water, are brought about by the interference of the white light which falls on the very thin films. If we consider a very much magnified section of a soap film, we see that light falling on it can suffer reflection at the first surface (Fig. 45) ; then, of the light which is refracted

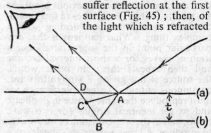

Fig. 45. *Reflection and refraction from a soap film.*

into the soap film, some is reflected at the surface (b) and will emerge, as shown, parallel to the first ray. When we think of a wide beam of light as being incident, instead of one ray, we find that the reflected beam is made up of millions of rays, some of which have been simply reflected at (a) and an equal number reflected at (b).

What an eye sees by these reflected rays depends largely on the way in which the two sets of rays behave when they unite. If the extra path, ABC, which the one set of rays have to travel, is equal to a whole number of waves, we should expect that the two sets of rays would reinforce, crest to crest, and produce a brightness. In fact, when reflection takes place at a more dense medium from air, as at (a), there is introduced the equivalent of half a wavelength path difference, whereas at (b), where the surface separates a more dense medium (soap solution) from a less dense (air), there is no such change of phase.

Wave-Length Path Differences. Thus the mere difference in the nature of the reflection surface introduces a path difference, and, therefore, we find that if the path ABC is a whole number of waves in length, the light of this wave-length destructively interferes and neutralizes. That is, in this direction there is no light of the colour corresponding to the particular wave-length, and if white light is incident, the reflection is devoid of this one colour, and, therefore, the complementary colour (i.e. white minus this particular colour) is produced and the film appears to be coloured. The colour will, of course, change when the thickness of the film changes, because the extra path ABC is thereby changed, and so is the wave-length which interferes at this particular path difference.

Again, if the path difference is a whole number of waves' lengths plus a half-wave of one colour, this will be reinforced at the particular angle which gives this condition, and there will thus be an excess of one colour on a white background. In both ways the reflected light gives rise to colours. In light which goes through the films, the colour seen is the complementary colour to that given by reflection.

Film of Molecular Thickness. Suppose we blow a soap bubble and watch the colour change, it will be found that this change is continuous as the film gets thinner. When the thickness is very greatly reduced, we find that a large area has the same colour, which in turn becomes red, then changes to blue through all the intermediate colours of the rainbow. If we are lucky in our soap solution we may be able to get the film so thin that a black patch appears and gradually spreads over the bubble, which at this stage might break at any instant. The black patch means that we have reduced the thickness of the bubble to something much less than the wave-length of blue light, i.e. of the order of much less than ·00004 cm. In fact, the path difference between the two reflected rays is negligibly small (only a minute fraction of the wave-length of blue light), and all that is happening is that the difference in phase caused by reflection at the upper surface, as we saw above, introduced a path difference of half a wave and all waves, therefore, interfere, and we obtain the perfectly black spot. The film is only a few molecules thick at this stage. A certain amount of patience is required to produce this effect, but the experiment can easily be tried with a clay pipe and a soap solution.

The same explanation accounts for many well-known beautiful colour schemes, such as those produced by thin oil films on the surface of water. The colours of opals and many gems of the same kind, butterflies' wings, peacock feathers and the like can all be explained in terms of interference,

as such, or in terms of an allied effect, which is called *diffraction*. The difference between interference and diffraction is quite arbitrary : the methods are similar, as we shall see.

Newton's Rings. Before we go on to consider this other interesting phenomenon, there is one particular form of interference fringe system which is worth consideration because of its wide application. If we take a curved surface and put it in contact with a perfectly plane surface, we find that beautiful coloured rings appear when illuminated with white light. These rings are called Newton's rings. Many elaborate instruments, called *interferometers*, have been devised to produce them, and to measure by their aid the dimensions of small objects and the change in length of longer objects when subjected to change of physical conditions.

If we take a piece of good plate glass and rest a weak convex spectacle lens on it and illuminate with white light, the rings appear. If the light enters at right angles to the plane, as at 0.1.2 in Fig. 46, it is clear that ray 1 can reflect at AOB

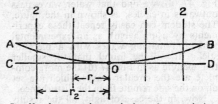

Fig. 46. A convex lens and plate glass producing Newton's diffraction rings, a simple form of interferometer.

or at CD. These reflected rays, coming together, reinforce or interfere if the path difference is half a wave or a whole wave, and so produce rings of light or darkness about O, as the path difference is the same in a circle about O. If we use monochromatic light we get bright and dark rings of the colour used. Now, if CD moves away parallel to itself, we find that the rings appear to move in or out. For a movement of CD equal to half a wave, the path difference made is a whole wave, and so the rings seen move so that they take the place of their former neighbouring rings. This is used to measure small movements in physical and engineering practice. It has the virtue of enabling an accurate measurement to ·000005 cm. without using anything more harmful to the apparatus than a beam of light, which

is reflected from the apparatus itself. The
interferometer has important applications
in astronomy in the calculation of star
distances (*see* Astronomy, Lesson 23, Vol. I).

A Difficulty in the Wave Theory. When
we discussed the properties of waves in
Lesson 9 (page 354), we saw that, in cases of
water waves, the motion was able to go
round a small obstacle, Fig. 47 (b), whereas
a long breakwater casts shadows, Fig. 47
(a). If water waves are directed to an

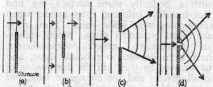

Fig. 47. *Behaviour of wave in water passing between obstacles.*

opening between two obstacles, they pass
through, not only in the original direction,
but in a fanlike direction, spread outwards,
as shown in Fig. 47 (c).

If, now, we make the opening small, as in
Fig. 47 (d), we find that water waves pass
outwards in circles, as shown in the figure.
The student can easily repeat these experiments by using a bath as an experimental
tank and making waves with a piece of
stick. It will be found that the smaller
the opening as in Fig. 47 (d) the more complete are the circular waves which are set
up on the side remote from the disturbance.

Now, in the case of light, all the results
which we have seen in this Course up to
date appear to fit in with a wave propagation, but we also know that if the experiments shown in Fig. 47 be performed with
light, instead of water, waves, the type of
result does not appear—at first sight, at
any rate—to agree with the results given in
these cases for water waves. Fig. 48 shows
the results we are accustomed to expect.

At one time it was believed that this
apparent disagreement was a decided blow
to a wave theory for light. It was, therefore, a matter of great scientific interest to
see whether light by any chance behaved
as in Fig. 47, to some degree, and to explain
the bulk disagreement. Now there is a
very important difference between the two
waves. Water waves are long ; light
waves are very small. In the water waves
in Fig. 47 (b), for example, the size of the
obstacle is comparable with the wave-
length, whereas in Fig. 48 (b) the obstacle
is some hundred thousand times as great as

the wave-length. The same may be said
of the opening between the obstacles in
Figs. 47 (d) and 48 (d).

To make a fair comparison, therefore, it
seems desirable so to reduce the size of the
obstacle, or the opening, as to be at any
rate of the same *order* as the wave-length of
the light used, and then to see if the bending
of the light waves takes place, as shown in
Fig. 47 for water waves.

We are so accustomed to recognizing that
light travels in straight lines that it comes as
a mild shock to find that, when we deal with
extremely small openings, there appears to
be a variation from this rule. For example,
if the sun is shining on a room darkened
by means of a black blind and there is a very
minute pin-prick in the blind, we are able
to see the sun shining at the small pin-prick
even when the eye is not in a straight line
with it and the sun—in fact, the light will
reach us in almost all directions if the hole
is small enough ; and so we have an
experimental realization of the water wave
case illustrated in Fig. 47 (d). The question which then arises is, ' Why should a
very small portion of the wave front behave
differently when separated from the rest of
the wave ?' The suggested answer is that
it does not do so ; that, in fact, all points
of the wave send out new waves, but, owing
to interference, all we realize when the full

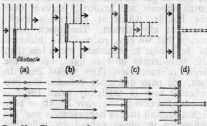

Fig. 48. *The upper figures represent wave fronts,
the lower figures the corresponding rays of light
using obstacles and apertures the same as in Fig. 47 :
(a) a long obstacle ; (b) a short obstacle ; (c) a
wide opening ; (d) a narrow opening.*

wave is present is the new wave front,
parallel to the old.

Bending of Light Waves. If we look more
carefully into the shadow cast by an object
with a straight edge in a darkened room, for
example, we find, using a low-power
microscope for the study of the shadow,
that there is no sharp line of demarcation
between brightness and darkness, but that
a gradual shading off to zero light takes
place within the shadow. Further, we find
that near the edge of the shadow, in the part

which appears to be bright to the naked eye, there is a fluctuation of intensity of the light, forming a set of straight line fringes parallel to the straight edge and rapidly closing up into the general illumination. Of course, all these fluctuations, etc., take place in a very small distance. For example, at a distance of 1 metre from the straight edge all the fringes are seen in a distance of 0·3 cm., and the diffraction, or bending, of the waves is, therefore, very small indeed ; but so is the wave-length of the light.

Close examination of many of the simple experiments yields equally interesting results. If, for example, we take a smooth-edged threepenny piece and set it up at right angles to a parallel beam of light in a darkened room, we find on examining the shadow that at certain distances away there is intense light at the centre of the shadow. This repeats along a line at right angles to the coin. It is merely a case of the waves having bent round the coin, reinforcing and producing the light seen. All the portions of light falling on the edge of the coin set up waves which pass into the shadow, but in most directions these waves destructively interfere, and darkness results.

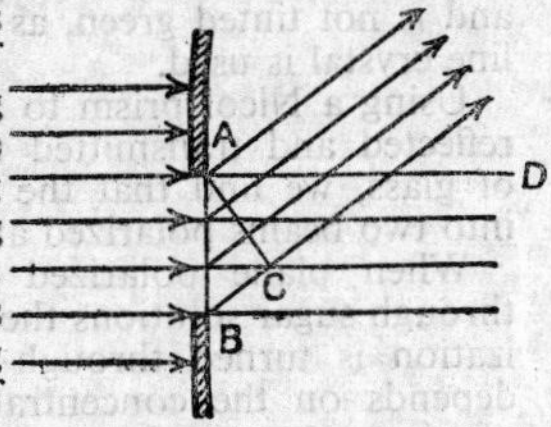

Fig. 49. Production of diffraction fringes.

Producing Diffraction Fringes. The point is, perhaps, best studied in the case of a narrow slit on which a parallel beam of light is falling. As seen in Fig. 49, there is no doubt that a direct beam goes through, but if each point across the slit AB sends out waves, as in Fig. 47 (d), the illumination in any other direction simply depends on what is the result of all the secondary waves from AB in the direction chosen. It can be shown that if BC is equal to half a wave-length of the light used there is reinforcement and the light so formed can be viewed by means of a telescope. When BC=λ there is darkness ; when BC=1½λ there is a second bright light, and so on. In fact, there are bright and dark *diffraction* fringes arranged symmetrically about the 'straight through' position shown. The positions of these

fringes depend on the colour of the light used, the red light diffraction fringe being at a greater angle than the violet. Once more we produce colours when white light is used to illuminate the slit.

Measuring Wave-Lengths. At the National Physical Laboratory at Teddington there is a machine which is able to rule a very large number of lines per cm. on glass and metal, and so produces what is called a *diffraction grating*. This ruling of lines makes alternate transmitting slits and opaque lines of the order of 14,000 lines per inch. Light falling on these gratings is diffracted at an angle which depends on the colour of the light used ; the angles are bigger for the longer wave-lengths. The result is the production of a spectrum ; the same thing occurs at an angle almost double the first, and the colours are practically twice as far apart. If conditions permit, this is again repeated and we have *spectra of the 1st, 2nd and 3rd, etc., order.*

The diffraction grating provides an excellent means of measuring the wave-length of the light falling on it, and it is often used instead of a prism as a means of analysing the spectra of light sources.

This brief discussion of diffraction, taken in conjunction with what we saw in page 369 in discussing interference, leads us to believe that light is undoubtedly a wave motion. Of course, there are two kinds of wave motion, as we saw in Lesson 9 (page 354) ; and the experiments we have described so far do not differentiate between the two, as both exhibit interference and diffraction. However, there are many very beautiful experiments which decide the point for us.

Light waves are transverse, i.e. they vibrate at right angles to the direction of motion of the wave. If we take a stretched cord, pass it through two slits, S_1 and S_2, and vibrate the end A in all directions at right angles to the cord (*see* Fig. 50), it is found that only those vibrations which are parallel to slit S_1 are able to pass through it ; and if we arrange the slit S_2 at right angles to S_1 we find that the cord at C is not moving. We speak of the waves

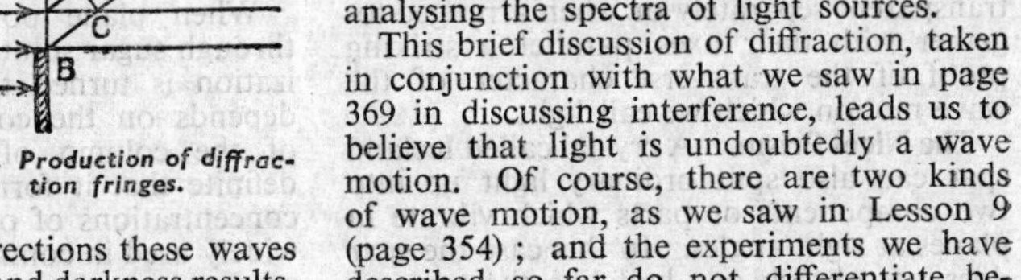

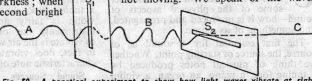

Fig. 50. A practical experiment to show how light waves vibrate at right angles to the direction of motion of the wave. Direction of vibration at A in all directions, B in one plane, and C no vibration.

between S_1 and S_2 as being *plane polarized,* i.e. vibrating in one plane only. Now, if light is a *transverse* vibration it may vibrate as does the string at A, and it should be possible to produce plane polarization.

Polarization of Light. Various ways have been found to accomplish this. There is a green crystal called tourmaline, which has the property of splitting light up into two vibrations at right angles, and further, absorbs one of the vibrations and only transmits light vibrations in one plane, like the string at B in Fig. 50. It is to be noticed that the tourmaline is *not a slit,* but merely acts to light as the slit S_1 does to the string. When ordinary light has passed through such a crystal and becomes plane polarized, it does not appear different from ordinary light. If, however, a second crystal of tourmaline is placed in the path of the plane polarized light it is found that, as the second crystal is rotated, it comes to a position when its axis is at right angles to the first (the crystals are said to be 'crossed') and all the light is cut off. The beam of a powerful arc lamp cannot penetrate these two crossed crystals, which are transparent separately or when arranged together with their axes parallel a striking proof of the transverse character of the wave motion which we call light.

The Nicol Prism. A crystal called Iceland spar can also split ordinary light up into two components or parts which vibrate in planes at right angles. In this case the spar does not absorb one half like the tourmaline. However, it is found that the two rays in the crystal are plane polarized in planes at right angles to each other, and that one ray obeys the ordinary laws of refraction as we discussed them. The other ray does not follow the same laws, and is

aptly called the 'extraordinary ray.' In general, the two rays separate in going through the crystal, and when the light comes out it is doubled. If such a crystal is placed on this print a double set of images is seen through the clear crystal, as shown in Fig. 51. If these images are again viewed through tourmaline it is found that

Fig. 51. Double image from Iceland spar.

they disappear in turn when the axis of the tourmaline is turned through a right angle. By a simple method, too long to describe here, it is possible to construct a Nicol prism with a rhomb of calcite (Iceland spar) ; this allows the extraordinary light to pass through, but cuts off the ordinary ray ; and so ordinary light, when passed through the 'prism,' is plane polarized, and is not tinted green, as when a tourmaline crystal is used.

Using a Nicol prism to analyse the light reflected and transmitted through a sheet of glass, we find that the light is split up into two beams polarized at right angles.

When plane polarized light is passed through sugar solutions the plane of polarization is turned through an angle which depends on the concentration and length of the column of solution. This is so definite that it forms a method of testing concentrations of organic solutions, and is widely used in commerce and pure scientific work where the measurements of rotation are carried out with a *saccharimeter.*

There are many other experiments which we might consider in connexion with polarization, but we have at least established the fact that our light waves are transverse in character.

LESSON 13

Physical Aspects of Sound

CONTINUING our survey of the elements of Physics, we will now consider some of the physical aspects of sound—how it is produced and propagated, and something of its nature.

The first essential for a sound is, of course, the source or starting point. Whether we think of musical notes produced by a tuning fork, a piano, an organ, a violin, a saxophone, or simply a noise such as is produced by a pneumatic drill, we realize

that one common feature in these sources is vibration. The vibration of the prong of a tuning fork, the string of a piano or a violin is fairly apparent, but in wind instruments the only possible substance to vibrate is the air within the tubes—which, in fact, does vibrate and so produces the characteristic note of this type of instrument.

Sound Sources. Assuming that the vibration in the source is the starting point of the sound, the question which arises is, how does the vibration change to produce the different notes which are emitted, on the one hand, or the mere *noise*, on the other ? We find that the size of the source determines the pitch of a musical note ; why, then, does this change in the size of the source produce the difference in pitch ?

In the first place, all sources of musical notes give out regular vibration of a definite frequency (i.e. number of vibrations per second). One definite pitch corresponds to a definite frequency. For example, if a source vibrates in a regular manner 256 times per second, the note given out is what we call middle C (on some scales this number is modified slightly). In other words, we associate pitch with the frequency of vibration of the source. Mathematically, we can calculate the frequency of vibration of a string of a given material of known thickness and length when stretched with a known tension, and we find that the frequency (n) is proportional to the square root of the tension and is inversely proportional to the length and the square root of the mass per centimetre. In other words, if the tension of the given string of a fixed material is constant, we find that the frequency is inversely proportional to the length, i.e. if we double the length we halve the frequency and make the pitch an octave lower.

Similar rules can be deduced to apply to columns of air, vibrating plates such as telephone diaphragms, etc. Some sources vibrate in a complex manner. In a violin string there is, in addition to the simple vibration, a possibility of other waves of half and other simple fractions of the length and of the first being superimposed on it. These *overtones* give the distinctive note of a violin. In a noise there is no *regular* vibration, and the frequency emitted is an assortment of a vast number of individual frequencies, each of which would produce a musical note, but together result in *noise* only.

Sound Waves. We have seen that the source of sound is a vibrating body, and we will now consider how the vibration sets up what we call 'sound waves,' which travel from the source to the listener. If we consider a tuning fork vibrating in a regular manner, it is clear that the prongs of the fork will compress the air as they move outwards and endeavour to rarefy the air as they move inwards, thus giving rise to a pressure wave in the air. In this way the maintained movement of the fork is communicated to the air.

The fork itself vibrates in S.H.M. (*see* Lesson 9, page 356), and so does the air particle next to it. The air particles in the neighbourhood gradually take up a S.H.M., but the phase of the vibration differs as we consider particles more removed from the source. In other words, we realize that we have here all the conditions for the production of wave motion, as we discussed it in Lesson 9. The great difference which we notice between this wave and light waves is that the air particles vibrate in the direction in which the wave is moving.

We have seen that the alternative way of regarding this is to consider the pressure set up by the moving air particles. No *transverse* S.H.M. movement is possible because, of course, there is no force set up in air or liquids to restore such a transverse displacement ; but a movement in the line of propagation can be propagated, for the movement itself sets up a force, which restores the particles to their original position.

Wave in Air Particles. Our picture of a sound wave in air, therefore, is of propagation by the movement of the individual air particles, each about a position of rest ; the particles have a phase difference in their movement which results in compressions and rarefactions of the particles. Under no circumstances do we visualize transverse movement. It is to be noticed that for a sound wave in air it is the *air* which moves. The same in water, wood, wires, etc. This is again different from light. We are here stating that the material medium is the transmitting agent.

We can easily show that sound requires a material medium for its transmission, for if we hang an electric bell in a glass vessel, using the wires as support, and then apply an air pump (*see* Lesson 3, page 338) to withdraw all the air from the vessel, we find that the noise of the ringing bell gets fainter and fainter as the air is withdrawn. When we have almost a vacuum in the glass vessel the sound is almost inaudible. All the time we can *see* the bell hammer hitting the gong, i.e. light can be transmitted through the vacuum, but not sound.

Velocity of Sound. Sound travels through air at 0° C. with a velocity of about 1,090 ft. per second or 331 metres per second, and not with the tremendous velocity of light. The early determinations of velocity were made by observing a distant flash of a gun firing, and by noting the time which elapsed before the explosion of the charge was heard a measured distance away. It is the reverse process to that we use as a method of estimating the distance of a thunderstorm, in which the number of seconds between seeing a flash of lightning and hearing the corresponding roll of thunder is recorded. In each 5 seconds the sound has travelled 5,450 ft., which may be taken as approximately one mile (5,280 ft.), i.e. the distance from the storm, the time taken by light being negligible.

Sound travels in different substances with very different speeds, as may be seen in the following table:

Speed of Sound in Four Substances

Substance	Velocity (approx.).
Air at 0° C.	331 metres per sec.
Water	1400 ,, ,, ,,
Steel	5000 ,, ,, ,,
Wood, pine deal ..	3300 to 4900 ,, ,, ,,

It will be seen from these figures that it is possible for an observer to see at a distance a hammer strike a railway line, then to hear the sound which has travelled along the steel, and then, a little later, hear the sound carried through the air.

The relation between wave-length (λ), frequency (n) and velocity (v) is $v = n\lambda$, as before ; therefore in air the wave-length of middle C ($n = 256$) is 33,000/256 cm., i.e. almost 129 cm. In other words, the wave-length is fairly long. Such things as reflection, refraction, interference and diffraction are to be expected with these waves, of course, and we realize that the general order of results are those we anticipate with long waves. If we remember the effects discussed in Lesson 12 (page 370) we shall realize that the bending or diffraction of sound round buildings is what is to be expected with the waves, and that the lower the note, the longer the wave and, therefore, the bigger these effects will be. We have an example of reflection in echoes, when sound is reflected by mountain faces, etc.

Sound a Wave Motion. Interference of sound waves can be demonstrated by using the apparatus illustrated in the diagram (Fig. 52). It consists of two tubes A and B, which slide within each other,

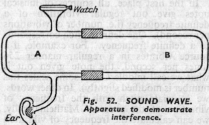

*Fig. 52. SOUND WAVE.
Apparatus to demonstrate
interference.*

trombone fashion. At an opening on one side a watch is used as source, and at a corresponding opening at the other side the ear listens to the sounds. When B is pushed in so that the sound has an equal path each way, i.e. via A or B, a loud tick is heard, but when B is pulled out a position is reached when practically no noise is heard. The path via B has been increased by half a wave-length of the note given out, and interference of the waves has been operative in dimming the intensity.

From what has been said it appears that sound is undoubtedly a wave motion in material media. That no polarization is possible indicates that the wave is longitudinal. It appears to be produced by vibrating bodies, and takes on a frequency of those bodies. Scales of musical notes have frequencies simply related, and are used in musical composition because to our ear they form pleasing combinations.

LESSON 14

Basic Principles of Magnetism and Electricity

IN the preceding Lessons in this Course we have considered in turn the outlines of mechanics, properties of matter, heat, light and sound ; now to complete the survey of the wide-spreading subject of physics we will investigate some of the chief properties of magnetism and electricity. This allied pair of subjects is of great importance to the physicist because of the very far-reaching nature of the results of practical investigation and theoretical speculation. Some of these applications are considered more fully in the Course on Engineering.

Permanent Magnetism. The text books recall that the beginnings of magnetism are to be found in a discovery of great antiquity ; this is that certain magnetic oxides of iron were observed to have the property of setting always in one direction when freely suspended. These magnetic ores were used in much the same way in which a compass is now used, and acquired the name of 'leading stone' or lode stone. They are in fact naturally occurring magnets. If a piece of iron or steel is rubbed, always one way, with such a lodestone, it is found that the iron or steel itself becomes a magnet (an 'artificial' magnet). These artificial magnets in turn can impart their magnetic power to pieces of iron and steel by exactly the same process.

One common feature of both sorts of magnet is that they attract to themselves small pieces of iron and steel. No doubt the earliest memory most of us have of magnetism is this very property. Most schoolboys used to have a horse-shoe magnet as a very cherished possession and performed the experiment just referred to by using pins or tin tacks as the small iron objects (Fig. 53). Large numbers adhere to the ends marked N and S when brought near the magnet. In a laboratory the ordinary bar magnet is most often used. This is made from a straight piece of steel instead of the horse-shoe shape. If this is placed on a sheet of paper and then entirely covered with iron filings, it is found that when the bar is lifted, the filings adhere in two tufts, round the two ends of the bar magnet (Fig. 54), just as the tacks remained only at the ends of the horse-shoe magnet. We say that at the ends we have the *poles* of the magnet.

When a bar magnet is hung so that it can swing freely in a horizontal plane we find that one end always points north. The pole at this end we call the north-seeking pole (often contracted to N pole) ; the pole at the other end is called the south-seeking pole (or S pole).

We find that if we bring the N pole of a magnet near the N pole of the suspended magnet, the latter turns away ; we say it is repelled. If we bring a S pole near the S pole of this suspended magnet, this also is repelled ; but we find that a N and S attract each other. This is summarized by saying that 'like poles repel, unlike poles attract.'

Magnetic Field. Obviously the force of repulsion or attraction depends on how strong the two poles are and how far apart they are. As in all physics we like to have a definition of the units in which to measure, so we define a unit pole in terms of the force : 'A unit north pole is such that if we place it one centimetre away from another unit N pole, in air, the force of repulsion is one dyne.'

If two north poles are of strengths m and m^1 and are separated by a distance of d cm. of air, it has been found that the force of repulsion (F) is given by

$$F = \frac{mm^1}{d^2}$$

This expresses what we call the *inverse square law.*

To account for the fact that one magnet tends to turn or attract, we say that in the space around a magnet there is a *magnetic field.* If we take a bar magnet and cover it with a sheet of glass and scatter iron filings on the glass, we find that after tapping the glass gently in order to allow the filings to turn,

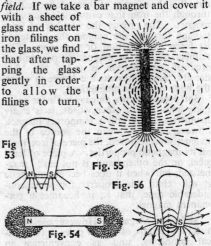

Fig 53

Fig. 55

Fig. 56

Fig. 54

MAGNETIC FIELDS. Fig. 53. Tacks on horse-shoe magnet. **Fig. 54.** Filings on ends of bar magnet. **Fig. 55.** Lines of force shown by iron filings with bar magnet. **Fig. 56.** With horse-shoe magnet.

a very definite picture is obtained. The iron filings take on the form of Fig. 55. If we used a horse-shoe magnet, the result is shown in Fig. 56. We say that the filings map out the *magnetic fields* of the magnets in each case.

Lines of Magnetic Force. It is clear, too, that if we were able to place a unit north pole near the N pole of either magnet in Figs. 55 or 56, the N pole would go to the south pole and it would in fact travel along the line marked out in the figure. We say that the lines are *lines of magnetic force,* and alternative to the iron filings we say that the line of magnetic force is the path a freely moving N pole would take if placed near the magnet. If there are a lot of lines in a given area we say that the magnetic field is strong. If there are few lines we say the magnetic field is weak. We define the actual magnetic field at a point as the force in dynes which acts on a unit north pole placed at the point. Now, like all forces on unit poles or anything else, there is a direction as well as magnitude, so we always put arrows (*see* Fig. 56) to indicate this.

Flux Density. If a piece of iron or other metallic material be introduced into the field of the magnet, i.e. into a region containing these lines of magnetism, the lines will be diverted towards the piece of iron and will pass through it in preference to the air. It is the passage of these magnetic lines through the iron that causes it to act as a magnet. The greater the number of lines passing through the magnet the greater is its force of attraction or repulsion. The number of lines of magnetism per unit of area of cross-section is called the 'flux density,' and represents the degree to which the body has been magnetized.

Soft iron presents an easy path for magnetic lines, or, in other words, it is easily magnetized. It is only a temporary magnet, however, because when the source of the magnetism is removed, the piece of iron loses all its magnetic properties. A piece of hard steel, on the other hand, is not easily magnetized, but when it does become magnetic it will retain this property for some considerable time, that is, it becomes a permanent magnet.

Molecular Magnets. However useful and valid it is to talk of unit N poles in theoretical problems, and as convenience in defining fields, etc., no such thing can be isolated in practice. For example, if we magnetize a steel hack saw blade and then break it into two in an attempt to isolate the N pole and the S pole, we find that we have two complete magnets. Again, if each half is broken to make two quarters, each quarter is itself a complete magnet, as shown in Fig. 57.

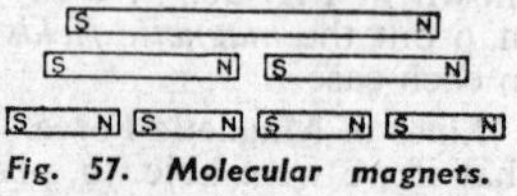

We are led

Fig. 57. Molecular magnets.

to the conclusion that in iron and steel the molecules are magnets which are in general arranged in a haphazard fashion. When stroked with a magnet the molecules aline themselves in one direction, so that however small the portion which we break away from the main magnet, the molecules, being in alinement, show north and south polarity in the segment of steel detached.

The Earth a Magnetic Field. But to return to the question of the magnetic fields, we now assume that whenever a field is applied to a magnet, it causes a force to act on the magnet. In terms of this definition we say that in the first place a magnet sets in the meridian because there is a magnetic field due to the earth. In fact, the earth produces magnetic effects which are the same as if a huge magnet had its S seeking pole near the north geographic pole and its N seeking pole near the south geographic pole.

No such magnet exists, of course, but the magnetic field around the earth is similar to that which would be produced by such a distribution of magnetic poles. Naturally over an area so small as England (compared with the area of the earth) the magnetic lines of force may be taken as parallel, and the field is said to be uniform. Suppose the strength of this magnetic field is H dynes per unit pole (or H *gauss*) and that a magnet is pivoted so that it can rotate in a horizontal plane, it is clear that when the magnet is not setting in the magnetic meridian (i.e. the direction of the earth's line of force) it is acted on by forces which tend to turn it to there. For example, in Fig. 58 suppose H is the direction of the earth's horizontal magnetic field, and NS is the position of the magnet. We have in the

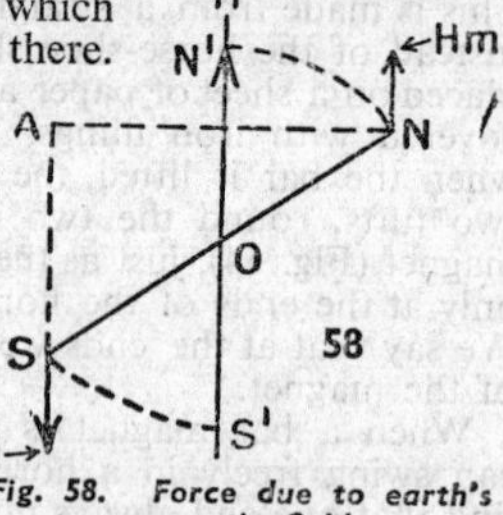

Fig. 58. Force due to earth's magnetic field.

magnet two poles at N and S each of the same pole strength, say *m* units. The force at N on the pole there is $H \times m$ (since by definition H is the force on *unit* pole). A similar force acts at S in the opposite direction and so these forces produce a turning couple which will tend to move the magnet round until it lies along N^1S^1, where the two forces are acting in the same line and are opposite in direction.

If a uniform magnetic field of strength F now acts on the magnet, in a direction at right angles to that of H, the magnet will turn round through some angle, say θ°, from the meridian, and it can be shown that the strength F and force H are related by the expression

$$F = H \tan \theta.$$

We can use this relation to compare field strengths whether the fields are due directly to magnets, or, as we shall see later, to electric currents.

Electrification. The name electricity is derived from the Greek *elektron*, which means amber. This is a constant reminder of the fact that the earliest recorded method of producing electricity is by rubbing amber. When any two different substances are rubbed together, electricity is produced by the friction. For example, if an ebonite fountain-pen is rubbed on the coat or on the hair it is found that the pen acquires the property of attracting light pieces of tissue paper towards it. If we suspend a light gilded ball of elder pith by means of a dry silk thread and hang near to it a glass rod which has been rubbed with silk, we find that the ball is attracted to the rod and then is repelled. Any attempt to take the rod near the charged pith ball results in repulsion.

The same sequence of events is witnessed if an ebonite rod rubbed with flannel replaces the glass rod. But it is found that the ball, when charged from the glass rod, is subsequently attracted by the ebonite rod. We recognize two kinds of charges : the one on the glass is now called positive, the one on the ebonite is called negative, and we find that 'like charges repel and unlike charges attract.' In the process of producing a charge by friction, we manufacture equal positive and negative charges from the two uncharged bodies. In the case of rubbing ebonite with flannel the positive charge goes to the flannel and the negative to the ebonite, whereas in the case of glass and silk the positive goes to the glass and the negative to the silk. If two equal charges of + and — values are mixed, the net result is no net charge. When a charge is hung up by means of a wire or a damp silk thread, the charge is conducted to the support and leaks away. Using insulators like dry silk, sulphur, ebonite, etc., the charge remains on the pith ball.

Electric Charges. As with magnetic poles, which obey similar laws, we can define a unit positive charge as 'that charge which will repel an equal charge, when one centimetre away in air, with a force of one dyne,' and also we deduce a similar inverse square law, viz. : if two charges of q and q^1 are d cms. apart in air the force (F) of repulsion in dynes is given by

$$F = \frac{q\,q^1}{d^2}$$

In the same way we define *electric-field strength* at a point as 'the force in dynes which acts on a unit positive charge placed at that point' ; e.g. if a charge of +10 units is placed in a uniform electric field of 50 dynes/unit pole, the force acting on it is $10 \times 50 = 500$ dynes.

Potential and Current Flow. Another useful electrical conception may be obtained from this introductory account of electricity, produced by friction and remaining as a stationary charge, namely, *potential*. If we have two charges of opposite kind, positive and negative, and we join them together by a conducting path, e.g. a wire, we find that positive electricity flows from the positive to the negative, and we say we have an electric current flowing. This only lasts for a very small interval of time.

If a positive charge is joined by a wire to the earth, a current of electricity flows to the earth and the body loses its charge, whereas when we join a negative charge, by means of a wire, to the earth, the current flows from the earth to the body, and the flow, which is almost instantaneous, discharges the body. We take the earth as our zero in these cases. We say the free negative charge has a negative potential and the free positive, a positive potential, and the earth is said to be at zero potential.

In the same way, if we have two bodies charged with positive electricity and join them together by means of a wire, there will in general be a flow of electricity (a current) from the body at the higher potential to the body at the lower potential. In the case of a sphere we can find that the potential is equal to the charge on it divided by the radius of the sphere. This is deduced by defining potential in a quantitative manner as being equal to the work done in bringing up a unit positive charge to the body from a long way away (infinity). We may take it as axiomatic that if an electric potential difference exists on a conductor, there will be a flow of electricity from the place at the higher to the place at the lower potential, which tends to equalize potential.

Law of Electric Charges. As we have seen (page 376), the law of force between charges is similar to the law of force between magnetic poles. If a sphere is charged, the effect on outside charges is as though the charge was concentrated at the centre ; for example, if a large region of space has a charge Q spread evenly throughout a volume of radius R, then at any point outside the sphere the force is the same as if Q were at the centre of the sphere. If a charge q units of the opposite sign be placed a distance d away, the attraction is :

$\dfrac{qQ}{d^2}$, so long as d is greater than R.

For points within the distance R, the force is no longer governed by this result. The fact is that when within a charge there is no force from that charge. So we see in Fig. 59, which illustrates this, there

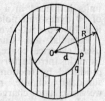

Fig. 59. Electric capacity of a sphere.

is no force on q at P due to the part of the charge Q which is in the vertical shading, and the force is given by the inverse square law as :

$$q \times \frac{\text{(charge within sphere of radius } d)}{d^2}$$

Now the enclosed volume is $\frac{4}{3} \pi d^3$, which is a fraction of the total volume, $\frac{4}{3} \pi R^3$, which is obviously $\frac{\frac{4}{3} \pi d^3}{\frac{4}{3} \pi R^3} = \frac{d^3}{R^3}$

and therefore, since Q is uniformly spread throughout the volume, the charge within the small sphere is $\frac{d^3}{R^3}$. Q, and so the force q is

$$\left(\frac{d^3}{R^3}. Q\right) \frac{q}{d^2} = d \left(\frac{Qq}{R^3}\right)$$

that is, the force within the charge is directly proportional to the distance from the centre. This is again analogous to what happens in the gravitational case for any two portions of matter.

Potential and Capacity. The second idea which we have already noted is the important electrical term, *potential*. We saw that an electric charge raises the electric potential of a body just as a quantity of heat raises the temperature of a body, or a quantity of water raises the level or pressure in a container. The 'electric temperature,' or 'electric pressure' as we sometimes call potential, exists in stationary charges and also by our definition is present to cause a movement of charges, when we say that a current flows. It must be maintained as long as electricity is to pass.

Consider first the stationary charges. When a sphere of radius r cm. is given q units of electricity we saw that the potential may be calculated to be q/r. It will be apparent that, if we divide the charge by the potential, we obtain the radius ($q \div q/r = r$). We find in all cases that if a body is fixed in space the ratio of

$$\frac{\text{charge}}{\text{potential}} \text{ is a constant}$$

which we call the *capacity* of a body.

In our example above we see that the electrical capacity of a sphere is equal to the radius. Now the capacity can be increased by increasing the area of the body, by bringing another earth-connected body near the first, and by displacing the air between the two bodies by inserting shellac, glass, mica, etc. This arrangement is called a *condenser*, and is usually made by taking parallel plates which are separated by waxed paper, or sheets of mica. In the *air* condenser the plates are separated by air. In wireless variable air condensers the capacity is changed by rotating the plates so that a change in the area of the facing plates is brought about.

The Electric Cell. If we now consider the movement of charges due to a difference of potential, we find that if two stationary charges at different potentials are joined a current flows until the two potentials become equal. This is almost instantaneous in action. To maintain the current we must maintain the potential difference. The friction methods are abandoned for most practical purposes, and we utilize the fact that when any two dissimilar metals are placed in a dilute acid, suitably chosen, a potential difference is set up which is maintained even when a current flows, as shown in Fig. 60, which is a typical example of a simple *cell*.

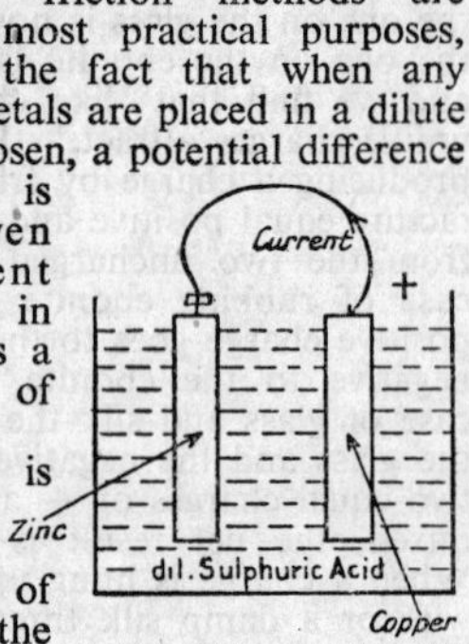

In practice it is found that the cell soon polarizes (i.e. bubbles of gas appear on the copper plate in Fig. 60 and so increase

Fig. 60. Diagram of simple electric cell.

the resistance that the current stops) and special modifications are introduced to overcome the difficulty. Accumulators, or secondary cells, which can be charged with electricity, provide a source of constant current.

If we take any form of cell or battery and allow a current to flow by joining the poles, $+$ and $-$, by means of a wire, we find several effects are produced by this current.

There are : 1. Physiological effects. 2. Magnetic effects. 3. Heating effects. 4. Chemical effects, etc.

In addition we find that when acted on by a magnetic field we produce an important interaction.

The physiological effect referred to is most marked when several cells are joined together. Cases are reported in the newspapers of the fatal results of applying the ends of such a battery either by accident or design (U.S.A. electric chair). The physiological effect observed on a freshly killed frog led to the discovery by Galvani of the simple cell, which was developed by Volta.

Electro-magnetic Effects. When a current is passed along a wire the region about the wire has a magnetic field set up in it in the form of circular lines of force. In Fig. 61 the dot represents the section of a wire conveying a current into the plane of the paper; the magnetic field is represented by the circles. If the current is reversed the magnetic field is reversed.

Fig. 61. Field due to electric current.

There is a simple useful rule to determine the relative directions of the magnetic field and the current. This was given by Clerk-Maxwell, formerly professor of Physics at King's College, London, and subsequently appointed the first Cavendish professor of Physics at Cambridge. His main work was the electro-magnetic theory, the importance of which is of first rank. His simple little rule is called the *corkscrew rule*. If you imagine that a corkscrew is being driven in the direction of the current, the direction of rotation gives the direction of the magnetic field.

Measuring Magnetic Field Strength. If a wire is bent into a circular coil and a current passed through it, the magnetic field is still in circles about the wire ; i.e. if we draw planes at right angles to the *wire* the field is in circles in the plane. So that at the centre of the coil of wire the magnetic field is at right angles to the plane of the coil, and is made up of the effects produced by each bit of current in the wires. Our mental picture of the magnetic field is somewhat like the smoke in a smoke ring. Now we can make use of this magnetic effect to define current, so that we have a unit for measurement. We define it in terms of the strength of the magnetic field it sets up.

It was found by experiment that the magnetic field due to a short length l of conductor conveying a current was proportional to the length and inversely proportional to the square of the distance, r, away from the wire, as well as to the current itself, and therefore at the centre of a circular coil of wire of radius r the magnetic field, F, is proportional to

$$\frac{2\pi r}{r^2} \times \text{strength of current}$$

i.e. F = constant $\times \dfrac{2\pi}{r} i$,

where i is the current in some unit.

The E.M.U. and the Ampere. Now we define unit current in terms of the magnetic effect (called the electro-magnetic unit, or E.M.U.) by saying that if it flowed in a circle of radius 1 cm. it would produce a magnetic field of 2π dynes per unit pole at the centre. This makes the constant equal to unity, and we write,

$$F = \frac{2\pi i}{r}$$

where i is in E.M.U.

The theoretical unit is too large for many practical purposes, so we use the *ampere*, which is one-tenth part of the unit we have defined. Not only does this give us a definition of a unit current, but the same ideas are underlying a practical method of measuring current in an instrument called a galvanometer, the principle of which is shown in Fig. 62. A coil of wire shown in section at A, A, and of a known number of turns is placed in the magnetic meridian and at its centre a small magnet is pivoted.

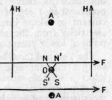

Fig. 62. Principle of the galvanometer; AA, section of a coil of wire; NS, magnet pivoted at O; H, the earth's magnetic field in horizontal plane; F, field due to current in coil; N'S', position of magnet when currents pass.

When a current is sent round the coils a magnetic field F is set up which is

$$n \times \frac{2\pi i}{r} :$$

this moves the needle through an angle θ, which is given by

F = H tan θ (*see* page 376),

so that $\dfrac{2\pi n i}{r}$ = H tan θ

or $i = \dfrac{Hr}{2\pi n} \tan \theta.$

If we know H, r, and observe θ we can calculate i in theoretical units, or, if we multiply by 10, we obtain i in amperes. This is the principle of the tangent galvanometer (or current measurer), and is the fundamental idea in all galvanometers using a moving magnet.

Measuring Current. We see at least from this that if we *define* current in terms of the magnetic effect it produces, we can also *measure* the current by similar means. The ammeter generally used for current measurement makes use of another principle, which is discussed later in these Lessons, but all moving magnet instruments are based on the above theory.

The unit of quantity of electricity in E.M.U. is obtained by considering the amount of electricity which is conveyed by the current in unit time. For example, if an ampère flows for one second the quantity of electricity passing any point is a *coulomb*, which is 1/10 of the quantity conveyed past a point in one second when a theoretical unit of current flows.

Of course, the current flows because a potential difference exists. From a theoretical point of view we define unit potential difference as being set up between two points when 1 erg of work is done by the current in taking one unit of quantity of electricity from the point at higher to the point at lower potential.

The Volt and the Ohm. This is much too small a unit for practical purposes, so we select a suitable number of this unit and call it a practical unit—just the same as in measurement of length, 1 inch is a suitable unit for some measurements, whereas for long distances we take 63,360 of these and call them a mile. The practical unit of potential is called the *volt*, and this is 100 million (10^8) theoretical units.

It was found by Ohm that if a wire was maintained at constant temperature there is a constant relation between the potential applied to its ends and the current which results. Thus if i is the current and E is the potential Ohm found that

$$\frac{E}{i} = \text{constant.}$$

This constant was called the resistance, R, and the relation above, which is called Ohm's Law, may be written

$$\frac{E}{i} = R.$$

If E and i are in theoretical units R is also in theoretical E.M.U. of resistance. This unit has many advantages in calculations, as have i and E, but for practical purposes it is much too small, so we take what is a convenient large number of these units, 1,000 million (10^9) and call this the *ohm*.

In terms of practical units we have, where i is in ampères, and E is in volts,

$$R = E/i.$$

In practical work usually written $R = E/I$

Thus if the mains are at 100 volts and a current of 5 ampères passes through an apparatus, its resistance is

$$\frac{100}{5} = 20 \text{ ohms.}$$

Measuring Resistance. Actually, the resistance of a wire is not constant, but in most cases goes up with an increase of temperature, so that if the resistance at $0°$C. is R_0 and at $t°$C. is R_t, we have a relation connecting the two of the form

$$R_t = R_0 (1 + \alpha t + \beta t^2) ;$$

for small ranges of temperature this becomes

$$R_t = R_0 (1 + \alpha t)$$

because the constant β is small. The constant α for pure metals has a value of about ·0036. The change in resistance of a wire which has been carefully measured at three known temperatures and thereby standardised can be used to measure unknown temperatures.

This is used, for example, in the measurement of furnace temperatures. The wire is encased in a porcelain cover and inserted in the furnace. The measurement of resistance can be carried out, through as long as a circuit as necessary, in a cool office some distance away, using a modified form of Wheatstone bridge.

The Wheatstone bridge is really a simple enough scheme. Two fixed resistances P and Q (usually equal, or P is 10 or 100 times Q) are connected as shown in Fig. 63. R is a known resistance which may be varied, and S is the unknown. A battery sends

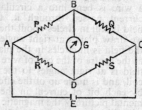

Fig. 63. Scheme of the Wheatstone bridge; lettering is explained in the text.

a current via ABC and ADC and R is adjusted until the galvanometer G shows no deflection, when it can be simply shown that the following relation holds :

$$\frac{P}{Q} = \frac{R}{S},$$

from which the unknown S may be calculated.

LESSON 15

Effects of Electric Energy

WHEN a current flows between two points where a unit of potential difference exists, the work done on each unit of quantity of electricity passing is, by definition, equal to one erg. Now the quantity, q, of electricity is given by $I\,t$ where I is the current and t the time in seconds for which it flows. Therefore the work done by the current when flowing between two points where the potential difference is E is q E or $I\,t$ E ergs. This work is done in overcoming the resistance, etc., in the wire, and the energy appears as heat in the wire unless some definite extra work is done by the current. In Lesson 5, page 345, we saw that as a result of Dr. Joule's experiments we are able to find the thermal equivalent of the work W, done, using the mechanical equivalent of heat J ($=4.2 \times 10^7$ ergs per calorie). We therefore anticipate that an amount of heat H cals. is given when the current I flows for a time t between two points at potential difference E, where

$$J = \frac{W}{H} \text{ or } H = \frac{E\,I\,t}{4.2 \times 10^7}, \text{ cals.}$$

When we measure the electrical quantities in practical units we remember the relations given in Lesson 14, and we then say that for I in amperes we have I/10 theoretical units; for E volts, 10^8 theoretical units, and therefore we have

$$I \times E \times 1/10 \times 10^9 \text{ ergs}$$
$$\text{or} = I\,E\,t \times 10^7 \text{ ergs, i.e. the heat is}$$
$$\frac{\text{amps.} \times \text{volts} \times \text{secs.}}{4.2} \text{ cals.}$$

We see the energy supplied *per second* in amps × volts × 10^7 ergs, or *amps × volts* joules (since the joule is the large unit of work which is equal to 10^7 ergs). The *rate* of working in the electric circuit is E I joules per second.

Ohm's Law in Practice. Now in the C.G.S. system we have a unit for measuring the rate of working, just as in the British System we employ a unit, the *horse power*. When the energy is used at the rate of 1 joule per second we say the rate of working is one watt; therefore in our case the rate of working is volts × amps. watts. When the energy consumed is at a large rate, comparable with a horse power, we use a larger unit— in fact, 1,000 watts—called a *kilowatt*.

Obviously, the rate of working in kilowatts is $\dfrac{\text{volt} \times \text{amps}}{1000}$ kilowatts.

For the purpose of illustrating this point we may consider a well-known example. The ordinary electric lamp is rated at so many watts. A 60-watt lamp on a 100-volt mains passes a current, i, given by $100 \times I = 60$ or $I = 0.6$ ampere. On a 240-volt main a lamp made for *this* voltage, and called a 60-watt lamp, takes I, where

$$240 \times I' = 60 \qquad I' = \tfrac{1}{4} = .25 \text{ amp.}$$

In the first case of 100-volt mains the resistance of the lamp is given by Ohm's Law

$$R = \frac{E}{I} = \frac{100}{.6} = 166\tfrac{2}{3} \text{ ohms.}$$

In the second case (240 volt)

$$R = \frac{E}{I} = \frac{240}{.25} = 960 \text{ ohms.}$$

Obviously, if we put the lamp marked 60 watt 100 volt on the 240 volt mains, the current which would pass would be, by Ohm's Law :

$$I = \frac{E}{R} = \frac{240}{166\tfrac{2}{3}} = 1.44 \text{ amperes,}$$

assuming there is no change in the resistance of the lamp. It is important to avoid this in practice. In all electrical apparatus the voltage of the mains must be that marked on the apparatus.

Consider the second case a little further. The lamp wrongly used on 240-volt mains has a current 1·44 amperes. In proper use it should take ·6 ampere. The heat produced in normal running on its correct voltage is :

$$\frac{.6 \times 100}{4.2} \text{ cals. per second,}$$

and the second case is

$$\frac{1.44 \times 240}{4.2} \text{ cals., i.e. } \frac{345}{60} = 5.7 \text{ times as much.}$$

The obvious will happen—the heat developed is nearly 6 times the normal, so the metal wire will melt and the lamp becomes useless.

This kind of thing happens when a wire is overloaded. In wiring a house the electrician uses wires which are sufficiently thick, and therefore sufficiently low in resistance. He ensures that when the full load is taken the heating of the lead wires will be negligibly small, as it would not be safe to allow encased wires to heat up. Sometimes the consumer adds electric irons and other devices and overloads the circuit.

The Domestic Fuse. To safeguard the house against possible fire, *fuses* are placed in each circuit. At the point near the meter where the wires are branching off to subsidiary circuits a box contains these fuses. They are simply lengths of wire made of tin/lead alloys, which join the outgoing and ingoing wires. When the current in any of the circuits exceeds the safe current in that circuit the fuse becomes so hot that it melts. A 5-amp. fuse melts when 5 amperes are passed continuously through it, so if the wiring is safe up to 5 ampères and a 5-amp. fuse is in circuit, any increased load would break the weakest link—the fuse—and save overheating of the rest of the circuit. If the fuse ' blows ' it is easily replaced by first switching off the main switch and then inserting a new length of fuse wire of the same kind.

Measuring Electric Supply. The method of charging for electrical supply is to charge for the *energy* ' consumed,' as the supply is ultimately from energy used at the power station. Now if we use at the rate of 1 kilowatt for one hour we use energy equivalent

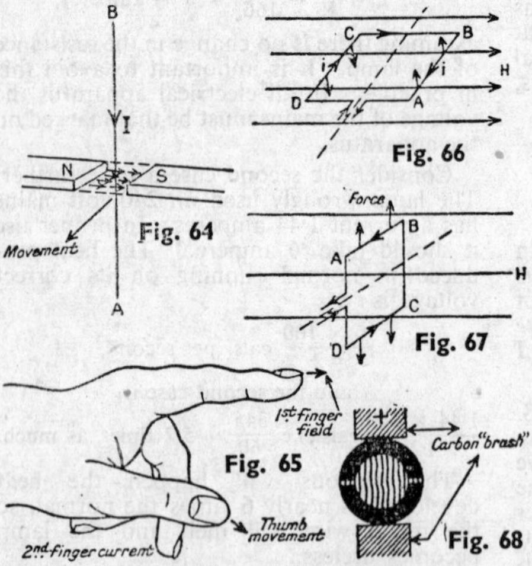

to $(1000 \times 10^7) \times 60 \times 60$ ergs. This method of calculating the ergs introduces too many noughts ; we simply say 1 kilowatt hour, the Board of Trade unit of supply.

Suppose we use four 60-watt lamps for four hours per night for one week, the energy in kilowatt hours is

$$\frac{4 \times 60 \times 4 \times 7}{1000}$$

In addition, one electric fire rated at 1 kilowatt (a 1-bar fire) for the same time consumes $1 \times 4 \times 7 = 28$ kilowatt hours, and the bill at 3d. per unit is

$$(6\cdot72 + 28) \times 3 \text{ pence} =$$
$$\frac{34\cdot72 \times 3}{12} \text{ shillings } \frac{104\cdot2}{12}$$

= 8s. 8d., of which 7s. is for the fire !

The above heating effects are referred to as the Joule heating effects. The expression for the energy, EIt, can be changed, by Ohm's Law, substituting $E = IR$, to I^2Rt, and the engineer usually refers to energy 'lost' in this way as 'the I^2Rt loss.'

The Left-Hand Rule. When a current passes along a wire there are other ways in which the energy may be practically used. If a straight wire AB, Fig. 64, conveys a current I as shown, and is in a magnetic field set up, in this case, by two magnets, it is found that the wire is acted upon by a force tending to move the wire in the direction of the arrow. If either I or the magnetic field, H, is reversed the direction of movement is reversed. If we extend the first two fingers and thumb of the left hand so that they are mutually at right angles, and then point the first finger in the direction of the magnetic field and the second finger in the direction of the current, the direction of the thumb indicates the direction of the resulting motion of the conductor (Fig. 65). This *left-hand rule* summarizes the results of observation on the interaction between magnetic field and current.

The Electric Motor. The movement, of course, takes energy from the source of supply of the current in addition to the I^2Rt energy, which is a loss if our main object is to produce movement. From a simple observation of this kind the modern electric motor has been developed. We will consider one stage in this development.

A rectangular coil of wire is mounted

Fig. 64. Movement of an electric wire in a magnetic field. Fig. 65. The left-hand rule (see text). Figs. 66 and 67. The behaviour of a coil of wire relative to magnetic forces. Fig. 68. Principle of commutator in electric motor by means of which current is reversed and continuous revolution of the armature maintained.

to rotate about a central axis, shown as a broken line in Fig. 66 and a uniform magnetic field, H, is applied at right angles to this axis. The side AB is acted upon by an upward force, as may be seen by applying the left-hand rule, and the side DC is acted upon by an equal downward force. This causes the coil to rotate. When, as in Fig. 67, the coil is at right angles to the field, the forces are parallel to the plane of the coil and do not tend to turn the system. Actually, when the coil turns it overshoots this position, but the upward force on AB rotates it back to the position shown in Fig. 67. If, however, we reverse the current as the coil passes the position of Fig. 67, the coil rotates a further half turn, thus giving one complete revolution. If this reversal is done each time the plane of the coil is at right angles to the field, the rotation becomes continuous.

This reversal is brought about by the use of a *commutator*, seen in Fig. 68, which shows the section of the axis. Two metal sectors, shown in black, are joined to the ends of the coil, and the current is led away via the carbon brushes. When the coil is in the ' dead centre' position of Fig. 67 the gaps between the metal sectors are against the brushes, and a slight continued movement reverses the current automatically. So much for the physics of the motor. Development of this idea is the province of the electrical engineer (*see* Engineering, Vol. III, Lesson 19).

Galvanometers and Voltmeters. If we hang up a coil of wire by means of a very thin wire between the poles of a magnet, as in Fig. 69, we find that when a current is passed the coil moves through an angle and so twists the wire XY which supports it. When the wire is twisted it sets up a turning effect, tending to restore the coil to its original position. If now we fix a soft iron core by means of a screw to a piece of brass as shown in the section diagram given in Fig. 70 (b), and let the coil move in the space between the magnetic

poles and the soft iron cylindrical core, we find that the angle of twist is proportional to the current. This constitutes, therefore, a simple galvanometer with a moving coil, where I is proportional to θ, the angle of deflection, and forms the basis of ammeters and voltmeters. Instead of the supporting wires XY and the flexible lead Z, the coil is mounted on two jewels and the current is led in and out by two hair springs, which also act as control.

When used as an ammeter, the two

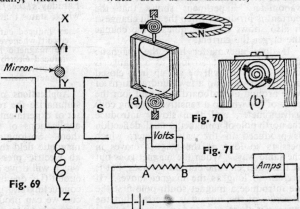

GALVANOMETERS AND VOLTMETERS. *Fig. 69. Diagram showing principle of mirror galvanometer. Fig. 70 (a) and (b). Moving parts of an ammeter or voltmeter. Fig. 71. Voltmeter in parallel and ammeter in series.*

ends of the hair springs are connected to a low resistance (called a shunt), which allows most of the current to be side-tracked and which makes the net resistance of the instrument very small. The instrument is then placed in series with the circuit in which the current is to be measured. Instead of using a mirror, as in the galvanometer, a pointer N gives a direct reading on a scale graduated in amperes.

When used as a voltmeter a very high resistance is placed in series with the coil, so that the total resistance of the whole instrument becomes so high that only a small current is passed through it ; therefore the instrument is always used in parallel with the circuit in which the potential is to be measured. These points are illustrated in Fig. 71, which incidentally shows a ready way of measuring a resistance AB. If the voltmeter reads 15 volts and the ammeter reads 1·5 amperes :

$$\text{Resistance AB} = \frac{15}{1\cdot 5} = 10 \text{ ohms.}$$

LESSON 16

Laws of Electro-Magnetic Induction

WHEN a coil of wire is joined to a sensitive galvanometer no current passes, as there is no source of potential. Now it was found by Faraday that if the magnetic field which passes through the coil is altered, current flows through the coil as shown by the deflection of the galvanometer. Experiment shows that the current is produced when the field changes ; it also shows that the quicker the change the bigger the current.

It does not matter how the magnetic field is produced ; so long as a change is made a current will be set up in a closed circuit. If we wrap a few hundred turns of wire around a cardboard tube and join the ends of the wire to a sensitive (moving coil) galvanometer, and then slowly introduce the north pole of a magnet, a small deflection is produced in the galvanometer, which persists so long as the magnet moves in the same way. When the magnet goes out at the other end the current reverses, but is present so long as the magnet moves. If we introduce a magnet south pole first the *direction* of the current is reversed, but the current is there.

Now if we do the same two experiments at a quicker rate the deflection is bigger, i.e. the current is bigger, but, of course, lasts for the smaller time taken to move the magnet. We shall see later that this principle of inducing currents by means of moving magnets, or changing magnetic fields, is of immense importance for it lies behind the whole field of application of electric energy. From this apparently simple experiment of Faraday grew the vast modern electrical industry.

Laws of Lenz and Faraday. If we find the direction of the current we see that the induced currents set up a magnetic field in opposition to that which has caused them. For example, when the north pole is introduced, the current which is set up in the coil produces a magnetic field which tends to push the north pole out of the coil. When the north pole is taken out the current reverses and so sets up a magnetic field tending to bring the north pole back again.

This is summarized in the *Law of Lenz*, which says that—

> when an induced current is produced it is in such a direction as to oppose the motion which causes it.

The first observations are summarized in Faraday's *Law of Electro-Magnetic Induction*, which states that—

> an induced current is set up in a closed circuit whenever there is any change in the magnetic flux in that circuit. The induced electromotive force (potential) is proportional to the rate of change of the magnetic field (i.e. change per second).

Applications of the Laws. These laws summarize the results of a very important set of experiments, and we find many useful applications of the principles involved in them. So long as there is a change in the magnetic field threading through a circuit, an electric pressure (potential) is set up which will drive a current through a closed circuit (i.e. one in which there is a complete conducting path). We saw that with a fixed coil we can produce this effect by bringing a magnet up to, and into, the coil. Another way is to have a second coil within the first, as in Fig. 72. When a current is sent in coil AB, which is called the *primary coil*, a second current passes through the circuit C G D (which is called a *secondary coil*), containing a galvanometer G, which shows that the current only passes when the key in the primary circuit is being closed or opened. When the key remains down or up (i.e. when there is no change of primary current) there is no 'secondary current.'

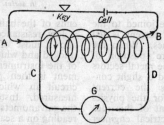

ELECTRO-MAGNETIC INDUCTION.
Fig. 72. *Current produced in secondary circuit.*

This is consistent with what we saw above, for when the current passes in AB it sets up a magnetic field in AB. If we apply the corkscrew rule to each turn of wire in the primary coil, we find that the field produced by all the turns is along the axis of the coil (called a *solenoid*). If the current is set up in the direction of the arrows, the magnetic field runs in the coil from left to right. Therefore, as far as the secondary coil is concerned, we have introduced a magnetic field in this direction, and therefore, to be consistent with Lenz's law, a current will be induced in the secondary in the opposite direction, in order to make a transient magnetic field to oppose the motion which causes the induction.

When the current in the primary coil is established, the magnetic field becomes fixed, and since there is now no movement of the field there is no induction and, therefore, the secondary current ceases. When the current in the primary is stopped, by opening the key, the magnetic field goes, and so again a transient current is induced in the secondary coil, this time in the reverse direction from the last. In the secondary coil the electric pressure set up depends on the number of turns. Each turn has a definite pressure, so that the total potential at the ends of the secondary is proportional to the total number of turns in the secondary. In the device known as the *induction coil* we can produce very high potential by automatically or otherwise 'making' and 'breaking' the primary current.

High Voltage Secondary Currents. For example, if 100 volts are used in the primary it is possible to obtain, with ease, 80,000 volts in the secondary. Of course, to do this we use large currents in the primary and only obtain small currents in the secondary, because the power put in is never exceeded by the power taken out, i.e.

$$I_p \times E_p = I_s E_s$$

under ideal conditions, where I and E are the currents and potentials, and the suffix *s* refers to the secondary and suffix *p* to primary.

Suppose that, using 100 volts mains, the current that is taken is 15 amperes, and that 75,000 volts are produced in the secondary, then the maximum theoretical current (which is never quite obtained) in the secondary is

$$I_s = \frac{100 \times 15}{75,000} = \frac{1}{50} \text{ ampère.}$$

These small currents are usually measured in a smaller unit called the milliampere (=1/1000 amp.). Therefore, the current is 20 milliamperes. This kind of device has been largely used in X-ray practice.

Theory of Generators. An alternative method of producing a current by relative movement of a magnetic field and a coil is to leave the field fixed and rotate the coil. Fig. 66, in Lesson 15 (page 382), illustrates this case. When the plane of the coil is at right angles to the field (Fig. 66) there is a maximum number of lines of magnetic force through the coil. When the latter turns through a right angle there are no lines of force through the coil. Therefore, in the act of turning, an electric current goes through the coil and the external wires which join its ends. Let us examine this case a little further with the help of Fig. 73.

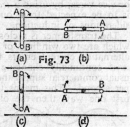

Fig. 73 (a) (b) (c) (d)

Fig. 73. Movement of coil in magnetic field produces current.

Starting with the coil shown in section in Fig. 73 (a) with a maximum magnetic flux passing through it, we pass to Fig. 73 (b), where the position of the coil after moving through a right angle is set out. During this movement lines of magnetic force have been taken out of the left-hand face, and as the coil moves on to position (c), lines of magnetic force are pushed into the former right-hand face, which amounts to the same thing. Therefore, a potential is set up always in one direction.

The rate of cutting the lines is very small in positions (a) and (c), but is quick at position (b); therefore there is a big potential at (b), and, as a matter of fact, there is no potential in the exact positions (a) and (c). As the coil continues to rotate for the next half revolution the potential reverses in direction, for in going from (c) to (d) lines are now taken out of the face into which they were previously inserted.

We see, therefore, that this method of producing potential results in the direction being reversed every half revolution, and if the ends of the coil are each connected to a separate circular ring (called a *slip ring*) on the axis of rotation, a current may be caused to pass through an external circuit by allowing carbon brushes to press on these slip rings. If, on the other hand, the ends of the coil are connected to a commutator (as illustrated in Fig. 68 of Lesson 15) the current in the circuit is reversed every half revolution and so becomes unidirectional.

A.C. and D.C. The first type of current is called alternating current (A.C.), and the second direct, or continuous, current (D.C., or C.C.), which has similar properties to that type of current already discussed. These are illustrated in Fig. 74. A.C., which is more generally supplied by the electric lighting undertakings, has certain advantages over D.C. It can be 'transformed' from high to low potential, or vice versa, by using a *transformer*. This is to be expected from our previous considerations of induction.

The transformer is a closed iron core on which are two windings of wire. When an alternating current enters PP (*see* Fig. 75) it is continually changing direction. In usual commercial supply there are 50 cycles per second. This means the current goes first one way, then the other, completely

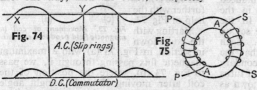

Fig. 74. Alternating and continuous current shown diagrammatically; X, Y is one cycle of A.C. **Fig. 75.** Simple transformer. A, soft iron; P, primary winding, S, secondary.

50 times per second, and so the magnetic field, set up in this core, performs similar reversals. This reversing field induces a potential in the secondary S S of the same frequency (i.e. 50/sec.).

If the number of turns in S S is 20 times that in P P, the potential set up is about 20 times as big, and the transformer is said to be a ' step-up ' transformer. If the secondary has fewer turns than the primary, the potential is less (and therefore the current can be bigger) and the apparatus is called a 'step-down' transformer. The student who wishes to follow this further should study wireless telephony, where understanding of these ideas is of fundamental importance (*see* Radio and Television, Vol. V).

Electrolysis. When a current passes through a liquid which conducts electricity, we find that its passage is accompanied by a chemical decomposition of the liquid. This chemical effect is of importance to the chemist, who has been enabled to isolate substances by its aid. An account of the process of electrolysis is given in Lesson 20 in Chemistry (Vol. III).

Study of these Lessons will show that electricity is conveyed through liquid by means of *ions*, which are charged particles of matter. By the mere act of dissolving a salt in water the molecule breaks up into groups of atoms with equal positive and negative charges. Thus a solution of common salt, NaCl—sodium chloride—contains molecules of NaCl together with positively charged sodium atoms called sodium ions, also negatively charged chlorine atoms called chlorine ions. The number of molecules which dissociate or break up into ions depends on the concentration of the solution. The main point is that the solution contains the ready-made ions.

When two electrodes are inserted in the liquid and a potential difference is applied, the + ions are conveyed down the electric field and reach the − ive electrode, and the − ive ions move up the field and reach the + ive electrode. When they arrive at their destination they give up their charge to the electrodes. The current, therefore, depends on the number of ions passing, on their velocity, and the charge on each ion. By finding the total mass of an ion deposited and the total quantity of electricity passed, the charge per ion (e) can be calculated, if we know the number of ions per gram. If the mass (m) of the ion is known the ratio of e/m can also be found.

When the charged ions reach the electrodes it sometimes happens, for gaseous ions, that they form layers on the electrode and, as they are charged, they set up a back electrical potential. Thus, if E^1 is the value of this potential when a current I flows as a result of the application of a potential E, the resistance of the liquid, as stated by Ohm's Law, is not, as in current flow through metallic conductors,

$$\frac{E}{I} \text{ but } \frac{E - E^1}{I}.$$

It seems, therefore, that Ohm's Law holds for liquid conductors as well as solids, provided we state the law as

$$\frac{\text{effective potential}}{\text{net current}} = \text{total resistance.}$$

In finding the resistance of a liquid it is customary to use alternating current to overcome the electrode effect just referred to. The experiment is simply conducted using the arrangement of a Wheatstone Bridge as seen in Fig. 63, in Lesson 14 (page 380). Alternating current is used for current supply instead of the cell E, and a pair of telephones instead of the galvanometer. The adjustment of R is then made until the buzz in the telephone is reduced to a minimum when P/Q = R/S as before.

Conduction in Gases: Ions, Electrons and X-rays

IF we remove the two electrodes from the electrolyte of a solution, through which a current has been passing, and fix these—say, 1 cm. apart in air—we find that no current passes. We say that, for the potential applied, the air is an insulator or non-conductor. Similarly, if the electrodes are placed in really pure water no current passes. We need the introduction of some ions to the liquid to allow the current to pass. The question arises, is it possible to introduce ions to the air in the space between a pair of metal plates to which a potential difference is applied ?

Obviously we cannot do this by the same means as for the liquid—solids will not dissolve in the air. Ions of positively and negatively charged *gas* molecules can be introduced, and we can make the air conducting in that way. Before discussing this, let us consider the ordinary air between two metal plates A B (Fig. 76). If we attach one cell and have a very sensitive recorder of current at Q, we find no current passes. By adding cell by cell we can build up quite a high potential and still find no current. It is clear that Ohm's Law is not obeyed in this case.

Fig. 76. Investigation of conductivity of gases.

Ionizing Gases. If we continue adding cells we finally reach a potential sufficiently high to break down the air resistance, and a spark passes. When we replace the plates by two pointed rods the spark passes at much lower potentials. Once the spark has passed the air seems to act as though it were a conductor—a poor one, it is true. The air in the spark seems to have taken on conducting properties. It is in fact *ionized*, or split up into +ive and —ive molecules of air which convey the current.

If the potential is cut off and then, after a short interval, once more applied, the spark appears to pass more easily, because some of the gaseous ions are present from the last spark. If a little time elapses before switching on we must again raise the potential to be as high as in the first case. The reason is that the ions have opposite charges, and, being readily movable, attract each other and recombine to be neutral air molecules.

We see from the above that the formation of gaseous ions is possible by raising the potential to 'sparking potential' for the gap. There are other means available. For instance, if we send a beam of X-rays through the gas, or allow the radiations from radioactive substances to pass, the air is ionized so that even with a potential of only 2 volts a current will pass, so long as the ionizing agent acts on the gas.

Both the ionizing agents, X-ray and radioactive bodies, are able to produce a definite number of ions per second, and when a potential sufficiently high is applied to the electrodes, all the ions produced per second are carried across the space in that time and no more can be carried, i.e. the possible current will reach a maximum, and for any increase in potential there will be no increase in current simply because there are no more ions produced to be conveyed across the space. This maximum current is called the *saturation current*. In Fig. 77 the relation between E and I shows that, except for small potentials, the Law of Ohm is again not applicable to conduction through gases. Incidentally, the 'strength' of a beam of X-rays

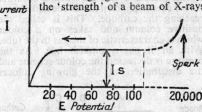

CONDUCTION IN GASES. Fig. 77. Graph of conductivity of ionized gases. Ohm's Law does not hold here.

or the rays from a radioactive body is often compared by measuring the saturation currents which they produce in the air between two plates.

The effect of the applied potential is, of course, to direct the ions, the +ive ions to the —ive electrodes, and —ive ions to the +ive electrodes. As the potential is increased the speed of travel of the ions becomes bigger, and, finally, when a sufficiently high potential is applied, the ions attain such a speed that in their course between the plates they collide with other uncharged air molecules and ionize them. This process is called *ionization by collision.* The very large number of ions so formed repeat the process, and the result is that a very large current passes, again as a spark, between the plates.

When we consider a gas at ordinary atmospheric pressure, the conductivity is not in accordance with Ohm's Law. Now a very interesting and important sequence of observations may be obtained from a study of what happens to the conductivity of a gas when the pressure of the gas is reduced. Fig. 78 shows a section of a glass apparatus which can be exhausted in slow degrees by connecting to an exhaust pump.

Low Pressure Ionization. When ordinary atmospheric pressure prevails the discharge does not take place until the potential is raised to be sufficient to cause a spark to pass between the anode and cathode within the tube. (This may be as high as 30,000 volts for an inch space in air.) If there is an alternative spark gap as shown, the spark will all take place at this place, as there is a shorter air path in the gap. Now when the pressure is reduced we find that the spark ceases to pass at the spark gap, but at the same time there is evidence of a current passing through the tube in the form of a thin, line-like glow. As the pressure decreases there is a wide glow with a beautiful colour extending from the anode and almost reaching the positive column. This is called the positive column and takes on a colour which is characteristic of the gas in the tube. With air it has a pinkish hue. As the pressure is decreased the colour scheme and the distribution of the glowing colours

within the tube alter. A dark space is apparent between the cathode and the positive column, which now recedes towards the anode.

This is followed by the appearance of *Crookes' dark space,* and then a glow about the cathode, as indicated in Fig. 78. For a further diminution of the pressure the resistance of the tube decreases, and the Crookes' dark space advances towards the cathode. Finally, the Crookes' dark space fills the tube and the resistance gets bigger, as evidenced by the appearance of spark in the spark gap.

In the early stage the positive column and previous thin glow represent the actual path of the current. We can deflect this glow by using a magnet, and so on, just as we have been able to deflect wires conveying current. But when the Crookes' dark space fills the tube there is naturally no glow to deflect. The glass walls of the tube at this stage, however, take on a greenish glow. This represents a new phase in the gaseous discharge.

The electricity is conveyed through the tube by gaseous ions, which are made obvious in the early stages by the glow produced. In the later stages no glow is apparent to mark the ionization, but the actual electric current is still conveyed by ions.

When the positive ions hit the cathode they give rise to what was called the 'cathode rays' or the 'cathode stream.' At one time it was thought that this stream was, like light, an electro-magnetic radiation. The English school of physicists led by Crookes, however, maintained that the cathode stream consists of discrete particles, or corpuscles as Sir J. J. Thomson called them. This point of view seems to be the correct one.

The Cathode Rays. Let us see what experiment showed to be the case. The cathode stream on hitting the glass wall opposite the cathode caused a vigorous green glow; also when certain crystals were placed in the beam (which leaves the cathode at right angles and goes in straight lines) fluorescence, and in some cases phosphorescence, is produced.

For example, certain sulphides glow when placed in the beam. These crystals, when powdered and gummed to a sheet of cardboard, form an excellent screen for detecting the cathode ray beams. If a solid cross is placed between the cathode and such a screen placed within the tube, it is found that a 'shadow' is formed, just as if the

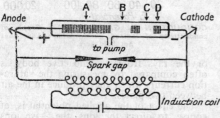

CATHODE RAYS. Fig. 78. A, glowing positive column; B, Faraday's dark space; C, Crookes' dark space. D, cathode glow.

fluorescence were caused by a light shining from the cathode; i.e. the cathode rays travel in straight lines.

If the cathode is cup-shaped, the rays, leaving at right angles to the cathode, all converge to the centre of the cup. If a thin sheet of platinum is placed there, it is found to be heated to a bright red glow by the bombardment of the cathode rays. A light windmill placed on horizontal rails is caused to rotate by the cathode rays hitting the vanes. It is clear, therefore, that these rays are capable of showing their energy by the heat produced or, indirectly, by the rotation of the vanes.

Effects of Magnetic Field. A most important piece of information may be obtained as to the nature of cathode rays

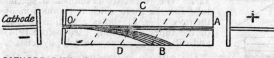

CATHODE RAYS. *Fig. 79. OA, path of rays when no magnetic field is acting; OB, path of rays with magnetic field acting at right-angles to the plane of this page.*

by applying a magnetic field. In Fig. 79 is a section of a suitable apparatus. A sheet of card covered with powdered zinc sulphide, CD, serves to indicate the path of the cathode rays which pass from the cathode through the slit O towards the anode, making a line of fluorescence OA. When the magnetic field is applied into and at right angles to the plane of the paper, the line OA is displaced into the splayed out line OB.

Applying the left-hand rule, we see that this is what would happen to a current going from A to O, and since the effect has its origin at O, we are led to speculate that the cathode stream is made of negative charges going from O to A. In other words, a wave theory for the beam appears to be wrong, and we have excellent grounds for supposing that the stream consists of negatively charged corpuscles. At this stage of exhaustion of the tube, therefore, we are led to visualize the current passing by means of ions, and where the positive ions bombard the cathode we have a cathode stream of negative charges moving off at right angles to the cathode. These negative charges are additional to the negative ions which go from cathode to anode.

Theory of Electrons. Sir J. J. Thomson, by a most ingenious set of experiments, was able to measure the speed of the cathode corpuscles and also to obtain a value of the ratio of the charge to the mass (e/m). The essence of the experiment was to deflect the corpuscles by a magnetic and an electric field. From the amounts of the deflections he calculated the quantities mentioned. From the value of e/m which was found, and a knowledge of the probable value of e, it was calculated that m was approximately one two-thousandth part of the mass of a hydrogen atom.

Now the hydrogen atom is the smallest particle of matter which can exist alone, and the conclusion was reached that the corpuscles, which were called *electrons*, were a 'fourth state' of matter—actually they were considered to be discrete particles of negative electricity free from all matter. They are, indeed, the 'atoms of electricity.' Modern theory suggests that atoms are built up of a central core of positive electricity of a definite value with one or more of these electrons moving about it in orbits. The charge on the electron is taken as a fundamental unit, and is usually written as e. Thus Fig. 80 represents the hydrogen atom with a core of $+e$ and one electron moving about it. The possible orbits for the electron have been the subject of much theoretical speculation, and certain paths or orbits are regarded as being possible. In the case illustrated the attraction which would result would be

Fig. 80. Hydrogen atom.

$$\frac{ee}{r^2}$$ (according to the inverse square law).

This is balanced by the effect of the rotation. When the electron jumps to an orbit nearer the core, the potential energy is less, and the difference in these energies is regarded as being spent in radiation. The characteristic lines of the line spectrum of the elements are regarded as originating in this manner. The ionization of the element is produced by the removal of the electron from the atom.

Electron Emission. From this brief statement of the theory of the atom it becomes clear that if the theory is at all correct, the electron which was 'isolated' by J. J. Thomson in the very artificial manner in the discharge tube should be available in all forms of matter, since it is the fundamental brick from which the matter is made. This conclusion has since been verified.

We can produce electrons in a variety of ways, and from all forms of matter.

When any matter is bombarded by X-rays or γ-rays from radioactive bodies, such matter becomes a source of electrons. When ultra-violet light falls on polished zinc plates a copious supply of electrons is given out. A most important method of obtaining electrons was discovered by O. W. Richardson. When a wire is raised to incandescence it emits an electron stream which is stronger the higher the temperature of the wire. This phenomenon was called 'thermionic emission,' and has been utilized in the thermionic 'valve' or vacuum tube, where it is noticed that the

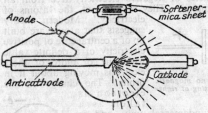

X-RAYS. *Fig. 81. Early form of tube used for production of the rays.*

thermionic current, I, is bigger the higher the temperature, T, of the wire, which is controlled by the heating current or filament current. In fact, I, by Richardson's law, is equal to

$$AT^{\frac{1}{2}}e - \frac{b}{T}$$ when A and b are constants.

Discovery of X-Rays. But let us return to our discharge tube where the electron was first discovered, as there is another property of the electron to discuss. When the electron is stopped by a platinum foil we saw that heat was produced. In addition to this a very small fraction of the energy of the electron stream is changed into a radiation which is called *X-rays*.

This was accidentally discovered by Röntgen when he was investigating the properties of the cathode ray stream. Röntgen had a discharge tube covered entirely with black paper. Outside the tube was a screen covered with crystals of barium-platino-cyanide. When the potential was applied to the tube in a dark room it was found that the screen lit up, owing to a fluorescence of the crystals. When solid bodies were placed between the tube and the screen the shadows enabled him to locate the origin of the radiation.

This he traced to be the spot where the cathode rays were arrested. The energy of the cathode rays which were so changed was small, but the radiation was relatively penetrating. It was further found that the radiation passed through substances like flesh and tissue, but was absorbed by bone. The denser and the higher the atomic weight of a substance, the more it absorbed the rays. When a hand was placed between the tube and the screen the latter showed a faint outline of the fingers, at the centre of which was a shadow picture of the bones.

The medical application of the discovery was very soon realized and many used it for the location of foreign bodies—e.g. a needle in the hand, etc.—and for the diagnosis of fractures, and so on (see page 327). The physicists developed a special tube for the more efficient production of the rays. Fig. 81 shows a section of one of the tubes universally used before 1914, and still used by some research physicists.

The cathode is cup-shaped, and at the centre of the sphere of which the cup is part is placed a massive lump of copper, faced with tungsten or similar hard metal. As shown by the broken lines, the X-rays set up on this 'anti-cathode' radiate out in all directions in the hemisphere nearest to the cathode ; the other half is absorbed in the mass of the anti-cathode. The tube is excited by connecting to the secondary of an induction coil. The higher the potential which is applied to the tube the quicker the speed of the electrons, and consequently the more sudden is their stoppage when they hit the anti-cathode. In these circumstances it is found that the rays are more penetrating—they are said to be 'hard X-rays,' With small potentials the rays are 'soft,' i.e. easily stopped.

The Coolidge Tube. About 1914 a new type of tube, called the Coolidge tube, was introduced ; it has now largely replaced the ordinary gas tube which was described above. The new ideas involved aim at complete control of the radiations given out, both as to penetrating power and strength or intensity of the beam.

These ideas may be readily understood, for if we return to our glass vessel (Fig. 78), we find that when the tube is exhausted of the gas beyond the stage when the cathode rays appear, the more the gas is exhausted the bigger the resistance becomes. The current is conveyed by ions ; when an ion travels down the tube it hits the gas molecules and produces more ions by the collisions. As the pressure gets less, the number of the gas molecules gets less, and so the longer is the path any molecule or ion can go without hitting another molecule or ion. When, finally, the pressure is so low that an ion can go from one electrode to another without hitting a molecule, that is, when 'the mean free path is longer than the distance between the electrodes, it goes from one end of the tube to the other without producing more ions. Instead of the thousands of ions normally produced, only one goes through the tube. The current is, therefore, reduced to practically zero value, and the resistance of the tube becomes enormous.

This is the state inside the Coolidge tube, which is shown in Fig. 82. Even when very high potentials are applied no current passes ; and as there is no appreciable number of ions passing there are no electrons produced and consequently no X-rays.

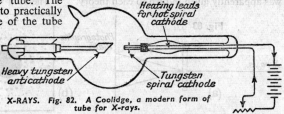

Heating leads for hot spiral cathode

Heavy tungsten anticathode

Tungsten spiral cathode

X-RAYS. Fig. 82. A Coolidge, a modern form of tube for X-rays.

To produce the necessary electron stream, the cathode is made in the form of a spiral of wire which can be made incandescent by a heating current, just as in the more modern thermionic valve. To make the electrons so produced go down the tube at a high speed and set up X-rays when stopped at the anti-cathode, a potential is applied from an induction coil or a large step-up transformer. By making the potential high, penetrating X-rays are produced ; by making the filament current high, an intense beam is produced.

X-rays are not electrically charged particles since they are not deflected by a magnetic field. Because of the great penetrating power of the 'hard' rays and because they cannot be deflected, or reflected or refracted, they must be of a wave-length

much shorter than any ultra-violet ray.

In Angstrom units they have an average wave-length of 1 compared with 2,000 for very short ultra-violet light.

Medical Use of X-Rays The use of X-rays in medicine is fairly apparent for diagnosing fractures of the bones, whose shadow picture can be produced on a screen. A permanent record of these shadow pictures can be made by allowing the rays to cast a shadow picture on to a photographic plate instead of the fluorescence screen. The plate, when developed, produces photographs as shown in in page 327.

When photographs are wanted there must always be a difference in density of the materials, otherwise the shadow picture produced will not show any difference. For example, when used to help in diagnosis in the alimentary tract, the patient is given a 'meal' of bread-and-milk containing a heavy barium salt, which fills the stomach, etc., and allows the radiologist to determine, both from the shape and the time the meal remains, whether or not the patient is normal ; without the meal nothing could be gained in the case quoted.

In addition to the more obvious medical applications, X-rays have been of extreme importance in helping the physicist to obtain information about the structure of the atom.

LESSON 18

Outline of the Quantum Theory

PRODUCED in a manner described in the preceding Lesson, X-rays have been most fruitful of results in investigations on atomic structure. When the rays were first discovered the theories as to their nature also led to much physical research, which yielded results of importance. In the early years of this century the speculations on the nature of X-rays were very

similar to those which were advanced in Newton's time to account for the nature of ordinary light. In those years two serious theories were rivals in the field. The first postulated that light was produced by 'corpuscles' shot out from the source and travelling in straight lines at great speed to the receiver, in much the same way as bullets from a machine-gun. A light source, on this theory, was analogous to a machine-gun nest firing its 'corpuscle' bullets in all directions. This led to results which were contrary to experimental findings, and was abandoned. The other theory, which has held the field from that time until recently without serious challenge, is that light is a wave motion. This theory we have discussed in previous Lessons (see pages 366–372 and 389–390).

X-Rays and the Wave Theory. Many X-ray properties were such that support was apparently given in turn to each theory.

The scheme of the first experiment is shown at (a) in Fig. 83. A narrow beam of X-rays was sent at right-angles to a thin piece of crystal, and a photographic plate, arranged as in the diagram, was found to have a pattern on it when developed, showing a symmetrical set of images about the central area which marked the direct beam, as shown in (b). This pattern was produced by the diffraction of the X-rays at the regularly arranged molecules within the crystal (see also page 328).

The idea was developed by Sir W. Bragg and his son Prof. W. L. Bragg; it was found that the equivalent of reflection could be obtained.

Further, they were able to calculate the distance between the molecules and also the wave-length of the rays used.

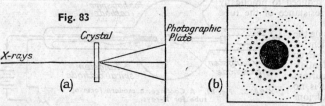

Fig. 83

Crystal

X-rays

Photographic Plate

(a)   (b)

X-RAYS. *Fig. 83. Experiment to determine nature of wave-length of the rays.*

Reflection, refraction, interference, diffraction, etc., which are to be predicted on a wave theory, and occur with light, were not found with X-rays, and so some support was forthcoming for a corpuscular theory.

Now, when we discussed diffraction of light we saw that the amount of diffraction to be expected depended on the relative size of the wave and the slit used. Also in such a simple thing as reflection, the *regular* reflection of the wave only occurs if the surface is free of irregularities of the size of the wave. A sheet of white paper does not reflect light in the same way as a mirror, simply because the surface is not smooth to the order of a wave-length of the light used. It merely gives a diffuse reflection in most directions. This was the kind of result obtained in early experiments with X-rays.

Ultra-Short Waves. However, a theory which was new about 1908, called the Quantum theory, led to the suggestion that X-rays were waves of a *very* short wave-length—something of the order of one hundred millionth part of a centimetre (10^{-8} cm.). This is of the same order as the distance between the molecules in a solid. It was then suggested that in crystals the molecules are arranged in regular patterns as evidenced by the constant shape of crystals of all sizes, and that if crystals were used, some sort of diffraction or interference should be made apparent. The experiments performed to check this theoretical pointer were successful.

This settled the point, in outline at least ; X-rays are of a wave character of measurable wave-length. They are found to be $\frac{1}{1000}$ part of the wave-length of visible light, but are of the same general nature as light—a very dwarf member of the family of radiations which we have previously discussed. Incidentally, the crystal methods have led to a very certain way of investigating the arrangement of molecules and atoms within crystals and powders (*see* illustrations in page 327).

As technique has advanced it has been found possible to produce reflection at polished metal surfaces and also to produce refraction by thin prisms which in the early days was not obtainable.

Incidentally again, the consequences of such refraction show that a beam of X-rays is bent in the opposite way from light, i.e. towards the refracting angle of the prism. The refraction is small, but measurable. Diffraction by diffraction gratings has also been obtained in the last few years, and it is safe to say that in nature the rays are very similar to light waves.

Photo Electrons. When light falls on certain metals it causes the emission of electrons from the metal. If an electric field is set up by arranging a positive charge near the metal, these electrons are attracted to the charge and consequently a current passes. The electrons ejected as a result of the action of light are called *photo electrons.* The photo-electric cell, which now has a wide application, is based on this principle. The current passing fluctuates with fluctuation of intensity of the light falling on the metals.

In this respect, too, X-rays strongly resemble visible light. If a beam of X-rays falls on any substance it ejects electrons from that substance. By analogy with the photo electrons with light, these ejected electrons are called X-ray photo electrons. When X-rays are used the speed of the photo electrons is much greater than when they are excited by visible or ultra-violet light, and when hard X-rays (i.e. short wavelength X-rays) are used the velocity is greater than for soft X-rays (longer wavelength X-rays). These photo electrons cause ionization in gases, which, in the case of X-rays, is almost entirely due to such secondary action.

The result of investigations on the velocity of photo electrons for different wave-length X-rays led to similar conclusions as in the case of visible radiations. A beam of one wave-length gives out electrons at one speed. Whatever the strength of the X-ray beam, the speed of the electron is the same so long as the wave-length is the same.

Now, the classical, established theory would not predict this sort of result. If, for example, we think of the electron as being ejected by the incoming wave we should anticipate that the stronger the beam, the bigger the force and, consequently, the quicker the speed of ejection.

Planck's Quantum Theory. About 1908 Prof. Max Planck propounded a theory, called the Quantum theory. The theory as developed from Planck's first observations has many widely differing aspects, and covers much scientific ground. Since he first propounded it, it has invaded almost every branch of physics until it has become the most important and dominating of all physical theories. It is not too much to say that the Quantum theory has created a radically new outlook on the physical world.

Planck propounded the theory in order to explain the results of observations on the radiation of energy from a hot body. In this case there was the first serious example of results obtained with radiation which did not agree with deductions based on the established or classical ideas. According to these ideas if a body is giving out radiations—and in so doing is really converting its energy into radiation—it may do so in a continuous manner. In the same way it presupposes that an atom may absorb energy continuously.

Unfortunately, this apparently obvious assumption leads to results contrary to experience. Planck postulated that when there is an interchange of energy from matter to radiation or *vice versa* this interchange takes place in multiples of a unit of energy, and that the size of the unit is different for each wave-length in the radiation. He did not use *wave-length*, however, but *frequency*. As we know, these are *simply* related, for

$$\text{frequency} = \frac{\text{velocity}}{\text{wave-length}}.$$

The Quantum of Energy. The unit of energy used in these interchanges was called the quantum of energy, for the particular frequency used. It is really equivalent to saying that when a radiation is falling on a body the latter is not taking in the radiation continuously, but in small packets, or quanta ; for a fixed frequency the number of quanta received per second depends on the intensity of strength of the beam.

The size of the quantum for any frequency n was postulated to be a constant $h \times n$, i.e. $=hn$. This constant is called *Planck's constant* and is very small. When we are dealing with a large-scale effect removed from critical regions we find that, since the quantum is small, the effect is similar to the classical ideas, but when we consider *individual atoms* absorbing energy, there is a sharp demarcation in the results of the application of two theories.

In the case of X-ray photo-electricity, for example, where we are ejecting single electrons by absorbing energy incident on a material, we find, by Planck's Quantum theory, that if the X-rays have a frequency n, the unit of energy absorbed is $hn=W$, say, and this energy is given to the electron which is emitted. The kinetic energy acquired, $\frac{1}{2}mv^2$, is therefore given by

$$W = hn = \tfrac{1}{2}mv^2 \ldots \ldots (i)$$

and so we have a relation between frequency, n, and v, the velocity of the electron, assuming that all the energy is used in imparting movement to it. By measuring v for X-ray photo electrons an estimate of n and, consequently, wave-length of X-rays, was made before crystal analysis was first introduced.

Application to X-Rays. Applying this theory to the X-ray case in all stages, we find that the photo electron emitted has the same velocity as the electron in the X-ray tube, for suppose that the velocity of the electron in the cathode ray beam in the X-ray tube is v, the energy of the electron is $\frac{1}{2}mv^2$. If this changes to X-radiations, causing the formation of radiation of one quantum, we anticipate that the ray will have a frequency n given by

$$\frac{1}{2}mv^2 = hn \ \ldots \ldots (ii)$$

When this radiation ejects a photo electron from matter it causes the latter to move with a velocity given by

$$hn = \frac{1}{2}mv^2 \ldots \ldots (iii)$$

therefore this velocity is the same as that of the parent cathode ray electron—a fact which had been shown experimentally to be the case before the Quantum theory was developed.

A Model of the Atom. The Rutherford-Bohr Model of the atom considers it to be made up of a positive nucleus with electrons rotating about it in orbits. The higher the atomic weight the larger the number of electrons. When an electron from an outer orbit is removed—say, by being hit with another electron or by impact of a radiation —the atom which is left without one of its negative charges is ionized. When an unattached electron is attracted to the incomplete atom it loses potential energy with respect to the positive nucleus or core. Suppose this energy lost as potential energy is W, then, according to the Quantum theory, there will be radiated from the atom a radiation of frequency n given by $W = hn$, where again h is Planck's constant. Accordingly, if n comes to be within the limits of the visible spectrum the radiation will be what we call light.

On older ideas we were content to think that the radius of the orbits of the electrons may have any value (considering circular orbits for simplicity) within the limits of the atom. But the Quantum theory postulates that only relatively few radii are permissible. The radii are of such magnitude that the energy of the electrons in these orbits is a simple multiple of a unit value. Therefore, when we consider the electrons in the atom, we have only to visualize possible paths, which are relatively few.

Atomic Radiation Frequencies. Suppose we return to the atom again and consider the removal of an electron from the orbit next to the outer one. We find that the atom can be made complete once more, this time either by an electron from the outer orbit or alternatively from outside the atom. In each case there is a specific amount of energy lost as potential energy and, consequently, radiated out as a radiation of one or two frequencies given by equation (i) above.

It will be apparent to the student, at least in a general way, from what has been said, that in the way briefly outlined a set of radiations of definite frequencies will be radiated from the disturbed atom. For a different atom a similar set of frequencies will be possible, but of different absolute values—each atom can give out its own waves of frequencies, which can be calculated. If these frequencies come within the visible range they correspond to the line spectra discussed in Lesson 11 (page 365).

When very fast electrons bombard the atoms it is possible to remove electrons from the orbit or near to the nucleus itself. These electrons move out as photo electrons. The incomplete atom which is left gets back to normal by the falling in of electrons from the outer orbits and, finally, from outside the atom itself. In processes of this kind the energy change may be as much as 1,000 times that visualized above. Consequently, the frequency n of the radiation emitted is 1,000 times as great, or the wave-length 1,000 times smaller. It is in fact no longer a light wave, but an X-ray wave which is given out.

There are in the X-ray regions, as in the light regions, many possibilities of replacing the 'lost' electron. Consequently, there is radiated a range of wave-lengths, and X-ray spectra result. The most penetrating X-rays have their origin in the removal of an electron from the orbit nearest the nucleus, and the consequent completion of the atom by the falling in of an electron to that orbit.

Atomic Disintegration. In Lesson 26 in Chemistry (Volume III) an account is given of the physics of radio-activity, and in Lessons 27 and 28 in the same Course are summaries of the theories of the atom, together with an account of the work of such physicists as Lord Rutherford. From these accounts it will be realized that in a radio-active disintegration of an atom it is possible to obtain α, β and γ 'radiations.' It is realized that the α and β 'rays' are not rays, but are charged helium nuclei and swift electrons respectively. The γ radiation is a true radiation of the same nature as X-rays. The question which may perhaps occur to the student is, 'What is the source of origin of the γ ray, if this is shorter in wave-length than the most penetrating X-ray which can be excited in the element, say, radium?' It seems that the γ ray is due to some cause within the nucleus itself, as also is the origin of the α and β rays.

The chemical property of an atom depends among other factors on the number of positive charges on the nucleus. Therefore if this charge is altered, either by altering the weight of the atom or otherwise, the chemical nature of the residue will be charged. Now when an α particle is removed there is a removal of a helium atom of atomic weight 4 and also a removal of two positive charges, so the net charge is two units less, and on both counts it is clear that the atom has been spontaneously transmuted to a lighter atom having entirely different properties.

When a β particle is shot out of the nucleus the effect is an inappreciable loss of mass —i.e. the atomic weight remains the same, but since there is a loss of one unit of negative charge, the net positive charge left on the nucleus is one more than before. We have, in fact, an entirely different atom although it has the same atomic weight.

A study of the table of the radio-active series of uranium in Chemistry, Volume III, Lesson 26, will make these points clear; the fact to notice here is that in these emissions of β particles in particular we have a phenomenon similar to the photo electron we have discussed above. If the β particles are stopped they give rise to radiations according to the equation (i), above. These naturally occurring, quickly moving charges, however, provide material for considering the application of another modern theory, the theory of relativity. (For modern developments in splitting the atom *see* Vol. III, Chemistry, Lesson 27.)

LESSON 19

The Theory of Relativity

THE so-called radiations from a radio-active body include, as we saw in the preceding Lesson, the β 'radiation,' which is merely a stream of very rapidly moving electrons which are ejected from the nucleus itself. According to the particular source of the β particles it is found that their velocity has distinct values, and these velocities, although very great, have been measured by deflecting the particles in strong magnetic fields. From the deflection produced, calculation has yielded the values of *v*. Combined with the magnetic deflection experiments, the deflections produced by strong electric fields have given data from which the ratio of e/m (electronic charge to mass) has also been calculated for the electrons from different sources.

The velocities have been found to be very great indeed. For example, from Radium B, velocities of 1 to 2×10^{10} cms. per sec. have been allotted to the β particles.

Electron Mass and Velocity. The interesting fact emerges that e/m has smaller values for the higher velocity β particles, and we are led to one of two obvious alternatives to account for these results— either the mass of the electron has a bigger value, or the charge becomes less when the speed is increased.

Now *e* has been determined by a very large number of varied experiments, and invariably its value comes to the same number. At the same time we remember that one of the fundamental concepts of our older mechanics is that mass is constant.

This latter notion is the basis of the older mechanics founded by Newton, and it has been adequate to account for all observed facts from his day to the present century. In 1905 Einstein first formulated his celebrated principle of relativity, and this provides an explanation of the variation of e/m with velocity.

Systems of Reference. In dealing with movement we have to realize that all measurements are of motion relative to some 'system of reference.' The speed of a car, e.g., is measured with respect to the ground, which may be taken as our 'system of reference' in this case. In other words, our measurements of the speed of a body on the earth are relative to the earth, which is itself moving. We say a car is moving at 60 miles per hour, whereas, actually, it is only moving 60 miles per hour with respect to the earth. It is actually travelling at some great speed through space in addition to the 60 miles per hour developed by the engine. The expression for velocity is very dependent, therefore, on the exact way in which it is measured.

As a further example, consider raindrops falling towards the ground. If there is no wind they fall directly downwards. To a man stationary on the ground the drops are falling vertically with a definite speed. If the man runs in any direction on the ground, however, the drops no longer appear to fall either vertically or with the same speed as before. Even when no wind is blowing the drops seem to be beating into his face (i.e., coming on the slant) with a greater velocity than before. If a wind is blowing a further complication ensues, for now the drops are in a medium which is itself moving. To have some idea of the actual speed of the drops of rain in this case it is necessary to measure them with respect to a stationary observer (stationary, that is, compared with the earth), and then also to determine the movement of the air, or, what is the same thing, the velocity of the wind.

Actual and Relative Speed. If we were in a closed carriage of a railway train which was such that the movement of the wheels could not be heard or felt, and if we had no means of measuring except in length and time, we should be able to find the velocity of a fly in the carriage, and this would be relative to the carriage itself. The train might travel with uniform velocity, or be retarded or accelerated, but, as far as our measurements go, the velocity of the fly in this limited region would be the same if it continued its motion uniformly in the carriage. Actually, the true velocity with respect to the earth would be variable, and the variation would depend on the train's movement. Regarding the earth for the moment to be at rest, the only way to measure the fly's velocity is to get outside the carriage and measure from the 'stationary' earth.

Now, when it comes to the normal measurements, we have to realize that we are in precisely the same position as the observer in the closed carriage. The earth is moving as part of the solar system. Our measurements of velocities can be made with respect to this system just as those in the carriage are made with respect to the carriage.

It is clear, therefore, by analogy, that the *actual* velocity of movement of a particle in our solar system cannot be determined by measurements made within the system. We need outside, stationary reference points from which to measure and to decide whether we are moving with a uniform speed or not.

The Michelson-Morley Experiment. Attempts were made to reach such a method of measurement when it was assumed that the ether was the system of reference and the absolute value of a velocity was supposed to be that measured with respect to the ether. Now light is propagated in the ether, as we have seen, and, therefore, if it travels with a constant speed, the time it takes to pass from one point to another should depend on whether we travel with the light or against it—i.e. there should be a difference in the observed velocity as measured on the earth—it should apparently go quicker against the direction of movement of the earth than when moving with it.

An elaborate optical experiment was performed by Michelson and Morley to test this point, and it was found that there was no observed difference. It appears that the light travels in the ether just as though the earth were still. This experiment showed the impossibility of measuring or even detecting the velocity of the earth with respect to the ether. Other experiments have also demonstrated this failure. This indicates the uselessness of the ether as a system of reference, and a theory was developed which omits any reference to it. It does not accept or deny the existence of the ether, but merely does not refer to it. This theory is Einstein's Theory of Relativity.

Einstein's Theory. Unfortunately, his method of procedure is far too complex to put into simple language, but by an application of a system of mathematics which appears to be very involved to the uninitiated he deduced many important consequences. He showed that if measurements of length are made there is the equivalent of a contraction of the measuring rod in the direction of motion which does not occur when the measuring rod is at right angles to the movement. The velocity of light, according to the theory, is to be taken as the maximum speed attainable, and it is regarded as constant.

Another conclusion he arrived at is quite opposed at first sight to the accepted, classical mechanics of Newton, namely, that the mass of a body is not invariant—i.e. has not always the same value. It is to be noticed that although this statement appears to be in direct contradiction to the ideas which were taken as absolutely fundamental before 1905, in reality it only becomes different from Newtonian mechanics when we are dealing with masses moving with very great speeds—in fact, with speeds approaching what is regarded as the limiting value, that of the velocity of light.

In effect, he says that if the mass of a body at rest is m_0 (and this was the invariable mass of that body in terms of Newtonian mechanics), the value of the mass, when moving with a velocity v, is m where

$$m = \frac{m_0}{\sqrt{1 - \left(\frac{v}{c}\right)^2}} \quad \ldots (i)$$

where c is the velocity of light.

The exact nature of this change of mass he showed to be equal to the gain of kinetic energy divided by c^2. When we remember that $c = 3 \times 10^{10}$—i.e. thirty thousand million centimetres per second— we see that $c^2 = 9 \times 10^{20}$, and we realize that a gain in kinetic energy, which is to be divided by this number, must be very great in order to produce an appreciable quotient. In other words, ordinary masses moving at normal speeds have no measurable change in mass.

Referring to equation (i) above, we see that if it were possible for the moving body to have a velocity c equal to that of light, the mass, m, would become

$$\frac{m_0}{\left(1 - \frac{c^2}{c^2}\right)^{\frac{1}{2}}} = \frac{m_0}{o} \quad \ldots (ii)$$

Now, the quotient obtained by dividing any finite number by o is infinitely large, that is, a body going with the velocity of light would acquire infinite mass.

Masses at Definite Speeds. Perhaps the student will appreciate the predictions of the theory of relativity in this respect much better by considering the values of the masses acquired for definite speeds. If a body has a mass of m_0 at rest, substitution in equation (i) shows that it will have the following values for the velocities quoted :

Velocity	Mass
0·5 c. $= 1·5 \times 10^{10}$ cm. per sec.	1.15 m_0
0·9 c. $= 2·7 \times 10^{10}$,, ,,	2·3 m_0
0·99 c. $= 2·97 \times 10^{10}$,, ,,	7·0 m_0

Now, ordinary large-scale objects never approach these tremendous speeds. The tremendous high speed records obtained in flying have not been much greater than 480 miles per hour, or 704 ft. per sec., which is about 21,120 cm. per sec. If we say 25,000 cm. per second could be about this is only a minute fraction of c of the order of ·0000008 c, so m would be

$$m = \frac{m_0}{\sqrt{1 - (·0000008)}} = m_0 (1 + 3·2 \times 10^{-13})$$

i.e. $m = 1·00000000000032 \times m_0$

If we imagine that we are flying a machine at this high speed of 480 miles per hour

and that the machine were to have a mass at rest of 50,000 kilograms (about 50 tons), the gain in mass would only be about ·00000015 gm. or ·000000005 oz.

Newtonian Mechanics and Electron Speeds. It seems almost an obvious comment that, if this be so, there does not seem to be much wrong with the Newtonian mechanics, which does not make all this fuss and indulge in large flights of higher mathematics to show that the change in mass is of this absurdly minute amount. The Newtonian mechanics certainly is, for all practical purposes, correct when dealing with large-scale phenomena of this kind, and only breaks down when we consider such a case as the electrons in the β ray streams ejected by radioactive bodies. In this case the correction for the variation in mass of the corpuscles gives a value of e/m which agrees with experiment and emphasizes the constancy of e, the electronic charge.

The theory of relativity also offers an explanation of an outstanding discrepancy between theory and observed result in connexion with the planet Mercury. There was a minute yet observable difference in its path with time which had long been a puzzle. The slight correction which the principle introduces clears up this point.

Radiation and Gravitation. Again, according to the principle of relativity, there should be an interaction between radiation and a strong gravitational field. If light were a stream of particles, then we should expect that when the stream passed near a large body there would be an attraction, just as there is on a body near the earth. Now there is an equivalent effect, according to the theory of relativity, on ordinary waves such as light waves. Any radiation, in fact, has allotted to it its equivalent energy, and this allows calculations to be made of the effect of the pull of a heavenly body on a ray of light which happens to travel near it.

The expeditions which have set out to observe stars during a solar eclipse have aimed at finding out if such a pull is exerted by the 'gravitational field' of the sun, for the change in direction of the rays of light should make the stars appear slightly out of place. The position stars should occupy during eclipse is calculated beforehand, and those stars which are normally invisible as the line of sight is just grazing the sun are chosen. The exact position they appear to occupy is calculated from photographs, and there is some reason to believe that the shift predicted by the theory is measurable.

Nowadays there are many interesting speculations as to the nature of radiation or waves in space, and we shall see in our next Lesson something of these modern speculations as to the nature of waves and corpuscles in the theory of Wave Mechanics.

LESSON 20

Protons, Neutrons and Wave Mechanics

IN many branches of Physics the investigation of small-scale phenomena and the effect of great speed has led the physicist and the mathematical physicist to a collaboration that has yielded results which some twenty or thirty years ago would have seemed fantastic. We have seen from a consideration of the Quantum theory that when there is an interaction between radiation and matter, the former always deals in energy bundles, or quanta, of size hn where h is Planck's constant and n is the frequency of the radiation. In fact, the quantum is often regarded in much the same way as Newton regarded his corpuscles in the celebrated corpuscular theory of light, and in this respect there is a reversion to this old theory.

The beam of radiation (light and any other electro-magnetic wave) is regarded as conveying its energy in *photons*, each of which carries the quantum hn. The use of the word photon itself suggests a discrete corpuscle of the radiation, and the application of this idea has led to some recent developments.

Photons and Electrons. For example, A. H. Compton made a theoretical investigation of what happens when a beam of X-rays falls on electrons. He assumed that the energy in the X-ray beam was conveyed by photons (quanta) which behaved as discrete corpuscles and hit an electron in such a way that one can make use of many of the laws of impact that are applicable when two billiard balls collide.

Fig. 84 shows his method of treatment. An incident beam of X-rays enters from left to right and hits an electron at O. It is assumed that in the impact we are dealing with a photon of energy hn, and an electron. After impact the photon rebounds in one direction, as shown, having a new energy value hn' (i.e. as a quantum of another radiation which is less than hn because some energy has been imparted to the electron), and the electron recoils, as shown, in another direction. Compton calculated the values of hn' and the velocity of the

electron after impact by applying the principles of conservation of momentum *and of energy*. The interesting conclusions which were arrived at lead one to expect that after such a collision the radiation has a smaller frequency n' and that recoil electrons move in the space with a pre-determined value.

It will be seen, as the frequency n' is less than n, the wave length of the 'scattered' X-ray will be larger than the incident beam. Not only was a lengthening of the wave-length predicted, but also the amount of wave-length change was shown to depend on the actual angle at which it happened to be scattered.

Photographing Electron Tracks. All these conclusions were verified by experiment. Using an X-ray spectrometer, the wave-lengths of the scattered X-rays were measured for different angles of scattering, and the wave-length change was found almost exactly as theory predicted. Also, using a cloud condensation apparatus, photographs of electrons tracks (*see* page 328) showed the presence of short tracks which exactly fitted the anticipated recoil electrons. In this case there certainly seemed to be ample proof that the X-ray 'waves' behaved as corpuscles, and there was support for the use of the term photon to describe the phenomenon. Since the same laws are applicable in the case of all the electro-magnetic radiations, it seemed that many

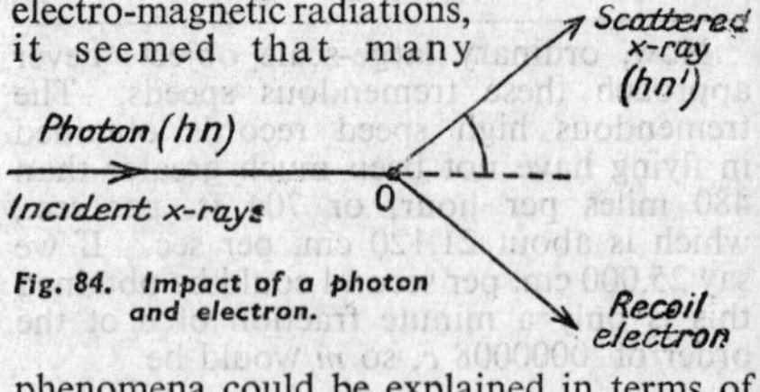

Fig. 84. **Impact of a photon and electron.**

phenomena could be explained in terms of a common conception, that of a corpuscle.

On the other hand, this notion is not so useful in giving an explanation of such things as interference, diffraction, etc. There still remains this curious fact, that one set of properties of radiation can be best explained in terms of a wave theory, and another set of observed results can be better explained if we use the photon development of the Quantum theory as a theoretical background. In almost all cases the wave theory gives the broad outline explanation and the Quantum theory developments give the detail and account for those observed results for which the wave theory has no explanation.

Protons. There are many corpuscles which, it would appear at first sight at least, are beyond doubt discrete particles and which do not develop from radiation ideas. Of these the first we met in this Course was the electron. This particular corpuscle was shown to be a negative charge of a mass so small, compared with the mass of the hydrogen atom, that we say it is not associated with matter at all.

All the *positive* charges we have so far met with in this Course have been of a much more massive structure. The smallest positive charge is that on the nucleus of the hydrogen atom. This charge is associated with the mass of the hydrogen atom and is equal in size but opposite in sign to the charge on the electron. It will be remembered that the hydrogen atom was considered to be a nucleus with one electron moving about it. For the heavier atoms we have a similar simplified picture. The heavier the atom the bigger the positive charge of the nucleus, and correspondingly bigger is the number of electrons rotating about that nucleus.

Now, since for the heavier atoms the nuclear charge is a whole number of times that of the hydrogen nucleus, it seems obvious why a theory has developed on the lines of assuming that a tentative unit of positive electricity is that associated with the matter forming the hydrogen nucleus. The *proton*, as this unit is called, is then used in building up other atoms. For example, the atom of sodium is supposed to be made of a nucleus containing eleven protons and surrounded by eleven electrons.

Until the end of the year 1932 positive electricity had never been isolated in a state free from matter as had the negative charge. But in the course of very intensive researches in those years, one experiment in 1933 seemed to produce clear evidence that the *positive electron* was isolated. Cloud condensation experiments were performed and the tracks of electrons and other ionizing agents, liberated by penetrating, cosmic radiation, were photographed.

The action of magnetic fields causing the tracks to be bent was also investigated. In some of the photographs tracks were obtained which were bent in a direction opposite to that in which the electron tracks were bent. This showed that the track was produced by a positively charged particle.

Now, from a knowledge of the magnetic field it is a fairly simple matter to estimate the magnitude of the particle if its charge is known. The estimated mass of the newly discovered particle was much less than that of a proton, so that it could not be associated with matter (unless, indeed, the hydrogen atom is not the smallest portion of matter which can be isolated). There seems to be little doubt that this experiment isolated the positive electron, although it made no *definite* measurements of the mass, etc., of it (page 328).

The Neutron. Yet another corpuscle is known to modern Physics under the name of the *neutron*, which, as its name suggests, is neutral in charge. This uncharged corpuscle is released when certain substances are bombarded by α rays and swiftly-moving protons. A full account of the experiment which led Dr. Chadwick to isolate and describe this corpuscle, is, however, too long to include here.

It is thus seen that the number of different corpuscles which have been isolated has increased, and more and more phenomena receive an explanation in terms of them. However, important work has been carried out both on the theoretical and experimental sides, which has had an effect just the reverse of that produced by the introduction of the photon. This work is classified under the title of the New Quantum Theory, one aspect being Wave Mechanics.

Wave Mechanics. Schroedinger, who was a pupil of Count de Broglie, advanced a mathematical idea that was first introduced by de Broglie, in which a study of a moving corpuscle led to a mathematical form to express its movement, which was similar in general appearance to that which describes waves travelling through space. A moving electron, for example, in this treatment is expressed by an equation which looks very similar to that of a wave.

The analogy led to the suggestion that, in effect, the moving electron might be similar to waves of suitable wave-length. This does not mean quite that the new wave mechanics suggests that we must change this accepted *corpuscle*—the electron—and in its place substitute a wave ; but it does suggest that in the close analogy which the mathematical development has deduced there is a chance that in some respects the electron should exhibit wave-like properties.

To use an imperfect analogy, if we have a quickly-moving ship steaming over the smooth surface of the sea, and we view this from an aeroplane well above the surface, we shall be able to see a set of bow waves moving over the surface, or we shall see the ship moving over the surface. In this analogy the ship represents the electron and the waves correspond to the wave-like structure which the waves mechanics suggests.

Now, for a corpuscle moving with a velocity v, the length of the associated wave form is deduced to be equal to h/mv, where h is Planck's constant and m the electron's mass.

Experimental Evidence of Electron Wave-Lengths. Experiments have been performed to try to detect any effect of the waves, and it is a surprising fact that the results in most cases have been positive. A stream of electrons, when sent at right angles to very thin sheets of metal, instead of going through with a reduced intensity or reduced speed, have been found to spread out into definite rings, in a way very similar to the X-ray waves on passing through a thin crystal (*see* diagram, Lesson 18, page 392). This may be due to the diffraction of the waves and is, in fact, in agreement with the diffraction expected with waves of wave-length $\lambda = h/mv$.

For quickly-moving electrons the calculated value of λ is of the same order as X-ray wave-lengths; Professor G. P. Thomson was the first to demonstrate the effect clearly.

Now, although the diffraction was that given for waves of X-ray wave-length, the absorption of the electrons still continues to obey the laws of absorption for electrons, i.e. they are still very easily absorbed in thin sheets, whereas X-rays of the same wave-length are able to penetrate relatively thick slabs of the same substance.

Another set of striking experimental evidence of the wave nature to be associated with the moving particle was obtained by the production of diffraction with ruled diffraction gratings. Here, again, one experimenter found the diffractions to produce lines just as would be produced by waves of length $\lambda = h/mv$. Although this has not been confirmed, there is striking evidence that there must be some wave-like property associated with the electron. Experiments have also been made with uncharged particles—as there is no need, according to the theory, for the particle to have a charge—and confirmation is again forthcoming to support the new theory.

Cosmic Rays. Another subject of interest in modern Physics concerns the very penetrating radiation which is found to be present when all known sources of radiation, e.g. radioactive bodies, etc., are excluded. This penetrating radiation, which is sometimes referred to as cosmic radiation, is present at great height above the earth's surface. At the moment the origin of the radiation is quite unknown. It certainly seems to be external to the earth. Also, we cannot say whether it is photons of a very short wave-length radiation or whether it is truly corpuscular in character.

It will be seen that this very brief résumé of some of the more recent theories advanced to account for the results obtained by experiment shows clearly the interplay which is going on between the work of the theoretical and experimental physicist.

There are no definite answers to the modern questions set, but 'intelligent guesses' and considered theories, followed by the critical test by experiment, constitute very promising attempts.

SHORT BIBLIOGRAPHY

General. 'A Text Book of Physics,' Duncan and Starling; 'The Mechanism of Nature,' E. N. da C. Andrade (Bell); 'Infra Red Photography,' Rawlings (Blackie). 'Aspects of Science' and 'Science, A New Outline,' J. W. N. Sullivan (Nelson); 'New Pathways in Science,' Sir A. Eddington (Cambridge U. Press); 'The Revolution in Physics,' E. Zimmer (Faber); 'Science for the Citizen,' Lancelot Hogben (Allen & Unwin).

Radioactivity. Sir W. Bragg, 'Studies in Radioactivity' (Macmillan); 'Radio-activity & Radioactive Substances,' Chadwick (Pitman).

Relativity. 'Three Men Discuss Relativity,' J. W. N. Sullivan (Collins); 'A.B.C. of Relativity,' Bertrand Russell (Kegan Paul).

Light, Heat and Sound. 'Heat and Light,' Sir R. T. Glazebrook (Cam. U. Press); 'Treatise on Light,' R. A. Houston (Longman); 'Heat for Advanced Students,' G. Edser (Macmillan); 'The World of Sound' and 'The Universe of Light,' Sir Wm. Bragg (Bell).

Electricity. 'Electricity,' W. L. Bragg (Bell); 'Everyday Electricity,' Lunt (Macmillan); 'Electricity Today,' T. B. Vinycomb (Oxford Press); 'Electrical Technology,' H. Cotton (Pitman); 'The Electrical Encyclopedia,' S. G. B. Stubbs (Waverley Book Co.).

Advanced. 'Electrons and Ionising Radiations,' J. A. Crowther (Arnold); 'The Nature of the Physical World,' Sir A. Eddington (Cambridge University Press); 'Monographs in Physical Subjects,' (Methuen); 'Theory of Light,' Max Planck (Macmillan); 'Theory of Heat,' Max Planck (Macmillan).

ARCHAEOLOGY

*I*N *this Course we are concerned with the fundamentals of History. Without the science of Archaeology; in exploring and examining the remains on ancient sites throughout the world, the history of its earliest cultures could not be written. After discussing the latest archaeological methods the Course proceeds to a careful evaluation of the facts of pre-history from evidences of primitive man to the early civilizations of Egypt, the Near East and Europe. Brief accounts of the cultures of India, Byzantium, the Far East and of South America conclude the survey. For an expanded treatment of the life of ancient peoples the student should refer to the Course on* SOCIAL HISTORY *in Volume III. Prehistoric life is studied from another point of view in* GEOLOGY *in Volume V. Other closely associated Courses are* ANCIENT HISTORY *in Volume II and* ANTHROPOLOGY *in Volume V.*

32 LESSONS

N

LESSON ONE

Recovering the Past

ANYONE who asks what there is in Archaeology that those who study it are filled with the desire to know more and more about it, is recommended to read the last chapter of Petrie's ' Methods and Aims in Archaeology,' where will be found a full and lucid explanation of why

human beings long for the recovery of the past, why we desire to know what our ancestors in our own and other countries did and felt, and why we wish to follow back to their sources the social institutions which are now so much part of our lives that we hardly realize that they had a beginning in time.

SIR W. M. FLINDERS PETRIE (1853–1942). *Egyptologist and pioneer of practical archaeology.*

Archaeology began in antiquarianism, just as chemistry began in alchemy. The early antiquarian was the uncritical collector, a kind of human magpie, who collected objects only because they were strange or were what he considered beautiful or interesting. Then came a stage when the antiquarian collected books, statuary and coins, whose only interest to him was that they must be old. Age was the one quality that he insisted on.

The archaeologist, though he may be as ardent a collector as the antiquarian, cares for things only because they throw light on the past history of mankind. But he does not merely collect ; he studies objects from two aspects : he learns all he can from the object itself, its material, the method of its making, and the use to which it was put ; he then studies it in relation to the objects with which it was found, and compares it with similar objects found in other countries or periods, noting similarities and differences. To put the matter shortly, the antiquarian values things for their own sake, while the archaeologist values them for what they *mean*.

The primitive conception of an antiquarian's field work is that it consists of digging up buried treasure of gold and jewels, all of fabulous value, or of unearthing beautiful statues which are the admiration of the whole artistic world, or

of finding marvellous manuscripts on the interpretation of which the greatest scholars of the universities may expend their energies. The earliest recorded antiquarians of this type were the ancient Egyptians, who held the wisdom of their ancestors in such respect that they literally left no stone unturned in their temples in their search for documents. When their efforts were crowned with success, the document was considered to have a religious value so great as to be almost divine. In ancient Egypt all medical remedies, to be efficacious, were recommended as having been in use for several centuries, and were dated if possible from the reign of some well-known king of antiquity.

Early Antiquarians. The first antiquarian, whose taste as a collector ran almost

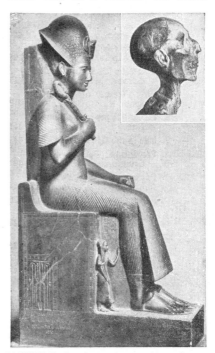

RAMESES II. *A zealous antiquary, whose collection of papyri was retrieved by Sir Flinders Petrie in 1898.*
Photos, Mansell

entirely to books, was the great Pharaoh Rameses II (1300–1234 B.C.). At the back of his mortuary temple at Thebes he built a vast number of living rooms and storehouses for the accommodation of the officials and servants in attendance on himself as both king and god In one of these rooms he kept his library, and inscribed over the doorway were the words, ' The Medicine of the Mind.' When Diodorus visited Thebes in the first century B.C. the inscription was

AN ANCIENT MUSEUM. In this mortuary temple at Thebes Rameses II had a library of Egyptian MSS. of much earlier date than his reign.
Photo, Donald McLeish

still in place and the priests translated it for him. When Flinders Petrie excavated part of these ruins in 1898, nothing remained of the inscription, but the library was found containing papyri, all of much earlier date than the reign of Rameses, showing that the Pharaoh, 3,000 years earlier, had devoted much time to collecting early MSS.

The next recorded antiquarian was Nabonidus, king of Babylon (555–538 B.C.). He is perhaps better known to us as the father of that Belshazzar who saw the writing on the wall. The great delight of Nabonidus was to dig in the temples for ancient records, historical and religious, and from his finds he made compilations of historical events and dates which modern historians find of the utmost use. His mania for collecting proved his downfall, for he took away the ancient figures of gods from their own centres of worship and brought them all to his capital, where he could gloat over them at his leisure.

He probably did not realize the horror which his sacrilegious action inspired in the priests and worshippers of the temples that he ravaged. Therefore when Cyrus the Persian invaded Babylonia, the offended people flocked to meet him, and his entry into the country was as much a triumphal procession as a warlike conquest. As soon as Cyrus had taken full possession of the country, he repaid the confidence of the priests and people by sending back the

images, each to its own temple. In Babylonia the first beginnings of the true science of archaeology are found when a princess made a collection of antiquities, and labelled each piece with the name of the place where it was found.

Founders of Archaeology. Antiquarians are found in all periods and all countries, but in England there are two men who rise above the ordinary level, Elias Ashmole and Colt Hoare. Ashmole (1617–92) had a certain critical faculty, his collections, though unscientific in the modern sense, have always been of interest and value, and form the basis of one of the greatest museums of modern times. Sir Richard Colt Hoare (1758–1838) was a recorder rather than a collector, and his records and measurements are still used by the archaeologist on account of their accuracy.

ELIAS ASHMOLE (1617–92). English antiquary; founder of the Ashmolean Museum, Oxford.

From these beginnings the science of archaeology has arisen. Though it has not long passed its half century the old type of antiquary no longer exists. Sculpture and inscriptions, coins and gems, even manuscripts, are valued now for the light they shed on the civilization to which they belong. The main objective of the archaeologist is not the accumulation of pretty things but a wide and accurate view of the long dead and almost forgotten past.

This change has been brought about by the genius of one man, Sir Flinders Petrie. When he began his life's work antiquarianism held the field ; museums refused to accept objects which were not considered beautiful according to the taste of the day, and most universities were scornful of a subject which took little note of language as an end in itself—for in archaeology the language of a country is often merely auxiliary, as in ancient Egypt, or does not even exist, as in early Britain. Petrie founded the science of archaeology by showing the importance of the objects of daily life. In these can be traced the changes in civilization, the foreign contacts, and even the evolution of the ritual of religious worship. When, in addition to Petrie's work, Miss Amelia B. Edwards founded in 1893 a professorship of Egyptology at University College, London, so that practical archaeology could be taught and students trained in the latest methods, the triumph of archaeology over antiquarianism was assured.

Scientific Methods of Excavation

THERE are four main subjects in which archaeologists should be trained : (1) excavation ; (2) study in museums of objects already excavated ; (3) study of published material ; and (4) study of living races. Each of these will be treated separately, but as excavation is the foundation of all archaeological knowledge it must be considered first.

To many people archaeology means only the excavating of ancient cities and tombs, and, above all, the finding of buried treasure. Excavation, however, is not an end in itself : it is only the preliminary to the serious study, merely the means of obtaining the material on which the real study is based. But as it is the foundation of the whole subject it must be scientifically done.

Choice of a Site. First of all, the site must be chosen. Accident may bring a site to light, as when the plough unearths a quantity of flint implements or when a landslip shows stratified walls and habitations. But no archaeologist worthy of the name would depend on chance. Nowadays an aerial survey is usually made of areas which are judged likely to be archaeologically rich. By this means was discovered the Iron Age site at Woodbury, on the hill south of Salisbury, which in 1938 was selected by the Prehistoric Society as a training ground for young archaeologists.

If an aerial survey is impossible there are other means of learning from the surface of the ground what lies beneath. There are, of course, indications which even

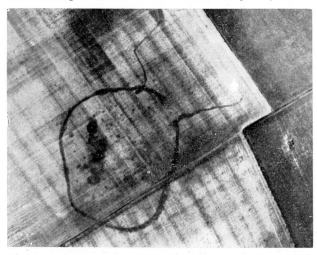

ARCHAEOLOGICAL TRAINING-GROUND. At Woodbury, on the hill south of Salisbury, a site for training amateur archaeologists was acquired in 1938 by the Prehistoric Society. Aerial survey disclosed rings of dark colour in the corn; excavation proved the site to be an Early Iron Age settlement.
Photo, 'The Times'

Scientific Excavation

the untrained eye can see, as, for instance, circles of megalithic stones, burial barrows, ruined walls, broken columns, or mounds covered with potsherds.

When there is nothing on the surface, and an air photograph is not obtainable, the method must necessarily be different. In Egypt the rare rain, which falls on the narrow strip of desert bordering the cultivated land of the Nile valley, is a godsend to the excavator. Under the hot sun the moisture evaporates more quickly from the sand which covers buried walls than from the deeper layers. Half an hour's sun after rain will often show the whole plan of a building of which not a trace can be seen on the surface in dry weather.

Before the tomb of Tutankhamen was found it was known to be in that neighbourhood, for the excavators had already found the huts of the workmen who had made it. It had escaped pillage because the falls of rock from the cliff above had hidden the entrance, and it was discovered on removing the mass of débris at the foot of the cliff down to bed-rock.

The remains of the palace of Cnossus were laid bare because the tradition as to the site had been preserved by some of the classical authors, and when the topographical indications given by those authors were identified, the find was made.

TRIUMPHS OF ARCHAEOLOGY. Top, entrance (bottom right) to the tomb of the Pharaoh Tutankhamen at Thebes. Below, long-buried Cnossus, in Crete, as resurrected by the late Sir Arthur Evans. These remarkable remains of the once great Minoan capital lie on the slope of a hill about 3½ miles from Candia. The skeleton tower in the middle distance was built to enable the excavations to be seen as a whole.

Photos, 'The Times' and G. Maraghianni

Having chosen his site, the excavator must decide on the method of digging. He will have a general idea of what he expects to find. In a town-site it will be houses and probably a temple, perhaps a palace ; in a tomb he may find bodies, or at least bones, and a certain number of objects. The unscientific excavator will excavate both sites in the same way, merely digging them out, keeping no records of levels, preserving only the pretty things and throwing away the rest.

The site must first be surveyed and a datum fixed by which all levels can be measured ; the plan should be divided into squares, so that the position of everything found can be entered at once.

Plans and Records. In excavating a town-site the digger must decide exactly what he wants to do. Then he will have to remove tons of earth or sand, and must arrange that the dump-heaps are conveniently near the dig and yet not covering any part of it. If he chooses the position of the dump-heaps wisely, many of his difficulties are solved.

The ideal method of excavating a town-site is to excavate the whole surface, descending foot by foot till bed-rock or virgin soil is reached. The fullest records must be kept as to levels and objects found, besides plans of every building and wall, so that the place could be reconstructed by any future archaeologist. By this method of excavation, as will be seen, all evidence on the spot is destroyed, and it is also the costliest of all methods, for the digger must be prepared to spend fully half his time and half his money on an elaborate and careful publication. In a large site, therefore, it is better to attempt the full excavation of only a portion, working within strict limits and leaving the rest of the area as a ' control ' for those who come after.

In excavating tombs, whether single graves or a whole cemetery, the survey must be made first as for a town-site. Generally, the original burial for which the tomb was made will be found at the bottom of a shaft or at the far end of a passage—in other words, as far as possible from the entrance. The shaft or passage may have been used later for intrusive burials, and these will give a sequence of dating to the objects found, the earliest being at the far end, the latest at or near the entrance. Each burial, as it comes to light, must be carefully cleared so that the position of each object can be planned and photographed.

As objects are unearthed they must be so carefully marked that their provenance cannot be lost ; if broken, each piece must be marked. When the objects arrive in the camp they should be photographed and copied in facsimile by hand.

The excavator's life is not a happy one. In the Near East the language of the workmen is Arabic and this, therefore, he must learn to speak fluently ; he has to be up early in the mornings so as to begin work with the men ; he has to oversee them continuously and assess their work if they work by the piece ; he must also assess the rewards for objects found and see that the men understand his system of payment, for it is essential to gain their confidence if he is to get the best out of them. His evenings and spare time will be spent in drawing, photographing, planning, and all the miscellaneous jobs that occur in camp. He will have to work hard and with great accuracy, for in archaeological excavation evidence once lost is lost for ever and can never be recovered. But if his work is done well and scientifically he has his reward in having added something to our knowledge of the origin and progress of our present civilizations.

LESSON THREE

Steps in the Training of an Archaeologist

THOUGH excavation is the foundation of archaeology, the training of the archaeologist should begin with the study of the material already excavated by others. This is most conveniently done in a museum, where the student is generally in a position to handle the objects.

The first thing that every archaeologist must know and understand is pottery.

Archaeologically speaking, a knowledge of pottery is essential. Pottery is the commonest of all objects and is practically indestructible ; fire or water will not destroy it ; and if a pot is broken the shards can be put together and the form identified. Pottery was always so common that even the poorest person would have at least one vessel buried with him. It is bulky, heavy and fragile, and therefore travels badly, so that it is rarely carried any distance from the place of making. The ware of each country is distinctive ; the sandy, gritty pottery of Egypt is totally different from the finely levigated clay of the Aegean, which again is unlike the pottery of western Europe or of India. In each period of every country there occur one or more distinctive shapes which never recur there or elsewhere in the whole history of pottery (*see* Lesson 9).

Methods of Making Pots. The technique of pottery making is

POTTERY ' THROWER ' at work in the corner of the factory at Etruria, Stoke, where in 1769 Josiah Wedgwood made his first six vases while his partner turned the wheel, one of the earliest devices invented.

also of the utmost importance. The ancient world knew three methods of making a pot—pinching, coiling, and the wheel ; the modern potter has introduced a fourth, casting. Pinching is the most primitive of all the methods ; the potter took a lump of clay, hollowed it with his hands, smoothed the outside, and the pot was ready. By practice he was able to shape his pot so exactly that it is almost impossible to tell a pinched pot from a wheel-made pot by sight alone. It is only by touch that the irregularities in the thickness of the walls of the vessel can be sensed, and the very slight differences in the form can be observed.

Coiling is done by rolling the clay into long 'sausages,' and then laying these round, one above the other, in the desired shape. The hollows between the coils are filled by pressing the clay of each coil upwards and downwards till

the hollow is hardly visible. This is a more elaborate method than pinching. A coiled pot can be distinguished from a pinched pot by the fact that there are slight horizontal ridges where the coils were set in place ; these, when regular, make it difficult to be certain in many cases whether a vessel is made by coiling or on the wheel.

The potter's wheel is not only of great importance in itself, but is remarkable as one of the earliest mechanical appliances ever invented. It is a flat table which moves round and round on a pivot ; a lump of clay is placed in the middle, and as the table spins the vase springs up under the potter's hands. The earliest wheel was merely a small board, or thin slab of stone, pivoted probably on another stone and turned by an occasional push of the potter's hand or foot. Wheel-made pottery is found in Egypt in the 1st dynasty, but whether the wheel was invented there or was introduced by the dynastic invaders is still uncertain.

THE POTTER'S WHEEL. Breton pottery-maker at his wheel in Quimper. This device in its various forms has been in use for over 5,000 years, and wheel-made pots which have survived from dynastic Egypt and later civilizations furnish evidence which is of the utmost value to the archaeologist.
Photo, E.N.A.

For some centuries it was too primitive to admit of making a large vase completely ; two sections had to be made separately and joined together, the junction being masked and strengthened by a band of clay.

Another method of making a large vessel was to turn the upper part on the wheel, making it with the mouth downwards ; then the lower part could be finished by hand. This method is still followed by the Bedawy (Beduin) potters in southern Palestine. Gradually the wheel-made pottery superseded the hand-made, because, though the machine was very primitive, it enabled the worker to increase his production, and even a beginner could produce better pots on the wheel than could be produced by hand.

Here it may be noted that archaeology has corrected a literary trâdition. According to the Greeks, the potter's wheel was invented by one of the Seven Sages in the seventh century B.C., but the archaeological evidence shows that in Egypt and Mesopotamia it was in use before 3000 B.C., and in Italy about 1000 B.C. North of the Alps the Celts were the first people to adopt the potter's wheel along with other devices of civilization.

In making pottery, whether by hand or wheel, the vessel after being shaped must be allowed to dry thoroughly. In Egypt this was always done in the sun. Large vessels were often bound with rope to prevent sagging during the drying process. When thoroughly dry the pot was fired in a kiln, and the clay when thoroughly baked became pottery. The skill of the potter is shown not only in shaping the vessel, but also in his method of firing it.

Decoration. There are three ways of decorating pottery—slip, paint, and incisions. Slip is one of the earliest. Finely ground clay is mixed with water till like a thick liquid ; it can be applied as a wash over the whole surface, or when quite thick it can be laid on in a raised design.

Paint can also be employed to cover the whole surface or in decorative patterns. The surface of a vessel is covered only when the clay of which it is made burns to a dull or ugly colour ; the slip is then of a different clay or mixed with paint and applied, or the paint is washed over the surface. Both slip and paint are applied when the vessel is dry and before firing. Sometimes the slip will scale off, leaving the dull-coloured surface visible underneath.

Incised designs are made while the clay is still wet. Usually they consist of straight lines without curves, and after firing the hollows were often filled with gypsum so that the pattern was in white on the darker background of the pottery. The ropes which bound the large pots while drying often left marks on the soft clay, and these suggested another form of incised ornament which we call nowadays a ' rope-pattern.'

Glazed earthenware is not met with till comparatively recent times, but burnished pottery was not uncommon even in the prehistoric periods of Egypt. It is found in the Neolithic period of Malta and in the Bronze Age throughout Europe. The method of making is to polish the surface, whether plain or slipped, with some smooth material, such as a smooth stone, a shell, a bone, or even a pad of wool. This was done when the vase was dry before firing, and the polishing was repeated after the baking. As will be noted, this process cannot properly be called glazing, which means that a coating of glass has been laid over the object. Glass itself was used under the Egyptian Empire for making ornamental vessels, inlays and sometimes statuettes.

In studying pottery the points to be noted are material, shape, method of making, method of firing, colour, and decoration. Each point should serve as a guide and should tell its own story as to the date and place of origin.

PRE-DYNASTIC POTS OF EGYPT. The degree of technical excellence attained by the earliest Egyptian potters is truly amazing. The pot on the right has painted animal motives, while that on the left, owing to the fashion for stonework, is crudely painted to imitate marbled stone.

British Museum

How to Date Pottery. The knowledge of different types of ware can only be learnt by continual handling of the material ; consequently, study in a museum is an essential in the training of an archaeologist. The best method of studying is to draw the pots, for the range of shapes is so vast that it is impossible to remember them until the eye is trained by drawing. Each vase should be drawn to scale, either half or quarter size, in plain outline without any attempt at perspective or shading. With eyes and fingers well-trained by drawing pottery, the student will find that he can carry shapes of vases in his memory and will be able to compare them without always referring to the originals. Each class of object must be studied with the same meticulous care as the pottery, until the student feels he can recognize types of objects at sight.

While working at the actual objects, the student must also study the published material. Here again he should confine himself at first to pottery, until he can recognize and date shapes with complete accuracy. The evidence given in the publications as to levels at which pots were found, and the objects found with them, must be carefully noted ; and in this way the budding archaeologist not only learns archaeology, but also discovers how to publish his own excavations when that exciting time arrives. He very soon sees which books give him the information he requires, and which are the most easy of reference ; and he will model his own publication on the ones he finds best, and avoid the imperfections which he has noticed. He will also discover the imperative need of good publication of material as soon as possible after excavation, and will realize that to hold back results for more than three years constitutes an archaeological crime.

Study of Anthropology. The next item in the training of an archaeologist is the study of the living races of mankind, for archaeology has been well described as the ' anthropology of the past.' The modern anthropologist, by his work on the more backward peoples of the present day, has thrown a flood of light on the ancient civilizations in every part of the world. There are races still in existence

HANDIWORK OF PREHISTORIC POTTERS. *These vessels are typical primitive Greek pottery, and may be assigned to the Stone or early Bronze Age.*
British Museum

to whom the use of metal is unknown, and whose tools and weapons are of stone. These peoples live, in many respects, the life led by Neolithic man. We see so exactly how the stone tools and weapons were made and used that, instead of their being merely dull lumps of stone, they become instinct with vivid meaning.

Among more advanced peoples we can trace the use of mechanism applied to the making of various objects. The pointed stick rotated between the hands could be used to pierce small, smoothed pieces of dried clay to make beads ; when fed with emery or sharp sand the pointed stick would pierce stone. The stick could be turned more rapidly if a piece of string were twisted round it and the ends of the string attached to a piece of wood, when the movement of the stick horizontally to and fro, or vertically up and down, causes the drill to move much faster than if rotated by the hands alone. These two methods of working with a string and a piece of wood are known respectively as the bow drill and the pump drill.

These inventions largely increased the speed of the worker and consequently the amount of production. With a copper point or copper tube attached to the cutting end of the drill, the capacity for working stone would be immensely increased. The tubular drill was commonly used by the sculptors of ancient Egypt for blocking out their statues, and they were thus able to carve stones which are regarded as too hard by the modern sculptor.

Though the main work of the archaeologist is with the concrete remains of ancient civilizations, there are other aspects of those civilizations which can also be studied in the light of anthropology. Of these the most important is religion.

Systematized Religions, such as those of Egypt, Babylonia, India and Greece, had organized priesthoods, temples and temple furniture. The more organized the priesthood the greater is always the amount of material objects connected with the worship. In order to understand the use and meaning of many of such objects it is necessary to study some of the religions which are still in existence. Votive offerings made to the gods are often merely elaborated forms of objects of daily life, and by analogy with living religions we are justified in concluding that the offerers of those objects regarded their god as a kind of superman with the same needs and desires as a human being. Thus in ancient Egypt the carved slate palettes found in the temple of Hierakonpolis are large and elaborate forms of the slate palettes on which the primitive

Egyptian ground and prepared green malachite for painting his eyes. As the man required this protection against eye disease, so also did the god, but as the god was greater than the man his palette had to be much bigger than that needed for human use. With the palettes were found huge stone mace-heads, elaborately carved and far too heavy for use ; but they were clearly placed there for the benefit of the god, whose worshippers had found similar, though smaller, weapons extremely effective.

Buried in the Egyptian tombs, we find models of food and drink, and of the bakers, butchers and brewers who were to provide these necessities in the future life ; there are models, too, of the servants who were to minister to the dead man, and of his chariot and his ship. These symbols served instead of the actual persons and things ; it was held that they would become what they represented.

In many cases the social conditions can be inferred from the burial customs. If it is found that the tomb of a woman is as elaborate and the offerings buried with her as rich as those of a man, we may well conclude that the position of women in that community was high. Often, also, we can learn from the objects in a grave what the dead person's trade was, and whether certain trades were regarded as belonging specifically to one sex.

In countries where the language can be read, literary evidence must also be used ; but literary evidence alone is not a safe guide in archaeology. The greater part of European archaeology must be worked without the help of language, and anyone who has studied the amount of information available as to the Bronze and Iron Ages in the British Isles will realize that archaeology is in no way dependent on language and literary evidence but on the correct recognition and interpretation of concrete remains brought to light.

SUCH AS A GOD MIGHT USE. *Slate palette (left) and carved stone mace-head from Hierakonpolis. On the latter the ' Scorpion,' apparently the first king of the first dynasty, is seen with hoe in hand, to symbolize his public works or the opening of the agricultural year.*

Quibell, Hierakonpolis and Ashmolean Museum

When the Ice Sheet Covered Europe

As the earliest phase of archaeology begins with geology, a few words must be said on that subject, although it has a Course to itself in Vol. V. The great geological periods are named Primary, Secondary, Tertiary and Quaternary ; the last of these is the one in which we now are. With the first two periods archaeology has nothing to do, and it is therefore not necessary to consider them ; but in the tertiary, mammals first made their appearance, and it is here that the beginnings of Man and his works must be sought.

The tertiary period has four subdivisions, the Eocene, the Oligocene, the Miocene and the Pliocene; the Quaternary period has two subdivisions, the Pleistocene and the Holocene.

The first consideration in treating of these remote epochs is the condition of the land surfaces and the climate. The surface of the earth in Pliocene and Pleistocene times was altogether different from what it is now. The Mediterranean consisted of two comparatively small lakes entirely shut off from the Atlantic and from each other. The Nile was still a roaring torrent, cutting its way through the limestone plateau of northern Africa and emptying itself into the Mediterranean lake, where it deposited the mud which it carried in solution. African and European animals passed freely from one continent to the other across the land bridges which enclosed the Mediterranean lakes(*see* Chart, Vol. V, *f.p.* 128).

A glance at the map of the modern Mediterranean will show exactly where those ancient land bridges were situated. The British Isles were then part of the main land mass which we now call Europe, and that continent probably extended far into the Atlantic Ocean. On the mainland the configuration was not the same as now. Ranges of mountains, originally due to volcanic action, were not in existence, and there were open plateaux where there are now valleys. Therefore in the Pleistocene period we are dealing with land surfaces in

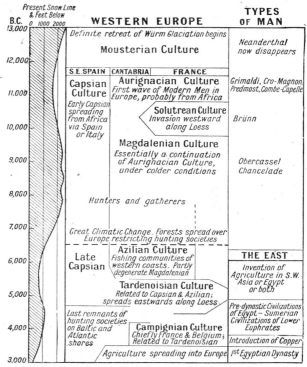

LATE STONE AGE RACES AND CULTURES. The colour-chart of Man's descent that appears in Geology, Vol. V, f. p. 128 carries on the human story from the Pliocene Period to the coming of ' true men ' towards the close of the fourth Ice Age ; but it is too compressed to show in detail the cultures that multiplied towards the end of the Palaeolithic (Old Stone) Age in Europe. The diagram given above amplifies the Chart, and carries on the story to the beginnings of agriculture in Europe and of recorded history in Egypt. It should be borne in mind that the dates and lengths of periods in prehistoric Archaeology are still the subject of controversy.

which the present barriers to intercourse did not exist. This is an important fact to remember when considering the spread of palaeolithic culture. Up to the present Europe has been more intensively studied than the other continents.

At the end of the Pliocene period the climate of Europe appears to have been temperate or even warm, for animals which occur now only in tropical and sub-tropical climates lived freely as far north as Germany. The climate then changed and gradually became exceedingly cold, with a spread of polar ice over the whole of northern Europe, forming a cap like that at the polar regions of the present day. The ice forced itself as glaciers into the warmer parts, cutting out valleys in the underlying rock. The pace at which the glaciers moved cannot be estimated, but it was probably faster than at present, owing to the tremendous pressure of the accumulated snow behind them. Their extent can be measured by the moraines which they have left, and their positions can be clearly seen by the valleys which they carved out. Another method by which their extent and position can be judged is by the so-called ' erratic ' blocks and boulders which they carried for immense distances on their surface and deposited when they retreated.

Four Ice Ages. The polar ice retreated more than once ; in fact, geologists recognize four great glaciations or ice ages. These are called by the names of the four Alpine valleys in which the evidence for their existence was first established. The names were purposely selected from many others as they occur in order alphabetically, and there is thus no difficulty in remembering their relative chronological position. These names are : (1) Günz, (2) Mindel, (3) Riss, and (4) Würm. The warm periods which occurred between the four glaciations are known as Günz-Mindel, Mindel-Riss, and Riss-Würm.

The reasons for these alterations in climate must be sought in geology. The archaeologist who studies the earliest remains of Man must understand the evidence of the various boulder clays which are the result of glaciation.

These immense masses of snow and ice must necessarily have had an effect on the climate, which would be extremely cold when within range of the glaciers and excessively rainy in the tropical and sub-tropical regions. The climate would affect the vegetation, and the vegetation would in its turn affect the types of animal which could live on it and successfully withstand all the rigours of an Arctic winter.

EUROPE IN THE ICE AGE. *This photograph of the Morteratsch Glacier in the Upper Engadine, Switzerland, shows the kind of scenery that predominated in Europe during the Ice Age. Note the lateral and medial moraines, ice-falls and upper ice-fields.*   *Courtesy of Swiss Federal Railways*

of the original nodule of flint is left at the butt for convenience of holding. In the later forms this crust has been cut away, perhaps because some method of hafting had been evolved. The typical tools are known as *coups-de-poing* or hand axes, although it is still a matter of conjecture what use they were put to. (Another name frequently given to them is *bouchers*, after the French archaeologist, Boucher de Perthes, 1788-1868.)

The Acheulean tools appear to be a development of the Chellean ; they are thinner and flatter, and the flakes were taken off in smaller chips. As the use of the tools is unknown one cannot say whether the change in the working was an improvement or a degradation of the Chellean tools. Flakes are also found among Chellean and

Attempts are being made by many archaeologists to correlate the pluvial or rainy periods of sub-tropical Africa with the glacial periods of Europe. This is one of the many problems which an archaeologist is called on to solve, and perhaps one of the most fascinating. It is difficulties such as this which give life and action to the subject, for a subject which is already thoroughly known and completely cut-and-dried is never inspiring, whereas archaeology is still in its infancy.

The actual appearance of Man on the earth must be sought in these remote epochs

of the world's history. In this quest there is nothing to guide the student but the archaeological method, assisted by geology and zoology. The position of the remains in, under, or above certain geological strata and the animal bones which accompany those remains must be thoroughly understood before any opinion can be formed as to the period to which the remains can belong, for it is possible to mistake the skull of an ape for that of a man, and it is also possible to think that a flint has been artificially chipped when the chipping is really due to natural causes.

LESSON FIVE

First Traces of Primitive Man

IT must always be remembered when dealing with the ages before history that our knowledge is still fragmentary, and that, therefore, the theories which are advanced to explain the various phenomena are not in any sense like ' the law of the Medes and Persians which altereth not.' On the contrary, though a working hypothesis is necessary, that hypothesis must be capable of modification in the light of such new evidence as may arise.

In the present state of knowledge only three glaciations—Mindel, Riss and Würm — and their respective interglaciations are accepted for England and France ; and as these are the two countries in which the Palaeolithic periods are well marked it is best to confine our attention to them.

It is as yet impossible to fix with any accuracy the period at which Man appeared on the earth. Actual human remains, such as bones and skulls, are not found till well into the quaternary era, but flints showing artificial chip-

ping have been discovered in the strata formed at the junction of the tertiary and quaternary epochs. These early stone implements are known as eoliths (Greek, *eos*, dawn ; *lithos*, stone).

Eolithic Period. The most interesting eoliths are the rostro-carinates, or keel-backed implements. The shape is characteristic, and is not found

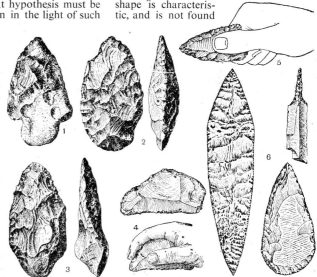

FLINT IMPLEMENTS OF PALAEOLITHIC MAN. 1, Pre-Chellean ; 2, Chellean ; 3, Acheulean ; 4, Acheulean knife, showing method of use ; 5, Mousterian ' point,' probably an implement of all work ; 6, beautifully fashioned Solutrean implements (Upper Palaeolithic).

British Museum; V. Commont, 'L'Anthropologie'; De Mortillet, 'Musée Préhistorique'

First Traces of 1

LESSON

Earliest Types of 1

THE attempt to investigate the origin of Man is one of the most absorbingly interesting subjects of study. It is a wide field, as it comprises the whole of the Old World, and it is always possible for a student to make epoch-making discoveries. Human remains of the Pleistocene era are rare, for earth movements and climatic changes have destroyed them. Stone implements fashioned by the hand of Man can survive long immersion in water or being dashed about in a torrent ; sudden and heavy falls of earth and rock will not break them or grind them to powder. But human bones are much more fragile than stone, and the wonder is that any have survived at all.

Prehistorians and anatomists are agreed that no human bones of the Tertiary period have survived ; the earliest appear to belong to the Riss-Würm interglacial epoch. All authorities are of opinion that the earliest type of Man was nearer to the ape than our present more developed species, though the missing link is still not found. The apes which are nearest to Man are the chimpanzee and the gorilla, but there

THE OLD STO	
Period	*Cli*
Upper Palaeolithic	Post-cold dry
Middle Palaeolithic	Würi glac cold moi
Lower Palaeolithic	Riss- inter tion

at any other period ; it is like an upturne boat with a keel running the whole leng of the back, a downward-curving beak the front, and with the chipping so arrange as to give a firm grip to the thumb ar fingers of the right hand.

At Foxhall, near Ipswich, in the same ty of strata as contains the rostro-carinate were found a number of burnt flint impl ments and pot boilers, i.e. stones whic had been made red-hot in the fire and the thrown into water to heat it. This show that the use of fire had been discovered eve at this remote period of time. Eoliths other forms, known as Pre-Chellean, ar found in many countries.

The making of tools and the discovery fire mark two of the greatest epochs in th evolution of Mankind. The making tools differentiates Man from the animal and though all the types of eoliths ar extremely primitive they are a definit advance on the unworked stones whic must be Man's earliest tools. A regards fire, the literary evidence ha always suggested that it was a late dis covery, but the evidence of archaeolog proves that it was one of the earliest of al the epoch-making inventions which hav carried Man so far from his primitive be ginnings and have differentiated him from his animal ancestors. It is extremel

PREHISTORIC, BUT IN USE TODAY. Most back-ward of the world's peoples are the Australian aborigines, one of whom is seen here chipping flints much as did his ancestor of 20,000 or so years ago.

Spencer & Gillen, 'Across Australia,'
Macmillan & Co., Ltd.

Early Human Remains. The most primitive of all the early skulls discovered is one which was found in Java in 1891. The stratum in which it lay belongs to the earliest Quater-nary period, almost to the Tertiary. Only the upper part of the skull was found, and with it were a thigh bone and three teeth. The creature had many ape-like characters, such as the heavy bony ridges above the brows, the crestlike ridge up the back of the skull and the size and shape of the teeth ; but it had also certain human characters. The brain cavity, though smaller than the human, was larger than in any known ape, whether fossil or living ; the straightness of the thigh bone showed that the animal stood erect in a position that apes cannot assume, and the anatomical evidence showed that in all probability the creature was capable of communicating with its fellows in a more complex manner than do the animals ; in other words, the capacity for speech had already begun. This Java find was named *Pithecanthropus*, to indicate that it combined the char-acters of both ape and Man.

In 1937 the dis-covery in Central Java of two new skulls of *Pithecan-thropus*—those of a female and of an infant — established that the so-called ape-man was a very primitive human being.

Other early human remains are a jaw found at Mauer, near Heidel-berg, which, though not of the type of modern Man, is certainly human. It can be dated to the early Pleistocene period by the ani-mal bones which occur in the same stratum, and is, therefore, one of the earliest speci-mens of the human race that is known. Next in date is the

skull found at Piltdown, in Sussex. This is not complete, but the greater part of the face and the lower jaw remain. The upper part is somewhat of the type of modern Man, with a high forehead and a fairly large brain capacity ; but the jaw and teeth are more ape-like than the Mauer jaw. Sir Arthur Smith Woodward assigned this skull to a human genus now extinct. Skulls of a very early type (*Sinanthropus*) have been found near Peking ; and the late Sir G. Elliot Smith called attention to the fact that early Man must have spread across the whole land-mass of the Old World, from Peking in the east to Sussex in the west, with *Pithecanthropus* and the Mauer remains intermediately.

Neanderthal Man. It is with the advent of the Middle Pleistocene that a well-defined type of Man appears. This is called after the place where, in 1856, the first skull of the type was found—Neanderthal, near Bonn,

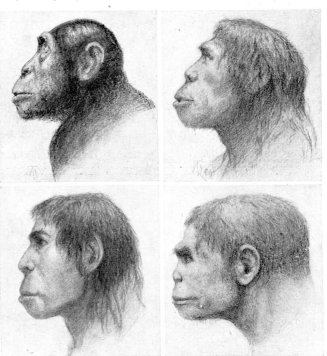

MAN-LIKE APE AND APE-LIKE MAN. Top, left, Chimpanzee. The three other drawings are reconstructions by Mr. H. Forestier, showing the probable appear-ance of Java Man (Pithecanthropus erectus, top right) ; Dawn Man (Eoanthropus, bottom left), skull fragments of whom were found at Piltdown, Sussex ; and Peking Man (Sinanthropus).

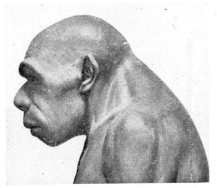

NEANDERTHAL MAN. *Reconstruction based on the well-preserved skull discovered in 1939 by Dr. A. C. Blanc in a cave at San Felice Circeo, Italy.*

on the Rhine. It belongs essentially to the Mousterian culture, and was spread chiefly over south-west Europe, though it is found also in Germany and Croatia. The best early example of this type was found at La Chapelle-aux-Saints, where much of the skeleton was also preserved. This creature when living must have stood about five feet three or four inches in height, but it is clear from the shape of the skull that he did not stand quite erect, but carried the head well forward, though not so much as an ape. Though the heavy brow ridges and the strong, projecting jaws are reminiscent of the ape, the shape of the jaw and the teeth are human.

In February, 1939, the best-preserved Neanderthal skull hitherto found was discovered by Dr. A. C. Blanc, of Pisa University, in the interior of a cave at San Felice Circeo, about halfway between Rome and Naples. The cave, also newly discovered, had evidently become blocked in Mousterian times, and its contents had remained untouched for a period of between 70,000 and 100,000 years. The skull, found lying among stones which appeared to have been disposed in a circle, is nearly complete. Under it were antlers and fossil bones of beasts, some showing intentional flaking.

Probably Neanderthal Man is not a direct ancestor of the present human race, but he is undoubtedly Man, and on the road to civilization. He lived in caves, possibly because of the coldness of the climate, but this may also show the beginnings of settlement. He was a hunter, killing even large animals for food, and he was well acquainted with the use of fire, and therefore probably

cooked his food. In Croatia he seems to have practised cannibalism, but this has not been observed elsewhere.

An interesting point in regard to Neanderthal Man is that we have here, it would seem, the first indication of religion. The skeleton from La Chapelle-aux-Saints had received ceremonial burial, for with it were stone implements of Mousterian types, as well as bones of food animals. This suggests that already Man had evolved the idea of a hereafter, and the tribesmen had sent their great chief to the next world well equipped. The stones surrounding the skull at San Felice Circeo also implied careful burial.

How many thousand years the Lower and Middle Palaeolithic periods lasted is quite unknown. The lapse of time must have been very great, for the implements show slow changes, and the development of Man must have been slower still. Nevertheless, in this most important period Man develops from an almost ape-like form to a certain degree of culture. Though he was not yet civilized, the beginnings of civilization can be traced.

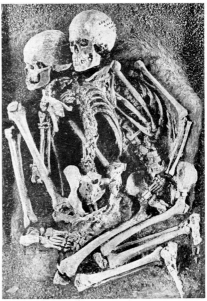

PREHISTORIC BURIAL. *These skeletons of an old woman (left) and a young man, found in the Grimaldi caves at Mentone, suggest careful and reverent sepulture—if not an actual belief in a life beyond the grave—for the man's head was encircled with a chaplet of shells and there were bracelets on the woman's arm.*

From Dr. R. Verneau, 'Les Grottes de Grimaldi'

Life in the Old Stone Age

THE great advance in civilization so noticeable in the Upper Palaeolithic era appears to be due to the advent of Homo sapiens, the forerunner of modern Man. Homo sapiens was contemporary with Homo Neanderthalensis, as is proved by the animal remains found with skeletons of both races. His ancestry is probably as remote as that of Neanderthal Man, but the difference between the two is so great that, had they been merely animals and not the genus Homo, they would have been classed as different species.

Neanderthal Man vanished completely before the onset of Homo sapiens ; but with the evidence at present at our disposal it is impossible to determine whether his disappearance was due to deliberate extermination by the invaders, or to his inability to withstand climatic changes and consequent changes in the food supply. Bones of Neanderthal Man have been found pierced with flint arrows of the type used by Man of the Upper Palaeolithic, but there is nothing to show whether these were accidental or premeditated killings.

Homo Sapiens Appears. Whatever the cause it is certain that in Europe Neanderthal Man became as extinct as his contemporary, the mammoth. Though there is some evidence that a remnant of this race migrated to, and survived in, Africa until within the Metal Age, Neanderthal Man is generally regarded as a belated form surviving only where conditions were favourable to him, but without the capacity to change with his environment. From the beginning of the Upper Palaeolithic until the present day—a period, on some calculations, of about 15,000 years—Homo sapiens has held his own. From the remote epoch of the last great Ice Age down to our own times, the history of the world is the history of Homo sapiens.

The Upper Palaeolithic Period is divided into three parts : Aurignacian, Solutrean, and Magdalenian. It is better to regard these as neither strictly chronological nor strictly geographical, but as a mixture of the two (*see* Diagram, page 415).

The people of the Upper Palaeolithic age lived in caves and rock shelters, where their tools and weapons and the remains of their food have been found. Usually their homes were close to streams, partly because the inhabitants were fishers, partly because they were hunters and the game would frequent a stream, and partly because they required water for their own needs. They were also traders, exchanging their tools and weapons and their personal ornaments with other communities. They probably bartered decorated objects and hides. Pierced shells were made up into necklaces and girdles and may have served as amulets as well as trinkets.

Their tools were far more varied than those of the earlier periods, showing that their requirements had increased as their civilization advanced. The simple savagery of the Lower and Middle Palaeolithic people was now left entirely behind, and in this period the old saying, ' the luxuries of one generation become the necessities of the next,' is well exemplified. Though even the Magdalenians were lower than the lowest of modern savages, yet they were definitely advanced in civilization compared with the races who preceded them.

Stone was not the only material used for implements at this time ; horn, bone and ivory were freely employed, and it is clear from their shape that many of the tools were hafted, probably with wood, though this has not survived. The weapons of the chase were smaller and lighter, showing that the large fierce animals of the Ice Age had disappeared with the approach of a more genial climate. Bears were no longer trapped in pits in the caves and killed by heavy stones thrown down on them from a height. Man of the Upper Palaeolithic period made sharp flint arrows with shafts of reed or wood, which could pierce through to the heart of deer or wild horse, but were entirely useless against the hide of a mammoth or the thick fur of the cave bear.

The Aurignacian Period shows an increase in the number of forms of tools over the Mousterian. Bone pins were used, probably for fastening the skins worn as garments, and there are various implements which may have been employed in dressing the skins. It has been suggested, on account of the absence of weapons of war, that the Upper Palaeolithic was the golden age, when there was no fighting. But it must be remembered that primitive weapons, such as stones, wooden clubs and slings, might not be recognized, or might have perished by disintegration in the course of centuries; and the arrows which have been found in the bones of Neanderthal skeletons must not be forgotten.

The Solutrean civilization does not occur in every site, and it is suggested that these people were not indigenous in Europe, but entered as invaders from the east. Their flint working is very fine ; the type of work is known as pressure flaking. It was done by breaking off the flake from the nodule by pressing, instead of by a blow, a method which leaves a series of transverse ripples across the surface of the cleavage. The size of the implements is markedly smaller than in the Mousterian, and the characteristic forms are called laurel leaves and willow leaves on account of their shape (*see* Fig. 6, page 413). So exquisitely fashioned are some that they are thought to have had a ceremonial use.

Eyed needle in reindeer horn and bodkins of ivory and bone, used by Solutrean housewives.
Photo,
Prof. D. K. Absolon

The **Magdalenian Period** is as important for the Upper Palaeolithic as the Mousterian is for the Lower and Middle Palaeolithic ages. The flint implements are not only surprisingly varied in shape, but occur in immense numbers. They are always small and appear to have been intended for fine work only, not for the rough usage of cutting down trees. Probably the men of the Upper Palaeolithic brought down a tree by ringing the trunk with fire, as is done by certain primitive peoples still even at the present day.

Bone implements are also numerous. Harpoons show a definite sequence of development, beginning with a shaft with a single notch on one side and gradually changing into a more formidable weapon with barbs down both sides of the shaft ; these objects were for spearing fish and in skilled hands would be very effective. Among the most interesting developments of bone implements are needles, both long and short, sharpened to a point at one end and pierced at the other. As the only use for a needle is sewing, it is clear that the Magdalenians were able to sew ; but as there is no evidence that they could spin or weave, the sewing must have been on leather, with sinews or fine strips of leather

HAUNT OF PALAEOLITHIC MEN. *The cave whose entrance is shown here is at Font-de-Gaume in the Dordogne, southern France, and contains one of the most famous picture-galleries of prehistoric art. The studies of animals—elephants, reindeer, bison and wolves—are remarkably realistic and brilliantly executed.*
Capitan, 'Caverne de Font-de-Gaume '

as the thread. Many of the small flint tools so common at this time may have been for dressing and cutting the leather and preparing the sewing materials.

It is as yet uncertain whether the people of the Upper Palaeolithic had learned the use of pottery, for no pottery which can be dated to this period has been found. The meat must, therefore, have been roasted on some form of spit or eaten raw, as boiling without a vessel capable of withstanding both fire and water is impossible.

Prehistoric Paintings and Sculptures

THE most surprising survival of the Upper Palaeolithic age, and one which most appeals to the modern mind, is its art. Even as far back as the Aurignacian period, artists had begun to record their impressions in the form of sculpture, both in the round and in relief. Occasionally also they made line drawings with a sharp tool on bone, horn or stone ; these crude artistic efforts become more frequent among the Magdalenians.

The Aurignacian confined his efforts to the representation of the human being. The greater number of his statuettes are of women, and are carved in mammoth ivory, in limestone and in steatite (*see* illus. in Vol. III, page 4). This type of female beauty is not one which appeals to modern taste, but it is one which must have been admired for many centuries in the ancient world, for statuettes of the same type are found in Egypt in the prehistoric (Amratian) period and in Malta in the Neolithic era, and it still survives among the Bushman women of Africa.

The chief characteristic is a marked fatness of the thighs and buttocks. Many of the Palaeolithic women were also immensely fat in the body as well, though the arms and lower part of the legs were

REALISM IN PALAEOLITHIC ART. *To carve so virile and individual a horse's head as this from reindeer antler, the Palaeolithic artist must have had real genius, together with a very intelligently developed technique. The carving was found in the Magdalenian deposits at Mas d'Azil.*

slender, even according to modern standards. It is noticeable that the faces of the statuettes and reliefs are never fully delineated and are often left blank. Traces of colour show that the figures were originally painted. The engravings are often of human beings clothed in animal skins, with the animal's head covering the face like a mask. Such figures occur in several sites of the Upper Palaeolithic era, even in Derbyshire. The motif is highly developed among the Magdalenians, and will be discussed later.

Magdalenian Paintings. In this period sculpture became of less consequence than painting. This is a sign of intellectual advance, for among primitive peoples a model may be understood when a drawing or painting would be regarded only as unmeaning lines and patches of colour. As Spearing says (' Childhood of Art,' p. 59), ' If you put up a painted sign of a fiercely barking dog, would that scare even the most timid cat ? ' Even at the present day there are many races who, like the cat, do not see the meaning of a picture. Consequently, when Magdalenian man produced his paintings and engravings he showed that artistically he had far outstripped his predecessors.

An artist is always more or less limited by his material. The Aurignacian worked in ivory, and in that almost ideal substance was able to produce really fine work in the round. The Magdalenian was not so fortunate, for the mammoth had deserted the warmer country and there was no more ivory to be had. The artist was restricted to bone and horn, neither of which is well adapted for carving in the round ; he, therefore, developed a technique called by the French *contour découpé*, in which the figures, though carved on both sides of the bone or horn, are really flat, the outlines being incised, but the roundness is that of the object and is not effected by modelling.

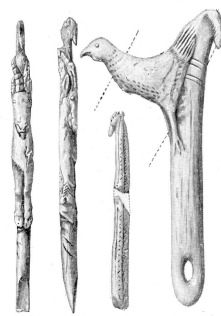

MAGDALENIAN CARVING. *Left, chamois carved on spear-throwers of reindeer horn. Centre, the notch to hold the spear-butt is well defined in this broken thrower. Right, skilfully carved grouse, partly restored.*

From Mas d'Azil, after Breuil and Piette

These decorated objects are numerous, but the uses to which they were put are uncertain. Occasionally some can be identified by a similarity with objects now in use among savage tribes. Among these are the spear-throwers that are used to lengthen the throw of the weapon ; there are also the handles of daggers or knives, but the long *bâtons de commandement*, which appear to have been of the utmost importance to the people who used them, are still unidentified by us. All these small carved objects are classed under the head of *art mobilier*, or chattel art, as they belong to the chattels of these primitive folk. Chattel art is at its finest in the Aurignacian period.

Cave Art. The real glory of the Upper Palaeolithic period is the cave or mural art. This may have begun when the technique of *contour découpé* was developing and the outline was becoming more important than the modelling. Such a technique was easily transferred to a rock surface, and the artist began to realize that in paint he could have a substitute for sculpture. The human statuettes of Aurignacian times were certainly painted, but there the colour was subsidiary to the modelling ; on a rock surface the artist discovered that paint could be used as a medium in itself. It is possible that the new method took its rise in the custom of smearing the hand with colour and the nmaking an impress on a smooth part of the rock ; or by placing the hand on a piece of rock previously prepared and then powdering the paint over it, leaving the form of the hand in the natural colour of the rock imprinted against a background of colour.

Animal Paintings. Sketches begin very tentatively, gradually becoming free and naturalistic ; and there is a sudden advance when the painted outline was softened by rubbing to produce the effect of shading. Then came the full tide of Palaeolithic painting, the splendid art of the caves, which was never equalled by any ancient nation. The greater number of the subjects are animals. Not only is the drawing brilliant, but the pigments are so laid on as to produce the effect of light and shade as well as the natural colouring of the animal represented. The method used was to cut on the rock surface parts of the outline of the figure ; the rock within those lines was then carefully scraped till quite smooth, and the pigments were laid on, either as a paste or a liquid, until the whole surface was covered. The artist now proceeded, with flint or bone scrapers, or perhaps with a piece of hide from which the hair had not been removed, to wash and scrape away the paint until he had obtained the result he desired ; then with a little black paint he added the horns, hoofs and other details. The colours used were mineral products. They are forms of iron ore, such as the different ochres. The lumps were powdered with pestles in stone mortars, and both pestles and mortars have been found in the settlements. The powdered paints were kept in hollow tubes of bone. The outlines were drawn with sharpened pieces of iron ore. Examples of these cave paintings are reproduced in colour in plates accompanying the Course on Social History in Vol. III.

Ideas of the Supernatural. Besides the large number of remains of his cultural environment, Palaeolithic Man has left some indications of his religious beliefs. These have to be interpreted by our knowledge of the religions of modern savages, for though the savage of the present day is farther advanced both intellectually and in the capacity for intellectual improvemen than Palaeolithic Man, yet he has retained certain beliefs and customs which seem to date back to a more primitive stratum.

Of the earliest periods nothing remains to show what the beliefs were—if, indeed, any existed ; but Neanderthal Man has left at least one burial, by which it is possible to learn something of the religious views of the Mousterian people. In a small cave at La Chapelle-aux-Saints, in the department of Corrèze, France, there was found the fossilized skeleton of an elderly man. It was a burial conducted with as much ceremony as the kinsmen and friends of the dead man had been capable of. The man had perhaps been a chief, a leader in war or hunting ; though elderly, he was strong and well built, but, like all his race, unable to stand or walk entirely upright. Round about the body had been placed numerous flint implements, and the bones of animals laid beside him show that the dead man had been provided with food.

Belief in Survival. All this indicates that this early race had arrived at the belief that death was not the end, had conceived the idea of a hereafter—childish and primitive, no doubt, but a factor affecting the religious development of Mankind. It should be noted that there are no signs of human sacrifice ; the dead man does not appear to have been a victim, and human beings were not killed at his grave to accompany him to the other world. Such

rites were reserved for the more developed and systematized religions of a later date. Homo sapiens also buried his dead with ceremony. There is, for instance, in the Grimaldi caves a burial of a man, who was laid on his back with his head turned slightly to one side in the attitude of sleep ; he lies, in fact, ' like a warrior taking his rest.' In Franconia and in Switzerland other cave burials have been found of a different type. In these the skulls only had been preserved ; they were arranged between the side of the cave and a little wall, which had been built so as to form a kind of chamber. The preservation of the skull only may perhaps be explained by the custom of certain aboriginal tribes in India who, after the burial of a kinsman, dig up the skull and place it with those of his ancestors in a shrine, believing that the spirits of the dead survive and inhabit the skulls, and that, being treated with honour, they will protect and help their descendants.

In many cases the bones are found covered with red ochre—for a reason which is still obscure. It may have been done with some view of placating the spirit of the dead, who is often supposed by primitive minds to be incensed at being driven out of the body. Burials of women are as common as those of men, showing that the women were treated as being on the same level with men.

Though the burial customs are interesting, they are never so vivid as the beliefs of the living ; and among the people of the Upper Palaeolithic such beliefs are indicated in their art—especially the art of the caves. The decorated caves were never inhabited by Man, who always lived in shallow caves with wide entrances, or in rock-shelters. This was quite natural, inasmuch as wild beasts have an affection for dark caverns as dwelling-places. But the decorated caves are almost invariably long and very tortuous, and the decoration is in the innermost passages, where no light could ever penetrate. The artist worked by the dim light of a sandstone lamp in which animal fat was burnt. In short, the paintings and sculptures

MASTERPIECE OF A PRIMEVAL LANDSEER. *These amazingly realistic bison, male and female, in the cave of Tuc d'Audoubert, French Pyrenees, have been preserved through the ages owing to a nearby subterranean river which has kept moist the clay of which they are composed. The numerous prints of naked feet, with heels deeply impressed, in their neighbourhood, add weight to the theory that they are symbols of fertility, and that the devotees danced out their litanies after the way of the modern savage.*
From Bégouen, ' L'Anthropologie '

were hidden in the darkness of un-inhabitable caves, placed in positions which are often difficult to see, and in winding passages where it is easy to lose the way. It is very evident that they were not for the vulgar to gaze upon, nor were they made by the artist for the sheer joy of creation ; clearly they were for something higher and greater.

Religious Motive of Cave Art. The paintings and sculptures of the period represent, with few exceptions, food animals, which are almost invariably shown drawn singly and often as though pierced with arrows. There are seldom any human figures, and these are never shown in the act of hunting ; they are represented as masked with animals' heads, clothed in animals' skins, and performing some kind of dance. By analogy with modern primitive races, it becomes certain that the figures, whether animal or human, were not merely the expression of the artist's feelings, but had an underlying religious meaning.

The belief in the efficacy of sympathetic magic is deeply rooted in the primitive mind. To imitate an action is to ensure its fulfilment ; to paint a bison or deer pierced with arrows would ensure that at the next hunt game would be secured. If the life of a tribe depended on the continual killing of wild animals for food, the hunters would use every means, spiritual as well as physical, to attain that very desirable end. This belief explains the representation of the pierced animals ; and it also explains why the animals are often depicted as standing quietly and thus affording a good target for the huntsman.

The Dance. The dancing figures can also be understood by reference to other cults. Modern savages have ceremonial fertility dances for the animals on which they live. Sometimes these dances are performed by the whole community, sometimes by one man alone. In the latter case, the single performer is usually the chief or king, in whom is supposed to reside the magical power of fertility. When he is clothed in the skin of an animal he is regarded, and regards himself, as the animal he represents. He apes the actions of the animals—rhythmically, as a dance.

Early Migrations. Where modern man originated is still a subject for conjecture. In looking back across the whole range of the early periods we see that the movements of peoples have been in progress since the beginning. The origin of Eolithic Man is unknown, but his remains have been dis-

PREHISTORIC SORCERER. *Although in the examples of Palaeolithic art known to us there are no paintings of the human figure at all comparable to those of animals, there are several vigorous representations of men in animal guise. The most famous of these is ' The Sorcerer ' in the cavern of Les Trois Frères, showing a man disguised with stag horns, reindeer mask, and legs and tail of other animals. It has been suggested that the figure represents a magician leader comparable to the Chief Wizard of the medieval Witches' Sabbaths, the make-up being adopted to bring success in game-stalking.*
Courtesy of M. C. Burkitt

covered to a large extent in England. The Chellean culture entered southern Europe from Africa, probably by way of the land-bridge at Gibraltar ; it may have originated in Asia Minor and worked round the north coast of Africa. The Acheulean, which was possibly only a more developed Chellean, moved from at least three centres—France, Russia and Asia Minor. The Mousterian began in central Europe, whence it was driven southwards by the increasing cold of the last great glaciation. The Aurignacians were partly of African origin, but there was also a spread from a centre in Italy. The Solutreans were from eastern Europe and came westwards, but never reached the Mediterranean. The Magdalenians started in the west and moved eastward. In every period, therefore, there was movement throughout the Old World.

Archaeology

LESSON NINE

Pottery as a Guide to Prehistory

IN the Neolithic period the centre of civilization shifts from the western to the eastern Mediterranean—Egypt and Crete begin to take a prominent part in the history of the world.

The civilization of Egypt has been so carefully studied that it is taken as a standard for dating in all countries of the Near East until they can establish a dating of their own. Before the beginning of history—that is, of the written word—it is impossible to date by years ; some other method has to be adopted. For Egypt, the simple and effective method of progressive arithmetical notation, first used by Petrie, is followed ; it is known as sequence-dating (abbreviated to S.D.). This was worked out entirely on the pottery by numbering each successive type ; thus, if a type of pot belongs to S.D.35 one knows that it is earlier than 36, though later than 34. The difference in time is not given, but the sequence is clear. To use a geological term, sequence-dating gives the ' horizon ' in a named period. By this method it was shown that between S.D.38 and 43 there was a great change in early Egyptian civilization, due apparently first to peaceful penetration and afterwards to conquest.

There are five prehistoric periods in Egypt : Tasian, Badarian, Amratian, Gerzean, and Semainian, each called after the place in which the civilization was first found or specially studied. The original discoveries, which entirely revolutionized the whole of Egyptology, included only the last three periods ; but, realizing from the type of civilization that a long and settled civiliza-

tion must have preceded the Amratian, Petrie began the first sequence-dating at 30, leaving room for a whole series when found.

Badarian Civilization. Miss Caton Thompson's work at Badari is a fine example of the important results of good field-work. The first indication of this new civilization was the discovery of some potsherds of unknown type from a site near the village of Badari, in Upper Egypt. The site was a small mound, which Miss Caton Thompson cleared in six-inch slices. On the upper layers she found the characteristic pottery and flint tools of the Gerzean age, S.D.50-60 ; these grew fewer as the work progressed and sherds and flints of Amratian age appeared, till there were no more of the Gerzean period, but only Amratian. Still lower, potsherds of the new type, now called Badarian, were found with the Amratian ; the Amratian decreased in number, till at ground level there were only Badarian flints and pottery. In this excavation the sequence of the pottery abundantly proved Petrie's typological method of sequence-dating. The Badarian civilization ends at S.D.30, and goes back probably to S.D.22. More recently Brunton claimed a still earlier civilization, which he called Tasian. This is certainly Neolithic, but the Badarian shows the incoming of the use of metal. From the Tasian period onwards the cultural history of Egypt can be traced without a break to the present day.

First Potters. The Tasian period is represented chiefly by pottery, for it is in the Neolithic era that pottery first appears. The Tasian pottery is coarse, as is the Neolithic pottery of western Europe. The shapes are uncouth, and the whole style of the pottery suggests that the potters were unskilled. The tools were always of flint ; there is not a trace of any kind of metal.

The Badarian civilization was considerably higher than the Tasian, and towards the end had reached the period known as Chalcolithic, when metal was coming into use, though in such small quantities that stone was still the common material for tools and weapons. Metal at this period was a luxury—one of those luxuries which in course of time became a necessity.

The pottery is fine-grained and fairly well baked. The ware is often covered with a

BADARIAN WARE. *The pottery of the Badarian civilization, so called because of the remains first found at Badari, near Assiut, in Upper Egypt, is characterized by its rippled surface, as is seen on the bowl pictured here.*

wash of haematite (iron ore), which burns to a fine dark red in an open kiln or to a lustrous black when the air is excluded. The Badarian potters seem to have made the discovery of this property of haematite, and used it with good effect by placing the pot mouth downwards in the kiln and then covering it for a few inches with ashes. When thus fired the pot is dark red with an irregular band of lustrous black at the top. The pot was usually burnished both before and after firing, which brings out the beauty of the colour. Such pots are known as 'black-topped.'

Decoration. The characteristic method of decoration of Badarian pottery is the rippling of the surface. This began—as so much decoration of all kinds begins—with the object of serving a useful purpose, in this case by thinning the walls of the vessel. The ripples were produced by some kind of comb—perhaps a piece of wood with notches—with which the sides of the pot were lightly scraped, the lines going diagonally. Many of the pots were polished after being rippled, for the ridges are often rubbed down or even erased. A special

type of decoration is a slightly incised and highly burnished design on an unburnished surface ; the designs are drawn in fine lines and often appear to represent palm-branches. Occasionally the palm-branches are laid across one another, and the intersection of lines produced an effect of cross-hatching, which was used in other designs merely because the potter admired it. The shape peculiar to the period is a shallow bowl with a sharp keel, possibly a copy in pottery of a leather vessel, such as were, doubtless, in everyday use.

Earliest Wheat. The Badarian era is, so far, the earliest period with definite evidence of the cultivation of wheat. Grains of wheat were found, and flint-toothed sickles were also discovered. Wheat does not grow naturally in Egypt, but the kind called emmer wheat is native in Syria and Palestine, where, presumably, it was first cultivated, and whence it could have been easily introduced into Egypt. Egyptian tradition supports this theory, for the legend of Isis and Osiris states that the two deities came from the north bringing with them corn and the vine. There is no proof that the vine

3,000 YEARS OF POTTERY FORM. *Pottery is a most useful index for classifying the undated ages of prehistory, and from the progressive alterations in its form archaeologists are enabled to construct a series of ' sequence dates ' for the peoples who made it. The sequence in the above illustration covers 3,000 years and shows the connexion between a large globular jar and a little conical pot fitted only for ceremonial use.*

Courtesy of Sir Flinders Petrie

was introduced so early, as no seeds or leaves have been found.

Another proof of the foreign connexions of the Badarians is seen in the remains of pine and cedar woods. As no conifers grow in Egypt these woods must have been imported, perhaps from Lebanon or the Aegean. The obvious way of transporting wood from either of those two regions is by sea, but though water transport can be inferred there is no evidence that the people of the Badarian epoch—Egyptian, Syrian or Aegean—used boats for this purpose. The flint implements used by this prehistoric people are peculiar in that

they were invariably made of nodules of flint which were picked up on the desert, although there were veins of better material to hand. Miss Caton Thompson suggests that the Badarians were an intrusive people, who were not accustomed to finding their flint *in situ*, and had not realized the inexhaustible supply which lay close by. ' I am tempted to see in the preference of the Badarians for a raw material of rough derivative nodules of which to fashion their tools and weapons, while far finer material lay at their very door, a perpetuation of enforced habits acquired in their ancestral home outside the Nile Valley.'

LESSON TEN

Advent of the Neolithic Age

IN the history of the world, as in the history of a country, there are times when civilization appears to fall below its previous level. This is the case in the Neolithic period. The junction of the Palaeolithic and Neolithic ages is not satisfactorily determined. Not many years ago the gulf was regarded as impassable, but the discoveries in the Mas d'Azil (Pyrenees) and elsewhere have helped to narrow the space. This intermediate period is called the Epipalaeolithic. It probably lasted a very long time, for the climate changed—a fact causing or being caused by changes in the configuration of the land, both in outline and on the surface. **Retreat of the Ice.** The problem of the northward retreat of the ice belongs to geology, but the effect on the history of Mankind concerns archaeology. According to some geologists and zoologists the evidence shows that earth movements were the cause of the changes. The rising of the land brought with it an increase of ice and snow, while the sinking of the land and the consequent advance of the sea had the opposite effect, and resulted in a warmer climate (*see* Colour Plate Vol. V, f. p. 128.)

Throughout Europe subsidence was of the utmost importance. The eastern lake of the present Mediterranean increased in size by forming the Adriatic ; the two lakes were joined together and broke through to the Atlantic ; the British Isles were cut off from the continent of Europe ; the Baltic, after various oscillations, was united with the newly formed North Sea. In short, Europe had assumed her familiar shape.

The storm-zone, which rings the earth and brings with it the rain-bearing winds, followed the retreating glaciers ; it no longer traversed the Mediterranean, but moved northwards beyond the Pyrenees and Alps. The Sahara, once a grassy plain full of game, dried up and became a desert waste. Europe was filled with forests and marshes, the only open spaces being the limestone hills, chalk downs and sandy heaths. The whole aspect and conditions of life had changed.

Capsian Period. The magnificent Upper Palaeolithic period had passed away, leaving only degenerate forms of art and flints. The African hunters followed the game from the drying Sahara into the more fertile continent of Europe, bringing with them their art and flint tools. The art differs from that of the Upper Palaeolithic by being more diagrammatic, though full of life and vigour. In some ways also it is more advanced, as the artists often attempt to represent groups, such as a dance or a hunt, which was never done by Aurignacian or Magdalenian Man. This type of civilization, which is the last of the Palaeolithic, is called Capsian, and remains of its culture have been found in eastern Spain.

The Capsians appear to have amalgamated with the degenerate folk of Europe, whose painted pebbles and pygmy flints are found in many places. The cave of Mas d'Azil and the type-station of Tardenois have given their names to this period, and the microliths (pygmy flint tools) are known as Azilian and Tardenoisian. Capsian art degenerated in course of time, though there is some evidence to show that the diagrams, which took the place of careful drawings, indicate a higher mental development, the mind being sufficiently educated to realize that a symbol was quite as valuable as a naturalistic representation ; in fact, these diagrams may be the beginnings of writing.

Homo sapiens, who first appeared in the Palaeolithic era, was long-headed (dolichocephalic) ; so also was Capsian Man. Some time during the intermediate period there came into Europe from the east a new type of people, who were broad-headed (brachycephalic). These settled among the long-heads and perhaps intermarried with them, but the exact effect of the intermixture as regards civilization is not yet certain. It should be noted that, although Europe may be the original home of Neanderthal Man, it is fairly certain that the later races of Man entered Europe either from the east, i.e. Asia, or from the south, i.e. Africa. It is possible that even the African invaders were people who had first migrated from Asia.

Neolithic Man, when he first appears on the scene, was a hunter, like his Palaeolithic predecessor. The animals of the chase were, however, different from those of earlier times. The reindeer and other Arctic animals had followed the retreating ice northward ; the rhinoceros and elephant could no longer cross into Europe ; their places were taken by red deer, wild cattle, and other creatures which flourish in the temperate zone.

It was in the temperate zone that the mixture of races took place which has produced our modern civilization. Though Palaeolithic Man may be our ancestor physically, Neolithic Man is our ancestor in civilization. The struggle for existence in the Ice Age was severe, and, until the climate moderated, there was little time for the amenities ; but the milder climate brought with it opportunities for improvement of living conditions, and each improvement gave more leisure to invent further improvements. The hunting age gradually passed either into the pastoral or the agricultural, according to the opportunities afforded.

On open grassy plains Man domesticated animals and became the owner of flocks and herds ; on rich fertile soil he took to farming and had corn-fields, keeping only a few animals to provide meat.

Neolithic civilization, therefore, varies according to the country in which it flourished. It cannot be studied as a more or less complete whole, like the Palaeolithic period ; each part must be examined separately. The pastoral people, whether nomad or settled, developed a different civilization and different social customs and religious ideas from those of the settled agriculturists. This difference between the two types of culture underlies the Biblical story of Cain and Abel—a story which has been handed down from a race of pastoral people who regarded the settled agriculturist with contempt and some fear.

As long as a people are merely food-gatherers, progress must necessarily be slow ; hunters and gatherers of wild fruits and roots live a rough, exacting life, where there is little opportunity for improvement. The food-producers can provide for hard times by domesticating animals and by growing grain and other foods ; the women and children are better fed and the race improves intellectually and physically.

Neolithic Culture in Crete. The beginnings of Neolithic civilization must be sought in the Near East. Crete is only a later development of the culture of Egypt, Mesopotamia, and Asia Minor ; but, as Gordon Childe puts it, ' the true originality of our ancestors was displayed in the manner in which they adapted and improved the inventions of the Orient. In this sense the inhabitants of our continent were truly and remarkably creative.' In Crete the Neolithic stratum extends to a depth of 6½ metres below the oldest layers of the Minoan culture at Cnossus. The vast length of time required for the accumulation of this mass of débris puts the beginning of the Neolithic age in Crete at a very early period. Although the inhabitants of Crete did not possess any metals, they were far from being primitive barbarians. Already they were well advanced in the art of

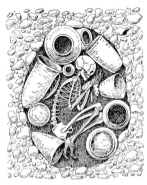

CAREFUL SEPULTURE. The care with which the dead were interred in the Neolithic age, with their possessions grouped about them (as in the Egyptian burial seen here), is evidence of a well established belief in the continued existence (and potential vindictiveness) of the disembodied soul.

From de Morgan, ' Prehistoric Man '

pottery making ; their vessels are provided with handles and spouts. Stone axes were ground down to an edge instead of being chipped, and grinding was also applied as a method of drilling holes in stone implements to facilitate hafting. The boring was done with sand, either wet or dry, and a pointed piece of stick or a hollow reed. This method was perhaps borrowed from the Badarian people of Egypt who, however, appear to have used it only for drilling stone beads. Spools and spindle-whorls of clay show that they could spin and work in textiles.

The Neolithic Cretan built himself a square house with stone foundations—unlike the Egyptian, who always seems to have preferred . mud. Trade must have come already to the island, as obsidian is found —which establishes the fact that water traffic had begun in the Aegean area.

Greece. Contemporaneously with Crete, on the mainland of Greece the people were using polished stone axes, hafted probably with wood or antler. The forms of pottery suggest metal prototypes ; this is not impossible, as coast-dwellers are more in contact with other nations and civilizations than the inland folk, who as a rule tend to be slightly more backward. It may be that the coast-dwellers had already begun to use metal before the inland people, who, therefore, could only imitate the new shapes in their ancient material.

Italy and France. In northern Italy and southern France the Neolithic folk were now herdsmen and hunters, living in caves or huts partially sunk below the level of the ground. The pottery is more primitive in form and ware than that of the more eastern civilizations, and is suggestive, therefore, of being a copy by less experienced potters. In southern Italy and Sicily the connexions are entirely with the eastern Mediterranean. Though some families lived in caves, there were many villages of built houses, often defended by trenches and ramparts. The inhabitants were herdsmen, and kept goats, sheep, pigs and cattle ; but it is doubtful whether they had arrived at the agricultural stage. Their pottery was remarkably fine and highly decorated with

NEOLITHIC LAKE DWELLERS. Some of the new-comers to western Europe during the New Stone Age lived in huts raised on piles over shallow lakes and marshes and connected with the land by wooden causeways, easily removed in time of danger. This is an impression of a typical lake-village (see p. 444.)

After Prof. J. M. Tyler. 'New Stone Age' (Scribners)

incised designs filled in with white gypsum. Occasionally also they used paint for the ornamentation of their vases, usually black or red. The stone implements of this period are poor in style and few in quantity.

Malta. The Neolithic period of Malta cannot as yet be brought into connexion with that of any other country. Its age is determined by the fact that the remains found on the rock-floor of the temple of Tarxien were covered with a layer of more than three metres deep of wind-blown detritus ; above this sterile layer, which represents the period when the temple was abandoned, there were found pottery and objects of the early Bronze age. The Neolithic pottery of Malta is characterized by the beauty of the ware and the fineness of the finish. The shapes of the vases are peculiar, and the handles are almost invariably of the ' tunnel ' kind. That the pottery is indigenous to the island is shown by the fact that several of the vases, including a very large one, were broken in the firing ; they must, therefore, have been made in Malta, and not imported. With these vases were found figures of human beings made in clay or stone, all being of an early type.

The Mediterranean culture was clearly spread by sea, and as it proceeded farther west and north it shows signs of degeneration and of admixture with other elements. In the meantime, far north, a remnant of the Epipalaeolithic people carried on the older culture, having little or no contact with the higher civilization of the south.

Scandinavia. Much work has been done in the Scandinavian countries, with the result that our knowledge of the conditions of life on the shores of the Baltic is fairly extensive. The Maglemose culture began when that sea was a landlocked fresh-water lake, now known to us as the Ancylus lake, from the name of a fresh-water mussel, the most characteristic of its denizens.

Maglemose people were food-gatherers, mostly fishermen, but there is some evidence that they trapped wildfowl and hunted deer. They had implements of flint and of horn and bone, and they had advanced so far beyond their Palaeolithic predecessors that they hafted their tools with wood or horn. They made pygmy flint points as barbs for harpoons. Their dwellings were wooden rafts on the lake or wooden platforms on its shores ; this shows that they were able to fell trees and work wood.

By a further oscillation of the land the sea broke through into the Ancylus lake and brought with it the salt water new types of water creatures. The extension of the sea also caused a change of climate, which became warmer. The changes affected the civilization, and the Maglemose culture developed into that of Ertebolle. The people were still food-gatherers at the beginning of this epoch, but by the end of the time they were to some extent food-producers. The great shell heaps or kitchen-middens of Denmark belong to this period, and in the upper layers of the heaps are found the remains of a few domestic animals, some grains of wheat and pieces of coarse pottery.

LESSON 11

The Megalithic Voyagers

THE Near East passed rapidly through the transition period between the Stone and the Metal Ages, and arrived at the knowledge and use of copper long before the peoples of western Europe. The contemporary civilizations of East and West are entirely different at this period. That two kinds of civilization should run parallel at the same time is not surprising. Even at the present day the Australian aborigines and some tribes of American Indians use nothing but stone tools and are ignorant of metals ; in other words, their civilization is Neolithic, while ours has passed beyond the Bronze and Iron Ages to a stage when all metals are used.

Though western Europe was backward in many ways, there is a considerable amount of evidence to show the existence there of several centres of culture which affected even the Mediterranean civilization. Spain and Portugal contained more than one early focus from which civilization radiated northward along the Atlantic coast and eastward through the Mediterranean. The influence from these centres must have been waterborne, for even as far north as Scotland a dugout boat plugged with cork has been found with Neolithic objects. Though it is as yet doubtful whether Palaeolithic Man learned how to make boats, it is quite certain that Neolithic Man moved freely on the face of the waters. The first sailors would be the people living on the banks of rivers or by the seashore, and the latter would be the more daring and skilful.

The most important feature of the Neolithic era is the beginning of the megalithic culture, which lasted through the Bronze Age down to the Iron Age. North-west Spain and Portugal may be responsible for its spread, which was certainly due to sea traffic—at least, in its earlier stages.

Dolmens. The oldest form of megalithic tomb is known as dolmen, perhaps from two Cornish words meaning ' stone hole.' Four types of dolmen exist. The earliest, which is undoubtedly Neolithic, consists of a chamber formed by setting up three or more blocks of unhewn stone to form a roughly rectangular or oval enclosure, which was then roofed with a single block or slab of unhewn stone ; the roofing block is called a capstone. The upright stones which formed the walls were arranged to leave a gap as a doorway.

The second type was also Neolithic. It consisted of a chamber like that of the first type, but two stones were set up, one on each side of the doorway, to form a kind of entrance or rudimentary corridor, which was often covered with a second capstone. In course of time the entrance corridor was elongated and was roofed throughout its length with blocks or slabs of stone. This type is known as the passage-grave—in French as *dolmen à galerie*. The later stages of this type may belong to the Bronze Age.

The third type of dolmen belongs to the Bronze Age, but it is more convenient to describe it here, in order to show the development of these structures. In this stage the passage became more important than the chamber, which was now little more than a kind of annexe. This is called the covered gallery tomb or ' long stone cist '—in French, *allée couverte*.

In the fourth type the gallery fell into disuse and became smaller, until, in the final stage, it had shrunk into nothingness and only the cist or small stone chamber was left. This is so like the original primitive form of the first type that it is

only possible to distinguish between the two stages by the objects found. All types of dolmen were originally covered with a mound of earth, called in English a barrow ; in many places the barrow has disappeared, leaving the dolmen exposed.

Dolmens were always collective tombs, a kind of family vault, though it is clear that more than one family was buried in each dolmen. It would perhaps be more correct to call them tribal burial places. In the third type the long gallery was also used as a receptacle for the dead.

MEGALITHIC MONUMENTS. Typical of the less elaborate dolmen tombs is Kit's Coty House (upper photograph) at Aylesford in Kent. Originally the whole structure was enclosed within an earthen barrow. The lower photo shows the central chamber of the elaborate dolmen at La Hougue Bie in Jersey, built of huge monoliths and situated in a vast tumulus composed of some 20,000 tons of earth.
Lower photo, Société Jersaise

There is evidence of an elaborate funerary ritual. Offerings of many kinds were often placed with the dead, and it is to these objects that we owe a great part of our knowledge of the civilization of the Neolithic period in the west of Europe. Pottery was common; it was handmade, usually badly baked, and the walls of the vessels are thick and coarse. In England the rims are always carefully made, and the vessels are generally in the form of a round-bottomed bowl. The decoration is incised and is simple in style. A variation from the plain incisions is made by impressing a piece of coarsely-twisted string on the soft clay ; this makes the marks known as ' maggot-pattern.'

Brittany and Ireland were among the chief centres for the megalithic voyagers of the Neolithic era. The dolmens in both those countries are often highly decorated with various sculptured designs. Of these the most important are at Newgrange in Ireland and at Gavr'inis in Brittany ; in both places the whole of the inner faces of the stones is sculptured. In other parts of the British Isles and western Europe the sculptures consist of hollows cut in the stones, which are called ' cup-marks.' Their significance is quite unknown.

The stream of trade, which carried the megalithic folk from north-west Spain northwards, seems to have divided into two parts. One went up to Brittany and thence to Scandinavia ; the other went up the west coast of Ireland and Scotland, and reached Scandinavia by a longer voyage. After the modifications resulting from contact with another people and with another climate, the trade came southwards ; but now the route appears to have been only by way of Brittany. Consequently, it is in Brittany that the meeting of both influences is to be found.

The Danubians. While the megalithic culture was spreading westwards, a different civilization began in central Europe. Here the geographical conditions are of the greatest importance in following the course of the civilizing peoples. An agricultural race pushed up the Danube, coming from south and east. They settled on the fertile soil on each side of the river, and, as the population increased, colonists went farther afield in search of pastures new. The sides of the Danube and its tributaries were peopled in this way. In its upper reaches the Danube is not far from two great tributaries of the Rhine, the Neckar and the Main ; and thus the Danubian civilization reached the North Sea. Then, by the valley of the March and through the Moravian Gate, the headwaters of the Oder and the Vistula are reached. By those rivers access to the northern plains was easy, and so the civilization of the eastern Mediterranean filtered through to Europe.

LESSON 12

Two Later Periods of Prehistoric Egypt

METAL was used in the eastern Mediterranean long before it came to the West. Egypt and Mesopotamia led the way in this new development, and there is some evidence that the use of metal may have been introduced from India. The Amratian civilization of Egypt seems to have developed from the more ancient Badarian. The pottery was of the same type and many of the Badarian shapes continued in use. Obviously, however, new influences were at work—the keeled bowls disappeared ; tall trumpet vases and small egg-shaped vessels became common. The Amratian potters introduced a new method of decoration by applying white slip on the burnished red ground, a totally different ornament from the fine lines of the Badarians, though the cross-hatching was continued. The thick white cross-hatched lines give the effect of basket-work so strongly that it is generally supposed that many of the shapes originated in basketry. The actual ware was not so good as in the previous period, but the decoration became more varied and interesting, and includes human and animal figures as well as geometric designs. An open dish in the form of a boat has a slip decoration representing the oars, cabins, and other details ; this is the first actual evidence of water transport in this early era.

The decadent forms of the Amratian stone vases show a long and uninterrupted period of decline. The prevalent shape is a cylindrical vase, too tall for its width, and standing on a high and narrow foot, which gives a top-heavy effect. In course of time the foot decreased in height and width, till in the end it became merely a button-like excrescence with a rounded base. The vase was evidently not intended to stand, but was meant to be suspended by a string through the handles. The stones used were basalt, alabaster, and limestone, all of which are obtainable in the Nile valley. The slow decadence of the shapes shows that the change from the Badarian to the Amratian was peaceful, and was probably caused by the settlement in the country of Amratian foreigners who intermarried with the native Badarian inhabitants.

Use of Copper. The great advance in civilization made by the Amratians was in the use of metal, i.e. copper. At first the introduction of metal was slow, quickening by degrees as the new material proved its value. Pins to fasten the goatskin, in which the body was wrapped, were the first metal objects to be made ; harpoons for spearing fish were invented next ; and shortly afterwards chisels made their appearance. The superiority of the metal chisel over the flint tool was indicated in the picture-writing which developed into hieroglyphs, for the accompanying picture of the copper blade set in a wooden handle became the sign for the word *excellent* ; the wooden handle was coloured brown to represent wood, and the blade blue for the copper. Though writing was unknown, the Amratians used signs as marks on property, scoring them on pottery vessels. Owners' marks are well-known in many countries ; our own broad arrow, as indicating Government property, carries on the same custom. Another advance in civilization is seen in the more decided views on religion. A definite ritual was followed in the burials, and the objects placed in the tomb for the use of the dead make it clear that there was among these primitive people a firm belief in the Hereafter.

Stone Pottery. Near the Nile valley lived a people, workers in stone, who penetrated into Egypt at S.D. (sequence-dating) 38, had taken complete possession by S.D. 43, and had introduced a new type of civilization. Instead of the clumsy unsteady stone vessels of the Amratians, we now find barrel-shaped vases with flat ledge-rims ; there is no foot to the vase, which stands firmly on a flat base. The stones are porphyry and other hard kinds which do not occur in the Nile valley. Gold is first used in this period ; it was beaten out into thin sheets, cut into strips, and then laid over the rims and handles of stone vases ; beads were also made by overlaying a stone core with sheet gold. Gold was only used for ornamentation, being valued for its colour and sheen ; it never rivalled copper, which was of use for tools.

Gerzeans. In the Gerzean era a great advance was made by the building of houses and tombs with sun-dried bricks. This industry continued throughout the whole historical period of Egypt, burnt bricks being introduced only when the Romans came. The houses of the Badarians and Amratians were probably reed huts smeared with mud and thatched with straw or reeds.

The Gerzean boats are a characteristic feature of the period. They were large rowing galleys, steered by two long oars at the stern, and big enough to carry a considerable amount of cargo. In the centre of each boat the sacred emblem of the port from which the vessel came was displayed on a tall pole. From these it appears that there was a trade as far south as the Cataract and across the sea to Crete ; and it is highly probable that there was a land route for trade from the Red Sea reaching the Nile at Koptos, a few miles to the north of Thebes. Egypt, even at this early time, was in touch with far-distant lands.

The first worked iron in the world belongs to the Gerzean period. It is in the form of beads, and was considered so valuable that the beads were strung with the most precious materials then known, gold, carnelian and agate. It has been suggested that these examples, which were found in tombs, may be meteoric in origin. Iron is not found again in Egypt until two thousand years later.

From Badarian times till the beginning of the historic period slate palettes were in use among the Egyptians. These were for grinding green malachite into powder, which was mixed with water and applied to the eyelids as a paint. The Badarian palettes are long and narrow, with straight sides and hollowed ends ; the Amratian forms are often very artistic, and represent birds, fish and animals ; the Gerzean are degenerate forms of the Amratian.

The painting of the eyes in this primitive period was to shelter them from the glare which strikes upwards, and, as copper is a germicide, the use of malachite must have been a preventive of infectious eye-diseases. Later on in the history of the world the eyes were painted with antimony, which is also a germicide and, being black, would be considered more becoming.

LESSON 13

Cultural Beginnings in Ancient Egypt

THE last part of the prehistoric period in Egypt shows evidence of more than one warlike invasion. Ever since the Nile valley has been fit for cultivation its fertility has brought wealth to its inhabitants ; its neighbours have cast covetous eyes on it, and desired it for their own. The history of Egypt shows a recurring rise and fall of civilization almost as regular as that of the Nile. A series of strong rulers would make Egypt prosperous and wealthy. Then there would be a period of decadence, after which would come an invasion of foreigners ; these might prove to be the next series of strong rulers, or they might be driven out by a native Egyptian prince, who would found another strong dynasty. This cycle of continual change began with the Badarian civilization, which became decadent in the Amratian period. The invasion of the Gerzeans was probably more warlike than peaceful, but the remains show that the wealth of Egypt increased greatly at this epoch. Decadence set in again under the Semainians, and the wars of invasion and conquest by foreigners ushered in the historic period. The cycle of change continued throughout the whole period of Egyptian history, and can be traced even down to the present time.

It is still undiscovered who the people were who successfully invaded the Nile valley at the end of the prehistoric period. The indications point to a people coming from the north or east, but until our knowledge of ancient India and ancient Persia is more advanced nothing definite can be even suggested. The conquest is recorded in a series of representations carved on slate palettes, on stone maceheads, and on an ivory knifehandle. These are carved in low relief, and depict the scenes of battle and conquest, sometimes naturalistically,

sometimes emblematically, but always with great spirit. The ivory knife-handle found at Gebel Araq shows that the native inhabitants defended their country both by land and water. The difference between the type of boat employed by the Egyptians and that used by the conquerors is extremely interesting ; the one is of the felucca type, perhaps derived from reed-bundles, and the other a dug-out of folk from a forested land. The reverse of the handle is decorated with a motif of a central figure having a supporter on each side ; balanced designs of this type are un-Egyptian, but are common in Mesopotamia and early Persia. The man's thick garments and the heavy pelts of the animals between which he stands indicate that the artist was accustomed to a cold country. Other pictorial records of the conquest show the conqueror

HISTORY ON A KNIFE-HANDLE. Both sides of the famous knife-handle found at Gebel Araq are shown above. The pictorial details of pre-dynastic boats, costume, etc., are of very great interest to students of the development of civilization.

The Louvre

O

as a bull buffalo trampling on an overthrown enemy, and another scene is of a battlefield strewn with dead.

The most important of the slate palettes records the conquest of northern Egypt by the invaders, who had established themselves in the south. On one side of the palette is the king, who is wearing the crown of the south and is in the act of slaying a northern chief, while his falcon totem leads the north captive ; on the other side is the king, wearing the crown of the north and going to see the sacrifice of ten human victims. The few hieroglyphs, which explain the scene, suggest that the king is taking possession of and sanctifying the Great Door (i.e. the chief port), perhaps the harbour now known as Alexandria.

EGYPT'S CONQUEROR. *Slate palette—the reverse is seen in p. 410—showing Narmer, a southern invader who subdued northern Egypt.*
Quibell, 'Hierakonpolis'

The stone mace-heads are obviously votive offerings ; they are too large for human use. The scenes on them record religious ceremonies of Egyptian type, in which the foreign king plays a leading part.

Early Writing and Numeration. These foreign people, who invaded Egypt and founded a kingdom that was to last for more than four thousand years, brought with them the art of writing. Hieroglyphs for use in the monumental script and hieratic for writing in ink appear at this time and simultaneously, and with them there appears a whole system of numeration, with figures denoting numbers from one to a million. The method of numeration was by special signs for units, tens, hundreds, thousands, and so on, as in the Roman numerals. Our present method of numeration comes from India, and was not introduced into Egypt till after the Christian era. The early writing was at first little more than names of kings, but it soon developed into the careful record of events, and even to the writing of books. From this time forward the archaeologist has in Egypt written documents—inscriptions or papyri—to assist him in his investigations. It was the custom of the Egyptian scribes to record every event, usual or unusual.

Two other inventions introduced by the invaders were a form of potter's wheel and some kind of mechanical means for drilling stone. Glass must have been invented elsewhere, since only a very few examples of this period have been found in Egypt, and always in places where the value put on it appears to have been very great. It was probably brought in through trade. Besides glass, Egypt also imported timber. The Nile valley has never produced any good building timber ; all wood for that purpose had, and still has, to be imported.

New Building Developments. At the beginning of the historic period new types of building had been introduced : the royal tombs of the First Dynasty show the development in the construction of all parts of a building. The walls at first were of mud-brick, with which also the floors were paved, but the roofs were of wood, the beams being taken across the whole span of the roof without intermediate supports. As in many cases the shortest span was twenty feet, a long piece of timber capable of standing the strain was required. The appropriate wood would be some kind of conifer, but no trees of the kind grow in Egypt, the nearest places from which they could be obtained being the Lebanon or the Aegean islands ; from either of these places timber could have easily been shipped to Egypt. Later in the dynasty another advance was made in building when stone was used for paving the floors of the royal burial chambers. The stone was granite, which was laboriously hammer-dressed. It was not until the Second Dynasty that stone was used for building walls—and then only walls of tombs, not of houses.

Even at the beginning of history Egypt had little to learn from her foreign conquerors. Long before they entered the land, methods of agriculture had been evolved to suit the peculiar conditions of the Nile valley ; a system of canal irrigation had developed which, with modern improvements, is in use today. The Nile itself was the highway for all traffic.

Like all primitive countries, Egypt before the conquest was divided into a number of small states, each under its own petty king ; but their union under one supreme ruler gave peace to the land and made it possible for civilization to develop rapidly.

Early Civilizations of Mesopotamia and Minoan Crete

THE early civilization of Mesopotamia is not so clearly dated as that of Egypt. The country was divided into two parts—Akkad in the north and Sumer in the south, both contained within the narrow plain lying between the Euphrates and the Tigris. Till within comparatively modern times the two rivers flowed separately into the sea ; now they join together to form the Shat-el-Arab, into which the rivers Karun and Kerkha also flow. The Euphrates has shifted its course many times even during the historic period, and few of the ancient cities are to be found situated on the present stream ; Eridu, Ur, Borsippa, all lie at some distance to the west of it.

Susa was probably the place from which culture spread to the Land of the Two Rivers. It lies on the eastern bank of the Kerkha river, at the foot of the western slopes of the Zagros mountains. Here in the lowest levels was found fine painted pottery, which, though of great beauty, was clearly not intended for domestic use. The walls of the vases are so thin and the clay is so badly fired that the vessels would have collapsed with the weight of their contents ; they must, therefore, have been only for funerary purposes. Although flint tools were commonly used by the people who inhabited Susa I, copper mirrors and copper daggers show that they were well acquainted with metal and were skilled smiths. This stratum at Susa is of great importance, as it is the earliest agricultural village yet excavated, and developed directly from the hunting stage. No domestic animals, except the dog, were known, and the evidence shows that it was at first a village of hunters, but that before it came to an end the inhabitants were producing their own food by cultivating the earth. The site was abandoned for several centuries, and was then re-inhabited by a people who wore pigtails and made pottery with polychrome decoration. This is the stratum

known as Susa II, which is contemporary with the first dynasty of Kish. The two successive civilizations were probably due to a migration which seems to have originated from Anatolia.

Much has been said of the connexions between Susa and Sumer, but it must be remembered that there is evidence of a strong civilizing influence entering from the south also ; the origin of that civilization is still unknown, and will remain so until further excavation reveals the secret. The Sumerians founded the city of Erech, and were thus the beginners of that series of independent city-states so characteristic of Mesopotamian civilization. This method of government was entirely unlike the monarchical rule of Egypt, and approximates more to the Greek ideals.

First Script. Writing is first found at Tel-el-Ubaid. The Mesopotamian script shows a form of picture-writing which rapidly lost its pictorial character, largely because of the material used. In Egypt stone and papyrus lent themselves to the preservation of the most beautiful and artistic writing of the ancient world, but in Sumer and Akkad the only material was clay, on which the characters had to be scratched with a sharp point ; the forms, therefore, tended to become angular and conventionalized. The Mesopotamian writing is known as cuneiform. i.e. wedge-shaped, on account of the shape of the characters, which were written with a metal style.

The dating of the Mesopotamian civilization is still uncertain. Like the ancient Egyptians, the ancient dwellers by the Two Rivers made lists of their kings, ascribing a fabulous length to the reigns of the early rulers. This merely means that there was a tradition of a settled government over a long period before the beginning of real history, but the dates given in the king lists are, like Manetho's lists of Egyptian kings, still open to question. Up to the present there has been no actual connexion

HEAD-DRESS of a Sumerian queen, about 3000 B.C., from a stone tomb at Ur.

Courtesy of Joint Expedition to Ur

found between Mesopotamia and the two well-dated civilizations of Egypt and Crete. The gold-tombs of Ur are probably contemporary with the Old Kingdom of Egypt. The objects found in those tombs show a combination of wealth and barbarism unknown in Egypt or Crete. The chaplets of golden leaves were clearly made by the dozen, without any of the artistic feeling which characterized Egyptian and Aegean jewelry, and the clumsy masses of lapis lazuli suggest that the main idea of artificer and owner was the display of wealth.

Minoan Crete. In turning to Crete one is struck by the European effect of the objects found. Though there is much Egyptian and Syrian influence, Cretan civilization always retained its European character. The dating of the Cretan periods is founded on that of Egypt ; the coincidence is by periods and dynasties, not by years. Thus Early Minoan I was contemporary with the Ist dynasty of Egypt, Middle Minoan II with the XIIth dynasty, and Late Minoan III with the XVIIIth dynasty. This dating is established by the only method which, in the absence of astronomical data, can be considered as accurate before the adoption of a fixed era, viz. the finding of dated objects of one country with dated objects of the other country. Cretan pottery of the Early Minoan period

has been found in Egypt with objects of the Ist dynasty, and Egyptian stone vases of the characteristic forms of the Ist dynasty occur in Crete in the Early Minoan levels ; the other two chronological contacts have been dated in the same way. The dating of the Cretan civilization is of the utmost importance for European archaeology, for though Egyptian influence was strong in Crete and in the Aegean, it did not go farther west, whereas Cretan influence spread all over the Mediterranean lands.

From the time that the island was first inhabited the Cretans were mariners, for all foreign products could only have reached them from overseas, and their own products are found not in Egypt only but westward as far as Italy. They were potters even before they knew the use of metal, but their pottery, when compared with that of Egypt or Mesopotamia, is European in style and feeling. They were builders in stone at a time when the Egyptians were still living in reed or mud structures. They were weavers evidently, for great numbers of clay spindle whorls have survived—the looms, being probably made of wood, have perished. Oxen and sheep were domesticated, but there seems some doubt whether grain was known. In this the Cretans were more backward than the Egyptians, who had been agriculturists from Badarian times.

Earliest Metal Workers

THERE are four great stages in the development of human culture : the Stone Age, the Bronze Age, the Iron Age, and the Mechanical Age, in the last of which we are now living. Each of these can be subdivided into smaller sections, and in the Bronze Age, which we are now about to study, the first section is known as the Copper Age, because pure copper without any deliberate admixture of another ingredient was the metal in use.

The use of metal began with the laborious method of hammering out nuggets of copper with one stone as a hammer and another as an anvil. The sheet of metal thus obtained was then cut into the desired shapes, and the edges ground down to the required sharpness. This was a slow process, slower than the manufacture of flint tools, but it was the precursor of the great development following on the dis-

covery of the arts of smelting and casting. When this discovery was made is still unknown, but it must have been in the Old World, for the most advanced American Indians had not gone beyond the stage of hammering the metal at the period when European civilization was first introduced into the New World.

The first metal to be used, either for hammering or smelting, was copper, but the Copper Age is found in very few countries—Egypt, Mesopotamia, Hungary, north Italy, and perhaps Ireland. The difference in hardness between different ores of copper must have set inquiring minds at work, for before 2000 B.C. the mixed metal, bronze, was not only in use, but the mixture of copper and tin was in the proportion of 9 to 1, a proportion which in modern times is regarded as the best. As it seems likely that the deliberate mixture of copper and tin would be used first in those countries where both metals occur together, it is worth while noting the countries in Europe where this happens. They are surprisingly few : the Caucasus, Bohemia, Spain, Cornwall. It is for this reason that many authorities consider that the Bronze Age took its rise in Spain. It must, however, be remembered that the two metals occur together in south China, and an inventive people like the Chinese might well have been the first discoverers of the method which revolutionized the world and rescued civilization from the ' blind alley of the Stone Age.' The archaeology of the countries intermediate between China and Europe has not been investigated yet, but geographically there is no reason why the knowledge of the mixed metal should not have travelled from the Far East to the shores of the Atlantic ; it could come across the Ural mountains and Altai range, southwards to the Caucasus, and from there be distributed to Egypt, Mesopotamia and Europe.

The fact that not a single bronze object of this early period has been found farther east than the Nile valley and the Land of the Two Rivers does not necessarily militate against this theory, for ' negative evidence is no evidence,' and while we await serious excavation in those intermediate countries, and in China itself, no real knowledge can be obtained of the origin of bronze.

From Copper to Bronze. Metal-workers soon found that pure copper was unsuitable for tools, being too soft and losing its edge quickly ; in this way, it is inferior to stone. On the other hand, it is not brittle, and many more tools can be made from one mould and one ' pouring ' than could be made in the same length of time from stone. Even with all its disadvantages it was so superior to stone that the workman's scope was greatly enlarged by using it.

Bronze very soon ousted copper for the manufacture of tools and weapons. Copper requires a very high temperature for melting, always a difficulty in primitive furnaces ; but the addition of tin lowers the melting point appreciably. Copper can be cast only in open moulds, which limits the shapes of tools to the simplest forms, and the object has to be cast solid ; bronze can be cast in a closed mould or by the *cire perdue* (waste wax) process, a method which enables an object to be cast hollow and at the same time economizes the metal. The reason for this is that the mixed metal is less likely

to have bubbles, which produce flaws in the finished tool. Above all, bronze is a hard metal, can take and keep a finer edge than copper, and does not break like stone ; in other words, it has all the advantages and none of the disadvantages which are found with stone and copper.

The introduction of smelted metal is extremely important in the history of human culture. Those countries where both copper and tin occurred increased their trade relations by exporting either the raw material or the manufactured articles. Other peoples imported the metal and worked it up themselves or bought the tools ready-made.

The Smith. Conditions of life were now changed. In Neolithic times each village, probably each family, was self-supporting ; every man could make his own flint tools, every woman could make her own pots or weave her own baskets. But metal-working, especially smelting and smith's work, needed special training. This was the beginning of specializing in work, the smith being one of the first to become an expert in his craft. In all probability it was kept a profound secret, to which only initiates were admitted, for the position of the metal-worker was clearly a high one. In Bronze Age villages there was always one hut, and never more than one, which was set apart for the smithy almost as though it were a sacred place.

Bronze, however, was not used for rough work. Almost to the Iron Age sickles and other farming tools required for rough work were fashioned of flint which was set in wooden handles, and arrow-heads for hunting were also made of stone.

The increase in trade gave an impetus to methods of communication. Wheeled vehicles came into being for land transport and vessels with sails for water traffic ; and, more important still, writing was invented. It is possible that some kind of arithmetic also came into use, some system by which barter could be effected. All these changes indicate that for some considerable length of time conditions were peaceful. The steady spread of the use of bronze, quite unlike the sporadic appearance of copper, added to the fact that tools and weapons were actually carried in trade from the east to the west of the Mediterranean and even to the Atlantic seaboard, shows that at the beginning of the Bronze Age there were no great wars, no vast upheavals, no migration of immense hordes overwhelming a weak population or being hurled back by a strong people.

LESSON 16

The Bronze Age in Europe

THE Bronze Age was an age of trade and the intercourse of nations—peaceful on the whole, but with interludes of savage warfare. Both copper and tin are required for making bronze, and though copper is sufficiently common, tin is comparatively rare ; therefore, those peoples who inhabited the countries where tin occurs were brought rapidly into contact with other civilizations. Equally fortunate were the dwellers by the sea or by the side of large navigable rivers, such as the Nile, the Euphrates and the Indus. But the very factors which brought to these countries riches and leisure to develop the arts of life, roused the cupidity of other races, so that invasions and other warlike manifestations occurred.

Successive Cities of Troy. Among the most important of the maritime peoples were those who lived in Anatolia (Asia Minor) on a site which was called by the Greeks in later times Troy. It was the key position for all trade between the Mediterranean and the Black Sea, and was thus in touch with the Danube and the Caucasus, as well as with Crete and the whole of the eastern Mediterranean. It is not surprising, then, to find that a settlement existed there from remote antiquity. On this site one city after another rose on the ruins of its predecessor, till seven or eight cities of varied importance had risen and perished, leaving only a huge mound to cover their ruins. The lowest level is known as Troy I, Homer's Troy being Troy VI.

The first settlement was hardly more than a large village, but even at this early period bronze was already coming into use. Troy II is of the utmost importance in any study of conditions in the Bronze Age in Europe. It was a big city ; its fortifications had stone foundations with brick battlements, and within the circle of the defences the houses were large and handsome. Troy II must have existed for many centuries, and perhaps had resisted more than one warlike attack, for the protecting wall had been rebuilt twice. Then came disaster ; the city was stormed, and so ruthlessly destroyed that it remained desolate for many generations. The inhabitants of the captured town had, however, buried much of their wealth before the conquerors burst in and sacked the city, and from these hoards we learn what the civilization of Troy II was like. Small villages succeeded one another on the site till the rise of Troy VI, which, about 1500 B.C., again dominated the trade of the Mediterranean and the Black Sea. This city lasted till the Greeks besieged and took it.

FROM TROY TO YORKSHIRE. In the Bronze Age settlement at Troy, the second city on the site, a characteristic owl-face design appears on the pottery found there. Trade communications carried this and other designs all over Europe, and as far away as Yorkshire such designs carved on Bronze Age chalk drums (top) are found. Similar designs are found in Malta, Greece and Spain.

From Schliemann, 'Atlas Trojanischer Alterthümer' and British Museum

The finds belonging to Troy II show cultural relations with other parts of the Near East and Europe. One remarkable example is the ' owl-face ' ornament on pottery and other objects, which is found in the Greek islands, in Malta, in Spain, and as far away from Troy as Yorkshire. In Saxony finger-rings of gold wire coiled in spirals, in Sicily bone ornaments, in Spain small figures of deities, all show that objects from Troy II were carried in trade right across Europe.

Crete as a Trade Centre. The importance of Troy was spasmodic, but the civilization of Crete was continuous over a long period. The whole of the Aegean area exercised a vast influence over Europe and the Near East, but as the chief excavations have been made in Crete and Troy it is natural to regard those two places as the principal centres from which civilization radiated. Cretan objects of the Early Minoan I period are found in Egypt with objects of the 1st dynasty, and Egyptian objects of the same date are found in Crete ; while in the islands near Crete are copies in local stone of the Egyptian stone vases of this early period. At the beginning of the Bronze Age the connexion between Egypt and Crete is so close that the generally received opinion now is that there was a migration of Egyptians to Crete, due perhaps to the conquest of the Delta and expulsion of the inhabitants by King Menes. The trade and close communication did not end with the 1st dynasty, for stone bowls and perfume vases of the characteristic form of the Egyptian Old Kingdom are found in Crete, and also the Cretan copies of those forms. Again, in the 12th dynasty vases of Kamares pottery are found in Egypt, exactly dated to the reign of Senusret II, while scarabs of that king are found in Crete. The first discovery of Kamares ware was in Egypt, at Kahun, the town which was built for the workmen engaged in erecting the pyramid of Senusret II. The type of ware, with a polychrome decoration on a black ground, was then entirely unknown. Petrie, with his usual perspicacity, at once realized that it was from the Aegean, but not until Evans's excava-

tions in Crete some years later was the exact provenance found.

Crete was in constant trade communication with the islands of the Aegean, where independent little civilizations arose, of which the most notable is the Cycladic. The Cyclades group was too small to support a large population, but their mineral and metallic resources, added to their geographical position, gave the islands unusual importance in the early Bronze Age. The group lies between Asia Minor and the mainland of Greece, and thus offered convenient ports of call between Crete, northern Greece and the Black Sea.

Iberian Culture. The Bronze Age civilization of western Europe seems to have owed its origin to the Aegean culture. Carried by trade from the eastern Mediterranean, it first took root in Almeria on the east coast of Spain, spreading round the Iberian coast and also inland.

The aboriginal inhabitants of Spain and Portugal on the Atlantic sea-board were already hardy and daring mariners, and as traders they carried the new civilization north to the British Isles and the Scandinavian countries. The result of this trade is seen in the jet and amber found in the tombs in Almeria and Portugal, and in the purely Mediterranean decoration on vases in the Danish graves of the same

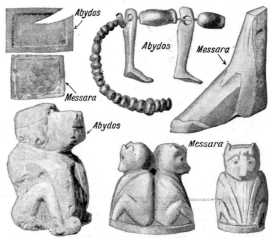

COMMERCE BETWEEN EGYPT AND CRETE. Evidence of close relations between early Egypt and the Bronze Age culture of the Minoans (for the latter see page 442) is supplied by these trinkets found in the Cretan tombs of Messara with their prototypes from Abydos in Upper Egypt.

From Xanthoudides 'Messará,' and Petrie, 'Royal Tombs '

period. The collapse of the Iberian civilization began with the use of a new and shorter trade-route for amber from the Baltic to the Aegean, across central Europe and down the Adriatic. Then came the discovery of tin in Bohemia, which supplanted the tin mines in Spain and Britain. Finally the fall of Crete and Mycenae ended the eastern Mediterranean trade, on which the whole of the Iberian culture had been built.

Danube Civilization. During the dry climate of the Bronze Age the broad and fertile plain of the Danube offered great inducement to agriculturists, for the loess, of which it is in large measure composed,

SIGN OF WIDESPREAD WAR. *These bell-beakers are found right across Europe, and wherever relics of this culture, which arose after the Neolithic period, appear there are signs of bitter warfare.*

is one of the finest soils for growing grain. The population gradually spread along both sides of the great stream and its tributaries. The civilization of the peoples who lived on the upper and middle Danube and the adjacent rivers is known as the Aunjetitz culture. The objects found in the early strata of this culture show that the people were in close touch with Anatolia. Clearly they were trading with Troy II, for when utter destruction befell that city, the Aunjetitz people were forced to use their own productions instead of exporting them. Though these people were farmers—peasant proprietors, as we should now call them—the trade in amber, copper and gold passed through their hands. It was not a civilization which exercised a profound influence on Europe at the beginning. 'The Danube valley does not seem so much an original focus from which culture radiated as a secondary centre where new elements, derived from without, were elaborated.'

Beaker Folk. There is, however, a theory which many archaeologists accept, whereby the Danubians play in the end a great part in the formation of European civilization. The end of the Neolithic period saw great changes in many parts of the world. In Spain there arose a type of culture characterized by a peculiar form of pottery known as the *bell-beaker.* Where this culture originated is as yet unknown ; it may possibly have been North Africa. The people who used this form of beaker were clearly a warrior folk, for the bell-beakers, wherever they appear, are a storm signal of profound disturbances, from Denmark to Budapest. These people flooded across Europe, fighting and all but exterminating many of the previous populations. It is the combination of these warrior races with the inhabitants of the banks of the Danube which brought into existence, according to some authorities, the people whom we now call Aryans.

The peaceful, rather dull, farmer folk of the Danube plain appear to have developed into a more or less warlike people. The social conditions changed also, and instead of peasant communities there appears to have risen an aristocracy,

MIDDLE BRONZE AGE EUROPEANS. *Every detail of this reconstruction drawing of the dress and equipment of a man and woman of the second millennium B.C. is based upon contemporary material remains. The woman's necklace, belt, pins and pot came from a Württemberg grave containing a female skeleton. The man's sword is a Middle Bronze slashing weapon and the cloaks, jerkin, and half boots are drawn from existing fragments of the same period.*

a change probably due to the necessity of a military organization to repel the attacks of invaders. At this period there came into use the slashing sword, a weapon greatly superior to the dagger or the rapier, with which the ancient world had hitherto been armed. Daggers and rapiers are thrusting weapons, but the sword can be used in more than one direction, and its superiority was manifest at once. Military organization led to the alliance of villages for mutual defence; and as these must, for effective purposes, be under the leadership of one ruler, a chief or king would be appointed. The rigid individuality of village communities was thus destroyed, and a rapid development of art and culture became possible.

In the part of the Danubian plain which is now Hungary, metallurgy was extensively practised, and many objects in bronze were manufactured and exported up and down the Danube, and into Germany and as far as the Ukraine. The ancient Hungarians wore ornaments which were not made elsewhere; one, which is very peculiar, was a bronze ribbon wound spirally round the arm or leg. Other ornaments were bronze pendants for girdles, necklaces and for hair ornaments. Occasionally, gold was used for this purpose; though it is rare, the mere fact that it occurs indicates the wealth of these communities. The bronze pendants were made chiefly for export; the commonest type is in the form of an ivy leaf. Copper axes with a hole for hafting appear in south Russia and Hungary; they are of Mesopotamian type, and show that intercourse with the Near East was constant. Another indication of the contact is the occurrence in central Europe of the Mesopotamian 'adze-axe.' More positive proof of the continual and close connexions with more easterly peoples is afforded by the houses with porches, and the concentric fortifications.

Black-Earth Lands of Russia. Stretching right across Galicia, Wallachia and southern Russia is a wide belt of park-like grassy country, dotted with woods and clumps of trees. These areas, known in Russia as black-earth lands, are of great importance for the study of the early civilization of central Europe.

Just to the north of the Transylvanian Alps there once stood a small city, of which the modern name is Erösd. It was perched on a precipitous spur of the mountain, a site obviously chosen as being easily defended because only one side needed fortifying. There were three levels of occupation, but even in the lowest metal was found. The pottery on this site is very remarkable, and shows that the first settlers were already experts in ceramic art. The vases were painted with spirals and meanders in various colours, and the ware itself was fine and well fired. Part of an actual kiln and a pottery model of a kiln were discovered, so that the exact method of firing the pots can be seen. They built rectangular houses with posts to support the walls of mud and interlaced boughs.

In Rumania, at a site called Cucuteni, pottery painted with spiral designs has been found. Like Erösd, this settlement was fortified with a walled rampart of stones enclosing the village, and a deep ditch encircled the rampart.

The black-earth lands are inadequately explored as yet. A few sites on

VILLAGE STRONGHOLD. In the latter part of the Bronze Age villages in various parts of Central Europe were heavily fortified, as in this remarkable example in Upper Swabia. Here it has been found that the village, which stood on an island, was completely surrounded by a palisade of more than 50,000 pine trunks driven into the bed of the lake. The village buildings had outer walls of heavy timbers arranged in regular courses like log cabins. The whole excavation work here reveals a vivid picture of continuous invasion and disturbance.

Urgeschichtliche Forschungsinstitut, Tübingen

the Dnieper have been cleared; in the largest of these, known as Tripolye, two periods can be distinguished, which are labelled A and B. The pottery on these sites had the same kind of painted spirals as that found farther west. Metal was known, and the ancient inhabitants of these villages possessed all the domestic animals, but it is not certain whether they were cultivators of the soil.

The spread of the painted pottery gives the clue to the origin of much of the civilization of Central Europe in the Bronze Age. It is clear that it came from the east, and the evidence points to the Caucasus and Asia Minor. The people who carried the painted pottery across eastern Europe to the Danubian plain are perhaps the same people who pushed southwards and affected the civilization of Susa and Mesopotamia.

LESSON 17

Cretan Commerce in the Bronze Age

THROUGHOUT the Bronze Age the influence of Crete in the eastern Mediterranean was very great, though naturally the effect is best observed in the Aegean area. The civilization of Crete is called Minoan ; it lasted from the period when metal was first introduced almost to the rise of the Iron Age. Even at the beginning of this era Crete, like Egypt, had already had a long period of civilization, but, unlike Egypt, she expanded rapidly and fell as rapidly. This was due to her geographical position, for, being an island, water-traffic was soon established with the other islands which were within easy reach, and for the same reason she was liable to attack on her coasts.

After trade connexions had been established Crete sent out colonies ; some of these were founded peacefully, some were due to conquest. The nearest land was the island group of the Cyclades, which had an original culture of their own, but which soon fell under the sway of their larger and stronger neighbour. Colonies were planted by degrees on the mainland of Greece, till the whole of southern Greece was so much under Cretan influence that it is possible that Minoan rulers reigned there. The most important of these colonies on the mainland were Tiryns and Mycenae, but other places in the eastern Mediterranean were still known as Minoan in later times, showing their Cretan origin. It is very noticeable that the great towns of Crete were built in close proximity to harbours, without regard to the agricultural value of the land, an indication that the maritime trade was of more importance to the islanders than farming.

In the Middle Minoan period the two great towns were Cnossus on the north and Phaestus on the south, in both of which

there were magnificent royal palaces. It is as yet uncertain whether these were the centres of two separate principalities, or whether they were two capitals of one kingdom. Until the Cretan script can be deciphered our knowledge of the method of government and of the division of the island into kingdoms must remain imperfect.

The whole of Cretan civilization was based on sea-power and commerce. The ancient world brought its trade to the island-harbours, and the wealth of the inhabitants increased accordingly. It should be noted that none of the Cretan palaces, no matter where they were situated, ever had ramparts or other warlike defences ; in this they differ from palaces on the mainland, which were often only fine houses in the centre of strong fortifications. An island which has command of the sea has no need of walls and ramparts to ensure the safety of its subjects and its treasures.

Palace of Cnossus. The description of the building—the Labyrinth of tradition—shows the enormous wealth that was lavished on its decoration. The few frescoes which have escaped destruction give a faint idea of the beauty that adorned its walls. One fact, however, proves that the civilization which built this splendid structure was essentially European and not Oriental in type ; this fact is that great attention had been paid to the drainage, both surface drainage and for sewage. The whole system is entirely modern, but Europe took ' more than three thousand years to regain the sanitary knowledge which was lost when the Minoan Empire collapsed.'

Crete was at her zenith when Egypt was rising to power, about 1600 B.C. Tradition places Minos at this period, visualizing him as a single king, though more probably the legendary figure embodies a dynasty.

Crete in the Bronze Age

According to the story Minos went every nine years to the Dictaean cave, the birthplace of Zeus, there ' to converse with the god.' Frazer has pointed out that this is probably a euphemism for the killing of the divine king at the end of a term of years. This rite is found so commonly throughout Europe and the Near East that it must have arisen at an early period of the world's history, possibly even in Palaeolithic times. The Greek tradition also states that Zeus died in Crete, which again suggests that the god died in the person of his human representative. The goddess of Crete was known to the Greeks as Britomart; nothing is known of her cult, but the figures of priestesses, made in ivory or faience, indicate that a snake goddess was worshipped. (*See* Vol. III, page 13.)

The commerce of Crete carried her wares, particularly her pottery, to all parts ; and this was not surprising, as the pottery was unsurpassed in beauty of decoration. Beginning, in the Middle Minoan II, with

OCTOPUS MOTIF. The Late Minoan potters excelled in the portrayal of marine life, as may be seen from the octopus shown amid shells and seaweed on this jar.
British Museum

the polychrome Kamares ware—the colours laid on a dark ground—it passed to white line drawings on a pale ground, and then to dark designs on a light ground. The designs were spirals and conventionalized forms of natural objects, especially shells and marine creatures. One of the most characteristic motifs was the octopus. When first introduced the decorative effect of the semi-naturalistic form is very fine, but in course of time it degenerates, till in late Minoan III the tentacles are merely a series of loops; the final stage is seen at Tell Fara (Beth Pelet), in Palestine, where after many generations of copying it has become almost unrecognizable.

The palace of Cnossus was destroyed by fire at the end of Middle Minoan II, but rose again soon afterwards in greater magnificence. It was not the exclusive personal abode of a monarch and his court, but a vast communal building. Among the remains are the 'Corridor of Magazines,' shown below, and the throne, a dignified

KING MINOS' STOREHOUSE. This photograph shows the ' Corridor of the Magazines ' in the palace at Cnossus. It is 200 ft. long and flanked on one side by twenty long and narrow store-rooms containing a large number of immense jars. These were probably used as receptacles for the grain and oil brought by the Cretan voyagers from overseas.
From Daniel Baud-Bovy and Frédéric Boissonns, ' Des Cyclades en Crète '

chair of white stone. It lasted till the beginning of Late Minoan III ; then invaders broke in, and sacked both town and palace with such a fury of violence that it has lain desolate and in ruins ever since. Fugitives from the invasion sought refuge in other parts, and carried with them some of the Minoan culture, thus prolonging for a time the remembrance of the island civilization.

An interesting part of the culture of the Cretans was their fondness for sports and public games. ' The dancing-ground which Daedalus made in broad Cnossus for fair-haired Ariadne ' has been identified with a paved area, which has rows of steps at the sides on which the spectators could sit and watch the shows. Bull-fights were common,

as is proved by the frescoes (*see* Vol. III, page 14), where youths and girls are represented leaping over a charging bull ; there is nothing, however, to show that the bull was killed, as in a modern bull-fight. There was probably some degree of sanctity attached to these displays, for one of the deities of Cnossus was the Minoan bull, which was stabled within the palace itself.

Among the most interesting of the descendants of the island-kingdom were the Philistines, who at a later date gave their name to that part of Syria now called Palestine. It is possible that these colonists took with them to their new home the form of linear writing which they had used in Crete, and that the Phoenician script is merely a later form of the Cretan.

LESSON 18

Advancing Culture in Barbaric Europe

THE history of lake-dwellings begins in the Neolithic period. The inhabitants of these villages were so commonly of the broad-headed (brachycephalic) type that it seems probable that the lake civilizations are due entirely to that race of Mankind. Lake-villages built on piles have certain peculiarities which are not found among the people of land settlements. From its very construction a lake-village could hold only a certain number of people, and if it became over-populated colonies had to go out from their homes and found new settlements elsewhere. The lakes of the

Alps show many such settlements of different periods. Then came a wider diffusion of these people and their peculiar method of living ; they passed along the Danube and into the plain of northern Germany, moved down the Rhine, across France and Belgium, and so into Britain. Their settlements were so peculiarly adapted for living in waterlogged areas, such as swamps and morasses, that they were able to inhabit places which, during the greater part of the Neolithic and Bronze Ages, were utterly unsuitable for human habitation.

Lake-Villages. The earliest representations of pile-dwellings are on the walls of the temple of Deir el Bahri in Upper Egypt. These houses were in the country known to the ancient Egyptians as ' the Land of Punt,' which seems to have been situated on the east coast of Africa, in the estuary of a river flowing into the Red Sea or the Indian Ocean. These representations date to the Middle Bronze Age, about 1500 B.C. The making of a pile-village is described at a considerably later date by Herodotus, when writing of the dwellers on Lake Prasias (Lake Takino) in Macedonia. ' Planks fitted on lofty piles are placed in the middle of the lake, with a narrow entrance from the mainland by a single bridge. These piles that support the planks all the citizens placed there at the common charge. Every man has a hut on the planks, on which he dwells.' The inhabitants of a

PILE-DWELLINGS OF 1500 B.C. This relief from Queen Hatshepsut's mortuary temple at Deir el Bahri depicts a dome-shaped pile-dwelling of ' the Land of Punt,' believed to have been near the present-day Somaliland.

From Schäfer, ' Kunst des Alten Orients '

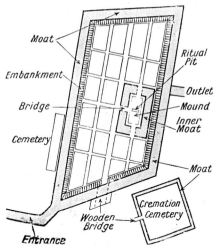

TOWN PLANNING OF THE BRONZE AGE. *Italian 'terramara' villages were constructed on a trapezoidal plan and surrounded by an embankment and wide moat. A single bridge gave access to the enclosure, in which huts, built on pile foundations, stood in parallel streets.*

After T. E. Peet, 'Bronze Age in Italy'

lake-village lived chiefly on fish, but they cultivated the land in the vicinity of the lake, and grew various cereals, including wheat, barley and millet, and as they also grew flax, it is certain that they practised spinning and weaving. A typical lake-village of the Neolithic Period is illustrated in page 428.

Terremare. The spread of these people into Italy took place in the Bronze Age. They settled first on Lake Garda and other eastern lakes, then gradually colonized southwards to the Apennines. The peculiarity of these Italian colonies was that they no longer made their villages over the water, but built their pile-dwellings on dry land. The special name of *terremare* (in the singular, *terramara;* Latin *terra amara,* bitter earth) is given to these sites. The terremare were built on a definite plan; they were oblong, and were defended by an earth rampart surrounded by a moat. The houses within the rampart were built on piles and were arranged in streets, which ran

TERREMARE POTTERY. *The terremare folk practised cremation, and buried the ashes of their dead in cinerary urns such as the one from Serbia shown above. Szombathely Museum, Hungary*

parallel with or at right angles to one another. At the east side of the enclosure was an area of solid earth surrounded by another moat and entered by a bridge. A trench was always made across this area, and in it pits were dug to contain ritual offerings of pottery, animal bones and other objects ; this was probably the part of the settlement set apart for religious ceremonies.

The terremare people knew the use of metal : they had tools and weapons of various kinds, and, in particular, they possessed very fine two-edged swords. It is not merely the cultivation of flax which shows that they understood the making of fabrics, but the occurrence of the ' violin-bow ' fibula, which was common among them, indicates that they wore some kind of loose garment or cloak. The dead were invariably cremated and the ashes, with a few metal ornaments, were buried in a pottery urn. In this method of disposing of their dead in ' urn-fields ' the people of the terremare were following the custom of their predecessors, the lake-dwellers.

Turning now to western Europe, on which the lake civilization had little effect, it will be found that the region rises into importance in the Iberian peninsula, now divided into the countries of Spain and Portugal. From the Late Palaeolithic period onwards this land received continual impulses from the south, and one of the invasions of Spain by Africa is known within historic times. On the east side the peninsula was in touch with the Aegean civilization, but the physical condition of the country prevented the spread of that culture by land—it could be carried only by sea-borne traffic round the coast. On the west side of the peninsula there arose a type of burial, with consequent culture, which exerted a profound influence on the countries to which it was taken. This was the megalithic culture which has already been dealt with in some detail in Lesson 11 (*see* page 430).

Dolmen Tombs. It was in the lowlands of South Portugal that the Late Neolithic people began to bury their dead by erecting over the bodies a stone chamber of upright blocks and covering slabs, all of unhewn stones as large as the survivors could move. Such chambers are known nowadays as dolmens. The spread of this practice eastward was not very great ; it passed northward into Catalonia and up the Rhone into France. On the west it expanded to all those Atlantic coasts which the hardy Iberian sailors could reach. Great Britain, Ireland and the peninsula of Brittany were among the chief centres of

this culture ; it spread also to Scandinavia and across the plain of Germany, and it followed the course of those French rivers which flow into the Atlantic. Everywhere it is clearly the same culture, for in every region where it is found the type of tomb varies in the same order of development, as also do the implements buried in the grave. The pottery, too, that has been discovered follows a certain standard with only slight local variations.

LESSON 19

Monuments of the Neolithic and Bronze Ages

MEGALITHIC building began in Neolithic times, but it reached its finest stage at the beginning of the Bronze Age. The most magnificent of these monuments are found in the British Isles, Brittany, Malta, and in the islands lying between Spain and Italy. In Malta, Ireland and Brittany the megalithic builders enriched the dolmens and temples with carving. The temples of Tarxien in Malta are decorated with spirals of an elaborate and advanced type ; these were cut with stone tools and occur in the Neolithic stratum. In Ireland and Brittany the decoration suggests that the artist was not making a merely decorative design, but was conveying some meaning to the spectator.

AVEBURY MENHIRS. *Though many of the stones have been removed and destroyed by local farmers, Avebury is still a thing to inspire wonder. Originally the rampart and fosse enclosed an outer circle and two inner circles of massive uprights. The largest building of its kind in existence, it is presumed to have been a temple of the megalithic voyagers.*
Photo. W. F. Taylor

Of megalithic monuments other than tombs the most remarkable are the stone circles of Great Britain, the alignments of Brittany, the *taulas* of the Balearic Islands, and the temples of Malta.

Stone Circles. In England, the most important circles are at Avebury and at Stonehenge. The blocks at Avebury are unhewn ; there were originally two circles, and although only a few stones still remain *in situ*, the two circles can be clearly traced. They are enclosed in a vast circular earthwork. The size of the enclosure and the fact that the ditch is on the inner side of the rampart preclude the idea that this was a fortified area. As it is too large for defence and was not intended for habitation it can have been only for religious purposes. Excavations have added little to our knowledge of the site, except that no metal has been found and the only objects discovered are of the Stone Age ; therefore, the enclosure of Avebury is generally accepted as being of the Neolithic period.

But it is far otherwise with Stonehenge. This structure is unique in plan, though probably a development from the enclosure of Avebury. Stonehenge stands within a circular earthwork ; inside this and following its curve is a circle of holes (now known as the Aubrey holes), in which upright stones once stood. Of the part which still stands the plan is peculiar. There are two concentric rings. The outer is of the local sarsen stone, and, when complete, consisted of uprights on which cross-bars or lintels were laid, the whole forming a complete circle with the lintels touching each other all the way round. The inner circle is of the ' foreign ' stone brought from Prescelly, near Milford Haven. Within these two circles stood five great trilithons, forming not a circle but a horseshoe; within these is another horseshoe of Prescelly stones, and within that again a stone lying flat known as the altar stone. All the stones have been squared, and the cross-bars of the outer ring and of the trilithons are fixed to their supports by mortise-and-tenon joints. This is a technique of wood-working, and suggests that the builders may have been carpenters rather than stonemasons. Only in one spot are there any toolmarks still visible; these marks were certainly made with stone tools. The consensus of opinion, however, places Stonehenge in the Bronze Age, the suggestion being that for religious reasons metal was not used.

Avebury and Stonehenge are the largest and most magnificent of these circular structures, but minor groups of stones are found in many parts of Great Britain.

Stone Alignments. In Brittany the most important non-funerary structures are the alignments. The three largest are at Carnac, where they are set up end to end and are over two miles in length. The stones are arranged regularly in rows, standing a little apart from one another, and forming wide avenues which lead up to a cromlech, or small stone circle. At the end of each row near the cromlech the stones are huge unhewn blocks; they diminish in size the

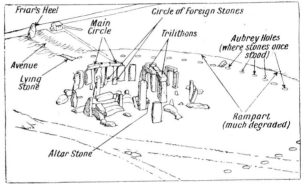

STONEHENGE FROM THE AIR. The circular arrangement of the great structure on Salisbury Plain is clearly revealed in this aerial photograph. The ring of white marks indicates the points—called the 'Aubrey holes,' after the antiquary John Aubrey (1626-97)—where once stood the outermost ring of standing stones. An earthwork encloses the whole. The component parts are designated in the key diagram given above.

Photo, Central Aerophoto Co., Ltd

NEOLITHIC MALTA. The temple at Hal-Tarxien is the most majestic of Neolithic ruins in Malta. It is built of massive stone pillars, and plain spirals constitute the principal decoration.
Courtesy of Professor T. Zammit

farther they are from the cromlech, till at the far end they are quite small. The cromlechs are supposed to be burial-places, and the alignments of monoliths processional avenues.

Maltese Temples. The chief megalithic monuments in Malta are the temples. They are all built on the same plan, which is peculiar to the island. There is a main aisle leading from the entrance to a semicircular sanctuary, and on each side of the aisle are two (in a few cases, three) semicircular transepts. The temple is always built of carefully squared slabs set upright, and the whole structure is surrounded by a wall of rough-hewn blocks; the transepts appear to have had corbelled stone roofs, but the main aisle was open to the sky. These temples usually occur in groups, often in pairs, one being always slightly larger than the other. The sculpture of spirals in relief with which the temples were decorated is so advanced in type that doubt has been expressed as to the early date of these buildings, but the excavated evidence proves conclusively that they belong to the Neolithic period, probably just before the Bronze Age reached the Mediterranean cultural centres. The vast buildings at Hal-Tarxien are the most impressive of these remains.

Balearic Is. Taulas. Peculiar to the Balearic Islands is the megalithic monument known as the *taula* or table. It consists of two slabs. The lower is comparatively thin for its height and width; the wide faces are the natural cleavage of the stone, but the narrow sides have been hammer-dressed so as to form surfaces at right angles to the wide sides. Each end of the slab was slightly bevelled, and the great mass was

SOME OF CARNAC'S MEGALITHS. At Carnac, in the department of Morbihan, Brittany, the plain is dotted with thousands of monoliths standing in definite alignments. This photograph shows the avenue of Ménec, about a thousand yards in length and composed of more than a thousand uprights arranged in eleven alignments. The orientation of the avenues indicates some connexion with the worship of the sun.

then raised upright and set into a shallow groove in the flat rock. It was probably held in place with rocks and earth until the upper stone was placed in position. The upper stone, though not so large, is always considerably thicker than the supporting slab ; it also was hammer-dressed, but the working is far more careful. It is bevelled downwards, and on every side it overhangs the upright, to which it is fixed by a mortise-and-tenon joint like the cross-bars at Stonehenge.

Though the construction is the same as Stonehenge, the form of the structure is entirely different. At Stonehenge the trilithon has the form of a doorway ; in the Balearic Islands the taula has the form of a table. A taula stands in a more or less circular enclosure, round which is a stone wall built without mortar, the wall being of

A TYPICAL TAULA. This photograph of a taula at Trapuco, Minorca, shows the characteristic megalithic monument of the Balearic Islands.

later date. The earliest objects found in these enclosures are of the Bronze Age, though the working of the taula shows the Neolithic technique. Like Stonehenge, it would seem that the sacred stones were worked with the tools of a past civilization.

How the Bronze Age Reached Britain

IN view of the possibility that much of the civilization of Europe originated in India, it is essential to consider the archaeology of south Russia, for it is by that route that the Oriental culture must have come to the West.

Kurgan Builders. In the region known as the Kuban, north of the Caucasus, and also on the steppe between the Volga and the Dnieper, there are burial mounds like our barrows. They are called locally *kurgans*, but to archaeologists they are often known as ' ochre-graves,' because the bodies interred in the mounds had been thickly covered with red ochre. The custom of smearing the dead with red paint began in the Palaeolithic period in western Europe and continued in Neolithic times in central Europe. The reason for the custom is still unknown to us.

In the kurgans the body was usually laid in a contracted position, sometimes in a stone chamber like a dolmen, built of well-squared blocks. The peculiarity of the chamber is that it is divided into two compartments by a slab which has a hole cut right through it. No objects have been found in these dolmen-like structures, so that it is difficult to assign a date to them. Where there were no megaliths, a single burial was made in a pit and the mound heaped up over it ; at a later date the burial was in a ' catacomb-grave.' In both types of burial metal objects occurred ; in the pit-graves there were but few, whereas in the catacombs two-thirds of the tools and weapons were of metal. Silver ornaments were fairly frequent ; this is a rare metal for so early a period and suggests an Oriental taste. Very important also are the glass beads, for the country where the making of glass originated has not yet been identified with any certainty.

The people of the kurgans were probably partly agricultural and partly nomadic. The remains of horses and sheep have been found, showing that they had some domestic animals, and there are indications that they practised a primitive form of agriculture. Two facts point to their nomadic type of life. First, no settlements have been discovered, though the burial places are known ; and, secondly, models of wagons occur in the tombs.

These people were undoubtedly warriors and traders, as can be seen by their weapons and by the foreign objects which are found buried with the dead. The battle-axe, which is a marked feature of the cultures of central Europe, and the adze-axe, a peculiar type which was known in Hungary and was the prototype of the Nordic stone axe, are found in their most primitive form in the Kuban. A people who could invent these effective weapons are not likely to have settled peacefully in one country ; they evidently spread westward, carrying their weapons with them. That they traded with the Mediterranean civilizations is very certain : copper beads of peculiar form and marble statuettes from the Cyclades are found in the catacomb-graves ; gold vessels and spiral earrings, like those of Troy II, also occur ; and many of the tools and weapons found here

show a close connexion with Mesopotamia. As yet the connexion with India cannot be traced, but there is some evidence to show that the kurgan-makers were Asiatic in origin, and some authorities regard them as the proto-Aryans.

Bronze Age in Britain. Although the Bronze Age in Britain may have developed later than in the eastern Mediterranean, it was a brilliant period when it arrived. The Neolithic method of burial in barrows continued for some considerable time after the immigration of the metal-workers, but there is a fundamental difference between the two types. The Neolithic long-barrows were family or tribal vaults, but the barrows of the Bronze Age were for single interments, showing a development from the communal village, where all had equal rights of burial, to the single-ruler type of government. The objects in the Neolithic barrows show that the inhabitants of Britain were poor and had little to take with them to the next world, while the Bronze Age people could afford to give their dead supplies of food, of weapons and of personal adornments.

The people who brought the knowledge of metal to Britain probably started from the steppes of Russia, but their progress was slow, and when they arrived they were a mixed race, broad-headed with an admixture of Nordic blood. They passed from central Europe, down the Rhine, and then across the sea to the British Isles. The Cornish tin may have been discovered by the megalithic builders, but the sudden development of the Bronze Age in Britain coincides with the first wave of Aryan invaders about 2000 B.C.

The trade connexions of the British Bronze Age were with the south, the north and the north-east ; the amber d i s c o v e r e d shows trade with the Baltic, and the segmented blue-paste beads found in round barrows near Stonehenge belong to the Middle Minoan III p e r i o d of Crete. Similar beads have been found in Spain and

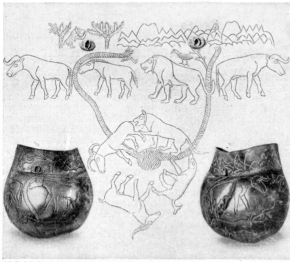

ART OF THE KURGAN-MAKERS. *This silver vase, found in a kurgan, or mound grave, at Maikop in the Caucasus, is covered with finely carved drawings of the animals who roamed the south Russian steppes with the kurgan-makers. In the left-hand view may be seen a species of horse represented today by the Mongolian wild pony. The people of the kurgans were possibly Aryan nomads, immigrants from Asia.*

From 'Materials for the Archaeology of Russia'

in the south-west of France, which shows that the trade-route was by water round the Atlantic seaboard. The pottery and the foreign objects found in the round barrows are excellent for dating purposes, and it is therefore possible to date the beginning of the Bronze Age in Britain as from about 2000 B.C., and the Middle Bronze Age from about 1600 B.C.

Britain was well ahead of all her continental neighbours in the use of bronze, and it is noticeable that throughout the ages she has retained her supremacy in the working of metal. Before the Roman invasion the jewelry and ironwork were remarkable, and at the present day British steel machinery has not been surpassed. The Bronze Age saw the first development of this faculty in the inventions of new types of spear-heads ; and metal tools, weapons and ornaments, in bronze or gold, were carried in trade from Britain throughout north Europe and spread southwards

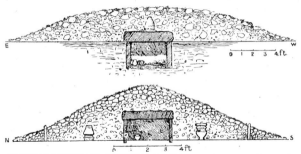

ROUND BARROWS IN SECTION. *A widely prevalent type of grave in the Bronze Age was the round barrow composed of heaped earth and rubble.* **Many, like the Northumbrian examples seen above, contain stone receptacles or chambers in which the body was placed ; and the depositing of pottery with the dead seems to have been a universal practice. There are some 2,000 round barrows in Wiltshire alone, and many more elsewhere in Britain.**
British Museum

along the Atlantic coasts of France and Spain. As Gordon Childe puts it :

Britain had achieved a truly original and independent culture already in the Early Bronze Age by 1600 B.C. But it is only fair to add that Britain did not partake in the brilliant development which marks the Middle Bronze age in Italy, Central Europe and Scandinavia. Cults and superstitions inherited from the Atlantic culture stifled progress and left these islands a prey to later invaders from Central Europe armed with more modern weapons

LESSON 21

Ancient Egypt as a World Power

BEFORE the middle of the Bronze Age a great movement of peoples took place in the Near East. Part of these hordes came southwards and invaded Egypt, where they were known as the Hyksos. Their civilization was of a lower type than that of the people they conquered ; the objects they have left are few, and as they were ignorant of writing, the records of their invasion and subsequent expulsion were made by their enemies. They appear to have been horsemen and archers. The Egyptians could never be induced to accept the bow as a weapon, but they took to horse breeding ; at the beginning of the Iron Age they were exporting horses.

Egypt's Conquest of Syria. The Hyksos were driven out, and Egypt became a united country under a dynasty of indigenous rulers. But as the Nile valley can never be secure from invasion unless the

countries to the north and south are held in check, the great warrior-king, Thothmes III, found himself obliged to subdue and hold Syria. This conquest is an important factor in the development of religious and social ideas in the Near East and, consequently, throughout Europe. Up to this time raids and invasions were well known —raids in which the victors massacred young and old and retired to their own country with all the booty on which they could lay hands, and invasions when the conquerors settled in the conquered country after killing or enslaving the population. For the first time in the history of the world a clear view is given of a human personality in the annals of this reign. The great Egyptian conqueror is depicted, quite unconsciously, in his recorded words and actions.

In the capacity of general, Thothmes was daring and cool and won the confidence of his army ; as a conqueror, he was merciful and generous ; as a statesman, he was far-seeing. When a town was taken by assault there was no massacre or sack, as in the wars between the Israelites and the Midianites ; terms were offered and the population was spared. Egyptian governors were appointed over the conquered districts ; or, if the local chiefs were prepared to swear fealty to the Egyptian Pharaoh, they were left to rule the country, provided they ruled it in peace. To allow a country the enjoyment of its own produce and to protect its inhabitants from attack were new ideas in the ethics of warfare. This one fact alone would show the high state of civilization at which Egypt had arrived, for not only the ruler but his armies must have been imbued with the same spirit. Though material culture is often the only means of gauging the civiliza-

QUEEN HATSHEPSUT'S TEMPLE. *Partly built and partly excavated, the great queen's mortuary temple at Deir el-Bahri rises in three terraces, of which the central and upper are seen here. The temple has many striking reliefs.*

Photo. Lehnert & Landrock

tion of a people, the written record, when it exists, throws light on the ideals which inspire that culture.

The condition of Syria, as given in the Egyptian and the Israelite records, shows that the country was split up into a number of little principalities, each governed by its own king. Wars between these little states were common, and political intrigues were rife. Syria suffered continually from civil war or from invasion. Thothmes III (*see* Vol. II, History, Ancient, Lesson 4), introduced the idea of peace to these warring peoples, who found that subjection to Egypt meant safety to themselves, as their suzerain was strong enough to protect them against all enemies. This is the first instance in history of an empire, i.e. of one country so ruling another as to allow the subordinate nations the opportunity to develop their own civilization without molestation. Thothmes III extended his conquests as far as the Euphrates, and his subjects prospered under his rule.

Worship of Amon. Another important step was now taken. In Egypt, as in all other countries, each district had its own tribal deity, who was regarded as the only god in his own territory. When the princes of Thebes united all Egypt under their rule in order to expel the Hyksos, the local god of Thebes, Amon, became the supreme god of Egypt ; and when the Pharaoh of Egypt became the overlord of other countries, Amon became thereby the overlord of the gods of those countries, and thus rose to the position of chief god of the known world.

The material magnificence of the period is reflected in its architecture. The conquests and trading expeditions of the early XVIIIth dynasty, combined with the piety of the Pharaohs, raised the priesthood to power. Temples were built whose very ruins still fill the beholder with wonder. Amon, as supreme god, was honoured with endow-ments of gold and lands, and with buildings in his own city such as Egypt had never before seen. Costly stones from distant quarries were brought to deck the shrines in the temples, and golden vessels were dedicated to the service of the god. The courts of his temple were filled with native and foreign artisans employed in beautifying the structure raised in his honour. Other gods also received worship and gifts, though in a lesser degree, and throughout the country the priesthood was favoured beyond all other classes of the community. The preferential treatment given to the priests,

EARLIEST DRAWING OF A COCK. *Thothmes III introduced many foreign plants and animals— domestic fowls, e.g.—into Egypt. This, the earliest known drawing of a cock, comes from a tomb dating from the XVIIIth Dynasty, the dynasty to which Thothmes belonged.*

British Museum of Natural History

as described in Gen. xlvii, 22, 26, applies very well to this period also :

Only the land of the priests bought he not ; for the priests had a portion assigned them of Pharaoh, and did eat their portion which Pharaoh gave them : wherefore they sold not their lands.

And Joseph made it a law over the land of Egypt unto this day, that Pharaoh should have the fifth part ; except the land of the priests only, which became not Pharaoh's.

Botany and Zoology. With the expansion of the Egyptian Empire, new interests came into the country. The famous Queen Hatshepsut and her immediate successor, Thothmes III, must be credited with the first recorded attempt to acclimatize foreign plants and animals in Egypt. Hatshepsut's trading expedition to the land of Punt brought back large numbers of incense-bearing trees, which were planted in pits of earth to form a shady avenue up to the gate of her temple at Deir el-Bahri ; others were planted in the garden in the outer court. Excavation has laid bare these pits of earth, which still contain the roots of the trees.

Thothmes endowed his temple at Karnak with a garden of strange plants and animals, and his artists depicted on the walls of one of the chapels examples of these exotic creatures and flowers. One of the artists who drew the plants was also something of a botanist, for he has represented several consecutive stages of the germination of a seed. These are, as far as we know, the first scientific drawings in the world.

Egyptian Trade Links. The position of Egypt as the great world power in the 16th and 17th centuries before Christ brought her into contact with other lands and peoples ; it is possible to gauge, from her records and from the objects found in her tombs and towns, the condition of culture at which those peoples had arrived.

Trade in resins and spices for perfumes and for religious and burial purposes was carried on with the land of Punt. The actual position of Punt is still uncertain ; it appears to have been on the east African coast, at least as far south as Somaliland, for the trading expedition sent by Queen Hatshepsut reached it by way of the Red Sea. The Egyptian expedition bartered beads, trinkets and weapons for raw materials, such as frankincense, gold in dust and in rings, wood of different kinds, elephant tusks and panther skins. Among the people of Punt negroes are represented, showing that trade from the interior of Africa passed through the seaport. The sketches made by the artists accompanying the Egyptian expedition give a vivid picture of the landscape and houses of Punt (*see* illus., p. 444), as well as the costume and ornaments of the inhabitants. Ebony stools, inlaid with ivory, and with leather seats, were the products of Africa at a later date ; the finest example was found in the tomb of Tutankhamen, and a picture of the same stool is seen in the tribute of the negroes depicted in the tomb of Huy, vizier of Tutankhamen. Elaborate but barbaric goldwork also came from Africa, and with it were brought unworked ebony and ivory,

CRAFTSMANSHIP OF ANCIENT AFRICA. *Among the imports into Egypt from the mysterious south were ebony stools, inlaid with ivory. The specimen shown above—collapsible, with legs inlaid to resemble ducks' heads—was part of the treasure found in Tutankhamen's tomb.*

and stuffs woven in brilliant red and yellow patterns.

But it is from the north that the most interesting products came. Syria, Mesopotamia and the Aegean all traded with Egypt and vied with each other in the Egyptian markets. At the time that the Hyksos invaders were subjugating Egypt, the North Syrian kingdom of Ugarit (Ras Shamra) was a centre of intellectual and artistic culture, and of international commerce. Excavations made for ten years from 1929 brought to light innumerable examples of jewelry in gold and lapis lazuli, amber and cornelian beads, copper and ivory statuettes, the oldest 'steel' weapon known—a battle-axe—and evidence of a remarkable system of modern drainage and of well-equipped stables for race-horses. Later the Egyptian protectorate over Syria brought the two countries into close contact, Egyptian products being carried into Syria in return for Syrian manufactures. Syrian artisans entered Egypt, sometimes as prisoners of war, sometimes as free men, and brought their crafts with them. This is perhaps why glass-making became so great an industry in Egypt at this time. At first only beads of black and white glass were made ; then, under Amenhotep III and Akhnaton, the whole range of colour was used for beads and small vases. Inlaid glazes, which had not been seen from the time of the 1st dynasty, were

EGYPTIAN GLASSWARE. Bottles made of glass, opaque and cast over a mould by dipping ; the variegated effect was produced by threads and bars of different colours laid on and softened by heating.
Courtesy of Egyptian Exploration Society

re-introduced, and at Tell-el-Amarna were brought to perfection. It is possible that glass-making came into Egypt from Syria, though there is also the possibility that the invention was European ; it was certainly not indigenous in the Nile valley, where it first appears in a form too elaborate to be considered primitive.

Syria was famous for its metal-working ; gold vases and bowls, chased or repoussé and often jewelled, were brought as tribute to the Pharaoh. The hereditary ruler of Keftiu—the Hebrew Caphtor and the Greek Cappadocia—sent embassies with gifts ; the men who formed the cortège of the ambassadors wore loin-cloths woven in colours of brilliant tints. Some of the pottery found in Egypt at this period is not identified, though it is probably from Syria. A certain type of wide-necked vases decorated with lines of red and

OLDEST 'STEEL' WEAPON KNOWN. This superb battle-axe from Ras Shamra (Ugarit), here mounted on a dummy haft, was made by Mitannian craftsmen in the second millennium B.C. The head, which is ornamented with a boar and two lions' masks, was very ingeniously shrunk on to the blade, obviating the use of rivets.
Photo, Prof. Claude Schaeffer

dark brown is peculiar to the reign of Thothmes III and his immediate successors ; as the import of these into Egypt lasted only a short time, the connexion between Egypt and the land of their origin must have been severed when the Egyptian protectorate slackened.

In the reigns of the Tell-el-Amarna Pharaohs (Amenhotep III, Akhnaton and Tutankhamen) foreign imports are found on every hand and foreign connexions are strongly visible. It is generally agreed that the impulse given to the art of that period came from abroad, though the actual sculpture and painting were carried out by Egyptian artists. For the first time since the Palaeolithic period there was an attempt to represent light and shade in painting, the only example being in a scene which is otherwise entirely Egyptian in design and style. Much of the art of Tell-el-Amarna is regarded as due to Minoan

CRETE AND EGYPT. *The typically Late Minoan vase borne by this dark-skinned Egyptian is evidence of commerce with the Minoan Cretans.*

influence, but no real prototypes can be found in Crete. Some of the motifs, such as the running bull, may be an Egyptian form of Cretan art, but the portraiture of

Egypt at this period is unique. A possible connexion may be found in the scene of Ay showing to his servants the gloves which had been presented to him by the king, for the earliest known representation of gloves is in a picture of a Cretan lady of an earlier date than the tomb of Ay.

Babylonia and Mitanni also sent their products to Egypt, for these were found in the tomb of Tutankhamen. Among the mass of objects placed with the dead Pharaoh were three large couches, a throne and a footstool, all of wood overlaid with gold, some being decorated with ivory. The beds are made in four pieces and are put together with bronze hooks and staples, obviously for convenience of carriage. These are mentioned in a letter from Kallima-sin, king of Babylon, to Amenhotep III, in which he says that he sends to the Pharaoh ' three couches of *ushu*-wood and gold, a throne of *ushu*-wood and gold, and a footstool of *ushu*-wood.' The couches were evidently made in portable form for transport between the Euphrates and the Nile.

EGYPTIAN LIFE-MASKS. *In the workshop of the sculptor Thothmes, at Akhetaton, were found a number of casts, taken 3,000 years ago from living and dead, as guides for portrait statuary ; the two above are life-masks. Not all were Egyptian in type ; the lady, shown full-face and in profile, is definitely European.*
Berlin Museum

The Tell-el-Amarna letters—a collection of diplomatic correspondence called after its place of discovery—show the condition of trade in the Near East in the 15th century B.C. Communication was constant and fairly regular, though delays must have occurred at times, for apologies were sent by the king of Alashiya that he had not heard in time that Akhnaton was celebrating a sacrificial feast, but he sends a belated and very handsome gift. On the land routes the local princes were charged with the duty of protecting and providing for the caravans which passed through their provinces. On the sea there was always the danger of piracy, and measures had to be taken to secure the safety of merchant vessels. Custom-houses were established both in Egypt and in Crete for the commodities which paid duty, and there appears to have been a preferential tariff in Egypt in favour of Alashiya. The state of trade and inter-communication in the eastern Mediterranean at this period must have been very much like the conditions in that part of the Near East after the fall of the Roman power until the policing of the seas during the Napoleonic wars put an end to piracy.

LESSON 22

The Culture of Tiryns and Mycenae

TIRYNS and Mycenae were offshoots of the great Cretan civilization, colonies planted when the island-kingdom was still at the height of its power. The evidence shows that at Mycenae, if not at Tiryns, the civilization represents the result of actual conquest and the abrupt and wholesale displacement of a lower by an incomparably higher culture. There was no gradual Minoization of the native Helladic community thus submerged.

Tiryns was founded on a low rocky hill rising out of the swamps of the plain of Argos, about a mile from the sea. An earlier village, probably inhabited by aborigines who used obsidian implements, crowned the hill-top ; the natives were ejected by the colonists, who made a settlement surrounded by a wall of megalithic blocks built without mortar. The wall was from 25 to 50 feet thick, with passages in the thickness ; the stone blocks range from 7 to 10 feet in length, and from 3 to 4 feet in width and depth. The citadel, which was probably also the palace, contained a number of rooms and courtyards, with colonnades and flights of steps. The frescoes on the walls are definitely Cretan in character, particularly the bull-leaper, which must have been painted by a Cretan artist. The alabaster frieze is of exceptional interest because it is carved and inlaid with blue glass which is of the same date as the glass of Thothmes III, or possibly a little earlier.

Mycenae. Golden Mycenae—Mycenae of the Wide Ways—was also founded by colonists from Crete. It began as a small but strong citadel on a rocky inland hill, where the invading settlers could hold their own against the aboriginal inhabitants. In the foundations of rock shafts were dug for the burial of the Mycenaean princes. Here all the wonderful golden objects were of Cretan workmanship imported by the colonists from the homeland. Though the technique is often very fine, the artistic beauty—with the exception of the Vaphio cups—cannot compare with similar objects of Egyptian work ; the gold masks of Mycenae, when placed beside the gold mask of Tutankhamen, emphasize the rudeness of this early phase of Mycenaean art. The wealth of the city must have been immense, as the rulers could afford to bury so great a mass of treasure. At a later date the royal cemetery was enclosed with a circular wall of upright slabs, possibly the original gravestones.

TWO GOLD CUPS *from a Mycenaean tomb at Vaphio. They display such exquisite craftsmanship that they may have been imports from Cretan workshops. One (right) shows a wild bull in a ' flying gallop ' ; on the other is a man leading captured bulls.*

National Museum, Athens

The goldwork of Mycenae, though splendid in some ways, is often disappointing in technique. Among the seven hundred circular and leaf-shaped plates of gold found in the shaft-graves there are only fourteen designs, repeated over and over again without variation. They seem to have been produced either by casting from moulds or by hammering the soft sheet-gold into flat moulds. The same method must have been used to produce the gold buttons and the strange ornaments in the shape of cuttlefish. The whole of the gold-work is, therefore, a study in mass production, by which the greatest display of wealth is effected with the least possible cost of time and labour. This is like the jewelry of Ur, but entirely unlike any known Egyptian goldwork, in which there is always the touch of the individual artist.

MYCENAEAN SEPULTURE. Upper photo, the so-called Treasury of Atreus, the most magnificent and best preserved of the great beehive tombs—domed structures built of upward-narrowing rings of masonry—that are sunk in the flank of rising ground at Mycenae. Near by is the grave circle (lower photo) containing the shaft-graves wherein the German archaeologist, Heinrich Schliemann, made a rich find of buried treasure in 1876. The slabs surrounding the circle were probably the original gravestones, rearranged as a fence when, owing to the city's growth, the ancient burial place became incorporated within its walls.

British School at Athens Annual; Underwood Press Service

After the shaft-grave dynasty came to an end, a new family of princes rose to power. These increased the area enclosed by fortifications, and to them belongs the famous Lion Gate, which gave admission to the fortress (*see* illus., p. 457). The gate derives its modern name from the sculpture of a pillar with two lions as supporters, which is placed above the entrance ; the Cretan origin of the design is seen in the shape of the pillar, which narrows to the base like its prototypes in the Labyrinth. The royal burials were at this period

A STIRRUP-VASE. Mycenaean pottery was carried by traders all over the eastern Mediterranean. This typical 'stirrup-vase' came from Rhodes.
British Museum

in buildings which are called, from their shape, ' Beehive Tombs.' These tombs were scattered all down the slopes of the hill, and in spite of their solid masonry and thick walls they were completely plundered long before any written record of Mycenae was made. Remains of the royal palace show that the walls were decorated with painted stucco, the style and motifs being entirely Cretan.

After the fall of Cnossus (c. 1400 B.C.) and the utter collapse of Minoan culture, caused perhaps by an invasion of the half-Greek, half-Cretan colonists, only Troy remained to dispute with Mycenae the supremacy of the Aegean. It was a confederation of the semi-civilized tribes of the Greek mainland, led by the ruler of Mycenae, which broke the power of Troy and completely destroyed that great city.

Mycenae in her turn sent out colonies, which settled in the island of Rhodes, along the coast as far as Macedonia, in Cyprus, Corfu, Italy and Sicily. The products of Mycenae were carried in trade to Egypt. The most easily recognizable of these products are the small vases known as stirrup-vases from the shape of the handles ; they are of pottery covered with a fine polished slip and painted with lines and geometrical designs in red or brown ; they probably contained perfume or some precious liquid, and are clearly luxury objects.

Mycenae fell when barbarian tribes from the north invaded peninsular Greece, and by the end of the 5th century B.C. she had lost all her traditional glory and had degenerated into a small and insignificant village. (*See* Vol. III, Lesson 5 in Social History.)

The rise and fall of Tiryns and Mycenae give a view of what must have happened many times in the ancient world. Colonies of some great world-power grew and developed until they united with barbarian tribes to overwhelm the homeland and seize its power. They carried on the tradition of culture, though in a lower form, and flourished partly by trade and partly by conquest, until in their turn were overwhelmed by barbarians and that cycle of civilization came to an end.

MYCENAEAN FRESCOES IN MINOAN STYLE. Although the frescoes at Mycenae were discovered in a very fragmentary condition, they have been arranged to form convincing restorations. One of these is shown above and represents horses being led by grooms.
British School at Athens Annual

Migration of the Sea-Peoples

IN the historical period there are many movements of peoples which must be regarded as parallel with those unrecorded movements of early times that can be traced by the material remains only. One of these events was the great coalition of the Sea-peoples of the eastern Mediterranean which descended on Egypt in the twelfth century B.C. and is recorded in the Egyptian annals of the period.

The Cretan colonies gradually became independent and identified themselves with the countries in which they were settled. In this way the Minoans on the southern coasts of Syria began as the overlords of that country, but were known later as the Pulasati or Philistines ; Gaza, one of their chief towns, was still called Minoa in Roman times. The condition of Syria was extremely unsettled after the Egyptian protectorate was slackened under Akhnaton, who lost almost all the Asiatic provinces ; and the land fell into the hands of the warlike Hittites, who were the driving force in the confederacy of the north Syrian princes against Egypt. Seti I regained some of the lost provinces after much hard fighting ; but when Rameses II became Pharaoh the Hittites were pouring southwards, and he was forced to fight to check their rush.

Because the Hittites were not fully established in the country the Egyptians were able to pass to the north of Syria as far as Kadesh and even to Mitanni. After a war of twenty years both sides were equally exhausted and were glad to make peace on equal terms. Continual fighting broke the Hittite power, but Egypt was in no case to resume the Syrian protectorate, being engaged under the Pharaoh Merneptah in fighting for life against an invasion of confederated tribes from the west, and afterwards in clearing the Delta of the foreigners who had settled there and ousted the native inhabitants.

The eastern Mediterranean lands were, there-

ONE OF THE PULASATI. Prominent among the migratory Sea-peoples were the Pulasati who, emanating probably from Crete, attacked Egypt and settled in Palestine as the Philistines.

fore, in a turbulent condition : the old powers had fallen, the new ones were not yet consolidated. The Peoples of the Sea saw their chance and combined for conquest and plunder. The Philistines, Danai, Shardana and other tribes from the islands and coast-lands moved on Egypt, which had never been plundered and was consequently the richest country of the ancient world. After the death of Merneptah it had been distracted by civil war, but a strong ruler had arisen who had restored order. His son and successor, Rameses III, was one of the greatest soldiers Egypt ever produced.

Advance from Syria. The advanced hosts of the confederated Sea-peoples passed south and joined with the Libyans in an attack from the west on Egypt. The battle was by land and sea, and the invaders suffered a terrible defeat at the hands of Rameses III. The check, however, was no more than temporary ; the main body of the allies were established in Syria and advanced steadily southwards. It was a migration rather than a war of aggression. Whole tribes were on the move, bringing their women and children and all their possessions in carts. It was like a swarm of locusts. The fighting men captured the land fortresses and the warships seized and plundered the coast towns ; no nation or citadel could stand against them. As they neared the south, Egypt braced itself to withstand the shock. Battle was joined on land and sea, and Egypt was victorious. The disappointed invaders united with the western tribes and attacked again on the Libyan frontier, but without success. But though Rameses III raided Syria and brought back much plunder, Egypt's resources had been overstrained in the struggle for life ; she sank into insignificance, and her power passed, first to Israel, then to Assyria.

The records and sculptures in the temple of Rameses III at Medinet Habu tell us much about

RING MONEY. *Arising out of the golden ornaments worn by barbaric peoples, ring money was a form of currency in use in Egypt, Gaul, Britain, etc., during the Bronze Age. The specimens shown above were found in Ireland.*

the culture of the peoples who attacked Egypt. Foremost among the enemy were the Philistines, with their high feather-crowns which hid the helmet ; they wore a protective corslet covering the whole body, but leaving the arms free ; the helmet was fastened with a leather strap under the chin. Their weapons were short two-edged swords and they carried round shields.

Their galleys were equipped with rams at the prow, and at both bow and stern there was a high protective bulwark. The Egyptian crews were armed with bows and arrows, spears and maces ; at the summit of the Egyptian ship there was a fighting top, from which a slinger cast his missiles. A weapon used with deadly effect by the Egyptians was the grappling hook, of which four tied together are shown as having been thrown at and entangled in the sail of the Philistine craft which they are tearing to ribbons. Metal helmets appear to have been worn by the other invaders, many of whom also had earrings ; these are suggestive of the golden earrings of the Midianites from which Gideon made an

ephod (Judges 8, 24–27). The weapons and armour of the invaders were of bronze, and the short sword is the slashing sword of central Europe, probably introduced into the eastern Mediterranean by the tribes who destroyed Mycenae.

While eastern Europe was convulsed with war, the west was undergoing changes, though less violent. The culture of the urn-field people, who disposed of their dead by cremation instead of burial, was carried from Central Europe to Holland, Belgium and France, and thence to Great Britain. It was a peaceful infiltration, for there is no sign of extermination of the previous civilization. This Late Bronze Age invasion brought with it new burial customs : the dead were burned and the ashes buried in urns ; objects placed with the dead were few in comparison with the burials of the earlier period, and metal tools are rare.

A peculiarity of the Late Bronze Age in Britain is the occurrence of ' founder's hoards.' These appear to have belonged to travelling smiths, who moved from place to place, making and selling metal objects in the villages through which they passed. Many of the objects in the hoards are of Italian types ; and the round buckler, such as the Philistines used, is also found. Buckets and cauldrons are not uncommon ; though the buckets are of Italian form, the cauldrons are purely British. In the hoards the connexions with all parts of Europe are clearly visible, showing that the old trade routes were still in use. Gold objects are frequent, the most important being a peculiar type of ring or bracelet, which is supposed to have been a form of currency, and is usually called ' ring money.' These objects are generally of pure gold, but some are of alternate bands of gold and silver.

LESSON 24

The Iron Age

THE Iron Age, like all other great changes in civilization, was ushered in with continual wars, general unrest and redistribution of power until conditions were adjusted and became stabilized. After the great upheaval in the eastern Mediterranean Egypt retired from the contest and left the world to fight. Assyria flared up like a volcano, but soon became extinct ; the Assyrian time of power was too short for it to exercise much influence on the

surrounding countries, and Assyria vanished, leaving little or no trace.

It is difficult to understand why so complicated a process as bronze-making should have preceded the simpler method of working iron. A little iron was always in use in Egypt from the Gerzean period onwards, but it was not a steady industry and the iron objects seem to have been imported. In the same way, iron was used in Crete as early as Middle Minoan II, but it is very

TUTANKHAMEN'S STEEL DAGGER. An early instance of iron displacing bronze for weapons of offence is one of the famous daggers of Tutankhamen (c. 1358-1353 B.C.). The haft is of jewel-encrusted gold with a crystal knob ; but the blade is excellently tempered steel.

From Howard Carter, 'Tomb of Tutankhamen'

rare till the 12th century B.C. The use of iron among the Hittites seems to have begun rather earlier than in Crete. The Dorian invasion brought iron into Greece, and with it came geometric designs on pottery. Iron ousted bronze gradually. In the ' Iliad ' the Achaeans wore bronze armour and fought with bronze weapons, though iron was coming into use for agricultural and household purposes. In Mycenae iron was still sufficiently rare to be considered fit for jewelry. In Egypt iron was brought in from Syria as a costly gift to the Pharaohs, and Tutankhamen possessed a dagger with a steel blade. In Palestine the earliest known iron is from a Philistine grave at Tell Fara, dating from the 15th century B.C. At that time the Israelites were just emerging from their Bronze Age, but two hundred years later the Philistines still kept the traffic in metal in their own hands, and the Israelites were not permitted to sharpen, much less to make, their metal implements ; ' there was no smith found throughout all the land of Israel. . . All the Israelites went down to the Philistines to sharpen every man his share, and his coulter, and his axe, and his mattock' (I Sam. xiii, 19, 20). Though the reason given was that the Hebrews might arm and rise against their overlords, the true motive was probably the wealth that accrued to the metal-workers. Goliath's panoply of war was of bronze, with the exception of his spear, which was of iron (I Sam. xvii, 7).

Phoenician Trading Posts. The immense importance of Phoenician trade during the Iron Age is one of the chief features of the period. Tyre and Sidon had trading posts on the African shore of the Mediterranean by 1100 B.C., and were already in active communication with Tartessus (Tarshish) on the Atlantic coast at the mouth of the Guadalquivir river. Here the mineral wealth of Spain was exchanged for goods from the Near East. Gradually other trading posts were established along the south-eastern coast of Spain, and finally Tartessus was seized and forced to become a vassal of Tyre. All along the coast of north Africa there was a string of trading centres, of which the latest was Qarthhadasht, the New Town, known to us as Carthage. This city came into existence about the end of the 9th century B.C., when the Phoenicians had already made settlements in the islands of Sardinia, Malta, Sicily and Iviza. It

CARTHAGINIAN COPYISTS. The Carthaginians, and the Phoenicians generally, were copyists rather than creators. Their copying propensity may be seen from the crudely fashioned dancing-girl (right), strongly suggestive of Grecian influence. It may be compared with the flute-player (left), definitely Greek in conception and execution.

From Musée Lavigerie, E. Leroux, Paris

was in Sicily that the Greek colonial settlements and Phoenician trading posts first came into contact ; their relations appear to have been unfriendly from the first.

Rise of Carthage. When Tyre collapsed Carthage rose and established herself as the chief trading power in the Mediterranean. It was not an altogether peaceful rise, but it was manifestly successful, as she vanquished her two most powerful rivals by destroying Tartessus in Spain, and by driving, with the help of her Etruscan allies, the Greek colonies out of Sicily and the Greek shipping off the seas. Her traders ventured far afield and are said to have reached the coasts of Cornwall, evidently following the old trade-route of the Bronze Age. Phoenician sailors circumnavigated Africa, the expedition being undertaken at the instigation and expense of Pharaoh-Necho of Egypt. They started from the Red Sea and came back by way of Gibraltar.

Carthage never developed a civilization of her own, though she was the means of developing it in other lands. She was entirely a trading power and held the whole of the carrying trade in the Mediterranean. All Carthaginian objects, whether found actually at Carthage or at her trading centres, show that her workmen were copyists without originality. Her models were Greece and Egypt. In some ways her political constitution was like that of primitive Egypt, in that the army was composed of foreign mercenaries officered by the citizens of the country. The religion seems to have been copied equally from Tyre and Egypt. To Tyre the Carthaginians yearly sent envoys to take part in the worship of Melkart, the great god of Tyre ; and the greater number of amulets and figures of gods show Egyptian influence.

Hallstatt and La Tène. In Europe the Iron Age is divided into two parts. The earlier is called the Hallstatt period, from the famous cemetery in Austrian Tirol where this civilization was first studied ; the second part, which is known as La Tène, from the Celtic settlement on Lake Neuchâtel, is subdivided into four sections. The beginning of the Iron Age saw the first spread of the Celtic peoples, and in the La Tène period the Celts were the chief power in continental Europe. They were hardly a nation, but consisted of tribes more or less closely allied, who acted sometimes in concert, sometimes alone ; the real bond among them was a common language. The Bronze Age culture was carried from the east, but the civilization of

the Iron Age was spread by a people who were clearly Nordic, for the Celts had fair hair and light eyes and were a tall race. They are first located in central Europe, especially in south-west Germany, whence they migrated in successive waves in every direction, reaching Britain in the west, Greece and Asia Minor in the east, and penetrating southward into Italy. The civilization of the Hallstatt II period (beginning about 700 B.C.) was carried in their early migrations, and the spread of the La Tène culture (beginning about 500 B.C.) was also due to them.

Iron Age in Britain. Throughout the Hallstatt period central Europe and the region of the Rhine were perpetually invaded

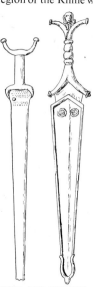

from the south. The invaders exterminated or drove out the inhabitants, or else settled and were absorbed. The pressure of these moving hordes was so great that even Britain was affected at last. Evidence of Hallstatt culture is not yet completely recognized in Britain, though excavation is bringing it to light in many places. The presence of the characteristic leaf-shaped sword shows that the Hallstatt invaders did not always come peacefully ; another type of Hallstatt sword is also found which is known as the 'anthropoid,' and is derived from a sword with 'antennae.' It is

IRON AGE SWORDS.
Left, a Hallstatt sword of the 'antennae' type ; right, an 'anthropoid' sword found in the river Witham.

probable that the attacks of the invaders were short but continuous, like the Danish invasions of historic times, and a certain number of settlements were founded in the south of England. A few Hallstatt objects appear to have come by trade ; the most important of these, for dating purposes, are the fibulae (safety-pin brooches). Italian types occur in Suffolk, Dorset and Wiltshire; this suggests that they were brought by sea traffic, and worked their way inland.

Pottery of Hallstatt types, but made locally, has been found near Cissbury in Sussex, at Hengistbury in Hampshire, and at All Cannings Cross in Wiltshire. There is so much pottery on all these sites that it is highly improbable that it was imported ; it is more likely that the Hallstatt people settled near the sea first, and only founded their inland village at a somewhat later date.

The geographical conditions of Great Britain are extremely important in the study of British archaeology. As C. F. Fox says :

Britain, south of the Forth-Clyde isthmus, consists geographically of two parts, the highlands and the lowlands. A diagonal line drawn from Teesmouth to Torquay roughly indicates the boundary of the two areas . . . the lowland is easily overrun by invaders ; it lies opposite those Continental shores whence nearly all our recorded invaders have come. In the lowlands of Britain new cultures of Continental origin tend to be imposed ; in the highlands these tend to be absorbed. In the lowlands you get replacement ; in the highlands fusion. Hence a given culture brought across the Straits or the North Sea tends to manifest itself much later in the highland than in the lowland ; less distinctively, more feebly.

These remarks apply very closely to the La Tène culture in Britain. The people who brought in that culture are known as Celts. There were two invasions of the Celtic-speaking peoples, each of a rather different type ; and it should be noted that these were not mere raids, but were true invasions, where the invaders entered and took possession. The two invading tribes are called by the Celtic dialect they spoke. The first invasion was by the Goidels, whose language has a *q* where the latter had *p* (Latin, *quin*que ; Greek, **p**ente) ; this language was the foundation of the Gaelic of Scotland and the Isle of Man, and of the Erse of Ireland. The second invasion was by the Brythons, from whom Britain takes its name ; they pushed the Goidels westwards across the sea and northwards into the mountainous and less fertile regions, and then took possession of the rich agricultural lands. Still later another wave, known as the Belgae, dispossessed the Brythons, who were driven westwards into Wales.

The Celtic occupation of France took place rather earlier than the invasions of Britain.

Here the Celts were known as Galatae or Gauls, notably on the banks of the river Sequana (abbreviated to Seine).

Both in Britain and France chariot burials are characteristic of the Iron Age. These burials are always very rich and clearly belonged to chiefs and kings. The body was buried in the chariot, and the harness for two horses was placed in position, but as no remains of horses are found it is evident they were not slaughtered when their master was buried. The metal-work of the harness shows beautiful workmanship ; it is often of open-work bronze, sometimes set with coral, and in England enamel ornaments are also found. The use of enamel, i.e. the fusing of glass on metal, is found in the La Tène II period in central and western Europe, and reached its highest development in England in La Tène III. It seems to be an entirely European art, as it is not found in the Near East or Egypt till introduced by the Romans. The metal used in England was a golden bronze, and the design is so arranged that the metal forms part of the colour scheme with the enamel.

Hill Forts. The Iron Age invaders left remains other than weapons and household objects. The ' camps ' or hill forts found all over the country were for tribal defence, the settlers living outside and taking refuge when necessary in the fort. The defensive works usually consisted of a single rampart and a ditch, enclosing an area which could be as much as sixty acres in extent. In this enclosure were the huts in which the permanent garrison lived. The camps are placed on the tops of hills, whence a wide view can be obtained, so that an enemy's approach could be seen from a distance. Many of the forts are so strongly defended that they were probably impregnable.

Another type of monument is peculiar to this period in Britain; these are the figures cut in the chalk on a hillside, of which the White Horse of Uffington and the White Horse of Westbury are the best known. The latest theory assigns these figures to a period just before the Roman invasion, on the ground of a supposed resemblance between the White Horse and the horse figures on contemporary coins. It may be, however, that the chalk figures belong rather to the early than to the late Iron Age.

ENAMEL was a typically Celtic art. Here is a mirror back, beautifully engraved and enamelled, found in Gloucestershire.
British Museum

LESSON 25

Archaeology's Debt to Ancient Rome

THE great claim which the Roman Empire has on the respect of all archaeologists is that it took the best from the civilizations of the earlier periods of Europe, Asia and Egypt, and carried the complex through the known world. The Romans' method of doing this was entirely their own. Underlying the whole of their policy towards the countries they ruled was the determination to be supreme. They allowed no political or other associations within their dominions ; the allegiance of subjects was due to Rome alone, and Roman rulers tolerated no breach in that allegiance. But the privilege of citizenship could be granted where Rome would. Under the republic, to some of the Italians Rome gave full citizenship (so long at least as the citizen body needed recruits), to others partial citizenship, to others a smaller share of privilege, to all a certain measure of local self-government, always as the occasion and Rome's welfare directed. Under the empire this policy was continued among the provinces ; towns as well as individuals were admitted to the honour, till Rome had bound the greater part of Europe into a single unit and reigned unchallenged over it.

This position was held in all its splendour for two centuries ; then the inevitable change set in. The frontiers, continually menaced by barbarian tribes, required larger and larger armies, and Rome as the central authority began to lose ground, till finally it was possible for the Praetorian guards to murder the emperor and put up the empire to auction. Then came an alteration in the government : the empire was divided into two parts, with an emperor and a capital city in each, Rome still retaining a hold on the West while Constantinople ruled the East.

In the West the government was subdivided into ' dioceses,' probably following old tribal divisions. The force of tradition was such that the empire survived invasion after invasion from the Germanic barbarians and from the Scythic Huns. No emperor ruled in the West after the end of the fifth century, but Rome of the East was still a power to reckon with.

Roman Colonization. The effect of Rome on the outlying provinces was almost as great as on those nearer the centre of government. Everywhere Rome followed the example first set by the Persian empire and made good roads and ensured the safety of travellers, for the Romans realized, as Persia had done, that easy and safe communication between countries is the basis of all advance ; the high road of commerce is the high road of civilization. The Romans displayed genius for colonial government in all parts of the empire, educating subjects to look to Rome as the giver of all gifts, and Romanizing as far as possible the barbarian tribes within the imperial pale. Everywhere the barbarian nobles and chiefs modelled themselves on Rome; they built towns with a suite of public buildings— market-place, town hall, baths, amphitheatre outside the walls—they built villas in Roman style with tessellated pavements, they imported Roman products and tried to make their own manufactures resemble Roman goods,

THE ROMAN ROAD. Next to the Roman Law, the Roman road is the most permanent memorial of the greatest empire of antiquity. Throughout the lands that were once part of the imperial dominion there are still many traces of the Roman thoroughfares. This photograph shows the Roman Fosse, between Northleach and Bourton-on-the-Water in the Cotswold country.

Photo, J. Dixon-Scott

they incorporated Latin into their language, they introduced Roman customs and Roman ways into their daily life, and they wore Roman dress in preference to their own. Only in marriage rites and the methods of disposal of the dead did the provinces retain their ancient ways.

ROMAN PROVINCIAL BANKER. *Wherever Roman colonization extended capitalistic development followed and the banker became a familiar figure. Here we see one, with two Roman clerks, receiving payment from Celtic peasants of the Moselle region.*
Trèves Museum

Trade. Intercommunication was safe, but that very safety brought with it other dangers. The mineral wealth of the provinces was often exploited by speculators; and foreigners, greedy of riches, often poured into a new province in hope of making their fortunes. Spain, as has always been the case from the beginning of the Bronze Age, produced gold and copper, wine and oil, and by reason of its natural wealth was one of the richest and most important of the provinces ; it also did a thriving trade in steel blades, as well as in linen and woollen textiles. Flour from the Balearic Islands came much into favour with the epicures of Rome. The chief industries of Gaul were textiles, but there was quite a large output of pottery in imitation of the fine red Arretine ware. This imitation, often called Samian pottery, is characterized by a brilliant polished slip of a sealing-wax red colour. The bowls of this material were cast in a mould and were decorated with wreaths and cupids in the approved Roman style. The imitation Arretine ware was carried all over the provinces and was even taken to Italy ; it is found on Roman sites in all countries.

Britain's minerals were not so important as those of Spain, for zinc instead of tin was used by the Roman metal-founders for alloying copper, the mixture producing brass, not bronze. Enamels still continued to be made, but Britain's chief exports were hides, corn and textiles. Germany, being on the border of the Roman empire, did a large carrying trade of Roman products to the barbarians, but manufactured besides pottery, glass and brass, all for export to the more distant provinces. The trade of Rome on the east went as far as southern India and Ceylon, with which countries there was steady and regular communication, the imports being cotton, spices and other Oriental luxuries. This trade passed across Egypt, with the result that Alexandria was as important under Rome as under the Ptolemies. Rome even sent an embassy to China, probably in connexion with the overland silk trade. One of the most lucrative of all the trades was the traffic in slaves, which was carried on with all countries throughout the known world.

A modern practice first begun under the Romans was the fashion of visiting interesting or beautiful places ; this tourist traffic was in full swing in the second century. Greece owed its prosperity to the tourists, Mediterranean cruises were very popular, and a journey up the Nile became fashionable after Hadrian's visit to Egypt.

Freedom of Worship. Rome was very tolerant of the religions of other countries ; her provincials could worship as they chose. The persecution of the Christians was due not to hatred of their religion but to their refusal to acknowledge the supremacy of the emperor in the usual manner by burning incense before his statue. This was to the Romans a form of high treason, a political not a religious offence ; it was punished, just as high treason was always punished throughout the Middle Ages by Christian monarchs and Christian pontiffs, with torture and death. The eastern part of the empire became officially Christian under Constantine in the fourth century, and not long afterwards the West abandoned paganism. In the West the Roman legions had brought the worship of the soldiers' god, Mithras, to all parts of the empire ; when, therefore, Christianity was established as the official religion, it was carried far and wide and superseded, at least on the surface, the old pagan cults wherever Rome's power prevailed. Christianity followed the Eagles and became co-terminous with the empire.

Indian Archaeology

THE archaeology of India is as yet hardly touched ; there is very little written concerning the prehistory of the country, and excavations are few. Until the twenties of the present century, the knowledge of ancient India extended only to the time of Alexander the Great's invasion, a period when the empires of Egypt, Babylon, Crete, Israel, the Hittites and Assyria had passed almost into oblivion. But India must have had as long a civilization as Europe or the Near East. There is a rich harvest awaiting the archaeologist.

Geographical Conditions. To understand the problems which India presents, the geographical conditions must be taken into account. For archaeological purposes India can be divided into four regions : (1) the Indus basin, which has affinities with Persia and central Asia ; the Ganges valley, which also has connexions with central Asia and is in touch with the more eastern countries ; (3) a *massif* of barren hills and deserts, which forms a barrier running across the whole country from the north-west corner of the Bay of Bengal on the east almost to the Indian Ocean on the west ; (4) the peninsula of India. It is clear, then, that northern India's contacts with other countries, which were chiefly by land, must be entirely different from those of peninsular India, which were always by sea.

In the north, Afghanistan must be reckoned as part of India, for the Kabul river is a tributary of the Indus, and the passes—of which the Khyber is the most celebrated—are practicable for traffic, either commercial or warlike. Afghanistan lies at the foot of the mountain range of the Hindu Kush, through which passes lead to the headwaters of the Oxus and so down into Bactria and thence into central Asia or Europe. The land route from Persia lies through Kandahar, which controls the southern passes, and therefore controls the trade, through these passes, to Sind and Multan. The sea-borne traffic from Persia and the Persian Gulf entered India at the country of Makran, between Baluchistan and the sea, and went up the Indus valley.

The contacts and, therefore, the civilizations of the Ganges valley and of the Peninsula differ from each other and from those of the Indus valley. So little excava-

tion of prehistoric sites has been done in the Ganges region that the archaeology is hardly known. In the Peninsula the contacts were by sea almost entirely. The belt of barren hills which divides India into a northern and a southern region reaches the sea on the east, and to the south of that belt lies the Chilka lake, which effectually blocks all access from the north to the Peninsula on the east except by sea. On the west there is a strip of land between a belt of hills and the sea ; through this trade could filter to some extent. There are some good harbours down the west coast, so that sea-borne traffic could enter the Peninsula more easily on the west than on the east, where the harbours are poor.

Stone Age Cultures. The Palaeolithic cultures are well represented in India, and it is a remarkable fact that the implements of the Lower Palaeolithic periods (Chelles and St. Acheul) are found there as in all other parts of the Old World. The forms are completely stabilized and the methods of chipping are the same wherever the implements are found ; and on the sites where they occur they are found in great quantities. The wide distribution of these highly specialized implements is one of the many problems of archaeology. In the Neolithic period the people lived, as in Europe, on high rolling country, where there were neither forests nor swamps. On such sites Neolithic implements are found, but, unlike the Palaeolithic people, the Neolithic folk made very few tools.

Until excavations were carried out at Mohenjo-Daro and Harappa, the Bronze Age was hardly represented in India. Even now it appears to be known only in the Indus valley, where it may have been imported from the north or west. The Iron Age, however, begins so early and is so important that many authorities are of opinion that the smelting and working of iron began in India, and that the art filtered by slow degrees through the usual channels of communication to the Near East and Russia, and so to the West. The debt of pre-Roman Europe to India is as yet unknown, but it was probably very great.

Bronze Age Centres. The two principal excavations in the Indus valley are at Harappa and Mohenjo-Daro, which are about four hundred miles apart. Mohenjo-

Daro (the Mound of the Dead) lies in the Sind desert, about three and a half miles from the Indus, but as the river is constantly changing its course the town was probably at one time actually on the river bank. Nine strata of buildings have been identified, all belonging to the Bronze Age. It is interesting to note that burnt brick was already the main material for all buildings at this early period ; it was known, though little used, in Mesopotamia in the contemporary period, but in Egypt it is not found till Roman times. The town was laid out with two arterial streets thirty-five feet wide, crossing each other at right angles ; other smaller streets and lanes branched off these, also at right angles. The houses were built, like modern Oriental houses, round a courtyard. The alluvial plain in which Mohenjo-Daro stands has no metal and no stone ; both these materials had to be imported. The few large slabs, used for covering drains and for similar heavy work, were quarried a hundred miles or more farther up the river and brought down by boat. Small semi-precious stones came with the metals from some other part of India, or even from Afghanistan or Tibet.

Some of the small stone seals found at Mohenjo-Daro and Harappa show connexions with seals discovered in Mesopotamia and Elam; by these the date of the upper levels of Mohenjo-Daro can be considered with some certainty to be 2500 B.C. Other connexions with Mesopotamia and Elam are seen in the fragments of steatite vases carved with a mat pattern, found in all three places, and also the strangely etched carnelian beads which are known at Mohenjo-Daro and in Mesopotamia and Russia. Cotton was used for weaving, but no flax. The actual fibres of the cotton have been found preserved by being corroded on a silver vase ; the threads which formed the fabric show its texture.

The whole civilization revealed at Mohenjo-Daro indicates a trading town. Everything was severely practical—there was no attempt at art ; and though religion was manifest, the great temples with their beautiful architecture, which are a feature of Egypt and of later India, do not occur. Mohenjo-Daro existed for trade alone.

Archaeology of Buddhist India. When India first comes into the light of history, about 600 B.C., the northern part of the country was already subject to Hinduism. The expedition of Alexander the Great is, however, the beginning of detailed and consecutive history. From that date until the beginning of the Middle Ages the chief periods are as follows : (1), Mauryan (in the Ganges valley), 323 B.C.-A.D. 100; this includes the Sunga, and also the Bactrian and Parthian intrusions into the northwest ; (2) Kushan (Indo-Scythian), A.D. 100-320 ; (3) Gupta (in the Ganges valley), A.D. 320-6th century, conquered all western India ; (4) Vakataka (in the Deccan) ; (5) Pallava (in peninsular India), A.D. 642-11th century ; this includes the Chola. The chief king of the Mauryan dynasty was Asoka (273-232 B.C.), who made Buddhism the state religion of his great

DOMESTIC COMFORT IN PRE-ARYAN INDIA. One of the principal archaeological sites so far excavated in India is Mohenjo-Daro in the Indus valley. A Bronze Age settlement, it was for centuries a trading town, with well-drained streets and substantial houses. The latter had private wells and paved bath rooms.
Courtesy of Sir John Marshall, Director-General of Archaeology in India

FRESCO AT AJANTA. *At Ajanta in Hyderabad there is a remarkable collection of rock-cut monasteries and shrines forming a Buddhist university that flourished from about 200 B.C. to A.D. 600. The walls of the caves are covered with frescoes, of which the above is an example. It represents a group of Devas—the Shining Ones who had their home among the snows of the Himalayas and who occupy so great a place in Indian mythology.*

doctrine, monasteries were founded, hermits withdrew to the desert, until nearly a third of the inhabitants of Egypt were under religious vows. The missionary spirit, emanating first from India, was also introduced into Christianity, with far-reaching effect on the civilization of medieval and modern Europe.

Asoka appears to have been the first to use stonework for his monuments. His inscriptions were on stone, his commemorative pillars were of stone, and his buildings were of stone; the earlier temples and palaces were probably of sun-dried brick. The change was brought about by foreign influence, and as the beautiful monolithic pillars show a Persian style, it is evident that the influence was from Persia.

empire. This empire comprised practically the whole of the north of India, and stretched from the Hindu Kush mountains in the north to the barren belt of hills which divides northern India from the peninsula. As the most powerful kingdom in India ambassadors and traders flocked in, and Asoka's subjects traded with the lesser kingdoms of the south, including Ceylon, and with the whole of western Asia, eastern Europe and Egypt. With the full force of a remarkable character Asoka sought to introduce the tenets and practices of his religion into other countries. To this end he sent out missionaries, who established themselves in many lands, east and west.

Asoka's Missionaries. In Ceylon and farther east their efforts were crowned with success. In the west the most important for Europe was the mission to Egypt, which preached and practised asceticism and the necessity of withdrawing from the wickedness of this world. The effect of this preaching and of the long contact of Egypt with Buddhist India was not seen till Christianity, which also preached renunciation of the world, swept over Egypt like a flood. Egypt grafted Buddhist asceticism on Christian

After the fall of the Mauryan dynasty the Sunga kings continued as Buddhists; so also were their successors, the Kushan kings. The religious building of this period is the *stupa*, a solid mound of brick or stone surrounded by stone railings and carved stone gateways, with monasteries and chapels adjacent. The railings and gateways are obviously copies of constructions in wood, but the detailed and delicate carvings with which they are adorned suggest that the carver learnt his art on ivory or some equally fine material. Wood was largely used in the construction of private houses, a temple being usually only a more elaborate dwelling-place. In the Mauryan and Kushan periods are found the prototypes of those rock-cut halls and cells which, later on, became so characteristic of Buddhist art in northern and central India.

Ajanta and Ellora. Kings of the Gupta dynasty were patrons of all the arts. The earliest stone buildings which still survive belong to this period, and it must be noted that they are all Hindu, not Buddhist; they show a stage of development between the primitive caves and the fully developed temples and shrines of Ajanta, Ellora and other caves of medieval India. Working in metal on a large scale is characteristic of this age. Statues are known which weigh about a ton, and the celebrated Iron Pillar at Delhi, which stands nearly twenty-four feet high and weighs about six tons, dates from this dynasty.

Our knowledge of the archaeology of this period is derived chiefly from the sculptures in the temples ; the general life of the people cannot be understood without excavation of ancient towns. As in Egypt, working in stone, when once introduced, improved rapidly, until the artificial caves of Ajanta and the rock-hewn temple of Ellora are among the greatest achievements in stone-working that the world has seen. The Ajanta caves show in their sculptures and frescoes the progress of Hinduism and the decadence of Buddhism ; they are still Buddhist in type, but progressively Hindu in feeling. At Ellora the cave technique resulted in the carving of a temple out of a rocky hill. The hill has been completely cut away above and at the sides, leaving a solid four-square mass of rock standing ; this mass has been hollowed out and forms

the temple, which is enriched with carving. It stands upon a great rock plinth, surmounted by a remarkable frieze of elephants which appear to carry the temple on their backs.

The names of Hindu gods occur on cuneiform tablets of the fifteenth century B.C. found at Boghaz Keui in Asia Minor, showing that some of the Vedic deities are connected with the Near East and the eastern Mediterranean. As the fifteenth century B.C. is the time of the Aryan invasion of northern India it is very possible that the spread of this culture may have been due to that great movement of peoples which convulsed the ancient Mediterranean civilizations and resulted in the collapse of Minoan culture and the loss to Egypt of northern Syria. Though the people who entered India spoke an Aryan language, Sanskrit, which is the foundation of a great number of the languages of India, it must not be supposed that the invaders were all of one race. They were probably a mixture of races speaking one language, like the Celts of the Iron Age and the Arabs of the Middle Ages ; they were united by language but not necessarily by blood.

ELLORA'S ROCK-HEWN TEMPLE. *Begun about A.D. 760 as a thank-offering for a victory, and called the Kailasa after Siva's mountain paradise in the Himalayas, this magnificent specimen of Hindu architecture was carved out of the living rock. A rectangular trench was first cut downward from the top of the cliff, and then the great central block thus left was carved into a Siva temple, flat-topped save for the pyramidal ' vimana,' symbolic of the snowy mountain, crowned by the stupa of Siva.*
From Havell, ' Ancient and Medieval Architecture of India,' John Murray

Archaeology of the Byzantine Period

THE Byzantine period begins after the accession of the emperor Constantine (306–337), when he laid the foundations of his new capital on the Bosporus in the year 324. Its history is largely the history of the Christian Church in the east, and the objects which remain are chiefly of religious significance or definitely Christian, because Byzantine art advanced along purely religious lines, Christianity being identified with the State. Archaeologically, the period can be divided into four parts: (1) foundation of Constantinople to the beginning of the Iconoclastic period: 324–725 ; (2) Iconoclastic period: 725–842 ; (3) accession of Basil I to the sack of Constantinople: 867–1204 ; (4) restoration to the Turkish conquest: 1261–1453.

From the accession of Constantine till the Moslem invasion the history of the Mediterranean is one of continual warfare, either between nations or between Churches. In the west the great empire of Rome collapsed under the continued attacks of barbarians ; Goths, Huns and Persians were pushing in, and many of the outlying provinces were lost. Towards the end of the 5th century the last emperor of Rome was deposed, and the centre of government in the west shifted to Ravenna under one of the conquerors. In the east, Byzantium not only stood firm, but carried on the old tradition of Rome's greatness. The advance of the Moslem hordes began in the first half of the 7th century ; Persia, Egypt, Syria, North Africa and Spain were reft away, but Constantinople remained undefeated until the final capture by the Turks in 1453.

During this troubled time the Churches were fighting among themselves. Persecutions were instigated by one sect against another with an animosity greater than that of

the pagan emperors against the Christians ; heresies flamed up and were quenched in blood. The turmoil of the Church was reflected in the world. In Alexandria street riots were so common that in the reign of Justinian the barges laden with corn from Upper Egypt had to be moored within a fortified wall to protect them from looting by the rioters.

One of the chief cities of the Byzantine empire was Alexandria, which was famous for its libraries and its school of medicine. It was an Alexandrian architect who built the Hall of the Thousand-and-One Columns at Constantinople ; alabaster and porphyry were exported from Egypt ; there were shipbuilding yards at Alexandria, and Egyptian hemp was considered the best for the rigging of ships.

A peculiar art of Byzantine times was ivory carving, influenced by the great Syro-Egyptian school. The Christian art of Egypt, during the Coptic period beginning at the end of the 4th century, remained Egyptian, though it was marked by a decorative freedom and humanity. The wealth of Byzantium brought traders from all parts, and pilgrims passing to and from the holy places carried the Byzantine influence to distant countries, so that bronze vessels of Coptic type have been found in Anglo-Saxon cemeteries. Silk weaving was established in Syria under Justinian, and silk became one of the most important fabrics in use. In the 3rd century it was imported from China and was worth its weight in gold ; in the 4th century bishops denounced the use of it as a luxury, and in the 5th all wealthy people dressed in silk. Dye works were also established in Syria, and the woven stuffs and embroideries of Byzantium became famous.

The beginnings of Christian art are not easily traced. Greek influence penetrated central

BYZANTINE CARVING. This 5th century panel of St. Michael, superbly modelled, is typical of the artistic excellence of the Byzantine ivory carvers.

British Museum, photo Mansell

Asia ; out of central Asia streamed forces which influenced the west. Symbolism was at first paramount, and there was no attempt to represent scenes or portraits of sacred personages. The Oriental influence of Syria gradually crept in ; Hellenistic art was regarded as pagan and was discarded in favour of historical and dogmatic representations. Religious art was steadily orientalized till the 8th century, when Oriental influence reached its height in western Europe.

Moslem Influence. The Persian invasion, with the capture of Jerusalem and then of Egypt, drove the Christians elsewhere, and they carried the art and civilization of the east to other countries where they settled. But the great change came with the rise of Islam. The Moslems were animated with love of military adventure, lust of conquest and the consciousness of a divine mission, a combination which rendered them invincible. They moved forward like a flood, and the south, west and part of the east of the Mediterranean came under their rule.

The Iconoclastic period of Byzantium was probably due to Mahomedan influence. It was a revulsion against the superstitious reverence paid to pictures ; all mosaics, frescoes, pictures and even illuminated manuscripts were ruthlessly destroyed. A new art grew up in which the solemn monumental figures were no longer used ; scenes of daily life were portrayed, books of science were illustrated, and a rich foliate ornament was introduced. This continued till, under Basil I, the ' Golden Age ' of Byzantine art arose, in spite of the fact that some of the artists were often little more than copyists and imitators, and painted with theological intention or to illustrate some dogma. Though this naturally developed a tendency towards routine, a great religious and a great decorative art remained. The glory of its sensuous colour and appeal, its aesthetic unity, won praise from Ruskin, despite his prejudice in favour of Greco-Roman standards to the exclusion of other forms of beauty.

In the 10th century Byzantine ivory carving and precious-metal work reached their zenith ; in the 12th, illumination of manuscripts was carried to a pitch of perfection which was unsurpassed. Byzantine architecture may be seen in Venice and other places in western Europe ; Byzantine mosaics—an art form adopted from oriental sources but colour-perfected by the Byzantine artists—which were employed for decorating the walls of churches, also inspired the revival of this art in Italy. The sack of Constantinople drove her inhabitants to seek other and safer countries, and thus Byzantine civilization was carried westward to enrich the countries under her influence. The end of the great Byzantine empire came with the Moslem triumph in 1453

LESSON 28

Dawn of Culture in China and Japan

THOUGH the history of China is late as compared with that of the countries of the Near East, the discovery of the remains of Palaeolithic Man shows that China was inhabited as early as the more western parts of the Old World. Accurate dating does not begin till the ninth century B.C., but scientific excavation is carrying our knowledge of ancient China back to a still earlier period. The Bronze Age appears to have been established as early as in Europe, and there is some reason to suppose that the use of the mixed metal, bronze, may have originated in China. By the twelfth century B.C. the Chinese, who have always been craftsmen, understood the full value of bronze, and were already producing those bronze vessels which are the wonder and despair of all metal workers. Many of these vessels were used to contain the votive offerings dedicated to the worship of the ancestors, and on them was lavished all the skill of the artist.

A Chinese Invention. Glazing of faience was known in Egypt before the beginning of the historic period, and elsewhere there was a certain amount of glazed pottery ; but porcelain appears to have been a Chinese invention, and was made by them so extensively that the common word in modern English for that material is the name of its country of origin, *china.* The invention consisted in subjecting a special kind of clay to sufficient heat to make it crystalline and translucent. The Chinese were using glazed ware about the second century B.C., having perhaps learned this art, together with the art of making glass, from the western peoples with whom they came in contact by trade ; porcelain, however, does

EARLY CHINESE BRONZES. *As early as the twelfth century B.C. Chinese craftsmen were producing vessels of bronze of exquisite workmanship. These two great sacrificial bowls date from the age of the Chous, which closed 250 years before the beginning of our era. The lower bowl measures 33 inches across and is inlaid with gold and silver.*
British and Victoria & Albert Museums

not occur till the seventh century A.D. The Chinese potters were not content with merely inventing a beautiful material ; being artists, they used that material to form beautiful shapes, and decorated the objects with exquisite and appropriate designs. No other country can show such a continuity of high achievement in these arts or such a rich variety in their application.

In Honan Province excavations have been made on the sites of important centres of ancient Chinese life and culture. At one, on the left bank of the Hwan river, royal tombs of the Shang or Yin dynasty (B.C. 1766-1122) have yielded many masterpieces of Chinese art, including superb bronzes and beautifully carved limestone figures, stated to be the earliest examples of sculpture yet found in the Far East.

Tomb tiles of the third century B.C., found at Old Loyang, in the valley of the Lo river, Western Honan, depict hunting scenes and wild geese in flight of a remarkable naturalism, as well as stylized designs of birds, horses and human figures (*see* illustration below).

The earliest known contacts between China and the Near East took place within two centuries after Alexander the Great's expedition to India, when Europe first became conscious of vast territories lying far away to the east. Rome was spreading her empire across Europe and the countries of the Levant, and so came in touch with Persia and India. China was in close contact with India, and Buddhist missionaries carried their religion and their religious art— with its dogmatic symbolism, a bad element in art, and its devotion, a vitalizing element —to China. There is also a record that Chinese envoys visited the court of the Kushan kings at the very beginning of the Christian era, a fact that shows that relations between the two countries were not only amicable but probably frequent.

Early Silk Trade. A regular route for trade from China to Europe ran north of the Hindu Kush, across the Pamirs, along the chain of oases bordering the Taklamakan desert. The silk trade, which followed this route, was very important for China. It began when the Han emperors were at war with the hereditary enemies of China, the Nomads. These fierce people rode small active horses, and the emperor desired large horses that he might overwhelm his foes in cavalry charges. In order to obtain such horses he sent missions to other countries, which resulted in regular communication with the west ; for if the emperor desired horses, the Europeans desired silk with equal fervour. The trade became so important that the production of silk was a jealously guarded monopoly of the emperors. No silkworms or eggs of the insect might be exported ; only raw or woven silk was permitted to leave the country. This rigid monopoly continued until

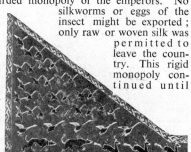

ANCIENT CHINESE MASTERPIECES. *Left, an owl carved in limestone. It stands about 32 cm. high, was discovered in a Shang or Yin dynasty tomb, and is the oldest example of sculpture yet found in the Far East. Right, ink squeeze of a tomb tile of the 3rd century B.C. The dogs, the deer and the flying geese are superbly designed and instinct with movement.*
Academia Sinica, Nanking

about the year 550 A.D., when, at the instigation of the Byzantine emperor, two monks smuggled out of China a quantity of eggs hidden in a bamboo cane.

The first emperor of the Ch'in dynasty, Shi Hwang Ti, lives in the world's memory on account of his connexion with the Great Wall (*see* Vol. II, History, Ancient, L e s s o n 25). It forms the northern boundary of China, and

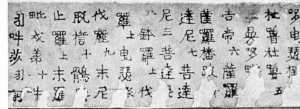

EARLIEST SPECIMEN OF CHINESE PRINTING. *Found at Kichik Hassar in Turkestan, these Chinese Buddhist charms printed in black and red date from the 8th century A.D.*
British Museum; Stein Collection

runs from the Yellow Sea to the mountains of Tibet. There had been other walls along the boundary, but to Shi Hwang Ti belongs the honour of combining them into one, which is 1,500 miles in length. It was originally an earth rampart, faced with either stone or burnt brick ; and the towers—there are said to be twenty-five thousand great towers and fifteen thousand watch-towers —were of sun-dried or burnt brick and only occasionally faced with stone.

Confucianism and Taoism were probably the indigenous religions of China, though Buddhism, which was introduced from India, took root and flourished. Another foreign religion was Christianity, which came in from Persia in the form known as Nestorianism. It grew so popular that in the eighth century it appeared likely to become the state religion, but the opposition of Confucianism and Buddhism, and perhaps of Mahomedanism, overwhelmed it, and although it still survives it is far from being the national religion.

Whether the Chinese invented their own method of writing or whether they received the idea from the Near East is still unknown, but it is certain that they were able to write at a very early period. They never evolved an alphabetic script like the peoples of the Near East, but they were the first to use movable wooden blocks for printing.

Japan. The civilization of the island of Japan is founded on the Chinese. Japan appears to have been inhabited in early times by a primitive race, perhaps originating in western Asia ; these are called Ainu. And there are even legends of a still earlier dwarf people who preceded the Ainu, which shows that the islands have a long, though almost forgotten, history. The people whom we call the Japanese appear to have come from the mainland by way of Korea during the Bronze Age, for they were already well acquainted with the use of metal. The history of Japan traditionally begins at 660 B.C., when the imperial dynasty was first founded. Continual wars with the Ainu and other savages, and perpetual conquests and reconquests of Korea, gave the Japanese little leisure to evolve a civilization of their own. They therefore turned to China, and in the third century A.D. established close cultural contact with that highly civilized power. Chinese writing and all the Chinese arts and crafts were introduced into Japan, and with them priests from Korea also brought the religion of Buddha, which gradually overshadowed the earlier Shintoism and became the state religion.

PREHISTORIC AINU POTTERY. *In the Neolithic age the art of pottery making was established in the southern islands of Japan but never reached the north. The features of these curious little human figures are indicated partly by dabbing on bits of clay and partly by making incisions with some implement.*
From Maeda, 'Japanische Steinzeit'

Temples and Shrines of the Far East

IN the Far East the religious influence of India, whether as Buddhism or Hinduism, is visible throughout the Middle Ages ; it extends to Ceylon, Burma, Siam, Cambodia, Malaya, Java, China and Japan. The great Shwe Dagon of Lower Burma is one of the holiest shrines in the East, for here are preserved eight hairs which the Buddha plucked from his own head and gave to two pious Burmese traders who visited him. This is the legend, but the extreme sanctity of the temple suggests that it was built on a site which was already regarded as sacred by the pre-Buddhist people. Like the stupas of India, the Shwe Dagon is a solid mass of brickwork with shrines round it. It was begun before the Christian era, but was not finished in its present form till 1584, and during all those centuries it was one of the chief places of pilgrimage in the Far East. The great dome is covered with sheets of gold, and the belfry-pinnacle on the top is encrusted with precious stones and hung with numbers of little silver bells which are rung by the wind.

Upper Burma. The Shwe Dagon is in Lower Burma, but in Upper Burma between the 9th and 13th centuries there was a wealthy and powerful kingdom whose capital was Pagán. In the 11th century one of its kings married an Indian princess, showing that there was a considerable amount of intercourse between the two countries. This queen's son built at Pagán a magnificent temple, which has many features in common with Indian architecture. The city of Pagán was full of splendid pagodas, for each king tried to outdo his predecessors in lavish piety. It was utterly destroyed by a Chinese army sent to avenge the murder of some Chinese envoys. Even after its fall some of the pagodas retained their sanctity, and the holy relics of Buddha which they contained made them the objects of pilgrimage for all devout Buddhists throughout the Middle Ages. This custom of making pilgrimages to sacred places and visiting holy relics dates from the time when ancestor-worship was the vogue.

Ceylon. In Ceylon the dagobas, or ' relic-receptacles,' take the place of the stupas of India, and, like their prototypes, are solid masses of brickwork. The shape is not

SHWE DAGON PAGODA. *One of the greatest of Buddhist shrines, the Shwe Dagon at Rangoon, Lower Burma, was traditionally founded in 585 B.C., and has been little altered since the 16th century A.D. Rising from a platform 900 feet long by 685 feet wide, the pagoda is covered from spire to plinth with gold leaf or gold plating, and is decorated with thousands of jewels and hundreds of gold and silver bells. The main building is surrounded by about fifteen hundred smaller shrines.*

Photo, Col. W. J. P. Rodd

unlike an inverted basin or a bell, with the little belfry-pinnacle at the top like the handle of the bell. Each dagoba stands on a base, which may be circular, quadrangular or polygonal ; these rise in three terraces, and round them the religious processions made their way. In some of the dagobas there is a secret chamber hidden in the mass of the building, where the sacred relic was kept. On the walls of the terraces were carved scenes from the life of Buddha. The impulse underlying these carvings is the same as that which produced the Poor Man's Bible of the Middle Ages in Europe ; those sacred pictures and sculptures by which the illiterate learned the dogmas of their faith are similarly exhibited in an easily understood form.

Cambodia. In Cambodia Hindu influence is more manifest than in Burma and Ceylon—an interesting fact, showing that Hinduism had its missionaries as well as Buddhism. The magnificent temple of Angkor Vat was built to honour Hindu gods, but later it became a shrine of Buddha ; it was finished in the 7th century A.D., and has remained untouched ever since. Three miles away lay the city of Angkor Thom, where dwelt the Aryan invaders who brought Hinduism to the country. They built not only Angkor Vat, but many other temples in Cambodia in the same style and as vast in size. The Aryan invaders came from India, not in one overwhelming mass, but in a series of waves, so that they were gradually absorbed into the general population. Buddhism smothered the old Hinduism, as the Aryan blood, not being reinforced by further migration from India, died out.

In all these countries, though Buddhism became the official religion, the old primitive beliefs can often be traced underlying the temple cults. Many of the old gods, dispossessed by the Lord Buddha, are still revered and still receive sacrifices from the people in the village shrines.

Japan. The original religion of Japan was ancestor-worship, the modern name of which is Shinto, ' the Way of the Gods.' Though Buddhism never completely ousted Shinto, ' the influence which it exerted upon Japanese civilization was immense, profound, multiform, incalculable.' It was about the middle of the sixth century that Buddhism was first introduced into Japan, and with it came the arts of civilized China. It was due to the Buddhist doctrine that all living creatures should be treated with consistent kindness that the emperor Temmu decreed in the seventh century that no traps or pitfalls should be used for catching game and that certain animals should not be used as food. As long as Buddhism kept within the bounds of religion all went well, but when in 1575 the priests tried to usurp the temporal power the emperor put them all to the sword. In the following century the same danger to the Government arose through the Jesuit and Franciscan missionaries, and the same means were used to suppress the danger. To prevent any further peril from ' religious intrigues,' Japan shut herself off from the rest of the world, and until the year 1868 foreigners were rarely permitted to enter the country.

LESSON 30

Civilizations of the Mayas and Aztecs

CENTRAL America is divided geographically, and to a certain extent archaeologically, into two parts by the depression across the isthmus of Tehuantepec. To the east the countries of Guatemala, Honduras and Yucatan belong to the Maya civilization, while those to the north-east of the isthmus were Aztec. The history of Central America resolves itself into a series of migrations coming in from the north, sometimes by way of southern California and Jalisco, sometimes by the eastern route. The invaders were probably all of the same race but at different stages of civilization, for they appear to have arrived as nomadic hunters and adopted agriculture after settling in the country. The continued immigration of new tribes brought in fresh ideas and so raised the level of civilization.

The Maya people were of the same race and closely connected with the pre-Aztec (Toltec) inhabitants of Mexico. Their architecture, their calendar, their vigesimal (proceeding by twenties) system of counting were the same ; and the Maya civilization, like the Toltec, ended before the Spanish invasion. The collapse of the Mayas appears to have been due to internal decay ; they gradually relapsed into small insignificant communities. In Mexico the allied culture of the Toltecs also died under the invasions of the Chichimecs, whose kingdom served as the foundation on which the still later invaders, the Aztecs, raised their empire. The Toltec kingdom began in A.D. 752 ; the Aztecs founded their city and established their supremacy in 1325.

Mexican Temples. The architecture of the people of Central America is peculiar to the country. The most remarkable of all the buildings were those dedicated to the service of religion, i.e. the temples. These were raised on high platforms or foundation-mounds made of earth and stones faced with masonry ; and as the Mexicans had a special reverence for the points of the compass, the mounds were built four-square. The steps by which access was obtained to the temple on the top of the mound were always on the west, the temple being built on the flat platform on the top. The reason for such a structure seems to be the desire to build the earthly habitation of the god as close as possible to his heavenly abode in the sky. In many places the walls of these erections are decorated with geometric designs clearly derived from the technique of weaving and basketry. The patterns are often worked in mosaic and the variations of design are amazing. Throughout Central America weaving and basket-work have exerted an immense influence on the art ; the squareness so characteristic of the painting and relief-sculpture indicates its origin.

It is a strange fact that, though the pottery is often very elaborate in design, the potter's wheel was entirely unknown. The elaborate forms were made by hand, and were often fitted with pedestals or legs (*see* the illus. of pottery in Vol. V, Anthropology, Lesson 1) ; the decoration was always geometrical in design.

The most important of the artistic products of the Mexicans was their stone mosaic ; this was a product not found elsewhere in the ancient world, and may have been an invention of their own. One of the finest examples of this art is a human skull covered with horizontal bands of turquoise and jet set in resin ; the eyes are iron pyrites surrounded with a ring of shell, and the nose is inlaid with pink shell. This object represented the god Tezcatlipoca, who was a fertility deity to whom human sacrifices were made. That the worship of this god began in very early times is shown by his emblem of a flint knife.

Two Types of Calendar. The Mexican calendar has always attracted a great deal of attention owing to its peculiarities. There were obviously two calendars, one superimposed on the other. The solar calendar, which was presumably the later of the two, gave 365 days to the year. The year was divided into eighteen months of twenty days each, and there were five intercalary days at the end of the year ; these were known as ' useless days ' and were regarded as unlucky. The monthly festivals, eighteen to the year, followed this calendar, and it was then that human sacrifices were made, the victims being men, women and children as occasion or custom demanded. The whole of the ceremonies were connected with agriculture ; and, the length of the year being that of the agricultural year, it would seem that this calendar evolved when the tribes settled in the country. The ritual calendar, known as the Tonalmatl, had a year of 20 weeks, each week being of thirteen days, making a total of 260 days to the

AZTEC TEMPLE OF THE SUN. The vast pyramid at Teotihuacan, 216 feet high, on a base line of nearly 1,000 feet, is the largest in all Central America. Flights of steps lead upward to the summit where stood the actual temple on a flat platform. For centuries after the Spanish conquest the pyramid was buried in vegetation, but it has now been thoroughly excavated.

Photo, Hugo Brehme

other walls extend for miles. At Tia[l]
naco stood a great megalithic struct[ure]
probably a temple, of which there remai[ns a]
huge doorway cut out of a single l[arge]
block of stone (*see* illus. in facing page).

Inca Supremacy. When the Inca civil[iza]
tion emerged from the storms which [fol]
lowed the Tiahuanaco II period some of [the]
ancient arts still remained. The I[nca]
masonry had not the careless freedom of [the]
earlier builders, but what was lost in [?]
was gained in accuracy ; the blocks u[sed]
were smaller, but were more evenly squa[red]
and fitted. The monotony of long strai[ght]
walls was broken by niches ; these ha[ve]
been likened by superficial observers [to]
Egyptian doorways, but the Egyptian do[or]
way has invariably vertical sides, where[as]
the Inca doorway broadens out from [the]
top to the bottom.

The most amazing part of the In[ca]
civilization was the organization of [the]
country, which, owing to natural conditio[ns,]
had never before been unified. The In[ca]
made roads, built causeways and bridg[es,]
and so linked together all outlying distr[icts.]
They removed the inhabitants of any ne[wly]
conquered country and settled them in t[he]
Inca-ized parts, sending Inca colonists [to]
fill the empty villages in the new territo[ry.]
Inca garrisons were stationed in outlyi[ng]
parts, and large trading centres were esta[b]
lished. Agriculture was improved—no m[an]
was exempt from agricultural labour [or]
military service, except by special privilege[;]
and great irrigation works increased t[he]
wealth of the land. Mining, metallurgy a[nd]

LE[SSON ?]

Archaeology an[d ?]

IN looking back across the ages it [is]
possible to see how little Man ha[s]
changed in essentials since he fir[st]
appeared on the earth. The same force[s]
that surround him now surrounded hi[m]
then, forces which he cannot control, y[et]
which mould him and to which he mu[st]
adapt himself if he would survive. It [is]
possible to see how settlements arose [in]
various parts of the world, each with i[ts]
own organization. These became linke[d]
together by trade or by conquest, bot[h]
these forces having a high value in th[e]
promotion of civilization. That clash [of]
warring peoples and the subsequent com[]
promise between victor and vanquished ar[e]

year ; this was the calendar
for movable feasts and for
divination, and conforms to
no other calendar in existence. There was also an
elaborate system of naming
the days, so that it was only
the priests who could use the
calendars with any facility.

The Mexicans had ad-
vanced far beyond the system
of picture-writing common
to the Indians of North
America, and had evolved
a form of script in which
the signs were symbolical and
not mere pictures. They
were able to make maps and
town-plans.

Aztec Religion. The religion of the Aztecs, which
so horrified the Spaniards,
throws a great deal of light
on the beliefs and religious
customs of early peoples.
Death by sacrifice was the
normal death of the fighting
man, and ceremonial cannibalism was
regarded as an act of communion with the
god who was identified with the sacrificed

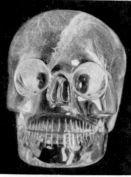

**TEZCATLIPOCA'S SKULL. This
masterpiece in stone mosaic, the
work of a primitive Mexican, is
composed of turquoise, jet, iron
pyrites, and pink shell. It represents Tezcatlipoca, a fertility god
who was also god of the sky and
the night—hence his association
with death, as evidenced by this
gruesome creation.**
*British Museum; photo, Beck
and Macgregor*

victim. To primitive people
death is neither abhorrent
nor to be greatly feared, and
this fact must always be borne
in mind by the archaeologist
when studying the remains
of any ancient religion. The
Mexican burial customs suggest that there was a strong
belief among the Aztecs in
the hereafter, for when the
body was burnt the possessions of the dead man were
burnt also, clearly that they
might go with him to the next
world. Sometimes, as in
other primitive countries,
human beings were slaugh-
tered at the grave to accompany their masters, and the
Mexican was careful to take
his dog also with him. The
Aztec civilization is specially
interesting as a case of
arrested development ; had
the Spaniards not conquered
the country the tribes might
have produced a civilization as high as, if
not higher than, that of Peru, of which we
give an outline in the next Lesson.

LESSON 31

Developments of Culture in Peru

THOUGH Peru is indissolubly linked in
modern minds with the Inca civilization in power at the time of Pizarro's
expedition, yet there was a great empire in
that region before the Incas. The geographical features of that area of South
America played a large part in influencing
the development of culture. There are
three main lines of country running roughly
parallel from north to south : (1) the coastal
desert, known to the Spaniards as Los
Llanos, (2) the highlands and plateaux of
the Andes, the Sierra, and (3) the forested
eastern slopes of the Andes, the Montana.
Streams and small rivers flow from the
Andes through the coastal desert, forming
valleys, and it was by the sides of these
streams that civilization arose and developed in that almost rainless land. The
areas between the river valleys were, and
still are, uninhabited, except by a few fisher
people living in tiny hamlets on the seashore,
who cultivated maize.

Knowledge of the early periods depends
chiefly on legends and oral tradition, and
by this means, supplemented by some
not very scientific excavation in Peru and
Bolivia, it is possible to date approximately
some part of the history :

	A.D.
Early Chimu (on the coast) .. ..⎫	500
Tiahuanaco I (in the mountains) ..⎭	
Tiahuanaco II (coast and mountains)	600–900
Chaotic period	900–1100
Inca supremacy	1100–1530

About the beginning of the Christian era
—a time of great movements of peoples
throughout the world—tribes in small
groups came into Peru from the north and
settled in the mountains and in the river
valleys of the coast. This period lasted
till about 900 A.D., and was followed by a
period of chaos, the causes of which are
not known. Then the Inca tribe rose to
power among the mountain people, conquered and held the coast, and ruled the

country successfully until finally destroyed by the Spaniards.

Chimu Period. The accounts of the Chimu period are legendary but with foundations in fact, for these people had a system of record-keeping peculiar to themselves. This was a kind of tally formed by a series of knots tied on string—called quippu—the record-keepers being instructed as to the event associated with each knot, and passing on their knowledge orally. The method continued through the Inca period, and the history thus chronicled was collected by some of the Spanish Jesuits. During the early Chimu period the country was divided into small independent communities, each ruled by its own chief. This is the invariable beginning of all civilized nations, and it is not until two or more small states coalesce one large community that any adv be made.

The chief product of the Chimu the pottery, found buried in tombs. the potter's wheel was unknown t pottery-making was highly de There were two contemporary '

TIAHUANACO'S MEGALITHIC GATEWAY
monoliths for architectural purposes is a c
pre-Inca civilization of Peru. The gateway
a solid block of stone ; the crack was ca

power. That decay was produced either by exhaustion following on a long-continued or violent war, or by stagnation from a peace undisturbed by invasion or battle. At the same time it must be remembered that civilization advances without regard to the oscillations of world-power. The process is slow, and it is only by looking back across the ages to the hardly human creatures, like Neanderthal Man, from whom we descend, that progress is clearly visible.

Geography and Climate. It is obvious that geography and climate determine the conditions of life. A mountain people will not produce the same culture as the people of the plains or of the sea-shore ; the tropics will create a different civilization from the temperate zone ; the desert or forest people have other requirements than those of the fertile agricultural land. Climatic changes, such as the drying up of a region, will drive out the inhabitants to seek their living elsewhere ; overcrowding of a settlement will have the same effect. From the very earliest period of which we have any knowledge Mankind has always been in movement, leaving traces of his handiwork wherever he settled. Palaeolithic Man made his typical stone implements in all parts of the Old World. Metal-working spread with immense rapidity over large areas ; the only barriers to the advance of civilization were waterless deserts. In every part of the world little civilizations have been established, sometimes growing and spreading from very small beginnings until they became great centres for the distribution of culture, making their mark on the world as the chief contributors to the advance of mankind ; among these can be reckoned the ancient empires of the Near East. Others, like the Incas of Peru, were crushed by a less civilized power before they reached their full glory, and never had the strength to recover from their defeat ; thus they had no effect on the general culture of the world.

Origin of Religion. There are also other factors which control civilization—these spring from Man's own impulses. Of them one of the most important and powerful is the religious impulse. When Man first used his brain to think, he found himself amid the marvels of Nature ; and not knowing which were under his control and which were not, he attempted to propitiate all. Seen from the point of view of modern science, Man's progress may be regarded as a series of more or less successful attempts to free himself from superstitious bonds into

which he was forced by his own ignorance and its consequent terror.

Though the primitive religious impulse was responsible for the savage rite of human sacrifice practised by the early Hebrews as by the more modern Aztecs, it was also responsible for the high ethical code of the ancient Egyptians, for the consciousness of sin among the Babylonians, for the realization of the sufferings of animals among the Buddhists. As Man rises in the scale of civilization, so does his conception of God also rise ; his beliefs and his civilization are so closely linked that one cannot rise or fall without affecting the other. The religious impulse is also responsible for some of the most remarkable and beautiful creations of human hands ; the Palaeolithic paintings, the vast and magnificent temples in all lands, the sculptures of ancient Egypt and Greece, all owe their being to Man's desire to reach up to the Power Beyond.

Artistic Impulse. Closely connected with religion in its earliest expressions is, therefore, the artistic impulse. This is manifested when Man has attained to a little leisure, when the struggle for life is not too severe. Leisure implies wealth, and wealth implies civilization. The desire for beauty, however, is always present, even in the races that are regarded as of low mentality or culture. The method of expressing that desire—whether in music, art or words— necessarily varies according to the natural surroundings, the state of civilization, and the immediate conditions of the country in which that desire is shown. Poetry and music leave no trace until they are recorded, but there is no doubt that they were among the earliest of the arts. The finest epics were inspired by war. Love songs, lullabies and hymns arose from the primitive impulses of sex, maternal love and religion.

It is only when Archaeology is studied from the standpoint of the rise of Man that it assumes its true importance, for it brings into one connected whole the struggles, the defeats and successes of Mankind throughout the world.

BOOK LIST

' Digging Up the Past,' C. L. Woolley (Benn) ; 'Seventy Years in Archaeology,' Sir Flinders Petrie (Sampson, Low) ; 'Corridors of Time,' Peake and Fleure (Oxford) ; 'Our Forerunners,' M. C. Burkitt (Home University Library) ; 'Downland Man,' H. J. Massingham (Cape) ; 'Ancient Hunters,' W. J. Sollas (Macmillan) ; 'The Most Ancient East,' V. Gordon Childe (Kegan, Paul) ; 'Wonders of the Past,' Amalgamated Press.

ENGLISH LANGUAGE

*F*OLLOWING *a lesson on the essentials of grammar which are
common to most languages, ancient and modern, comes our
Course on English. In this the student will read of the origins and
history of English, and of those particular rules of grammar which
apply to it, thus learning to make the right use of his own tongue
in speech and writing.*

*Courses which are complementary to this on the English Language
are those on* ENGLISH LITERATURE *in this Volume and on* PHILOLOGY
*in Vol. II. The student who wishes to pursue his study of languages
further will find Courses on* LATIN *and* GREEK *(Vols. II and III),*
FRENCH *(Vol. I),* GERMAN *(Vol. II),* ITALIAN *(Vol. III),* SPANISH
and PORTUGUESE *(Vol. IV) and* RUSSIAN *(Vol. V).*

Introductory

LANGUAGE STUDY: First Things to Know
about Grammar .. .. *page* 482

16 LESSONS

First Things to Know About Grammar

THIS Lesson is introductory to the whole series of language Courses. It contains in summarized form information concerning parts of speech, inflexion and conjugation, number and gender, case and comparison and so on, which should be mastered before the student turns to the Courses dealing with specific languages—Latin, Greek, French, German, Italian, Spanish, Portuguese, Russian, and, first, English.

Language is the expression of thought by means of words. Words are combinations of elementary sounds, to which a certain meaning is attached. The meaning of the word is what is thought of when the word is used.

Words are generally used in groups called sentences. A sentence is an expression of a complete thought, as when we say ' We know ' ; ' To be or not to be ; that is the question.'

The rules for changing the form of words to express differences in meaning, and for grouping words in sentences, are called Grammar. English grammar, and all other grammars, are those portions of the general science of language which treat of the speech of the English, French, German, and other peoples.

The grammar of any language falls naturally into two parts. The first is that which deals with separate words ; the second is that which deals with words combined to form sentences. The first part treats of the variation of form which words undergo to mark changes in their relation to other words, and of the manner in which they are formed out of simpler elements. The name accidence is given to this, because it shows what changes may befall words—Latin *accidere*, to befall.

The second main division of grammar, dealing with words combined in sentences, is called *Syntax*, from the Greek *syntaxis*, arrangement. The rules of syntax are statements of the ways in which the words of a sentence are related to each other. Syntax deals both with the order of words in a sentence and with the particular inflexions that are required in any given sentence to express the desired meaning.

The classes in which words may be arranged are called parts of speech. These are the same in most of the European languages. The English names for the eight parts of speech—all derived from their Latin equivalents—are as follows :

1. A Noun (*nomen* = name) is a word used as the name of something—e.g. bird, *avis* (Latin), *oiseau* (French) ; James, Jacques.

2. An Adjective (*adjectivus* = that is added to) is a word used with a noun to describe, to measure, to count, or to indicate that for which the noun stands—e.g. *hot* days, *four* boys, *this* man.

3. A Pronoun (*pro* = instead of) is a word used instead of, or to avoid repeating, a noun—e.g. ' When Elizabeth died, *she* was seventy years old.'

4. A Verb (*verbum* = word) is a word by means of which we state something—' Birds *sing*.'

5. An Adverb (*ad verbum* = to a word) is a word which shows how an action, state, or quality is modified or limited—' He speaks *eloquently*.'

6. A Preposition (*prae-positus* = placed before) is a word which shows how things, or their actions and attributes, are related to other things—' The Mill *on* the Floss ' ; ' Come *unto* Me.' It is usually placed before the noun which it governs.

7. A Conjunction (*con-junctio* = joining together) is a word which joins together words or sentences—e.g. ' Man proposes, *but* God disposes ' ; ' Come, buy wine *and* milk.'

8. An Interjection (*inter-jectus* = thrown between) is a word thrown in to express some feeling or emotion. It has no grammatical relation to the sentence in which it stands : ' Alas ! ' ; ' Hurrah ! '

Inflexion. Inflexion (Latin, *inflectere*, to bend) is a change made in the form of a word to denote a modification of meaning, or to show the relationship of the word to some other word in the sentence.

Nouns, pronouns and adjectives are inflected to mark number, gender, and case. This is called declension. Thus, in Latin there were five methods of declension, in Greek three, in German the strong and the weak declensions, etc. The old grammarians used to speak of the subject (or nominative case) as the ' upright ' case, and all the other cases as ' oblique.'

Case. The word case means ' a falling,' and the oblique cases were conceived of as falling away or ' declining ' from the nominative. Hence the declension of a noun is a statement of its cases—i.e. of the forms which it assumes in various relations. The full number of cases is seven, but the actual number in use varies in different languages.

Nominative (including the Nominative of Address, sometimes called the Vocative)—e.g. ' *He* is going out.' ' *The man* is well known.' ' *John,* come here ! '
Accusative (the case of the direct object)—e.g. 'The man saw *the dog* ; he saw *me.*'
Dative (the case of the indirect object)—e.g. ' I give *him* a book.'
Genitive (the case denoting origin or possession)—e.g. the *horse's* head.
Ablative (the case denoting separation from).
Locative (the case denoting place at which).
Instrumental (case denoting association with).

The last two became merged in the ablative in Latin. In English the last three case-relations and that of the dative (except for pronouns) are expressed by phrases with prepositions—e.g. 'It comes *from London.*' ' He killed him *with a dagger,*' etc.

Gender. The distinction between male and female in nature is called sex. The distinction between masculine and feminine in words is called Gender. In English we adopt the natural distinctions of gender : names of animals of the male sex are masculine, names of animals of the female sex are feminine, names applied to animals of either sex are common, and names of things of neither sex are neuter. This is perfectly simple, but other languages, such as Latin, French, and German, often distinguish gender by noun endings, irrespective of meaning ; thus, in German, *Mädchen*=a little maid, is neuter : and in French, *la table*= the table, is feminine.

Number. Number is the difference in words to express one or more than one—singular or plural. Some languages have special forms to denote two persons or things ; this is called the dual.

Comparison. Adjectives and adverbs are inflected to mark degree. This inflexion is called Comparison. There are three degrees of Comparison—Positive, Comparative, Superlative. A Positive adjective compares a thing with all other things, and ascribes to it a certain quality—e.g. *long, beau* (French), *altus* (Latin). A comparative adjective compares the thing named with one other, and shows that the former has more of a certain quality than the second—e.g. *longer, plus beau, altior.* A superlative adjective compares the thing named with several others—at least two—and shows that it possesses a certain quality in a higher degree than any of the others—e.g. *longest, le plus beau, altissimus.* The same applies to adverbs.

Conjugation. Verbs are inflected to mark voice, mood, tense, number, and person. This inflexion is called Conjugation. Voice is the form of the verb by which it is shown whether the subject of the sentence stands for the doer or for the sufferer of the action spoken of by the verb. Most languages have two voices—Active (where the subject of the sentence is the doer of the action) and Passive (where the subject of the sentence 'suffers,' or is the object of the action). Greek has a middle or reflexive voice in addition.

Mood is that variation of the verb used to express the mode or manner of an action or of a state of being, e.g. simple statement (Indicative Mood), command (Imperative), possibility (Subjunctive). When a verb has no subject expressed or implied, it is said to be in the Infinitive Mood ; the other moods are finite.

Tense indicates the time to which an action or event is referred ; in all languages the natural division is into past, present, and future, with different varieties and shades of meanings of each.

Person is a modification of the form of a verb by which it is shown whether the speaker speaks of himself (first person), or of the person or persons addressed (second person), or of some other person or thing (third person).

To conjugate a verb is to give all its tenses and moods, and the full Conjugation of a verb is the formation of all the inflexions and combinations used to indicate voice, mood, tense, number and person. Thus, when we speak of the four Conjugations in Latin or French, we mean the four modes of forming the tenses in those languages. In English there are two 'conjugations,' strong and weak ; the former modifies the vowel-sound of the root to form the past tense (*write, wrote*) ; the latter adds *-ed* or *t* to the stem (*love, lov-ed*). Prepositions, conjunctions, and interjections are not inflected.

Analytic and Synthetic Languages. A language which is rich in inflexions, like Latin or Greek, is called *Synthetic* (Greek, synthetikos = able to put together), because it puts many meanings and relations into one word. A language which has simplified its inflexions, like English or French, and uses separate words instead, is called *Analytic* (Greek, analytikos=able to split up or take to pieces : cf. the noun analysis).

The tendency of languages is to pass from synthetic to analytic, and the languages which are today analytic were originally far more synthetic, if not entirely so. We see this tendency in the passage from Latin to French, and in that from Old English to Modern English. Old English, for example, was an inflexional or synthetic language : its nouns had four cases, and there were different declensions : adjectives were declined, and had three genders ; pronouns had more forms than they have today, and some had a dual number, as well as a singular and plural ; the verbs had more variety in the terminations. Gradually, in the three centuries following the Norman Conquest, most of these inflexions were dropped, and separate words (such as prepositions and auxiliary verbs) were used in their stead. For example, the Old English word hām (=home) was declined thus:

Case	Singular	Plural
Nominative	hām	hāmas
Accusative	„	„
Genitive	hāmes	hāma
Dative	hāme	hāmum

There is no short cut to the acquisition of a language, that is, to the thorough understanding of it. Of course, a language can be very easily picked up, as we say, by a short residence among the people who speak it. But merely to repeat certain sounds is not to know a language, even if we pronounce the sounds quite correctly. To know a language we must understand the why and the wherefore of all the inflexions of its words and their relationship one with another in any sentence of that language.

Undoubtedly, therefore, the best way to study a language and to learn its grammar is to begin with sentences, not with single words. The unit of speech is the sentence, and we cannot fix an exact meaning to a word until we see it in a sentence. It is thus a great mistake to start learning the grammar of a language by committing to memory pages of rules and paradigms, or by confining oneself to acquiring a large vocabulary of its words.

It is with the sentence that the pupil should begin his study. When once a sufficient number of sentences has been assimilated it will be easy to analyse them into their component parts, and to show the relations that these bear to one another. As Professor Sayce says :

In this way the learner will be prevented from regarding grammar as a piece of dead mechanism or a Chinese puzzle, of which the parts must be fitted together in accordance with certain artificial rules, and will realize that it is a living organism which has a history and a reason of its own. The method of nature and science alike is analytic ; and if we would learn a foreign language properly we must learn it as we did our mother-tongue, by first mastering the expression of a complete thought, and then breaking up this expression into its several elements.

ENGLISH LANGUAGE

LESSON ONE

Outline History of Our Racial Speech

THE history of the English language is the history of the English people. As we trace the growth of the nation, we trace the growth of the language. Words are fossilized history. They speak to us of waves of conquest, of eras of strife, of the gradual victory of the arts of peace over the arts of war ; they tell us of the hopes and fears, the expectations and disappointments, the laws, customs, dress and manners of those who dwelt in this land of ours long centuries before us.

Up to the year A.D. 450 our islands were inhabited by different Celtic races, speaking various dialects of the Celtic group of languages. These races were closely allied to the inhabitants of Gaul (as France was then called), and spoke practically the same tongue. About the beginning of the Christian era both Britain and Gaul were conquered and overrun by the Romans, but with strikingly different results as far as language was concerned. The conquered Gauls adopted the Latin language, while Latin made singularly little impression on the Celts of Britain, who largely retained their own dialects. The Latin language was destined, however, to have its revenge ; for the Franks and Normans, who subsequently occupied France, adopted the language of that country, and were instrumental in introducing it (in an altered form, of course) into Britain about the time of the Norman Conquest.

Celtic Words. Among the earliest elements in our language, therefore, are the old Celtic words, that have survived in the struggle for existence and have come down to us through two thousand years and more. These are not many, for the language of the Britons was displaced by that of their Saxon conquerors.

The Celtic words consist chiefly of geographical names—e.g. *Devon, Dor(set), Kent, Exe* ; *Avon, Ouse,* and *Usk* (all three meaning water), *Trent, Dee, Don, Severn, Wight, Bute, Pen* (as in *Penrith*). Also, as we should expect, words dealing with household matters, names of implements used by serfs, etc.—as : *ass, brock* (a badger), *druid, down* (a hill), *cross* (noun) ; and indirectly (through the Norman-French) words like *basket, bran, gown.* One of the Celtic dialects is still spoken in Wales. The Romans left singularly few words as the result of their occupation of these islands.

Coming of the Anglo-Saxons. Not long after the departure of the Romans from this country, fresh conquerors descended on its defenceless shores. From about A.D. 450 to 550 a constant succession of Jutes, Saxons, and Angles streamed over from the lowland region in north-west Germany. Conquering the Celtic inhabitants, they drove them steadily northward and westward into the lowlands of Scotland, and into Cumberland, Westmorland, Wales, and Cornwall. These tribes were of Germanic stock. As their area of conquest extended, their language naturally became more and more prevalent, until in course of time (long before the Norman Conquest) it was spoken from the Firth of Forth to the English Channel. This language, which became gradually broken up into a number of dialects, is known as Old English ; and it is the direct ancestor of the English of today.

Second Latin Influx. The introduction of Christianity brought into the language many Latin words of an ecclesiastical nature. Words thus introduced are mostly the names of Church dignitaries, ceremonies, and the like. They came either directly from the Latin, or indirectly through Latin from the Greek. Examples of the latter are *bishop, presbyter, baptism, eucharist, monk,* and *clergy.*

Scandinavian Elements. Meanwhile during all these centuries the Norsemen and Danes were constantly landing on our shores, in more or less successful attempts at conquest. These were men of Scandinavian race, whose language was of the same group as English (Germanic). Owing to their settlement here, we have many of their words in our language today. A number of place-names in the north and east of England are Scandinavian—e.g. Grimsby, Whitby (*by* = town) ; Furness, Skegness (*ness* = headland) ; Troutbeck, Welbeck (*beck* = brook) ; Orkney (*ey* = island) ; Aira Force, Scale Force (*force* = waterfall) ; Thorpe, Grimsthorpe (*thorp* = village) ; Dingwall, Thingwall (*thing* or *ding* = place of meeting) ; Langwith (*with* = wood) ; Lowestoft (*toft* = small field).

The Norman Conquest. The Normans introduced their language (a descendant of Latin) when they introduced themselves. This is the third, and perhaps the most important, invasion by the Latin tongue. Norman-French became the language of the upper classes and of the law courts : even today our Sovereign uses this language when he gives his assent to, or withholds his assent from, bills that have passed the two Houses of Parliament. For a time, however, the mass of the English people clung tenaciously to their old language, but gradually the two races began to blend, and English assumed the form which it has today—a fusion of Old English and Norman-French. Nevertheless, the basis of the language, including the commonest words and all the grammar, remains thoroughly English.

The majority of the words in our language which relate to feudal institutions, to war, law, and the chase were introduced in this way, and, to quote but one example, to this day the town crier perpetuates the Norman-French word 'Oyez' (the imperative of *oyer*, to hear) in his 'Oh yes,' 'Oh yes,' 'Oh yes.'

Influence of the Renaissance. The Renaissance, the great revival of the study of the classical languages that took place in the sixteenth century, gave an immense number of Latin words to our language. This is the fourth, and practically the last, invasion on the part of Latin. A perfect craze arose for using long, cumbersome, and unwieldy words taken straight from Latin, and even from Greek. The authors of this period and school are often painful reading.

In their works we find, for example, the following uncouth creations : torve and tetric = *stern, severe ;* cecity = *blindness ;* insulse = *tasteless ;* facinorous = *guilty.*

Many of the words thus introduced have long since perished, and during the last hundred years or so there has been a reaction in favour of a return to a purer English diction.

In many cases the same Latin word has given us two words in English, one direct from the Latin, the other through the medium of Norman-French. For example:

Latin	Direct from Latin	Through Norman-French
Fragilis	fragile	frail
Ratio (-nem)	rational	reason
Potio (-nem)	potion	poison
Quietus	quiet	coy
Punctum	punctuate, etc.	point
Factum	fact	feat

Borrowed Words. In later times English has borrowed words from almost every language under the sun. Some of the chief of these sources may be mentioned:

Chinese. Caddy, junk, gong, nankeen, tea.

Turkish. Bey, ottoman, sash, tulip.

Persian. Bazaar, attar, sherbet, turban, chess, dervish, hookah, lilac, musk, taffeta.

Hebrew. Sabbath, seraph, cherub, amen, leviathan, jubilee, Satan, ephod.

Arabic. Alchemy, alcohol, algebra, almanac, alembic, tariff, zenith, zero, nadir, talisman, naphtha, coffee, mosque, fakir, giraffe, harem, sultan, vizier.

Hindustani. Muslin, calico, rupee, lac, pundit, sepoy, thug, suttee, chutney, jungle, pariah, nabob, bungalow, coolie, curry.

French. Etiquette, soirée, menu, eau-de-vie, chef, ennui, bouquet, bon-bon, trousseau, carte-de-visite, tête-à-tête.

Spanish. Alligator, armada, matador, toreador, battledore, galleon, cargo, bolero, eldorado, tornado, renegade, verandah, castanets, chocolate, don, negro, mulatto, grandee, pillion.

Italian. Banditti, macaroni, folio, quarto, stiletto, stucco, incognito, gazette, brigand, gondola, influenza, motto, opera, concert, and nearly all the terms used in music.

Dutch. Boom, schooner, sloop, skipper, yacht, reef, skate.

Gaelic. Clan, tartan, pibroch, slogan, plaid.

Portuguese. Caste, cocoa, palaver, porcelain, marmalade, commodore, fetish.

Polynesian. Taboo, tattoo, boomerang, kangaroo, wombat.

American Indian. Squaw, wigwam, pampas, papoose, tobacco, tomahawk, maize, pemmican, potato, hammock.

Scientific words used in botany, medicine, etc., mostly come from Latin or Greek.

The Five Periods of English. It is possible to trace five distinct periods or stages through which the English language has passed.

1. OLD ENGLISH. This period extends practically up to the time of the Norman Conquest, at the close of the eleventh century. There were four main dialects of the language—*Northumbrian* and *Mercian* (the two together sometimes called *Anglian*) in the north, and *West Saxon*

and *Kentish* in the south. The S.E. Midland variety of the Anglian branch, which included the dialect of London, became the parent of modern standard English.

2. EARLY MIDDLE ENGLISH. This lasted from about A.D. 1100 to A.D. 1250. The most noticeable feature is the influence of Norman-French on spelling and vocabulary. During this period many of the inflexional endings became confused and often vanished.

3. MIDDLE ENGLISH. This lasted from about A.D. 1250 to 1350. The weakening influence of Norman-French was still more pronounced, and the language became rapidly analytic. The English of these first three periods is very different from that of today, and needs to be studied almost as though it were a foreign tongue.

4. LATE MIDDLE ENGLISH. But when we come to this period (1350–1450), of which Chaucer is the shining light, we approach much nearer to our modern language. A great deal of Chaucer can be read right off by any person of average education. It was during this period that the London dialect became predominant.

5. MODERN ENGLISH. 1450 to the present day. During this period many changes in sound took place, though these were not followed up by corresponding changes in the spelling, owing to the fact that the early printers adhered to the conventional spelling of the fourteenth century.

Germanic v. Romance. These two elements have blended together to form our modern language. But we must never forget that the basis, or framework, is Germanic. It is true that there are more than twice as many classical or Romance words in our language as Germanic, the numbers given by some authorities being respectively 29,000 and 13,000. Yet the majority of those used belong to pure English stock, and when we want to express our finest feelings, or to interpret the deepest things of life, we naturally resort to that language. As a rule, the Germanic words are the shorter. Most words of three or more syllables, and many of those of two, are classical; while in most words of one syllable, and very many of two, the Germanic element prevails. It is at once the simplest and the most dignified. A wise writer, of course, will avail himself of both elements. He will never choose a classical word when a Germanic one will do equally well, but he will see to it that while the superstructure may be Romance, the basis of his language will be English.

Germanic Words. The following are the chief Germanic elements in the English language : pronouns, numerals, prepositions, conjunctions, adjectives of irregular comparison, auxiliary verbs, all verbs of strong conjugation and some of weak, also most words relating to house, farm, family, parts of the body, common natural objects, common actions and things, trades, etc. On the other hand, words relating to law, religion, government, war, science, art, and philosophy are mostly classical.

One great advantage given to the English language by this blending of two distinct elements is that it is particularly rich in words of similar though not identical significance. It can, therefore, express delicate shades of meaning that are impossible in other languages. Notice, for example, the following list of pairs, one word being Germanic, the other classical :

Germanic	Classical	Germanic	Classical
cold	frigid	breadth	extent
hard	difficult	feeling	sentiment
bitterness	acerbity	life	existence
God	deity	love	passion
work	labour	worship	adoration
bloom	flower	fire	conflagration

This list might be extended to almost any length. It will be noticed that, on the whole, the Germanic words are more 'nervous' and expressive than the classical. As a rule, they come first to one's mind, the others being employed subsequently to avoid repetition, or to amplify the meaning. Naturally, our finest poetry is largely composed of the Germanic element. Shakespeare is well worth studying from this point of view alone. The Authorized Version of the Bible, Bunyan, and Defoe contain whole paragraphs composed almost entirely of English words. For simplicity and pathos there is nothing to beat pure English. In large measure the charm of such a piece as, say, Tennyson's 'Crossing the Bar' lies in the fact that it contains hardly any but Germanic words :

Sunset and evening star,
  And one clear call for me,
And may there be no moaning of the bar
  When I put out to sea,

But such a tide as moving seems asleep,
  Too full for sound and foam ;
When that which drew from out the boundless deep   •
  Turns again home.

Classical Style. A very good example of the classical style is to be found in the works of Walter Pater. If we open them at any page we find majestic, sonorous sentences, almost every other word of which is of classical origin—e.g. from 'Marius the Epicurean' :

His old native susceptibility to the spirit, the special sympathies, of places—above all, to any hieratic or religious significance they might have—was at its liveliest, as Marius, still encompassed by that peculiar singing, and still amid the evidences of a grave discretion all around him, passed into the house. That intelligent seriousness about life, the absence of which had ever seemed to remove those who lacked it into some strange species wholly alien from himself, accumulating all the lessons of his experience since those first days at Whitenights, was as it were translated here, as if in designed congruity with his favourite precepts of the power of physical vision, into an actual picture. If the true value of souls is in proportion to what they can admire, Marius was just then an acceptable soul.

Aryan Languages. The languages of the world are arranged in families, according to original identity in grammar and vocabulary. One of these families is known as the Indo-Germanic or Aryan family. It includes :

1. *Sanskrit*, which is the classical language of India, and exhibits the Aryan grammar in its most perfect form.

2. *Persian*, the earliest literary form of which is called Zend.

3. *Balto-Slavonic*, including Russian, Polish, Czech, Serb, Lithuanian, Lettish, etc.

4. *Hellenic*, including all Greek dialects.

5. *Italic*, including Latin, together with the Romance languages derived from Latin, e.g. French, Italian, Spanish, Portuguese.

6. *Celtic*, comprising Gaelic (i.e. Irish, Manx, and Scottish Gaelic) and Cymric (i.e. Welsh, and the Armorican of Brittany).

7. *Germanic*. This group now consists of two main sections, Scandinavian and West Germanic. *Scandinavian* includes Icelandic, Swedish, Norwegian, and Danish. *West Germanic* comprises High German (the languages spoken in South Germany), Low German (the languages spoken in the northern lowlands of Germany), English, Frisian, Dutch, and Flemish.

Not all the European languages are of Indo-Germanic stock. Thus, Turkish, Finnish, and Hungarian were introduced from Central Asia in fairly modern times.

In addition to words that have been imported into English, there are many English words, or roots of words, that are common to most of the Aryan languages. These have not been borrowed one from another, but all the different languages have received them from an earlier source. English thus ceases to be an independent language, arbitrarily invented for our exclusive use.

We see it to be a gradual growth, a single member of a large family of related tongues.

EXERCISE

1. From what Latin words are the following doublets derived ? *Hospital* and *hotel ; pauper* and *poor ; redemption* and *ransom ; senior* and *sir ; rotund* and *round ; junction* and *joint.*

2. From what languages are the following words borrowed ? *maize, tattoo. cocoa, slogan, yacht, quarto, pillion, bouquet, jungle, zero, leviathan, attar, ottoman, tea-caddy.*

3. Re-write in modern English :
   Whan that Aprillè with his shourës soote
   The droghte of March hath percëd to the roote,
   And bathëd every veyne in swich licour
   Of which vertu engendred is the flour ; . . .
   Thanne longen folk to goon on pilgrimages.
       CHAUCER (*Prologue to Canterbury Tales*)

4. What words of classical origin are to be found in Tennyson's 'Crossing the Bar' ?

LESSON TWO

The Alphabet and Spelling

THE English alphabet is the ordinary Roman alphabet, with the addition of the letter w. It consists of twenty-six letters, which are written both as small letters and as capitals.

Capital letters are used at the beginning of proper names ; also at the beginning of every new sentence, and of every line of poetry. The pronoun I and the interjection O are always capitals. Capitals are also used when speaking of the Divine Being, e.g. Thou, He, and in such expressions as His Majesty, etc.

CAPITALS. A, B, C, D, E, F, G, H, I, J, K, L, M, N, O, P, Q, R, S, T, U, V, W, X, Y, Z.

SMALL. a, b, c, d, e, f, g, h, i, j, k, l, m, n, o, p, q, r, s, t, u, v, w, x, y, z.

The English alphabet is both redundant and defective : redundant, because it contains three letters (c, q, x) indicating sounds which are also indicated by other letters (c=k or s, q=k, x=ks or gs) ; defective, because there are only twenty-six letters (twenty-three really) to express at least thirty-four sounds. For the eleven sounds which have no special letters, we use certain combinations of letters, as ng, ee, au, sh, etc. We want a new alphabet of at least thirty-four letters, one for each sound.

Vowels. The letters a, e, i, o, u represent sounds which are called Vowels (Lat. *vocalis*=soundable), because they can be fully sounded with no check in the passage of the breath. The remaining letters represent sounds called Consonants ('sounding with') ; during their articulation the air-stream is wholly or partially checked. W and y may represent either a consonant or a vowel ; when they are followed by a vowel sound in the same syllable, they are consonants, as *world, yield.* When a vowel precedes them in the same syllable in spelling they combine with it to form either a diphthong (see below), or a simple vowel sound, as *buy, few.* Y is a pure vowel when followed by a consonant, as *Ygdrasil :* this was its original use ; it was first used as a consonant after the Norman Conquest.

When two vowel sounds are pronounced as one syllable we have a diphthong ('double sound'). The chief diphthongs in English are listed.

DIPHTHONGS

1. *i*, as in *bind, find* (cf. the same sound in *aye*). This sound = ă+i.
2. *oi* or *oy*, as in *hoist, boy, buoy.* It = the sound of o+i.
3. *a*, as in *make, may.* This sound = e+i.
4. *ou* or *ow*, as in *how, pound.*
5. *o* as in *stone, know ;* = o+u.

NOTE. In cases where two vowels are written, but only one pronounced (gauge, boat, mien), we have not a proper diphthong.

The vowel sounds in modern standard English are as follows :

SHORT VOWELS : *a* as in m*a*n ; *e* as in m*e*n, r*ea*dy ; *i* as in b*i*t ; *o* as in n*o*t, wh*a*t ; *u* as in b*u*t, sh*o*ve ; *oo* as in p*u*ll, b*oo*k ; the unstressed vowel heard in *u*pon, fath*e*r.

LONG VOWELS : *ah* as in f*a*ther, p*a*rt ; *ē* as in b*e*, b*ea*n ; *aw* as in c*aw*, c*au*se ; *ē* as in f*i*r, w*o*rd, l*ea*rn.

Consonants. These are classified thus :

1. STOP CONSONANTS, e.g. *b, d, k.* In the formation of these the air-stream is completely (but momentarily) checked in some part of the mouth-passage.
2. OPEN, e.g. *f, s, th, w.* In these the air-stream is perceptibly hindered, but not entirely stopped.
3. NASAL, e.g. *m, n, ng.* Here the air-stream is stopped in the mouth, but the air is released through the nose.

4. DIVIDED, e.g. *l*. The air-stream is stopped by the middle of the tongue (regarded lengthwise), but passes out at either side.

5. TRILL, e.g. *r*. Here the tongue or uvula vibrates rapidly (less in English than in other languages).

Consonants are also grouped according to the part of the mouth used in producing them : the point, blade, front, or back (of the tongue), represented respectively, for instance, by *t, s, y* (in *y*ou), *k ;* the lips (*m, b*, etc.) : the teeth, which may be used with the point of the tongue (as in *th*), or the lower lip (as in *f*). Thus *k* is a lip stop consonant, *l* a point divided, *m* a lip nasal, *f* a lip-teeth open, and so on.

Finally, consonants are divided into two classes, according to the presence or absence of the 'buzz' which accompanies the vibration of the vocal cords. Examples of consonants in the formation of which the vocal cords vibrate, and the 'buzz' (technically known as *voice*) is heard, are *v, z, m, g ;* these are called *voiced* consonants. In the *unvoiced* sounds *f, s, k*, etc., the vocal cords do not vibrate.

There are two pairs of consonants which are very closely linked : *t*+*sh* (usually written *ch* or *tch*) and *d*+*zh* (usually written *j, g* (before *e, i*, as in *gem*), or *dge* (as in bri*dge*).

The sound *h* is produced by putting special stress on the ordinary air-stream as it passes out through the throat. It is called an aspirate. In many English words, *h* is written where it is not pronounced, e.g. in *h*our, *h*onour.

Defects in Spelling. A perfect system of spelling or writing would be *phonetic*, i.e. would indicate exactly the sounds made in speaking. For this purpose it is necessary :

1. That there should be a letter for each spoken sound ;
2. That each letter should stand for only one sound ;
3. That in writing a word, no sound should be omitted and no unpronounced letters should be added.

English spelling breaks all these rules :

1. As there are only twenty-three letters for thirty-four sounds, there are eleven sounds without corresponding letters.
2. The letter *a*, for example, represents four simple vowel sounds, as in *fall, far, fat, want*, and a diphthong, as in *fate* ; *e*, five sounds (*mete, pet, herd, clerk, pretty*) ; *i* represents two simple sounds (*pit, fir*) and one diphthongal (*bite*) ; *o* represents three sounds (*poke, pot, for*) ; *u* represents four (*rude, pull, fun, fur*). Cf. *his* and *this ; dough* and *cough*.
3. Letters are often written which are not pronounced ; these are useless as signals of the spoken word :

E.g. *c* is useless in *duck, scene*.
    g   „   „ *gnat, reign*.
    k   „   „ *knee, know*.

Syllables. A syllable consists of a single vowel or a collection of sounds pronounced together, and has only one vowel sound. Words consisting of one, two, or three syllables are called respectively monosyllables, disyllables, and trisyllables ; words of more than three syllables are called polysyllables (Gk. *polys*, many).

In dividing a word into syllables we must as far as possible indicate the significant parts of which the word is composed, e.g. trans-act, not tran-sact ; e-rect, not er-ect. There is, however, a limitation to this rule, for words must be divided in writing according to the way in which the elementary sounds are grouped in speaking, i.e. the division is usually made after the vowel, and the following consonant is carried on to the next syllable, e.g. hu-mour, fa-cing.

Accent is the stress of the voice upon a syllable—as cátaract, pervérsion, corróde. Difference of accent is often the only distinction between nouns and verbs, e.g. rébel and rebél, prógress and progréss. Many words have changed their accent, and the tendency of English is tó throw the accent back towards the beginning of a word. Thus Shakespeare uses *contráry*, Milton *blasphémous*, Pope *compénsated* and *effórt*, etc.

Letters and syllables lead on to words, and these, grouped according to parts of speech, will be next discussed.

Key to Exercise in Lesson 1

1. *Hospitale* (low Latin from *hospitem*)— *pauper—redemptum—seniorem—rotundum —junctum*.
2. See the list in page 486.
3. When April with its sweet showers has pierced the drought of March to the root and bathed every vein (of the plant) in such liquor by virtue of which the flower is engendered (brought forth)—then folk long to go on pilgrimages.
4. Clear (Lat, *clarum*), bar (Low Lat. *barra*), moving (Lat. *movère*), sound (Lat. *sonus*), bound(less) (Low Lat. *bodina*).

LESSON THREE

The Noun and Its Three Cases

IN English there are eight parts of speech —noun, adjective, pronoun, verb, adverb, preposition, conjunction and interjection. The article is sometimes regarded as a ninth part of speech, but it is more customary to include it with the adjective.

A noun is a word used as the name of something (Lat., *nomen*=name).

Classes of Nouns. There are two main classes of nouns : Proper and Common.

1. A proper noun is a name appropriated (Latin, *proprium*) to one particular thing or person, e.g. Abraham, Mont Blanc.

2. A common noun is a name which all things of the same kind have in common (*communis*=shared by several). All nouns not proper are common. Examples : cat, town, coal, water.

NOTE. Proper nouns may be converted into common, e.g. 'he is the *Rupert* of debate.' Similarly, a common noun may become proper, e.g. 'I am going up to *Town*' (London).

Common nouns are subdivided into :

1. Ordinary class names, i.e. names belonging to each individual of a class, or to each portion of some material, e.g. tree, iron.

2. Collective nouns, denoting a number of persons or things forming one body, e.g. committee, jury, herd. In the plural such nouns stand for several similar collections : e.g. the parliaments of Europe. As a rule, a collective noun has its verb in the singular : 'the Government has abdicated' ; but when attention is directed to the individuals composing the subject, the verb is plural : e.g. 'the jury were right in finding him guilty.'

3. Abstract nouns, denoting not objects, but quality, action, or state, e.g. drowsiness, walking, manhood. Also names of arts and sciences, as music, biology.

In English there are only two numbers, singular and plural. A noun is said to be singular when it denotes a single object, and plural when it denotes two or more things of the same kind—e.g. book, books.

Forming the Plural. The plural is formed from the singular in several ways :

1. By far the commonest method is to add *es* (Old English *as*) to the singular : this becomes *s* when the pronunciation allows.

(a) The full syllable *es* is added only when the singular ends in a sound of *s*—i.e. *s*, *sh*, *ch* (except when it = k), *x*, *z*. Examples : churches, foxes, lashes (but monarchs).

(b) The letters *es* are also added after several words ending in -*o* (cargoes, potatoes, mosquitoes) ; they are not, however, sounded as a separate syllable in this or the two following cases. (A few words in -*o* simply add *s*, as solo, tiro, canto, grotto, quarto, and all in -*io* and -*oo*.)

(c) *es* is also added after *y* preceded by a consonant, the *y* being changed to *i* : body, bodies. *Qu* counts as a consonant : soliloquy, soliloquies. But if a vowel precedes the *y*, *s* alone is added, the *y* remaining unchanged—e.g. chimneys, boys, monkeys.

(d) *es* is also added to words of Old English origin ending in *f*, *fe*, and *lf*, preceded by any long vowel sound except *oo*, and the *f* is changed into *v*. Examples : life, lives ; calf, calves ; loaf, loaves. But nouns in *oof*, *ff*, *rf*, and nouns in *f* of Norman-French origin, take simple *s*, and retain the voiceless sound of the *f*— e.g. chiefs, roofs, skiffs, turfs, reefs.

NOTE : thief, thieves ; staff, staves ; wharf, wharves : scarf, scarves.

All other nouns except those that are to be immediately mentioned add *s* to the singular —e.g. cats (voiceless *s*), dogs (voiced *s* = z).

2. By adding *en*, as ox, oxen ; brother, brethren ; child, children (children is a double plural, the old English plural being cild*ru*) ; eye, eyne (Spenser, Shakespeare) ; shoe, shoon ; cow, kine ; hose, hosen.

3. By changing the vowel sound of the word, as man, men ; foot, feet ; mouse, mice ; tooth, teeth. To this head also belong brethren and kine, as well as to 2.

4. By leaving the singular unchanged— e.g. sheep, deer, swine. Cf. also : twenty brace of partridges, ten thousand horse (i.e. cavalry), ten sail of the line.

In the case of some nouns there are two plurals, differing in meaning :

brother	brothers (*by birth*)	brethren (*of a society*)
die	dies (*for stamping*)	dice (*for play*)
penny	pennies (*separate coins*)	pence (*lump sum*)
index	indexes (*of a book*)	indices (*in Algebra*)
pea	peas (*separate seeds*)	pease (*collective*)
genius	geniuses(*gifted men*)	genii(*spirits, ghosts*)
cloth	cloths (*kinds of cloth*)	clothes (*garments*)

Nouns used only in the singular are names of materials or substances, and of qualities : as water, gold, humour. These nouns can, of course, take a plural, denoting different sorts of the same thing—e.g. mineral waters.

Nouns used only in the plural are names of instruments or articles of dress made double (scissors, trousers) ; portions of the body, diseases, games, ceremonies, etc. (entrails, mumps, billiards, matins).

Alms, riches, and eaves are really singular, though often treated as plural. Amends, means, news, pains, wages are strictly plural, but are often used as singular.

In most compounds the constituent parts have so completely coalesced that there is no difficulty about forming the plural in the ordinary way—e.g. rainbow, rainbows ; horse-box, horse-boxes.

But compounds of a noun and an attributive word or phrase, in which the parts have not coalesced into a single word, add the *s* to the noun—e.g. courts-martial, knights-errant, fathers-in-law. When the compound consists of two nouns imperfectly coalesced, both take the sign of the plural—e.g. lords-justices, men-servants.

Some nouns borrowed from foreign languages retain their proper plurals. Thus :

Latin

Nouns in *a*	make *ae :*	nebula, nebulae
„	*um*	„ *a :*	erratum, errata
„	*is*	„ *es :*	axis, axes
„	*ix* (*ex*)	„ *ices :*	vertex, vertices; appendix, appendices
„	*us* (masc.)	„ *i :*	terminus, termini
„	*us* (neut.)	„ *era :*	genus, genera
„	*ies*	„ *ies :*	series, series

Greek

Nouns in *on*	make *a :*	automaton, automata
„	*sis*	„ *ses :*	crisis, crises
„	*ma*	„ *mata:*	miasma, miasmata

Miscellaneous. Cherub, cherubim ; seraph, seraphim ; beau, beaux ; madame, mesdames; bandit, banditti ; virtuoso, virtuosi.

The Three Cases. Cases are the different forms which a noun or pronoun assumes to denote its relation to other words in a sentence. In modern English we have three cases—nominative, possessive, objective. The objective (except in pronouns) no longer has a different form in English ; its position shows its relation to the rest of the phrase or sentence.

The nominative is the case of the subject of the sentence, and denotes the person or thing about which we are speaking. It answers the question Who ? or What ?

with the verb—e.g. Time flies. When the nominative names the person spoken *to*, it is called the nominative of address, or sometimes the vocative (Latin, *voco* = I call) —e.g. ' *Son*, go work in my vineyard.'

The possessive is the case by which we show that something belongs to the person or thing for which it stands—e.g. Joseph's brethren. It is the only case in nouns in which a case-suffix is now used. The possessive case in the singular, and in those forms of the plural not ending in *s*, is formed by adding *'s* to the nominative case—e.g. the boy's father ; women's rights. But when the plural ends in *s*, the possessive is indicated in writing by putting the apostrophe after the *s*, as boys' clothes, Their Highnesses' coach.

NOTE.—The use of the apostrophe is modern. The old possessive suffix was *es* (seen, for example, in Wednesday—i.e. Woden's day).

The simple apostrophe is sometimes used with singular nouns that end in an *s* sound— e.g. for justice' sake ; for righteousness' sake. This is admissible, but we must write Jones's Dairy, St. James's Palace, not Jones' Dairy, St. James' Palace, for we do not omit the *'s* in speaking. In the case of a complex name, the possessive suffix is attached only to the last word of the name—e.g. the Prince of Wales's carriage ; with Mr. and Mrs. Brown's compliments.

The objective case is that form or relative position of a noun (or pronoun) which denotes that the noun or pronoun stands for the object of the action indicated in some verb in the active voice, or which comes after a preposition. A noun is therefore in the objective case when it is the object of a verb or is governed by a preposition. The objective case answers the question ' Whom ? ' ' What ? ' after the verb. In nouns the objective case is the same in form as the nominative ; usually, therefore, we distinguish the two by their position in the sentence, the nominative coming before the verb, and the objective after—e.g. 'The Greeks (nom.) defeated the Persians (obj.).' ' The queen (nom.) was in the parlour (obj. after *in*).'

The objective, besides corresponding to the Latin accusative (direct object, as above), also corresponds to the Latin dative (indirect object, *to* or *for*)—e.g. ' Tell me your story '—where *me* is indirect and *story* direct object. ' I wrote him a letter ' (I wrote a letter to him). 'Give him the money.'

Syntax of the Noun. The syntax of the noun deals with the manner in which a noun is related to the other words in a sentence.

NOMINATIVE CASE. 1. Complementary nominative. The verbs to be, to become, and passive verbs of naming, making, appointing, deeming, etc., take a nominative after them as well as before : ' It is *I*.' ' Descartes was called the father of modern philosophy.' In colloquial language we say, It's me, That's him.

2. Nominative absolute (corresponding to ablative absolute in Latin, and genitive absolute in Greek). The nominative may be used with a participle, forming with it a clause grammatically independent of the rest of the sentence, i.e. an absolute clause—e.g. ' They pressed on into the heart of the mountains, *the scenery becoming more sombre at every step.*' This sentence is complete grammatically even if we omit the words in italics.

POSSESSIVE CASE. This is rarely (though oftener than formerly) used except where the noun denotes a living thing. In such expressions as the cannon's mouth, the earth's surface, the objects are personified. Traces of the old genitive case in *-es* (which the possessive replaced) are seen in : a month's notice, a day's wages, at their wits' end.

OBJECTIVE CASE. 1. The objective usually follows the verb, but when it differs in form from the nominative, or when the subject of the sentence in which it stands has a distinctive form, it may stand before the verb, without causing any ambiguity : as ' He saved others : *Himself* He cannot save.'

2. Verbs of making, appointing, calling, thinking, take a complementary object in addition to the direct object ; as, ' They elected him (direct) president ' (compl. obj.).

3. The verbs ask, teach, forgive, banish, etc., sometimes take a second objective —e.g. ' We banish you our territories.' ' I ask you pardon ' (N.B.—Such expressions are rather archaic). These verbs can take an objective even in the passive voice : ' He was denied his rights.'

4. The cognate objective, or objective of kindred meaning, is used after many intransitive verbs : ' I have fought the good fight.' ' He laughed his great laugh.'

Apposition. When two or more nouns are used together, as names of the same thing, they are said to be in apposition ; they are always in the same *case* : ' He brought his children, two little girls ' (obj.). ' Mr. Smith, my cousin, came with me.'

Sometimes a noun stands in apposition to a whole sentence : ' They dragged her away shrieking, *a sight* to move the hardest heart.'

EXERCISE

Correct the following sentences :
1. The boy stood on the burning deck, Whence all but he had fled.
2. Whom do men say that I am ?
3. This injury has been done me by my friend, He whom I treated like a brother.
4. Oh, a cherubim thou wast that did preserve me.
5. Where nothing save the waves and I Shall hear our mutual murmurs sweep.

LESSON FOUR

Adjectives and Articles

A N adjective is a word added to a noun to qualify it, or limit it by reference to quality, quantity, or position. There are, therefore, three main classes of adjectives : adjectives of quality, adjectives of quantity, and adjectives of position or relation. Examples of the three classes are :

1. Qualitative, or descriptive, adjectives, denoting some quality or attribute : e.g. *white, ugly, thick, French, such.*

2. Quantitative adjectives, denoting *how much* or *how many.* These include :

(a) cardinal numerals : *one, two,* etc. ;
(b) indefinite numerals : *many, few, some, all, enough, any, much, more, most, several, sundry, certain, none* or *no* (=*not any*), *less, least, both.*

3. Adjectives of relation, or demonstrative adjectives. These include :
(a) ordinal numerals : *first, second,* etc. ;
(b) pronominal adjectives (adjectives which are also used as pronouns): *a, an, the, this, that, these, those, other, yon ; my, thy, his,* etc. ; *which, what, whether ; each, every, either, neither.*

The words, hundred, thousand, million are nouns ; we can say 'a hundred,' though not 'a twenty.' One hundred men is therefore one hundred *of* men, and in Old English men was put in the genitive case.

When *many* is used with *a* or *an* to denote a number of persons or things looked at individually, it takes a singular verb : 'Full many a flower is born to blush unseen' (Gray's 'Elegy').

No is a form of *none*, which equals 'not one.' The use of *none* as an adjective is archaic : 'There is none other name under heaven' (Acts).

Just as many adjectives are used as pronouns (e.g. 'The *other* day,' adjective ; 'Hate the one and love the *other*,' pronoun), so also many adjectives are used as nouns : 'The *merciful* ; 'All is lost' ; 'Enough is as good as a feast' ; 'I will not destroy it for *twenty's* sake' ; 'We count by *tens*.'

Adjectives are indeclinable (except *this* and *that*, which have as plurals *these* and *those*).

Comparison of Adjectives. There are three degrees of comparison : the *positive*, the *comparative*, and the *superlative*. The positive is the simple adjective, as 'a *bright* light.' The comparative compares one thing with another, and asserts that the one possesses a certain quality in a higher degree than the other : as 'a *brighter* light.' The superlative compares one thing with many, and asserts that it possesses a certain quality in a higher degree than any of the others : as 'the *brightest* light.'

Certain adjectives, from their meaning, are incapable of comparison : e.g. *one, two, first, second, this, that, square, triangular, perfect*, etc.

The comparative is formed as follows :

1. By adding *-er* to the positive (or *-r*, if the positive ends in *e* mute) : e.g. *long, longer ; scarce, scarcer*. If the positive ends in *y* preceded by a consonant, the *y* becomes *i* : *lofty, loftier*. If the positive ends in a single consonant preceded by a single vowel, the consonant is doubled in writing : *fit, fitter*.

2. By prefixing *more* to the positive, in all cases where the positive has more than two syllables (*alarming, more alarming*), and in most cases where the positive is disyllabic (*decent, more decent*). The disyllabic adjectives that form their comparatives in *-er* are those ending in *y, ble, er, ow*, and those that have the accent on the last syllable (*prettier, nobler, tenderer, narrower, politer*). It is very much a matter of taste in these cases ; what sounds best is oftenest used.

The superlative is formed as follows :

1. By adding *-est* to the positive (or *-st*, if the positive ends in *e* mute) : e.g. *longest, largest*.

2. By prefixing *most* to the positive : e.g. *most alarming*. The remarks on the formation of the comparative apply equally here.

The superlative is sometimes used to denote that a thing possesses a certain quality in a high degree ; this is expressed by prefixing *a most* or *a very* to the positive : as 'a most extraordinary thing.'

Double comparatives and superlatives are found in old writers : e.g. 'worser' ; 'The most unkindest cut of all' ; 'The most straitest sect' ; and (even in modern English) 'lesser.'

Not all comparisons are regular. Examples of irregular comparison are :

Positive.	Comparative.	Superlative.
good	better	best
bad	worse	worst
little	less	least
much *or* many	more	most
old	older *or* elder	oldest *or* eldest
far	farther	farthest
(forth, *adverb*)	further	furthest
fore	former	foremost, first
nigh	higher, nearer	highest, nearest, next
late	later, latter	latest, last

NOTE. *Elder* is not used when two persons are definitely compared in point of age.

An adjective is said to be used attributively when it immediately precedes or follows a noun ; but when the verb 'to be,' or some similar verb, comes between it and the noun it is said to be used predicatively. Thus : 'The *wise* men of Gotham' (attributive) ; 'Heap on more wood, the wind is *chill*' (predicative).

The Articles. *A, an*, and *the* are sometimes called articles (Latin, *articulus* = a joint), but they are really adjectives. *The* has been termed the definite article, because it points out or defines : as 'The pied piper of Hamelin ' ; 'The Maccabees.' It is a weak form of the demonstrative 'that.'

A, an, have been termed indefinite articles : they are weakened forms of the numeral *one*. They show that it is *one* thing of the class which is meant, but do not specify *which*. *An* is used before words beginning with a vowel or *h* silent ; *a* before words beginning with a consonant or *h* aspirated, or *u* when sounded *yu* : e.g. *an army, an heir, a cat, a horse, a unicorn* (but *an umbrella*). But *an* may stand before a word beginning with *h* aspirated when the accent is not on the first syllable of the word : *an historical parallel, an hypothesis.* Writers differ very much on this point.

EXERCISES

(I) Pick out all the adjectives in the following passage, classify them, and give the comparative and superlative forms ; say whether used attributively or predicatively :

All the earth and air
  With thy voice is loud,
As, when night is bare,
  From one lonely cloud
The moon rains out her beams, and heaven is
  overflowed.
    Chorus hymeneal
    Or triumphant chant,
    Matched with thine, would be all

But an empty vaunt—
A thing wherein we feel there is some hidden want.

(*Shelley*, 'Ode to a Skylark.')

(II) Correct the following sentences :
1. He is the tallest man of all the rest. 2. Which of these two do you like best ? 3. He wore a large and a very shabby hat. 4. The King sent for the Chancellor and Treasurer. 5. Milton is greater than any poet. 6. I can see two different flags, a white and green.

Key to Exercise in Lesson 3

1. *He* should be *him*, as *but* is here a preposition meaning *except*. 2. *Whom* should be *Who*. 3. *He* should be *him*, to be in apposition to *friend*, which is in the objective case. 4. *Cherubim* should be *cherub*. 5. *I* should be *me* for the same reason as in the first sentence.

LESSON FIVE

Classification of Pronouns

A PRONOUN is exactly what its name implies, a word used for a noun : e.g. ' Love took up the glass of Time, and turned *it* in his glowing hands.' *It* is here used to avoid repeating 'the glass of Time.'

As a pronoun is a substitute for a noun, it has number, gender, and case, just as would the noun for which it stands.

Pronouns are often confused with adjectives. To test a pronoun, ask the question—does this word stand instead of a noun ? If so, it is a pronoun ; if not, it is something else, probably an adjective. Thus : in 'give John that book,' *that* does not stand for a noun, and is therefore not a pronoun ; it is a demonstrative adjective. But in ' give John his book and that of his brother,' *that* stands for 'the book,' and is therefore a pronoun.

Pronouns are classified as follows : Personal, Demonstrative, Interrogative, Relative, Indefinite, Distributive.

Personal Pronouns. These are : *I, we, thou, ye* or *you, he, she, it, they,* and all their cases. *I* and *we* are personal pronouns of the first person (the person speaking) ; *thou, ye* and *you* of the second person (the person spoken to) ; *he, she, it* and *they* of the third person (the person spoken of). These pronouns are thus declined :

	FIRST PERSON		SECOND PERSON	
	Singular	*Plural*	*Singular*	*Plural*
Nom.	I	we	thou	ye, you
Obj.	me	us	thee	you
Pos.	my	our	thy	your
	or mine	*or* ours	*or* thine	*or* yours

THIRD PERSON

	Singular			*Plural*
	Masc.	*Fem.*	*Neuter*	*All genders*
Nom.	he	she	it	they
Obj.	him	her	it	them
Pos.	his	her	its	their
		or hers		*or* theirs

The possessive cases of these pronouns are always adjectival, and are best classed as adjectives. The forms *mine, thine, ours, yours, hers, theirs,* are used only predicatively : e.g. 'the loss is ours.' Sometimes, however, in poetry and stately diction we find *mine* and *thine* used attributively, but only before a noun beginning with a vowel : ' Give every man thine ear but few thy voice' ('Hamlet'). The forms *my, thy, our, your, her, their,* are used only attributively : ' my fault.'

Thou and *Thee* are now rarely used, except in poetry or addressing the Divine Being, and in the Society of Friends. The plural *you* gradually supplanted the singular forms.

It is the Old English *hit*, the *t* being a neuter suffix (as in *what, that*). Its original possessive was *his*, and *its* is a modern form : e.g. 'The iron gate . . . opened to them of his own accord' (Acts).

The following are sometimes called *reflexive* pronouns, but are really personal :

Singular	*Plural*
myself (ourself)	ourselves
thyself (yourself)	yourselves
himself, herself, itself	themselves

Also the modern form *oneself*, which has no plural ; it was originally written 'one's self.' *Self* (which means *same*), though originally an adjective, came to be regarded as a noun ; hence *myself*, etc. The form 'ourself' is used by royalty.

They are called *reflexive* because they are used when the action 'bends back' and affects the doer : as, ' He hurt himself '; 'He saved others ; *Himself* He cannot save' (*himself* being here *objective*). Sometimes they have no reflexive force, but are used for emphasis : as, ' God Himself is with us'; 'myself am hell.' Here *himself* and *myself* are in the *nominative* case.

Demonstrative Pronouns. As already explained, when used to prevent repetition of the preceding noun, *this*, *that*, with their plurals, *these* and *those*, are demonstrative pronouns, but when used with nouns they are demonstrative adjectives. *This* and *that* in the following sentence are pronouns : 'We offer you either war or peace : this means prosperity, that destruction.'

Interrogative Pronouns. These pronouns —*who*, *what*, *which* and *whether*—are used in asking questions—either direct questions, as : who is there ? or indirect—i.e. questions depending on a previous verb, as : he asked who was there. *Who*, *which* and *what* are also used as relative pronouns. *Who* is thus declined :

Singular and Plural
Nominative　　Who
Objective　　　Whom
Possessive　　Whose

Which and *what* are indeclinable. *What* is the neuter of *who* (*cf. it, that*). *Whether* means which of the two ? (*who-ther*).

Who is used with reference to persons only, never to things : it is always a substantive. *Which* and *what* are used both substantivally and adjectivally—e.g. 'What did you go out to see ?' (substantivally) ; 'What sneaking fellow comes yonder ?' (adjectivally) ; 'Which was the braver ?' (substantivally) ; ' Which way went the Spirit of the Lord ?' (adjectivally).

Who and *what* ask quite indefinitely : *which* asks for one out of a selected class or group. *What* (interrogative) is often used in exclamations, as : 'What dreadful sufferings, with what patience, he endured !' (Charles Lamb).

Whether, as an interrogative pronoun, must be carefully distinguished from the conjunction—e.g. 'He asked whether you were in ' (conjunction) : 'Whether of the twain will ye that I release unto you ?' (pronoun). This usage is now obsolete.

Relative Pronouns. Almost all the pronouns relate to some previous noun, but those particularly designated relative pronouns also connect the clause which they introduce with the former part of the sentence. In the sentence just written, for example, *which* is a relative pronoun referring to *clause* (called the *antecedent*), and connecting the clause, ' which they introduce, with the earlier part of the sentence.

Relative pronouns, therefore, introduce clauses which are *adjectival* to some noun or pronoun in another part of the sentence, for the words, 'which they introduce,' limit or qualify the meaning of the clause.

If we examine any sentence containing a relative pronoun—e.g. 'The man whom you saw has gone'—we see that but for the use of the relative the sentence must have been broken up into two separate parts : 'He has gone' : and, 'you saw him.' A relative pronoun is thus really a pronoun and conjunction combined.

As a relative, *that* is always substantival, and may refer to either persons or things ; it is also indeclinable. It is used for *who* or *which* only when the antecedent is incomplete and requires further definition—e.g. 'All is not gold that glitters.' *That* may be (1) conjunction, (2) demonstrative adjective, (3) noun, (4) relative pronoun, (5) demonstrative pronoun. In the following sentence *that* illustrates each of these parts of speech in the order named : ' He said that that '' that'' that the boy had written was that of a bad writer.'

Both *who* and *whom* are now used only of persons, but the possessive *whose* can be used even of lifeless things—e.g. 'We bought a bookcase whose height was four feet.' *What* is used only of things, and never related to any antecedent except *that* (which is always understood and never expressed) ; it is therefore used in the singular only—e.g. 'What all desire, must be good'=that which all desire, etc.

The ordinary relative referring to animals or things is *which*, as *who* to persons. It was formerly used of persons as well. In the English Bible it is often preceded by 'the'—e.g. ' In the which ye also walked.' It differs from *who* in that it can be used as an adjective—e.g. 'Which things have indeed a shew of wisdom' (Colossians). *Who* or *which* can always be used where *that* (relative) is used.

Who, *which*, and *what* may each be compounded with -*ever* and -*soever*, and *who* also with -*so* (whoso). The forms in -*so* and -*soever* are not often used now.

Relative and Antecedent. A relative pronoun must have an antecedent, expressed or understood. This may be a noun, a pronoun, a noun-phrase, or a noun-clause. The antecedent of *who* and *that* is sometimes understood in earlier literature—e.g. 'Who reads Incessantly, and to his reading brings not A spirit and judgement equal and superior . . . Uncertain and unsettled still remains' ('Paradise Regained'). Here *he* is understood before *who*.

The relative agrees with its antecedent in number, gender, and person ; but its *case* is determined by its own clause—e.g. 'The boy, *who* knew him well,' *who* is third person, singular, masculine, agreeing with antecedent *boy* ; its case is determined by its own clause, it being nominative because subject to *knew*. 'Those (nom.) whom (obj.) the gods love die early,' *whom* is plural, common gender, agreeing with *those*, objective after *love*.

NOTE. *Who*, both as relative and interrogative, presents many difficulties. All such expressions as 'Who did you see ?' 'Who did you speak to ?' 'I know who you mean,' should be avoided in writing, but are often used colloquially by good speakers.

Omission of the Relative. The relative is often omitted, but only when, if expressed, it would be in the objective case. This is common in colloquial English : 'The book he gave me is lost' ; *which* is understood.

The relative should never be omitted—(a) when, if expressed, it would be in the nominative ; (b) when the relative clause, instead of defining or restricting the antecedent, states some further circumstance attending the antecedent, and is continuative or ampliative rather than restrictive. If we compare the two sentences : 'He broke the pen which I lent him,' and 'His eldest son, whom he had lost many years before, had always been his favourite,' we see the difference. In the former, *which* defines, limits and restricts the meaning of *pen* ; in the latter *whom* amplifies and enlarges on *his eldest son*. The *which* in the first sentence could be omitted, but *whom* in the second could not be left out.

As is often used as a relative pronoun, after 'same' and 'such'—e.g. 'This is the same as that' ; 'A noise such as I had never heard before.'

Indefinite Pronouns. The Indefinite Pronouns are : *One, none, aught, naught, any, other, another, some*. The pronoun *one* is used either (a) adjectivally, meaning 'some,' 'a certain,' as : 'I shall one day learn Italian,' or (b) substantivally, like the French *on* and the German *man* : 'One can never say what will happen.'

None is used for *no* when the noun is omitted, as : '. . . those kindnesses that I have done for you. I know of none.'

Aught : naught. These are not often used now, 'anything' and 'nothing' usually taking their places.

Other means 'one of two.' It is used as an adjective and as a pronoun ; in the latter case it is declined :

	Singular	Plural
Nom. and Obj.	other	others
Poss.	other's	others'

'The one . . . the other' are used when only two are spoken of ; 'one . . . another' when more than two. Similarly, the expression 'one another' is not correct when used of only two persons : we should then use 'each other.'

Distributive Pronouns. These are : *Each, every, either, neither.*

Each denotes all taken separately ; it can be either adjective or pronoun—e.g. 'Each morning she practises singing exercises ' (adjective) ; ' The guests arrived, each in his own car' (pronoun).

Every (ever-each) is very similar to *each*. It is usually an adjective—'Every child enjoyed the circus'—though originally it stood as a pronoun by itself.

Either ; neither=one of the two (but not both) ; not one of the two. 'Either' and 'neither' should be used only when there are two alternatives : 'either of the three' is wrong. *Each, every, either, neither* should always be followed by a singular verb, as they are always singular—e.g. 'Each man knows what suits himself.'

EXERCISE
In the following passage pick out and classify all the pronouns :

There was once a dog who was crossing a bridge, carrying a bone in his mouth. Looking into the water, he saw another dog, that also had a bone in his mouth. 'I should like that,' he thought to himself, 'better than this.' So he dropped his own bone to seize the other and lost them both. Who could believe that any dog could be so foolish as he ?

Key to Exercise II in Lesson 4
(II) 1. Omit 'the rest.' 2. 'Best ' should be 'the better.' 3. Omit the second 'a.' 4. If one man fills both these offices this is correct ; otherwise insert 'the' before 'Treasurer.' 5. Insert 'other' before 'poet.' 6. Insert 'a' before 'green.'

English Verbs : Their Moods and Tenses

A WORD which says something about a person or thing, or groups of persons or things—as 'time *flies*,' 'dogs *bark*'—was originally called verb (Latin *verbum*=a word) because it is the most important word in a sentence. Every grammatical sentence must contain at least two words, the one naming a person or thing (or groups of persons or things), the other telling us with regard to the first that it does something, or is in some state, or has something done to it. The first is a noun and is called the subject, the second is a verb and is called the Predicate. Verbs are classified as transitive and intransitive.

A transitive verb (Latin *transire*=to go across) is a verb of action which affects an object ; the action 'goes across' from the doer to someone or something else. Therefore every transitive verb must have an object—e.g. 'Shut the door ; open the window.'

An intransitive (or neuter) verb cannot affect an object ; it denotes a state or condition, or an action confined to the doer—e.g. 'Men sleep,' 'The top spins.'

Many transitive verbs are sometimes used intransitively—e.g. 'He *burst* his chains ' (trans.), and 'The bubble *burst*' (intrans.) ; 'He *cut* his finger', and 'This knife *cuts* well.'

Transitive verbs can be used reflexively, with the reflexive pronoun either expressed or understood—e.g. 'He *wounded* himself,' 'Planets *move* (themselves) round the sun.'

Voice. There are two Voices, Active and Passive. A verb is in the Active Voice when its subject stands for the *doer* of the action. A verb is in the Passive Voice when its subject stands for the *object* of the action. Examples : 'I *brushed* the dog' (active) ; 'The dog *was brushed* by me ' (passive). Intransitive verbs have no passive voice, as they pass over no action to an object.

The Passive Voice is formed by prefixing to the past participle of a transitive verb the different tenses of the verb 'to be'—as, 'I shall be *praised* ' ; 'He was *hit* by a golfball.' Be sure, however, that the past participle is that of a transitive verb ; if it is that of an intransitive verb, the voice is active—e.g. 'He *is* dead'; 'I *am* come.' We could equally well say, 'He *has* died ' ; and 'I *have* come.'

Moods. When a verb makes a direct statement or asks a direct question, we say it is in the *Indicative* Mood (Lat. *indicare*= to point out). When a verb conveys a command it is said to be in the *Imperative* Mood (Lat. *imperare*=to command). When we wish to express, not so much a fact (in which case we should use the Indicative) as our conception of the fact, we are said to use the *Subjunctive* Mood. These are the three Finite Moods—called 'finite' because the action or state denoted by them is limited by consideration of number, person, and time.

There is the fourth Mood, the *Infinitive*, in which the notion expressed by the verb is absolutely 'infinite,' unlimited by number, person, or time—e.g. 'I cannot *speak* for laughing' (i.e. 'I am not able *to speak*').

Indicative. In the English verb there is an infinitive mood, a gerund and two participles and three finite moods—the indicative, imperative, and subjunctive. The indicative mood is used whenever we make a statement or ask a question about something which we regard as a matter of fact : e.g. 'London *is* burning' ; 'How *are* you ?' The indicative may even be used to express condition, provided that the condition or supposition relates to some matter of fact rather than to some matter of conception ; e.g. 'If he *betrays* me, he will be sorry for it.' This will be more fully explained later.

Imperative. This form expresses a command, and is strictly used only in the second person : 'Come here ; read this letter to me.' When we wish to express a command or exhortation in connexion with the first or third person, we use either the imperative (second pers. sing.) of *let*, followed by the infinitive (e.g. 'Let us go to the theatre'), or the subjunctive mood of the verb in question —e.g. 'God *save* the King' ; this usage is archaic. The future imperative is not often used now ; it was common in prohibitions (cf. the Ten Commandments : 'Thou *shalt* not . . .').

Subjunctive. This mood was so called because it was most often used in subordinate (subjoined) sentences. It is impossible for the subjunctive to be used in a simple direct statement or question. It is used chiefly in (1) conditional clauses, introduced by *if* (though not always, as we have seen with regard to the indicative) ; (2) purpose clauses, introduced by *in order that* or *so that*, as 'Take an umbrella, so that you *don't* get wet' ; (3) wishes, as 'O that he *were* here !'

The subjunctive mood is becoming more and more rarely used in English. It is being replaced (1) by the indicative (instead of 'If he *were* here, all would be well,' it is becoming increasingly common to say, 'If he *was* here,' etc.) ; (2) by the use of some auxiliary verb, as *may, might, should*.

Infinitive. This is a really verbal noun. It is a noun because it can stand as the subject or the object of a verb, as '*To be* is nobler than *to have*' (subject) ; 'Learn to *dance* well' (object). It is a verb because it can govern an object, as 'It is a good thing to avoid over-work.'

Although the infinitive is generally used with the preposition *to* before it, the *to* is not a part of the infinitive. Many verbs are followed by the infinitive without *to* ; these include the auxiliaries *do, shall, will*, the verbs *bid, dare, make, let, can, may, must, need*, and some verbs denoting the operation of the senses, as *hear, see, feel*. Originally, the *to* was prefixed only when the infinitive was used to denote purpose, as 'I have come *to mend* the window.' The infinitive is sometimes used in exclamations, as '*To think* that I could have been so foolish !'

It is most important to avoid using the *split infinitive* caused by inserting any word or words between the *to* of an infinitive mood and its verb. It is correct to say 'I must ask you *kindly to excuse me*,' and not 'I must ask you *to kindly excuse* me.'

The past infinitive (e.g. *to have seen*) needs careful handling when used after another verb in the past tense. Many people will say 'I should *have liked* to *have seen* you,' which is, strictly speaking, incorrect : it should be 'I should *have liked* to *see* you.'

Gerund. The gerund (Latin *gerere* = to carry on) is a verbal noun like the infinitive, and has a similar meaning. The participle is a verbal adjective (Latin *participare* = to partake, because it partakes of the nature both of verb and adjective). As these are not finite moods, they are sometimes classed as infinitive moods.

The gerund, being a verbal noun, can be used in most of the constructions of a noun. It is formed from the verb by adding *-ing*. Gerunds are often confused with abstract nouns ending in *-ing* (Old English *-ung* and *-ing*), though they are really quite distinct.

Thus, it is correct to say either ' By *dredging* the river ' (gerund), or ' By the *dredging* of the river ' (noun). The rule is quite simple : when *the* precedes, *of* must follow ; but if *the* is omitted, *of* must also be omitted. We thus see that a gerund, when formed from a transitive verb, can govern an object just like any other part of the verb. The gerund, like the infinitive, can be either the subject or the object of a verb—as, ' *Walking* is capital exercise ' (subject), ' I like *walking* ' (object). Although the gerund has the same meaning as the infinitive, the two are not always interchangeable ; for instance, after prepositions the gerund is almost always used, as ' I had no idea then of *going* abroad.' The gerund can, of course, be used in the passive voice as well as in the active—as, ' The joy of *being loved*.'

In such archaic expressions as ' I go *a-fishing*,' ' There came three ships *a-sailing* ' (where the *a-* represents *on*) we must treat the form in *-ing* not as the gerund, but as a modern form of the old abstract noun.

Many compound nouns are formed from gerunds, as ' *skipping*-rope ' (a rope for skipping). Contrast such a compound noun with others like ' *humming*-bird ' which does not mean ' a bird for humming,' but ' a bird which hums.' ' Skipping-rope ' could not be rendered ' a rope which skips.' This shows the difference between a gerund (skipping) and a participle (humming), and we thus come to participles, or verbal adjectives. These, like all adjectives, refer to some noun about which they specify something.

Participles. There are two participles formed by inflexion, the *Present* or *Imperfect*, and the *Past*. The present participle is always active and always ends in *-ing* (like the gerund, with which it is often confused), e.g. ' *Thinking* he had come, I opened the door.' *Thinking* is a verbal adjective agreeing with *I*.

Words in ' -ing.' It is most important for the student to be able to differentiate between the three parts of speech ending in *-ing* : the Abstract Noun, the Gerund, and the Present Participle. To distinguish a gerund from a present participle, ask the question ' Does the word in question play the part of a noun or an adjective ? ' If the former, it is a gerund ; if the latter, a participle. Contrast ' By *talking* my throat gets tired ' (gerund) with ' *Talking* loudly, they left the room ' (participle, agreeing with *they*).

It is a very common mistake to use the participle where a gerund should be used.

To say ' I heard of *you* winning the prize ' is wrong ; it should be *your*, because *winning* is the gerund (i.e. a noun). *You* could only be used if *winning* were a participle—e.g. ' You, *winning* the prize, are a happy man.' In the case of personal and relative pronouns, the gerund and the possessive (*my, thy, his*, etc.) should be used, not the participle and the objective—as, ' I am sorry for *his* (not *him*) lapsing into bad ways ' ; ' They told me of *his* (not *him*) running away.'

We thus see that there are three totally different classes of words in -*ing*. (1) The abstract noun, as ' The *courting* of danger is foolish.' (2) The gerund, as, ' He perished in *courting* danger.' (3) The participle, as, ' The foolish fellow, *courting* danger, met his death.'

The past or passive participle ends in -*d*, -*ed*, -*t*, or -*en* : ' *Refreshed* by our night's rest, we resumed our journey next morning.'

The past participle can be compounded with the verb ' to have ' to form an active verb, and with the verb ' to be ' to form a passive verb. The Old English past participle usually had *ge*- (pronounced *yĕ*) prefixed to the verb ; traces of this remain in the words : *yclept* (called), *yclad* (clothed), *yslaked* (slaked).

Participles often come to be used as mere adjectives—e.g. ' a *frowning* hill,' ' a *broken* reed.' The following compound participles are used in English : (*a*) the past participle compounded with ' having,' to form a perfect participle active, as, ' *Having spoken* these words, he died ' ; (*b*) the past participle compounded with ' being,' to form an imperfect participle passive, as ' *being warned* ' ; also the same compounded with ' having been,' to form a perfect participle passive, as, ' *having been warned* ' ; (*c*) a loose kind of future participle, as ' *About to die*, we salute you ' ; ' *about to be killed*.'

CORRECT THE FOLLOWING SENTENCES: 1. I had wanted to have seen him. 2. Trusting you are well, believe me yours truly. 3. In the reading the Psalms, the clerk made many mistakes. 4. Had he have gone he would have regretted it.

Divisions of Time. The different forms assumed by a verb to indicate time are called Tenses (Latin *tempus*=time). There are three natural divisions of time—Past, Present, and Future ; and corresponding to these are three main tenses in Grammar. But an action in each of these three tenses can be looked at from three distinct points of view—as Incomplete, as Complete, and as Indefinite. We thus get nine Primary Tenses, as follows :

	INCOMPLETE	COMPLETE	INDEFINITE
	(1)	(2)	(3)
PAST *Act.*	I was loving	I had loved	I loved
„ *Pass.*	I was being loved	I had been loved	I was loved
	(4)	(5)	(6)
PRES. *Act.*	I am loving	I have loved	I love
„ *Pass.*	I am being loved	I have been loved	I am loved
	(7)	(8)	(9)
FUT. *Act.*	I shall be loving	I shall have loved	I shall love
„ *Pass.*	I shall be being loved	I shall have been loved	I shall be loved

In addition to these nine Primary Tenses there are three Secondary ones, called Perfect Continuous (in the Active voice only) :

1. I have been loving.
2. I had been loving.
3. I shall have been loving.

Nearly all the tenses are formed by using auxiliary verbs, *be, have*, etc. Such tenses are called Compound tenses, as opposed to Simple tenses, which contain only a single word (*I love, I loved*). An alternative form of the past and present indefinite is ' I *did* love,' ' I *do* love.' Sometimes the *do* and the *did* are used for emphasis, as ' I *did* think you would have come earlier.' Do and *did*, however, are used in questions and in the negative, as ' *do* men say ? ' rather than 'say men ? ' ' I *do* not like you' rather than ' I like you not.'

Past Tense. The simple past tense (past indefinite) is used in three ways : (1) it points out, without any qualification, that something occurred in the past, as : 'William of Normandy *conquered* England in 1066 ' ; (2) it is used with the meaning of an imperfect tense : ' As they *sat* by the stream they watched the birds' (=*were sitting*) ; (3) it expresses what happened frequently or customarily : 'In those days men *travelled* well-armed' (=*used to travel*).

Present Tense. The simple present tense (present indefinite) is used in the following senses : (1) it states what is actually taking place, as 'The rain pours down the windows' ; (2) it denotes what regularly takes place, as : 'Each morning the postman comes' ; (3) it often stands for the future, especially after *when, as soon as*, etc., as : 'As soon as I *hear*, I will let you know' ; 'When he comes, I will ask him what to do' ; (4) it is sometimes—chiefly in rather archaic verse—used in describing past events, the speaker adopting the present tense in order to be more graphic.

Future Tense. The future tense is formed with the auxiliary verbs shall or will. Thus I shall (or will) come, thou wilt come, he will come, we shall (or will) come, you will come, they will come. In the first person, singular and plural, shall and will are interchangeable ; in the second and third persons, however, the verb 'shall' denotes obligation or authority, e.g. ' you shall not go' ; 'He shall not enter this house again.' On the other hand, 'will' in the first person sometimes implies determination, e.g. ' I *will* do it, though the heavens fall.'

Sequence of Tenses. Generally, if the verb in the principal clause is past, the verb in the dependent clause will be past likewise ; if it is present or future, then the verb in the dependent clause will be present or future.

LESSON SEVEN

Conjugation of Verbs

IN English, verbs, like nouns, have two numbers, singular and plural. The latter is without inflexion in all verbs save 'to be.' Verbs are inflected, however, for person. There are three persons, first, second and third—the person(s) speaking, spoken to, and spoken of.

The two principal auxiliary verbs are: 'To Be' and 'To Have.'

Conjugation of Verb TO BE

INFINITIVE MOOD

Present	*Past*
to be	to have been

PARTICIPLES

being   been, having been

GERUNDS

Simple	*Compound*
being	having been

INDICATIVE MOOD

Past	*Present*	*Future*
	Indefinite	
I was	I am	I shall be
	Complete	
I had been	I have been	I shall have been

SUBJUNCTIVE MOOD

Past	*Present*
	Indefinite
I were, or might be	I be, or may be
	Complete
I had been, or might have been	I have been, or may have been

NOTE.—A third form of the subjunctive past tense is formed with *should* instead of *might* : I should be ; I should have been.

IMPERATIVE MOOD

Singular	*Plural*
Be (thou)	Be (ye)

The full conjugation of the Present Indefinite Indicative is : I am, thou art, he is, we are, you are, they are ; and of the Past : I was, thou wast, or wert, he was, we were, you were, they were.

In the compound tenses there is no inflexion, except of the auxiliary verbs 'have,' 'shall,' etc., to be given later.

All tenses of *to be* can be used as auxiliaries to form compound tenses of other verbs (e.g. 'I shall have been writing').

Conjugation of Verb TO HAVE

INFINITIVE MOOD

Present	*Past*
to have	to have had

PARTICIPLES

having   had, having had

GERUNDS

Simple	*Compound*
having	having had

INDICATIVE MOOD

Past	*Present Indefinite*	*Future*
I had	I have	I shall have
	Incomplete	
I was having	I am having	I shall be having
	Complete	
I had had	I have had	I shall have had
	Perfect Continuous	
I had been having	I have been having	I shall have been having

SUBJUNCTIVE MOOD

Past	*Indefinite Present*
I had	I have
I might have	I may have
I should have	
	Incomplete
I were having	I be having
I might be having	I may be having
I should be having	
	Complete
I had had	I have had
I might have had	I may have had
I should have had	
	Perfect Continuous
I had been having	I have been having
I might (or should) have been having	I may have been having

IMPERATIVE MOOD

Singular	*Plural*
Have (thou)	Have (ye)

The full conjugation of the Present Indefinite Indicative is : I have, thou hast, he has, we have, you have, they have ; and of the Past : I had, thou hadst, he had, we had, you had, they had.

Only the Indefinite tenses of *to have* can be used as auxiliaries for the purpose of forming compound tenses of other verbs.

Conjugation of an Ordinary Verb. We will now give in tabular form the conjugation of an ordinary verb (other than an auxiliary) in its various voices, moods, and tenses. The alternative forms for the indicative indefinite (*did see, do see,* etc.) are used only in negative, interrogative and emphatic sentences.

Impersonal Verbs. In such expressions as 'it thunders,' 'it hails,' 'it seems,' the subject is general and undefined. These verbs are, therefore, called impersonal, there being no person expressed or understood as subject. They are always in the third person singular, though, of course, they can be of different tenses—e.g. it thundered, it will hail. While *it* is usually employed as the grammatical subject of such verbs,

---

COMPLETE CONJUGATION OF THE VERB 'TO SEE'

(A) Active Voice. INFINITIVE MOOD
Present Indefinite : (To) see
Present Incomplete : (To) be seeing
Perfect : (To) have seen
Continuous Perfect : (To) have been seeing

PARTICIPLES
Present : Seeing. *Perfect :* Having seen
Continuous Perfect : Having been seeing

INDICATIVE MOOD

Past	Present	Future
	Indefinite	
I saw (*or*, did see)	I see (*or*, do see)	I shall see
	Incomplete	
I was seeing	I am seeing	I shall be seeing
	Perfect	
I had seen	I have seen	I shall have seen
	Continuous Perfect	
I had been seeing	I have been seeing	I shall have been seeing

Imperative Mood
Singular : See (thou) *Plural :* See (ye)

SUBJUNCTIVE MOOD

Past	Present
	Indefinite
I saw	I see
I might see	I may see
I should see	
	Incomplete
I were seeing	*I be seeing
I might be seeing	I may be seeing
I should be seeing	
	Perfect
I had seen	I have seen
I might have seen	I may have seen
I should have seen	
	Continuous Perfect
I had been seeing	I have been seeing
I might have been seeing	I may have been seeing
I should have been seeing	

(B) Passive Voice. INFINITIVE MOOD
Indefinite — To be seen
Perfect — To have been seen

PARTICIPLES
Indefinite : Being seen
Perfect : Seen, *or* having been seen

INDICATIVE MOOD

Past	Present	Future
	Indefinite	
I was seen	I am seen	I shall be seen

Passive Voice (*cont.*)

	Incomplete	
I was being seen	I am being seen	*I shall be being seen
	Perfect	
I had been seen	I have been seen	I shall have been seen

(No Continuous Perfect in the Passive.)

IMPERATIVE MOOD
Singular : Be (thou) seen
Plural : Be (ye) seen

SUBJUNCTIVE MOOD

Past	Present
	Indefinite
I were seen	*I be seen
I might be seen	I may be seen
I should be seen	
	Incomplete
*I were being seen	*I be being seen
*I might be being seen	*I may be being seen
*I should be being seen	
	Perfect
I had been seen	I have been seen
I might have been seen	I may have been seen
I should have been seen	

Note. The forms marked with an asterisk are seldom, if ever, used in modern speech. It will be seen that many forms in the Subjunctive of the Active Voice are the same as in the Indicative.

The four simple tenses of the Active Voice are now given in full :

INDICATIVE MOOD

Past Indefinite		Present Indefinite	
I saw	we saw	I see	we see
thou sawest	you saw	thou seest	you see
he saw	they saw	he sees	they see

SUBJUNCTIVE MOOD

Past Indefinite		Present Indefinite	
(Same as Indicative.)		I see	we see
		thou see	you see
		he see	they see

occasionally there is no subject expressed at all ; as methinks (=it seems to me), meseems, maybe ; also, if you please (=if it please you).

Auxiliary and Principal Verbs. If we compare the sentences 'I have lost sixpence' and 'I have sixpence,' we see a great difference in the two uses of *have*. In the first sentence it simply helps to form the present perfect tense of ':lose.' In the second sentence it has a meaning of its own, namely, 'I possess.' In the first case it is an auxiliary (helping) verb, in the second a principal verb. The same applies to *shall, will, may, do, be*—e.g. 'I shall go tomorrow' (*auxiliary*), and 'You *shall* (i.e. must) do it' (*principal*). 'I will see you before long' (*auxiliary*), and 'I *will* have my own way' (*principal*). 'It may be wet tomorrow' (*auxiliary*), and 'You *may* (i.e. are permitted to) go' (*principal*). 'Do you think so ?' (*auxiliary*), and 'What will you do ?' (*principal*). 'I am coming' (*auxiliary*), and 'I *am* a man' (*principal*).

All the above-mentioned verbs (except *have* and *be*), when used as auxiliaries, are deficient in certain tenses. They have no infinitive and no participles and, therefore, have no compound tenses. Of course, when used as principal verbs, they are not necessarily defective. Thus, 'to will' (meaning 'to resolve') has all the compound tenses 'I have willed,' etc.

Key to Exercise in Lesson 6

1. I had wanted to see him. 2. Trusting you are well, I remain, yours truly. (In the faulty sentence the participle *trusting* agrees with *you*, which is the suppressed subject to *believe ;* it therefore means : ' Do you, trusting you are well, believe me,' which is nonsense.) 3. The sentence should run either ' In *reading* the Psalms ' (gerund), or ' In the *reading* of the Psalms ' (abstract noun). 4. If he had gone (*or*, had he gone), he would have regretted it.

LESSON EIGHT

Some Defective Verbs

IN this Lesson we note the defective verbs and their uses. Some of their parts were already missing in the Old English period. At this time also they were employed chiefly as auxiliaries, though their uses did not correspond exactly with those of Modern English. In English, helping or auxiliary verbs are numerous, and most auxiliaries can be also employed as independent verbs : e.g. *have* meaning *possess*, and *do* meaning *perform*. We now give the conjugation of the auxiliary verbs *do, will, shall* and *may*. The two principal auxiliaries, *to be* and *to have*, are conjugated in page 500.

Conjugation of Verb DO
INFINITIVE MOOD

Present	Incomplete	Past
(To) do	(to) be doing	(to) have done

PARTICIPLES
doing   done

INDICATIVE MOOD

Past		Present	
I did	we did	I do	we do
thou didst	you did	thou doest	you do
		or dost	
he did	they did	he doeth	they do
		or doth	
		or does	

NOTES. When used as a notional verb (i.e. a verb expressing a complete idea), *do* is conjugated in full (Future: *I shall do ;* Incomplete: *I was doing*); but when as an auxiliary, only present and past indefinite are used (*do* and *did*). *Doest* and *doeth* are used only in the notional sense, e.g. ' *Doest* thou well to be angry ? ' and are now archaic.

Conjugation of Verb WILL
INDICATIVE MOOD

Past	Present
I would	I will
thou wouldest	thou wilt, or willest
or wouldst	
he would, etc.	he will, or wills, etc.

NOTES. The past of the subjunctive is the same as the past indicative (*I would*, etc.) ; there is no present tense in the subjunctive. The forms *willest* and *wills* (Pres. Indic.) are not used when the verb is an auxiliary. When *will* means 'to exercise the will,' or 'to bequeath by will,' it has a full conjugation. The past indicative *would* is used as an auxiliary only in reported (or indirect) speech, to take the place of *will* in direct speech, e.g. 'he *will* come soon' (*direct*) ; ' he said that he *would* come soon' (*indirect*).

Will is also used to express a customary action, as : ' He *will* play for hours' ; 'When he was young, he *would* spend whole days in the fields.' When *will* is an auxiliary verb, it has no compound tenses.

Won't comes from *wol* (not), an old form of *will*.

Conjugation of Verb SHALL
INDICATIVE MOOD

Past	Present
I should	I shall
thou shouldst	thou shalt
he should, etc.	he shall, etc.

NOTES. The past of the subjunctive is the same as the past indicative ; there is no present subjunctive, nor any infinitive, imperative or participles, whether *shall* is used as auxiliary or notional verb. The past indicative *should* is used as an auxiliary only in reported speech, representing *shall* in direct speech.

Shall comes from *sculan* = to owe, and hence arose the meaning of obligation, e.g. = 'He *shall* do it' ; 'You *should* answer when your mother speaks.' When *shall* retains this idea of obligation it is a notional verb ; used as an auxiliary it loses this force.

Conjugation of Verb MAY
INDICATIVE MOOD

Past	Present
I might	I may
thou mightest	thou mayest
he might, etc.	he may, etc.

NOTES. The subjunctive mood is the same as the indicative. *May* has no infinitive, imperative, or participles ; and in its indicative mood it is never auxiliary, but always notional, e.g. 'You *may* go' (i.e. 'You are permitted to go') ; 'The fish *might* be seen rising at any hour almost' (i.e. it was possible to see them). In the subjunctive mood, of course, it can be an auxiliary, e.g. 'We eat in order that we *may* live' ; 'May it be so' ; 'I came early so that I *might* see you.'

We have now discussed all the auxiliary verbs, namely, *be, have, do, will, shall*, and *may*. Three verbs, *can, must*, and *ought*, are sometimes called auxiliaries ; but they do not help to form any tense, mood, or voice of any verb. *Can* is from an old verb *cunnan*, meaning 'to know.' 'I can read' therefore means 'I know how to read' : e.g. 'He knew to sing' ('Lycidas'). We have this meaning still preserved, in 'to con,' and in the Scottish 'to ken.' 'Cunning' is the old imperfect participle of this verb, and *couth* the past participle (cf. *uncouth*, which means *unknown* and therefore *strange*).

As *can* originally meant 'to know,' it required no infinitive ; cf. 'They *can* well on horseback' (' Hamlet') ; 'Other prayer *can* I none' ('Lay of the Last Minstrel'). Bacon even has 'not to *can*.'

Can is always a notional or principal verb : e.g. 'I *can* write' (i.e. 'I am able to write') ; 'I would if I *could*' (i.e. 'I would if I were able').

Conjugation of Verb CAN
INDICATIVE MOOD

Present	
I can	We can
Thou canst	You can
He can	They can

Past	
I could	We could
Thou couldest *or* couldst	You could
He could	They could

SUBJUNCTIVE MOOD

Present	Past
(None)	(Same as Indicative)

No Infinitive, Imperative, or Participles.

Like *can*, the verb *must* is always a notional verb. It has no inflexions for tense or person, all the persons of each number of each of the two indicative tenses being alike *must*. It has no subjunctive, infinitive, imperative or participles.

Ought is the past indefinite tense of *owe*. Thus, in Shakespeare's 'Henry IV,' the hostess says, 'He said this other day you *ought* (= owed) him a thousand pounds.' It is now used as a present, in the sense of moral obligation, as 'I *ought* to be a better man.'

Owe originally meant *to own, to possess*, as 'This is no mortal business, nor no sound that the earth *owes*' ('Tempest') ; 'I am not worthy of the wealth I *owe*' ('All's Well'). *Owe*, 'to be in debt,' is quite regular : *I owed, I shall owe*, etc.

In the verb *dare* (to venture) the third person singular of the present indicative is properly 'he dare,' *not* 'he dares.' The reason is that 'I dare' is an old *past* tense and is not really a present at all : e.g. 'Mine unworthiness that *dare* not offer,' etc. ('Tempest'). We now use 'I durst' as the past tense of *dare*, followed by the infinitive without *to* as 'he durst not do it.' When *dare* is a transitive verb meaning to challenge it is a perfectly regular weak verb.

When *to need* means to lack, to be in want of, it is perfectly regular. But when it means to be under the necessity of doing a thing, the third person singular present indicative is often 'he *need*' not 'he *needs*,' as 'he need not go.' Contrast this with 'he *needs* brains.'

Wit (to know) has present, *I wot*, past, *I wist*, and present participle, *witting* or *wotting*. This verb is not used now except in the infinitive *to wit*, in the sense of *namely* ; together with *wit*, the verbs *quoth, methinks, list, hight, dight* and *worth* are practically obsolete in Modern English, except in archaic or poetic diction.

Quoth is used only in the first and third

persons singular, for 'said I,' 'said he.' Examples: *'Quoth* the raven, " Nevermore,'' ' '' "To tame your fierce temper,'' *quoth* she.'

Methinks is only used in the forms *methinks* and *methought. List* in the archaic *melists* (it pleases me) and *him-listed* is an impersonal verb. It is also used personally as 'The wind bloweth where it *listeth.*'

Hight is used only in the meaning 'was called.' *Dight* means, decked, adorned. *Worth,* expressing a wish, is used only in the third person singular present subjunctive, as : 'Woe *worth* the day'= 'May woe befall the day.'

EXERCISE

Explain every *should* and *would* in the following :

She would often say ' Would I were a man. I *should* have been, for then I would have shown the world a lesson it would never forget.' I would reply that I should not attempt to argue with her lest she should get angry ; but I now often think that I should have done so. For perhaps I should have convinced her that it would not have been so easy. Should I, or should I not, I wonder ?

LESSON NINE

Strong and Weak Verbs

ENGLISH verbs are divided into *strong* and *weak,* according to the manner in which they form their Past Indefinite tense. Verbs that form this tense by modifying the vowel of the present tense (without adding any suffix) are said to belong to the *strong* conjugation—as : *shine, shone.* The past participle of all strong verbs originally ended in *-en,* and this ending still remains in many of them (sometimes in the form of *-n*)—as : *break, broke, broken.*

Verbs that form their past indefinite by adding the suffix *-ed, -d,* or *-t* to the present tense are said to belong to the *weak conjugation,* as : *treat, treated ; feel, felt.* When the present tense ends in *e, d* only is added, as *love, loved.* The vowel *y* preceded by a consonant becomes *i* before this suffix, as : *bully, bullied ; pay, paid.* A single final consonant preceded by a single vowel is usually doubled before the suffix, as : *drug, drugged ; travel, travelled.* The past participle of weak verbs is usually the same in form as the past indefinite. If the present tense ends in *d* or *t,* the suffix is often dropped, and present, past, and past participle have all the same form, as in the following example : *cost, cost, cost.*

Strong Verbs. The most interesting strong verbs, particularly those that present any difficulty, are given in the Table below, grouped according to vowel modification.

VERBS OF THE STRONG CONJUGATION

Present	Past	Past Participle	Present	Past	Past Participle
bind	bound	bound	slide	slid	slid
find	found	found	strive	strove	striven
grind	ground	ground	strike	struck	struck
wind	wound	wound	thrive	throve	thriven
cling	clung	clung	write	wrote	written

Present	Past	Past Participle	Present	Past	Past Participle
fling	flung	flung	bite	bit	bitten
sling	slung	slung	eat	eat	eaten
slink	slunk	slunk			(pron. *et*), *or* ate
stick	stuck	stuck	beat	beat	beaten
string	strung	strung	bid (to	bade,	bidden,
swing	swung	swung	order)	*or* bid	*or* bid
wring	wrung	wrung	give	gave	given
begin	began	begun	forsake	forsook	forsaken
drink	drank	drunk (-en)[1]	shake	shook	shaken
			take	took	taken
ring	rang	rung	come	came	come
sing	sang	sung	bear	bore	borne,[3]
sink	sank	sunk (-en)[1]			*or* born
			break	broke	broken
spin	span, *or* spun	spun	tear	tore	torn
			wear	wore	worn
shrink	shrank	shrunk (-en)[1]	weave	wove	woven
			speak	spoke	spoken
spring	sprang	sprung	steal	stole	stolen
stink	stank	stunk	swear	swore	sworn
swim	swam	swum	choose	chose	chosen
win	won	won	freeze	froze	frozen
blow	blew	blown	fly	flew	flown
grow	grew	grown	abide	abode	abode
know	knew	known	awake[4]	awoke[4]	awoke[4]
throw	threw	thrown	stand	stood	stood
draw	drew	drawn	tread	trod	trod, *or* trodden
hold	held	held			
fall[2]	fell[2]	fallen[2]	lie	lay	lain
(to recline)			sit	sat	sat
slay	slew	slain	get	got	got
see	saw	seen	hang[4]	hung[4]	hung[4]
drive	drove	driven	run	ran	run
ride	rode	ridden	burst	burst	burst
rise	rose	risen	shoot	shot	shot
smite	smote	smitten	seethe[5]	sod	sodden, *or* sod
chide	chid	chidden, *or* chid	spit	spat, *or* spit	spit
hide	hid	hidden, *or* hid	fight	fought	fought

Notes on Strong Verbs

[1] *Drunken, sunken,* and *shrunken* are now used only as adjectives, as : a *drunken* man ; *sunken* rocks : *shrunken* flannel.

[2] *Fall, fell, fallen* is intransitive ; but the kindred verb *to fell* is transitive, weak and regular, as : 'The woodman *felled* the tree.'

[3] *Borne* means *carried* ; *born* is used of *birth,*

chiefly after the verb 'to be.' Examples: 'Their voices were *borne* by the winds'; 'I was *born* in this village.'

'Awake, as a strong verb, is intransitive, meaning 'I wake up.' When it is transitive, meaning 'I rouse someone,' it is weak, and has *awaked, awaked* for its past tense and past participle. *Hang* is strong except in the sense of 'execute by hanging,' when the past tense and past participle are *hanged*, and in such phrases as 'hanged if I know.'

⁵Seethe, meaning *to boil*, is very seldom used now, except in a figurative sense, as: 'a seething mass of men.' The original sense is seen in the expression, 'And Jacob *sod* pottage' (Genesis xxv, 29). The past participle *sodden* now means 'soaked through.' *Seethe* is now usually weak, making *seethed, seethed.*

Weak Verbs. New verbs which have been introduced into English from foreign sources are conjugated like weak verbs. These include verbs of French origin, such as *passed, finished*, etc., and more scientific borrowings such as *electrified, radiographed,* etc.

VERBS OF THE WEAK CONJUGATION

Some verbs of the weak conjugation shorten the vowel as:

Present	Past	Past Participle	Present	Past	Past Participle
bleed	bled	bled	meet	met	met
breed	bred	bred	read	read	read (*pr.* red)(*pr.* red)
feed	fed	fed	speed	sped	sped
lead	led	led	light	lit	lit

Some keep the vowel, but they change the final *-d* into *-t.*

Present	Past	Past Participle	Present	Past	Past Participle
bend	bent	bent	build	built	built, *or* builded
lend	lent	lent			
rend	rent	rent	blend	blended	blent
send	sent	sent	gild	gilt, *or* gilded	gilt, *or* gilded
spend	spent	spent			
wend	went, *or* wended	wended	gird	girt, *or* girded	girt, *or* girded

The following have the same form throughout: *Cast, cost, cut, hit, hurt, knit, let, put, rid, set, shed, shred, shut, slit, split, spread, thrust,* and *bid* (meaning 'to offer at an auction').

Some shorten or otherwise alter the vowel:

Present	Past	Past Participle	Present	Past	Past Participle
beseech	besought	besought	deal	dealt	dealt
buy	bought	bought	dream	dreamt, *or* dreamed	dreamt *or* dreamed
catch	caught	caught			
bring	brought	brought	feel	felt	felt
sell	sold	sold	flee	fled	fled
seek	sought	sought	hear	heard	heard
teach	taught	taught	keep	kept	kept
think	thought	thought	kneel	knelt	knelt
tell	told	told	lean	leant, *or* leaned	leant
work	worked, wrought	worked, wrought	leave	left	left
can	could	—	lose	lost	lost
may	might	—	mean	meant	meant
will	would	—	sleep	slept	slept
shall	should	—	sweep	swept	swept
bereave	bereft, *or* bereaved	bereft	weep	wept	wept
			lay	laid	laid
creep	crept	crept	say	said	said
			shoe	shod	shod

VERBS OF MIXED CONJUGATION

Present	Past	Past Participle	Present	Past	Past Participle
shear	sheared, shore	sheared, shorn	saw	sawed	sawn, sawed
cleave (to split)	clove, cleft	cloven, cleft	shape	shaped	shapen, shaped
dig	dug, digged	dug, digged	shave	shaved	shaved, shaven
crow	crew¹ crowed	crowed	shew,	shewed,	shewn,
			or show *or* showed		shown
hew	hewed	hewn, hewed			showed (rare)
lade	laded	laden	sow	sowed	sown, sowed
lose	lost	lost, lorn (*forlorn*)	strew	strewed	strewn, strown, strewed
melt	melted	melted, molten	swell	swelled	swollen, swelled
mow	mowed	mown, mowed	wax (to grow)	waxed	waxed, waxen
rive	rived	riven, rived	do	did	done
			go	(went)²	gone

Notes on Mixed Verbs

¹*Crew* (from *crow*) is rarely used now, and only of the literal crowing of a cock—e.g. 'the cock *crew.*' When used of the crowing of babies, etc., the past tense is always *crowed*. Some of the strong past participles are used as adjectives—e.g. a *molten* image, the *cloven* hoof, a *shaven* head.

²*Went*, used in the past tense of *go*, is the past tense of *wend*—as in 'to wend one's way.'

Special Forms. *Clothe, have* and *make* form *clad, had* and *made*, which are contracted from *clothed, haved* and *maked.*

Tight and *straight* (adjectives) are weak past participles of *tie, stretch. Distraught* is an irregular past participle of *distract. Fraught* is the past participle of the obsolete Middle English verb *fraghten*, to load. (Cf. Modern English, *to freight*).

Lie and Lay. Much confusion arises between the verbs *lie* and *lay*, and their differences should be well noted by comparing the principal parts:

Present	Past	Past Participle
(1) lie (to recline)	lay	lain
(2) lay	laid	laid

To lie is strong and intransitive. *To lay* is weak and transitive.

Examples of *to lie*: The sofa that I *lie* on is comfortable; He *lay* where he fell; I *have* never *lain* on a softer bed.

Examples of *to lay*: Just *lay* the parcel on the table; He *laid* down the book; Hens *lay* eggs; That hen has *laid* five eggs this week.

By using *lay* with the reflexive pronoun myself (me), etc., as object we have an alternative to (1): I *lay* myself (me) down, for I *lie* down. I *laid* myself (me) down, for I *lay* down. I have *laid* myself (me) down, for I have *lain* down.

Formation and Use of Adverbs

JUST as adjectives qualify nouns, so adverbs modify or limit verbs, as, 'He bowed to me *politely.*' 'He gives *twice* who gives *quickly.*' This usage has been extended, and adverbs can now modify adjectives and other adverbs in addition to verbs, as : '*Too* many cooks spoil the broth' (*too* modifying the adjective *many*) ' It struck me *very* forcibly' (one adverb *very* modifying another, *forcibly*).

Adverbs, like adjectives (from which they are mostly formed), are usually classified according to their meaning ; just as adjectives are divided into qualitative, quantitative, and relational, so we can divide adverbs. Thus :

1. ADVERBS OF QUALITY : *Well, ill, badly,* and all the adverbs in *-ly* derived from adjectives ; *how, however, so, as, likewise,* etc. (sometimes called adverbs of manner).

2. ADVERBS OF QUANTITY : *a.* Degree : *Very, nearly, almost, too, quite, enough, rather, much, more, most, little, less, least, only, but, just, even, any, the* (as in '*the* more *the* merrier'). Also the adverbs of affirmation and negation: *Not, no, nay, aye, yea, yes.*

b. Repetition of Time—as, *once, twice, thrice, often, seldom, always,* etc.

3. ADVERBS OF RELATION, which show :

a. Time : *Now, then, after, before, soon, ago, instantly,* etc.

b. Place and Arrangement : *Firstly, secondly, thirdly, here, there, hither, thither, hence, thence, inside, outside, up, down,* etc.

c. Cause and Consequence : *Why, therefore, wherefore, accordingly, consequently,* etc.

It will be noticed that some of the words appearing in this list of adverbs have previously appeared as other parts of speech. *As,* for example, was included under relative pronouns ; and *much, little, no, any,* were included under adjectives. To determine what part of speech a word is in a given sentence, we must consider the purpose it serves. Thus, 'This is the same *as* that' (relative pronoun='this is the same which that is') ; '*As* I spoke the sun came out' (adverb denoting the time of the action). Again, 'Give him *no* peace ' (adjective) ; 'This is *no* better than that ' (adverb). Similarly, *much,*

little, and *any* before comparatives are adverbs.

Formation of Adverbs, 1. FROM ADJECTIVES. Most adverbs are formed by adding *-ly* to the corresponding adjective— e.g. *wild, wildly ; cheerful, cheerfully.* The termination *-ly*=like.

Adjectives ending in *y* preceded by a consonant change *y* into *i* before *-ly* : e.g. *hearty, heartily ; speedy, speedily ;* but : *shy, shyly ; gay, gaily.*

Adjectives ending in *-le* change the *e* into *y* : e.g., *noble, nobly ; horrible, horribly.* When the adjective already ends in *-ly* the same form is generally used for the adverb : e.g. the adverb of *godly* is usually *godly* : 'We should live soberly, righteously and *godly* in this present world.' So also *likely* : 'A *likely* story' (adjective) ; 'He will very *likely* come' (adverb). Other adverbs derived from adjectives are *once, twice, thrice* (for *ones, twyes, thries*), *unawares.* Some adjectives, in addition to those ending in *-ly,* are used as adverbs without any change of form : e.g. 'run *fast*,' 'stand *firm*,' 'strike *deep*,' '*pretty* good.'

2. FROM NOUNS. *Needs* (as in 'If I must needs leave you'), *whiles, sideways, lengthways, straightways, noways,* are genitive cases of nouns. *Whilom* ('at whiles,' 'formerly') and *seldom* are dative cases plural of Old English *hwil* (=space of time), and *seld* (=rare). Other adverbs derived from nouns are *headlong, sidelong, piecemeal* (meal=part), *sometimes, always, perhaps, otherwise, midway,* etc. Many adverbs are compounds of the preposition *a* (meaning *on*) and a noun, as *afoot, abreast, aside, asleep ;* while some are compounds of other prepositions with nouns, as *betimes* (by times), *besides, indeed.*

3. FROM PRONOUNS. *Thus, then, than ; here, hither, hence ; there, thither, thence ; where, whither, whence ; why, how* (for *whow*), and all the other adverbs formed from the relative pronouns, such as *wherefore, whereat, wherein, whereby,* etc.

These adverbs, that are derived from the relative pronouns, with the addition of *as* and *than,* are *connective* or *conjunctive* adverbs, that is, they retain the connective power which we have seen belongs to relative pronouns. A connective adverb introduces a subordinate clause and modifies the predicate of this clause.

Negative Adverbs. *Not* is shortened from *nought* or *naught*, and literally means 'in no whit, in no degree.' In Old and Middle English, *ne* (=*not*) is employed before the verb, and a form corresponding to *naught* after the verb, the two negatives strengthening each other; thus, in Robert of Gloucester's Chronicle (A.D. 1298) we find '*Ne* be thou naught so sturne' ('Be thou not in any way so stern'), and in Chaucer's 'Canterbury Tales' we have

' There was also a Doctour of Physik,
In all the world *ne* was there *none* him like.'

Also 'Nor hath not one spirit to command' ('Tempest').

In Modern English, two negatives, so far from strengthening each other, neutralize each other.

No and *nay* are from *na*, meaning *never*, while *aye* (affirmative) is from *a*, meaning *ever* (cf. *for aye*, meaning *for ever*. 'This world is not for aye,' 'Hamlet'). *Yes* is from Old English *gese* (pronounced *yĕs-ĕ*), from *gēa* (yea) and *swā* (so).

Comparison of Adverbs. Most adverbs are compared by prefixing *more* and *most* to the positive, as *willingly, more willingly, most willingly*. But a few, and especially those which have the same form as the corresponding adjectives, are formed by the suffixes *-er, -est*, as in the table following.

Positive	Comparative	Superlative
firm	firmer	firmest
fast	faster	fastest
soon	sooner	soonest
early	earlier	earliest

The following are irregular (see 'Comparison of Adjectives,' Lesson 4, p. 493):

Positive	Comparative	Superlative
well	better	best
badly, evilly *or* ill	worse	worst
much	more	most
far	farther	farthest
forth	further	furthest
nigh *or* near	nearer	nearest, next
late	later / latter	latest / last
[rathe, *adjective*]	rather	—
—	ere	erst
lief	liefer	—

Rathe meant *quick, early; rather*, therefore, means *quicker, earlier, sooner*. Milton in 'Lycidas' has 'the *rathe* primrose' (adjective).

Ere is the Old English *ær*, a comparative adverb of time. It is now used mainly as a conjunction. *Erst*, from *ærest*, means *formerly*.

Adverbs are usually placed as near as possible to the words they modify, and generally *before* an adjective, or other adverb, and *after* a verb. For emphasis, however, an adverb may precede the verb, and even be the first word of a sentence.

LESSON 11

Prepositions, Conjunctions and Interjections

A PREPOSITION is a word which shows how things, or their actions or attributes, are related to other things: e.g. 'Coming *through* the rye' (*through* showing the relation of the action *coming* to the thing *rye*); 'London is full *of* people' (*of* showing the relation of the attribute *full* to the thing *people*). The noun or pronoun following a preposition is in the objective case, governed by the preposition. Prepositions may be classified as *Simple* and *Compound*. The simple prepositions are *at, by, for, from, in, of, off, on, through, till, to, up, with*.

The most important compound prepositions are:

aboard	amid(st)	athwart
about	among(st)	before
above	(a)round	behind
across	aslant	below
against	astride	beneath
along		

beside(s)	down, adown	toward(s)
between	except	underneath
betwixt	inside	after ⎫ formed by
beyond	outside	over ⎬ comptve.
but (by-out)	since	under ⎭ suffix *-er*

Beside is used of *place*, to denote either nearness to, or remoteness from: thus, 'They wandered beside the stream' (meaning *by the side of*); 'She was almost *beside* herself with grief' (meaning *out of her mind*). When, however, the sense of *over and above* is intended, *besides* is generally used, as '*Besides* Latin, he is also learning Greek.'

But is a preposition when it means *except*. It should then be followed by the objective case, as 'No one was saved but *me*.'

Sans and *Maugre* are found in Shakespeare, Milton, etc. *Sans* is the French preposition, meaning *without*: e.g. 'A confidence *sans* bound' ('Tempest'). *Maugre* is the French *malgré*, in spite of: e.g. '*Maugre* the Roman' ('Paradise Regained').

Certain participles, such as *considering, concerning, respecting, pending, during, notwithstanding, saving, save,* are often used as prepositions, though they are not really such. Thus, in '*Notwithstanding* your cruelty, I forgive you,' the true construction is, 'Your cruelty *notwithstanding,* I forgive you,' the first three words being in the nominative absolute, and *notwithstanding* filling its proper part as a participle.

Many prepositions are also adverbs, but it is easy to distinguish the two uses. If the word in question governs a noun or some substitute for a noun, it is a preposition; if not, it is probably an adverb. We say 'probably,' because it might be a conjunction, or even occasionally some other part of speech.

Examples: 'He walked *along* the river' (preposition); 'He walked *along* very fast' (adverb). '*Since* his death I have lived here' (preposition); 'He died long *since*' (adverb); '*Since* he is dead, we must not speak evil of him' (conjunction).

In 'But me no buts,' *but* is used first as a verb, secondly as a noun.

When *to* is used as an adverb, it is spelt *too* ('It is too cold for you to go out today').

A preposition should, if possible, immediately precede the word which it governs. Even in relative and interrogative sentences this order should be observed. It is better to say 'Of whom are you speaking?' than 'Whom are you speaking of?' When, however, in a relative sentence, the relative pronoun is omitted, the preposition is usually placed at the end of the sentence, as: 'He is not a man I am fond of' (i.e. 'of whom I am fond').

Conjunctions. Conjunctions are words which join sentences together—as: 'I will wait *till* you come.' Here *till* joins together the two sentences, 'I will wait' and 'you come.' Not every word, however, that connects two sentences is a conjunction, for we have seen that relative pronouns (*who, which,* etc.) and relative adverbs (*when, where,* etc.) often connect one sentence with another. With these two exceptions, all words which join sentences together are conjunctions.

The conjunction *and* is peculiar, because, in addition to joining two sentences, it can also join two words, provided they are both of the same kind and stand in the same relation to some other word in the sentence: e.g. 'Two *and* two are four,' 'Egg *and* milk are a good mixture.' But in a sentence like 'My parents and my cousins are here,' *and* joins two *sentences* ('my parents are here' and 'my cousins are here'), not two words. *And* is the only conjunction that can join words, though it is sometimes said that *but, or,* and *nor* join words. We shall find, however, that in every case these conjunctions really join sentences: e.g. 'Neither this nor that is right' stands for 'This is not right, that is not right.' Such sentences are contracted compound sentences.

Co-ordinative Conjunctions. Conjunctions are divided into co-ordinative and subordinative. Those in the former class join co-ordinate sentences, that is, sentences of the same rank (Latin *ordo*=rank), neither of which is dependent on the other. The co-ordinative conjunctions are *and, both, but, either, or, neither, nor* (and, according to some grammarians, *because, for, as,* and *whether*).

Either is the distributive pronoun, and *whether* the relative pronoun, used as conjunctions: e.g. '*Either* of the two suits me' (pronoun); '*Either* you or I shall perish' (conjunction).

But was originally a preposition, meaning *without, except.* In phrases like 'I cannot but think,' 'There is no one but knows,' it is a conjunction; also in all cases where it joins two sentences, as 'Strike, but hear me,' 'He loved not fatherland, but himself.'

Subordinative Conjunctions. The conjunctions in this second class join subordinate clauses to a main clause, that is, they unite sentences one of which is dependent on the other; e.g. 'He'll kill himself yet, *though* he has been lucky so far.' Here, the second clause depends on the first, or is subordinate to it, therefore the conjunction uniting them is subordinative. Such a sentence as the above is called a *complex* sentence, as opposed to a compound sentence, which consists of two or more co-ordinate clauses united by a co-ordinative conjunction. In a complex sentence, one clause is called the principal clause, and all the other clauses are called subordinate. These subordinate clauses play the part of adverbs, adjectives, or substantives, and are called accordingly, *Adverbial, Adjectival,* or *Substantival Clauses.*

The most important subordinative conjunctions are:

1. *That,* introducing substantival clauses: e.g. 'He said that he was cold.'
2. *If, unless, except,* etc. (conditional).
3. *Though, although, albeit* (concessive).
4. *That,* meaning 'so that' (consecutive) as: 'It was so cold that the water froze.'

5. *That*, meaning ' in order that,' *lest* (final) as : ' He went out that he might get warm.'

6. *After, before, till, until, ere, since, now, while, as* (temporal).

7. *Because, since, for, as* (causal).

8. *Than* (comparative).

Than is now regarded as a conjunction, though it is strictly a relative adverb, meaning *when, at which time*. The noun or pronoun following *than* may be in the nominative case or in the objective, according to the predicate to be supplied, thus : ' I know you better than he (does)' ; ' I know you better than (I know) him' ; 'He hates me more *than* you' may mean 'He hates me more than he hates you' (*you* being objective), or 'He hates me more than

you hate me' (*you* being nominative). A relative pronoun following *than* is always put in the objective case, even when it is strictly nominative, as : 'Caesar is dead, than *whom* no greater Roman ever lived.' *Whom* ought to be in the nominative, as the sentence stands for 'Caesar is dead, and no greater Roman ever lived than *he*.'

Interjections. These are words interjected or ' thrown in' to express some emotion. They do not stand in any grammatical relation to other words, and are independent of the construction of the sentence.

Examples: *Hurrah* ! *Alas* ! *Oh* ! *Ah* ! *Pshaw* ! *Ha, ha* ! *Good-bye* ! (God be with you). *Hullo* ! *Whoa* ! *Welcome* ! *Hail*!

LESSON 12

Analysing the Sentence

WE may not only consider words as independent units (the study of *Accidence*) and parse them, but we may also deal with them in their relationship to other words grouped with them to form a sentence (the study of *Syntax*). The unit of speech is the sentence, and it is quite as important to be able to break a sentence up into its component parts as it is to be able to compare an adjective or conjugate a verb. We cannot properly parse a word—that is, say to what part of speech it belongs—until we see it in a sentence ; and before we can parse it then as it should be parsed, we must make a mental analysis of the sentence. The practice of analysis, then, logically comes before that of parsing.

A simple sentence has only one subject and one predicate. The subject is that about which something is asserted ; the predicate is what is asserted concerning the subject. In every sentence there must be a subject and a predicate ; this is the irreducible minimum, as ' Fire burns.' In addition, there may be a word or words limiting or qualifying either the subject or the predicate, or both, as : '*This* fire burns *well*.' Finally, if the predicate contains a transitive verb, this will take an object, and this

object, too, may have a word or words limiting it, as : 'Fire burns your finger' (*finger* being the object and *your* the limitation of the object).

As a rule, a simple sentence does not consist of more than the following parts : subject ; limitation of subject ; predicate ; limitation of predicate ; object ; limitation of object.

For example : 'The freshening breeze of eve unfurled that banner's massy fold' consists of five parts, which may be isolated as in the table given below.

Analyses of Simple Sentences, Showing Their Structure

'The freshening breeze of eve unfurled that banner's massy fold.'

Subject	Limitation of Subject	Predicate	Object	Limitation of Object
breeze	1. The freshening	unfurled	fold	that banner's massy
	2. of eve			

'Here rests his head upon the lap of earth, A youth to fortune and to fame unknown.'

Subject	Limitation of Subject	Predicate	Limitation of Pred.	Object	Limitation of Object
youth	1. A	rests	1. Here	head	his
	2. to fortune and to fame unknown		2. upon the lap of earth		

'Cromwell's enemies have often called him a bloodthirsty monster.'

Subject	Limitation of Subject	Verb	Predicate Complement	Limitation of Complement	Limitation of Predicate	Object
enemies	Cromwell's	have called	monster	a bloodthirsty	often	him

Analyses of Complex Sentences
(1) 'There is some soul of goodness in things evil would men observingly distil it out.'

Subject	Limitation of Subject	Verb	Limitation of Verb	Object	Limitation of Object
soul	(a) some (b) of goodness	is	(a) in things evil (b) would men observingly distil it out	—	—
men	—	would distil	(a) observingly (b) out	it	—

(2) 'If you catch him when you reach home, give him the message which I will give you now.'

| (you) | — | give | (a) him (b) if you catch him when you reach home | message | (a) the (b) which I will give you now |

(a) 'If you catch him when you reach home.'

| you | — | catch | when you reach home | him | — |

(b) 'When you reach home.'

| you | — | reach | home | — | — |

(c) 'Which I will give you now.'

| I | — | will give | (a) you (b) now | which | — |

Sometimes the predicate consists of a verb and a complement, especially with verbs of *making, calling,* and so on. For example : 'Cromwell's enemies have often called him a bloodthirsty monster.' An analysis of this sentence also appears in the table in the previous page.

Analysis lays bare the structure of the sentence. From a grammatical point of view, a sentence is not grasped until it has been mentally analysed and all its component parts set forth in their nakedness.

We can now go a step farther to the dissection of a sentence containing a principal clause and one or more subordinate clauses, i.e. a complex sentence. To analyse this we first pick out the principal clause, and insert the subordinate clauses as parts of the sentence. Then, omitting the connecting words, we can analyse the different subordinate clauses in turn. The student should be familiar with the various kinds of clauses. There are three kinds of subordinate clauses :

(1) SUBSTANTIVAL. Clauses that play the part of a substantive in relation to some part of the sentence. Examples : 'We know *that you are wrong*' (this clause is the object of 'know') ; '*When the election will come* is uncertain' (this clause is the subject of 'is').

(2) ADJECTIVAL. Clauses that play the part of an adjective in relation to some part of the sentence. Examples : 'Give me the portion of goods *that falleth to me*' (qualifies 'portion') ; 'That is the spot *where Nelson fell*' (qualifies 'spot'). Care must be taken, however, to distinguish such clauses from clauses involving an indirect question—as : 'Tell me *where Nelson fell,*' 'I asked *where I was,*' 'I know *why you have come.*' In these sentences the dependent clauses are substantival, representing substantives ; there is no antecedent to which they could relate.

(3) ADVERBIAL. Clauses that play the part of an adverb in relation to some part of the sentence. Examples : 'I like her, *because she is cheerful*' (modifying 'like') ; 'Do *as I tell you*' (modifying 'do').

Sentences must always be grouped according to their subordination or coordination. Example :

There at the foot of yonder nodding beech
That wreaths its old fantastic roots so high,
His listless length at noontide would he stretch,
And pore upon the brook that babbles by.

He would stretch his listless length at noontide, there, at the foot of yonder nodding beech. *Principal.*
And (he would) pore upon the brook. *Co-ordinate Principal.*
That wreathes its old fantastic roots so high. *Subordinate Adjectival, qualifying ' beech.'*
That babbles by. *Subordinate Adjectival, qualifying ' brook.'*

The formal analysis in the table above shows the structure of the sentences :

(1) 'There is some soul of goodness in things evil
Would men observingly distil it out.'

The principal clause is 'There is some soul of goodness in things evil,' and the subordinate clause '(If) men would observingly distil it out.'

(2) 'If you catch him when you reach home, give him the message which I will give you now.'

The principal clause is 'give him the message' ; the other three clauses are subordinate.

Simple Schemes in Parsing

WE have in our Course in the English Language now gone through all the parts of speech in detail, and have been 'parsing' words, perhaps unconsciously, throughout the process. For to 'parse' a word is simply to say to what part of speech it belongs, and how it is related to other words in the same sentence. The following is a parsing scheme :

1. NOUN. Give (1) general class—i.e. proper, common, abstract, collective ; (2) gender ; (3) number ; (4) case ; (5) reason for the case.

2. ADJECTIVE. Give (1) class, whether of quality, quantity or relation ; (2) degree, whether positive, comparative or superlative ; (3) its qualification of the substantive. If the adjective in question is pronominal—i.e. also used as a pronoun—state this in parsing it.

3. PRONOUN. Give (1) class ; (2) gender (if possible) ; (3) number ; (4) case, with reasons for the number and the case.

4. VERB. If a finite verb, give (1) voice ; (2) mood ; (3) tense ; (4) number ; (5) person and the subject with which it agrees or the object it governs ; (6) principal parts—i.e. present indicative, past indicative and past participle.

If an infinitive or gerund, give (1) voice ; (2) tense ; (3) case, with a reason for the case.

If a participle, give (1) voice ; (2) tense ; (3) number ; (4) case, and the substantive with which it agrees. In *all* moods, say whether the verb is transitive or intransitive, whether of weak conjugation or of strong, and give the principal parts.

5. ADVERB. Give (1) class ; (2) degree ; (3) what it qualifies.

6. PREPOSITION. State what it governs.

7. CONJUNCTION. Give its class, and say what sentences or words it connects.

It should be noted that all grammarians do not adopt precisely the same nomenclature. Some insist that adjectives ' qualify ' but adverbs ' modify.' Such distinctions are not vital, and the student should not attach too much importance to them. It is important, however, to note that a word is not necessarily one *fixed* part of speech, but differs according to its function. Thus ' frequent ' is an adjective in ' It is a frequent occurrence,' and a verb in ' We frequent the same club.' Similarly in ' Sleeping is necessary for life,' and ' Let sleeping dogs lie,' sleeping is a gerund in the first example, and an adjective in the second.

Example of Parsing

'*But then the mind much sufferance doth o'erskip,*
When grief hath mates, and bearing fellowship.' ('King Lear.')

But. Co-ordinative conjunction, connecting this sentence with what has gone before.

Then. Adverb of time, modifying 'doth o'erskip.'

The. Demonstrative adjective (sometimes called definite article), pointing out 'mind.'

Mind. Abstract noun, neuter, singular, nominative because subject of 'doth o'erskip.'

Much. Adjective of quantity, positive, qualifying 'sufferance.'

Sufferance. Abstract noun, neuter, singular, objective, governed by 'doth o'erskip.'

Doth o'erskip. Verb, transitive, weak conjugation, active, indicative, present, singular, third person, agreeing with its subject 'mind,' from *o'erskip, o'erskipped, o'erskipped.*

When. Relative adverb (or conjunctive adverb) of time, modifying 'hath.'

Grief. Abstract noun, neuter, singular, nominative because subject to 'hath.'

Hath. Verb, notional (not auxiliary here), transitive, weak, active, indicative, present, singular, third person, agreeing with its subject 'grief,' from *have, had, had.*

Mates. Common noun, common gender, plural, objective after 'hath.'

And. Co-ordinative conjunction, joining the two sentences 'grief hath mates,' and 'bearing (hath) fellowship.'

Bearing. Abstract noun, neuter, singular, nominative, subject to 'hath' understood.

Fellowship. Abstract noun, neuter, singular, objective after 'hath' understood.

NOTE. Parse compound tenses of a verb : e.g. *have been, shall be leaving,* all as one word. We could, of course, parse the words separately, but there is no need to do this.

EXERCISE

Parse fully the words in italics : ' And *so*, neither condemning the delights of *others*, nor altogether *distrustful* of our own, we must *advance*, as we live *on*, from what is promised to what is *fulfilled.*'

Notes on English Punctuation

PUNCTUATION is the right method of inserting stops (Latin *puncta*, points). Stops are written marks to represent oral pauses. If we speak to anyone for a few minutes, and notice carefully the manner of our speech, we shall find that we make pauses of greater or less duration, mainly—though not entirely—for the sake of clearness. If our remarks were then written down, these different pauses would be represented by different stops. Where we completed a sentence, a *period*, or *full stop* (.), would be used. Where we made a decided pause, but not so decided as in the first case, a *colon* (:) or *semi-colon* (;) would be used. Where only a slight pause was made, a *comma* (,) would be used.

The meaning of a sentence ought to be plain without the aid of any stops whatever. Stops are a comparatively modern invention; they do not appear on ancient manuscripts, and at one time they were not allowed in our Acts of Parliament. At the present day, too, in legal documents stops are most often conspicuous by their absence.

Very often the entire meaning of a sentence can be altered by a slight alteration of punctuation—a fact of which full advantage is taken in many riddles that are propounded, and in many traps that are set for the unwary. Thus, in the well-known statement, 'King Charles walked and talked half an hour after his head was cut off,' nonsense becomes sense by the insertion of a colon after 'talked.'

Full Stop. This is used to mark the completion of a whole sentence, whether simple or complex. It is also used after abbreviations: i.e. R.S.V.P., Rev., D.D., M.P., Dr., Mr.

Colon. The *colon* originally marked off the parts of a compound sentence. It is now used after a sentence which, though grammatically complete, is followed by another closely connected in sense: here a full stop would mark too great a break. A colon is also used to introduce a quotation. For example:

' Cowards die many times before their deaths :
The valiant never taste of death but once.'

Semi-colon. This is a modern form of the colon. It is impossible to lay down rules for their respective use, but, roughly speaking, the semi-colon marks a less complete pause than the colon. The semi-colon is usually placed between the co-ordinate members of a compound sentence *when the connexion is marked by a conjunction*, as : 'You do not understand the lessons you have learnt ; but this is only because you are inattentive.' If the sentences are short, and closely connected in meaning, commas are used instead of semi-colons, as :

' We carved not a line, and we raised not a stone,
But we left him alone in his glory.'

Comma. The *comma* is not used as frequently as formerly. A sentence should not be overloaded with commas ; they should be used only where it is absolutely necessary for the sake of clearness. Common sense must be the guiding element in their usage. But a few points may be mentioned :

1. A comma should be used to mark the end of a substantive clause forming the *subject* of a verb, as : 'That the days are longer in summer than in winter, admits of no dispute.' But if the clause either follows the verb, or is the object of the verb, no comma is used, as : 'He said that he was cold.'

2. In a list of words of the same nature—nouns, adjectives, adverbs, etc.—brought together in the same connexion, a comma is inserted after each word except the penultimate when it is followed by 'and,' as : 'The fence was painted in stripes of green, brown, black and white.'

3. The comma is used after an adverbial clause that comes before the verb which it modifies, as : 'When he comes, tell me.' But if the adverbial clause *follows* the verb, the comma is not needed, as : 'Tell me when he comes.'

4. There is no need of a comma between the antecedent and the relative pronoun if the relative introduces a limiting, or restricting, clause ; but if the relative is continuative or ampliative a comma must be introduced.

Restrictive. 'He broke the pen which I lent him.'

Continuative. 'His eldest son, whom he had lost many years before, had always been his favourite.'

5. A comma is used to separate a noun in the vocative (or nominative of address) from the rest of the sentence, as : ' Mother, may I go out to play ?'

Other Stops. The *note of interrogation* (?) is placed at the end of all direct questions, as : ' Who is there ?' It is not used after an indirect or reported question, as : ' He asked who was there.'

The *note of exclamation* (!), used after interjections and exclamations, e.g. ' Alas !' is also sometimes used after the vocative case, as : ' All hail, great master !'

Curved and square brackets ( ), [ ], are used to separate certain words from the rest of the sentence, to add an explanation of a difficult word, etc.

Inverted commas, double " — ", or single ' — ', are used to mark quotations. When a quotation occurs within a quotation the inner quotation should be carefully rendered distinct by single inverted commas inside double, or double inside single, as :

' Breathes there the man with soul so dead,
Who never to himself hath said,
" This is my own, my native land " ? '

LESSON 15

On the Writing of Good English

THE main object of our study of the English language is that we may be able to express ourselves clearly in it, whether in writing or in speech. We must aim not only at meaning exactly what we say, but also—and this is all-important—at saying exactly what we mean.

Absolute clearness of style is the result of long and careful discipline, but it is a result that will well repay the labour. It can be cultivated better in writing than in speech, because we can revise what we have written, whereas the spoken word is usually forgotten as soon as uttered. We should, therefore, make it a practice at first to read and re-read everything that we write, looking carefully for any ambiguity or any loophole for misunderstanding. We may be certain that if a thing is not quite clear to the writer of it, the chances are that it will be far from clear to anyone else.

Perhaps in no matter is this more important than in one where it is as a rule most neglected—viz. that of writing business letters. The necessity for a clear style is a very practical matter indeed, as thousands of people have discovered.

It is impossible to mention all the errors of style that can be committed, but the following are the most common.

(1) Words are often left without any relation whatever. Examples : ' Your guilt is as great or greater than his,' where *as* has nothing to which to relate.

' He is not only acquainted, but well versed in English literature,' where *acquainted* should be followed by *with*, to bring it into relation with the rest of the sentence.

' Having crossed the stream the banks on either side fell in,' where *having crossed* has no relation to any other word of the sentence. As it stands, it agrees with *banks* : but the banks did not cross the stream.

' Alarmed at the appearance of the sky, a terrific peal of thunder shook the house, so that he ran out,' where *alarmed* is not related to any other word. Grammatically, it agrees with *peal of thunder*, but it was not the peal of thunder that was alarmed. The subject of the main sentence should, of course, be *he*.

(2) Many errors arise from a wrong or misleading *order* of words. As a rule, a sentence should run in its natural order : subject (and its limitations), predicate, object (and its limitations), adverbial limitations of the predicate—as : ' The dying hero spoke words of consolation and of cheer in the midst of his mortal agony.' For the sake of emphasis, e.g. ' Great is Diana of the Ephesians,' or for certain other reasons, the order may be altered. But whatever be the order of the words, the important point is that the meaning shall be clear.

Great care is needed in dealing with relative pronouns, lest they seem to refer to a substantive which is not intended to be their antecedent. For example : ' Much energy was displayed by Mr. Smith in running down the street after his silk hat, which he felt might have been devoted to a better purpose.' The only way of avoiding this pitfall is to place the antecedent *immediately* before the relative : ' Mr. Smith, in running down the street after his silk hat, displayed an amount of energy,' etc.

R

Equal care is necessary in dealing with adverbs or adverbial phrases, as these have an awkward knack of appearing to qualify words which they are not intended to qualify. Examples : 'The Moor seizing a bolster full of rage and jealousy smothers her.'

'Erected to the memory of John Phillip accidentally shot as a mark of affection by his brother.'

'The young man coloured with pleasure and promised to return in quite a gratified tone of voice.'

'You have already been informed of the sale of Ford's theatre where Mr. Lincoln was assassinated for religious purposes.'

(3) Further errors of style are : the use of unnecessary phraseology for simple words, e.g. 'the nasal organ' (for nose), 'the lower extremities' (for legs), 'the tender passion' (for love) ; the use of stereotyped expressions (clichés), hackneyed allusions and quotations, e.g. 'fit as a fiddle,' 'the Swan of Avon,' 'the cup that cheers but not inebriates' ; and the use of needlessly involved sentences, meaningless phrases, and abstract instead of concrete nouns.

A typical specimen of this kind of writing is the following extract from a newspaper article, reprinted in H. W. Fowler's 'The King's English ':

One of the most important reforms mentioned in the rescript is the unification of the organization of judicial institutions and the guarantee for all the tribunals of the independence necessary for securing to all classes of the community equality before the law.

Sir Arthur Quiller-Couch, in 'The Art of Writing,' presses the point well home by re-writing in what he calls 'jargon' the first nine lines of Hamlet's soliloquy 'To be or not to be' (Hamlet, Act III, scene i):

To be, or the contrary ? Whether the former or the latter be preferable would seem to admit of some difference of opinion ; the answer in the present case being of an affirmative or of a negative character according as to whether one elects on the one hand to mentally suffer the disfavour of fortune, albeit in an extreme degree, or on the other to boldly envisage adverse conditions in the prospect of eventually bringing them to a conclusion. The condition of sleep is similar to, if not indistinguishable from, that of death ; and with the addition of finality the former might be considered identical with the latter : so that in this connection it might be argued with regard to sleep that, could the addition be effected, a termination would be put to the endurance of a multiplicity of inconveniences, not to mention a number of downright evils incidental to our fallen humanity, and thus a consummation achieved of a most gratifying nature.

As a mental training the art of reading the English classics aloud is worth cultivating. Clearness depends on grasping the author's meaning, and then conveying that meaning adequately to others. Correct emphasis is essential, and monotony must be avoided by proper inflexion of the voice.

While it is highly important in the formation of style to read the great masters of English literature, it should be remembered that each person has a natural style of his or her own. The study of the great stylists should therefore be with the aim of perfecting the reader's particular style rather than with the idea of slavish imitation. The student will find the Authorized Version of the English Bible hard to beat in clearness and simplicity ; he will naturally not copy its archaic phrases. His first requirement is to write good, direct English, not to be led away by false gods of style ; to be able to read Carlyle without falling into his habits, to pass unscathed through the labyrinth of Lytton Strachey's winding sentences and to withstand Oscar Wilde's worst mannerisms.

LESSON 16

Paraphrasing and Précis Writing

A PARAPHRASE is the free rendering of a text into a clearer and fuller form than found in the original. Paraphrasing is a stimulating but difficult exercise which calls for exactness of vocabulary and concentration. An effort has to be made to penetrate exactly into the writer's thought so as to reproduce only what has been written. The student may find considerable difficulty at first, but with practice and as reading increases his vocabulary a steady improvement may be confidently expected.

Certain rules may be laid down as a help. (1) Always read through the original three or four times to make sure you have understood the author's idea. Try to reproduce the tone of the original passage. (2) There is no need to find a synonym for every word, though it is advisable to do so if possible. You must avoid making a paraphrase of a piece of verse consist of the same words written in a prose order. The thought in poetry is sometimes more compressed, sometimes more diffuse, than in prose. It is your business to make the meaning clear. (3) Do not hesitate to cut up long sentences into shorter ones. (4) As a rule your paraphrase will be longer than the original, but be as brief as possible. (5) The paraphrase should be a piece of prose intelligible to anyone who has not read the original. (6) Sometimes the paraphrase takes the form of changing a piece of archaic English into modern prose and spelling. You must look out for words which have changed their meaning. Thus 'presently' in Shakespeare's time meant 'now,' 'at present,' whereas today it means 'soon.'

Examples of Paraphrasing. Two exercises from verse and one from prose will make the process clear.

Perhaps in this neglected spot is laid
Some heart once pregnant with celestial fire :
Hands, that the rod of Empire might have
  swayed,
Or waked to ecstasy the living lyre.

Perhaps in this uncared-for spot is buried some being filled once with heavenly ardour ; hands which, had chance been otherwise, might have grasped the sceptre of an empire, or won from some instrument notes of exquisite music.

Here is the opening of Bacon's 'Essay on Gardens.' Notice the magnificent opening sentence is retained in the paraphrase.

God Almightie first Planted a Garden. And indeed, it is the Purest of Humane pleasures. It is the Greatest Refreshment to the Spirits of Man ; Without which, Buildings and Pallaces are but Grosse Handy-works : and a Man shall ever see, that when Ages grow to Civility and Elegancie, Men come to Build Stately, sooner then to Garden Finely : As if Gardening were the Greater Perfection. I doe hold it, in the Royall Ordering of Gardens, there ought to be Gardens, for all the Moneths in the Yeare : In which, severally, Things of Beautie, may be then in Season.

God Almighty first planted a garden. In truth gardening is the most unmixed of human pleasures. It is most refreshing to the mind of man, for without it all his fine buildings and palaces appear but unfinished work. As time goes on and we grow more civilized and tasteful, it will be found that men build in noble fashion ere yet they become skilled gardeners. By this it appears that gardening is the more difficult calling. I do believe that in the arrangement of royal gardens there should be gardens for each month in which beautiful things are at their best as they come into season.

One more verse example :

Proud word you never spoke, but you will
  speak
Four not exempt from pride some future day
Resting on one white hand a warm wet cheek,
Over my open volume you will say,
'This man loved me'—then rise and trip away.

Vaingloriously you never spoke, but one day you will speak four words not devoid of pride. This you will do when you rest a tear-stained cheek upon your white hand over the book that I have written. Then you will say : 'This man loved me,' and rise and lightly walk away.

Précis Writing. A précis is an abstract, abridgement, or summary. It is the term usually applied to a condensed report or narrative. The object of a précis is to enable anyone who reads through the digest to obtain a knowledge of the essential features of the matter of which it is a condensation. The journalist makes a précis of a minister's speech to enable readers of the paper to see at a glance its main points. The student takes lecture notes to make a précis of what he has heard. A business clerk may be called upon to prepare a précis from a mass of correspondence, and government clerks have constantly to present précis of documents for the use of ministers.

Précis writing is an excellent exercise in extracting the essential matter from books, documents, speeches, etc. It requires discrimination, tidiness of mind, and powers of compression. At first it may seem difficult, and it varies much according to the difficulty of the original matter, but skill will come with practice. Some useful rules can be stated.

(1) Be sure to master the subject-matter which you have to summarize. If you cannot do this in one reading, read it a second or third time, and make certain that you keep to the logical order of the thought.

(2) When you feel that you have mastered the passage, read it once again and underline the important passages. Then prepare a skeleton outline of your précis.

(3) Go over your outline again and strike out everything that does not now appear essential.

(4) You are frequently asked to suggest a suitable title, and to reduce the original matter to about one-third. This is usually a reasonable reduction and should present no undue difficulty.

(5) Be brief, but not telegraphic. Your final draft should read as a piece of continuous prose which conveys clearly all that is necessary of the original.

(6) Letters and speeches should always be given in the past tense and the third person. Direct quotation must be changed into reported speech. Never reproduce in a précis the actual words of the speaker. Should there be conversation in the passage, this should only be briefly summarized.

(7) You need not keep too closely to the words of the original, nor need you avoid them if they are the best to make your meaning absolutely clear.

(8) Connect sentences together by linking words such as 'therefore,' 'while,' 'thus,' etc., and cut out all repetition used for emphasis.

Example of Précis Writing. Give titles and reduce the following specimens to about one-third :

Who will ever be able to forget the heroic self-sacrifice shown by an English regiment drowned in a shipwreck ? On Feb. 25th, 1852, the transport 'Birkenhead' was carrying troops to reinforce the garrison at the Cape of Good Hope. The ship struck a hidden rock off Cape Agulhas, the most southern point of Cape Colony. She carried 500 soldiers, a crew of 134, a number of women and children, and some passengers who were invalids. Officers and men took their arms and drew up in battle line on the deck as calmly as if on parade on a barrack square in England. Such rescue work as was possible proceeded as the ship sunk slowly beneath the waves. There were hardly sufficient lifeboats to carry the women, children and the sick, and none to accommodate the troops. Not one of the strong, vigorous and fully armed young men stepped from the ranks and attempted to take the place of those going to apparent safety, and the entire regiment was swallowed up in the deep waters, martyrs to obedience and self-sacrifice. Only 192 people were saved. The name of 'Birkenhead,' and the date of the wreck, should be placed on the colours of this regiment in commemoration of a deed as truly glorious as the most brilliant of victories on the battle-field.

HEROISM ON THE 'BIRKENHEAD'

The self-sacrifice on the ' Birkenhead' is unforgettable. The transport, with reinforcements for the Cape, struck a rock when carrying 500 troops, a crew of 134, women, children, and invalids. The troops, drawn up in battle-order on the deck, went down with the ship. Lifeboats were insufficient to accommodate non-combatants, but no armed man attempted to escape, and the entire regiment was drowned. The name 'Birkenhead' should be placed on the regimental colours to perpetuate a deed as glorious as the most brilliant victory.

In the act of stepping out of the boat, Nelson received a shot through the right elbow, and fell ; but, as he fell, he caught the sword, which he had just drawn, in his left hand, determined never to part with it while he lived, for it had belonged to his uncle, Captain Suckling, and he valued it like a relic. Nisbet, who was close to him, placed him in the bottom of the boat, and laid his hat over the shattered arm, lest the sight of the blood, which gushed out in great abundance, should increase his faintness. He then examined the wound, and, taking some silk handkerchiefs from his neck, bound them round the lacerated vessels. Had it not been for this presence of mind in his step-son, Nelson must have perished. One of his bargemen, by name Lovel, tore his shirt into shreds, and made a sling with them for the broken limb. They then collected five other seamen, by whose assistance they succeeded at length in getting the boat afloat ; for it had grounded with the falling tide. Nisbet took one of the oars, and ordered the steersman to go close under the guns of the battery, that they might be safe from its tremendous fire. Hearing his voice, Nelson roused himself, and desired to be lifted up in the boat, that he might look about him.

NELSON IS SEVERELY WOUNDED

On stepping from the boat, Nelson was shot through the right elbow, and fell. Nisbet, his step-son, placed him in the bottom of the boat, and covered the wound which was gushing blood. He bound silk handkerchiefs over the torn blood-vessels, thereby saving Nelson's life, and a sling was made for the arm. The grounded boat was re-floated, and went close under the battery to avoid its fire. Nelson asked to be lifted to look around.

BOOK LIST

'The Making of English,' H. Bradley (Macmillan) ; 'A Short History of English,' H. C. K. Wyld (Murray) ; 'History of Modern Colloquial English,' H. C. K. Wyld (Blackwell) ; 'The English Language,' L. Pearsall Smith (Home University Library) ; 'Words and Idioms,' L. Pearsall Smith (Constable) ; 'English Past and Present,' R. C. Trench (Dent) ; 'The Writing of English,' W. T. Brewster (Home University Library) ; 'Crabb's English Synonyms' (Routledge) ; 'On the Art of Writing,' Sir A. Quiller-Couch (C.U.P.) ; 'The King's English' and 'Concise Oxford Dictionary,' H. W. and F. G. Fowler (Oxford) ; 'Everyman Dictionary,' D. C. Browning (Dent).

FRENCH

PRECEDED *by an introductory Lesson on 'How to Learn a Language,' which gives some very practical hints on language study in general, here is our Course on French. Essentially scientific, the 15 Lessons in this Course provide those essentials of French grammar and vocabulary which must be mastered, whatever may be the purpose for which the language is studied. Once this is achieved, the student should be able to enlarge his knowledge of French by reading.*

Courses on other foreign languages will be found in Vol. II (LATIN and GERMAN), Vol. III (GREEK and ITALIAN), Vol. IV (SPANISH and PORTUGUESE) and Vol. V (RUSSIAN), while a Course which is complementary to the study of all languages is that on PHILOLOGY in Vol II.

HOW TO LEARN A FOREIGN LANGUAGE

FOR *the first time in a compendium of self-instruction the principal foreign languages, French, German, Italian, Portuguese, Spanish and Russian, are here presented on an entirely new system which greatly simplifies the task of acquiring a practical proficiency in their conversational, literary and commercial use. By special arrangement with the Orthological Institute of Cambridge, and in collaboration with its editor Mr. Charles Duff, each of the six Courses named has been expressly prepared for* PRACTICAL KNOWLEDGE FOR ALL *from the respective handbooks and readers issued in pocket volumes for the Institute by Messrs. Nelson & Sons, Ltd., Edinburgh and London. The copyright of these Courses is strictly reserved by the Orthological Institute of Cambridge.*

How to Learn a Language

IT is highly desirable, before beginning the study of a foreign language, to know the answers to the following three questions :

1. For what *purpose* is this language to be learnt ?
2. What *standard of knowledge* is to be aimed at ?
3. What is the best *method* to achieve the desired standard for the particular purpose ?

If the prospective linguist can make up his mind as to the answers to these questions it will save him or her infinite time and trouble. Here, we propose to assist the learner in answering these very important questions, upon which all his studies and progress will depend.

For What Purpose ? Experience shows that most people learn a foreign language for one of the following purposes :

(1) For a career, in which a knowledge of the language is desirable or essential ;

(2) For a technical purpose, such as the ability to read works in that language—on science, engineering, or some branch of technology ;

(3) To be able to read and enjoy foreign literature, or to listen to foreign radio ;

(4) For purposes of travel—and this may be subdivided into two standards : (a) the ability to find one's way about with some ease, make purchases, read notices, order meals and, generally, to get about without feeling too helpless, and (b) do all these things plus obtaining an insight into the mentality and outlook of the foreign people with whom one mixes.

All these purposes demand different standards of knowledge, so let the student think out what his aim is, and then set out to achieve the necessary standard. *Begin by having a definite aim.*

What Standard of Knowledge ? Half the failures in language study result from inability to know for what purpose the language is being studied, or the standard of knowledge that is being aimed at. There is far too much vagueness about it. For the prospective student of one of the courses given in this book, let us consider standards of knowledge under three heads, as follows :

Mastery. The ideal. It means the ability to do everything with the foreign language that can be done with one's own : speak with the utmost ease and fluency ;

write any sort of letter ; read any sort of book ; play any sort of game ; engage in any trade or profession. Mastery of a foreign language is very rarely achieved, and then generally when the person has had altogether exceptional opportunities—for example, has lived through childhood in the foreign country. While it is all to the good that we should aim at mastery as the ideal, it is as well to know that it demands years of effort. One can hope to master, to 'dominate' *one* foreign language ; to master two is well-nigh impossible.

Workaday Knowledge. This is what most of us want. It implies the ability to engage in the ordinary conversations of everyday life ; the ability to read, without continual recourse to the dictionary, an ordinary newspaper or magazine, a not too difficult author, or the average letter. Any person of average intelligence who persists can reach this standard through the material presented in these Courses. Four months' consistent study of one hour daily (six months for Russian) should lay a very solid foundation for this aim.

Reading Knowledge. This is the minimum standard to be aimed at, and it is one which can be achieved in a matter of weeks by anybody of normal intelligence. These Courses provide all the grammar that is ever likely to be required for it ; and all the word-material for a solid foundation of knowledge. In three to four months the standard of knowledge for reading can be achieved. It must be the *first aim.*

What Method ? There are as many methods in existence as there are teachers and exponents of methods—some good, some bad, some indifferent—but the results of modern research show that in all these methods except one there is a vast potential for wasted effort. In recent years C. K. Ogden, of the Orthological Institute, Cambridge, has blazed a new trail with his ' Basic English,' in which 850 words with a few simple rules of grammar can express almost any idea of which the human mind is capable. Great books have been translated into Basic English, and men so enlightened as George Bernard Shaw and H. G. Wells have not only approved it, but acclaimed it as an outstanding scientific achievement of the century. Basic English gave a pointer to the fact that the text books from which foreign languages are taught to English people are full of masses of quite unnecessary material, and that the minds of learners have been (and still are) filled with rules and words that may never be used in a lifetime. Investigation has proved that in each language there is a *basic vocabulary* and a *basic minimum of grammar* which, when mastered by the foreigner, will enable him to express the most frequently recurring ideas of life. With this basic knowledge he is rarely at a loss.

It is this basic minimum of grammar and vocabulary which is presented in these Courses.

This basic knowledge must be acquired, whatever the purpose may be, or whatever standard is aimed at in studying a foreign language. It is the shortest cut of all to either a reading knowledge, a workaday knowledge or mastery of any of these languages.

Not a rule, not a word is presented in these pages that is not essential. The languages are stripped bare of all useless material, and the students who learn from these Courses may do so in the full assurance that they are not wasting a moment over useless material, and that, if they master what is presented here, they will be possessed of a wonderfully flexible instrument. So much for that part of method represented by the material to be mastered.

How to Learn. Having decided upon an aim and a standard, and being put in possession of the very best material for learning, one can next consider the problem of how to learn. Here again system and method always triumph over haphazard study, and one must try to follow some rules that have been well tested. First, think of how a child learns its mother tongue. How quickly it does it ! Why not learn as a child learns ? A little thought will show that this is impossible. A child has a biological, a natural urge to learn all about the world into which it has plunged. And it has (in 99 per cent of cases) the best of all teachers—a loving mother, who also has a very natural urge to teach her offspring as much as possible. Language is the key to all knowledge for the child, and hence for the child language-learning is almost a full-time job. And it is undertaken in an entirely favourable environment, with all the promptings and help which environment can provide.

The adult wishing to learn a foreign language, especially while in his own country and not in the country where the language is spoken, has an entirely different and infinitely more difficult problem to solve. A teacher is not at his elbow all the time ; the people around him do not speak the language he wishes to learn ; and hearing and reading his own language all the time are powerful linguistic distractions which incessantly drive away the foreign language from his mind.

Ten Golden Rules. He must find ways and means of overcoming all these difficulties, and, without troubling with reasons or explanations, let him accept the following as golden advice resulting from very wide experience :

Fix upon a daily period for *concentrated* study : not less than half an hour nor more than one hour.

In that period, learn at least one rule of grammar and at least 10 new words ; or, alternatively, go over what has been already studied and is not yet fixed in the memory.

Devote one period a week to revision.

Once every four weeks re-read all that has been done, from the very beginning.

Attach more importance to the memorizing of words than to grammar. Keep a notebook with all new words printed in block letters (capitals), and without their English equivalents, to compel the memory to work and bring to mind the meanings.

In the course of everyday life do little mental exercises in the foreign language. For example, when in a sitting room look around at the different objects and try to bring to mind the words for them. Say to yourself in the foreign language 'What is this ?' and answer 'This is a table' ; or, 'What is that ?' and answer 'That is a chair' ; or, 'What colour is this ?' and answer 'It is blue.' As time goes on, make questions and answers a little more difficult. For example : 'What kind of chair is this ?' and answer, 'This is a very comfortable wooden chair with a yellow cushion, and is usually placed near the window.' And so on. This teaches you to think in the language, without translating.

When the numbers have been learnt, do little sums in the foreign language. Two and two make four ; six and six make twelve ; three times three make nine. And so on.

When learning a new word, if possible bring to mind a picture of the object. Thus, when learning the word for pencil, form a mental picture of a pencil ; or better still, have one and look at it while learning the word, when that can be done.

Learn words both ways. Thus, in French, *Un livre*, a book. A book, *un livre*.

It is desirable in the first few weeks to write out the foreign text of the exercises, or of some of them, as this also helps to fix words and grammar in the mind. But after five or six weeks try to make the memory retain all the grammar and words in them, without having recourse to writing.

Make your language a hobby, something that is not a task but an interesting, intellectual game which, if you want to play it seriously, requires some effort and attention. You cannot learn to play cricket or tennis, bridge or chess with anything but amateurish competence unless you take them fairly seriously, especially in the early stages, and, when possible, observe the results achieved by skilled exponents. This also applies to learning a foreign language.

The 'Gift of Tongues.' You often hear that Mr. So-and-So has the 'gift of tongues,' and you may suspect that you have not. There is nothing mystical about those people for whom it is claimed that they have the 'gift of tongues.' Investigate, and you will invariably find that they have devoted considerable care and concentration to study while in the learning stage. They are probably no more intelligent than you.

Remember that the language you are learning is more than just a series of rules and lists of words ; that it is a living instrument of human thought, the key to the psychology of a people, and a gateway to their literature. Knowing it, you can talk to the foreigner, read his newspapers and books, appreciate his theatre, listen to his radio—in fact, do everything you can do with your own language. Grammar and vocabulary are unavoidable 'mechanics' of language—parts which, like those of a clock, will work when assembled correctly but which, separate and unassembled as we meet them in the learning stage, may seem dull and uninteresting.

To learn a foreign language does not demand some curious kind of super-intelligence or gift. But it does demand work, patience, and perseverance. If your language-study is treated in a friendly way, as a hobby, and not as some dry-as-dust drudgery, then the more interest you have in it the quicker you will progress. You can learn at *any* age : men have learnt new languages at over seventy years of age so well as to be able to translate books from them. Persist, persist, persist !

The First of All Rules. If the above ten commonsense rules are observed, the student can hardly fail to make progress. There must be one rule overriding all others : Never let a day pass without doing something with the language—learning ten new words, one rule of grammar, reading or revision. If, by some circumstance, a day has been missed, then devote double time to the language for two days following. The reason is that at all costs the mind and memory must be kept 'in training' in the

new and still strange medium, until they are fully accustomed to it.

Do you remember how Robinson Crusoe taught his man Friday English ? If not, look it up. You will find that in a short time Friday was expressing himself (in bad English) and understanding. He got along —and quite nicely. Now, take to heart the lesson of Crusoe and Friday, and make up your mind that it does not matter in the least whether or not you make mistakes in grammar, so long as you can express what you want to express. Few foreigners are likely to cut you dead just because you make mistakes of grammar ! They often make them themselves.

The Englishman as Linguist. The record of the Englishman is one of far too much self-consciousness and shyness, and the story has got about that he is a ' bad linguist.' Absolute nonsense. The Englishman is no worse and no better a linguist than anybody else, but he does tend to be too self-conscious. You must shed all that from the outset, and make up your mind that, however you do it, you are going to express yourself in the foreign tongue. Far better to be able to do what Friday did, than nothing at all. And, with a little patience and perseverance, the Friday stage will be passed. You must strive hard to get to the stage at which you can read the foreign language slowly and understand what is read. With practice, easy reading will come. And, when you have reached the easy reading stage, your worst obstacles are passed. You have reached the stage of enjoyment and enter a vast new world.

Do not worry too much about accent, so long as you are understood. Time will correct it, if you just watch it. As soon as you can read with ease, begin to listen to radio in the foreign language. At first, you may not understand much. Again, perseverance and patience will win the day. Speaking follows, but only by practice, for preference with natives.

You may think from what has been said above that you face a difficult if not almost impossible task. Not at all. It seems difficult, because it has been analysed in some detail. But all this analysis is merely intended to put you on what experience has shown to be the right track—right from the beginning, and therefore in the long run the easiest, the most rapid and most productive of good results. With patience, it is possible to achieve a workaday knowledge of several foreign languages.

LESSON ONE

Essentials and Pronunciation

THIS Course consists of fifteen lessons, each of which should take the learner who is without a teacher from one week to ten days, assuming that he devotes not less than half an hour daily to study. For self-tuition an hour daily is advisable ; but never less than half an hour. On this basis, the Course can be mastered in from four to six months. With a teacher, much more rapid progress can be expected. A teacher should be found to help with pronunciation in the first few lessons, for good French pronunciation cannot be learnt from any book. It can only be acquired by ear from French people.

The beginner must be warned of something which has been (and no doubt will always be) a very common experience among language students. From time to time he may develop impatience and dissatisfaction with the progress he is making. He 'cannot see daylight' in what he is doing. But he must not be dismayed, for a language is like a clock, in that it will not 'work' until the parts have been assembled—of course, in the case of a language, mentally assembled ; in other words, until he has mastered and memorized what is put before him in the course of his lessons.

Experienced teachers agree that, when a moment comes at which the student feels that he is 'up against a brick wall,' the best thing to do is to revise what has gone before, and temporarily, for a week or so, to abandon the desire to start a new lesson.

Hasten slowly, is a very good principle in language learning ; and no day need be considered wasted if one rule and twenty new words have been learnt. It is most important to *learn something new every day*, or never to let a day pass without application to the language, even if it be only in revision. In the learning phase, a few days' slacking means that much will fade from memory and have to be begun almost afresh.

A notebook that can be carried in the pocket should be used from the beginning. Write down difficult rules and words and, in leisure moments, refer to them again and again. This is a golden rule—one that should be taken to heart.

Reading French. One other word of advice is necessary. From the outset, aim to read French first, especially if you have no teacher. Speaking and understanding follow rapidly when opportunities for them occur—and in these days of radio there need be no lack of opportunities for listening to French. If the language as written or spoken can be understood, speaking is merely a matter of practice.

Once the student has progressed to the stage of reading a book in French—and it can undoubtedly be achieved by any persistent person of average intelligence— the wonderful vista of French literature appears. Then, all the humdrum work and drudgery are rewarded many times over. Contact will have been established with great minds ; the variety of French literature is infinite ; and a wonderful culture is there to be explored.

Basic Requirements. This Course is essentially scientific, being based upon the latest advances in the selection and presentation of grammar and words that are absolutely essential, whatever the purpose may be for which the language is studied. Nothing that is given in these pages must be neglected, for it is the practical minimum required.

At the end of the Course some advice will be found for further study, and suggestions for reading. With very little extra reading and practice, the student who has mastered the lessons of this short Course will have reached matriculation standard, and need have no fear but that the knowledge acquired will be sufficient for all the purposes of everyday life.

Accents and Pronunciation. The letters of the alphabet are the same as in English.

There are **Three Accents** :

(´) the **acute,** (`) the **grave,** (^) the **circumflex,** which are placed over vowels (but not over capital letters) to distinguish sounds and meanings.

There is also (¨) the **diaeresis,** to show that two vowels coming together are pronounced separately (Noël, Christmas).

The **cedilla** (ç) is used when c must be pronounced **ss,** before **a, o, u,** as in **façade.** (The letter c is otherwise pronounced as k before these vowels.)

All words are *stressed* on the *last syllable*. (This is a most important rule.)

Vowels. The vowel sounds in French are pure. They are to be pronounced as indicated below (but see the warning Note at the end of this Lesson).

A like English **a** in father.

E „ „ e in demolish ; it is *silent* at the end of a word.

I or Y „ ee

O like „ o in mote.

U like Scotch guid—it has no equivalent in English. Say 'ee' with lips rounded and protruded.

OE, EU like u in burn.

OU like oo in moot.

Nasal vowels and OE, EU, Â are *long* when they are accented and followed by one consonant (or more).

All vowels are long if followed by final -ve, -se, -ge, -ble, -re. Vowels are short when followed (in the spelling) by a double consonant, or in an unaccented syllable.

ê is pronounced rather like ⎫
è „ „ ⎬ e in get
é „ „ ⎭ i in fit.

ai, ay and ei are pronounced like è long (where).

eau, au are pronounced like o (English oh, pure)

oi is pronounced like **wa** in water (oiseau, bird, is *wahzo*).

Other diphthongs follow the sounds of their simple vowels ; huile, *oil*, is pronounced almost like Scotch 'weel.'

Nasals. There are four simple nasal vowels, and they are shown in the spelling. When a vowel letter is followed, *in the same syllable*, by one m or n, e.g. **tant, en, emprunt,** the n's and m's are nasal vowels, but not in **ami** (which is a-mi) nor **comme** (not unlike English come).

a or e *followed by* m or n makes a nasal.

i „ y „ „ „ „ „
o „ „ „ „ „ „
u „ „ „ „ „ „

The pronunciation of French nasals must be acquired from a native by careful imitation. They have not even approximate equivalents in English.

Consonants. Unless mentioned below, consonants are pronounced the same as in English. Note the following special pronunciations :

CH is like *sh* in English.

-ER and -EZ at the end of words are like é.

-TION is like English *see-on* (last syllable nasal).

-STION is like English *stee-on* (last syllable nasal).

J is like English s in *pleasure.*

G *before* e *and* i is like J above, otherwise as in English go.

H is *always silent.*

S between vowels is like English z.

-ILL, -IL like English -y in Yes, except in ville, tranquille and mille, where it rhymes with eel, veal, etc.

-Y- between vowels as -y in English yes.

C *before* e, i, y, like ss.

Ç like English ss.

GN is like *gn* in mignonette or *ni* in onion.

GU is like g in go, get.

QU is like k.

TH is like t.

R should be strongly sounded (*i.e.* vibrated, as in Scotch 'braw, bricht').

-ISME is pronounced -*issme*.

W is like English v (wagon, pronounced *vagon*, last syllable nasal).

-ENT in *third person plural* of verbs is *silent.*

Liaison. A *Final Consonant* is generally silent in French, but it is pronounced and carried on as if it were part of the next word when this next word begins with a vowel or an h mute. To justify liaison or linking, there must be a logical connexion between the two words.

In liaison, s, x, z are pronounced like z : p is sounded only in **trop.**

There is *never* liaison with the word for *and*, et.

NOTE.—The English equivalents for pronunciation given above are **makeshifts.** Strictly, every letter in French and every combination of letters should be regarded as representing a sound or sounds quite distinct from any English sounds. Listen to French records, wireless broadcasts, and follow the speaker, mimicking exactly the pronunciation : this will give facility in making the sounds. Good French pronunciation can be learnt only by listening to native speakers.

EXERCISE

Now turn to the facing page and read to yourself slowly in accordance with the above rules the French words given, making certain that your pronunciation follows closely the rules given above.

LESSON TWO

The Definite and Indefinite Articles

IN this Lesson we shall study the definite and indefinite articles, their method of use and contractions ; also the few occasions when they are omitted in French and used in French though not in English. It is a rule that an article must precede every French noun despite a small number of exceptional cases.

The words the and a are called *articles*, the former the *definite*, the latter the *indefinite*, article.

The Definite Article. For *the*, the equivalents are :

LE before a masculine noun.
LA before a feminine noun.
LES before all nouns in the plural.

LE and LA become L' before words beginning with a vowel or h mute. Examples :

le père, *father.*   la mère, *mother*
les pères et les mères, *fathers and mothers.*
l'amour, *love.*   l'hiver, *winter.*

Used with the prepositions à *to* and de *of*, the following contractions are made :

AU takes the place of à le (but use à l' before a vowel or h mute).
DU takes the place of de le (but de l' before a vowel or h mute).
AUX and DES are used always in the plural.

NOTE.—To express the *possessive case* : '*The friend's name*' becomes '*The name of the friend*'—Le nom de l'ami, etc.

Use the article to express *parts of the body* and for *faculties* : J'ai levé la main, *I raised* MY *hand*, etc. Also, before names of *countries* and *seasons*, but not after en, *in*.

DU, DE L', DE LA and DES are used to express *some*, and are repeated before each noun :

Avez-vous du pain, de l'eau et des pommes ? *Have you* (*some*) *bread,* (*some*) *water and* (*some*) *apples?*

DE is used without the article when an adjective precedes the noun, or when it is part of *adverbs of quantity,* such as trop de, *too much,* peu de, *little* : plein de, *full of* : une foule de, *a crowd of.*

Or in negative sentences. Examples :

Nous avons de bons amis, *We have good friends*
Il fait trop de bruit, *He makes too much noise*
Nous avons peu de vin, *We have little wine*
Nous n'avons pas de vin, *We have no wine*

Bien de, *much, many,* always takes the article : Bien des choses, *many things,*

Bien du mal, *much evil, badness.* But Beaucoup de, with the same meaning, does not : beaucoup de pain, *much bread.*

Omit the Article before cent, *a hundred,* mille, *a thousand,* before names of towns and small islands, and before words preceded by avec, *with,* de, *made of,* en, *in,* and par, *by* :

cent francs, *a hundred francs*
avec plaisir, *with pleasure*
nous irons à Paris, *we shall go to Paris*
une chaise de bois, *a wooden chair*
en Angleterre, *in England*
par coeur, *by heart*

The Indefinite Article. Used as follows :

Un before masculine nouns : un homme, *a man.*
Une before a feminine noun : une femme, *a woman.*
Plural des, *some* : des hommes, des femmes, *some men, some women.*

The indefinite article is omitted when stating a nationality, rank, profession or calling :

I am a doctor, Je suis médecin, docteur.
He is an Italian, Il est italien.
He is a captain, Il est capitaine.

EXERCISE ON ARTICLES

L'article précède le nom.
The article precedes the noun.

Le nord de la France est très plat.
The North of France is very flat.

Paris est la capitale de la France.
Paris is the capital of France.

Demandez-le au (à +le) *facteur ou aux* (à +les) *employés là-bas.*
Ask (it to the) the postman or the officials over there.

Donnez-moi du (de +le) *pain, de l'eau, de l'huile et de la crème, s'il vous plaît.*
Give me (some) bread, (some) water, (some) oil and (some) cream, please.

Il y a beaucoup de monde sur la place.
There are many people *in* the square.

Voici un homme qui veut vous parler.
Here is a man who wants to speak to you.

C'est un film très joli : c'est une pièce amusante. Ce sont des spectacles qu'il ne faut pas manquer.
This is a very fine film ; it is an amusing play. These are shows which you should not miss.

L'honnête homme n'a qu'une parole.
The honest man keeps his word.

Elle a acheté bien des choses ce matin.
She bought a lot of things this morning.

Contractions of the Definite Article

La France est limitée *au* nord par la Manche et
France is bounded on the North by the Channel
and

le Pas-de-Calais : *au* nord-est, par la Belgique
the Straits of Dover : on the North-East by
Belgium

et le Luxembourg : *à l'*est par l'Allemagne et
and Luxemburg ; on the East by Germany and

la Suisse. *Au* sud-est, la chaîne des Alpes
Switzerland. In the South-East, the Alpine range

la sépare de l'Italie : *au* sud, ses côtes sont
separates her from Italy ; in the South, her
shores are

baignées par la Méditerranée : les Pyrénées la
washed by the Mediterranean ; the Pyrenees
then

séparent ensuite de l'Espagne. *Au* sud-ouest et
separate her from Spain. On the South-West and

*à l'*ouest, elle est limitée par l'Océan Atlantique.
on the West, she is bounded by the Atlantic
Ocean.

Omission of the Article

Je crois que vous avez raison.
I think you're right.

N'ayez pas peur.
Don't be afraid.

Nous irons en Angleterre par avion
We'll go to England by plane.

Il travaille avec soin.
He works carefully.

Je les ai vus par hasard.
I saw them by chance.

Marseille, grand port de France, est situé près
des bouches du Rhône.
Marseilles, *a* great port of France, is situated
near the delta of the Rhône.

On vient de le nommer ambassadeur *en* Espagne
He has just been appointed ambassador to
Spain.

Prenez garde de ne pas prendre froid.
Take care not to catch cold.

Definite Article Not Used in English.

Le printemps et *l'*été sont les saisons que je
préfère.

Spring and Summer are the seasons that I
prefer.

La vertu sera récompensée : *le* vice sera puni.
Virtue shall be rewarded : vice shall be
punished.

L'Angleterre et *la* France sont séparées par la
Manche.
England and France are separated by the
Channel.

Le Havre est le grand port de *la* Normandie.
Havre is the great port of Normandy.

Je vais le voir tous *les* samedis.
I go and see him every Saturday.

L'Amiral Nelson fut le héros de Trafalgar.
Admiral Nelson was the hero of Trafalgar.

Cet artiste joue *le* Bach à merveille.
This artist plays Bach marvellously.

General

Jean est le nom de mon ami.
John is my friend's name.

Le livre de mon père est sur la table.
My father's book is on the table.

Il prend le train de Londres tous les matins.
He takes the London train every morning.

J'ai trop de pain, mais je voudrais encore de
l'eau, s'il vous plaît.
I have too much bread, but I would like more
water. please.

Ne vous donnez pas tant de mal, je porterai
cette lettre en revenant de mon bureau.
Don't take so much trouble, I will deliver this
letter on my way back from the office.

M. (Monsieur) Dupont habite Lyon avec sa
famille : sa femme, Mme. (Madame)
Dupont,
Mr. D. lives in Lyons with his family : his wife,
Mrs. D.,

leurs enfants, ses soeurs, Mlles (Mesdemoiselles)
Jeanne et Marie, et sa grand'mère, Mme
Dupont-Villiers.
their children, his sisters, the Misses Jean and
Mary D., and his grandmother, Mrs.
D.-V.

M. Dupont est comptable chez MM. A et Cie,
marchands de charbon en gros.
Mr. D. is an accountant at Messrs. A and Co..
wholesale coal merchants.

LESSON THREE

Genders and Numbers of Nouns

HERE we consider French nouns, their
genders and numbers, with the
rules for their proper use. Examples
are given and the principal exceptions are
noted.

A noun is a word used for naming some
person or *thing*.

There are TWO GENDERS for French
nouns : masculine and feminine.

And TWO NUMBERS : singular and plural.

Gender.—There is only one rule of gender
which may be said to be without exceptions :
that the names of *men* and *male* animals

are *masculine* and the names of *women* and *female animals* are *feminine.*

Examples

le père, *the father*	le bélier, *the ram*
la mère, *the mother*	la brebis, *the sheep* (*ewe*)
le roi, *the king*	le chien, *the dog*
la reine, *the queen*	la chienne, *the bitch*

NOTE. This rule only applies where there are different words for each sex, otherwise, as in English, an animal is regarded arbitrarily as male or female :

> le rat, *the rat* (m. or f.)
> la souris, *the mouse* (m. or f.)

Hints Worth Noting

Masculine are : Names of trees, shrubs, seasons, months, days, colours, metals
nouns ending with a consonant
nouns ending with any vowel except -e mute
nouns ending with -ment, -age, -ège
the decimal weights and measures
other parts of speech when used as nouns.

Feminine are : Most nouns ending in -e mute
nouns ending in -té, -son, -ion
names of moral qualities, sciences and arts
names of qualities or states ending in -nce, -esse, -eur, -ade, -ude. Exception : le silence, *silence.*

Double Genders

un aide, *a helper*	une aide, *help*
un livre, *a book*	une livre, *a pound*
un poste, *a position*	une poste, *a post*[2]
un souris, *a smile*[1]	une souris, *a mouse*
un tour, *a turn*	une tour, *a tower*
un vapeur, *a steamer*	la vapeur, *steam*

[1]Rarely used. Say un sourire.
[2]bureau de poste=*post office.*

The Plural of Nouns.—The general rule is that the plural of all nouns is formed by adding -s to the singular—a ' silent ' s, sounded only in liaison.

Examples

Le baiser, *the kiss*   Les baisers, *the kisses*

Exceptions

Nouns ending in -s, -x, -z do not change.
Nouns in -u add -x.
Nouns in -ail, -al change these endings into -aux.

Examples

le fils, *the son*	le chapeau, *the hat*
les fils, *the sons*	les chapeaux, *the hats*
la voix, *the voice*	l'hôpital, *the hospital*
les voix, *the voices*	les hôpitaux, *the hospitals*
le nez, *the nose*	l'émail, *enamel*
les nez, *the noses*	les émaux, *enamels*

And remember :

le ciel, *the sky*	les cieux, *the heavens*
l'oeil, *the eye*	les yeux, *the eyes*

monsieur[1], MESsieurS[2].
madame, MESdameS
mademoiselle, MESdemoiselleS
[1]Pronounce : Me(r)sye(r), [2]Mésye(r).

The Feminine of Nouns. The general rule is to form the feminine of a noun by adding e.

Exceptions

Nouns ending in -eur change this into -euse.
Nouns in -teur (and not derived from Present Participles) change this into -trice.
Nouns in -x change it to -se.
Nouns in -f change it to -ve.

Nouns in -et, -en, -on, -ot, double the last consonant and add e.

Examples

un ami, *a friend* (m.)
une amie, *a lady friend*
un chanteur, *a singer* (m.) from chanter
une chanteuse, *a singer* (f.)
un instituteur, *a teacher* (m.)
une institutrice, *a teacher* (f.)
le boiteux, *the lame man*
la boiteuse, *the lame woman*
un veuf, *a widower*   un sot, *a fool* (m.)
une veuve, *a widow*   une sotte, *a fool* (f.)

A list of essential nouns will be found in Lesson 4 and a beginning should now be made of memorizing them. Learn *not fewer than ten daily.*

Note on Exercises. In all the exercises which follow, the student is advised first to work out in his mind the meaning of the French, covering the English text while so doing. When the French has become clear, he may then try to render the English into French. Once fully understood, the French must be read over again and again—until it has been almost memorized. Words not in the lists are occasionally introduced and should be learnt.

EXERCISE

The Feminine of Nouns

Mon ami est chanteur à l'Opéra, et sa femme est *danseuse* dans le ballet.
My friend sings at the Opera, and his wife dances in the ballet.

Après la mort du Roi *sa veuve* se retira dans ses propriétés.
After the King's death his widow retired to her estates.

La famille Dupont se compose, comme nous l'avons vu, du père, de la mère, du fils et de la fille, de deux soeurs et de la grand'-mère : quant à son grand-père, il était mort depuis trois ans.
The Dupont family is composed, as we have seen, of the father, the mother, the son and the daughter, two sisters and the grandmother ; as to his grandfather, he had died three years ago.

Pierre et Hélène sont le cousin et la *cousine* des enfants Dupont.
Peter and Ellen are cousins of the Dupont children.

Cette femme est docteur en médecine, et sa soeur est professeur : toutes les deux collaborent à différents journaux, et sont de fort bons écrivains.
This lady is *a* doctor, and her sister is *a* teacher ; both of them write in several papers, and are very good writers.
> (This is an instance of masculine professions recently adopted by women, for which there is no feminine form, although a form ' doctoresse ' is beginning to make its way into French.)

Le fermier aime son chien, qui garde ses moutons : la *fermière* aime sa *chatte*, qui garde la maison des souris et des rats.
The farmer loves his dog, which keeps watch over his sheep ; his wife loves her cat, which protects the house against mice and rats.

On dit que *la* reine Elizabeth était une *musicienne* de talent.
Queen Elizabeth was said to be a talented musician.

Mme. de Staël était *un auteur* célèbre par ses écrits politiques et littéraires.
Mme. de Staël was an author famous both for her political and her literary works.

Plural of Nouns

Sur la table il y a des *livres*, des *plumes*, des *journaux*.
On the table, there are books, pens, newspapers.

Les *fermes* de Normandie sont très pittoresques ;
The farms of Normandy are very picturesque :

elles ont des *toits* de paille, des fenêtres à volets de bois ;
they have thatched roofs, windows with wooden shutters ;

dans la cour des *pommiers* donnent de beaux *fruits* rouges ;
in the yard apple-trees yield beautiful red fruit ;

il y a aussi des *vaches*, des *chevaux*, des *moutons*, des *oiseaux* de basse-cour ;
there are also cows, horses, sheep, fowls (of the farm-yard) ;

les fermes sont généralement entourées d'*arbres*, pour les protéger des *vents* d'ouest.
the farms are generally surrounded with trees, to protect them from the west winds.

Le coiffeur dit : ' Au premier de ces *messieurs* ! '
The hairdresser says : ' Next gentleman, please ! '

Dans les trains express il y a souvent des *wagons-lits*.
In (the) express trains there are often sleeping-cars.

LESSON FOUR

The Essential Vocabulary of French

To express oneself for all practical purposes, fewer than 1,000 words which differ in French and English have to be memorized. In these lessons the vocabulary consists of 353 similar nouns and 427 dissimilar ; 126 similar adjectives and 120 dissimilar ; 156 verbs similar in the two languages and 174 dissimilar. To these are added 201 invariable words. This vocabulary, used in accordance with the grammar, will give a total working vocabulary of several thousand words.

Now, the 635 similar words can quickly be learnt ; the work of learning them is easy—a very slight obstacle.

The 721 words dissimilar in the two languages can be learnt—it has been ascertained—at a minimum rate of 10–30 per hour. After a few hours' practice up to about 50 can be memorized in an hour by an average student. Thus, the working vocabulary (and a *good* one !) can be mastered, if need be, in a very short time.

A vocabulary of essential words *well known* is much more than half the battle in learning any language.

Try to learn 20–30 words daily, but never fewer than ten.

ESSENTIAL NOUNS, OR NAMES OF THINGS

Section 1. Nouns which are alike or almost alike in French and English.

Section 2. Nouns which differ in the two languages.

Section 3. Days, months, seasons and countries.

Note.—Many thousands of nouns are the same in French and English, or almost identical in spelling. They can be recognized immediately in reading. But it is of the utmost importance that the French words which resemble the English for common objects and ideas should be on the tip of the tongue, and familiar to the ear. It is one thing to recognize **la bière** as the equivalent of BEER ; it is another thing to be able to think of **la bière** when ' beer' has to be expressed—or is offered.

Before proceeding to Section 2, the List of Nouns which are similar in form and usage should be mastered.   Then Section 2 will be found to be easier.

An image or idea of the thing should be present in the mind as each word is being memorized. This not only makes the process of learning more interesting, and therefore easier, but it **accustoms the learner to think in French.**

Thus, when **la brique** is being memorized, you must see in imagination a brick.   You must think of it as something not to be dropped.   And so on through the lists.

Know all the words both ways : un arbre, a tree ; a tree, un arbre. Know them by sight and by sound : and to pronounce without hesitation.

Section 1.   NOUNS SIMILAR IN FORM OR USAGE IN FRENCH AND ENGLISH

MASCULINE

un **acte**, *an act*
un **accord**, *agreement*
l'**air**, *air*
l'**ambassade**, *embassy*
l'**ambassadeur**, *ambassador*
l'**amusement**, *amusement*
un **agrandissement**, *increase*
un **animal**, *animal*
un **art**, *art*
un **automobile**, *motor car*
l'**automobilisme**, *motoring*
un **aide**, *a helper* ; **aide-médecin**, *assistant doctor*
un **arrêt**, *arrest, stopping place*
un **accident**, *accident*

MASCULINE

le **bébé**, *baby*
le **boeuf**, *beef, ox*
le **bifteck**, *beefsteak*
le **biscuit**, *biscuit*
le **bateau**, *boat, vessel*
le **bouton**, *button* (also *pimple*)
le **bureau**, *office*
le **bâton**, *stick*
les **bagages**, *luggage*

MASCULINE

le **corps**, *body, corps*
le **café**, *coffee, café*
le **capitaine**, *captain*
le **carburateur**, *carburettor*
le **cas**, *case*
le **chat**, *cat*
le **chèque**, *cheque*
le **commerce**, *commerce, business*
le **confort**, *comfort*
le **comité**, *committee*
le **cri**, *cry, shout*
le **contrôle**, *control, supervision*

MASCULINE

un **aérodrome**, *aerodrome*
un **autobus**, *omnibus*
un **avocat**, *lawyer (barrister)*

FEMININE

l'**addition**, *addition, bill*
une **adresse**, *address*
l'**approbation**, *approval*
l'**attention**, *attention*
l'**autorité**, *authority*
les **affaires**, *business*
une **assurance**, *insurance*
une **aide**, *assistance, help*
l'**attente**, *waiting (expectancy)*
l'**arche**, *arch*
une **armée**, *army*
l'**arrivée**, *arrival*

FEMININE

la **banque**, *bank*
la **base**, *base, basis*
la **bière**, *beer*
la **bicyclette**, *bicycle*
la **botte**, *boot*
la **bouteille**, *bottle*
la **brosse**, *brush*
la **boule**, *ball*
la **bande**, *band*
la **branche**, *branch*
la **brique**, *brick*

MASCULINE

le **coton**, *cotton*
le **crédit**, *credit*
le **crime**, *crime*
le **cigare**, *cigar*
le **cercle**, *circle*
le **col**, *collar*
le **coussin**, *cushion*
le **citron**, *lemon*
le **cinéma**, *cinema*
le **chauffeur**, *driver*
le **courant**, *current*
le **choc**, *shock*
le **commencement**, *beginning*
le **consul**, *consul*

MASCULINE

le **consulat**, *consulate*
le **cousin**, *cousin*
le **concert**, *concert*
le **compartiment**, *compartment (of a train)*
le **chef**, *chef, principal, head*

FEMININE

la **cabine**, *cabin*
la **conduite**, *conduct, behaviour*
la **carte**, *card*
la **cathédrale**, *cathedral*
la **couleur**, *colour*

MASCULINE

le **dictionnaire**, *dictionary*
le **danger**, *danger*
le **départ**, *departure*
le **degré**, *degree*
le **dessin**, *design, drawing*
le **désir**, *desire*
le **développement**, *development, expansion*
le **directeur**, *manager*
le **dîner**, *dinner*
le **domicile**, *home, domicile*
le **dommage**, *injury, wrong* (also *pity*)
le **doute**, *doubt*

MASCULINE

un **édifice**, *edifice*
un **essai**, *essay, trial*
l'**équilibre**, *balance, equilibrium*
un **effet**, *effect*
un **exemple**, *example*
un **expert**, *expert*
l'**effort**, *effort*
un **emploi**, *employment, occupation*
un **employé**, *clerk, employee*
un **étranger**, *stranger, foreigner*

FEMININE

la **compagnie**, *company*
la **condition**, *condition*
la **couverture**, *covering, blanket*
la **chambre**, *room*
la **conversation**, *conversation*
la **chaîne**, *chain*
la **cigarette**, *cigarette*
la **corde**, *cord, string*
la **chemise**, *shirt*
la **classe**, *class*
la **crème**, *cream*
la **commande**, *order, request*

FEMININE

la **discussion**, *discussion, argument*
la **danse**, *dance*
la **dette**, *debt*
la **destruction**, *destruction*
la **digestion**, *digestion*
la **direction**, *direction*
la **distance**, *distance*
la **douleur**, *pain, grief*
la **demande**, *demand, request*
la **déclaration**, *declaration, statement*
la **dame**, *lady*
la **douzaine**, *dozen*

MASCULINE

un **estomac**, *stomach*
un **étudiant**, *student*

FEMININE

une **éducation**, *education*
une **erreur**, *error*
une **existence**, *existence*
l'**érudition**, *learning*
une **enveloppe**, *envelope*
l'**essence**, *petrol*
une **éponge**, *sponge*
une **étude**, *study*
une **école**, *school*

Section 1. NOUNS SIMILAR IN FORM OR USAGE IN FRENCH AND ENGLISH (*continued*)

MASCULINE	FEMININE
le fonctionnaire, *functionary, official*	la forêt, *forest*
le front, *front, forehead*	la ferme, *farm*
le fruit, *fruit*	la fiction, *fiction*
le fracas, *smash*	la frontière, *frontier*
	la flamme, *flame*
	la figure, *face, form*
	la fleur, *flower*
FEMININE	la force, *force*
la famille, *family*	la forme, *form*

MASCULINE	MASCULINE
le gouvernement, *government*	le gaz, *gas*
le grain, *grain*	FEMININE
un guide, *guide* (*man and book*)	une gelée, *jelly*
	la graine, *seed*
le garage, *garage*	la grandeur, *size*
	la gorge, *throat*

MASCULINE	FEMININE
le hasard, *hazard, chance*	une histoire, *history, story*
un hôpital, *hospital*	une heure, *hour, o'clock*
un hôtel, *hotel, inn*	

MASCULINE	FEMININE
un indicateur, *railway time-table*	une idée, *idea*
un insecte, *insect*	une industrie, *industry*
un intérêt, *interest*	une invention, *invention*
	une instigation, *suggestion, instigation*
	l'instruction, *education*
	une île, *island*

MASCULINE	MASCULINE
le juge, *judge*	le kilomètre, *kilometre*
le journal, *newspaper*	le kilo, *kilo, kilogramme*
le jardin, *garden*	

MASCULINE	FEMININE
le liquide, *liquid*	la liaison, *connexion, link, friendship*
le litre, *litre*	la limite, *limit*
FEMININE	la liste, *list*
la lettre, *letter*	la lampe, *lamp*
la librairie, *bookshop*	la légation, *legation*

MASCULINE	FEMININE
le motif, *motive, cause*	la machine, *engine, machine*
le marché, *market*	la marque, *mark*
le métal, *metal*	la mesure, *measure*
le moteur, *engine (of a car*, etc.)	la mémoire, *memory*
le mécanicien, *mechanic, engineer*	la mine, *mine* (also *face, countenance*)
le marchand, *tradesman*	la minute, *minute*
le muscle, *muscle*	la montagne, *mountain*
le médecin, *doctor*	la multiplication, *multiplication*
le moment, *moment*	la musique, *music* (also *band*)
le ministre, *minister*	la matière, *matter, substance*
le mystère, *mystery*	la médecine, *medicine*
FEMININE	Madame, *Madam, Mrs.*
la mode, *fashion*	
la monnaie, *small change*	
la maladie, *illness*	

MASCULINE	FEMININE
le nerf, *nerve*	la nation, *nation*
le nom, *name*	la nécessité, *necessity*
le numéro, *number (in order)*	la note, *note*
le nombre, *number (total)*	

MASCULINE	FEMININE
un ordre, *order*	une offre, *offer*
	une opération, *operation*
FEMININE	une opinion, *opinion*
une odeur, *smell*	une organisation, *organization*
une offense, *offence*	une orange, *orange*
une observation, *observation*	

MASCULINE	FEMININE
le projet, *project, plan*	la partie, *part, section*
le propriétaire, *proprietor, owner*	la pâte, *paste, dough*
le papier, *paper*	la personne, *person*
le payement, *payment*	la place, *place, seat, square (in a town)*
le point, *point (also full stop)*	la plante, *plant*
le poison, *poison*	la pointe, *point (sharp end)*
le porteur, *porter*	la police, *police*
le produit, *product*	la position, *position*
le profit, *profit*	la prose, *prose*
le parent, *relation,* (plural) *parents*	la proportion, *rate, proportion*
le penchant, *slope, inclination, tendency*	la promenade, *promenade, walk*
le pot, *pot*	la punition, *punishment*
le pantalon, *trousers*	
le public, *public*	la parole, *word*
le passeport, *passport*	la plume, *feather, pen*
le plateau, *plateau, tray*	la pipe, *pipe*
le palais, *palace*	la poche, *pocket*
le prêtre, *priest*	la pompe, *pump*
le président, *president*	la planche, *plank*
le port, *port, harbour*	la pharmacie, *chemist's shop*
le plan, *plan (also map of a town)*	la poste, *post*
le paquet, *parcel*	la profession, *profession*
le pneu (*pneumatic) tire*	la paire, *pair*
FEMININE	la part, *part*
la propriété, *property*	la photo, *photograph*
la page, *page*	la prison, *prison*

MASCULINE	FEMININE
le quai, *quay, railway platform*	la qualité, *quality*
	la question, *question*
	la queue, *queue, tail*

MASCULINE	MASCULINE
le règlement, *regulation, adjustment*	le repos, *repose, rest*
le rond, *round*	le rythme, *rhythm*
le regard, *regard, look*	le rat, *rat*
le repas, *meal*	le reçu, *receipt*
le regret, *regret*	le radio, *wireless, radio*
le représentant, *representative*	le restaurant, *restaurant*
	le rapport, *report, record*

Section 1. NOUNS SIMILAR IN FORM OR USAGE IN FRENCH AND ENGLISH (*continued*)

FEMININE
la règle, *rule*
la répartition, *distribution*
la réaction, *reaction*
la raison, *reason, right*

FEMININE
la religion, *religion*
la rivière, *river*
la route, *road, route*
la république, *republic*
la rime, *rhyme*

MASCULINE
le télégramme, *telegram*
le téléphone, *telephone*
le tabac, *tobacco*

FEMININE
la théorie, *theory*
la table, *table*

MASCULINE
le sac, *bag*
le sentiment, *feeling*
le silence, *silence*
le soldat, *soldier*
le secrétaire, *secretary*
le sens, *sense*
le serpent, *snake*
le service, *service*

FEMININE
la science, *science*
la société, *society*
la soupe, *soup*
la scène, *scene*
la surface, *surface*
la serviette, *serviette, towel*

MASCULINE
l'usage, *use, usage*

FEMININE
une unité, *unit, unity*
une université, *university*

MASCULINE
le voyage, *voyage*
le vapeur, *steamer*
le vers, *verse*
le village, *village*

FEMININE
la vapeur, *steam*
la valeur, *value*
la vibration, *vibration*
la vue, *view*

MASCULINE
le tribunal, *law court*
le tarif, *scale*
le théâtre, *theatre, stage*

MASCULINE
le transport, *transport*
le tableau, *picture*
le train, *train*
le thé, *tea*

MASCULINE
le wagon, *carriage, car*

MASCULINE
le zéro, *zero, nought*
le zèle, *zeal*

FEMININE
la zone, *zone*

Section 2. NOUNS WHICH DIFFER IN THE TWO LANGUAGES

MASCULINE
un avion, *aeroplane*
un appareil, *apparatus, machine*
un ami, *friend*
un an, *year*
l'ascenseur, *lift, elevator*
un amour, *love*
l'argent, *silver, money*
(La monnaie is *small change*)
l'agent de police, *policeman*
l'acier, *steel*
un appui, *support*
un arbre, *a tree*
un anneau, *ring*

MASCULINE
le banc, *bench, form, seat*
le beurre, *butter*
le bouchon, *cork* ; (le tire-bouchon, *corkscrew*)
le bain, *bath*
le baiser, *kiss*
le brouillard, *mist*
le besoin, *need*
le bruit, *noise*
le billet, *ticket*
le billet de banque, *bank-note*
le but, *end, goal, aim*
le bouillon, *broth*
le bois, *wood*

MASCULINE
un après-midi, *afternoon*
un accroissement, *growth, enlargement, accretion*

FEMININE
une abeille, *bee*
une aiguille, *needle*
une assiette, *plate*
une araignée, *spider*
une aile, *wing*
l'actualité, *the present*
une allumette, *match (to light)*
une année, *year (duration)*

MASCULINE
le bas, *stocking*
le bras, *the arm*

FEMININE
la bougie, *candle*
la brume, *fog*
la bonne, *housemaid*
la baie, *berry*
une bibliothèque, *library*
la boîte, *box*
la bouche, *mouth*
une bouchée, *mouthful*
la bêche, *spade*
la boutique, *shop (small)*
la brûlure, *burn*
la boisson, *drink*

MASCULINE
le compte, *account*
le coup, *blow, stroke*
le coup de pied, *kick*
le cuivre, *copper*
le cuivre jaune, *brass*
le chou, *cabbage*
le charbon, *coal*
le concours, *competition (for a prize)*
le camion, *motor lorry*
le cuisinier, *cook*
le champ, *field*
le chômage, *unemployment*
le creux, *hollow*
le concierge, *hall porter*
le côté, *side*
le ciel, *sky, heaven*
les cieux, *heavens*
le choix, *choice*
le crayon, *pencil*
les ciseaux, *scissors*
le cuir, *hide, skin of an animal*
le clou, *metal nail*
le carré, *square (geom.)*
le caoutchouc, *rubber*
le cheval, *horse*
le chemin, *road*
le chemin de fer, *railway*
le coiffeur, *hairdresser*
le coin, *corner*
le cerveau, *brain (intellect, mind)*
le chien, *dog*
le cadre, *frame, picture*
le cheveu, *hair*

MASCULINE
le chapeau, *hat*
le cœur, *heart*
le crochet, *hook*
le congé, *leave*
le chaudron, *kettle, cauldron*
le couteau, *knife*
le cou, *neck*
le cochon, *pig*

FEMININE
la croyance, *belief*
la craie, *chalk*
la chaise, *chair*
la chair, *flesh*
la concurrence, *competition (in business, etc.)*
la courbe, *curve*
la chute, *fall*
la crainte, *fear*
la chaleur, *heat*
la connaissance, *knowledge*
la chanson, *song*
la chose, *thing*
la cire, *wax*
la cire à cacheter, *sealing-wax*
la croissance, *growth (abstract)*
la caserne, *barracks*
une cuiller, *spoon*
la consigne, *cloakroom, left luggage office*
une commande, *an order*
une côte, *coast, rib, hill*

Section 2. NOUNS WHICH DIFFER IN THE TWO LANGUAGES (continued)

FEMININE
la cuvette, *basin*
la cloche, *large bell*
la cervelle, *brains* (ana-tomical)
la charrette, *cart*
la corne, *horn*

MASCULINE
le dos, *back* (of the body)
le déjeuner, *lunch*
le débat, *discussion*
le petit déjeuner, *break-fast*
le drap, *cloth*
le drapeau, *flag*
le dégât, *damage*
le dégoût, *disgust*
le début, *start, begin-ning*
le doigt, *finger*

MASCULINE
un évêque, *bishop*
un exemplaire, *copy, sample*
un échantillon, *sample* (of merchandise, etc.)
un écrasement, *crush*
un endroit, *place*
un événement, *event*
un étage, *floor* (storey of a house)
l'esprit, *spirit, wit, mind*
un été, *summer*
l'enseignement, *teaching*
l'ennui, *trouble, annoy-ance, boredom*

MASCULINE
le frère, *brother*
un fait, *fact*
le fer, *iron*
le fer-blanc, *tin*
le frein, *brake*
le fromage, *cheese*
le fusil, *gun*
le four, *oven*
le fils, *son*
le fil, *thread*
le fil de fer, *wire*
le feu, *fire*
le fleuve, *large river*

FEMININE
la fille, *daughter, girl*

FEMININE
la clef, *key*
la charrue, *plough*
la chaussette, *sock*
la cuisine, *kitchen, cookery*
la colère, *anger*

MASCULINE
le doigt de pied, *toe*
le diable, *devil*
Dieu, *God*

FEMININE
la découverte, *discovery*
une dent, *tooth*
la douane, *Customs House*
la demoiselle, *girl*
la disparition, *disap-pearance*

MASCULINE
un éclat, *burst* (noise)
l'émail, *enamel*
l'escalier, *staircase*
un état, *state*

FEMININE
une espérance, *hope*
une empreinte, *print*
une épreuve, *proof*
une espèce, *species, kind, sort*
l'eau, *water*
l'écriture, *writing*
une église, *church*
une épingle, *pin*
une étoile, *star*
une encre, *ink*

FEMININE
la fin, *end*
la fumée, *smoke*
la femme, *woman* (pro-nounce *famme*)
la femme de chambre, *chambermaid*
la facture, *invoice, bill*
la fourmi, *ant*
la feuille, *leaf, sheet* (of paper), *blade of grass*
la fourchette, *fork*
la fenêtre, *window*
la fois, *time*
une fois, deux fois, *once, twice*

MASCULINE
le gérant, *business manager*
le garçon, *boy, waiter*
le genre, *sort, kind*
le goût, *taste*
le gâteau, *cake*
le gant, *glove*
le genou, *knee*
le guichet, *ticket win-dow*

MASCULINE
un homme, *man*
un hiver, *winter*
un habit, *coat*

MASCULINE
un impôt, *tax, rates*

MASCULINE
le jour, *day*
le jeu, *game*
le jambon, *ham*
le Juif, *Jew*

MASCULINE
le lavabo, *lavatory basin*
le lit, *bed*
le livre, *book*
le loisir, *leisure*
le linge, *made-up linen*
le lait, *milk*
le lieu, *place*
les légumes, *vegeta-bles, greens*

FEMININE
la livre, *pound*

MASCULINE
le montant, *amount, total*
le métier, *trade, busi-ness, vocation*
les moyens, *means*
les meubles, *furniture*
le morceau, *piece, lump*
le milieu, *middle, cir-cle, element*
le mois, *month*
le matin, *morning*
le marin, *sailor*
le mouton, *sheep*
le mari, *husband*
le mot, *word*

MASCULINE
les gages, *wages*
les gens, *people*

FEMININE
la glace, *ice*
la guerre, *war*
une goutte, *drop* (of water, etc.)
la grille, *railing*
la gare, *railway station*

FEMININE
l'herbe, *grass*
la haine, *hatred, hate*
l'haleine, *breath*
une huile, *oil*
la haie, *hedge*

FEMININE
la journée, *day* (dura-tion)
la jointure, *join, junc-tion*
la jambe, *leg*
la Juive, *Jewess*

FEMININE
la lutte, *struggle, fight, wrestling*
la langue, *tongue, lan-guage*
la loi, *law*
la lumière, *light*
la laine, *wool*
la lame, *blade* (of knife)
la laitue, *lettuce*
la lèvre, *lip*
la lune, *moon*
la lecture, *reading*

MASCULINE
le menton, *chin*
le marteau, *hammer*
le magasin, *store, large shop*
le mur, *wall*
le mouchoir, *handker-chief*
le maître, *master*
le maître d'hôtel, *head waiter*
Monsieur, *Sir, Mr.*

FEMININE
la morsure, *bite*
la mort, *death*

Section 2. NOUNS WHICH DIFFER IN THE TWO LANGUAGES (continued)

FEMININE
la moitié, *half*
la mer, *sea*
la mouche, *fly*
la main, *hand*
la maison, *house*
la muraille, *wall*

MASCULINE
le niveau, *level*
le nuage, *cloud*
le nœud, *knot*
le nez, *nose*
le navire, *ship*
le Noël, *Christmas*

MASCULINE
un oiseau, *bird*
l'or, *gold*
un os, *bone*
un oeuf, *egg*
un oeil, *eye;* les yeux, *eyes*

MASCULINE
le pain, *bread, loaf*
le petit pain, *roll of bread*
le pont, *bridge*
le pays, *country*
le partage, *division*
le père, *father*
le pli, *fold*
le plat, *flat, level*
le plaisir, *pleasure*
le pouvoir, *power, physical ability*
le prix, *price*
le pas, *step*
le faux pas, *slip, blunder*
le pourboire, *tip, gratuity*
le poids, *weight*
le poisson, *fish*
le panier, *basket*
le plancher, *floor*
le plafond, *ceiling*
le pied, *foot*
le poumon, *lung*

MASCULINE
le rire, *laughter*
le rayon, *ray*
le rhume, *cold (disease);* (être enrhumé, *to have a cold*)
le riz, *rice*

FEMININE
la montre, *watch, timepiece*
la matinée, *morning (duration)*
Mademoiselle, *Miss*
la mère, *mother*

FEMININE
la naissance, *birth*
la nourriture, *food, nourishment*
les nouvelles, *news*
la nuit, *night*
la neige, *snow*
la noix, *nut, walnut*

MASCULINE
un ongle, *finger (or toe) nail*
FEMININE
l'ouïe, *hearing*
une oreille, *ear*
une ombre, *shade, shadow*

MASCULINE
le parapluie, *umbrella*
le pardessus, *overcoat*
le poivre, *pepper*
le pouce, *thumb*
les Pâques, *Easter*
le peigne, *comb*
le poste, *position*

FEMININE
la pomme, *apple*
la pomme de terre, *potato*
la paille, *straw*
la poussière, *dust*
la peur, *fear*
la prise, *grip*
la perte, *loss*
la paix, *peace*
la peine, *punishment*
la pierre, *stone*
la pensée, *thought*
la porte, *door, gate*
la peau, *skin (of a person)*

FEMININE
la quinzaine, *fortnight*

MASCULINE
le rideau, *curtain*
le rabot, *plane (tool)*
le retour, *return*
le renseignement *information*
le roi, *king*

FEMININE
la racine, *root*
la rue, *street*
la roue, *wheel*

MASCULINE
le sang, *blood*
le soin, *care, attention*
le soulier, *shoe*
le siècle, *century*
le savon, *soap*
le secours, *help*
le singe, *monkey*
le saut, *jump*
le seau, *bucket*
le sel, *salt*
le sifflet, *whistle*
le sable, *sand*
le soir, *evening*
le soupir, *sigh*
le sucre, *sugar*

MASCULINE
le tiers, *third*
le tranchant, *cutting edge*
le trou, *hole*
le travail, *work, industry, labour*
le tas, *heap*
le tirage, *pull, towing* (also *circulation of a newspaper*)
le tonnerre, *thunder*
le temps, *time, weather*
le tour, *turn*
le taureau, *bull*
le tiroir, *drawer*
le tuyau, *drain-pipe, pipe*
le tort, *wrong, injury*
le trottoir, *pavement, sidewalk*
le trajet, *distance*

MASCULINE
le vol, *flight* (also *theft, robbery*)
le verre, *glass*
le versement, *payment (into the bank)*
le vernis, *polish, varnish*
le vent, *wind*
le vin, *wine*
le veston, *coat, jacket*
le vêtement, *garment*
le ver, *worm*

MASCULINE
le wagon-lit, *sleeping-car*
le wagon-restaurant, *dining-car*

FEMININE
la reine, *queen*
la remise, *commission*

MASCULINE
le sommeil, *sleep*
le sourire, *smile*
le soleil, *sun, sunshine*
le son, *sound*

FEMININE
la sonnette, *small bell*
la soie, *silk*
la semaine, *week*
la serrure, *lock*
la salle, *hall, room*
la salle à manger, *dining-room*
la santé, *health*
la soirée, *evening*

MASCULINE
le timbre, *stamp*
le toit, *roof*
le tapis, *carpet*

FEMININE
la toux, *cough*
la tante, *aunt*
la terre, *earth, land*
la tour, *tower*
la tasse, *cup*
la taille, *build, figure*
la toile, *linen (not made up)*
la tête, *head*
la tige, *stem*
la traite, *the draft (bank)*
la tranche, *slice, edge*
la tache, *stain, spot*
la tâche, *task*

FEMININE
la viande, *meat*
la voix, *voice*
la vague, *wave*
la voiture, *cab, car, vehicle, taxi*
la vingtaine, *score (twenty)*
la vache, *cow*
la volaille, *fowl*
la voile, *sail*
la vis, *screw*
la ville, *town, city*

Section 3. DAYS OF THE WEEK, MONTHS, SEASONS, COUNTRIES

Days of the Week

dimanche, *Sunday*   jeudi, *Thursday*
lundi, *Monday*   vendredi, *Friday*
mardi, *Tuesday*   samedi, *Saturday*
mercredi, *Wednesday*

Seasons

le printemps, *spring*   l'été, *summer*
l'automne, *autumn*   l'hiver, *winter*

Names of Countries

l'Angleterre, *England*
la Grande-Bretagne, *Great Britain*
le Royaume-Uni, *the United Kingdom*
les Etats-Unis, *the United States*
l'Amérique, *America*
la France, *France*
l'Allemagne, *Germany*
l'Italie, *Italy*
l'Espagne, *Spain*
la Russie, L'Union Soviétique, *Russia*

Months of the Year

janvier	juillet
février	août
mars	septembre
avril	octobre
mai	novembre
juin	décembre

The Disuse of Capital Letters in French

Capital letters are *not* used for days of the week, months of the year, national adjectives or personal titles. Il partira mardi. Le français est une langue assez difficile.

NOTE.—Je suis français, *I am French* (French is an adjective). L'Allemand, l'Anglais, *the German, the Englishman :* here Allemand and Anglais are nouns, and are written with capitals.

LESSON FIVE

Adjectives and Numbers

WE have dealt with definite and indefinite articles and the proper methods of their use and we have given the student a carefully selected vocabulary of essential nouns arranged in three sections. We next proceed to deal with the adjectives, their genders and numbers, comparisons and use with nouns. We then give a vocabulary of essential adjectives similar to the earlier one given for nouns, and an exercise makes clear the agreement of adjectives with nouns.

An adjective is a word used to describe the quality of a noun.

GENERAL RULE.—In French the adjective agrees in gender and number with the noun, and usually follows it : l'Académie française, *the French Academy*, les hommes sourds et muets, *the deaf and dumb men.*

Feminine of Adjectives. The feminine of an adjective is formed by adding -e mute ; those already ending in -e mute do not change.

Adjectives ending in -s, -l, -n, -t, double the last letter and add -e mute.

Those in -f change it to -ve.

,,	-x	,,	,,	-se.
,,	-eur	,,	,,	-euse.
,,	-eau	,,	,,	-elle.
,,	-g	,,	,,	-gue.
,,	-c	,,	,,	-que.
,,	-er	,,	,,	-ère.

Examples

exprès becomes in the feminine expresse
muet   ,,   ,,   ,,   muette
pareil   ,,   ,,   ,,   pareille
bon   ,,   ,,   ,,   bonne

NOTE WELL : beau, belle, *beautiful ;* nouveau, nouvelle, *new ;* fou, folle, *mad ;* mou, molle, *soft ;* vieux, vieille, *old ;* franc, franche, *free ;* blanc, blanche, *white ;* sec, sèche, *dry ;* doux, douce, *sweet ;* faux, fausse, *false ;* frais, fraîche, *fresh.*

The special masculine forms, vieil, bel, nouvel, fol and mol are used before nouns beginning with a vowel or an h mute.

Plural of Adjectives. The plural is formed by adding -s (silent) to the singular ; if this already ends in -s, there is no change.

Adjectives ending in -al change it to -aux in the masculine plural ; those in -eau add -x ; those in -x do not change in the masculine plural, but change -x to -ses in feminine plural.

Thus, égal, égaux, *equal*, heureux, heureuses (fem. plur.), *happy.*

NOTE.—bleu, bleus, *blue*, and tout, tous, toute, toutes, *all.*

Comparison of Adjectives

           1   2   3
Superiority :   plus (adjective) que *more ..than.*
               plus rouge que .. *redder than ..*

Inferiority :   moins (adjective) que *less .. than*
                  moins blanc que .. *less white*
                                        than ..

Equality :   aussi (adjective) que *as .. as.*
               aussi bleu que .. *as blue as ..*

Than before a number is always *de* ; plus
de trois, *more than three.*
Very : très, fort, bien.   Très bon, *very
good.*

le plus, le moins, *the most, the least.*
l'homme le plus brave, *the bravest man,* etc.

DISTINGUISH : bon, *good ;* meilleur,
better, le meilleur, *the best ;* mauvais, *bad ;*
pire, *worse,* le pire, *the worst* (also le plus
mauvais) ; petit has the forms moindre and
le moindre in addition to plus petit and le
plus petit.

From the adverbs : bien, *well ;* mieux,
better, le mieux, *the best ;* mal, *badly ;*
pis, *worse,* le pis, *the worst.*

NOTE.—beaucoup, *much ;* plus, *more,*

le plus, *most ;* peu, *little ;* moins, *less,*
le moins, *least.*

Adjectives Before the Noun. The following adjectives come *before* the noun (otherwise the adjective comes after) :

beau, *beautiful*   long, *long*
brave, *brave*   mauvais, *bad*
bon, *good*   méchant, *wicked*
cher, *dear, cherished*   meilleur, *better*
dernier, *last*   moindre, *less*
digne, *worthy*   petit, *little*
grand, *great, high, tall*   pire, *worse*
gros, *big, fat*   premier, *first*
haut, *high*   sot, *foolish*
jeune, *young*   vieux, *old*
joli, *pretty*   vilain, *ugly*

NOTE.—Un honnête homme, *an honest
man :* Un homme honnête, *a civil man.*
Le plus grand DU monde, *the greatest* IN THE
world.

Possessive Adjectives. My, your, his,
etc., are treated under pronouns.

Vocabulary—Essential Adjectives

Section 1. ADJECTIVES SIMILAR IN FORM OR USAGE IN FRENCH & ENGLISH

acide, *acid*
automatique, *automatic*
aimable, *kind*
avide, *greedy*

brillant, *bright*
brun, *brown*
blond, *fair*
blanc, *white*

capable (de), *able*
chimique, *chemical*
clair, *clear, light* (of
    colours), *bright*
complexe, *complex,
    complicated*
complet, *complete*
compliqué, *complicated*
cruel, *cruel*

dépendant (de), *depen-
    dent (upon)*
direct, *direct*
demi, *half*
délicat, *delicate*
différent, *different*

élastique, *elastic*
électrique, *electric*
égal, *equal*
étrange, *strange*

fertile, *fertile*
fixe, *fixed*
faible, *feeble*
fatigué, *tired*
femelle, *female*

actif, *active*
absent, *absent*
agréable, *agreeable*

bleu, *blue*
banal, *commonplace*
brave, *brave*

calme, *quiet*
certain, *certain*
convenable, *suitable*
commun, *common, or-
    dinary*
curieux, *curious*
charmé (de), *charmed
    (with)*
contraire (à), *opposite
    (to)*

délicieux, *delightful*
double, *double*
désagréable, *unpleas-
    ant*

drôle, *droll, odd*

extraordinaire, *extra-
    ordinary*
extrême, *violent*
exact, *exact*
élevé, *raised, exalted*

ferme, *firm, solid, hard*
futur, *future*
fameux, *famous*
frais, *fresh*
fin, *fine, delicate*

général, *general*
grand, *great*
gros, *coarse, bulky,
    stout*

humide, *damp*

important, *important*
inquiet (de), *uneasy
    (with)*

juste, *exact, right*

large, *wide*

maladroit, *clumsy*
mâle, *male*
masculin, *masculine*
marié, *married*
matériel, *material*

natural, *natural*
nécessaire, *necessary*

ordinaire, *common*

profond, *deep*
parallèle, *parallel*
passé, *past*
physique, *physical*
politique, *political*
possible, *possible*
privé, *private (intimate)*
particulier, *private (in-
    dividual)*

rouge, *red*
régulier, *regular*
rond, *round*
rude, *rough*

grave, *serious*
gentil, *nice, pleasant,
    kind*
grossier, *rude, vulgar*

international, *interna-
    tional*

long, *long* (of distance)

médical, *medical*
militaire, *military*
mortel, *mortal*
massif, *solid*
mystérieux, *mysterious*

normal, *normal*
naïf, *artless, naive*

présent, *present*
probable, *probable*
public, *public*
principal, *chief*
poli, *polished, polite,
    smooth*
plaisant, *pleasing,
    funny*
pur, *pure*

rapide, *quick (express,
    of trains, etc.)*
ridicule, *foolish*
rare, *rare, small*

Section 1. ADJECTIVES SIMILAR IN FORM OR USAGE IN FRENCH & ENGLISH (continued)

sage, *wise*
sauf, *safe*
second (deuxième), *second*
séparé, *separate*
sérieux, *serious (-minded)*
secret, *secret*

simple, *simple*
solide, *solid*
spécial, *special*
sûr, *certain, sure*
silencieux, *silent*
suspendu (à), *hanging (from)*

tardif, *slow*
tranquille, *quiet, peaceful, at rest*
uniforme, *equal, uniform*
uni, *united*
violent, *violent*

tendre, *tender*
troublé, *disturbed, uneasy*
utile, *useful*
unique, *unique*

Section 2. ADJECTIVES WHICH DIFFER IN THE TWO LANGUAGES

à part, *separate*
à venir, *future*
à bon marché, *cheap*
amer, *bitter*

aigu, *acute, sharp*
aveugle, *blind*
actuel, *present, contemporary*

mauvais, *bad, evil*
mort, *dead*
malade, *ill*
mêlé (de), *intermixed (with)*

mou, *soft*
malpropre, *dirty*
méchant, *wicked*
muet, *dumb*
mûr, *ripe*
maigre, *thin*

bouilli, *boiled*
bon, *good*
bas, *low*
brisé, *broken*

bête, *stupid, foolish*
boiteux, *lame*
beau (belle), *beautiful*
bienvenu, *welcome*

noir, *black*
nu, *naked*

nouveau, *new*

cassé, *broken*
coupé, *cut*
caché, *hidden*
collant, *sticky*
chaud, *hot*
courbé, *bent, curved*
cher, *dear*

en colère, *angry*
creux, *hollow*
chauve, *bald*
commode, *convenient*
croyable, *credible*
cru, *raw*

ouvert, *open*

propre, *clean*
plein (de), *full (of)*
pareil (à), *equal, similar (to)*
prêt (à), *ready (to)*

plat, *flat*
petit, *little, small*
puissant, *powerful*
pudique, *chaste, modest*

digne, *worthy*
droit, *right, straight*
dur, *hard*
doux, *sweet, quiet*
dernier, *last*

défendu, *forbidden*
délié, *loose*
défait, *undone*
disparu, *disappeared*

raide, *stiff*
rompu, *broken*

reconnaissant, *grateful*

épais, *thick*
éveillé, *awake*

étroit, *narrow*
estropié, *crippled*

semblable (à), *similar (to)*
sensible, *sensitive, tender*
sain, *healthy*
subit, *sudden, unexpected*
serré, *closed, tight*
sale, *dirty*

sec (sèche), *dry*
soigneux (de), *careful of, (to)*
sourd, *deaf*
seul, *alone*
salé, *salted*
sucré, *sweet*
sot, *foolish*

fâché contre, *angry with*
fâché de, en, que, *sorry for, to, that*
foncé, *dark* (of colours: bleu foncé, etc.)

fort, *strong, loud, violent,*
froid, *cold*
faux, *false, wrong, deceitful*
fier, *proud*

triste, *sad*
tranchant, *sharp, cutting*

tiède, *warm, lukewarm*
trompeur, *deceptive*
têtu, *obstinate, self-willed*

gras, *fat*
gris, *grey*

gauche, *left* (à la main gauche, etc.)

vivant, *living*
vif, *sharp, active, keen*
vrai, *true*
vert, *green*
vieux, *old*

vite, *swift, quick, speedy, rapid*
vide, *empty*
vilain, *ugly*
voisin (de), *neighbouring, next (to)*

haut, *high, tall* (of a building)
heureux, *happy*

à haute voix, *loud*
habile, *clever*

ingénu, *simple*

instruit, *educated*

jaune, *yellow*
jeune, *young*

joli, *pretty*

Adjectives of Nationality

libre, *free, loose*
lent, *slow*
lointain, *far*

lourd, *heavy*
léger, *light* (in weight ; *light* in colour is clair)

anglais, *English*
français, *French*
allemand, *German*
américain, *American*
chinois, *Chinese*

italien, *Italian*
espagnol, *Spanish*
russe, *Russian*
polonais, *Polish*
japonais, *Japanese*

même, *same*
mouillé, *wet, damp*

mélangé, *mixed (to a consistency)*

NOTE.—Adjectives of nationality are spelt with *small* letters in French.

EXERCISE ON AGREEMENT OF ADJECTIVES WITH NOUNS

Avant d'être comptable, M. Dupont était voyageur de commerce ;
Before being *an* accountant, Mr. D. was *a* commercial traveller ;

il était *jeune* alors, et très *bon* marcheur ;
he was young then, and *a* very good walker ;

il a pu voir ainsi presque *toute* la France :
he was thus able to see nearly the whole of France :

la Champagne et ses vignes *bleutées*,
the bluish vines of Champagne,

les villes du Nord avec leurs toits *pointus* et leurs églises *fameuses*,
the cities of the North with their pointed roofs and their *famous* churches,

Paris et ses cent merveilles toujours *variées*,
Paris and its hundred wonders, ever-varying,

les *longues* plaines de la Beauce,
the boundless plains of Beauce,

les ruines *romaines* de la Provence,
the Roman ruins of Provence,

les châlets *pittoresques* des Alpes,
the picturesque chalets of the Alps,

les côtes *rocheuses* de la Bretagne,
the rocky coasts of Brittany,

le bruit *charmeur* des vagues de la Manche sur des plages de sable *fin*.
the fascinating noise of the Channel waves on beaches of fine sand.

Une femme qui ne peut pas parler est *muette* ;
A woman who cannot speak is dumb ;

si elle ne peut pas entendre, elle est *sourde*.
if she cannot hear, she is deaf.

Si elle n'est plus *jeune*, elle est *vieille* ;
If she is no longer young, she is old ;

si elle a perdu la raison, elle est *folle*.
if she has lost her reason, she is mad.

Pauvre femme ! Parce qu'elle nous offre un exemple *commode* pour notre grammaire, nous la couvrons de calamités !
Poor woman ! Because she offers us a convenient example for our grammar, we heap calamities on her !

Elle est bien *bonne* de se laisser faire.
What a fool to allow herself to be treated thus!

NUMBERS

Cardinal Numbers

1 un, une	18 dix-huit
2 deux	19 dix-neuf
3 trois	20 vingt
4 quatre	21 vingt et un
5 cinq	22 vingt-deux
6 six	30 trente
7 sept	40 quarante
8 huit	50 cinquante
9 neuf	60 soixante
10 dix	70 soixante-dix
11 onze	80 quatre-vingts
12 douze	(-vingt-un, etc.)
13 treize	90 quatre-vingt-dix
14 quatorze	100 cent, cent un, etc.
15 quinze	1,000 mille, mille un, etc., deux mille
16 seize	
17 dix-sept	*A million,* un million

Six, pronounce **x** like ss, when the word comes alone.
Dix, pronounce **x** like ss, when the word comes alone.

Ordinals

1er premier, *first*		8e huitième	
2e deuxième, *second*		9e neuvième	
3e troisième, *third*		10e dixième	
4e quatrième, *fourth*		21e vingt et unième	
5e cinquième, *fifth, etc.*		31e trente et unième	
6e sixième		100e le centième	
7e septième		1,000e le millième	

Miscellaneous

une fois, *once*	le quadruple,
deux fois, *twice, etc.*	*quadruple, etc.*
le double, *double*	le demi-, *half-*
le triple, *treble*	la moitié de, *the half of*
le tiers, *third*	une centaine de,
le quart, *quarter*	*a hundred of*
la huitaine, *collection*	un huit jours, *a week*
of eight (also, *a week*)	il y a huit jours,
la dizaine, *collection*	*a week ago*
of ten	d'aujourd'hui en quinze
la douzaine, *the dozen*	(jours), *this day*
une quinzaine, *fortnight*	*fortnight*
une vingtaine, *score*	la semaine, *the week*
une paire de, *a pair of*	la semaine prochaine,
une couple, de, *a couple of*	*next week*
la plupart de, *most of*	la semaine dernière,
un grand nombre,	*last week*
a great number	

Different usage of numbers in French. Use cardinal numbers for : *Kings, dates, page, chapter,* and *verse*—excepting *premier* ;
Edouard VII. Le 10 mars. Chapitre vingt ; page soixante et un. Henri premier.

Time of Day.
Quelle heure est-il ? *What time is it ?*
Il est une heure, deux heures, minuit (midnight), midi (noon), cinq heures et quart, demi.
Il est six heures moins un quart.
Il est huit heures dix, quinze, etc.

Measurement.
Quelle est la longueur de cette chambre ?
Elle est longue de 10 mètres.
Haut[1] de, profond[2] de, épais[3] de.
Cette chambre a 20 mètres de long SUR 10 mètres de large.
[1] *high.* [2] *deep.* [3] *thick, broad.*

EXERCISE AND REVISION

Quel jour *sommes-nous* ? Mardi, le 10 (dix) Octobre.
What is the date today ? Tuesday, October 10th.

On célèbre en France la fête nationale *le 14* juillet, en souvenir de la prise de la Bastille, le *quatorze* juillet dix-sept cent quatre-vingt-neuf.
(The) National Day is kept in France on the 14th of July, in commemoration of the fall of the Bastille, on the 14th of July, 1789.

Deux *mille* hommes étaient présents à la cérémonie, jeudi dernier, 12 (*douze*) septembre, à trois heures de l'après-midi (à quinze heures).

Two thousand men were present at the ceremony, last Thursday, September the 12th, at three p.m.

Le roi François Ier (*premier*) fonda Le Havre en 1517.

King Francis the first founded Havre in 1517.

Henri IV (*quatre*) fut un roi populaire.

Henry IV was a popular king.

Nous partirons d'aujourd'hui en quinze.

We shall be leaving a fortnight today.

Galland publia en 1704 sa fameuse traduction des ' Mille et Une Nuits.'

Galland published in 1704 his famous translation of the 'Arabian Nights.'

Quelle heure est-il ? Midi et demi, exactement. Moi, je fais midi moins le quart. Votre montre *retarde* sans doute ? A moins que ce ne soit la vôtre qui *avance* . . . .

What time is it ? Half past twelve, precisely. *I* make it a quarter to twelve. Your watch is probably slow ? Unless it is *yours* which is fast. . . .

On affranchit une lettre à un franc vingt-cinq centimes.

The postage rate for a letter is Fr. 1,25.

J'ai dix-huit ans depuis hier. Bon anniversaire ! I was eighteen yesterday. Many happy returns!

Un billet *de* dix francs : un timbre *de* cinquante centimes : une pièce *de* vingt francs.

A ten franc note ; a fifty centime stamp ; a twenty franc piece.

Le français est une belle langue, avec une littérature riche et variée.

French is a fine language, with a rich and varied literature.

On le parle, en dehors de la France et de son Empire colonial, dans une partie de la Belgique (Bruxelles) et de la Suisse (Genève), au Canada, dans les Antilles (Haïti, la Martinique), aux Nouvelles-Hébrides.

It is spoken, outside France and her colonial Empire, in (a) part of Belgium (Brussels) and of Switzerland (Geneva), in French Canada, in the West Indies, and in the New Hebrides.

M.M. Meillet et Cohen écrivent : ' Le français est parlé par les gens cultivés de nombreux pays dans l'Europe centrale et sud-orientale, en Egypte et en Asie Mineure.'

Mr. M. and Mr. C. write : 'French is spoken by the educated classes of many countries in Central and South-Eastern Europe, in Egypt and in Asia Minor.'

C'est la langue officielle d'environ 100,000,000 de personnes, dont 48,000,000 la parlent comme langue maternelle.

It is the official language of about 100,000,000 people, 48,000,000 of whom speak it as their mother tongue.

Place of Adjectives

Ce chapeau est neuf : cette robe est *neuve*. Ces deux objets sont *neufs*, par conséquent.

This hat is new ; this gown is new. These two things are new, therefore.

C'était un petit homme, *vieux* et *sale*, qui portait un veston *noir* et un chapeau *mou décoloré*.

He was a dirty little old man, wearing a black jacket and a discoloured soft hat.

Il allait *nu-tête*, un *gros* sac *jaune* sous le bras *gauche*, et le *vieux* chien *fidèle* suivait . . .

He went bare-headed, a big yellow bag under *his* left arm, and the faithful old dog followed. . . .

'La *jeune* fille aux yeux *bleus*' est le titre de son *dernier* tableau.

'Girl with blue eyes' is the title of his last picture.

Tous les hommes sont égaux devant la loi.

All men are equal before the law.

Cet appartement est très confortable : les pièces en sont grandes et claires.

This flat is very comfortable : the rooms are big and light.

La rue est tranquille, et propre.

The street is quiet, and clean.

Il y a un jardin public tout près, où le petit Jacques peut jouer *toute* la journée.

There is a public garden close by, where little Jim can play all day long.

Paris a *plus* d'habitants *que* Lyon, mais *moins que* Londres.

Paris has more inhabitants than Lyons, but less than London.

Londres, capitale de l'Angleterre, est *la plus* grande ville du monde.

London, *the* capital of England, is the greatest city *in* the world.

La grammaire française est *plus* difficile *que* la grammaire anglaise.

(The) French grammar is more difficult than (the) English grammar.

Cette pièce est *plus* longue *que* large.

This room is longer than it is wide.

Jean est *plus* grand *que* vous.

John is taller than you.

J'en ai une, et vous en avez trois : c'est vous *qui* en avez *le plus*.

I have one (of them), and you have three : it is you who have the most.

Ce vin n'est peut-être *pas aussi* fameux *que* celui-là, mais il est *aussi* bon, et *moins* cher.

This wine is perhaps not as famous as that one, but it is just as good, and less expensive.

Irregular Comparison of Adjectives

Avec ce garçon il faut s'attendre au *pire*. From this boy one must expect the worst.

Il ne faut pas la punir ; elle a fait de son *mieux*. You must not punish her ; she did her best.

Ses affaires allaient de mal en *pis*. His business was going from bad to worse.

Practice on Pronouns (*page* 539)

Je suis étudiant ; *mon* nom est Robert. Mon père est docteur. *Ma* mère n'a pas de profession, mais elle aide mon père, et s'occupe de la maison : *mes* deux frères vont encore à l'école.

I am *a* student ; my name is Robert. My father is *a* doctor. My mother has no profession, but she helps my father, and looks after the house ; my two brothers are still going to school.

Ils y vont à bicyclette, car *elle* se trouve à deux kms. (kilomètres) de chez nous. Mon père n'en est pas fâché, cela *leur* donne de l'exercice. Je *me* lève en même temps qu'*eux*, et ils m'accompagnent jusqu'à la gare, où je prends le train de Paris à 8 h. 57.

They go there on their bicycles, for it is 2 kms. (=roughly 1 mile) from home. My father does not mind that, it is good exercise for them. I get up at the same time as they do, and they accompany me as far as the station, where I take the 8.57 to Paris.

Avez-vous lu ce livre ? *Ai-je* encore le temps de . . . ? *A-t-il* regardé s'il y avait des lettres ? *Iront-ils* à Deauville cette année ? Que *voulez-vous* que j'y fasse ?

Have you read this book ? Have I got enough time to . . . ? Has he seen whether there were any letters ? Will they be going to Deauville this year ? What do you want me to do ?

Voyez-vous ce paquet là-bas ? Donnez-*le* moi. Portez-le *lui* dès demain matin. Rendez-*les* nous aussitôt que possible. Quelle est la réponse de ce problème ? Attendez ! Ne me *la* dites pas ! Je veux la trouver tout seul.

Do you see that parcel over there ? Give it to me. Take it to him early tomorrow. Give them back to us as soon as possible. What is the solution of this problem ? Wait ! Don't tell (it to) me ! I shall find it myself.

Adjectives Preceding the Noun

J'espère que ce *beau* temps va durer jusqu'à la semaine prochaine.

I hope this fine weather will last until next week.

Le *digne* homme n'avait pas toujours *bon* caractère; il ne permettait pas la *moindre* infraction aux règlements de l'école. Les *jeunes* gens l'aimaient pourtant, et les *grands* élèves l'appelaient : " ce *cher* M. Lamouvette."

The worthy man was not always good-tempered ; he would not tolerate the least infraction of the school rules. The boys loved him though, and the older pupils called him : " that dear Mr. Lamouvette."

Regardez-moi ce *vilain petit* garçon, comme il est sale !

Just look at this bad little boy, how dirty he is !

Ennemi intelligent vaut mieux que *sot* ami.

Better a wise enemy than a foolish friend.

Miscellaneous

Mes amis, mes chefs, mes employés, tout le monde me trouve trop gros. Etes-vous de *leur* opinion ? Donnez-moi donc l'adresse de *votre* gymnase, que je perde *ce* poids inutile.

My friends, my superiors, my staff, everybody thinks I am too fat. Do you share their opinion ? If so, give me the address of your gymnasium, so that I can lose this useless weight.

Ce chapeau, *cette* canne ferrée, *ces* lunettes, *ce* sac ! Ah çà ! partiriez-vous faire l'ascension du Mont-Blanc ?

Why the hat, the alpenstock, the spectacles, the rucksack ? Dear me ! Can it be that you are going to climb (the) Mont Blanc ?

Veuillez croire, Monsieur, à l'expression de *mes* sentiments distingués.

Believe me, Sir, yours very truly (ending for a letter).

LESSON SIX

Practice on Lessons 1—5 and Exercises

A T this point it will be valuable to go over again the ground we have so far covered—both Lessons and Exercises. As emphasized already in page 519, it is essential in learning a language to make certain of the basis before advancing, and it is even more important, in the method adopted in this Course, to make completely sure of each step before proceeding to the next. Hence the necessity for revision work. This Lesson therefore consists of sentences and phrases which require the use of the vocabularies of essen-

tial nouns which should now have been learned, the articles, adjectives and numbers. It concludes with a few important idiomatic phrases.

GENERAL EXERCISE FOR REVISION

Chacun sait que Londres est la ville des brumes : *on* dit que

Everybody knows that London is a city of mists : they say that

Londres sans le brouillard n'est plus Londres. Pourtant, il ne

London without fog is no longer London. However, you

faut *rien* exagérer. Si *quelqu'un* était amené, les yeux bandés,
must not exaggerate anything. Were somebody to be brought, blindfold,
dans le parc de St. James, un beau matin de printemps, *rien ne* lui suggérerait
into St. James's Park, one fine Spring morning, nothing would suggest
la grande ville enfumée que *tout le monde* connaît :
to him the great smoky city (that) everyone knows :
Londres n'est *ni* la ville de la pluie et des brumes, *ni* la ville
London is neither a city of rain and mists, nor a city
des parcs et des jardins : c'est à la fois *l'un et l'autre.*
of parks and gardens ; it is both at the same time.

REVISION EXERCISES ON NUMBERS

La France adopta le système métrique après la Révolution.
France adopted the metric system after the Revolution.
L'unité monétaire est le franc, qui se divise en cent centimes :
monetary unit is the franc, which is divided into one hundred centimes ;
l'unité de longueur est le mètre, qui se divise en cent centimètres, etc.
the unit of length is the metre, which is divided into one hundred centimetres, etc.
Ainsi, toutes les opérations d'arithmétique
Thus, all (the) operations of arithmetic
se rapportant aux mesures de longueur, aux poids, à l'argent, etc., sont
relating to measures of length, to weights, to money, etc., are
très faciles. Soit par exemple vingt-sept mètres cinquante de
very easy. For example, take twenty-seven and a half
drap à neuf francs quarante *le* mètre : quel est le prix total
metres of cloth at nine francs forty centimes *a* metre ; what is the
du drap ? Nous multiplions le nombre de mètres par le nombre de
total cost of the cloth ? We multiply the number of metres by the number of
francs, nous séparons les deux décimales par une *virgule,* et
francs, we separate the two decimal figures by a *comma,* and
nous avons immédiatement le résultat : soit la multiplication
we have the result immediately ; thus :
27,5 × 9,4 = 258.50.
Le prix du drap est de deux cent cinquante
The cost of the cloth is two hundred and fifty-huit francs cinquante centimes. Combien *plus* compliquée serait
huit francs cinquante centimes. Combien *plus* compliquée serait
eight francs fifty centimes. How much more complicated would be
une opération semblable en mesures et en monnaies anglaises ! Soit
a similar operation with English measures and English money ! Let us say,

27 yards, 2 pieds et 3 pouces de drap à 2 shillings et 11 pence
27 yards 2 feet 3 inches of cloth at 2 shillings and 11 pence
le yard !
(a) yard !

La superficie de *la* France est *de* 550,926 Km. (kilomètres) carrés ;
The area of France is 550,926 square kilometres ;
sa population est *de plus de* quarante et un millions
her population exceeds forty-one million
d'habitants. De tous les fleuves de France, la Loire, qui
inhabitants. Of all the rivers *in* France, the Loire, which
passe à Orléans et à Nantes est *le plus* long ; il a environ
flows through Orleans and Nantes, is the *longest* ; it is about
mille kilomètres *de* long. Le Mont-Blanc est haut de quatre
one thousand kilometres in length. Mont Blanc is four thousand
mille huit cent dix mètres : c'est la montagne *la plus* haute
eight hundred and ten metres high ; it is the *highest* mountain
des Alpes. La Tour Eiffel a trois cents mètres *de haut.*
in the Alps. The Eiffel Tower is three hundred metres high.

REVISION EXERCISE

Nous savons que la France s'appelait autrefois la Gaule ;
We know that France was formerly called Gaul ;
elle était habitée par différentes populations, en majorité
it was inhabited by various populations, mostly
par des Celtes (les Gaulois), que l'on représente avec *des* cheveux
by Celts (the Gauls), whom one pictures with blonde
blonds, de grandes moustaches et *un* casque ailé. Il y
hair, big moustaches and winged helmets. There
avait aussi d'autres peuples, des Grecs par exemple, qui fondèrent
were two other peoples, e.g. (some) Greeks, who founded
une colonie dans le sud appelée Massilia (aujourd'hui
a colony in the South called Massilia (the Marseilles of
Marseille) vers 600 (six cents) avant J.C. Puis vint la
to-day) circa 600 B.C. Then came the
conquête romaine dirigée par Jules César, qui eut pour résultat
Roman conquest led by Julius Caesar, which resulted in

d'introduire la civilisation et la langue latines
en Gaule.
the introduction of Latin civilization and
language into Gaul.
Après les Romains vinrent d'autres invasions,
les Francs, les
After the Romans came other invaders,
Frank tribes,
Normands, etc. Mais le pays connut une
première unité avec le
Northmen, etc. However, the country knew a
first unity under
roi Clovis, que se convertit au Christianisme en
499 (quatre cent quatre-vingt dix-neuf)
après J.C.
King Clovis, who became converted to
Christianity in 499 A.D.
Ainsi la France grandit peu à peu pendant
le Moyen-Âge, sans
Thus France grew little by little during the
Middle Ages, without
avoir le sentiment réel d'être une nation dans
le sens que nous
having the real feeling of being a nation in the
sense that we
donnons à ce mot. C'est Louis XI (onze) qui
commença à centraliser
give to this word today. It was Louis XI
who began centralizing
les différentes provinces du royaume autour de
la personne
the various provinces of the kingdom around
the person
du Roi. Avec Louis XIV (quatorze) et sa
cour, groupée au
of the King. With Louis XIV and his court,
gathered at
château de Versailles, nous arrivons au ' grand
siècle ' et à
the château of Versailles, we come to the
' great century ' and the
la grande époque classique du français :
Molière, Racine, Corneille
Golden age of classical French ; Molière,
Racine, Corneille
en sont les grands noms. Les erreurs de la
monarchie
are among its greatest names. The errors of
absolute
absolue amenèrent une réaction sous Louis
XVI (seize) ; ce
monarchy led up to a reaction under Louis
XVI ; it was

fut la Révolution, symbolisée par la chute de la
prison de la
the Revolution, which is symbolized by the
fall of the prison of the
Bastille, le 14 Juillet 1789 (dix-sept cent
quatre-vingt neuf).
Bastille, on July 14th, 1789.
Cette date a été choisie comme Fête Nationale
par la République.
This date has been chosen as National Day by
the Republic.
La devise de la République française devint:
Liberté, Egalité, Fraternité.
The motto of the French Republic became :
Liberty, Equality, Fraternity.

IDIOMATIC PHRASES

De quoi parlez-vous ?
What are you talking about ?   •

Je vais *à l'école : à l'église : à la* **maison.**
I go to school ; to church ; home.

Je suis *chez moi,* **M. Dupont est chez** *lui,* **sa
mère est chez** *elle* **; nous sommes bien chez**
nous **; quand serez-vous chez** *vous* **? Je ne
suis pas allé les voir chez** *eux* **depuis longtemps.**
I am at home, Mr. Dupont is at home, his
mother is at home ; we feel comfortable at
home ; when will you be at home ? I
have not been to see them at their home for
a long time.

Jetez **donc un coup d'œil autour de vous.**
Do cast a glance around you.

Envoyez ce colis par *la* **poste ; par avion ; par
mer ; par un ami ; par voie ferrée.**
Send this parcel by post ; by air mail ; by
boat ; by a friend ; by rail.

Ce produit se vend *au* **poids, et non** *au* **mètre :
il vaut 10 frs.** *le* **kilo.**
This substance is sold *by the* pound, not *by the*
yard ; it is worth **10 frs.** *a* kilo (=2 pounds
approx.).

Il s'est cassé *la* **jambe.**
He broke *his* leg.

Qu'êtes-vous *en train de* **faire là ?   Je suis en
train de réparer cette machine.**
What are you doing there ? I am repairing
this machine.

Ça ne vous plaît pas, *non* **?**
You don't like that, do you ?

LESSON SEVEN

Pronouns and Their Use

IN the table given in the next page (1) is
the **Subject** pronoun, answering the
question *who acted ?* (2) is the **direct
object** pronoun, answering the question *who*
or *what* was the recipient of the action ?
and (3) is the pronoun for the **indirect object**
of the action.

Thus : **Je le lui dirai,** *I will tell it to him.*
Je, subject ; **le,** direct object ; **lui,** indirect
object ; and **dirai,** the verb representing the
action in this particular case.
EN, *of* : often used of persons and things,
instead of **de lui.**
Y, *to* : similarly, often replaces **à lui,** but
for things only. Also means *there.*

MÊME, *self* : **moi-même,** *myself,* etc.

SOI, *him, her, itself, themselves* : used only after on, *one,* **chacun,** *each,* **aucun,** *none,* **celui qui,** *he who.* **Chacun pour soi et Dieu pour tous. On ne doit pas parler de soi.**

Position of the Pronouns. The general rule is : *Before the verb in the order of person. After the verb in the order of object.*

NOTES : (1) Pronouns are placed *before* the verb in the order of persons. If both are in the same person, direct object first. **y** and **en** always next to the verb, in that order.

(2) In interrogative sentences, place subject *after* verb.

(3) In the imperative, place pronouns *after* the verb, direct object first.

Personal Pronouns	Reflexives, used with a Verb	Used apart from Verb, or for emphasis, or with Preposition
1 je, *I*		moi, *I, myself*
2 me, *me*	me, *myself*	moi, *me*
3 me, *to me*	me, *to myself*	à moi, *to me*
1 tu, *thou*		toi, *thou, thyself*
2 te, *thee* -ᵃ	te, *thyself* ⎱ b	toi, *thee* ⎱ c
3 te, *thee*)	te, *to thyself* ⎰	à toi, *to thee* ⎰
1 il, elle, *he, she*		lui, elle, *he, she*
2 le, la, *him, her, it*	se, *him-, her-, itself*	lui, elle, soi, *to him, her*
3 lui, *to him*	se, *to „ „ „*	à lui, à elle, *to him, her*
1 nous, *we*		nous, *we*
2 nous, *us*	nous, *ourselves*	nous, *us*
3 nous, *to us*	nous, *to ourselves*	à nous, *to us*
1 vous, *you*		vous, *you*
2 vous, *you*	vous, *yourselves*	vous, *you*
3 vous, *to you*	vous, *to yourselves*	à vous, *to you*
1 ils, elles, *they*		eux, elles, *they*
2 les, *them*	se, *themselves*	eux, elles, *them*
3 leur, *to them*	se, *to themselves*	à eux, à elles, *to them*

a, b, c To be avoided, except when speaking to very familiar friends or relatives

Examples

Je vous parle, *I speak to you.*
Elle ne me parle pas, *She does not speak to me.*
Il ne m'a pas parlé, *He has not spoken to me.*
Vous ne me l'avez pas dit, *You have not told me of it.*
Nous leur y en avons parlé, *We spoke to them of it there.*
Parlez-moi d'amour, *Speak to me of love.*
Donnez le moi, *Give it to me.*
Pensez à moi, *Think of me.*

NOTE.—The **e** of pronouns *is* dropped before a vowel or **h** mute.

Ne . . . pas : **Ne** after subject, **pas** after the auxiliary.

Possessive Pronouns. The six possessive pronouns with their genders and numbers are :

mon, ma, mes, *my*
ton, ta, tes, *thy*
son, sa, ses, *his, her, its*
notre, nos, *our*
votre, vos, *your*
leur, leurs, *their*

The possessive pronouns take the gender and number of the noun which follows them. **Son chapeau,** *his* or *her hat.* **Sa maison,** *his* or *her house.* **Ses souliers,** *his* or *her shoes.*

le mien, les miens ⎱
la mienne, les miennes ⎰ *mine*
le tien, le sien, *thine, his, hers*[1]
le nôtre, la nôtre, les nôtres, *ours*
le vôtre, la vôtre, les vôtres, *yours*
le leur, la leur, les leurs, *theirs*

[1] **La tienne, Les tiennes** : **La sienne, Les siennes** (fem.).

Leurs chapeaux ne sont pas si beaux que les nôtres, *Their hats are not so beautiful as ours.*

Demonstrative Pronouns. Ce, *this, that* and **celui,** *this, that,* with **-ci,** *here,* and **-là,** *there,* added : **ceci, cela,** *this, that ;* **ça,** *that*

Masculine : **Celui-ci, celui-là**
Plural : **ceux-ci, ceux-là.**
Feminine : **Celle-ci, celle-là**
Plural : **celles-ci, celles-là.**

These words follow the gender of the words to which they refer. The **-ci** and **-là** are dropped before **de** and **qui** : **Ceux qui sont ici.**

Relatives. A relative pronoun is one which connects the noun or pronoun to which it refers with the part of the sentence which follows. Thus : The man *whom* I know ; The house *that* Jack built : *whom* and *that* are relatives.

qui, *who, which, that* (of persons or things)
que, *whom, which, that* „ „
dont, *of whom, of which* „ „
lequel,[1] *who, which, that* „ „
duquel, *of whom, of which* „ „
auquel, *to whom, to which* „ „
de qui, *of whom, whose* (of persons only)
à qui, *to whom, whose* („ „)
quoi, *what* (of things only)
de quoi, *of what* („)
à quoi, *to which, what*

[1] *Which of* TWO.

Pronouns must *always* be expressed in French : *The house I sold,* La maison que j'ai vendue. Voici l'automobile qui me plaît, *Here's the car I like.*

Dont, quoi, qui and que are invariable, except that que becomes qu' before a vowel or h mute.

Interrogatives. All the above relatives except dont may be used as interrogatives, that is, to ask questions.

    qui est-ce qui, WHO ?
    qui est-ce que, qu', WHOM ?
    qu'est-ce qui, WHAT ? SUBJECT
    qu'est-ce que, qu', WHAT ? OBJECT

Quel, quelle, quels, quelles ; *which one ? What ?* (Note that quel agrees with the noun to which it refers.)

Miscellaneous Pronouns. Chacun, *each* ; on, *people* ; personne, *anybody* ; personne ne, *nobody* ; quelqu'un, *somebody* ; rien, *something* ; rien ne, *nothing* ; quelque chose, *something.* (Note that personne by itself means *nobody* ; rien *nothing.*)

L'un et l'autre, *both* ; l'un ou l'autre, *either* ; ni l'un ni l'autre, *neither.*

C'est and Il Est. *He, she, it is, they are,* when followed by a noun, proper noun, or pronoun, should be translated by c'est, ce sont. Qui est ce ? C'est le boulanger, le chauffeur. Ce sont mes amis. C'est moi. C'est Henri.

It is, followed by an adjective only, translate c'est : c'est mystérieux.

It is, followed by an adjective with à, or followed by a noun, pronoun or date, translate c'est : c'est difficile à faire. C'est le premier janvier. C'est un sot.

Use Il Est : (*a*) When the adjective following est is followed by a phrase : Il est facile de les apprendre (*to learn them*), Il est utile de savoir bien la grammaire ;

(*b*) to indicate the HOUR : Il est minuit ;
(*c*) When there is NO ARTICLE : Il est médecin.

LESSON EIGHT

The Verb: Basis and Essentials

DEFINITION : A Verb is a word of being or doing. The opening sentence of the chapter about Le Verbe in the *Grammaire de l'Académie française* is 'Le verbe est le mot essentiel de la langue.'

The French verb is not easy to master, that is, if you wish to know every form, every peculiarity, every subtlety and idiomatic usage. It may be some comfort to know that the members of the Academy quarrel over points in the grammar of the verb. But, for the foreigner to express him- or herself reasonably well, it is necessary to learn only the basis and essentials of the verb as outlined in the following pages. These must be known *thoroughly.*

Parts of the Verb which Must be Known. For most practical purposes, the parts of French verbs required are :

(*a*) The INFINITIVE, i.e. 'that part of a verb which names the action, without reference to any doer, and is therefore not limited by person or by number,' thus : MANGER *to eat,* LIRE *to read.*
(*b*) The PRESENT PARTICIPLE, ending in -ANT, and corresponding to the English ending *-ING* ; voyANT, *seeING* : allANT, *goING.*
(*c*) The PAST PARTICIPLE, which is used to form compound tenses (and is often used as an adjective.[1]). Thus : J'ai parlé, *I have spoken.* (It agrees with the subject after être, and with the direct object when this precedes all other verbs.)

  [1] For this reason many past participles are given in the list of adjectives, which see.

(*d*) The PRESENT TENSE, which represents the English forms, *I speak, I do speak,* or *I am speaking,* by one form : je parle.
(*e*) The PAST TENSE, which is formed with the AUXILIARY and the Past Participle, thus : J'ai parlé, *I have spoken* or *I spoke.* (This is the commonest form of the past tense.)
(*f*) The FUTURE TENSE, which is formed by adding to the Infinitive the ENDINGS of the PRESENT TENSE of AVOIR, as will be seen later. One can also use the verb *'to go'* to make a future—Je vais voir, *I shall see.*

The INFINITIVE of French Verbs has one of these four ENDINGS : -ER, -IR, -OIR, -RE ;

  parLER, *to speak*   recevOIR, *to receive*
  finIR, *to finish*   vendRE, *to sell*

General Rule. All verbs ending in -er are conjugated similarly to parler ;

All ending in -ir are conjugated similarly to finir ;

All in -oir to recevoir and all in -re to vendre.

Those which do not follow this general rule are called IRREGULAR VERBS, and all required for practical purposes are given after the 'Model' Conjugations in pages 543 and 544.

Formation of Tenses. For purposes of reference a Table and rules for the complete CONJUGATION OF VERBS in -er, -ir, -re, is given below. -oir will be found later, and the tenses of it not given would follow those below.

The **Future** is formed by *adding to the Infinitive the endings in the table.* Similarly the **Conditional.**

The **Present Participle** gives: **Present Indicative Plural** by changing -ant into the endings given in the table. It also gives similarly the **Imperfect Indicative** and the **Present Subjunctive.**

Note that in verbs ending -oir, c always changes to ç before a, o, u.

The **Past Participle** gives *all compound tenses, with an auxiliary.*

The **Present Indicative** provides the **Imperative,** simply by *dropping the pronouns*:

Prends, prenez, *take.*

The **Past Definite** (sometimes called the Preterite, or the Historical Past) used in narrative literature—never in speech—is formed by *adding the endings in the table to the infinitive without -er, -ir, -oir, -re.*

Thus, **je PARL-ai** (written **parlai**), **tu parlas,** etc.

The **Past Subjunctive** is formed by *adding the endings in the table to the second person singular of the Past Definite*:

Que je parlas-se, que tu parlas-ses, qu'il parlât, etc.

Note on the Subjunctive. The student who aspires to become an adept at translation *into* French must go to some other book for instruction in the use of the Subjunctive. For ordinary purposes, one should be able to recognize a tense in the Subjunctive, a mood which does not greatly matter in English. It *can* be avoided in French with a little ingenuity. For example:

I must go—il faut (*It is necessary*) que j'aille (*that I go,* subjunctive). Equally correct: **Il faut aller** (Infinitive): or, rather *more emphatic,* **je dois aller** (DEVOIR).

Analysis of the French Verb—for Reference. Today many French scholars prefer a new and slightly different approach to the conjugation of the verb. All verbs may be analysed into the following divisions for purposes of conjugation:

LIVING CONJUGATION: *All* verbs *ending in* -er, verbs *ending in* -ir which are *inchoate* (or indicate beginning).

DEAD CONJUGATION: *Non-inchoate* verbs in -ir. All others.

From this follows a very practical rule:

Learn the conjugation of a verb ending in -er, *and that of one ending* -ir, with plural in -iss (nous finissons) and consider *all other verbs are or may be irregular.* This acts as a warning.

Table of Past Participles

Infinitive		Past Part. always ends:
LIVING CONJUGATION	-er	é
	-ir	i
DEAD CONJUGATION	-ir	u or i
	-re	u, i, is, it
	-oir	u

Note that nearly all *living* inchoate verbs are *formed from an adjective* (**vert, lent**).

Also note that it is the -iss element which is missing from the dead verbs: **nous mourons, nous partons.**

It appears, however, from experience that English-speaking learners, if not all foreigners, find the old PARLER, FINIR, RECEVOIR and VENDRE classification to be more simple. The new approach is given for reference, or to drive home the old.

All new verbs formed from nouns, etc., end in **ER**: **Téléphoner,** *to telephone.*

TABLE OF CONJUGATION FOR REFERENCE

Pronoun	Present	Imperfect	Past definite	Future	Conditional	Present Subjunctive	Past Subjunctive
je	-e, -s	-ais	-ai, -s	-ai	-ais	-e	-se
tu	-es, -s	-ais	-as	-as	-ais	-es	-ses
il, elle	-e, -t, -d	-ait	-a, -t	-a	-ait	-e	^t
nous	-ons	-ions	-mes	-ons	-ions	-ions	-sions
vous	-ez	-iez	-tes	-ez	-iez	-iez	-siez
ils, elles	-ent	-aient	-rent	-ont	-aient	-ent	-sent

Infinitives: -er, -ir, -re.   Present Participles: -ant.   Past Participles: -é, -i, -u, -s, -t.

LESSON NINE

Auxiliary Verbs and Verbs in -er, -ir, and -oir

HAVING considered the basis of French verbs and how they are used, including the methods of conjugation, we proceed to the basically important auxiliary verbs Avoir and Être. This is followed by model conjugations for all verbs ending in -er and also models for those ending in -ir and -oir with various irregular forms.

The Auxiliary Verbs. The two verbs Avoir and Être are called AUXILIARIES, because they are used not only to express To HAVE and To BE, but also to form *compound tenses of all verbs.* Hence, they are of paramount importance. They are *both irregular.*

INFINITIVE : **AVOIR,** *to have*
PRESENT PARTICIPLE : **ayant,** *having*
PAST PARTICIPLE : **eu,** *had*

PRESENT TENSE	PAST TENSE
j'ai, *I have*	**j'ai eu,** *I have had or I had*
tu **as,** *thou hast*	tu as eu
il **a,** elle **a,** *he has, she has*	il a eu, elle a eu
nous **avons,** *we have*	nous avons eu
vous **avez,** *you have*	vous avez eu
ils, elles, **ont,** *they have*	ils, elles, ont eu

FUTURE TENSE
j'aurai, *I shall have*
tu auras
il, elle aura
nous aurons
vous aurez
ils, elles auront

Tu is used only where great familiarity exists between the persons speaking. **Vous** is the general word for *you.*

INFINITIVE : **ÊTRE,** *to be*
PRESENT PARTICIPLE : **étant,** *being*
PAST PARTICIPLE : **été,** *been*

PRESENT TENSE	PAST TENSE
je suis, *I am*	**j'ai été,** *I have been or I was*
tu **es,** *thou art*	tu as été
il, elle **est,** *he, she is*	il a été
nous **sommes,** *we are*	nous avons été
vous **êtes,** *you are*	vous avez été
ils, elles **sont,** *they are*	ils, elles ont été

FUTURE TENSE
je serai, *I shall be*
tu seras
il sera
nous serons
vous serez
ils seront

Model for All Verbs Ending in -ER

PARLER, *to speak*

PRESENT PART. :	PAST PART. :
parlant	parlé

PRESENT TENSE	PAST TENSE
je parle, *I speak*	**j'ai parlé,** *I spoke*
tu parles	tu as parlé
il parle	il a parlé
nous parlons	nous avons parlé
vous parlez	vous avez parlé
ils parlent (**-ent** *always silent*)	ils ont parlé

FUTURE TENSE
je parlerai, *I shall speak*
tu parleras
il parlera
nous parlerons
vous parlerez
ils parleront

Only two verbs ending in -er are conjugated differently from **parler** :

ALLER, *to go*

PRESENT TENSE	FUTURE TENSE
je vais	**j'irai**
tu vas	tu iras
il va	il ira
nous allons	nous irons
vous allez	vous irez
ils vont	ils iront

PARTICIPLES, **allant, allé**

ENVOYER, *to send*
FUTURE : **j'enverrai,** etc. (otherwise regular).

In the pages which follow, the essential parts of verbs will be stated as in the order of **PARLER** : the INFINITIVE, the PARTICIPLES, the PRESENT and FUTURE Tenses.

Model for Verbs Ending in -IR

FINIR, *to finish*

PRESENT PART. :	PAST PART. :
finissant	fini

PRESENT TENSE	PAST TENSE
je finis, *I finish*	**j'ai fini,** *I finished*
tu finis	tu as fini, etc.
il finit	
nous finissons	FUTURE TENSE
vous finissez	**je finirai**
ils finissent (**-ent** *always silent*)	tu finiras, etc.

A number of verbs ending in -ir do **not** follow exactly the model of **finir,** and of these the following should be known :

COURIR, *to run* — courant, couru
je cours, etc. — je courrai, etc.
DORMIR, *to sleep* — dormant, dormi
je dors, etc. — je dormirai, etc.
MENTIR, *to tell lies* — mentant, menti
je mens, etc. — je mentirai, etc.
PARTIR, *to start, to set out* : conjugate like **mentir.**

It is important to note that all verbs of motion are conjugated with **être** and NOT avoir. **Je suis parti,** *I have gone.*

SENTIR, *to feel* : conjugate like **mentir**

SERVIR, *to serve* : conjugate like **mentir**

MOURIR, *to die*   **mourant, mort**
je **meurs,** tu **meurs, il meurt**
nous **mourons,** vous **mourez,** ils **meurent**
je **mourrai,** etc.

OUVRIR, *to open*   **ouvrant, ouvert**
j'**ouvre,** etc., j'**ouvrirai,** etc.

COUVRIR, *to cover* : conjugate like **ouvrir**

OFFRIR, *to offer* : conjugate like **ouvrir**

SOUFFRIR, *to suffer* : conjugate like **ouvrir**

SORTIR, *to go out*
je **sors,** tu **sors, il sort**
nous **sortons,** vous **sortez,** ils **sortent**
Otherwise like **mentir**

VENIR, *to come* : **venant, venu**
je **viens,** tu **viens, il vient**
nous **venons,** vous **venez,** ils **viennent**
je **viendrai,** etc.
ju **suis venu,** *I have come*

TENIR, *to hold* : conjugate like **venir**

VÊTIR, *to clothe* : **vêtant, vêtu**
je **vêts,** tu **vêts, il vêt**
nous **vêtons,** vous **vêtez,** ils **vêtent**
je **vêtirai.** etc.

Model for Verbs Ending in -OIR

RECEVOIR, *to receive*

PARTICIPLES : **recevant, reçu**

PRESENT TENSE	PAST TENSE
je **reçois,** *I receive*	j'**ai reçu,** etc.
tu **reçois**	
ils **reçoit**	
nous **recevons**	FUTURE TENSE
vous **recevez**	je **recevrai**
ils **reçoivent (ent**	tu **recevras,** etc.
always silent)	

A number of verbs ending in -oir do not follow exactly the model of **recevoir,** and of these the following should be known :

DEVOIR, *to owe, to have to* : **devant, dû**
je **dois,** tu **dois, il doit**
nous **devons,** vous **devez,** ils **doivent**
je **devrai,** etc.

FALLOIR, *to be necessary.* PAST PARTICIPLE : **fallu**
il **faut,** *it is necessary*
il **faudra,** *it will be necessary*

PLEUVOIR, *to rain.* **pleuvant, plu**
il **pleut**
il **pleuvra**

POUVOIR, *to be able.* **pouvant, pu**
je **puis,** tu **puis, il peut**
nous **pouvons,** vous **pouvez,** ils **peuvent**
But : **je ne peux pas, tu ne peux pas,** etc.
(PRES. TENSE)
je **pourrai,** etc.

SAVOIR, *to know.* **sachant, su**
je **sais,** tu **sais, il sait**
nous **savons,** vous **savez,** ils **savent**
je **saurai,** etc.

VALOIR, *to be worth.* **valant, valu**
je **vaux,** tu **vaux, il vaut**
nous **valons,** vous **valez,** ils **valent**
je **vaudrai,** etc.

VOIR, *to see.* **voyant, vu**
je **vois,** tu **vois, il voit**
nous **voyons,** vous **voyons,** ils **voient**
je **verrai,** etc.

VOULOIR, *to be willing.* **voulons, voulu**
je **veux,** tu **veux, il veut**
nous **voulons,** vous **voulez,** ils **veulent**
je **voudrai,** etc.

As the model conjugations are learnt, the tenses should be compared with those set out in the Table of Conjugations in page 542. It will be found that in this way every part of a verb can be found in a short time.

LESSON TEN

Verbs in -re and Special Uses

WE complete in this Lesson the sets of model conjugations. These are for verbs ending in -re and their irregular forms and also for reflexive and impersonal verbs, and we add notes on the negative, interrogative, imperative, and passive. In the Lesson that follows we give an extensive vocabulary of essential verbs, the conjugations of which should be studied on the lines of this and the preceding Lesson.

Model for Verbs Ending in -RE
VENDRE, *to sell*

PARTICIPLES : **vendant, vendu**

PRESENT TENSE	FUTURE TENSE
je **vends,** *I sell*	je **vendrai**
tu **vends**	tu **vendras**
il **vend**	il **vendra**
nous **vendons**	nous **vendrons**
vous **vendez**	vous **vendrez**
ils **vendent (-ent** AL-	ils **vendront**
WAYS SILENT)	

j'**ai vendu.** *I sold*

The following **Irregular** verbs ending in -re should be known :

BOIRE, *to drink*   buvant, **bu**
je bois, etc.
je boirai

CONNAÎTRE, *to be acquainted with*
connaissant, connu
je connais, etc.
je connaîtrai, etc.

CONDUIRE, *to conduct, lead*   conduisant, conduit
je conduis . . . nous conduisons
je conduirai, etc.

CRAINDRE, *to fear*   craignant, **craint**
je crains, tu crains, il **craint**
nous craignons, vous craignez, ils craignent
je craindrai, etc.

CROIRE, *to believe*   croyant, **cru**
je crois, etc.
je croirai, etc.

CUIRE, *to cook* : conjugate like **conduire**

DIRE, *to say, to tell*   disant, **dit**
je dis, tu dis, il dit
nous disons, vous **dîtes,** ils disent
je dirai, etc.

ÉCRIRE, *to write*   écrivant, **écrit**
j'écris, etc.
j'écrirai, etc.

FAIRE, *to make, to do, to cause to*
faisant, **fait**
je fais, tu fais, il fait
nous faisons, vous faites, ils **font**
je ferai, etc.

LIRE, *to read*   lisant, **lu**
je lis, etc.
je lirai, etc.

METTRE, *to put*   mettant, **mis**
je mets, etc.
je mettrai, etc.

PARAÎTRE, *to appear* : conjugate like **connaître**

PLAIRE, *to please*   plaisant, **plu**
je plais, tu plais, il **plaît**
nous plaisons, vous plaisez, ils plaisent
je plairai, etc.

PRENDRE, *to take*   prenant, **pris**
je prends, tu prends, il prend
nous **prenons, vous prenez,** ils **prennent**
je prendrai, etc.

RIRE, *to laugh*   riant, **ri**
je ris, tu ris, il rit
nous rions, vous riez, ils rient
je rirai, etc.

ROMPRE, *to break*
Regular, excepting **il** or **elle rompt,** *he or she breaks*

S

SUFFIRE, *to suffice*   suffisant, suff*i*
je suffis, tu suffis, il suffit
nous suffisons, vous suffisez, ils suffisent
je suffirai, etc.

SUIVRE, *to follow*   suivant, suivi
je suis, tu suis, il suit
nous suivons, vous suivez, ils suivent

SE TAIRE, *to be silent* : conjugate **taire** like **plaire**
(See below for REFLEXIVE VERBS)

VIVRE, *to live*   vivant, **vécu**
je vis, tu vis, ils **vit**
nous vivons, vous vivez, ils vivent
je vivrai, etc.

Model for Reflexive Verbs, or verbs which express an action performed and suffered by the subject, or which are conjugated with two pronouns instead of one :

SE LAVER, *to wash oneself*

PARTICIPLES : se lavant, s'être lavé

PRESENT TENSE	PAST TENSE
je me lave, *I wash myself*	je me suis lavé, *I washed myself*
tu te laves	tu t'es lavé
il se lave	il s'est lavé
nous nous lavons	nous nous sommes lavés
vous vous lavez	vous vous êtes lavés
ils se lavent	ils se sont lavés

FUTURE TENSE
je me laverai, etc.

NOTE.—All reflexive verbs are conjugated with the auxiliary Être. No exception to this rule.

The verb **S'ASSEOIR,** *to sit down,* is conjugated as follows :

PRESENT : je m'assieds, tu t'assieds, etc.
PARTICIPLE : s'asseyant, s'être assis
FUTURE : je m'assiérai, etc.

The Negative of Verbs. This is expressed by placing ne before the verb and **pas** after : **Je ne parle pas,** *I do not speak.* **Je ne suis pas,** *I am not.* Used with the past Participle thus : **Je n'ai pas parlé.** In the Infinitive ne and pas both come before : **ne pas faire,** *not to do* ; **ne pas lire,** *not to read,* etc.

The following negatives should also be known :

ne .. **plus,** *no more, no longer*
ne .. **jamais,** *never*
ne .. **personne,** *nobody*
ne .. **rien,** *nothing*
ne .. **pas encore,** *not yet*

They are all used SIMILARLY TO ne . . . **pas** : **Il n'y a plus de vin dans la bouteille.**
Note also that ne . . . **que** means *only* : **Elle ne voit que la lune.**

To Use the Verb Interrogatively. To use a verb in this way, that is, *to ask a question* in simple sentences, the verb is placed first and the pronoun afterwards—the reverse of a *direct* statement :

Vous parlez, *You speak*
Parlez-vous ? *Do you speak, are you speaking ?*
Comprenez-vous ? *Do you understand ?*

For the sake of euphony it is necessary to place a **t** between the verb and the pronoun, *when the verb ends in a vowel :* **A-t-il ?** *Has he ?* **Aura-t-elle ?** *Will she have ?*

And when the *first person singular ends with* **e** mute, an **acute** accent ´ is placed over it in the interrogative form : **Donné-je ?** *Do I give ?* etc.

A most useful interrogative is the phrase **est-ce que,** followed by the direct statement :

Est-ce que vous allez à la gare ? *Are you going to the station ?*
Est-ce que vous chantez ? *Are you singing ?* etc.

In *negative-interrogative* phrases the order is : **ne,** *verb,* **pronoun, pas :**
Ne parlons-nous pas ? *Do we not speak ?*
The **Imperative,** or **How to Give Commands.** Use the second person plural of the Present Tense : **Parlez !** *Speak !*
And in the Negative : **Ne parlez pas,** *Do not speak.*

Impersonal Verbs

PLEUVOIR, *to rain*
  Il pleut, *it is raining.* **Il a plu,** *it rained*
  Il pleuvra, or **Il va pleuvoir,** *it will rain*

FALLOIR, *to be necessary*
  Il faut, *it is necessary* [*was necessary*
  Il faudra, *it will be necessary.* **Il a fallu,** *it*

Y AVOIR, *there . . . to be*
  Il y a, *there is or there are* [1]
  Il y aura, *there will be*
  Il y a eu, *there has been*

  [1] Also means *ago.* **Il y a un an,** *a year ago.*

And note the phrase : **IL S'AGIT DE** followed by an Infinitive : *the question is, the matter is.*

Il s'agit d'apprendre bien tout ce qui est écrit ici, *It is a matter of learning well all that is written here.*

AVOIR is used in the following PHRASES EXPRESSING SENSATION, etc. :

avoir	**froid,** *to be cold*
,,	**chaud,** *to be hot*
,,	**faim,** *to be hungry*
,,	**soif,** *to be thirsty*
,,	**raison,** *to be right*
,,	**tort,** *to be wrong*
,,	**sommeil,** *to be sleepy*
,,	**peur de,** *to be afraid of*
,,	**honte de,** *to be ashamed of*
,,	**envie de,** *to be inclined to*

In stating age : **J'ai dix ans,** *I am ten years old.* **Quel âge a-t-elle ? Elle a vingt ans.**

Also : **J'ai mal à la tête,** *I have a headache.*

The simplest and commonest way of forming the *passive* is by using **on** with **avoir** and the *past participle* of the verb of which the Passive is required. Thus, translate *I was told,* **On m'a dit** (*One has told me*), etc. **On** is greatly used : **On dit que,** *It is said that, they say that,* etc.

Most Infinitives make verbal nouns, thus : **Le boire,** *the drinking ;* **le manger,** *eating ;* **le parler,** *speech, manner of speaking.*

LESSON 11

A Vocabulary of Essential Verbs

MANY thousands of French verbs resemble their English equivalents but for the endings peculiar to French. These can quickly be learnt.

The lists which follow should be mastered, and each verb conjugated in accordance with its model, depending upon the ending of the Infinitive.

Section 1. VERBS SIMILAR IN FORM OR USAGE IN FRENCH AND ENGLISH

ENDING IN -ER

accepter, *to accept*
arriver, *to arrive* (être)[1]
aider, *to aid, assist*
améliorer, *to improve*

amuser, *to amuse*
abandonner, *to abandon*
avancer, *to be fast* (*watch, clock*), also *to advance*

  [1] All *VERBS of MOTION* and their compounds are conjugated with **être.** Never forget this rule. **Je suis arrivé,** *I have arrived,* etc.

accompagner, *to accompany*
briller, *to shine*
commencer, *to begin*
continuer, *to continue*
chanter, *to chant, sing*
changer, *to change*
comparer, *to compare*

augmenter, *to augment, increase*
contrôler, *to control, check*
compter, *to count*
commander, *to command, order*

Section 1. VERBS SIMILAR IN FORM OR USAGE IN FRENCH AND ENGLISH (*continued*)

conseiller, *to give coun-sel, advise*
copier, *to copy*
consoler, *to console, comfort*
chasser, *to hunt, chase*

demander, *to demand, ask*
danser, *to dance*
dîner, *to dine*
désirer, *to desire, wish*
discuter, *to discuss, debate*
se disputer, *to dispute, quarrel*
déclarer, *to declare*
développer, *to develop*
détacher, *to detach, un-do, untie*

étonner, *to astonish*
s'excuser, *to excuse oneself*
entrer, *to enter* (être)[1]
étudier, *to study*
essayer, *to attempt, try*

flatter, *to flatter*
fumer, *to smoke*

gagner, *to gain*

informer, *to inform*
inviter, *to invite*
interpréter, *to interpret*

juger, *to judge*

se marier, *to marry, get married*
nommer, *to name, nom-inate*

porter, *to carry*
payer, *to pay*
préférer, *to prefer*
passer, *to pass, also to spend time*

refuser, *to refuse*
retourner, *to return*
rencontrer, *to encount-er, meet*
regretter, *to regret*
rester, *to remain* (être)[1]
répéter, *to repeat*
se reposer, *to rest*
raconter, *to relate, tell*
réparer, *to repair*

séparer, *to separate*
se séparer (de), *to part company (with)*

téléphoner, *to telephone*
terminer, *to terminate, end*
traverser, *to traverse, cross*

charger, *to load*
cesser (de), *to cease (from)*
citer, *to cite, quote, mention*
célébrer, *to celebrate*

déranger, *to disturb*
dégoûter, *to disgust*
détester, *to detest, hate*
durer, *to endure, last*
décider (de), *to decide upon*
débarquer, *to disem-bark, land*
détailler, *to detail, de-tach*
déplacer, *to displace*
déterminer, *to deter-mine, decide*

expliquer, *to explain*
enregistrer, *to register*
exiger, *to exact*
employer, *to employ*
économiser, *to save*
embarrasser, *to em-barrass*

féliciter, *to congratu-late*
forcer, *to force*
garder, *to guard, keep*
imprimer, *to print*

limiter, *to limit*
monter, *to mount, go up* (être)[1]
numéroter, *to number (in order)*

persuader, *to persuade*
planter, *to plant*
profiter, *to profit*
présenter, *to present, introduce*

réserver, *to reserve*
respirer, *to breathe*
raisonner, *to reason*
recommander, *to re-commend, register a letter*
retarder, *to be or make late, slow (watch, clock)*
résulter, *to follow as a result*

sembler, *to seem*
signer, *to sign*

toucher, *to touch*
tourner, *to turn, to move round*
transporter, *to trans-port*

user, *to use, wear out*

visiter, *to visit*
varier, *to vary, change*

voyager, *to travel*
vouer, *to vow*

ENDING IN -IR

avertir, *to warn*

choisir, *to choose*
couvrir, *to cover*

convenir, *to be con-venient, to suit*
contenir, *to contain*

découvrir, *to discover*
désobéir, *to disobey*

dormir, *to sleep*
démolir, *to demolish*

s'endormir, *to fall asleep*

finir, *to finish*

nourrir, *to nourish, feed*

obtenir, *to obtain*
ouvrir, *to open*

offrir, *to offer*
obéir, *to obey*

punir, *to punish*
partir,[1] *to depart, go away*

polir, *to polish*

retenir, *to retain, hold back*

se repentir, *to repent*

sentir, *to feel*
servir, *to serve*
se servir de, *to make use of*

souffrir, *to suffer*
se souvenir de, *to re-member*

unir, *to unite, join to-gether*

ENDING IN -OIR

recevoir, *to receive*

ENDING IN -RE

admettre, *to admit*

apparaître, *to put in an appearance*

battre, *to beat*

se battre (à), *to fight*

convaincre, *to convince*
conduire, *to conduct, lead*

comprendre, *to under-stand*

déduire, *to deduct*
descendre,[1] *to descend, to take down*
détruire, *to destroy*

défendre, *to defend, also prohibit*
disparaître, *to disap-pear*

joindre, *to join*

permettre, *to permit*
promettre, *to promise*

paraître, *to appear*

répondre, *to reply*
suffire, *to suffice*

réduire, *to reduce*
surprendre, *to surprise*

---

[1] All *VERBS of MOTION* and their compounds are conjugated with être.

Section 2. VERBS WHICH DIFFER IN THE TWO LANGUAGES

ENDING IN -ER

ajouter, *to add*
apporter, *to fetch, bring*
acheter, *to buy*
appeler, *to call*
aller, *to go*

s'en aller, *to go out, away*
allumer, *to light*
aimer, *to love*
amener, *to lead, bring*

briser, *to break, crack*
baigner, *to bathe, bath*
baisser, *to lower, fall, go down*

brûler, *to burn*
blesser, *to wound*
bercer, *to rock, lull, delude*

couper, *to cut*
chercher, *to seek, look for*
coûter, *to cost*
cacher, *to hide*
se chausser, *to put on one's shoes*
se coiffer, *to do one's hair, to wear a hat*

chauffer, *to warm*
casser, *to smash, break*
constater, *to prove, establish, testify*
cheminer, *to walk, go, proceed*
couler, *to flow, glide, slip*

donner, *to give*
demeurer, *to live, dwell*
dépenser, *to spend (money)*
déshabiller, *to undress*

déchirer, *to tear*
diriger, *to direct, guide*
se dépêcher, *to make haste, to be quick*
déjeuner, *to have breakfast, to lunch*

s'écrier, *to cry out, yell, exclaim*
écouter, *to listen*
épeler, *to spell*
envoyer, *to send*
emballer, *to pack*
enseigner, *to teach*

s'emparer de, *to take hold of*
entourer, *to surround*
écraser, *to crush*
espérer, *to hope*
emprunter, *to borrow*
ennuyer, *to annoy*
emplir, *to fill*

fermer, *to shut*

grimper, *to climb*
goûter, *to taste, enjoy*

gêner, *to hinder, embarrass*
geler, *to freeze*

habiller, *to clothe*

jouer, *to play*

jeter, *to throw*

louer, *to let a house, and also to praise*
laver, *to wash*
lancer, *to throw, dart, toss*

laisser, *to let, allow*
lier, *to link, join*
lever, *to lift, raise, gather*

manger, *to eat*
montrer, *to show*
marcher, *to walk*
mener, *to lead, take, drive*

manquer, *to miss, be short of*
mêler, *to mix*
mouiller, *to wet, soak*

nettoyer, *to clean*
nager, *to swim*

neiger, *to snow*
nier, *to deny*

oublier, *to forget*

ôter, *to take off, remove*

prêter, *to lend*
se porter, *to be (as regards health)*
parler, *to speak*

penser, *to think*
plier, *to fold*
se passer de, *to do without*

partager, *to share, divide*
pleurer, *to weep*

pêcher, *to fish*
pencher, *to lean, stoop*

remercier, *to thank*
réveiller, *to awaken*
raccommoder, *to mend, repair*
rappeler, *to remind (someone else)*

se rappeler de, *to remember*
raser, *to shave*
railler, *to make fun of*

semer, *to sow (seeds)*
souhaiter, *to wish someone something*

siffler, *to blow, whistle, hiss*
serrer, *to press*
sauter, *to jump*

tomber, *to fall*
trouver, *to find*
travailler, *to work*
tailler, *to cut*
tromper, *to deceive*

tousser, *to cough*
tuer, *to kill*
tirer, *to draw, pull, shoot*
tâcher, *to try, endeavour*

verser, *to pour out*
se vanter de, *to boast*

voler, *to fly (also to steal)*
vider, *to empty*

ENDING IN -IR

appartenir, *to belong to*
bâtir, *to build*
bouillir, *to boil*
courir, *to run*
devenir, *to become*
mourir, *to die (être)*
mentir, *to tell lies*
remplir, *to fill*

revenir, *to return (être)*
réussir, *to succeed*
sortir, *to go out (être)*
tenir, *to hold*
venir, *to come (être)*
venir de, *to have just (done something)*
vieillir, *to grow old*
vêtir, *to dress, clothe*

ENDING IN -OIR

avoir, *to have*
avoir lieu, *to take place*
s'asseoir, *to sit down*
devoir, *to owe, to have a duty to*
falloir, *to be necessary*

pleuvoir, *to rain*
pouvoir, *to be able*
savoir, *to know*
valoir, *to be worth*
voir, *to see*
vouloir, *to wish, to want*

ENDING IN -RE

attendre, *to wait*
apprendre, *to learn*
boire, *to drink*
connaître, *to know, be acquainted with*
croire, *to believe*
cuire, *to cook*
coudre, *to sew (cloth, etc.)*
craindre, *to fear*
défaire, *to undo*
dire, *to say, tell*
être, *to be*
écrire, *to write*
entreprendre, *to undertake*
entendre, *to hear*
faire, *to make, do, cause to*
faire mal, *to damage*
faire un pas, *to take a step (See Idioms, page 555)*

lire, *to read*
mettre, *to put*
mordre, *to bite*
naître, *to be born*
nuire, *to injure*
omettre, *to omit*
perdre, *to lose*
plaindre, *to pity*
se plaindre, *to complain*
peindre, *to paint*
prendre, *to take*
rendre, *to give back*
rire, *to laugh*
rompre, *to break*
suivre, *to follow*
sourire, *to smile*
se taire, *to be silent*
traduire, *to translate*
tordre, *to twist*
vivre, *to live*
vendre, *to sell*

Exercises on Pronouns and Verbs

THE student should now have sufficient knowledge to enable him to work out the meaning of the following sentences.

Mostly translations are omitted, and this gives the student an opportunity of practising thinking in French, getting the meaning rather than translating laboriously word by word. The matters presented are, in order: personal, interrogative, relative and demonstrative pronouns; possessive pronouns; negation; the value and uses of tenses; an important note on the subjunctive (the use of which is deliberately avoided as far as practicable); the past and present participles; impersonal and reflexive verbs; verbs in -oir, -re and -ir; and, to conclude, notes on the use of il y a, y, and en. Instruction on all these, except the last named, has already been given.

Pardon, avez-vous encore besoin de ce livre ?
Oui, je ne *l'*ai pas fini.
Vous vous occupez de littérature, n'est-ce pas ?
Oui, je m'*en* occupe.
Etudiez-vous *le* français ?
Oui, je *l'*étudie.
Depuis combien de temps ?
J'en avais déjà fait à l'école ; mais je *l'*avais plus ou moins oublié.
*L'*apprenez-vous tout seul ?
Non, c'est M. Voisin qui *me l'*enseigne.
Tiens ! Il ne m'*en* avait pas parlé. *Que* vous fait-il faire ?

Il *me* corrige ma prononciation ; je *lui* demande des questions, il me *les* explique ; *nous* voyons ensemble différentes règles de grammaire, qu'il *est* difficile d'étudier *soi-même ;* nous passons plus de temps—cela va de soi—sur les points contraires à *mes* habitudes anglaises. Par exemple, j'ai toujours envie de dire : ' il' est un homme, ' elle' est une table—au lieu de *c'est* un homme, *c'est* une table.
Parlez-*moi* de *vos* lectures.
Oh ! je ne lis pas encore des livres très difficiles. Mais certains *me* semblent faciles, les Contes de Maupassant, par exemple. *Les* connaissez vous ?
Bien sûr. D'ailleurs, Maupassant est un normand, comme *moi*. Et il parle de choses que je connais bien.
Qui est là ?
C'est *moi*, Charles.
Entre. Qu'est-ce que *tu* fais dehors si tard ?

Je venais prendre de *tes* nouvelles.
Je vais mieux, merci. *Voici* les médicaments (medicines) **que je dois prendre ;** *ils* ont très mauvais goût.
À quoi le docteur attribue-t-il *ta* maladie ?
Les docteurs ne sont pas toujours bavards ; *le mien* n'a rien dit, il a écrit une ordonnance (prescription), *dont* je n'ai pas pu lire un seul mot.
Est-ce *votre* chapeau ?
Non. N'est-ce pas le *vôtre* ?
Non, le *mien* est brun. Quelqu'un a dû *le* prendre et oublier *le sien* par erreur.
Regardez bien parmi *ceux* qui sont ici ; *celui-ci* par exemple, ou *celui-là* ?
Merci, ne vous dérangez pas. *Ce* chapeau paraît *m'*aller (seems to fit me). Je *le* prends.
Les soieries (silks) *que* l'on fabrique à Lyon sont très belles. La vigne (vine) *que* j'ai plantée a poussé (has grown) beaucoup cette année.
Sont-ce là les livres *dont* vous m'avez parlé ?
À quoi fait-on allusion dans ce discours ?
Lequel de vos deux amis avez-vous invité ce soir ?
Voici *l'*agent *auquel* il faut vous adresser.
Qui avez-vous demandé ? *Que* dites-vous ?
Quoi ? *Qu'est-ce que* vous dites ? *Ce* téléphone ne fonctionne pas bien ; je n'entends pas *ce que* vous dites.
Quelle chance (luck) de vous rencontrer ici !
*Qu'est-ce qu'*il y a ?—Ce n'est rien, *c'est moi* qui viens de faire tomber une tasse.
Qui est-ce qui vous a répondu au téléphone ?
Qui est-ce ? C'est le facteur (postman), Madame, *il* est en bas. C'est aujourd'hui le 1er janvier et *il* demande ses étrennes (Christmas box).
C'est bizarre, je croyais avoir laissé mon livre sur la table. Quelle heure est-il ? *Il* est presque 4 heures.

POSSESSIVE PRONOUNS

The possessive pronouns take the gender and number of the noun which follows them : hence it is impossible to distinguish between *her* hat and *his* hat (both are son chapeau) unless you say : son chapeau à lui, son chapeau à elle. The same remark applies to the English IT, which has no equivalent in French. Study these points in the following sentences.

C'est *mon* chapeau neuf ; il me va bien, n'est-ce pas ? (It's probably a lady speaking !). Pour jouer au golf, je mets toujours *mon* vieux chapeau (Now, it's probably a man). Regardez *sa* robe, comme elle est laide ! (It must be a woman's, since men do not wear ' robes ' in France). M. Dupont parle de *son* ami Henri, et Mme. Dupont parle de *son* amie Juliette. Depuis *son* divorce, elle a *sa* maison à *elle*. Elle a *son* chapeau sur la tête (the pronoun ' elle ' makes it clear).

Il est tard, je vais me coucher. Donnez-la moi. Quoi ?—*La montre que vous m'avez* prise. Je viens de *le lire*. Quoi ?—*L'article* du journal dont vous m'aviez parlé. J'ai fini ma lettre, maintenant je vais *la* mettre à la poste ; est-*ce* loin d'ici ?

NEGATION

Aimez-vous ça (cela) ? *Non.*
Do you like that ? No.

Non, non, vous dis-je ; je *n*'en veux *pas*, je *ne* l'aime *pas*.
No, no, I tell you ; I don't want it, and I don't like it.

Me promettez-vous de *n*'en *rien* **dire ?**
Can you promise me not to say anything about it ?

Je *ne* **le dirai à** *personne ; nul ne* **le saura.**
I won't speak about it to anybody ; no one will know.

Je *n*'ai vu *ni* lui *ni* Jean.
I saw neither him nor John.

Redundant NE used in que sentences : i.e. sentences in which ne does not introduce a negation.
Evitez qu'on *ne* **vous entende en parler.**
Avoid being heard talking about it.

Partez avant qu'il *n*'arrive.
Go before he arrives.

Je crains qu'il *ne* **vienne** (compare **Je crains qu'il** *ne* **vienne pas**).
I am afraid he'll come (compare I am afraid he won't come).

Ce livre est plus intéressant que je *ne* le croyais.
This book is more interesting than I thought.

Voilà plus d'un mois que je *ne* les ai vus.
It is more than a month since I saw them.

VALUE OF TENSES

Notes de voyage.—Le soleil *se lève* (Present) et *entre* (Present) peu à peu dans ma chambre. Où *suis-je* (Present) ? Je ne *connais* (Present) pas ces rideaux, cette table, ce lit. Ah ! *c'est* (Present) vrai : je *suis* (Present) à Paris. Je *suis arrivé* (Past Part.) hier, vers 5 heures. Quel voyage !

Je *quittai* (Past Defin.) Londres vers 10 heures du matin ; comme il *faisait* (Imp.) de la brume, il ne me *fut* (Past Defin.) pas possible de *voir*

(Inf.) le paysage avant Newhaven ; en *arrivant* (Pres. Part.) au port, le soleil *apparut* (Past Defin.) tout à coup, encore rouge, dans un ciel qui *devenait* (Imp.) plus bleu de minute en minute.

Malgré tout, la mer *était* (Imp.) agitée, et le bateau *dansa* (Past Defin.) pendant presque toute la traversée. Beaucoup de voyageurs *furent* (Past Def.) malades, et je ne *valais* (Imp.) pas beaucoup mieux moi-même quand nous *arrivâmes* (Past Def.) à Dieppe.

Un marin me *promit* (Past Def.) cependant que le temps *allait* (Imp.) *se mettre* au beau, et, en effet, le ciel *était* (Imp.) clair quand je *montai* (Past Def.) dans le train. Le voyage *s'annonçait* (Imp.) bien.

Le train *partit* (Past Def.) lentement, *traversa* (Past Def.) la ville au pas (= at walking pace), puis *prit* (Past Def.) peu à peu de la vitesse. N'*ayant* jamais *vu* (Past Part.) la campagne normande, mon attention *fut* (Past Def.) naturellement attirée par les champs, les jardins plantés de pommiers, et les petits villages avec leur église au toit pointu.

Le pays *changea* (Past Def.) après Gisors, les maisons *se firent* (Past Def.) de plus en plus nombreuses, pour *se grouper* (Inf.) petit à petit en rues et en places. Nous *traversons* (Pr.) la Seine, et nous voici arrivés.

Comme *c'était* (Imp.) la première fois que je *venais* (Imp.) à Paris, je *pris* (Past Def.) un taxi. Si j'*étais* (Imp.) riche, je me *promènerais* (Condit.) toujours ainsi : *c'est* (Pr.) si agréable. Peut-être *deviendrai-je* (Fut.) riche un jour, qui *sait* ? (Pr.)

A peine le taxi *avait-*il *quitté* (Pluperfect) la gare que j'*eus* (Past Def.) une émotion : car je *croyais* (Imp.) que nous *étions* (Imp.) sur le mauvais côté de la rue. Mais en France les voitures *vont* (Pr.) à droite. Il *faut* (Pr.) *s'y habituer* (Inf.), quoique ce ne *soit* (Subj.) pas là une grande difficulté.

Je *n'ai* naturellement pas *pu* (Past Part.) *voir* (Inf.) grand chose pendant cette première soirée, quoique je me *sois* (Subj.) promené après dîner sur les Boulevards. Je *suis rentré* (Past Part.) d'assez bonne heure, et me voici maintenant prêt à *commencer* (Inf.) mon exploration par les bords de la Seine : *allons-y* (Imperat.) !

The progressive form in English : I am doing, *can be represented by the Present Indicative in French* : je fais, *or for emphasis by the idiom* : je suis en train de faire.

Qu'est-ce que vous *faites* **ici à cette heure-ci ?**
Je suis en train de rentrer ces plantes, les nuits sont froides maintenant.
What are you doing here at this time of night ? I am bringing these plants inside, the nights are cold now.

Voilà dix ans que je *vais* **à l'église le dimanche.**
I have been going to church every Sunday for 10 years.

Le facteur **lui** apporta une lettre alors qu'il
se *rasait*.[1]
The postman brought him a letter as he was
shaving.

Je suis en train d'écrire, ne me dérangez pas.
I am writing now, do not disturb me.

' Ma chère amie, Je vous *écris* d'un endroit
charmant, près de Z——.'
' My dear (Lady) friend, I am writing to you
from a charming spot, near Z——.'

Nous *irons* à la mer cet été, pendant que vous
irez à la montagne.
We shall be going to the seaside this summer,
while you'll be going to the mountains.

Il se coupa le doigt alors qu'il était en train de
tailler son crayon.
He cut his finger while (he was) sharpening
his pencil.

Il pleut ; il neige ; il vente; il fait un temps
à ne pas mettre un chien dehors ! Il
fait un froid de canard !
It's raining ; it's snowing ; it's blowing a gale ;
it's not fit for a dog to be out on a day
like this! Fine weather (cold) for
ducks !

NOTE ON THE SUBJUNCTIVE

It has not been possible to do away
entirely with the Subjunctive in this Course,
although it has been avoided whenever possible. Here are a few ways showing how
this can be done :

Il faut que j'*aille* = Il me faut aller.

Croyez-vous qu'il*s oit* nécessaire de . . =
Croyez-vous à la nécessité de . . .

Il vaudrait mieux que vous *veniez* ici = Votre
présence ici serait désirable.

Je ne crois pas qu'il *vienne* maintenant = A
cette heure-ci, sa venue m'étonnerait fort.

Craignez-vous qu'il ne *vienne* ? = Craignez-
vous de le voir venir ?

Il semble que cela *puisse* se faire facilement =
Il paraît possible de faire cela facilement.

Ne désirez-vous pas qu'il *soit* heureux ? = Ne
désirez-vous pas le voir heureux ?

Je ne permets pas que vous y *alliez* = Je ne
saurais vous permettre d'y aller.

Faut-il qu'il *soit* stupide pour faire ça ! =
Faut-il être stupide pour faire ça !

Pourvu que vous *arriviez* de bonne heure
nous prendrons un apéritif ensemble = Si vous
arrivez de bonne heure nous pourrons prendre
un apéritif ensemble.

Note.—In practice, it would be enough
to know the Subjunctive forms of **être** (*que
je sois*, etc.), avoir (*que j'aie*, etc.) and faire
(*que je fasse*, etc.). These forms would then
combine with infinitives and adjectives,

allowing for variety in style and introducing useful and common idioms. But,
and this is the point which should be
stressed, it is possible to write normal
French *without* the Subjunctive : *the whole
of* '*Conversation*' *and the* '*Gulliver*' *extract
given later have been translated without
using it once.*

PAST PARTICIPLE

Jean est *venu*. Marie est *venue*. Ils sont
venus tous deux.

Ces fleurs sont merveilleusement *colorées*.

Ces rois se sont *succédé* de père en fils
pendant 300 ans.

J'ai *écrit* une lettre, en effet : mais ce n'est
pas hier que je l'ai *écrite* (object preceding verb),
c'est avant-hier.

J'ai *vu* vos amis : je *les* ai *salués*.

Quelles fautes avez-vous *faites* dans cet
exercice ?

Que d'ennuis cette règle stupide m'a *causés* !

PRESENT PARTICIPLE

Étant arrivé trop tard, je n'ai vu que la
moitié du spectacle.

Le ministre entra en *saluant* très bas, puis,
prenant dans sa serviette (portfolio) un document, il en donna lecture au Roi.

Sa visite n'*ayant* aucun résultat, il alla voir
un autre ami.

Allant, venant, courant, travaillant sans
cesse, la fourmi (ant) a vite amassé de quoi
vivre pendant l'hiver.

IMPERSONAL VERBS AND IDIOMS

Il est avantageux de savoir plusieurs langues.

De quoi *s'agit-il?* Qu'y a-t-il? *Il se passe*
ici quelque chose de bizarre.

Il ne faut pas y aller avant demain matin.

Il me faudra 10 boîtes de conserves pour la
fin de la semaine.

Il pleut, il tonne, il fait un temps affreux: *il
fait* noir, *il fait* du vent, *il ne faut pas* sortir par
un temps pareil.

Il est question de faire une nouvelle route; *il
faut dire* que l'ancienne était trop étroite.

Il n'est pire sourd que celui qui ne veut pas
entendre.

Il lui a fallu rendre compte de toutes ses
dépenses.

REFLEXIVE VERBS

Je *me* lave les dents matin et soir. Le
dentiste *m*'a habitué à cela, et je *m*'en trouve
très bien.

Ne *vous* asseyez pas sur cette chaise, elle
n'est pas solide.

Il *se* regarde dans la glace : il *se* critique,
il *se* juge, il *se* déteste. Il ne *se* passe pas de
jours qu'il ne *se* désole d'avoir le nez trop long.

Nous *nous* sommes bien amusés au bord de la
mer cet été ; nous *nous* sommes baignés tous

---

[1] The Imperfect plays, in the Past, the same rôle as
the Present. Cf. also the rôle of the future in ' irons '
farther down.

les jours ; et vous, M. Dupont, *vous* êtes-vous
reposé à votre maison de campagne ?

Tu *te* trompes, je crois, le soleil ne *se* lève
pas si tôt en cette saison.

Je vous prie dè *vous* dépêcher pour ne pas
faire attendre le taxi.

Il se faut entraider, c'est la loi de nature (La
Fontaine). S'est-elle réveillée de bonne heure
aujourd'hui ?

Dites-vous bien qu'on peut *se* tromper ; ne
vous fiez pas (do not rely on) à un jugement trop
rapide.

Je ne *me* sens pas bien : je suis couché tard
hier, je crois que je vais aller *me* reposer ; je
m'excuse de vous quitter ainsi.

VERBS IN -OIR

The forms given in brackets are the
infinitives corresponding to each verb.
Grammars and dictionaries always take
the infinitive as a basis for classification.

Je reçois (*recevoir*) mes amis aujourd'hui ;
nous verrons (*voir*) s'ils sont exacts au rendez-
vous. Il faut (*falloir*) me dépêcher, si je ne
veux (*vouloir*) pas être en retard ; voyez-vous
(*voir*) cette table là-bas ?

Voudriez-vous (*vouloir*) la mettre près de la
fenêtre ? Pourrons-nous (*pouvoir*) nous asseoir
tous autour ?

Nos invités devraient (*devoir*) être là maintenant ; ah ! voilà Jean ! Eh bien, n'avez-
vous pas vu (*voir*) les autres ?—Non, mais
comme il pleut (*pleuvoir*) ils ont dû (*devoir*)
s'abriter quelque part en route. Il ne peuvent
(*pouvoir*) tarder maintenant.

VERBS IN -RE

Je connais (*connaître*) un restaurant sur le
Boulevard, qui vous plaira (*plaire*) certainement.
C'est un de mes amis qui m'y a conduit (*conduire*) ; et il paraît (*paraître*) s'y connaître.
Je crois (*croire*) que nous ferions (*faire*) mieux
de prendre un taxi ; je crains (*craindre*) qu'il
ne se mette (*mettre*) à pleuvoir.

Nous y voilà : oui, une table à deux nous
suffira (*suffire*). Prendrez-vous (*prendre*) un
apéritif ? Suivons (*suivre*) les conseils du garçon.
Voyons, ne croyez-vous (*croire*) pas qu'une
omelette cuite (*cuire*) à point, suivie (*suivre*)
d'un de ces 'plats du jour,' ferait (*faire*) notre
affaire ?

Et pour que nous ne rompions (*rompre*) pas
avec les bonnes habitudes, apportez-nous,
garçon, une bouteille de Bourgogne. Vivre
d'abord, philosopher ensuite ; je ne sais plus
qui a dit (*dire*) ça ; mais c'était un grand
homme. Buvons (*boire*) à sa santé !

VERBS IN -IR

En ouvrant (*ouvrir*) mon journal, je vois qu'il
y a courses à Auteuil cet après-midi. Je sors
(*sortir*) donc mon habit gris et mes jumelles[1] et

[1] = field-glasses.

me voilà parti (*partir*). L'autobus doit partir à
1 heure ; je vais l'attendre dans un café où l'on
me sert (*servir*) un vin blanc.

Je rencontre un ami et je lui dis : ' Viens
(*venir*) avec moi.' Nous partons ensemble pour
le champ de courses. Le cheval que je choisis
(*choisir*) est un des favoris ; mais, quoiqu'il ait
bien couru (*courir*), il n'arrive que second.

IL Y A

Il y a deux ans que vous êtes à Paris.
You have been in Paris for two years.

Y a-t-il déjà si longtemps ?
Have I been there so long ?

Il pouvait y avoir là deux mille personnes.
There might have been 2,000 people there.

Il y avait une fois un Roi et une Reine qui. . . .
Once upon a time there was a King and Queen
who. . . .

Il n'y a pas moyen de vous recevoir avant six
heures.
You cannot be received before six (i.e. there
is no way of receiving you).

Croyez-vous qu'*il y aura* beaucoup de monde ?
Do you think there will be many people there ?

Y (= à cette place, dans ce but)

Allez-vous au cinéma ? Oui, j'*y* vais.
Y pensez-vous encore, après un an ?
Pour *y* voir, mettez des lunettes.
Irez-vous en Bretagne ? Oui, j'*y* ai une petite
maison.

EN (= de là, de cela, de lui, de cette place)

Avez-vous des cigarettes ? Oui, j'*en* ai.
Ces fruits sont excellents. Mangez-*en* donc.
Etes-vous allé à Paris cette année ? Oui, j'*en*
viens.
Voilà une heure que j'attends ! J'*en* ai assez !
J'*en* veux une autre comme celle-ci, s'il vous
plaît.

AVOIR instead of ETRE

Il neige ; j'ai très *froid.*—Pour avoir *chaud,*
mettez donc des gants.—Vous *avez raison,*
malheureusement j'ai peur de les avoir perdus.

J'ai honte d'avoir *sommeil* ainsi ; mais je
me suis couché tard hier. Je n'*ai* vraiment
pas *envie* de jouer aux cartes ce soir. Mais si
vous *avez soif,* servez-vous, le porto est sur cette
petite table ; vous *auriez tort* de faire des
façons. Faites comme chez vous.

Use of ON

On dit que l'hiver sera très froid : c'est très
malheureux. *On sait,* en effet, que les pauvres
en souffrent beaucoup. *On a fait* ce qu'on
a pu pour eux, mais ce n'est pas assez ; *on
n'a pas* réussi à réunir assez d'argent.

Beaucoup devront se passer de chauffage, ce
qui est vraiment terrible. *On ne fera* jamais trop
pour le bien de l'humanité.

LESSON 13

Adverbs, Prepositions and Conjunctions

IN this short Lesson we break new ground. Necessarily adverbs, prepositions and conjunctions have been used in sentences for exercises and other purposes, but here we present brief rules for their uses.

An **Adverb** is a word used to qualify a verb, adjective or another adverb.

The general rule is that adverbs are formed by *adding* -ment to the *feminine of adjectives*, or to the masculine, when this ends in a vowel.

ADJECTIVE: courageux, courageuse,
courageous
ADVERB : courageusement, *courageously*
ADJECTIVE: heureux, heureuse, *happy*
ADVERB : heureusement, *happily*
Adjectives ending in -ant, -ent, form adverbs in -aMMent, -eMMent :
obligeant, obligeaMMent.
In French this ending -ment corresponds to the English -*ly*.

The *position of the adverb* is *after* a simple verb or the auxiliary in compound tenses :

Vous avez bien parlé, *You have spoken well.*
Il le fait souvent, *He does it often.*

Bien, *well* ; toujours, *ever, always* ; trop, *too much* precede the infinitive, while all other adverbs follow it. Il a peur de trop parler. Il a parlé haut.

COMPARISON : PLUS—plus courageux, *more courageous*, Le PLUS—le plus courageux, *most courageous.*

VOCABULARY OF ADVERBS

ainsi, *thus*
aussi, *also*
bien, *well*
fort, *very*
mal, *badly*
même, *even*
assez, *enough*
autant, *as much, many*
beaucoup,[1] *much*
environ, *about*
moins, *less*
très, *very*
ailleurs, *elsewhere*
auprès, *near*
peu, *little*
plus, *more*
presque, *almost*
si, *so*
tant, *so much*
trop, *too much*
contre, *against*

devant, *before*
en, *from there, thence*
ici, *here*
là, *there*
loin, *far*
où, *where* (distinguish ou, *or*)
partout, *everywhere*
y, *there*
en arrière, *behind*
en avant, *forward*
en bas, *below*
alors, *then*
aujourd'hui, *today*
aussitôt, *immediately*
bientôt, *soon*
pourtant, *yet, although*
cependant, *however*
demain, *tomorrow*
après-demain, *day after tomorrow*

[1]Never say or write '*Très beaucoup.*'

dedans, *inside*
dehors, *outside*
derrière, *behind*
dessous, *underneath*
dessus, *on, over*
avant-hier, *day before yesterday*
jamais, *ever*
maintenant, *now*
parfois, *at times*
puis, *then, afterwards*
quand, *when*
quelquefois, *sometimes*
souvent, *often*
tard, *late*
tôt, *soon*
toujours, *always*
tout à coup, *suddenly*
de jour, *by day*
de nuit, *by night*
à temps, *in time*

déjà, *already*
depuis, *since*
encore, *still, yet, again*
enfin, *at last*
hier, *yesterday*
en retard, *behind time*
combien ? *how much ?*
comment ? *how ?*
où ? *where ?*
pourquoi ? *why ?*
quand ? *when ?*
d'où ? *whence, from where ?*
non, *no*
oui, *yes*
si, *yes* (in reply to a *negative question*)
vraiment, *truly*
sans doute, *without doubt*
peut-être, *perhaps*
probablement, *probably*

PREPOSITIONS, CONJUNCTIONS AND INTERJECTIONS

These are invariable words of which the usage corresponds to the English. A list is given below. The words in this list are of great importance. Some of them are the most frequently recurring words in the language.

One should learn the use of the Prepositions en, dans and à (meaning *in*) *before proper names*. This is simple :

1 In the case of *feminine country* names use en, without the article.
2 With *masculine country* names use au, à l'.
3 With *towns and small islands* use à only (without article).
4 With *masculine or feminine* country names *qualified by some phrase*, use dans le, la, l'.

Thus : 1 En Chine, en Amérique, en France.
2 Au Maroc, au Portugal, etc.
3 A Paris, à Londres, à Jersey.
4 Dans l'Amérique du Sud, dans la Chine du Nord.

VOCABULARIES
1. PREPOSITIONS

à, *at, in*
après, *after*
avant, *before*
dans, *in*
de, *of, from*
depuis, *since*
en, *in*
entre, *between*
environ, *about*

jusque, *to, until*
pendant, *during*
vers, *towards*
avec, *with*
chez, *at the house of*
parmi, *among*
sous, *under*
sur, *on*
voici, *here is . . . .*

Note also : **Dans un mois** means *at the end of a month*, while **en un mois** means *in the space of a month*.

voilà, *there is*	**excepté**, *excepting*
à côté de, *beside*	**malgré**, *in spite of*
au-dessous de, *under*	**par**, *by*
au-dessus de, *over*	**sans**, *without*
au lieu de, *instead of*	**selon**, *according to*
en face de, *opposite*	**à cause de**, *on account of*
loin de, *far from*	**pour**, *for*
près de, *near*	**à travers**, *through*

2. CONJUNCTIONS

car, *for, because*	**que**, *that*
comme, *as*	**si**, *if*
donc, *then*	**puisque**, *since*
et, *and*	**quoique, bien que**, *al-*
mais, *but*	*though* (*subjunctive*)
ni, *neither, nor*	**aussitôt que**, *as soon as*
ou, *either, or*	**de manière que**, *so that*
quand, *when*	**parce que**, *because*

3. INTERJECTIONS

Attention ! *Pay atten-*	**Pas possible !** *You don't*
tion !	*say so !*
Tenez ! *Really !*	**Comment !** *How! Why!*
Bis ! *Again ! Encore !*	**Parbleu !** *Of course !*

Bon ! bien ! très bien !	**Allons donc !** *Tell that*
Good ! Well done!	*to the marines !*
Assez ! *Enough !*	**Vrai !** *Really !*
Paix ! *Silence !*	**A la bonne heure !**
Gare ! *Out of the way !*	*Excellent !*
Look out !	**Sapristi !** *Good*
	heavens !

4. MISCELLANEOUS

seulement, *only*	**aimé de tous**, *loved by all*
guère, *scarcely*	**boire dans un verre**,
de bonne heure, *early*	*drink out of a glass*
à droite, *to the right*	**la femme aux cheveux**
à gauche, *to the left*	**gris**, *the woman* with
tout droit, *straight*	*grey hair*
ahead	**pas à pas, mot à mot**,
à haute voix, *in a loud*	*step by step, word by*
voice	*word*
grâce à, *thanks to*	**en train de**, *in course of,*
en même temps, *at the*	*in the act of*
same time	**merci**, *thanks, no thanks*
s'il vous plaît, *please*	**Je vous remercie**, *thank*
	you

5. GREETINGS

Bonjour, *Good day,*	**Bonne nuit**, *Good night*
good morning	**Comment allez-vous ?**
Bonsoir, *Good evening*	*How are you?*

LESSON 14

Word Building

FRENCH, like other languages, has the means within itself of enlarging its vocabulary by virtue of word building. From the point of view of the beginner, it is at the same time a difficulty and an encouragement. A difficulty, because the *root* form on which the language builds is sometimes obscured—though never to a great extent—by vowel changes or more frequently consonantal changes ; and an encouragement, because of the wide vocabulary which rapidly comes within the bounds of comprehension.

When the Grammar and the essential or ' root ' vocabulary (already given) are known, and the principles of word-formation outlined here understood, the meaning of thousands of words will appear at once, or at any rate can be conjectured with fair certainty. Many of these new words will be found in the French exercises and texts, and the more difficult are explained.

The Four Ways of Word Building. There are, for practical purposes, four ways of making new words :

1 The same ' form ' can be used in different parts of speech. Boire, *to drink*, LE boire, *drinking* ; sage, *wise*, LE sage, *the wise*, etc.

2 By adding a suffix or ending, e.g. raison, *reason*, raisonNER, TO *reason*, raisonne-MENT, *reasoning*, raisonnABLE, *reason-ABLE*, raisonNEUR, *arguer, reasoner*.

3 By a prefix : faire, *to do*, REfaire, *to do* AGAIN, DEfaire, *to UNdo*, SURfaire, *to* OVERdo, PARfaire, *to complete*, etc.

4 By putting together two or more inde-pendent words : aigre-doux ; from aigre, *bitter*, and doux, *sweet*.

Prefixes Used in Word Building

IM (im, il, ir)	*Negation*	possible, IMpossible
		lisible, ILlisible
		religieux, IRreligieux
RE	*again*	venir, revenir
CONTRE	*against*	poison, contrepoison
EX (es, é)	*out of*	patrie, expatrier
		souffle, essouffler
MI	*half*	août, mi-août
SUR	*over*	voler, survoler
SOU, SUB	*under*	mettre, soumettre

Suffixes Used in Word Building
(a) To form NOUNS :
-et, -ette *diminutive* garçon, garçonnet
fille, fillette

-able	*agent*	compter, comptable
-age	*action*	laver, lavage
-eur	*agent*	voyager, voyageur
-aison,		
-ation	*action*	livrer, livraison
		administrer, administra-tion
-at	*profession*	professer, professorat
-ée	*fullness*	bouche, bouchée
-ier	*profession*	ferme, fermier
-ier	*fullness*	sucre, sucrier

(b) To form ADJECTIVES :
-ible	paix, paisible
-able	durer, durable
-ois, -ais	France, Français
	Hongrie, Hongrois
-el	mort, mortel
-iste	social, socialiste [1]
-é (the Past Participle ending)	limite, limité

[1] This ending often used to form nouns as well, e.g. un socialiste, un artiste, etc.

(c) To form VERBS :
-er	*to telephone*, téléphoner
	to shunt, shunter

Compounds

Of these there are four principal kinds :
1 two NOUNS : chou-fleur, *cauliflower*, timbre-poste, *postage stamp*
2. NOUN + ADJECTIVE : rouge-gorge, *red-breast*
3. ADJECTIVE +ADJECTIVE : petit-gris, *squirrel*
4 VERB + NOUN or ADJECTIVE : perce-neige, *snowdrop*
gagne-petit, *knife-grinder*

IDIOMS

An idiom is an expression peculiar to a language. The number of idioms in French is almost infinite, and there are many excellent lists of them available. For the practical purposes of a traveller what is given below should suffice for a beginning—but only for a beginning.

Que voulez-vous dire ?	*What do you mean?*
Qu'est-ce qu'il y a ?	*What is the matter?*
Qu'est-ce-qu'il a ?	*What is the matter with him?*
Il y a une heure que je suis ici	*For one hour I have been here*
Il n'y a pas de quoi	*Don't mention it*
Quel temps fait-il ce soir ?	*How is the weather this evening?*
Il fait { chaud / froid	*It is hot* / *It is cold*
Avoir { faim / soif / chaud / froid	*To be* { *hungry* / *thirsty* / *hot* / *cold*
Combien de temps faut-il pour aller de Londres à Paris ?	*How long does it take to go from London to Paris?*
Cette maison est à moi	*This house is mine*
Avoir mal à	*To have a pain in*
J'ai mal aux dents	*I have toothache*
J'ai mal au cœur	*I am not very well*

Elle est à plaindre	*She is to be pitied*
Il est à croire que	*It is probable that*
Me voici	*Here I am!*
Le voilà	*There he is!*
Le combien sommes-nous ?	*What is the date?*
Il me faut (followed by infinitive) / Il vous faut / Je dois / Vous devez	*I must, you must*, etc.
Veuillez (followed by infinitive)	*Please*
S'il vous plaît	*If you please*
Merci	*Thanks;* also *No thanks*
Être médecin, soldat, etc.	*To be* A *doctor.* A *soldier*, etc.
Comme il faut	*Correct : as should be*
Un homme comme il faut	*A respectable man*
Faites cela comme il faut	*Do that properly*
Avez-vous tout ce qu'il vous faut ?	*Have you everything you want?*
Payer (une bouteille)	*To pay* FOR (*a bottle*, etc.)
Être à même de	*To be capable of, up to*, etc. (*flying to Australia*, etc.)
Compter (followed by infinitive)	*To rely upon* (*doing something*)
Où en êtes-vous ?	*How far have you got?*
Quoi qu'il en soit	*Whatever the case may be*
Ça y est !	*That's it! It's all right!*
J'y suis !	*I understand*

Faire—
Cela ne fait rien	*That doesn't* MATTER
Faire une visite	PAY *a visit*
Faire un discours	DELIVER *a speech*
Faire plaisir à, de la peine, mal	GIVE *pleasure to, displease, to harm*
Faire 100 kilomètres	TO COVER 100 *kilometres* (*in a car*, etc.)
Faire des affaires avec	*To do business with*
Faire venir	*To send for, to fetch*

CORRESPONDENCE IN FRENCH

The DATE is written thus : le 1er janvier 1933, le 31 décembre 1934.

A FORMAL OPENING : Monsieur, Madame, Mademoiselle.

A MODERATELY FAMILIAR OPENING : Cher Monsieur, Chère Madame, Chère Mademoiselle.

A FAMILIAR OPENING : Mon cher Dupont, Mon cher Georges.

A FORMAL ENDING : Veuillez agréer, Monsieur, l'expression de mes sentiments distingués.

A MODERATELY FAMILIAR ENDING : Croyez en mes sentiments distingués.

A FAMILIAR ENDING : Croyez en mes meilleurs souvenirs, or : Tout à vous, *yours ever.*

LESSON 15

Conversation and Reading

THE student who has mastered the material so far provided should now have sufficient grammar and words to enable him to read French, with little difficulty beyond that experienced when he meets new words. New words should be looked up in a dictionary, and added to the notebook which was recommended at the beginning of the course. This Lesson should be regarded as a *test of knowledge*.

If the student feels that he can fully understand nearly all of the conversations and of the reading extracts, he can consider that good progress has been made. If not, there is only one thing to do. GO OVER THE COURSE AGAIN, paying particular attention to the parts not known. It is inadvisable to proceed to general reading until one is quite satisfied with the results of this test reading.

Dans un Grand Magasin

Monsieur X. : Ah, vous voilà ! Est-ce que je suis en retard ? Je suis d'abord entré par la porte de côté.

Une amie : Seulement une ou deux minutes. Ce n'est rien à Paris.

M. X. : Je me remets entre vos mains complètement, car je n'ai aucune idée des prix en France. Et d'ailleurs je suis toujours un peu perdu dans ces grands magasins.

Amie : Alors laissez-moi être votre guide ce matin. De quoi avez-vous besoin ?

M. X. : D'abord des articles de toilette ; c'est la première chose sur ma liste. J'ai été assez stupide pour partir sans ça.

Amie : Nous y voilà : c'est à notre gauche en entrant.

M. X. : Combien ces éponges ? [1]

Demoiselle de magasin : Il y en a à plusieurs prix, selon leur taille, à partir de 10 francs.

M. X. : Bien. Combien celle-ci, de taille moyenne ?

Demoiselle de M. : 20 francs, Monsieur.

M. X. : Je la prends. C'est un article solide, n'est-ce pas ?

Dem. de M. : Certainement, Monsieur. Nos éponges sont de première qualité. Et avec ça ?

M. X. : Une brosse à dents, aussi dure que possible. Oui, celle-ci fera mon affaire. Et de la pâte dentifrice[2], s'il vous plaît. Ce sera tout.

Dem. de M. : Trente-sept cinquante, Monsieur.

Amie : Et maintenant ?

M. X. : J'ai grand besoin de chaussures neuves.

Amie : Pour cela, il faut aller au rayon des articles d'hommes. C'est par ici.

Employé : Est-ce qu'on s'occupe de vous, Monsieur ?

M. X. : Non. Je voudrais voir des chaussures de ville.

Employé : En noir ou en brun ?

M. X. : En brun.

Employé : Combien chaussez-vous, Monsieur ?

M. X. : Je n'ai aucune idée des mesures françaises.

Employé : Je vais prendre votre pointure,[3] Monsieur. Vous chaussez du 41. Je vais voir ce que j'ai dans ce numéro. Voici une bonne chaussure, très forte. Elle peut aller aussi bien pour la ville que pour la campagne.

Amie : Essayez-les pour voir.

Employé : Comment vous sentez-vous dedans, Monsieur ?

M. X. : Mon pied gauche est un peu serré ici.

Employé : Je vais agrandir un peu la chaussure, c'est très simple.

M. X. : Et combien sont-elles ?

Employé : Cent dix francs, Monsieur.

Amie : C'est vraiment bon marché pour des chaussures de cette qualité. Je les prendrais, si j'étais de vous.

M. X. : Parfait. Mais n'oubliez pas d'agrandir celle de gauche.

Employé : Vous pouvez être tranquille, Monsieur, je vais m'en occuper. Voulez-vous les faire envoyer à votre adresse, ou les prenez-vous maintenant avec vous ?

M. X. : Faites-les envoyer chez moi. Je vais vous faire un chèque maintenant ; donnez-moi donc ma facture.

[1] éponge = *sponge*. *Notice that many English words in sp-, st-, sc-, correspond to French words in ép-, ét-, éc-, cf. school and* école, *stage and* étage, *stuff and* étoffe, *etc.*

[2] pâte dentifrice = *tooth-paste. In the same way, many English words in final -st correspond to French words in -ât-, ôt-, -êt-, cf. forest and* forêt, *roast and* rôt, *disgust and* dégoût, *etc.*

[3] pointure : taille du pied.